INTRODUCTORY
BOTANY

Photo by John O. Sumner, from National Audubon Society

INTRODUCTORY
BOTANY

ARTHUR CRONQUIST

HARPER & ROW, PUBLISHERS, NEW YORK AND EVANSTON

Contents

vi **Contents**

Preface

THE TWO MOST OBVIOUS ALTERNATIVES in the study of any subject are to start with the known and proceed to the unknown, or to start with the simple and proceed to the complex. In general botany, the first alternative is exemplified by beginning with the angiosperms, and the second by ending with them. The second alternative has been chosen for this text, both because it permits a natural evolutionary sequence and because few entering college students have more than a superficial familiarity with the structure, functions, and reproduction of angiosperms. Furthermore, the life cycle of angiosperms is best understood by the student who has some knowledge of the lower groups.

The text has been written, however, so that those who prefer to teach the angiosperms before the other groups of plants may do so. Terms used in discussing the angiosperms are introduced as new, even though they may have been used in earlier chapters on other groups. It is possible to move directly from Chapter 5 to Chapter 23, postponing or omitting the study of cryptogams and gymnosperms.

Both facts and interpretation are stressed in this text, in the conviction that facts without interpretation are meaningless, but interpretation without a solid foundation of facts is poorly grasped and soon forgotten.

Within the space limitations inherent in an introductory text, I have tried wherever possible to bring the student to the boundary of our knowledge, and to peer into the future. An earnest effort has been made to evaluate and include the results of current research.

In many branches of learning, certainly in much of botany, there are successively higher plateaus of understanding, separated by steep slopes of fact accumulation. The value of struggling up a slope of facts is limited if one does not reach the plateau of understanding. Throughout this text an effort has been made to reach the plateaus, and often to look upward to the next slope. The first plateau in genetics is simple Mendelism, but this provides such a limited and distorted view that we have climbed to the next level—an appreciation of multiple factors and multiple effects. Geneticists are still struggling toward an understanding of the precise structure of chromosomes and genes, and we merely gaze briefly at this slope.

Interpretative understandings reached at one level of study may themselves become the facts which permit some new or higher understanding. When Copernicus, and later Galileo, expounded the view that the earth is a sphere which turns on its axis and revolves around the sun, they were interpreting factual observations. Their interpretation, only slightly modified, has become a set of fundamental scientific facts which is part of the foundation for further improvements in our understanding of the universe. I hope that students using this text may likewise be able to utilize the interpretative understandings here reached, as facts which will help them to understand other problems they will meet.

ACKNOWLEDGMENTS

Many people have generously helped in the preparation of this book, either by reading manuscript or by providing illustrations or materials. While assuming complete personal responsibility for the entire text, I gratefully acknowledge the constructive criticism offered by the following botanists who have read parts of the manuscript: H. A. Gleason, ecology; John B. Hanson, water relations; Robert E. Hungate, bacteria; Henry A. Imshaug, lichens; R. M. Klein, physiology and some other segments; George F. Papenfuss, algae; Ruth Patrick, diatoms; D. J. Rogers, economic importance of angiosperms; D. P. Rogers, part of the fungi; Clark Rogerson, part of the fungi; R. M. Schuster, bryophytes; Alcides Teixeira, part of the fungi; and W. H. Wagner, vascular cryptogams. My wife, Mabel A. Cronquist, read the entire manuscript for form and clarity, and she did much of the final typing.

The original illustrations were drawn by Charles C. Clare and carry his initials. Many of the microscope slides used by Mr. Clare were kindly loaned for this purpose by M. S. Markle. Other illustrations are individually acknowledged in the captions. I particularly wish to thank the editors of Ginn and Company for generously allowing me to use a number of drawings from W. H. Brown's excellent text, *The Plant Kingdom*. Some other institutions and individuals who have provided large numbers of photographs are the Boyce-Thompson Institute; Chicago Natural History Museum; Cornell University, Department of Plant Pathology; General Biological Supply House (Chicago); Lakeside Biological Products (Ripon, Wis.); National Audubon Society; New York Botanical Garden; U.S. Department of Agriculture (Forest Service and Agricultural Research Service); Herman Becker; José Cuatrecasas; T. H. Everett; J. Arthur Herrick; W. H. Hodge; and Jack McCormick. The full page photographs of *Hydrodictyon, Euglena*, and a colonial diatom were made especially for my use by Elsa H. J. O'Donnell.

The full resources of the New York Botanical Garden library, herbarium, and living collections have been constantly at my disposal. The illustrations of *Anthoceros* were drawn in part from living material supplied by Wilbur H. Duncan. Fern gametophytes and *Isoetes* sporophytes were provided by my son, John Cronquist; the *Isoetes* stocks were originally sent him by Dr. Duncan. The phyletic chart of the divisions and classes of plants was designed by John Cronquist, under my supervision. The photograph of *Psilotum* shows a plant given me by David B. Dunn. My daughter Elizabeth and my son John assisted in the preparation of the index.

ARTHUR CRONQUIST

September, 1960

INTRODUCTORY
BOTANY

Botany as a Science

CHAPTER 1

THE NATURE OF SCIENCE

THE KINDS OF SCIENCE

Botany is the science which treats of plants. It is a branch of **biology**, the science which deals with living things, both plant and animal. Biology, in turn, may be considered as one of the natural sciences, which deal with nature—in its broadest sense. Some other natural sciences are chemistry, physics, geology, and astronomy. The natural sciences, exclusive of biology, may be referred to as the physical sciences. In addition to the natural sciences there are the social sciences, such as economics and sociology, and the exact sciences, such as mathematics.

Such an organization of the kinds of science is convenient but not wholly satisfactory for all purposes. The boundaries between the sciences are not sharp, and many special fields may include parts of two or more other sciences. Thus **genetics** (the study of heredity) and **ecology** (the

◀

Scene along the Kaweah River, western foothills of the Sierra Nevada, California. Yucca in the foreground. (Photo by John O. Sumner, from National Audubon Society.)

study of the relation between organisms and their environment) are parts of biology which transcend the distinction between botany and zoology; and **biochemistry,** the chemistry of living things, is on the borderline between chemistry and biology. The different sciences are, furthermore, so interdependent that a proper understanding of any one requires also a knowledge of several others. A good botanist must know some zoology, chemistry, physics, mathematics, and geology. An advance in any field of science may prove to be useful or necessary for the further progress in some other field. For example, the developments of the past several decades in the knowledge of radioactive elements have given plant physiologists and biochemists an important new tool for deciphering the chemical structure of living organisms and the processes which occur in them. Any of a number of elements used by a plant can be supplied in radioactive form, and the subsequent history of these tagged or labeled atoms can be followed because of their radioactivity.

In contrast to the organization given above, science may be divided into **pure science,** in which knowledge is sought for its own sake, without regard to its immediate economic importance, and **applied science,** in which an attempt is made to put knowledge to practical use. Efforts now being made by plant physiologists to find out just how a plant manufactures food from raw materials are an example of pure science. A solution to this problem in pure science will be aided by the use of radioactive isotopes and may permit the eventual application of this knowledge to the practical problem of producing food for human use. Today's minor bit of scientific knowledge may tomorrow be an essential part of some new development in pure or applied science.

THE CONCEPTS OF SCIENCE

It is commonly said that **science** is organized knowledge, but that is not a complete definition. Inherent in any concept of science is the search for objective truth or understanding, without regard for what would be pleasant or convenient to believe. Also inherent is the necessity for the facts or data to be sufficiently numerous and reliable to permit a solid core of agreement among essentially all serious students. Individual tastes and value judgments, which are so important in the arts and philosophy, are minimized in science. Ideally, all scientists working on a given problem should arrive at the same conclusion, and when experiment is possible, the results should be the same no matter who performs the experiment.

Scientists in all fields are continuously trying to add to the body of knowledge and understanding. The expansion of scientific knowledge involves both the discovery of previously unknown facts and the formulation of generalizations based on those facts. A scientific guess aimed at explaining certain observed facts is called a **hypothesis.** When additional information indicates that the guess is probably correct, the hypothesis may attain the status of a **theory.** If the theory proves to be correct and consistently applicable to a certain type of situation, it becomes a **principle** or **law.** The term *law* is applied especially to generalizations which can be used to predict accurately the results of the interaction of different factors or forces. Mendel's laws of heredity, taken up later in this book, are examples of scientific laws, although their applicability is now known to be more limited than was once believed.

Frequently, particularly in the observational as opposed to the experimental phases of science, it is convenient to continue to refer to a universally accepted principle as a theory. The **cell theory**, which states that living matter is characteristically organized into small, complex, definite bodies called cells, is an example of such a principle. The fact that some organisms (such as slime molds) are not composed of cells does not impair the usefulness of the cell theory in enabling us to understand the structure of living matter; in fact, the exceptions to the cell theory are best understood in the light of knowledge concerning cellular organisms.

Another scientific principle is the **theory of organic evolution.** It states that organisms of different kinds are related through a common ancestry, that the existing kinds of organisms have arisen from one kind of simple organism or a relatively few kinds of simple organisms, and that the whole process is very gradual and consists of small steps. The mechanisms of organic evolution are partly but not wholly understood; they are discussed in Chapter 36. The principle of organic evolution is no longer a matter of contention among scientists.

All scientific concepts, be they hypotheses, theories, principles, or supposed laws, are subject to re-examination, modification, or rejection as additional information is obtained. Often the additional information necessitates adjustment or refinement of existing ideas, so that successive concepts tend to represent ever closer approximations to the ultimate truth.

The Scientific Method

The methods employed by scientists in an effort to solve a problem have so much in common that the term **scientific method** is customarily used. In essence, the scientific method consists of (1) the acquisition of a body of facts pertaining to the problem; (2) the formulation of one or more hypotheses based on these facts; and (3) the testing of each hypothesis, either by the acquisition of new data of critical importance, or, when possible, by one or more experiments designed to determine whether a prediction based on the hypothesis is correct. The experiment, or the additional data, should be of such nature that if they confirm the applicability of one hypothesis, they exclude the alternatives. If no hypothesis is borne out by the third step, then the whole process, or the last two steps, are repeated until a satisfactory conclusion is reached.

Most scientific generalizations, particularly in the biological sciences, are subject to exception. In this book we shall give primary attention to the usual or typical conditions, and only passing (if any) mention to the unusual. The attentive reader will note the frequent use of qualifying words which admit exceptions to the statements made.

THE NATURE OF LIFE

THE CHARACTERISTICS OF LIFE

We have said that biology is the science which deals with life and that botany in the branch of biology which deals with plants. All of us know, in general, what is meant by "life" and "plant," but neither of these terms is precisely definable. There is no sharp boundary line between plants and animals, or even between living and nonliving things. The most characteristic features of **life** are growth, reproduction, and the carrying on of a complex series of chemical processes which are known collectively as **metabolism**. Of these, metabolism is the most important, since in any living thing growth and reproduction may be postponed or even eliminated, but if metabolism stops, the organism is no longer alive (except for the apparently suspended animation seen in certain viruses and spores). Living matter, called **protoplasm,** is (at least ordinarily) a complex organized mixture of proteins, fats, and many other substances, suspended in water, the whole in a state of continuous chemical activity. Any one of these substances, when isolated from the others, is not alive; it is the chemically active mixture that is alive.

One of the processes of metabolism is the breakdown of complex substances, called **foods,** into simpler substances, with energy being released as a result. The breakdown of foods may be divided into (1) **digestion,** a preliminary step which makes them more soluble or more readily diffusible without significantly changing the amount of stored energy, and (2) **respiration,** a further step in which some or all of the energy that was stored in the food is released. Respiration usually involves the use of oxygen, and the formation of carbon dioxide as one of the waste products. As used by biologists, the term *respiration* refers to the actual chemical processes within a living organism which result in the release of energy from food, not merely to breathing or to the exchange of gases which accompanies it. Some of the energy released in respiration is used to keep the protoplasm of a cell in constant motion; some of it is used in the formation, from raw materials and digested foods, of new compounds which become part of the protoplasm; but by far the largest part (commonly more than 90 percent) is transformed into heat. In warm-blooded animals the heat released in respiration is used to maintain a body temperature higher than the usual temperature of the outside environment; in other kinds of organisms the heat is largely wasted. The formation of new protoplasm from raw materials and digested foods is called **assimilation.** Digestion, respiration, and assimilation are among the essential processes of metabolism. The most continuous of these processes is respiration. With minor exceptions (some spores and viruses), continuous respiration is characteristic of all living things; if respiration completely stops, the organism dies. (It should be noted, however, that a state of suspended animation can be obtained in some kinds of cells by quick freezing and drying, under conditions far more extreme than exist in nature.)

Changes in the environment influence metabolic activities, and particular changes tend to call forth particular responses. This capacity to respond to stimuli, called **irritability,** is one of the most important characteristics of protoplasm. In both plants and animals responses to stimuli often result in movement, of either the whole organism or some part of it, and in plants they often also affect the direction of growth. Some types of plant response to stimuli are discussed in Chapter 32.

Protoplasm is constantly wearing out, breaking down, and being replaced by new protoplasm. When protoplasm is formed faster than it breaks down, the organism grows. Some or all of the cells increase in size, and these growing cells divide periodically, each into two. As a result, the organism appears to grow from within, rather than by merely adding material externally. Growth by **intussusception,** as this type of growth is called, is characteristic of living things. Nonliving things may swell by the absorption of water or other liquids (e.g., a raisin), or may grow by accretion, the mere addition of material of the same sort to what is already there (e.g., a hailstone, or a chemical crystal), but they do not grow by intussusception. If any one thing can be said to be the ultimate criterion of life, it is the ability to transform and organize food by chemical processes into body substance which in turn uses food in similar fashion.

THE ORIGIN OF LIFE

Many years ago it was generally believed that living things frequently originated from nonliving ones, i.e., by **spontaneous generation**. Cheese and old rags left undisturbed in a dark closet for some days were supposed to generate mice; meat exposed to the open air was supposed to generate maggots, etc. The concept of spontaneous generation still survives in popular superstition, as, for instance, that a horsehair in a watering trough will turn into a wireworm. Experiments by various scientists dispelled most of these ideas, but until well into the nineteenth century microorganisms were widely believed to arise spontaneously. The Italian biologist Lazzaro Spallanzani (1729–1799) demonstrated in 1768 that organisms did not reappear in cultures that were sterilized by boiling and then sealed by fusion of the mouth of the glass container. Schulz and Schwann in 1837 improved on Spallanzani's demonstration by permitting air to enter the sterilized flasks through red-hot tubes which killed any organism borne in the air. These experiments attracted relatively little attention, however. It remained for the French biologist and chemist Louis Pasteur (1822–1895) to deliver the deathblow to the theory of spontaneous generation. Apparently unaware of the work of his predecessors, he improved on their ex-

Fig. 1.1. Louis Pasteur (1822–1895), versatile French biologist and chemist, famous for his work on the cause and prevention of human and animal diseases and for his studies on fermentation, spontaneous generation, etc.

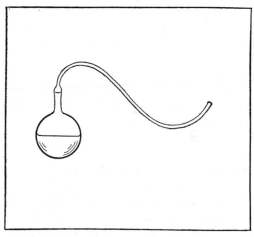

Fig. 1.2. Flask of a type used by Pasteur in his experiments on spontaneous generation.

periment (1862) by permitting air to enter the sterilized flasks through slender tubes twisted into such shapes that particles floating in the air could not fall into the flasks (Fig. 1.2). His work was well publicized, and the principle that all life arises from pre-existing life soon became standard scientific doctrine.

Spallanzani's experiments bore practical fruit long before the idea of spontaneous generation was fully discredited among biologists. François Appert, a French chef, founded the canning industry in 1804 and made a fortune from it. The French government awarded him a substantial prize in 1810 for making public his process, which consisted of sterilizing the food by boiling it and then sealing it in sterilized glass containers.

The ultimate origin of life still has not been explained satisfactorily on a scientific basis, although there are hypotheses of an original spontaneous generation at the molecular level, under environmental conditions quite different from those which exist today (see Chapter 36). Some of the viruses, which can be "crystallized" into apparently inert nucleoproteins but which return to apparent life when introduced into the proper host, appear to be on the borderline between the living and the nonliving. Since these occur only as parasites of more complex organisms, however, they are not likely to be the most ancient form of life.

THE NATURE OF PLANTS

Once we have arrived at the level of complexity of the most primitive existing organisms, which are microscopic and consist of single cells, three principal modes of nutrition are possible. The organism can **make** its food; it can **absorb** food from its surroundings; or it can **eat** (ingest) its food.

Organisms which make their own food have developed a series of features related to that way of life and are called **plants**. Organisms which eat their food have developed other features related to

this way of life and are called **animals**. Both plants and animals have given rise to (and may have arisen from) organisms which neither make nor eat their food but instead absorb it from their surroundings. Food-absorbing organisms are classified as plants or animals according to their probable evolutionary relationship as indicated by their structure and chemical processes. Some food-absorbing organisms, such as the fungi, probably originated prior to the divergence of plants and animals into wholly separate evolutionary lines.

A typical plant makes its own food from raw materials, with the aid of the green pigment chlorophyll. It is not motile, and it has neither a nervous system nor an excretory system. It is usually branched, with many similar parts; the size of the plant, the number of branches, and the number of organs of each kind are variable and subject to considerable modification by the environment. Increase in size is due largely to cell divisions in certain limited regions called meristems, and growth tends to continue indefinitely. The cells are bounded by a nonliving wall composed largely of cellulose, a complex carbohydrate. During cell division the protoplasm is divided into two parts by the formation of a cell plate, as described in Chapter 3.

A typical animal has no chlorophyll; it eats its food rather than makes it. It is motile and has both a nervous and an excretory system. It has a fairly definite mature form and size that are relatively little affected by the environment, and the number of organs of each kind is definite and usually not large. Increase in its size is due to cell divisions in all parts of its body, and growth stops when a certain size is reached. The cells, or most of them, are bounded by a flexible, living, proteinaceous membrane. Those cells which give a degree of rigidity to the body are surrounded by calcium salts, as in the vertebrates, or have a chitinous wall, as in the insects and other arthropods. (Chitin resembles protein to the extent that nitrogen is one of its essential constituents, although it is otherwise more like cellulose and other carbohydrates.) During cell division the protoplasm is constricted or furrowed into two parts, without the formation of a cell plate. (In both plants and animals there is ordinarily a precise division of one of the parts of the protoplasm, the nucleus, as is explained in Chapter 3.)

All these characteristics by which plants differ from animals are subject to exception, some more so than others; but among the more complex organisms there is rarely any difficulty in distinguishing a plant from an animal. The Venus's-flytrap (Fig. 1.3), a green plant which gets some of its food by snapping its leaves shut on unsuspecting insects, is still obviously a plant. Likewise dodder (Fig. 1.4), a twining nongreen plant that parasitizes other plants and absorbs its food from them, would never be confused with an animal; and tapeworms, although they absorb rather than eat their food, would scarcely be confused with plants.

As one considers progressively more simple organisms, the distinction between plants and animals becomes progressively more difficult. The fungi are generally con-

Fig. 1.3. Venus's-flytrap (*Dionaea muscipula*), an insectivorous plant native to North and South Carolina. (About natural size.) (New York Botanical Garden photo.)

Fig. 1.4. Dodder (*Cuscuta*), a twining, yellowish, parasitic plant lacking chlorophyll. It obtains its food through special absorbing organs (haustoria) which enter the tissues of the plant it grows on. (About natural size.) (Photo by Hugh Spencer, from National Audubon Society.)

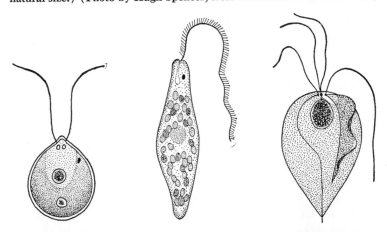

Fig. 1.5. Some single-celled motile organisms. Left, *Chlamydomonas*, which has an eyespot and a definite cell wall and makes its own food. (× 1200.) Center, *Euglena*, which has an eyespot and makes its own food but lacks a cell wall and has a mouth-like gullet at one end. (×500.) Right, *Trichomonas*, which lacks a cell wall and absorbs its food from its surroundings. (×3500; after Hinshaw.) All three organisms are commonly treated as protozoa (animal kingdom) by zoologists; *Chlamydomonas* and *Euglena* are also treated as algae (plant kingdom) by botanists.

sidered to be plants, although their cell walls are usually chitinous rather than being composed of cellulose. Many of the single-celled algae swim freely in water, and some of these are commonly studied in elementary courses in zoology as well as in botany. Among the most notable of these intermediate forms is *Euglena* (Fig. 1.5), which usually has chlorophyll and makes its own food, but which also has a gullet. Apparently *Euglena* itself does not ordinarily ingest food through the gullet, but some very similar and closely allied organisms without chlorophyll do. The cells of *Euglena* are bounded by a flexible, living, proteinaceous membrane; they have a simple excretory system; and the beginning of a nervous system is indicated by an eyespot which is sensitive to light. It is difficult to deny that any organism which contains chlorophyll is a plant, yet in other respects these organisms certainly resemble animals; and some of the close relatives of *Euglena* which lack chlorophyll are by all criteria animals.

The classification of organisms into the plant kingdom and the animal kingdom, based on the structural and chemical characters attendant upon their mode of nutrition, is natural, useful, and for the most part not difficult, but the cleavage between the two kingdoms is not absolute. Many of the chlorophyll-bearing unicellular organisms, which are treated by botanists as plants, are so obviously related to unicellular, nonchlorophyllous animals that zoologists regularly treat them as animals in spite of their chlorophyll. Once past the single-celled stage, however, the evolutionary development of plants and animals appears to have followed wholly separate channels, with no cross connections.

BRANCHES OF BOTANY

The increase in scientific knowledge during the past century, with the resultant impossibility for any individual scientist to comprehend all of it, has brought about a growing trend toward specialization. Proper understanding of any one segment of science requires some knowledge of several others, but the amount of detailed information now available is far too great for any one person to know more than a small fraction of it.

Botany, the study of plants, can be divided into several overlapping fields, all of which have zoological counterparts. The study of the form and structure of plants is called plant **morphology,** and this term is usually extended to cover also the changes in form and structure during growth and reproduction. Plant morphology includes plant **anatomy,** the study of the detailed structure of plants, particularly the kinds of cells of which tissues and organs are composed. The study of the structure of the living parts of cells (the protoplasm), including the changes in structure which occur during cell division, is called **cytology.** Still another specialized branch of morphology is **palynology,** the study of the structure of pollen grains.

The study of the processes occurring in plants and of the functions of plant parts is called **plant physiology.** Many plant physiologists now concern themselves chiefly with the chemical processes occurring in plants; they might equally well be called biochemists or plant biochemists.

The study of the relation between plants and their environment is called **plant ecology.** Plant ecology may be further divided into **autecology** and **synecology.** Autecology deals with individual plants, usually emphasizing the effect of the environment on the plant, rather than vice versa. It might almost as well be considered to be a branch of physiology, coordinate with the biochemical branch. Synecology deals with plant communities, including both the influence of the environment on the community and the influence of the community on the environment. **Plant geography,** the study of the distribution of plants and plant communities, is in large part a branch of synecology.

The study of heredity is called **genetics.** The principles of genetics are so similar in plants and animals that there is no clear division between plant geneticists and animal geneticists.

The study of the diseases of plants is called plant **pathology.**

The study of plant fossils is called **paleobotany.** Paleobotany may be considered to be a branch of **paleontology,** the study of fossils of all kinds, but the latter term (*paleontology*) is frequently used to refer primarily to the study of animal fossils.

The study of the mechanisms of evolution has attracted much attention, especially in the last half-century, but this branch of biology is not generally referred to by a special name. The study of the paths which evolution has followed, and thus of the relationships among kinds of plants, overlaps strongly with **systematic botany,** or plant **taxonomy.** Plant taxonomists attempt to classify plants into a system which reflects both evolutionary relationships and presently existing similarities and differences. Evidence from all sources is used in arriving at a taxonomic system, but external morphology is usually emphasized because it provides so many characters that can easily be seen and measured.

A large proportion of botanists devote their efforts chiefly to the study of the seed plants, which make up the dominant vegetation of the land surface. The study of other groups of plants is often designated by special names. **Pteridology** is the study of ferns and fern-like plants; **bryology** is the study of bryophytes (mosses and liverworts); **mycology** is the study of fungi; **phycology,** or **algology,** is the study of algae; **bacteriology** is the study of bacteria.

All the foregoing phases of botany have some economic significance. The study of the economic importance of plants is called **economic botany.** Economic botany is closely allied to agriculture, the culture of plants and/or animals for food or other economic use. A very specialized type of agriculture, in which plants are grown in tanks of water to which the necessary mineral nutrients have been added, is called **hydroponics.**

SUGGESTED READING

A *Century of Progress in the Natural Sciences, 1853–1953,* California Academy of Sciences, San Francisco, 1955, 807 pp. About half this book is botanical. Although it is not light reading, much of it should be intelligible to the general botany student. The better student will find it worth repeated attention in connection with chapter after chapter of this text.

Conant, James B., *On Understanding Science,* Yale University Press, New Haven, 1947, 142 pp. An essay on the nature and methods of science, with historical examples drawn mostly from chemistry and physics. No special background is needed to understand this book.

Cohen, I. Bernard, *Science, Servant of Man*, Little, Brown, Boston, 1948, 362 pp. A more enthusiastic and popularized approach than Conant's, with emphasis on current practical applications and future possibilities.

De Kruif, Paul, *Microbe Hunters*, Harcourt, Brace, New York, 1926. (Also in Pocket Book edition of 400 pp.) Chapters 2 and 3 of this fascinating and popular book deal with Spallanzani's and Pasteur's experiments on spontaneous generation.

The Structure and Function of Cells

◄

Western skunk cabbage, *Lysichiton kamtschatkensis.* This species and a number of its relatives respire so rapidly, as they come up in the spring, that the internal temperature of the inflorescence may reach 40 or 45 degrees C., several degrees higher than the normal human body temperature (37° C.). Skunk cabbage blooms at a time when the air temperature often drops below freezing, and the high rate of respiration may be of some importance in helping the plant to withstand low temperatures. (Photo by W. H. Hodge.)

CHAPTER 2

CHEMICAL AND PHYSICAL BACKGROUND

SUSPENSIONS, SOLUTIONS, AND COLLOIDS

The chemical and physical properties of any mixture of water and another substance undergo some variation according to the size of the particles of the substance in the water. In general, if solid particles in water are larger than about .0001 mm (a millimeter is about $\frac{1}{25}$ inch) in diameter, the mixture is cloudy or turbid, and the particles will eventually settle out. Such a mixture is called a **suspension.**

If the particles dispersed in the water are smaller than about .000001 mm in diameter, corresponding to the size of ordinary molecules or ions, the mixture is transparent and the particles do not settle out. Such a mixture is called a **solution.** The term *solution* may be applied to similar liquid mixtures which do not contain water and also to mixtures of gases. In a liquid solution, the substance whose particles are dispersed separately from each other is called the **solute,** and the substance through which the solute is dispersed is called the **solvent.** The solute is dissolved in the solvent. The most common solvent is water. The molecules of many substances in aqueous solution become separated into electrically charged, chemically active particles called **ions.**

If the particles dispersed in water are between about .0001 and .000001 mm in diameter, corresponding in size to very large individual molecules, or to groups of smaller molecules, the mixture may be either turbid or transparent, but the particles do not settle out. Such a mixture is called a colloidal suspension, a colloidal solution, or simply a **colloid.** Colloidal particles are often electrically charged, and they may tend to accumulate molecules of water or other substances on their surfaces. A colloid which tends to adsorb molecules of water on the surfaces of its particles is said to be **hydrophilic** (water-loving); and the swelling of a substance as a result of the adsorption of water by hydrophilic colloids is referred to as **imbibition.**

A colloid containing a relatively small amount of water is semisolid and is called a **gel.** A colloid containing a larger amount of water is more liquid and is called a **sol.** A gel can frequently be changed to a sol by raising its temperature, even without adding water, and the reverse change may occur when the temperature is lowered. Ordinary gelatin dessert is a colloidal gel which also contains sugar and flavoring.

Liquids which do not readily mix, such as oil and water, can form a physically stable mixture if the particles of one of the constituents are of colloidal size. Any colloidal suspension of a liquid in a liquid is called an **emulsion,** and the same term is commonly applied to any colloidal suspension of fat in water, or water in fat, regardless of whether the pure fat is liquid or solid. Cow's cream is an emulsion, as is also butter.

DIFFUSION

In any substance, be it solid, liquid, or gas, the molecules are in constant motion. In a solid the individual molecules move within a very limited range, but in a liquid or gas the individual molecules (or ions) are free to move throughout the solution. The molecules or ions of each substance eventually become uniformly distributed throughout the solution, even if they are introduced at only one point. The spreading of molecules or ions in solutions is called **diffusion.** Any substance in solution tends to diffuse from a region of its own high concentration toward a region of its own lower concentration, until a uniform distribution is achieved. After the solute has attained a uniform distribution throughout the solution, its molecules continue to move, but their movement does not change the equilibrium of the solution.

EFFECT OF TEMPERATURE ON CHEMICAL REACTIONS

The speed at which molecules and ions move increases with the temperature; temperature is in fact merely a measure of the speed of motion of these particles. Since any chemical reaction requires that different kinds of molecules or ions come into contact with each other, the rate at which these reactions take place also varies with the temperature. In the absence of other controlling or modifying factors, the rate of a chemical reaction approximately doubles with each increase of 10°C (18°F) in temperature. Often there is also a minimum temperature below which a reaction does not take place, and sometimes there is a maximum as well.

ENZYMES

Many chemical reactions between two substances occur whenever the two substances are brought together in solution. Other chemical changes require the intercession of a third substance, which takes part in the reaction but is not used up by it. Such substances, which facilitate chemical reactions between other substances, are called **catalysts.** Most of the chemical reactions characteristic of life involve catalysts. Catalysts produced by living organisms are called **enzymes.** Most enzymes have specific and limited functions, and every living cell contains many different enzymes.

CARBON CHEMISTRY

At the temperatures prevailing on earth, one element, carbon, differs from all others in the ability of its atoms to link with each other in chains, rings, and other structures, to which atoms of other elements are also attached, thus forming a very large number of different compounds. It was once thought that these complex carbon compounds could be produced only by living organisms; and carbon chemistry is still called **organic chemistry,** even though a great many organic compounds can now be produced in the laboratory and many of these do not even exist in nature.

When a chemical compound composed of two or more elements is produced, some electrons which previously belonged to one atom seem to be shared with another atom, and this sharing of electrons holds the atoms together into a molecule. The number of electrons which may be given or received by an atom in such an arrangement is referred to as the **valence** of the element. If electrons are given by the element, its valence is positive; if they are received by the element, its valence is negative.

In relatively simple compounds, carbon has a valence of plus 4 or minus 4. In more complex carbon compounds, it is difficult to distinguish the plus from the minus valences, since the carbon atoms are linked to each other. In organic chemistry, then, it is customary to think of each carbon atom as having 4 bonds, without worrying about whether these are positive or negative. On such an assumption it is possible to produce structural formulas for many organic compounds, with each atom represented by the symbol for its element and each bond represented by a line. The formula of carbon dioxide, a molecule which consists of 1 atom of carbon and 2 of oxygen, may be written as CO_2 or as

$$O \atop \underset{O}{\overset{\parallel}{C}}$$

. Likewise, methane, or marsh gas, may be written as CH_4 (the H representing hydrogen), or as

$$H-\underset{\underset{H}{\textstyle |}}{\overset{\overset{\textstyle H}{|}}{C}}-H.$$

Formaldehyde is CH_2O, or

$$\underset{\underset{H}{\textstyle |}}{\overset{\overset{\textstyle H}{|}}{C}}=O.$$

The reader will note that in each of these formulas hydrogen has a valence of 1, and oxygen 2. These are the characteristic valences of these two elements.

Often organic compounds will have 1 atom of hydrogen and 1 of oxygen collectively linked to a carbon atom by a single bond. Since hydrogen, like carbon, can have either a plus or a minus valence, whereas oxygen characteristically has a minus valence, it would be possible to show the oxygen atom connected to the carbon atom by one bond and to the hydrogen atom by the other. However, it is customary to write the OH as a single group, omitting the bond between the hydrogen atom and the oxygen atom in the diagram. Thus the structural formula of formic

acid is written H—C
$\begin{array}{c} O \\ \parallel \\ C \\ \backslash \\ OH \end{array}$, instead of

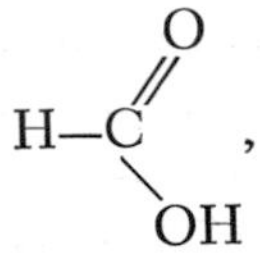

$\begin{array}{c} O \\ \parallel \\ H—C \\ \backslash \\ O—H \end{array}$. Organic acids regularly

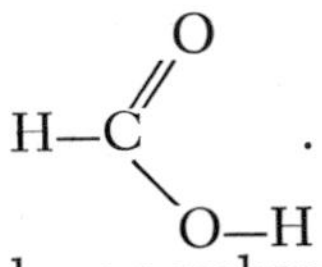

have a carbon atom which shares two of its bonds with an oxygen atom, one with an OH group, and one with some other atom. The acid effect is produced by the partial dissociation (in water) of the hydrogen atoms, without the shared electrons, from the OH group. Such hydrogen ions, as they are called, are characteristic of all acids, organic or inorganic. If one wishes to write the formula of formic acid without diagramming its structure, one writes HCOOH, the terminal COOH portion of the formula giving clear indication that the substance is an organic acid. The formula of acetic acid, a slightly more complex compound, may be written as CH_3COOH, or it may be diagrammed as

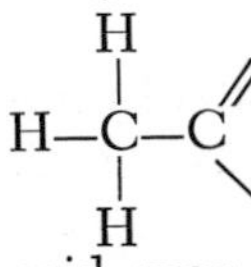

$\begin{array}{ccc} H & & O \\ | & & \parallel \\ H—C—C & \\ | & & \backslash \\ H & & OH \end{array}$. The formula of propionic

acid may be written as C_2H_5COOH or

diagrammed as

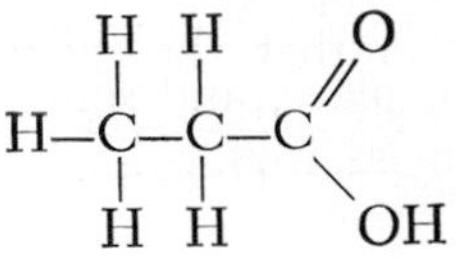

$\begin{array}{cccc} H & H & & O \\ | & | & & \parallel \\ H—C—C—C & \\ | & | & & \backslash \\ H & H & & OH \end{array}$

Foods

Any chemical compound which can be broken down by living organisms with release of energy is called a **food**. Most foods synthesized by plants may be classified into three general groups, **carbohydrates**, **fats**, and **proteins**. Typical fats and carbohydrates are composed wholly of carbon, hydrogen, and oxygen; proteins also contain nitrogen and usually one or more other elements (especially sulfur) as well. The simpler compounds from which foods are made, such as carbon dioxide, water, and various inorganic salts, are regarded as raw materials rather than as foods.

In carbohydrates there are characteristically twice as many atoms of hydrogen per molecule as there are of oxygen. One of the commonest carbohydrates is glucose (also called dextrose, or corn sugar), a simple sugar having the formula $C_6H_{12}O_6$. Glucose exists in two slightly differing forms, called α-glucose and β-glucose. A suggested structural formula for α-glucose, which explains most but not all of its chemical properties, is given in Fig.

Fig. 2.1. Structural formula of α-glucose. The heavy line indicates the near side of the ring.

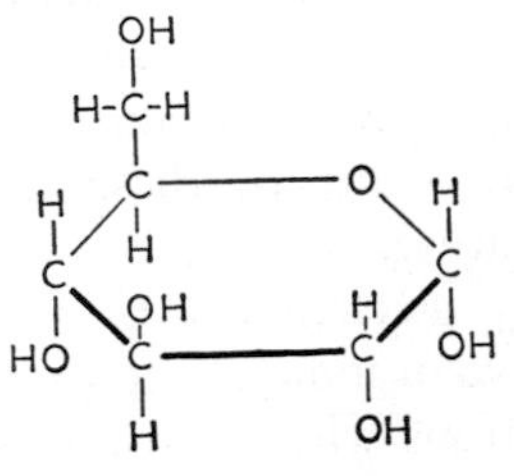

2.1. β-glucose apparently differs from α-glucose only in that the carbon atom at the farthest right, as in Fig. 2.1, has the OH above and the H below the plane of the ring.

Glucose is called a **hexose** sugar because it contains 6 carbon atoms. Some other hexose sugars, such as fructose (also called levulose) and mannose, also have the formula $C_6H_{12}O_6$ but have the atoms somewhat differently arranged. **Pentose** sugars, containing 5 rather than 6 carbon atoms, are also of frequent occurrence and have the general formula $C_5H_{10}O_5$. Simple sugars having 3, 4, or 7 carbon atoms are of less frequent occurrence. Any simple sugar, whether it has 3, 4, 5, 6, or 7 carbon atoms, may be called a **monosaccharide.**

A **disaccharide** is a sugar formed by the combination of two similar or different monosaccharides, the combination occurring in such a way that a molecule of water, H_2O, is released in the process. (It has been shown that water normally exists in aggregate molecules for which the formula is $(H_2O)_n$; but for most purposes it is still customary and adequate to write the formula H_2O.) One OH group from each of the two monosaccharides is affected in such a way that both of the hydrogen atoms are combined with one of the oxygen atoms to form a molecule of free water, and the remaining oxygen atom is bonded to each of the two monosaccharides, linking them into a disaccharide. Without resorting to a structural diagram, a typical example of such a process may be written $2C_6H_{12}O_6 \longrightarrow C_{12}H_{22}O_{11} + H_2O$. Under proper conditions, this reaction may be reversed, and 2 molecules of monosaccharide may be produced from 1 molecule of disaccharide, using up a molecule of water in the process. Many other chemical compounds may be broken down into simpler compounds in somewhat similar fashion, with water being used in the process. Such a chemical reaction is called **hydrolysis.**

The commonest disaccharide is cane sugar, or sucrose, which is formed from 1 molecule of glucose and 1 molecule of fructose, and which may be hydrolyzed to yield the original glucose and fructose molecules. Maltose is a disaccharide formed by the combination of 2 molecules of glucose.

Polysaccharides are formed by the union of several or many monosaccharide molecules in the same way that two monosaccharides are linked to form a disaccharide. Each such linkage results in the production of one molecule of water. A hexose polysaccharide may thus be thought of, in one way, as a series of $C_6H_{10}O_5$ groups linked to an original $C_6H_{12}O_6$. No matter how many monosaccharide molecules are combined to make the polysaccharide, the proportions of carbon, hydrogen, and oxygen never quite reach that of $C_6H_{10}O_5$ (so far as our information indicates) because the complete polysaccharide molecule always contains two additional atoms of hydrogen and one additional atom of oxygen. A generalized formula of a hexose polysaccharide may therefore be written as $(C_6H_{10}O_5)_n \cdot H_2O$. The n in the formula stands for any number, and in many polysaccharides it is evidently a high number, sometimes more than 1000. Two very common polysaccharides are starch, a reserve food, and cellulose, the principle constituent of the cell walls of most plants. The formation of complex molecules by the combination of a number of simpler molecules of the same or closely related kinds is called **polymerization,** and the resulting compounds are called **polymers.**

Some compounds which do not have exactly twice as many hydrogen atoms as oxygen atoms per molecule are still considered to be carbohydrates because of their close general similarity to other carbohydrates; and indeed there is no inherent and precise division between the carbohydrates and other organic compounds.

Fats differ from carbohydrates in the arrangement and proportion of atoms in the molecule, always having fewer oxygen atoms in relation to the number of hydrogen atoms than do carbohydrates. They have a higher energy content per unit of weight than do carbohydrates, and more oxygen is required to oxidize or respire them.

In general, any process which uses free oxygen and forms oxides, such as carbon dioxide and water as end products, releases chemical energy; whereas any process in which chemically bound oxygen is transformed into free oxygen absorbs energy. The use of oxygen with resultant release of energy is called **oxidation.** The opposite process, in which oxygen is released and energy is taken up, is called **reduction.** These definitions are adequate for our purposes, although modern chemists find expanded definitions of both terms more useful.

Fats are formed by the chemical combination of glycerol (glycerin), a kind of alcohol, with certain kinds of organic compounds known as **fatty acids.** Glycerol has the following structure:

$$
\begin{array}{c}
\text{H} \\
| \\
\text{HO--C--H} \\
| \\
\text{HO--C--H} \\
| \\
\text{HO--C--H} \\
| \\
\text{H}
\end{array}
$$

In the formation of a fat, 3 molecules of fatty acid (the same or different acids) are combined with 1 molecule of glycerin, and 3 molecules of water are released. If the convenient symbol R is used in each case to represent the majority of the structure of the fatty acid, the reaction may be shown as at the bottom of the page.

It will be seen that the chemical linkage of fatty acids to glycerin is accomplished in similar fashion to the linkage of monosaccharide molecules to form a disaccharide. In each case the formerly separate molecules are linked by an atom of oxygen at a point where each of the separate molecules had carried an OH, and a molecule of water is formed in the process. As might therefore be expected, fats can be hydrolyzed to produce glycerol and fatty acids, just as polysaccharides can be hydrolyzed to form monosaccharides.

Fats which are liquid at ordinary temperatures are frequently referred to as oils, but many substances called oils in general speech are of quite different chemical nature.

There are many compounds which, like fats, are insoluble in water but soluble in certain organic solvents such as acetone, ether, chloroform, and carbon tetrachloride. These, together with fats, are known as **lipids**. A large proportion of the lipids are formed in part from fatty acids and thus have some chemical similarity to fats, but some others are quite different in structure. An important group of lipids contains phosphorus as well as fatty acids; these are known as phospholipids. Some other lipids have fatty acids in combination with carbohydrates or with protein, thus breaking down the usual distinctions among these three types of foods.

Proteins differ from carbohydrates and fats in that they always contain nitrogen. They usually also contain sulfur, frequently phosphorus, and sometimes other elements as well. Proteins can be hydrolyzed to yield amino acids, which are organic acids having one or more amine, or NH_2, groups in place of hydrogen atoms. Most proteins are so complex that satisfactory structural formulas have not been produced for them, but the structure of the individual amino acids is known. The simplest amino acid, called glycine, or amino acetic acid, has the following structure:

$$\begin{array}{ccc} H & & O \\ | & & \| \\ H-C-C & & \\ | & & \diagdown \\ N & & OH \\ \diagup\diagdown & & \\ H & H & \end{array}$$

Some other amino acids are much more complex.

Protein molecules are usually very large, and many individual amino acid molecules go into the formation of each protein molecule. About 23 principal kinds of amino acids are involved, but not every protein molecule contains all these kinds.

An almost infinite number of proteins exist, varying in the acids used, their ratios to each other, and their positions within the molecules. Proteins usually occur as mixtures of slightly differing molecules, and it is doubtful that any protein has yet been obtained in a strictly pure form. The only protein whose structural formula has been clearly worked out is insulin.

Proteins which are formed solely by the linkage of amino acids, and which yield only amino acids on hydrolysis, are called **simple proteins.** Proteins which yield one or more other compounds in addition to amino acids when hydrolyzed are called **conjugated proteins.** Proteins may be conjugated with many other kinds of compounds, including carbohydrates. All or nearly all the enzymes which exist in plants are proteins or occur in conjugation with proteins.

HISTORICAL BACKGROUND

We have noted that a development in one field of science may be necessary to further advancement in some other field of science. The invention of the compound microscope in 1590 by Zacharias Jansen, a spectacle maker of Middelburg, Netherlands, was one of the most important events in the history of biology. It had long been known that a double-convex lens forms an enlarged visual image, but only a few diameters magnification could be obtained from most such lenses. Jansen found that by using two lenses, properly spaced, the magnified image produced by the first lens was again magnified by the second. His own microscopes were relatively crude, but they demonstrated the principle which enabled subsequent workers to make much more useful instruments.

The nature of light imposes practical limits to the magnification which can be obtained with a microscope of the type invented by Jansen. With ordinary present-day equipment this is a little more than 1000 diameters, and the most specialized accessory equipment does not extend the profitable range of magnification to more than about 3000 diameters. The

Fig. 2.2. **An electron microscope. (Courtesy of the Radio Corporation of America.)**

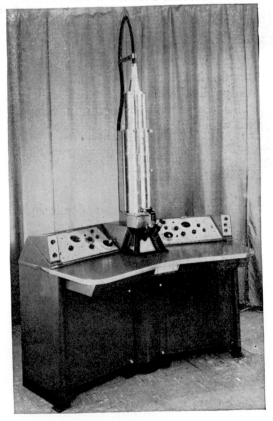

resolving power of the microscope, that is, its ability to produce distinct images of objects which are close together, is inherently limited by the wavelength of light. For practical purposes, structures less than about 200 millimicrons in diameter cannot be distinguished with microscopes using visible light. A micron is 1/1000 millimeter, and a millimicron is 1/1000 micron.

If a beam of electrons, instead of a beam of light, is thrown on the object to be examined, then with proper apparatus an image can be obtained which is profitably enlargeable to 100,000 diameters or more. The essential principle was discovered by a German physicist (Hans Busch) in 1924, and the electron microscope was developed during the 1930's. The design was much improved during the late 1930's and the 1940's by the Radio Corporation of America, and the instrument is now coming into general scientific use (Fig. 2.2). It has obvious advantages over conventional microscopes in the much greater magnifications which can be obtained, but manipulation and maintenance require considerable skill. It cannot be used on living material, since it operates in a vacuum, and the beam of electrons would in any case kill the object examined.

One of the first microscopists was Anton van Leeuwenhoek (1632–1723), a dry-goods merchant, and later custodian of the city hall in Delft, Netherlands. He used a simple rather than a compound microscope (Fig. 2.3), but he ground his lenses far more carefully than did any of his contemporaries. One of his instruments, preserved at Utrecht, magnifies about 280 diameters, which is extraordinarily good for a single lens, even by modern standards. He was probably the first man to observe bacteria, yeasts, and protozoa,

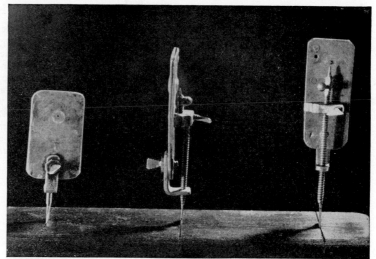

Fig. 2.3. Three Leeuwen-hoek microscopes, showing front, back, and side views. The lens is mounted in the small opening in the plate. The position of the needle point, which holds the object to be examined, is adjusted by the controls shown in the side and back views. (Slightly less than natural size.) (Copyright by Rijksmuseum voor de Geschiedenis der Natuurwetenschappen, Leiden.)

among other things. Many of his observations became known through his long correspondence with the British Royal Society.

Robert Hooke (1635–1703), a versatile British physicist, mathematician, and architect, devoted some time to improving and using the compound microscope (Fig. 2.4). His *Micrographia* (Fig. 2.5), published in 1665, included a description and illustration of the structure of cork. He introduced the term *cell* for the minute cavities into which the cork was regularly partitioned.

Subsequent investigators found that other parts of plants, and of animals as well, were also divided into cells. The German botanist Matthias Schleiden (1804–1881) and his zoologist friend Theodor Schwann (1810–1882) were impressed by the essential similarity of the structure of plant and animal tissues, and together they formulated, in 1838, the concept that all tissues, and indeed all organisms, are composed of cells. We now know that very small organisms often consist of but a single cell and that some kinds of organ-

Fig. 2.4. A microscope used by Robert Hooke. (Courtesy of the Medical Museum of the Armed Forces Institute of Pathology.)

isms, notably many fungi, are not divided into separate cells; but their idea was basically sound, and the **cell theory**, as it is called, is now one of the fundamental concepts of biology.

The Structure and Function of Cells 21

of other Vegetables to do to their bulk. But of these pores I have said more elsewhere.

To proceed then, Cork seems to be by the transverse constitution of the pores, a kind of *Fungus* or Mushrome, for the pores lie like so many Rays tending from the center, or pith of the tree, outwards; so that if you cut off a piece from a board of Cork transversly, to the flat of it, you will, as it were, split the pores, and they will appear just as they are express'd in the Figure B of the XI. *Scheme*. But if you shave off a very thin piece from this board, parallel to the plain of it, you will cut all the pores transversly, and they will appear almost as they are express'd in the Figure A, save onely the solid *Interstitia* will not appear so thick as they are there represented.

Fig. 2.5. A part of Robert Hooke's *Micrographia*.

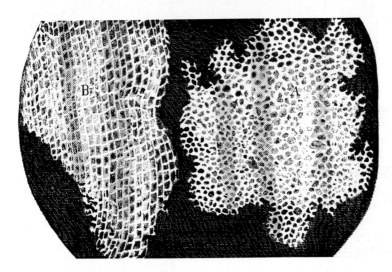

The cork cells observed by Hooke had no living contents, because cork cells die on reaching maturity and their protoplasm disintegrates. Even when living cells were studied, however, early observers apparently failed to recognized their protoplasmic contents, and such works as the *Anatomy of Plants*, published in 1675 by the Italian professor of medicine, Marcello Malpighi (1628–1694), are concerned entirely with cell walls rather than cell contents.

The first clear recognition of the living contents of a cell may have been made by the Italian botanist Bonaventuri Corti (1729–1813), who in 1772 observed protoplasmic streaming in the cells of *Chara*, an alga. In 1833 the Scottish botanist Robert Brown (1773–1858) described the nucleus as a regular component of living cells, but he did not understand its significance. The French zoologist Félix Dujardin (1801–1860) proposed the term *sarcode* in 1835 for the living substance of the cells of some simple animals which he was studying, but his term was not generally adopted. The Czech zoologist Johannes Purkinje (1787–1869) used the term *protoplasm* in 1840 for the formative substance of young animal embryos, and in 1846 the

German botanist Hugo von Mohl (1805–1872) applied this same term to the living contents of plant cells. The German botanist Ferdinand Cohn (1828–1898) suggested in 1850 that the protoplasm of plant and animal cells is essentially similar. In 1861 the German zoologist Max Schultze (1825–1884) set forth the doctrine (the protoplasm doctrine) that each unit of organization of living things consists of a mass of protoplasm, including a nucleus. Such an organized unit of protoplasm is now called a **protoplast.**

The role of the cell nucleus as the "vehicle of heredity" was tentatively suggested by the German naturalist and philosopher, Ernst Haeckel (1834–1919) in 1866. The soundness of Haeckel's speculation was independently and almost simultaneously confirmed by four other Germans—three zoologists and one botanist—in 1884–1885.

The concept of the cell has thus changed considerably from Robert Hooke's cavities surrounded by walls. Now we think of a cell as a protoplast which (in plants) is surrounded by a wall, or, in dead tissues or cells, as the wall itself. The empty space enclosed by the wall of a dead cell is now called the **lumen** and is of little scientific interest.

STRUCTURE OF CELLS

General Structure

Cells are extremely varied in size and shape and often have specialized functions related to these differences. Some bacteria are only about 200 millimicrons in diameter, which is barely large enough to be observed with the most powerful conven-

Fig. 2.6. Matthias Schleiden (1804–1881), German botanist who with Theodor Schwann proposed the cell theory.

tional microscopes. The cells which make up the juice sacs of citrus fruits are among the larger plant cells. The slender fiber cells of some plants are as much as 50 cm long, and nerve cells in some of the higher animals may reach a length of more than 1 meter. The largest cells of all, in terms of volume, are the yolks of the eggs of some of the larger birds, such as the ostrich. Most cells are so small as to be barely if at all visible to the naked eye, but large enough to be studied in fair detail under microscopes giving 100–400 diameters magnification.

A plant cell characteristically consists of (1) a protoplast which encloses (2) a **central vacuole** and is enclosed by (3) a cell wall. The central vacuole is not empty but contains the **cell sap.** The protoplast is the living part of the cell. It consists of a complex mixture of proteins, lipids, and

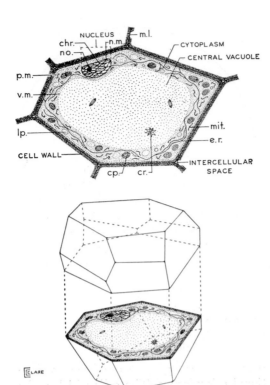

NUCLEUS
chr.
no.
m.l.
n.m.
CYTOPLASM
CENTRAL VACUOLE
p.m.
v.m.
lp.
mit.
e.r.
CELL WALL
cp.
cr.
INTERCELLULAR SPACE

CLARE

Fig. 2.7. A typical plant cell, much enlarged; chr., chromatin; cp., chloroplast; cr., crystal; e.r., endoplasmic reticulum; lp., leucoplast; mit., mitochondrium; m.l., middle lamella; n.m., nuclear membrane; no., nucleolus; p.m., plasma membrane; v.m., vacuolar membrane. For purposes of illustration the plasma membrane is shown slightly removed from the cell wall, instead of closely appressed to the wall as it would be in a normal cell.

other substances in colloidal suspension, plus some materials in true solution. It is usually divisible into two parts: (1) a mass of **cytoplasm**, in which is embedded (2) a distinctive body called the **nucleus**.

The Cell Wall

The cell wall is ordinarily composed of one or two layers. The thin outer layer is called the **primary wall;** the thicker inner layer, when present, is formed after the outer layer and is called the **secondary wall.**

The layers are not usually of uniform, homogeneous structure; each layer consists instead of an irregular latticework of slender rods called **micelles**, with many small openings and scattered larger ones (Fig. 2.8). Both the primary and secondary wall are usually composed largely of **cellulose**, a complex polysaccharide which can be broken down into β-glucose by hydrolysis. The chemical formula of cellulose can be written $(C_6H_{10}O_5)_n \cdot H_2O$. The n represents a large number, probably from 1000 to 2000. It is likely that the number represented by n in the formula is not entirely constant and that there are several or many different kinds of cellulose with differing values of n.

Occurring with the cellulose, but in smaller amounts, are usually one or more substances called **cellulosans**, or pentosans, which are polysaccharides that differ from cellulose in being formed of pentose sugars rather than of glucose, which is a hexose sugar. Another group of substances which commonly occur in the walls of plant cells are pectin and similar compounds, collectively called **pectic substances**. These substances differ chemically from cellulose in that some or all of the simpler molecules obtained by hydrolysis have the

projecting $\overset{\displaystyle H}{\underset{\displaystyle H}{\overset{|}{\underset{|}{C}}}}$—OH group of the glucose

replaced by a COOH group. In addition to occurring with cellulose in cell walls, pectic substances commonly form a thin layer, called the **middle lamella**, which holds adjacent cells together and is not regarded as part of the wall of either cell. The middle lamella between young cells is composed largely of pectin, which is soft and jelly-like. As the cells mature the pectin is often changed to calcium pectate,

24   Introductory Botany

a much harder cement which holds the cells firmly together. The cellulosans, pectic substances, and some other compounds related to the pectic substances have certain properties in common and are often collectively referred to as **hemicelluloses.**

Many cells, particularly those of wood, also contain **lignin,** a group of complex substances whose chemical composition is not yet fully understood. Lignin appears to be composed wholly of carbon, hydrogen, and oxygen, but unlike cellulose and hemicellulose it is not of carbohydrate nature and evidently is not formed by the polymerization of saccharides or saccharide-like molecules. Still other substances which occur in the cell walls of some

kinds of plants are discussed under the plant groups in which they are found.

THE CENTRAL VACUOLE

The protoplast commonly occupies essentially the whole space enclosed by the wall in young cells and often has numerous scattered small vacuoles. In mature plant cells, however, the protoplast usually forms a thin layer, just within the cell wall, which encloses a large central vacuole. The material contained in the central vacuole is called the **cell sap.** It consists of water, with a variety of other substances in true and colloidal solution, and it may also contain small crystals of

Fig. 2.8. Electron micrograph of cell wall in the root tip of an onion, showing loosely interwoven micelles of cellulose, with scattered openings of various sizes. Remains of plasmodesmata can be seen here and there as white blobs. This cell has a primary wall but no secondary wall. (×34,000.) (Courtesy of Flora Murray Scott.)

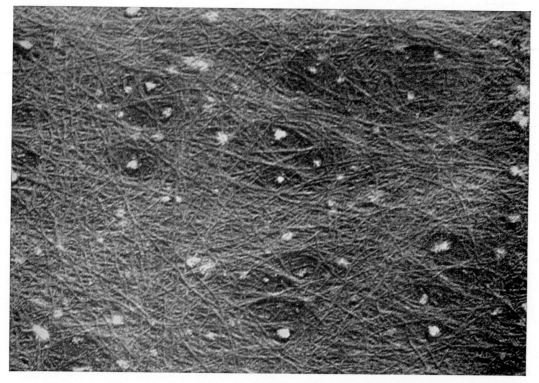

various sorts. Due to the colloids present, the cell sap is usually slightly viscous. The central vacuole is usually regarded as a nonliving inclusion of the cell, just as the cell wall is customarily regarded as a nonliving boundary to the cell, although, as has been pointed out, no one constituent of a living cell is alive when considered by itself. In general, the contents of the vacuole do not appear to be in a state of chemical activity, as are the constituents of the protoplast. Some of the vacuolar constituents are simply waste products. Others are, in at least some cases, food reserves which can be reincorporated into the protoplasm. Some kinds of pigments which give a characteristic color to certain plant parts also occur in vacuoles, although other pigments are borne in the cytoplasm. Notable among the pigments occurring in the vacuoles are the **anthocyanins,** which range in color from blue or violet to purple or red, and which are responsible for the colors of many flowers and some other plant parts such as the roots of beets.

THE CYTOPLASM

The cytoplasm of a typical plant cell consists of a clear, more or less viscous fluid (the **hyaloplasm**), an endoplasmic reticulum, and certain specialized bodies called plastids, mitochondria, and Golgi bodies. It may also contain small droplets, granules, and vacuoles, which are chemically relatively inactive and are therefore

Fig. 2.9.   Plasmodesmata in the very thick-walled cells of the endosperm (part of the seed) of persimmon (*Diospyros virginiana*). (Much enlarged.) (Copyright by General Biological Supply House, Inc., Chicago.)

customarily regarded as nonliving inclusions rather than as part of the living cytoplasm. The cytoplasm is bounded externally by a **plasma membrane** and internally by a **vacuolar membrane.** In multicellular plants the cytoplasm of adjacent cells is commonly continuous through numerous small holes in the cell wall. These connecting strands of cytoplasm are called **plasmodesmata** (Fig. 2.9).

The plasma membrane is exceedingly thin and consists of some of the same substances present in the rest of the cytoplasm, but in different proportions, with relatively more lipids. In some of its physical properties the plasma membrane resembles the surface film of a body of water, in which the molecules are believed to be closely arranged in a pavement-like layer. The existence of the plasma membrane as a discrete structure rather than as strictly a surface tension phenomenon was demonstrated by the American plant physiologist William Seifriz (1888–1955), who by careful micromanipulation was able to separate portions of the plasma membrane from the remainder of the cytoplasm in the cells of some plants.

Some recent experimental evidence suggests that the plasma membrane has numerous very small openings, so that it might be compared to an ultramicroscopic sieve. According to this viewpoint some of the smaller molecules and ions in solution can enter the protoplast by passing through the opening in the plasma membrane, while the larger ones can enter only by becoming dissolved in the material of the plasma membrane. Any openings which may exist in the plasma membrane are too small to be observed with conventional microscopes, and the structure of the membrane would doubtless be altered by any technique which would permit examination with the electron microscope.

The membrane separating the cytoplasm from the central vacuole is essentially similar to the plasma membrane. Each of any smaller vacuoles which may be scattered throughout the cytoplasm is bounded by a membrane of similar nature.

The **endoplasmic reticulum** (Fig. 2.10) is a loose network which permeates the cytoplasm and is connected to the nuclear membrane. It may even make up part of a plasmodesma which connects one cell with another. Minute, proteinaceous, chemically active bodies, called *microsomes,* have been isolated from macerated cells by use of a centrifuge, but careful electron micrographs do not disclose such bodies in intact cells. It is now strongly suspected that microsomes are really detached fragments of the endoplasmic reticulum.

Up to the present, studies of the endoplasmic reticulum have been carried out primarily in young, rapidly growing cells; it is not yet certain how nearly representative these are of cells in general. The full streaming of protoplasm commonly observed in mature cells would be difficult if the endoplasmic reticulum remained firmly attached to the nucleus and the cell wall at a number of points.

The cytoplasm contains a number of specialized, differentiated bodies called **plastids.** Colorless plastids are called **leucoplasts;** green plastids are called **chloroplasts;** and colored plastids other than chloroplasts are called **chromoplasts.** Since a chromoplast is, literally, a colored plastid, a chloroplast could be considered as one type of chromoplast, but because the chloroplasts are so different in function and structure from other chromoplasts it is

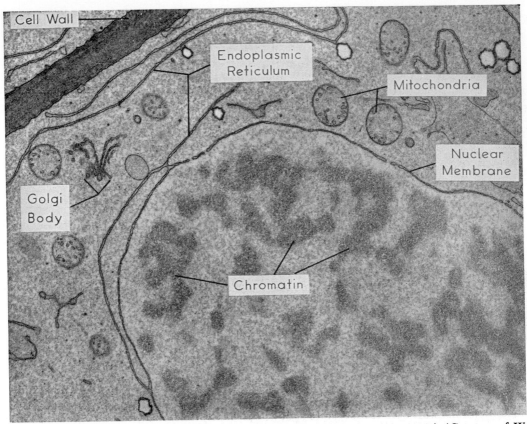

Fig. 2.10. Electron micrograph of part of a young cell of a corn root. (×11,000.) (Courtesy of W. Gordon Whaley, University of Texas.)

convenient to name and discuss them separately. Plastids are highly varied in form but are most commonly shaped like a double-convex lens, a disk, or a sphere.

Chloroplasts are characterized by the presence of a green pigment, **chlorophyll.** In the living cell chlorophyll and some associated pigments occur in conjugation with proteins, but they can be extracted from dead cells without the protein. As extracted, chlorophyll commonly exists in two slightly differing forms, called chlorophyll *a* and chlorophyll *b* (Fig. 2.11). The formula for extracted chlorophyll *a* is $C_{55}H_{72}N_4O_5Mg$; chlorophyll *b* differs only

in having one more atom of oxygen and two fewer of hydrogen. Still other variants of chlorophyll occur among some of the algae and bacteria. Chlorophyll was first synthesized from simple raw materials in 1960 by the American biochemist Robert B. Woodward.

The Mg in the formula for chlorophyll stands for magnesium. The core of the chlorophyll molecule consists of 1 atom of magnesium, surrounded by 4 nitrogen atoms to which are attached chains and rings of carbon, hydrogen, and oxygen. The hemoglobin of red blood cells in animals has an essentially similar structure, except that there is an atom of iron rather than of magnesium at the center. Iron is also used, in some way as yet not fully understood, in the formation of chlorophyll, but it is not present in chlorophyll itself.

Chlorophyll is always accompanied by one or more associated pigments which are not green. In the higher plants, two yellow pigments, **carotene** and **xanthophyll,** are customarily associated with chlorophyll, but their presence is masked by the more abundant chlorophyll. Carotene is the name for several closely allied compounds, all having the formula $C_{40}H_{56}$, but differing slightly in the arrangement of the atoms in the molecule. The xanthophylls differ from carotene in having one or several atoms of oxygen in the molecule; a common xanthophyll has the formula $C_{40}H_{56}O_2$. Carotene, xanthophyll, and some other mostly yellow to red or brownish pigments have certain structural features and chemical properties in common, and are called **carotenoid pigments.** Carotenoid pigments sometimes occur without chlorophyll, and they furnish the color of many chromoplasts.

In some algae, chlorophyll is accompanied and more or less masked by brownish, red, or blue pigments, some of which are carotenoids, while others are of a different type called phycobilins. It is often convenient to use the term *chloroplast* for any chlorophyll-bearing plastid, regardless of its color, and to restrict the term *chromoplast* to colored plastids which do not contain chlorophyll. That practice is adopted in this text.

Some other specialized parts of the cytoplasm, the **mitochondria** (also called chondriosomes), are colorless and might be considered as leucoplasts, but here again the function is so different that it is

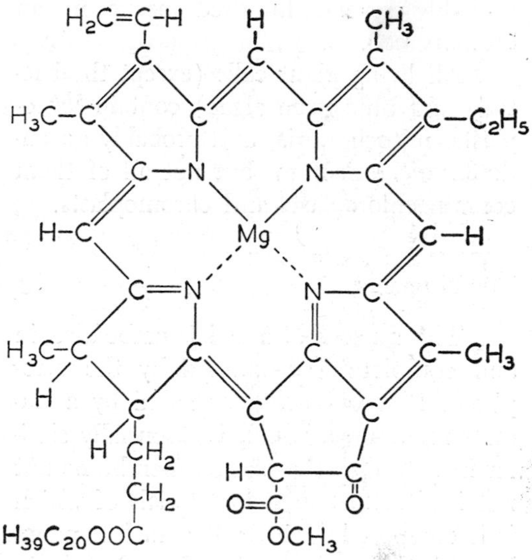

Fig. 2.11. Probable structural formula of chlorophyll *a.*

convenient to draw a distinction in the terminology. Mitochondria, like plastids, are variable in shape; most often they are crooked rods. In spite of their small size (up to about 5 microns long), they have a complex organized structure.

In addition to plastids and mitochondria, the cytoplasm also contains scattered minute bodies called **Golgi bodies** (Fig. 2.10), after the Italian zoologist Camillo Golgi (1844–1926), who in 1898 reported the existence of what may be these same structures in nerve cells of barn owls. Golgi bodies are in the size range of small mitochondria, and they are even more difficult to observe with ordinary techniques and conventional microscopes. Recent studies with electron microscopes have resolved some of the uncertainties, showing that the Golgi bodies characteristically consist of about half a dozen parallel platelets. It now seems likely that they are a regular constituent of both plant and animal cells;

The Structure and Function of Cells 29

probably several hundred occur in an ordinary cell.

All living plant cells (except the bacteria and blue-green algae) contain leucoplasts, mitochondria, and probably an endoplasmic reticulum, but not all of them contain chloroplasts and chromoplasts.

THE NUCLEUS

The nucleus of a cell is embedded in and completely surrounded by the cytoplasm. It is ordinarily bounded by a **nuclear membrane**, which is essentially similar in nature to the plasma membrane but not identical as to the materials of which it is composed. Within the nuclear membrane is the **nuclear sap**, or karyolymph, in which are embedded the **chromonemata** and a more or less spherical body called the **nucleolus** (or often two or more nucleoli). The nuclear sap, unlike the cell sap of the central vacuole, is chemically active and is regarded as living substance.

The chromonemata are slender, thread-like bodies which are so twisted and tangled that they appear to form a network. During cell division the chromonemata contract and become organized (with the addition of some previously undifferentiated material) into much shorter and thicker bodies, called **chromosomes.** The number of chromosomes in a cell varies according to the kind of organism, but, except for the regular and alternating changes during the reproductive cycle, discussed in Chapter 4, it is usually constant for each individual species. The number may be as low as 1, or more than 1000, but numbers of 6 to 50 are most common.

The word *chromosome* is derived from two Greek words: *chrōma*, color, and *sōma*, body. The name was originally proposed because some of the dyes used in preparing parts of plants for microscopic study have a particular affinity for these structures, which therefore appeared as colored bodies within the cell. The chromosomes consist in large part of a complex series of substances called **chromatin.** The individual units of chromatin, called **genes,** seem to be arranged in a linear sequence on the chromosomes, although recent experimental evidence indicates that this is probably an oversimplification. Each chromosome contains many different genes. The chromatin, or genic material, consists wholly or in large part of **nucleoproteins**, which are conjugated proteins formed by the combination of simple proteins with some complex organic acids called **nucleic acids.** It has been suggested that a chromosome, as seen during cell division, consists of a series of genes, or nucleoprotein units, extending out at right angles to a core of simple protein, but the evidence is still inconclusive, and even this may be an oversimplification.

All the many different nucleic acids contain nitrogen and phosphorus, as well as carbon, hydrogen, and oxygen. Most nucleic acids can be divided into two general groups, **ribonucleic acid,** commonly called **RNA,** and **deoxyribonucleic acid,** commonly called **DNA.** One of the blocks which goes into the formation of a molecule of RNA is ribose, a pentose sugar. DNA differs from RNA, among other respects, in that a ribose-like molecule, containing less oxygen than true ribose, is used in place of ribose in the formation of the DNA molecule. DNA occurs principally in chromatin, of which it is considered to be the essential constituent. RNA, on the other hand, occurs chiefly in the cytoplasm and in the nucleolus, being present also in minute amounts in the nuclear sap. Recent evidence suggests that there may be a consistent chemical difference between the DNA of higher plants and that of higher animals.

FUNCTIONS OF THE INDIVIDUAL PARTS OF CELLS

THE CELL WALL

The cell wall gives shape and some degree of rigidity to the cell. Unless it is impregnated with waterproofing substances, as is true, for example, of cork cells, it presents no significant barrier to the diffusion of water or other materials in solution. The middle lamella holds adjacent cells together.

THE NUCLEUS

The nucleus, and specifically the genes in the nucleus, govern most of the hereditary characteristics of the cell. The precise manner in which the genes act is not fully understood, but present evidence indicates that they govern the formation of molecules which migrate out into the cytoplasm and there, in turn, govern the formation of molecules of various cytoplasmic enzymes. Thus the kind and amount of enzymes in the cytoplasm are controlled mainly by the genes. Since the chemical activities and, indirectly, the physical properties of a cell depend largely on the enzymes present, this would explain the important role which the nucleus is known to play in controlling the nature of the whole cell.

A more detailed but less certain explanation of the mechanism of gene action is as follows: The nucleolus may act as a sort of factory and warehouse for low-polymer molecules of RNA. These low polymers migrate to the chromosomes, where they are assembled into high polymers. The assembly is governed by the genes,

Fig. 2.12. Results of an experiment using radioactive tracers. Excised root tips of broad bean (*Vicia faba*), growing in culture, were provided with cytidine (a precursor of RNA and DNA) that had been labeled with tritium, a radioactive isotope of hydrogen. The root tips were allowed to grow on the labeled medium for 1 hour, and were then fixed and immediately processed. The picture at the left is a photomicrograph of an unstained section seen through a phase microscope. The large nuclei and nucleoli of some cells are visible. The picture at the right is a radioautograph of the same section. The black dots, caused by radioactivity, are largely concentrated in the position of the nucleoli. If the preparation is first washed with a chemical which removes RNA but not DNA, the radioautograph is essentially blank. (Courtesy of Philip S. Woods, Brookhaven National Laboratory, Upton, N. Y.)

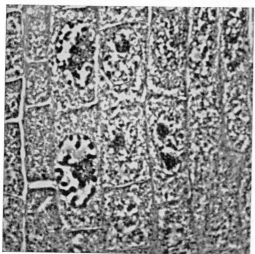 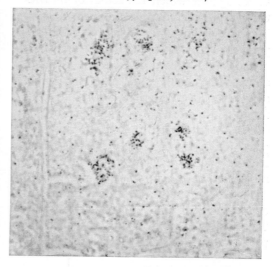

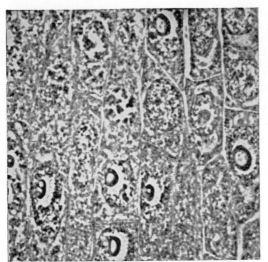 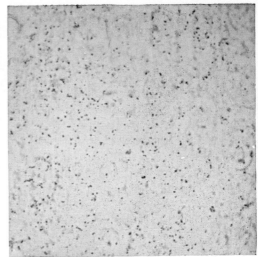

Fig. 2.13. Results of an experiment similar to that shown in Fig. 2.12, except that after 1 hour on the labeled medium the root tips were removed to an unlabeled (nonradioactive) medium and allowed to grow for 5 hours before being fixed and processed. The radioactivity is now scattered throughout the cell, with no special concentration in the nucleolus. These and some similar experiments support the hypothesis of nucleolar function suggested on p. 31, but a firm conclusion is not yet warranted. (Courtesy of Philip S. Woods, Brookhaven National Laboratory, Upton, N. Y.)

which act as templates against which the high polymers are formed in particular sizes and configurations. The high polymer molecules of RNA migrate out into the cytoplasm and become attached to the endoplasmic reticulum. As part of the endoplasmic reticulum they act as templates against which molecules of individual cytoplasmic enzymes are formed.

The action of genes as templates apparently sets narrow limits on the kinds of molecules formed in each case but does allow some small variation. Thus probably several very similar but slightly differing kinds of high polymers (probably of RNA) are formed in contact with each gene, and each of these RNA molecules likewise permits some variation in the molecules of enzymes which are formed against it. Doubtless the environmental conditions, including the relative nutrients available to the plant, influence the proportions in which the several slightly differing kinds of molecules which can form against each gene (and against each RNA molecule of the microsomes) are produced. The slightly varying forms of an enzyme may be expected to have slightly different chemical properties, and thus the influence of the environment on the plant possibly extends even into the mechanism of gene action.

Many suggestions as to the function of the nucleolus have been made and discarded in the past. The foregoing suggestion, although it is backed by some experimental evidence, is far from proved. The use of labeled (radioactive) elements in experimental studies promises to answer many such questions in the near future.

THE CYTOPLASM

The manufacture, storage, and digestion of foods are carried out in the cytoplasm, although some foods may also be

32   *Introductory Botany*

stored in the central vacuole. Respiration is largely a cytoplasmic function, but some of the processes occurring in the nucleus involve energy changes and might come under a broad definition of respiration. The formation of living substance is carried out both in the nucleus and in the cytoplasm.

Photosynthesis occurs on or in the chloroplasts; some of the principal steps of respiration ordinarily occur on the mitochondria; many cytoplasmic enzymes are probably formed on the endoplasmic reticulum; starch grains are often formed and stored in leucoplasts; entry to or departure from the cell of water and dissolved substances are governed in part by the plasma membrane and vacuolar membrane, and in part also by the kind and amount of dissolved and colloidal particles in both the cell sap and the cytoplasm. Other metabolic processes are in most cases not clearly demonstrated to be associated with particular parts of the cytoplasm, although it has been suggested that the Golgi bodies may be involved in complex lipid-metabolism.

METABOLISM AND RELATED PROCESSES

INTRODUCTORY REMARKS

The formation of living substance from raw materials is called **assimilation.** Assimilation is the phase of metabolism toward which all other metabolic processes are normally directed. Even in mature organisms, the formation of some new protoplasm is eventually necessary for continued life, inasmuch as existing protoplasm is constantly wearing out and breaking down. Living matter is chemically active and unstable and is therefore subject to attrition by the alteration or disintegration of its molecules.

Those phases of metabolism, such as photosynthesis and assimilation, which result in making more complex substances from simpler ones, are called **anabolism.** Those phases of metabolism, such as digestion and respiration, which result in making simpler substances from more complex ones, are called **catabolism.** For purposes of discussion and understanding, the division of metabolism into anabolism and catabolism is useful, but the distinction within the living cell is not precise. Both anabolic and catabolic processes ordinarily occur constantly and simultaneously, and some of the intermediate products of anabolic processes are the same as some of the intermediate products of simultaneously occurring catabolic processes.

OSMOSIS

One of the most important features of the plasma membrane (and vacuolar membrane) is that it constitutes a partial barrier to the passage by diffusion of materials in solution. Water passes through it freely. Some solutes pass freely, others more slowly, and others not at all. Such a membrane, which permits free passage by diffusion of some materials and restricts the passage of others, is commonly called a **semipermeable membrane,** although the term **differentially permeable membrane** would be more precisely descriptive.

An important characteristic of differentially permeable membranes of plant cells is that the permeability changes, so that a substance which is allowed to pass through at one time may be restrained at another. It has been suggested that one way in which these changes of permeabil-

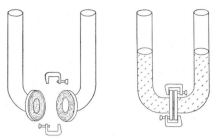

Fig. 2.14. Osmotic apparatus described in the text. Left, separated parts. Right, sugar solution in equal concentrations on both sides of the membrane after a period of diffusion.

ity occur is by a change in the nature of the lipid-water emulsion of which the plasma membrane is probably in part composed. In an emulsion consisting of colloidal particles of lipid dispersed in a continuous medium of water, the passage of water-soluble materials would be facilitated. The opposite condition, with colloidal particles of water dispersed in a continuous medium of lipid, would favor the passage of fat-soluble substances. Some substances usually present in the cell, such as sodium ions and some lipids known as phospholipids, favor a lipid in water emulsion; others, such as calcium ions and some other kinds of lipids, favor a water in lipid emulsion. Changes in the concentration of these substances at the surface of the cytoplasm would therefore be expected to affect the nature of the emulsion and thus the permeability of the membrane.

Since water and some solutes frequently move from outside a cell into the central vacuole, or vice versa, it is sometimes convenient to think of the cytoplasm itself as a membrane separating the central vacuole from the region outside the cell. Such a movement involves diffusion through both the plasma membrane and the vacuolar membrane, with passage through the intervening portion of the cytoplasm being accomplished partly by dif-

fusion and more especially by means of the constant streaming motion (cyclosis) of the cytoplasm itself.

If pure water is placed in one half of a U-shaped container and an equal amount of a solution of cane sugar is placed in the other half, the two halves being separated by a completely permeable membrane, as shown in Fig. 2.14, the proportions of sugar and water eventually become uniform throughout the container. Molecules of both substances pass through the membrane in both directions, but there is a net movement of the sugar into the side of the container which had held pure water, and a net movement of water into the side of the container which had held the original sugar solution. Each of the two substances, sugar and water, diffuses from a region of its own higher concentration toward a region of its own lower concentration, and the level of the liquids on the two sides of the container remains essentially unchanged throughout the process.

In a similar experiment using a membrane which is permeable to water and impermeable to sugar (Fig. 2.15), the results are quite different. The sugar is retained in one half of the container, and only the water moves from an area of its own higher to its own lower concentration. The level of the water falls, and the level

Fig. 2.15. Osmotic apparatus, showing changes when equal amounts of water and sugar solution are separated by a semipermeable membrane, as described in the text.

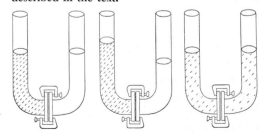

of the sugar solution rises. If the membrane remains unbroken and its differential permeability remains unimpaired, the level of the sugar solution may rise a considerable distance before the increased pressure of the sugar solution against the membrane results in an equilibrium, with as many molecules of water passing in one direction as the other. If the membrane merely retards the passage of sugar, rather than completely preventing it, the level of the sugar solution will at first rise, as more water enters it than leaves, and then it will fall as the equalization of sugar concentrations on the two sides of the membrane proceeds. Eventually the liquid will stand at the same level and have the same concentration of sugar on both sides of the membrane.

In the experiment in which the membrane wholly prevents the passage of sugar, the level of the sugar solution can be prevented from rising by inserting a plug in the tube down to the level of the solution (Fig. 2.16). Water will then enter the sugar solution until the pressure of the solution against the membrane is built up enough to cause the passage of equal amounts of water in both directions. The same results will be obtained if the two halves of the container merely have different concentrations of sugar molecules, or even if different kinds of solutes are used, as long as these solutes cannot pass through the membrane and as long as the concentration of water in the two solutions is not the same.

An oversimplification which might help one understand the process is to consider that whenever a molecule of water hits the membrane (and we have seen that all molecules are in constant motion) it passes through, whereas whenever a particle of the solute hits the membrane it is

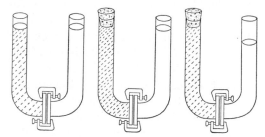

Fig. 2.16. **Osmotic apparatus developing pressure, as described in the text.**

restrained. A given amount of pure water will obviously contain more water molecules than the same amount of sugar solution, so that under the conditions of the experiment more molecules of water will hit and pass through the membrane into the sugar solution than in the reverse direction. With the volume of the sugar solution prevented from increasing, a pressure is built up within the solution, because more molecules occupy a given space than had previously occupied that space. When the pressure becomes so great that as many molecules of water hit the membrane from one side as the other, an equilibrium is established.

The diffusion of water through a semipermeable membrane is called **osmosis;** and the pressure exerted on a semipermeable membrane as a result of osmosis is called **osmotic pressure.** Obviously the actual osmotic pressure exerted by the cell sap of the central vacuole against the enclosing cytoplasm will be greater if the cell is immersed in pure water than if the surrounding medium contains any solutes. Also, other things being equal, the greater the concentration of solutes in the cell sap (and thus the less the concentration of water), the greater the actual osmotic pressure. The presence of hydrophilic colloids in the cell sap will still further increase the apparent osmotic pressure, since the colloidal particles adsorb water molecules on their surfaces and thus decrease the tendency for water to move back out of the cell. (Some physiologists exclude the effect of hydrophilic colloids from the concept of osmotic pressure, but this is purely a matter of definition, and in practice it is difficult to distinguish between the diffusional effect due directly to solutes and that due to the adherence of water to colloidal particles in solution. Actual measurements of osmotic pressure necessarily include the effect of colloidal adsorption in most instances.)

The **potential osmotic pressure,** or **osmotic potential,** i.e., what the pressure would be if the cell, otherwise unchanged, were immersed in pure water, with the volume of its protoplast and vacuole held constant, has considerable physiological importance as a measure of the water-absorbing and water-holding capacity of the cell. By long custom this osmotic potential rather than the actual pressure is meant in speaking of the osmotic pressure of a particular cell. The osmotic potential is usually expressed in atmospheres (i.e., the

Fig. 2.17. **Cell of the leaf of** *Elodea* **(a water plant); normal (left), and plasmolyzed (right). (×600.)**

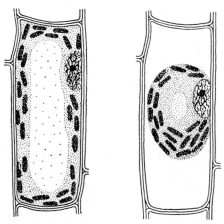

pressure of the atmosphere at sea level). There is a wide variation in osmotic potentials among the cells of different kinds of plants; potentials of 5 to 20 atmospheres are common.

Since the volume of a plant cell is held essentially constant by the cell wall, the osmotic pressure exerted by the central vacuole on the cytoplasm ordinarily forces the cytoplasm closely against the cell wall. The actual pressure of the cytoplasm against the cell wall is referred to as **turgor pressure.** The turgor pressure of cells is often so great that the cytoplasm would burst if the cell wall were not present.

If the concentration of solutes in the water surrounding a cell is raised to a level appreciably higher than that of the central vacuole (which means, also, that the concentration of water in the vacuole is greater than in the surrounding medium), osmosis tends to proceed in reverse direction, and water leaves the cell (unless hindered by hydrophilic colloids in the cell sap). If the process continues, the vacuole diminishes in size and the protoplast shrinks away from the cell wall (Fig. 2.17). The cell is then said to be plasmolyzed, or in a state of **plasmolysis.** A plasmolyzed but still living cell obviously exerts no turgor pressure, but its osmotic potential may be very high. If a more normal environment is restored, water re-enters the cell, and turgor is re-established, provided that plasmolysis has not been carried so far or continued so long as to kill the cell. The differential permeability of the cytoplasmic membrane depends on life, and when the cell dies the cytoplasm becomes wholly permeable.

In the foregoing paragraphs osmosis in living cells has been presented as a purely physical process, the only strictly metabolic contribution being the maintenance of an effective semipermeable membrane. This may not be the whole story, however. Some recent evidence suggests that the cytoplasmic membrane may not be equally permeable in both directions, under normal conditions, so that water enters the cell more readily than it leaves. It has been claimed that in many kinds of plants intake of water can proceed even against the concentration gradient (i.e., in the opposite direction from what would be expected on the basis of the relative concentrations of water and solutes). Rapid absorption of water by roots is associated with expenditure of energy, but the role of this expenditure (further discussed in Chapter 27) is not yet fully understood.

The entry of solutes into the cell proceeds in much the same way as the entry of water, but here it is clear that metabolic expenditure of energy can lead to absorption against the gradient. Certain minerals may be accumulated in concentrations many times higher than their concentrations in the surrounding medium, partly because the particles are removed from solution or are transformed into forms which do not pass readily through the plasma membrane. Absorption of water, on the contrary, can proceed against only a relatively mild (if any) concentration gradient, and only plants with very high osmotic potential can survive in water with a high concentration of solutes, or in soil containing such water. These matters are further discussed in Chapters 27 and 28.

PHOTOSYNTHESIS

Photosynthesis is the manufacture of food from raw materials, using light as a source of energy. All photosynthesis requires chlorophyll. In typical photosynthesis, carbon dioxide and water are com-

bined, through the agency of chlorophyll and with light as the source of energy, to form glucose, and oxygen is released as a by-product. The process has customarily been expressed by the following equation: $6 CO_2 + 6 H_2O + $ light energy $\rightarrow C_6H_{12}O_6 + 6 O_2$. (It may be noted here that 1 molecule of oxygen, like that of many other gases, ordinarily consists of 2 atoms.) The use or release of energy is not always indicated in an equation expressing a chemical reaction, but it is permissible to do so, and we wish to emphasize that energy from light is used in photosynthesis.

Photosynthesis is not really so simple a process as the foregoing equation might suggest. It certainly consists of several steps. In the first steps water molecules are split, oxygen is released, hydrogen is combined with some other substance in the cytoplasm, and light energy is used. In the ensuing several steps, which do not require additional energy and can take place just as well in the dark, carbon dioxide is used, carbohydrate is formed, and half the hydrogen which had previously been extracted from water is used in the formation of the carbohydrate, while the other half combines with some of the oxygen of the carbon dioxide to form more water. Thus for every two molecules of water that are broken down in the first part of photosynthesis, one molecule of water is formed in the following part. Although research is now actively in progress to determine just what compounds are formed in each step of photosynthesis, it is not yet possible to present with confidence a complete series of detailed chemical equations to explain the process. It was at one time thought that photosynthesis might perhaps involve the formation of formaldehyde, CH_2O, and the polymerization of 6 molecules of formaldehyde to form a molecule of glucose, but more recent evidence clearly indicates that this is not the case. An equation which summarizes our present knowledge of raw materials and principal end products of typical photosynthesis may be written:

$$6 \; CO_2 + 12 \; H_2O + \text{light energy} \longrightarrow$$
$$C_6H_{12}O_6 + 6 \; O_2 + 6 \; H_2O.$$

The glucose formed in photosynthesis is used as an essential material from which other more complex substances in the protoplasm are formed, but it is now evident that small quantities of some of these other substances are formed directly in photosynthesis without ever passing through a glucose stage. With minor exceptions regarding the bacteria (noted in Chapter 6) photosynthesis is directly or indirectly the source of all foods used by plants and animals.

The pigments associated with chlorophyll in the chloroplast are often called **accessory pigments.** The accessory pigments absorb light energy, and they transmit it into the photosynthetic process in a manner not yet fully understood. In some kinds of plants more light energy is absorbed by the accessory pigments than by the chlorophyll itself. The nature of the accessory pigments varies in the different groups of plants and furnishes an important criterion in the taxonomic delimitation of the groups.

Respiration

The photosynthetic process transforms light energy into potential chemical energy. The potential chemical energy is transformed into actual chemical energy, available for use by the cell, by means of **respiration.** Respiration is the oxidation of foods by living organisms. In the most typical form of respiration a simple sugar, such as glucose, is respired, oxygen is used, chemical energy is released, and carbon dioxide and water are formed as end products. The process may be represented by the following equation: $C_6H_{12}O_6 + 6 \; O_2 \longrightarrow 6 \; H_2O + 6 \; CO_2 + \text{heat and}$ chemical energy. It will be seen that as to materials used and products formed, the respiration of glucose is essentially the opposite of photosynthesis. Photosynthesis and respiration together constitute a means by which light energy is transformed into chemical energy available for use by the cell. The process is not highly efficient. Only a small fraction of the light energy to which plants are exposed is used in photosynthesis, and usually only about 2–5 percent of the energy liberated in respiration is liberated as chemical energy, the rest being mostly transformed into heat.

Like photosynthesis, respiration is not a simple chemical reaction but involves many steps. Some of the intermediate products of respiration appear to be the same as some of the intermediate products of photosynthesis, but the two processes are not opposites in all details. It is clear that some of the intermediate compounds in both respiration and photosynthesis contain phosphorus.

The manufacture of fats, proteins, and other complex substances in the cell requires energy. The constant streaming of the cytoplasm, called cyclosis, which occurs in most living cells, requires energy. Some other processes occurring in the cell also require energy. Excepting only the energy used in the manufacture of foods from raw materials by photosynthesis (and, in a few kinds of organisms, by a related process, chemosynthesis), all the energy required by a cell is obtained by respiration. Carbohydrates and fats are commonly used in respiration. Proteins can also be respired, but they are not ordinarily so used in any considerable quantity if an adequate supply of carbohydrates or fats is available.

Many different enzymes are involved in respiration. Some of these are borne on the mitochondria, and others are found free in the cytoplasm. The most important system of respiratory enzymes in most plants is called the **cytochrome** system. Some of the enzymes of the cytochrome system contain iron and are red. Usually the concentration of these enzymes is so low that they do not affect the visible color of the living plant cell.

Adenosine triphosphate, commonly called ATP, is the usual means by which respiratory energy is distributed into other metabolic processes. One of the three phosphate groups of the ATP molecule becomes part of that molecule through respiratory processes taking place on the mitochondria and elsewhere in the cytoplasm, and a relatively large amount of energy is transferred into the ATP as a result. This phosphate group readily separates from the ATP molecule again, releasing energy into other chemical reactions for which it is required. ATP is structurally (but not functionally) rather similar to the nucleic acids.

Ordinary respiration requires the use of free oxygen and is called **aerobic respiration.** An incomplete or partial respiration can sometimes be carried on without the use of free oxygen; this is called **anaerobic respiration.** Anaerobic respiration releases only part of the potential chemical energy of a food, and an end product is always

formed that can be further oxidized with release of energy. A familiar example of anaerobic respiration is the fermentation of sugar by yeast, in which ethyl alcohol and carbon dioxide are formed as end products. This process releases only part of the chemical energy stored in the sugar, and the alcohol retains a large amount of potential energy which can be released by aerobic respiration in other organisms. The chemical equation for the alcoholic fermentation of a simple hexose sugar is as follows: $C_6H_{12}O_6 \longrightarrow 2\ C_2H_5OH + 2\ CO_2 +$ energy.

Many modern plant physiologists would restrict the term *respiration* to aerobic respiration, and modify the definition of fermentation to cover what would otherwise be called anaerobic respiration. The distinction is largely theoretical, however, since even aerobic respiration consists of several steps, not all of which require free oxygen. Furthermore, many plant cells can carry on anaerobic respiration for a limited time under conditions of oxygen shortage and then aerobically respire the partly broken-down products of anaerobic respiration when a sufficient supply of free oxygen becomes available. A more traditional concept of **fermentation** is respiration, aerobic or more often anaerobic, of carbohydrates, fats, or products derived from the partial breakdown of carbohydrates and fats, in which only part of the energy stored in the food is released, and a normal end product (such as alcohol, lactic acid, or acetic acid) is formed that can still be oxidized with release of energy. As so defined, fermentation occurs chiefly or wholly among microorganisms, such as bacteria and yeasts.

Whether or not anaerobic respiration fits the definition of respiration as being oxidation of foods by living organisms depends on the definition of oxidation. In the traditional sense of oxidation, that is, a chemical process in which free oxygen is used and energy is released, anaerobic respiration is not oxidation. In the modern chemical definition of oxidation, which relates in part to the energy changes in a chemical reaction, however, anaerobic respiration *is* oxidation. The definition of respiration to include or exclude anaerobic processes is, of course, merely a matter of convenience. For purposes of understanding, we find it useful to classify the chemical processes of a cell into certain categories, but no such distinction is made by the plant itself. The term *respiration* is here retained in its traditional sense, to include both aerobic and anaerobic processes, because the concept is useful and no other term is available to replace it.

Food Storage

If all the glucose formed by a cell during photosynthesis were maintained in that form within the cell, it would upset the osmotic balance and interfere with metabolism in other ways as well. Glucose is seldom accumulated in large quantities; instead it is usually transformed into in-

Fig. 2.18. **Structural diagram of part of an amylopectin molecule. Each small hexagon indicates a glucose unit.**

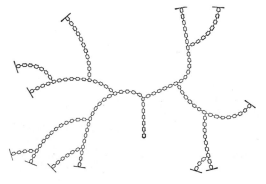

soluble, osmotically inactive reserves. The most common of these reserve foods into which glucose is transformed for storage is **starch.**

Starch is a mixture of at least two different polysaccharides, called amylose and amylopectin. A molecule of amylose is formed by the polymerization of about 300 molecules of α-glucose into a simple chain, and a molecule of amylopectin (Fig. 2.18) is formed by the polymerization of about 1300 molecules of α-glucose into a branched chain. (Amylose and amylopectin also contain minute amounts of phosphorus.) The number of molecules of glucose going into the formation of a molecule of amylose or amylopectin probably varies in different kinds of plants, or perhaps even in the same plant. Amylose turns a deep blue when a solution of iodine is applied to it; amylopectin turns red to purple; the resulting color of iodine-treated starch is a deep violet purple. No other common natural substance gives such a color when treated with iodine, and iodine is commonly used as a test for the presence of starch.

Another form in which food is stored is fat. The formation of fats from carbohydrates requires a series of chemical changes, of which the final step is the combination of 1 molecule of glycerin with 3 molecules of fatty acid (see p. 18). Energy is used in the formation of glycerin and fatty acids from carbohydrates and is retained in the molecule when these are combined to form fats. The respiration of fats, therefore, releases more energy than the respiration of the same amount (by weight) of carbohydrates. Fats are commonly stored as globules in the cytoplasm. Fats and other lipids also occur in colloidal form as part of the living protoplasm.

Food may also be stored in the form

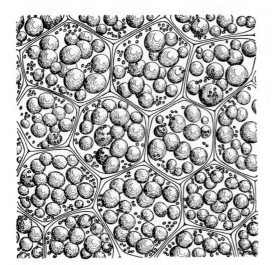 

Fig. 2.19.   Cells of endosperm of coconut: left, cut parallel to the surface (×400); right, cut perpendicular to the surface (×250). The large globules are oil and the small granules are protein. (From W. H. Brown, *The Plant Kingdom*, 1935; courtesy of Ginn & Company, Boston.)

of protein. Stored protein may exist as small crystals or granules in the protoplasm or cell sap; it is also frequently found in semiliquid globules, alone or with fats. Stored protein is usually used as building material for new protoplasm rather than for respiration. As might therefore be expected, it is especially likely to be found in specialized structures, such as seeds, which must draw on reserve foods for growth.

DIGESTION

Digestion is a chemical process by which insoluble or not readily diffusible foods are rendered more soluble or more readily diffusible. It is ordinarily a hydrolytic reaction, in which water is used, and large molecules are broken down into smaller molecules. A very small amount of energy is released in digestive hydrolysis, but the quantity is so negligible that it is customary to say that digestion does not involve the use or release of energy. The

chemical reactions in digestion are essentially the opposite of the reactions by which the substances digested were originally formed from less complex substances. Polysaccharides eventually yield monosaccharides when digested, although the process may be interrupted at any intermediate stage, as, for example, at the disaccharide level. The digestion of fats yields glycerin and fatty acids, and the digestion of simple proteins yields amino acids. The chemical equation for the digestion of sucrose may be written as follows:

$$C_{12}H_{22}O_{11} + H_2O \rightarrow C_6H_{12}O_6 + C_6H_{12}O_6.$$

sucrose   glucose   fructose

It is customary to name many enzymes, particularly digestive enzymes, according to the substance on which they act, followed by the suffix *-ase*. Thus enzymes which bring about the digestion of carbohydrates are called carbohydrases; enzymes which bring about the digestion of fats

The Structure and Function of Cells   41

are called lipases; and enzymes which bring about the digestion of proteins are called proteases. Enzymes are usually very specific in the compounds on which they will act, and there are many different kinds of proteases, lipases, and carbohydrases. The several different carbohydrases involved in the digestion of starch are collectively called amylase and have also been called diastase.

ELEMENTS NECESSARY FOR PLANT GROWTH

From the preceding discussion of cell structure and metabolism, it can be seen that several different chemical elements are necessary to the proper function or to the very existence of plants. Ten of these elements are ordinarily needed in sufficient quantity that their necessity is easily demonstrated by attempting to grow plants in an otherwise satisfactory artificial environment from which the test element is excluded. These are carbon (C), hydrogen (H), oxygen (O), nitrogen (N), sulfur (S), phosphorus (P), magnesium (Mg), potassium (K), iron (Fe), and calcium (Ca). All these, with the probable exception of calcium, are believed to be necessary for all plants. The necessity of calcium for some of the fungi, bacteria, and algae is doubtful. A simple mnemonic device to keep all these ten elements in mind is the phrase, "C HOPK'NS CaFe Mighty good," in which each element is represented by its chemical symbol, except magnesium, which is represented by "Mighty good."

Four other elements, aluminum (Al), chlorine (Cl), silicon (Si), and sodium (Na), are usually present in considerable quantity in plant cells. The necessity of these for plants in general remains to be demonstrated, but sodium is necessary to the growth of certain marine algae; silicon is necessary for the normal development of diatoms, although they can be grown in culture without it; and there is some evidence indicating that traces of both chlorine and aluminum are necessary for at least some of the higher plants.

In addition to the ten **macrometabolic elements** (i.e., those necessary in appreciable quantity for metabolism) and the four other elements usually present in some quantity but perhaps not necessary, several other elements are necessary in minute quantities for the growth of some (or all) plants. These are known as **trace elements.** All the currently known trace elements are toxic if present in more than minute amounts. Very careful experimental work is required to demonstrate the necessity of these trace elements, since they are usually present as impurities in the other substances used to set up the artificial environment; and even if they are rigorously excluded from the artificial environment they may be already present in the test plants in sufficient quantity to last for the duration of the experiment. It is sometimes necessary to grow plants in the artificial environment for several consecutive generations before the effects of lack of the test element appear.

Six trace elements are now generally admitted to be necessary for the growth of most or perhaps all plants. These are boron (B), cobalt (Co), copper (Cu), manganese (Mn), molybdenum (Mo), and zinc (Zn). Gallium (Ga) also seems to be necessary as a trace element for some kinds of plants, and further work may well enlarge the list of plants for which it is necessary. In some of the bacteria, at least, vanadium can substitute for molybdenum. It is probable that there will be additions in the future to the list of necessary trace elements.

One other element, selenium (Se), is necessary in considerable quantity for the growth of a few kinds of plants (Fig. 2.20) but is toxic to many others.

FUNCTIONS OF THE NECESSARY ELEMENTS

Most of the essential elements have several or many functions in plant metabolism. Some of these functions are fairly well understood for the macrometabolic elements, but the functions of most of the trace elements are much more obscure. Often their functions are merely inferred from the symptoms brought about by their lack.

Carbon is the essential element for all organic compounds, and a very large proportion of these also contain hydrogen and oxygen. All proteins contain nitrogen, and many of them (including some essential ones) contain sulfur.

Phosphorus is an essential constituent of nucleic acids and thus of nucleoprotein. It is also present in some of the intermediate products of both photosynthesis and respiration and is a constituent of phospholipids, which affect the permeability of the plasma membrane.

Magnesium is present in chlorophyll and is also necessary for plants which do not contain chlorophyll. Magnesium is involved in some way in phosphorus metabolism, and magnesium ions seem to activate some of the essential enzymes.

Iron is present in some of the enzymes essential for ordinary respiration. It is also necessary for the formation of chlorophyll, although it is not present in the chlorophyll molecule.

Calcium is involved in nitrogen

Fig. 2.20. *Stanleya elata*, in Death Valley, California. This plant requires selenium. (Photo courtesy of Rupert C. Barneby.)

metabolism; it also enters into a number of compounds in the cell, probably including nucleoproteins. Multicellular plants contain calcium in the middle lamella.

Potassium is certainly necessary for growth, but, unlike the other macrometabolic elements, it is not definitely known to be a component of essential organic compounds. Potassium ions appear to be necessary to the action of certain enzymes. Sodium can partly, but not wholly, replace potassium in metabolism.

Probably all the trace elements are either contained in or necessary to the formation of certain enzymes. Boron is involved in calcium and potassium metabolism and may also be involved in protein synthesis. Cobalt is a constituent of vitamin B_{12}, an enzyme which appears to be necessary for nearly all organisms. Copper is present in some of the respiratory enzymes. Manganese is involved in iron metabolism and is related in some way to respiration and to the formation of chlorophyll. Molybdenum is involved in nitrogen metabolism. The fixation of atmospheric nitrogen by some of the bacteria requires the presence of either molybdenum or vanadium. Zinc is necessary to the synthesis of indole acetic acid (an important growth-regulating substance) and is probably present in some of the essential respiratory enzymes.

Selenium belongs to the same chemical group as sulfur and can substitute for it in certain compounds. It probably substitutes for sulfur in some of the proteins of those plants for which it is an essential element, and its toxic properties for other organisms probably depend on this same sort of substitution.

SUGGESTED READING

Dobell, Clifford, *Antony van Leeuwenhoek and His "Little Animals,"* Staples Press, London, 1932, 435 pp. A biography and appraisal, with many excerpts from his letters to the Royal Society.

Downes, Helen R., *The Chemistry of Living Cells*, Harper, New York, 1955, 549 pp. A textbook in which the student who has some background in organic chemistry can find more detailed information, with many structural formulas.

Gabriel, Mordecai L., and Seymour Fogel (Eds.), *Great Experiments in Biology*, Prentice-Hall, Englewood Cliffs, New Jersey, 1955, 317 pp. A collection of some of the classic papers which established important new ideas. Well worth the student's attention in connection with this and many later chapters.

Cell
Division

CHAPTER 3

MITOSIS

INTRODUCTORY SUMMARY

Increase in number of cells is brought about by the division of existing cells. In typical cell division the chromatin material of a cell is precisely divided into two equal parts, and the cytoplasm is more roughly divided into two essentially similar parts, giving two daughter cells which are initially alike.

The process which results in the precise division of the chromatin is called **mitosis,** and the process which results in the division of the cytoplasm is called **cytokinesis.** With the notable exception of many fungi and some algae, mitosis and cytokinesis are usually closely associated, and the term *mitosis* is often loosely used to cover the whole process of mitotic cell division, including cytokinesis. Among animals, and among some plants, cytokinesis is ordinarily accomplished by the simple constriction, or furrowing, of the cytoplasm into two parts, but among most plants it (cytokinesis) ordinarily occurs by the formation of a distinct transverse membrane, the **cell plate,** which eventually becomes the middle lamella between the two daughter cells.

Cell division was noted by a number of observers between 1830 and 1840, and in 1847–1848 the German botanist Wilhelm Hofmeister (1824–1877) described much of the mitotic process, but without understanding its significance. A more complete understanding of the essential features of mitosis developed from the separate contributions of several men during the years 1873–1884.

The time occupied by the mitotic process varies according to the kind of organism, the kind of cell, the temperature, and other environmental conditions, but it is usually ½–2 hours. It is customary and convenient to divide mitosis into four stages, called, in order, the prophase, the metaphase, the anaphase, and the telophase. This is merely a convenient division of a process which is continuous from beginning to end. It should be emphasized that the division of the chromatin material which occurs in mitosis is qualitatively as well as quantitatively equal. Mitotic cell division is a means of increasing the number of cells without changing their hereditary potentialities.

THE PROPHASE

The **prophase** is the part of mitosis in which the chromonemata are modified into shorter, thicker chromosomes which can be visually recognized as separate bodies. The processes occurring in the assumption of the short, thick shape are not fully understood, but they include a compound coiling of the chromonemata and the appearance of a matrix or core (probably of simple protein) in which the chromonema is embedded, or around which the chromonema is wound in a close spiral. The coiling process has been roughly compared to what happens when a piece of string is twisted until it coils upon itself. Each chromosome, as seen at late prophase, has its own characteristic shape and consists of two equal, parallel bodies, called **chromatids.** Each chromatid consists of two strands which may be considered as half chromatids.

The nucleolus generally disappears

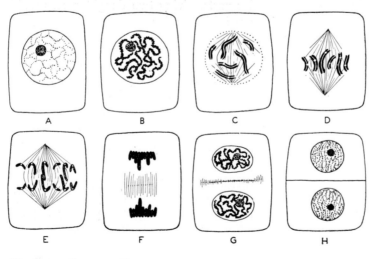

Fig. 3.1. Mitosis. Series of diagrams showing mitosis in a cell with six chromosomes. A, interphase; B, early prophase; C, late prophase; D, metaphase; E, anaphase; F, late anaphase verging toward telophase; G, late telophase; H, interphase.

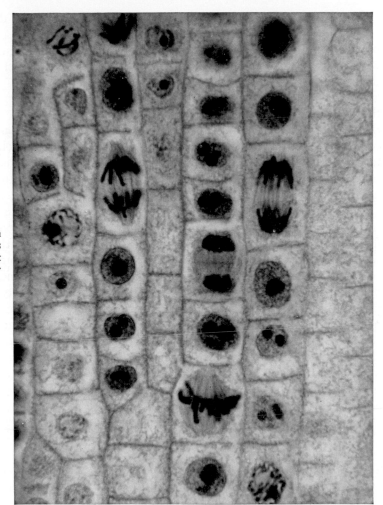

Fig. 3.2. Section of onion root tip, showing various stages of mitosis. (Copyright by General Biological Supply House, Inc., Chicago.)

during late prophase, approximately coincident with the appearance of the matrix of the chromosomes; but there is probably no direct relationship between the two events.

During late prophase a characteristic bipolar structure called (because of its shape) the **spindle** is formed in or around the nucleus. In most plants the spindle seems to be derived in large part from the nuclear sap, but it is likely that some chemical reaction with cytoplasmic con-

stituents is also necessary. In some instances the nuclear membrane gradually shrinks inward before its eventual disappearance at the end of the prophase, and the spindle is formed outside the membrane, coming to occupy the space formerly enclosed by the membrane. In other instances the spindle is formed entirely within the nuclear membrane, which does not shrink significantly before its disappearance at the end of the prophase. In either case the nuclear membrane probably becomes freely permeable before the spindle appears, permitting the mixing of nuclear and cytoplasmic constituents, which mixing results in the formation of the spindle. The spindle substance is organized into longitudinally oriented fibrils, the **spindle fibers.** These were at one time thought to be mere artifacts formed in preparing the cells for microscopic examination, but more refined techniques have recently made it possible to observe spindle fibers even in living cells.

In most animals, and among some plants (chiefly those, such as some of the flagellated algae, which lack definite cell walls), the spindle is formed in the cytoplasm, but here again the nuclear membrane probably loses its differential permeability and permits the mixing of nuclear and cytoplasmic constituents before the spindle is formed. In animals and in those plants which form spindles in the cytoplasm, there is also a specialized cytoplasmic body called the **centriole** or **cen-**

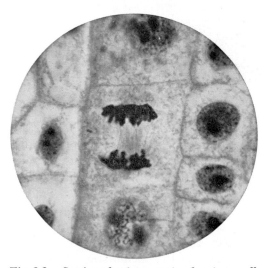

Fig. 3.3. Section of onion root tip, showing a cell in late anaphase. (Copyright by General Biological Supply House, Inc., Chicago.)

trosome, which divides during the prophase into two centrioles that come to mark the poles of the spindle. Such a structure does not exist in higher plants.

The Metaphase

The **metaphase** is the part of mitosis in which the chromosomes that have taken shape in the prophase become (and for a time remain) arranged in an **equatorial plate** (i.e., in a plane lying across the middle of the cell). The arrangement of the chromosomes into an equatorial plate occurs relatively rapidly and is followed by the formation of the so-called **tractile fibers** which lead from each chromosome to the two poles of the spindle. Each chromosome is attached to two tractile fibers, one leading from one chromatid to one pole of the spindle, the other leading from the other chromatid to the other pole of the spindle. The formation of each tractile fiber begins on each chromatid at a specialized point, called the **centromere,** and progresses from there to the spindle pole. The origin and physicochemical nature of the tractile fibers are not fully understood. The centromere may lie at any point along the chromatid, having the same position in corresponding chromosomes of different cells in the same or different individuals of any given kind of plant.

The Anaphase

The **anaphase** is the part of mitosis in which the two chromatids of each chromosome are separated and move toward the respective poles of the spindle. The mechanism which leads to the separation of the chromatids has received a great deal of study but is not yet well understood. It was at one time thought that the chromatids were pulled apart by contraction of the tractile fibers (whence the name for these), but more recent evidence makes this seem unlikely, and the function of the tractile fibers remains in doubt. It is believed that electrochemical repulsions (and perhaps also attractions) related to chemical changes occurring in the chromosomes have something to do with the separation and movement of the chromatids, and that the tractile fibers, even though not exerting any direct pull, also play some part in the process.

As soon as the two chromatids of a chromosome become separated during the anaphase of mitosis, each chromatid is considered (as a matter of terminology) to have advanced to the rank of a chromosome. Each chromatid as seen in metaphase and late prophase is also composed of duplicate halves, and these half chromatids are likewise advanced during anaphase to the rank of chromatids.

The spindle often elongates during the anaphase, so that the poles to which the chromosomes migrate become more widely separated.

THE TELOPHASE

The **telophase** is the part of mitosis in which each of the two groups of chromosomes (one group at each pole of the spindle) is formed into a distinct nucleus similar to the nucleus that existed at the beginning of the mitotic process. The processes in the telophase are in large part the reverse of those occurring in the prophase. A nuclear membrane appears around the group of chromosomes. The matrix of the chromosomes disappears, and the chromo-

somes without the matrix uncoil and are transformed into the slender, tangled chromonemata which form a quasi network. The nuclear sap and the nucleolus reappear, ordinarily more or less coincident with the disappearance of the chromosomal matrix. In a few cases the nucleolus persists throughout the mitotic process and is constricted at anaphase into two halves which migrate to the poles and are incorporated into the daughter nuclei. As the daughter nuclei develop, the spindle becomes shorter and broader, and eventually it disappears.

THE INTERPHASE

The time between the end of the telophase and the beginning of the next prophase is often called the **interphase.** Some of the essential preliminaries to the next mitosis occur during the interphase, but the interphase is not itself a part of mitosis. Each daughter chromosome, as seen in the later stages of mitosis, consists of two chromatids. Each chromatid is duplicated and comes to consist of two strands during the interphase. Each prophase and metaphase chromosome therefore consists of four strands, two making up one chromatid, and two the other.

Recent experiments by the American botanist J. Herbert Taylor (1916–   ), using radioactive isotopes, show that the duplication of chromatids during interphase occurs through the formation of a new strand in each case, rather than through the enlargement and splitting of existing strands (Fig. 3.4). Taylor's evidence further indicates that the two chromatids of an anaphase chromosome are not exactly identical and that they separate

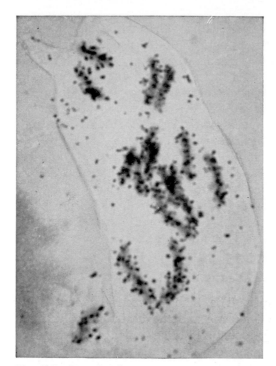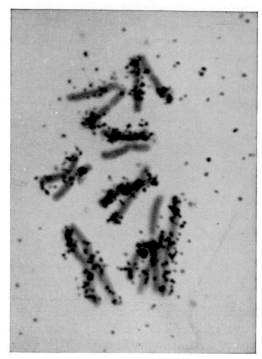

Fig. 3.4.   Use of radioactive tritium to investigate chromosome duplication. Plants of *Bellevalia* (family Liliaceae) have been provided with tritium-labeled thymidine, which is used in the manufacture of DNA. The supply of label is then removed, and the later stages of mitosis (from anaphase on) are prevented by treatment with colchicine. At the first division after labeling (left, above), all daughter chromosomes are labeled, as shown by the black dots, representing the effect of the radioactivity on the film. At the second division after removal of the supply of label (right, above), the label is largely confined to one chromosome of each pair, the exceptions being due to exchange of segments between sister chromatids before division. (×1650.) (Courtesy of J. Herbert Taylor.)

It is believed that the two chromatids of a chromosome separate slightly during interphase, and a labeled counterpart is formed against each, so that each chromatid consists of a labeled and an unlabeled strand, and all the chromosomes in the first division thereafter are therefore labeled. Each chromosome at the beginning of the next interphase thus consists of a labeled and an unlabeled chromatid; these in turn separate slightly, and an unlabeled counterpart is formed against each. One chromatid of each chromosome is now completely unlabeled (except for the effect of exchanges between sister chromatids), and the other consists of a labeled and an unlabeled strand. These chromosomes separate in the next mitosis as the mainly labeled and mainly unlabeled chromosomes seen in the illustration at the right, above.

during interphase. If two such paired chromatids are designated as A_1 and A_2, then a new A_2 strand is apparently formed against the A_1 strand, and a new A_1 against the A_2. The existing strands presumably act as templates against which the new strands are formed. Each of the two chromatids of the prophase and metaphase chromosome of the next mitosis thus consists of an A_1 strand and an A_2 strand in close contact with each other.

CYTOKINESIS

In both plants and animals cytokinesis commonly begins during the telophase of mitosis and is completed by or shortly after the end of telophase. In most plants cytokinesis occurs by the formation of a cell plate. The spindle becomes shorter and broader, and it evidently undergoes a chemical change, as indicated by a change in the stains or dyes which affect it. A thin fluid membrane, the **cell plate**, is then formed across the equator of the spindle. In some cases the constituents of the cell plate appear first near the equator as small droplets which grow and coalesce; in other cases the cell plate appears as a continuous film from the beginning. The spindle continues to shorten and widen, and the cell plate widens until the cell is completely divided into two parts. The remnants of the spindle then disappear. As soon as the cell plate has widened so as to extend from wall to wall, cytokinesis is completed, and the cell plate is thereafter referred to as the middle lamella. The cell plate is at first liquid and presumably proteinaceous, but it soon becomes impregnated with pectin, which is the chief constituent of the young middle lamella.

Among animals, and among those plants which do not have definite cell walls, cytokinesis usually does not involve the formation of a cell plate but results instead from a simple constriction or furrowing of the cytoplasm, with the cell membrane being progressively indented or impressed until division is complete. It is believed that the telophase spindle also plays a part in this type of cytokinesis, but its role is not yet well understood. In a few cases cytokinesis proceeds by a combination of furrowing and the formation of a small cell plate.

Wall Formation

Soon after the completion of cytokinesis, a primary cell wall, usually composed largely of cellulose, is generally deposited on each side of the middle lamella,

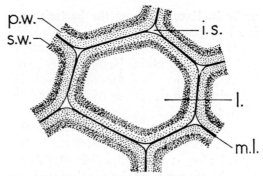

Fig. 3.5. Diagram showing wall layers of adjacent cells: i.s., intercellular space; l., lumen; m.l., middle lamella; p.w., primary wall; s.w., secondary wall

with the result that the plasma membrane of each cell lies against the cell wall rather than against the middle lamella. In many cases a secondary cell wall, usually also composed in large part of cellulose, is laid down against the primary wall. The partition between two adjacent cells then consists, in order, of (1) the secondary wall of one cell, (2) the primary wall of that cell, (3) the middle lamella, (4) the primary wall of the second cell, and (5) the secondary wall of the second cell (Fig. 3.5). As noted in Chapter 2, the partition, regardless of whether a secondary wall is present or not, usually has numerous small perforations through which the cytoplasm of adjacent cells is connected.

It has been suggested that cellulose is formed on the leucoplasts as minute granules which then migrate to the surface of the cytoplasm and become incorporated into the cell wall, but all this is not yet satisfactorily proved.

AMITOSIS

Nuclear division which results from the simple constriction of the nucleus into two or more parts, without the formation of chromosomes or a spindle, is called

amitosis. Except among the bacteria and the blue-green algae, amitosis occurs only rarely or under exceptional circumstances, and it is not always followed by cytokinesis. In some cases amitosis is associated with degenerating cells or tissues. The cells of bacteria and blue-green algae contain a central body of nuclear nature, but the nucleus does not seem to be of the highly organized type found in other organisms, and chromosomes in the usual sense have not been definitely observed. So far as is now known, cell division among the bacteria and blue-green algae is characteristically amitotic.

GENE MUTATION

To the best of our knowledge, a gene consists of one or a few molecules of nucleoprotein, and each gene has its own precise composition and structure. The effects of a gene in controlling the hereditary characteristics of an organism evidently depend on the kind and amount of nongenic molecules which are produced because of its activity. Any change in the chemical composition or structure of a gene would therefore be expected to modify the effects of that gene on heredity.

Every individual gene of every chromosome must be duplicated between one cell division and the next. Circumstantial evidence strongly suggests that this duplication of genes is ordinarily precise, so that each new gene which is formed is chemically identical with its forebear. If, through some mischance, the new gene differs in some respect from its forebear, the difference is ordinarily perpetuated in successive duplications of the modified gene. A change in the nature of a gene which is perpetuated in successive mitotic divisions is called a **gene mutation.**

The rate or percentage of mutation of individual genes is not accurately known, but it is evidently low. Since a gene is chemically very complex, many different mutations are possible in any particular gene. As might be expected on chemical grounds, the kinds of mutations affecting any one gene differ in their relative frequency, and the rate of detectable mutation varies in different genes. Among many genes the rate of detectable natural mutations in a generation is on the order of 1 per million. A few genes have been shown to have notably higher mutation rates, on the order of 1 per 2000. The visible effects of mutations vary from the quite obvious to the barely perceptible, and it is probable that the effects of many mutations are so small as to escape notice entirely. The actual rate of mutation may therefore be considerably greater than the apparent rate.

The rate of mutation can be increased by exposing the organism to extremes of environmental conditions, or by various kinds of radiation, notably X rays. Although cosmic radiation may be responsible for some natural mutations, plants protected from cosmic rays by lead shielding continue to mutate. Living substance is so complex and unstable that mutations should be expected even without the upsetting influence of external factors. The wonder is not that mutations occur but rather that they do not occur more frequently.

We have noted that in a living system there is a delicate balance of many kinds of compounds in a state of continuous chemical activity. Any gene mutation may be expected to alter that balance by changing one or more of the substances which are furnished to and become incorporated into the remainder of the protoplasm. It is always possible that the change might be favorable to the continued survival of the organism, but the greater likelihood is that it would be unfavorable. It is also possible that a change caused by a mutation will modify the environmental requirements of an organism, without being otherwise inherently favorable or unfavorable, or that the effects of the change will be so slight as to be insignificant. All these theoretical probabilities are borne out by observation. Of those mutations which are detected, far more are harmful than beneficial; many are so minor that their effect on survival is problematical; and some cause a shift in the environmental requirements of the organism or in the optimum conditions for survival.

Sexual Reproduction

CHAPTER 4

THE NATURE OF SEXUALITY

Reproduction, i.e., the formation of new individuals, occurs in a number of different ways. Among unicellular organisms, cell division is also reproduction, since the two daughter cells are physiologically independent of each other and do not remain attached. Multicellular organisms have various means of reproduction. One of the simplest means is the formation of special reproductive cells, called **spores,** which are liberated from the organism and develop directly into new individuals. Among the algae, spores often have one or more slender, whip-like structures called **flagella,** which enable them to swim freely. Motile spores such as these are called **zoospores,** because they possess the animal-like feature of motility.

Most kinds of organisms, whether they have any other means of reproduction or not, reproduce by the fusion of two different cells into a single cell which develops into a new individual. Any cell capable of fusing with another cell to form a new individual organism is called a **gamete,** and the cell formed by fusion of gametes is called a **zygote.**

Among some algae, the two gametes which fuse are similar in appearance and are therefore called **isogametes.** Some isogametes are so much like zoospores that they can be distinguished from zoospores only by their behavior (i.e., by the fact that two gametes fuse before a new individual develops, whereas a zoospore develops directly into a new individual). Even when the gametes which fuse are similar in appearance, however, they are often chemically unlike, and there are all transitions between typical isogamy and the more common condition in which the two gametes which fuse are distinctly unlike (heterogamy).

Heterogametes (morphologically unlike gametes which can fuse to form a zygote) are commonly of two types: a small, motile gamete, called the **sperm** and a larger, nonmotile gamete, called the **egg.** The zygote formed by the fusion of a sperm and an egg is called a fertilized egg. The sperm is the male gamete, and the egg is the female gamete. An individual which produces male gametes, but not female, is called a male; an individual which produces female gametes, but not male, is called a female; an individual which produces both male and female gametes is said to be a hermaphrodite.

Fusion of isogametes is called **conjugation,** and fusion of heterogametes is called **fertilization.** The term **syngamy** covers both conjugation and fertilization. Reproduction by fusion of gametes (either conjugation or fertilization) is called **sexual reproduction.** Sexual reproduction among the more familiar kinds of plants and animals always involves fertilization rather than conjugation.

When two gametes fuse, their nuclei generally also fuse into a single nucleus, but the individual chromonemata (and eventual chromosomes) retain their identity. The number of chromosomes present in subsequent mitotic divisions is equal to the sum of the numbers present in the 2 gametes; e.g., if each of the 2 gametes has 5 chromosomes, the number of chromosomes formed during the next division of the zygotic nucleus is 10. It is convenient to refer to the gametic number of chromosomes by the symbol n and to the zygotic number by the symbol $2n$. The number represented by n varies, according to the kind of organism, from 1 to more than 500, but numbers of 3 to 50 are more common. One complete set of chromosomes is called a chromosome complement. Ordinarily a gamete has one chromosome complement, and a zygote has two chromosome complements. A cell or nucleus which has one chromosome complement is said to be **haploid** (Greek *haploos,* simple), and a cell with two chromosome complements is said to be **diploid** (Greek *diploos,* double).

In any diploid nucleus, each chromosome from one complete haploid set is ordinarily matched by a similar chromosome from the other haploid set. Any two such matching chromosomes are called **homologous chromosomes.** Each of the chromosomes of any homologous pair carries genes affecting the same set of characters. For every gene on a given chromosome, there is ordinarily a similar gene in the same position on the homologous chromosome. Two similar genes occupying corresponding positions on homologous chromosomes may be exactly identical, or, due to past mutation, they may differ slightly in their chemical structure and resulting effect on the organism. The hereditary differences among individual organisms are largely due to such genic differences which have arisen through mutation. If, in a given individual, the two comparable genes from a pair of homologous chromosomes in a cell are exactly identical, the individual is said to be **homozygous** for that pair of genes; if the two comparable genes are not exactly identical, the individual is said to be **heterozygous** for that pair of genes. In most kinds of plants and animals, an individual diploid organism is usually homozygous for many genes and heterozygous for many others.

HISTORICAL SUMMARY

Any historical summary of scientific development requires oversimplification. Scientific knowledge grows by the efforts of many different workers in different countries, and a scientist trying to solve some problem must frequently refer to papers published in several languages. Fusion of gametic nuclei in plants was first reported by Eduard Strasburger in 1877, but Strasburger thought that the fusion nucleus then dissolved. It was another German botanist, C. J. Friedrich Schmitz (1850–1895), who first showed clearly, in 1879, that the essential feature of the sexual process in plants is ordinarily the union of two nuclei to form the primary nucleus of the new individual. The cell theory, which is generally attributed to Schleiden and Schwann (as on page 21 of this text), was foreseen by the French naturalist R. J. H. Dutrochet (1776–1847), who stated in 1824, "The globular corpuscles which make up all the tissues of animals are really globular cells of extreme smallness. . . . Growth results from the increase in volume of the cells, and from the addition of new little cells." Dutrochet did not distinguish between true cells and other globules visible in tissues, however, and he was unaware of the existence of the nucleus. It is clear that when sufficient data become available to permit the formation of a new concept, the concept will be formed. If one man does not do it, another soon will, and similar conclusions are often reached independently and nearly simultaneously by two or more scientists.

The importance of sperms in stimulating the development of the egg was suspected soon after the first observation of human sperm by Ludwig Hamm, a pupil of Leeuwenhoek. The way the sperm performs its function was not fully understood until two centuries later. The actual penetration of the sperm into the egg was first seen by the English zoologist Alfred Newport (1829–1907), who in 1854 reported his observations on the fertilization of frog eggs. Two years later the German botanist Nathanael Pringsheim (1823–1894) reported the penetration of the sperm into the egg in *Oedogonium*, a green alga. The fact that the penetration of the sperm into the egg is followed by fusion of the sperm nucleus with the egg nucleus was reported in 1876 by the German zoologist Oskar Hertwig (1849–1922); and fusion of gametic nuclei in plants was reported in 1877 by the German botanist Eduard Strasburger (1844–1912), working on *Spirogyra*, a green alga.

It can readily be seen that if each repetition of the cycle of sexual reproduction led to a doubling of the number of chromosomes in the nucleus of each cell, the number of chromosomes would soon increase beyond bounds. In 1883 the Belgian zoologist Eduard van Beneden (1846–1910) reported that the nuclei of the sperm and egg in the parasitic worm *Ascaris* contained only half as many chromosomes as the nuclei of ordinary body cells of the worm, and his results were soon duplicated in observations of other kinds of animals. In 1888 Strasburger demonstrated the existence of a similar reduction in flowering plants, and in 1894 he set forth the doctrine that reduction in the number of chromosomes is a normal and regular part of the life cycle of all sexually reproducing organisms, balancing the increase in number brought about by gametic fusion. This principle had been foreseen by the German zoologist August Weismann (1834–1914), who in 1887 even predicted the mechanism of reduction. Actual discovery of this mechanism was made almost simultaneously by several different investigators working independently in different countries, and it was elucidated in a series of papers published in 1890–1893.

Fig. 4.1. August Weismann (1834–1914), German biologist, who made important contributions to the theory of heredity, and who foresaw the necessity and the mechanism of reduction division.

MEIOSIS

The Typical Meiotic Process

The process by which the number of chromosomes in a cell is reduced from $2n$ to n is called **reduction division,** or **meiosis.** Meiosis may occur at any time in the life cycle, depending on the kind of organism. In some algae, the first division of the zygote after fertilization is a reduction division, and the zygote itself is the only cell in the life cycle that has $2n$ chromosomes. In many other plants, as in most animals, a diploid body of some size is formed from the zygote by repeated mitotic divisions, and reduction division affects only certain special reproductive cells or tissues of the mature diploid organism. Among animals the gametes are usually the immediate products of meiosis, but among most plants the cells formed in meiosis produce (by a series of mitotic divisions) a haploid body of two to many cells, on or in which the gametes are eventually borne. The essential features of meiosis are the same in both plants and animals, regardless of the point in the life cycle at which it occurs.

Meiosis (Fig. 4.2) typically consists of two successive nuclear divisions (with or without the formation of cell walls) during which the individual chromosomes are divided only once, so that four haploid nuclei are produced from an original diploid nucleus. The actual reduction occurs during the first division, but the second division is also an integral part of the process. Any cell capable of undergoing meiosis is called a **meiocyte.** Among plants

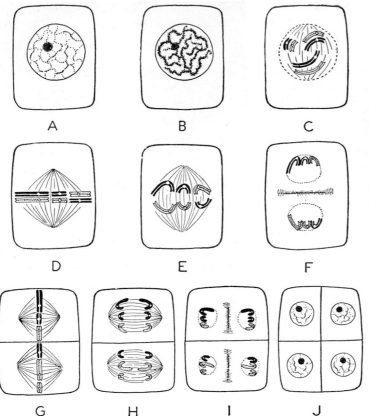

Fig. 4.2. Diagram of meiosis, with n = 3. The chromosomes of one complement are blacked in, and those of the other are stippled. A, resting stage, before meiosis; B, early prophase; C, late prophase, with paired chromosomes; D, first metaphase, with paired chromosomes; E, early anaphase, showing one possibility of segregation; F, telophase; G, second metaphase; H, second anaphase; I, second telophase; J, haploid cells after completion of meiosis.

the immediate products of meiosis are usually spores, and a meiocyte is therefore often called a **spore mother cell.** Spores formed as a result of reduction division are sometimes called **sexual spores** to distinguish them from other kinds of spores.

The prophase of the first division of meiosis is essentially similar to the prophase of mitosis, except that the homologous chromosomes become associated in pairs. Each chromosome becomes visibly double late in the prophase, just as in ordinary mitosis, and a pair of homologous chromosomes therefore consists of four chromatids. The chromosomes remain associated in pairs through the metaphase. At anaphase the members of the pairs are separated; one chromosome of each pair

moves to one pole, and the other moves to the other pole. Each of the daughter nuclei formed during the first division has the *n* rather than the 2*n* number of chromosomes. The first division of meiosis is followed immediately by the second division, in which the two chromatids of each chromosome are separated, just as in ordinary mitosis. As a result of these two divisions, which together comprise meiosis, the original 2*n* nucleus gives rise to four nuclei each with *n* chromosomes.

The actual reduction in the number of chromosomes per nucleus takes place in the first of the two divisions of meiosis, inasmuch as whole chromosomes rather than chromatids become separated at that time and move to the poles. The second division is essentially mitotic as regards the process itself, but the results differ from those of mitosis for this reason: when the two chromosomes of a pair become separated at anaphase of the first division of meiosis, they often exchange parts rather than separating cleanly. This **crossing over,** as the exchange is called, ordinarily involves only one of the two chromatids from each of the two chromosomes of a pair; of the two chromatids which make up a chromosome, one exchanges some parts with a chromatid from the homologous chromosome, while the other remains unaffected. As a result, the two chromatids which make up a chromosome are no longer identical in all respects. An example for a single pair of chromosomes is shown diagrammatically in Fig. 4.3.

Each of the two daughter cells formed in the first division of meiosis may contain some chromosomes whose two component chromatids are not identical in all respects, because one of the two chromatids of the chromosome has been affected by crossing over, while the other has not. The separation of chromatids during the second division of meiosis may result, therefore, in the formation of daughter nuclei which are not genetically identical, and this second division differs in that respect from ordinary mitosis. The amount of crossing over varies according to the size and number of chromosomes, and according to other factors. In general, the fewer and longer the chromosomes, the more abundant the crossing over.

VARIATIONS IN THE MEIOTIC PROCESS

Reduction division leading directly or eventually to the formation of either isogametes or male gametes ordinarily follows the pattern just described, and the four cells produced from each original meiocyte are similar in size and function. Reduction division leading directly or eventually to the formation of female gametes sometimes follows a slightly modified pattern, in which most of the cytoplasm from the original meiocyte is retained with one of the nuclei produced, and the other nuclei degenerate and disappear. The first division in such instances is similar to any other primary meiotic division, except that the cytoplasm is very unequally divided. The nucleus which gets only a small

Fig. 4.3. Diagram of crossing over. *A*, a pair of homologous chromosomes, each consisting of two chromatids; *B*, chromosomes twisted together; *C*, chromosomes separated again, after exchanging parts of chromatids; *D*, the four ultimate chromosomes after completion of meiosis.

amount of cytoplasm may or may not divide again; in any case, it or its daughter nuclei soon degenerate. The nucleus which gets the larger share of cytoplasm during the first division divides again, just as in any other second meiotic division, except that most of the cytoplasm is again retained with one of the daughter nuclei, and the other daughter nucleus degenerates. The original $2n$ nucleus thus gives rise to only one functional n nucleus, and this one functional nucleus with the reduced number of chromosomes retains most of the cytoplasm of the original $2n$ cell; otherwise the meiotic processes leading to the formation of female gametes are identical to those leading to the formation of male gametes.

The production of female gametes in higher animals regularly follows the meiotic pattern in which only a single functional haploid cell is produced from an original diploid meiocyte. Among plants this type of meiosis is less common, but tendencies toward it are shown by most of the plants in which some of the spores produced in reduction division are of the special type known as megaspores.

THE RESULTS OF MEIOSIS

There are two direct important results of meiosis. One is the obvious fact that the chromosome number is reduced from $2n$ to n. The other is that the resulting nuclei, with the reduced number of chromosomes, may carry different combinations of hereditary factors and thus be genetically unlike. Without allowing for the complicating effects of crossing over, a relatively simple case in which $n = 2$ may be considered. The two chromosomes in the diploid nucleus which are derived eventually from one of the ancestral ga-

metes may be called A_1 and B_1, and their homologues, derived eventually from the other ancestral gamete, may be called A_2 and B_2. At the metaphase of the first division of meiosis, these chromosomes are arranged in pairs: A_1–A_2, and B_1–B_2. In the ensuing separation, one of the A chromosomes and one of the B chromosomes go to one pole, and the others go to the other pole. One possibility is that chromosomes A_1 and B_1 will migrate to one of the poles and A_2 and B_2 to the other. The resulting nuclei will be similar to those of the parental gametes from which the zygote was formed (except for the effects of crossing over). The other possibility is that chromosomes A_1 and B_2 will migrate to one pole and chromosomes A_2 and B_1 to the other. These combinations are different from those of the parental gametes from which the zygote was formed. Each of the two chromosome complements, A_1–B_2, and A_2–B_1, has a complete set of genes governing the hereditary characters of the organism, but the two sets may not be alike in all their effects.

The larger the number of chromosomes making up the chromosome complement, the larger the number of different possible chromosome combinations as a result of meiosis. If $n = 2$, the number of possible combinations as a result of reduction division is 4, these being A_1–B_1, A_1–B_2, A_2–B_1, and A_2–B_2 (crossovers still ignored). If $n = 3$, then the number of possible combinations is doubled: each of the combinations already seen for the condition in which $n = 2$, may exist with the addition of chromosome C_1 or C_2. If $n = 4$, the number of possible combinations is again doubled, and so on. Mathematically, the number of possible combinations of chromosomes obtainable from normal meiosis may be represented as 2^n (that is,

2 to the power of n) if n represents the number of chromosomes in the cell after reduction. In human beings, for which n typically equals 23,[1] the number of possible combinations of chromosomes obtainable by normal reduction division in the reproductive cells of a single individual is 2^{23}, which is 8,388,608. Inasmuch as crossing over results in the formation of chromatids (and eventually chromosomes) having different combinations of genes from those that previously existed, the effect of crossing over is to increase still further the number of possible chromosome combinations produced by reduction division.

THE BIOLOGICAL SIGNIFICANCE OF SEXUALITY

The biological significance of sexuality is clear; it produces new and different combinations of hereditary characteristics. Mutation and sexual reproduction are the raw materials of evolution.

Consider two individual organisms of the same species, each of which has one beneficial characteristic not possessed by the other. Let one such beneficial character be designated as a_1, and its less beneficial state as a_2, while the other beneficial character is designated as b_1, and its less beneficial state as b_2. By sexual reproduction these two beneficial characters may be combined in the same organism. The principle is the same whether the mature organism is diploid or haploid but is perhaps best introduced at the haploid level. One of the two original haploid organisms will have the constitution a_1b_2, and the other will have the constitution a_2b_1. The zygote formed by fusion of gametes of

[1] Recent studies indicate that the number is 23 in most individuals, but 24 in some others.

these two organisms will have the constitution $a_1a_2b_1b_2$. If the factors governing a and b are borne on different chromosomes, then reduction division from the zygote gives us four possible combinations of these factors: a_1b_1, a_1b_2, a_2b_1, and a_2b_2. Two of these nuclei repeat the parental types, and the other two represent combinations different from the parental types. One of the two combinations different from the parental types embraces both the favorable characteristics from the two parents, whereas the other is burdened with both the unfavorable characteristics. If three pairs of characters are considered instead of two, and if each of these characters is governed by a single gene, then the number of possible combinations of these characters would be eight, and so on.

We shall see in Chapter 35 that many characters are controlled by groups of genes rather than by single genes, but this is merely an added complexity which does not change the basic situation. By gametic union and reduction division, new and different gene combinations are obtained, with correspondingly different kinds of individuals as a result. Most organisms produce many more offspring than can possibly survive, and the resulting competition for survival gives an opportunity for the more suitable gene combinations to be perpetuated. The mechanism of evolution will be further discussed in Chapter 36.

SUMMARY

Among the higher animals, including man, sexual reproduction is associated with the differentiation of distinctly male and female individuals, and in common usage this differentiation is considered the essential feature of sexuality. When some of the simpler kinds of organisms are also considered, however, an expanded concept is useful and proper. The most nearly characteristic feature of sexuality, in the broad sense, is the regular, alternating doubling and halving of the number of chromosomes in the nuclei. The doubling results from fusion of gametes; the halving is brought about by meiosis. Reduction division (meiosis) is just as much a part of the sexual cycle as is gametic fusion. Sexual reproduction results in the formation of new and different combinations of existing genes. The appearance of new characters (or the modification of existing ones) by gene mutation, and the formation of new and different combinations of existing characters by sexual reproduction, together constitute one of the most important forces in the march of organic evolution.

CHAPTER 5

Introduction to Taxonomy

PRINCIPLES OF CLASSIFICATION

INTRODUCTION

The diversity among living things is almost infinite. No two individuals are exactly alike in all details. Sometimes the differences between two individuals of very unlike appearance can be bridged by a series of other individuals, each differing so slightly from the next that there is no appreciable gap in the series. On the other hand, the variability among living things as a whole is not continuous but exhibits many distinct gaps of various sizes. The job of the taxonomist, or systematic biologist, is to organize the knowledge of the diversity and variability among organisms into a system of classification which reflects their evolutionary origin as well as their similarities and differences.

THE SPECIES

Any taxonomic unit of classification is called a **taxon** (pl., **taxa**). The basic taxon is

◄

Broom rape, *Orobanche uniflora*, a root parasite. (About twice natural size.) The family Orobanchaceae is a group of parasitic flowering plants which lack chlorophyll. Some members of the closely related family Scrophulariaceae, such as Indian paint brush (*Castilleja*), are partial root parasites, but still have chlorophyll. Other members of the Scrophulariaceae, such as the common snapdragon (*Antirrhinum majus*), are wholly autotrophic. (Photo by Hugh Spencer, from National Audubon Society.)

the **species** (pl., **species**). The word *species* is taken over from Latin, in which it means a particular kind or sort. In modern biological usage the species are the smallest groups of individuals which can be recognized as groups, and which are consistently and persistently different from other groups. Among sexually reproducing organisms, the members of a single species are usually capable of interbreeding freely, whereas interbreeding between members of different species is prevented or restricted by natural causes. In other words, a species is a particular kind of plant or animal, which retains its distinctness from other kinds in nature over a period of many successive generations.

Some species are more variable than others. Most biologists find it helpful to divide many of the more variable species into subspecies and/or varieties, which are populations within the species that are persistently different enough to merit some notice, but which are connected to each other by numerous intermediate individuals. Differences which are the direct result of the response of the individual to the environment are generally considered beneath taxonomic notice, as are also those hereditary differences which are customarily reassorted in successive generations because of interbreeding. Errors have been made, and will continue to be made, as to whether certain differences really mark separate, self-perpetuating natural populations, or whether they are merely differences between individuals in the same interbreeding population; but these errors are corrected when sufficient information becomes available.

The origin of one species from another, or the divergence of a single species into two or more, is usually a slow process which takes many generations. When two populations of a common origin have achieved a degree of divergence which permits the recognition of essentially all the individuals as belonging to one or to the other population, with few or no intermediates, they are considered to have become different species. Since evolution is an ever-continuing process, there are some taxa which are now sufficiently distinct so that some taxonomists call them separate species, but which are so closely related and so evidently connected by intermediate individuals that other taxonomists prefer to call them parts of one species. There is thus room for difference of opinion as well as for error in determining the limits of species, but taxonomists are agreed that the species is a fundamental natural unit.

The levels of classification above the species show the degrees of similarity and evolutionary relationship among species and groups of species. A group of similar species constitutes a **genus** (pl., **genera**); a group of similar genera constitutes a **family**; a group of similar families constitutes an **order**; a group of similar orders constitutes a **class**; and a group of similar classes constitutes a **division**. The division is the highest (most inclusive) category regularly used in the classification of the plant kingdom. It is customary and useful to classify all organisms into only two kingdoms, the plant kingdom and the animal kingdom, even though the cleavage between the two is not sharp. Except that the division of plant taxonomy is equivalent to the phylum of animal taxonomy, the terms used for the essential taxonomic groups are the same for both plants and animals.

The ending *-phyta* on a botanical scientific name indicates a division; the ending *-ales* indicates an order; and the ending *-aceae* indicates a family. Because of long-established custom which antedates the present rules of botanical nomenclature, the names of a few families and higher taxa take endings different from any of the foregoing ones. The ending for classes differs in different groups, and especially in the higher plants the usage is not yet stabilized.

The classification of the American elm is as follows:

Kingdom: Plantae
Division: Anthophyta
Class: Dicotyledonae
Order: Urticales
Family: Ulmaceae
Genus: *Ulmus*
Species: *Ulmus americana* L.[1]

The number of natural groups between the division and the species may or may not coincide with the number of categories given in the foregoing system of classification, but none of the categories is omitted. The maidenhair tree, *Ginkgo biloba* Salisb., is so distinct from all other living species that it is put into an order all by itself. Among living plants, the order Ginkgoales contains only the family Ginkgoaceae; the family Ginkgoaceae contains only the genus *Ginkgo;* and the genus *Ginkgo* contains only the species *Ginkgo biloba* Salisb. On the other hand, if more taxonomic categories are needed than the usual list provides, others can be inserted, usually with the prefix *sub-*. A subkingdom is a taxon between the kingdom and the division; a subdivision is a taxon between

the division and the class; a subclass is a taxon between the class and the order; etc.

SCIENTIFIC NAMES

The scientific name of any species of plant or animal consists of two words, usually Latin or of Latin form. The first word indicates the name of the genus to which the species belongs, and the second indicates the particular species of that genus. *Acer* is the scientific name of a particular genus which includes all the maples. The sugar maple is *Acer saccharum;* the Norway maple is *Acer platanoides;* and the red maple is *Acer rubrum.* The second of the two words making up the name of a species is called the **specific epithet.** A particular specific epithet may be used only once within a given genus, but it may be used repeatedly in different genera. The specific epithet *rubrum* has been used not only in the genus *Acer,* but also in *Allium* (the onion genus), *Chenopodium* (the goosefoot genus), and many other genera. By itself *rubrum* is merely a Latin adjective meaning red; it is not the name of a plant. As a scientific name, *rubrum,* or any other specific epithet, has meaning only if it is linked with the name of a particular genus. The names of genera and higher taxa, however, may stand alone. The specific epithet is usually a Latin or Latinized adjective, which takes its grammatical gender from that of the genus, but it is sometimes a noun in apposition to the generic name. It is customary to capitalize the names of genera and all the higher taxa and not to capitalize specific epithets, although the rules of botanical nomenclature permit the optional capitalization of certain specific epithets. Because the name

[1] As explained on p. 68, it is customary to add an abbreviation of the author's name after the specific epithet. L. stands for Linnaeus.

of a species consists of two words, scientific biological nomenclature is said to follow a **binomial system.**

It is a general principle of botanical nomenclature that each kind of plant can have only one correct scientific name, and each name can be used for only one kind of plant. In order to minimize the possibility of confusion resulting from the inadvertent use of the same name for two different species, the author's name, or more often an abbreviation of it, is frequently added after the specific epithet. In general, when two or more names have been used for the same species, it is the first name or usage which must stand, and subsequent ones are rejected.

USE OF LATIN FOR SCIENTIFIC NAMES

In Roman and medieval times, Latin was the language of learning in Europe. Those who wrote at all wrote Latin, regardless of the language they generally spoke. Those who wrote about plants naturally used Latin names for the plants.

The use of Latin for scientific names has been continued, in spite of the virtual abandonment of Latin in other writing, because of several advantages. Plants are not limited by national or linguistic boundaries, and if botanists in different countries are to understand each other's work, a plant should have the same name wherever it grows. Even within a single country, common names are unsatisfactory or confusing. The same common name may be applied to several different plants in different parts of the same country, or even in the same region, and the same plant may have several different common names in different regions or even in one region. A great many plants have no common names at all.

It is true that some common names coincide, at least in part, with the genera and species recognized by botanists. Such common names as spruce, fir, pine, oak, hemlock, ash, maple, elm, hickory, goldenrod, ragweed, and violet correspond in large part to botanical genera, and these names are readily converted to the binomial system by the addition of another word in each case to indicate a particular species. Longleaf pine, jack pine, slash pine, sugar pine, and Norway pine are common names for individual species of the genus *Pinus*; and American elm, slippery elm, cork elm, and English elm are common names for individual species of the genus *Ulmus*.

Even those common names which seem to conform to taxonomic groups cannot be depended on to do so, however. Most of the species which are called violets belong to the botanical genus *Viola*, which is a member of the family Violaceae, but the African violet belongs to the genus *Saintpaulia* of the family Gesneriaceae. Most of the species which are called pines belong to the genus *Pinus*; but the name pine is often loosely used for any of several different related genera, and the Australian pine is *Casuarina*, which belongs to a different botanical division from the true pines. Cabbage, brussels sprouts, broccoli, kale, kohlrabi, cauliflower, turnips, and black mustard all belong to the genus *Brassica*, a relationship which might be suspected from their flavor but never from their English common names.

Improvements in our understanding of the limits of species and genera sometimes necessitate changes in nomenclature, and scientific names are not always as stable and free from confusion as might be desired. The difficulty is minor, however, compared to that which would attend any attempt to organize common names into a comprehensive and scientifically accurate system.

HISTORICAL SUMMARY

The binomial system of nomenclature, which is now used for both plants and animals, was established by the Swedish botanist and naturalist Carl Linnaeus (1707–1778), whose name is also sometimes given as Carolus Linnaeus or Carl von Linné. His *Species Plantarum*, published in 1753, in which he attempted to name and describe all the species of plants in the world, is now the formal starting point for the scientific nomenclature of higher plants. Prior to Linnaeus' work, the botanical names of genera were customarily single Latin words, just as now, but the names of species were really short Latin descriptions, usually of several words, which attempted to give the characters by which they could be recognized.

The convenience of the binomial as opposed to the polynomial system and the thoroughness with which Linnaeus covered the known kinds of plants soon led to the general adoption of both his classification and his system of nomenclature. Linnaeus' classification of groups above the rank of genus has been abandoned, but the binomial system of nomenclature remains, together with most of his genera and species.

Linnaeus grouped all plants into 24 convenient classes. He freely admitted that this organization did not always put the most similar things together, but he felt that knowledge was not then adequate to permit the establishment of a comprehensive natural system. The development of a natural system, in which plants are classi-

Fig. 5.1. Carl Linnaeus (1707–1778), Swedish botanist and naturalist, who founded the binomial system of nomenclature.

fied according to the totality of their similarities and differences, has occupied the attention of post-Linnaean (and some pre-Linnaean) taxonomists to this day, and it is not yet satisfactorily completed.

For more than a century after the publication of *Species Plantarum*, biologists in general believed that each species had been separately created. The concept of organic evolution, which rapidly gained scientific acceptance after the publication of Charles Darwin's monumental *On the Origin of Species* (see Chapter 36) in 1859, gave new meaning to taxonomy. The progress that had been made toward a natural classification was so fully compatible with the principle of evolution that taxonomists in general soon accepted the concept and made it their own. No taxonomic system is now considered to be natural if it does not attempt to reflect evolutionary relationships as well as the present similarities and differences among organisms.

The basic classification of plants which was most widely accepted in the latter part of the nineteenth century and the early part of the twentieth century used certain outstanding morphological features to group all plants into four divisions: the Thallophyta, Bryophyta, Pteridophyta, and Spermatophyta. The most significant differences among these divisions are summarized in the following synoptical key[2]:

1. Plants without specialized conducting tissues, and not differentiated into true roots, stems, and leaves (the nonvascular plants)

    2. Gametangia (structures in which gametes are borne) unicellular or wanting; sporophyte (the part of the life cycle in which the cells have $2n$ chromosomes) not remaining attached to the gametophyte (the part of the life cycle in which the cells have n chromosomes), or the plants often asexual and thus without sporophyte and gametophyte generations   **1. Division Thallophyta**

        3. Plants with chlorophyll   1a. *Subdivision Algae*

        3. Plants without chlorophyll   1b. *Subdivision Fungi*

    2. Gametangia multicellular; sporophyte remaining attached to the gametophyte and more or less parasitic on it   **2. Division Bryophyta**

1. Plants with specialized conducting tissues (xylem and phloem) in the sporophyte, which is differentiated into roots, stems, and leaves (the vascular plants)

    4. Plants not producing seeds; both generations (the sporophyte and the gametophyte) physiologically independent at maturity   **3. Division Pteridophyta**

    4. Plants producing seeds; gametophyte parasitic on the sporophyte   **4. Division Spermatophyta**

        5. Seeds naked (i.e., exposed directly to the air); female gametophyte multicellular, with 500 or more cells (or nuclei)   4a. *Subdivision Gymnospermae*

        5. Seeds enclosed in a special structure, the ovary; female gametophyte composed of a few (typically 8) cells or nuclei   4b. *Subdivision Angiospermae*

[2] A key is any formal device to show the characters by which groups (or individuals) may be recognized. In dichotomous, indented keys, such as are used in this text, all organisms under consideration are first divided into two groups, and the contrasting characters of those groups are given in two opposing statements which start at the left-hand margin of the key. Each of these two groups is then divided into two lesser groups, and so on, until the ultimate categories are reached. Statements of the characters of the lesser groups are progressively indented under the larger groups to which they belong. The contrasting "legs" of a key are often marked by numbers as an aid to clarity. A synoptical key is one which attempts to show the important differences between the groups, regardless of how easy or difficult the characters may be to observe.

This relatively simple organization is readily comprehensible and has much to recommend it, but it has become increasingly evident that it misrepresents some of the evolutionary relationships. There is so much diversity among the algae that all algologists now consider them to represent several divisions, rather than a single subdivision. The development of seeds has occurred several times, and some abundant seed-bearing fossils are evidently not allied to present-day seed plants. The modern gymnosperms belong to two different groups that probably originated from the pteridophytes independently of each other. It is useful to retain the English equivalents for the names of the several divisions and subdivisions of the traditional classification, but it should be recognized that some of these are no longer considered to represent wholly natural groups.

PRESENT CLASSIFICATION

The necessity to recognize more than four divisions of plants is now widely admitted, but no general agreement on a comprehensive new system has yet been attained. The treatment in this text is the author's own synthesis of some of the proposals which have been made. The accompanying chart shows how the major groups here recognized compare with those of the older system previously referred to. Although only one of the divisions here recognized, the Bryophyta, corresponds exactly to any of the divisions in the older system, most of the others now admitted are also recognized, but at a lesser rank, in the traditional scheme. A synoptical key to the divisions and classes here recognized is presented in the appendix.

The student should also note at this point that the several divisions here recognized are grouped into two subkingdoms, the Thallophyta and Embryophyta. The thallophytes, corresponding to the division Thallophyta of the older system and comprising the first eight divisions of the present one, include the bacteria, molds, mushrooms, pond scums, seaweeds, etc. The embryophytes, corresponding to the Bryophyta, Pteridophyta, and Spermatophyta of the older system, and comprising the last eight divisions of the present one, include all the familiar green land plants large enough to be individually visible to the naked eye.

NUMBER OF SPECIES OF PLANTS

The number of species of plants in the world has not yet been accurately determined, both because many species remain to be discovered and because some species have unintentionally been named and described more than once. Probably not many bona fide new species of vascular plants remain to be discovered in temperate and boreal regions, but almost every collecting expedition into the tropics brings back its quota of things not previously known. Doubtless many species of fungi remain to be discovered even in temperate regions.

A rough estimate of the number of known species is given for each class of plants in the following chapters. They may be roughly summarized here as about 25,000 algae, 40,000 fungi, 20,000 bryophytes, 10,000 pteridophytes, 500 gymnosperms, and 200,000 angiosperms. Adding these together we obtain a figure of 295,500 species. Such a figure gives an impression of greater accuracy than actually exists, however, because the estimates in the various groups are not on the same scale of accu-

THE DIVISIONS AND CLASSES OF PLANTS

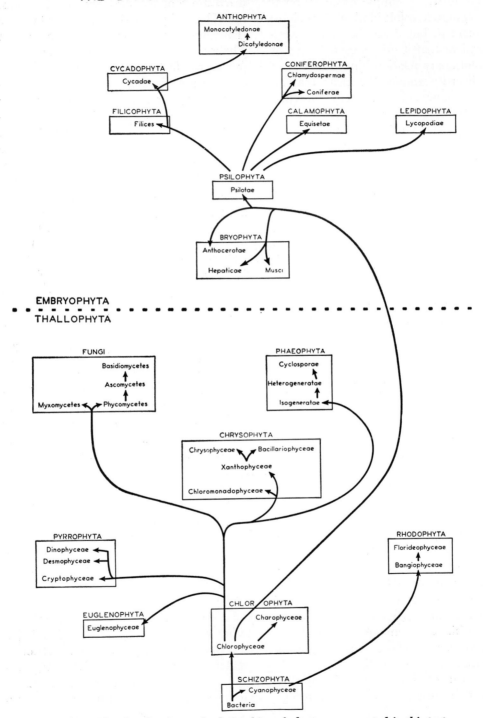

Fig. 5.2. The classification and relationships of plants, as presented in this text.

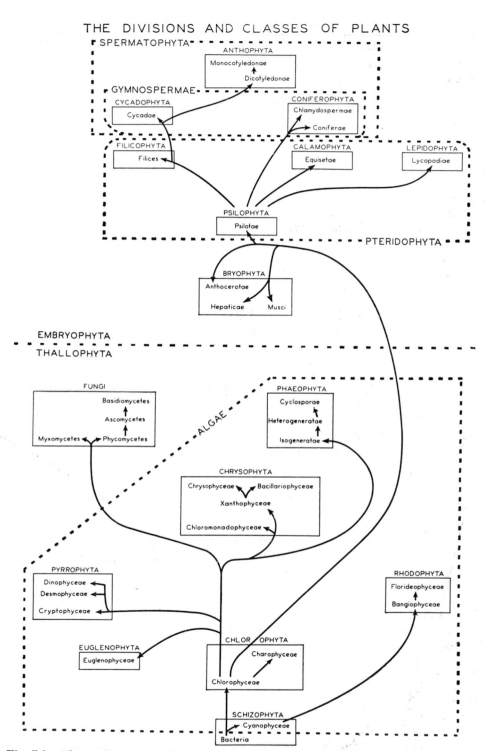

Fig. 5.3. The traditional four-division system of plant classification, superimposed on the system used in this text.

PRESENT SCHEME				TRADITIONAL SCHEME
Subkingdom	I.		Thallophyta	
Division	1.		Schizophyta	
Class	1a.		Schizomycetes (bacteria)	
Class	1b.		Cyanophyceae (blue-green algae)	
Division	2.		Chlorophyta (green algae)	
Class	2a.		Chlorophyceae	
Class	2b.		Charophyceae	
Division	3.		Euglenophyta	
Class	3a.		Euglenophyceae	
Division	4.		Pyrrophyta	Division Thallophyta
Class	4a.		Cryptophyceae	
Class	4b.		Desmophyceae	Subdivision Algae
Class	4c.		Dinophyceae	
Division	5.		Chrysophyta	
Class	5a.		Chloromonadophyceae	
Class	5b.		Xanthophyceae	
Class	5c.		Chrysophyceae	
Class	5d.		Bacillariophyceae (diatoms)	
Division	6.		Phaeophyta (brown algae)	
Class	6a.		Isogeneratae	
Class	6b.		Heterogeneratae	
Class	6c.		Cyclosporae	
Division	7.		Rhodophyta (red algae)	
Class	7a.		Bangiophyceae	
Class	7b.		Florideophyceae	
Division	8.		Fungi	(+ Bacteria)
Class	8a.		Myxomycetes (slime molds)	Subdivision Fungi
Class	8b.		Phycomycetes	
Class	8c.		Ascomycetes	
Class	8d.		Basidiomycetes	
Subkingdom	II.		Embryophyta	
Division	9.		Bryophyta	Division Bryophyta
Class	9a.		Anthocerotae (horned liverworts)	Class Hepaticae
Class	9b.		Hepaticae (liverworts)	
Class	9c.		Musci (mosses)	Class Musci
Division	10.		Psilophyta	
Class	10a.		Psilotae	
Division	11.		Lepidophyta	
Class	11a.		Lycopodiae (club mosses)	Division Pteridophyta
Division	12.		Calamophyta	
Class	12a.		Equisetae (horsetails)	
Division	13.		Filicophyta (ferns)	
Class	13a.		Filices	
Division	14.		Cycadophyta	
Class	14a.		Cycadae (cycads)	Division Spermatophyta
Division	15.		Coniferophyta	
Class	15a.		Coniferae (conifers, etc.)	Subdivision Gymnospermae
Class	15b.		Chlamydospermae	
Division	16.		Anthophyta (flowering plants)	Subdivision Angiospermae
Class	16a.		Dicotyledonae	Class Dicotyledonae
Class	16b.		Monocotyledonae	Class Monocotyledonae

The Major Divisions of Geologic Time				
ERA	PERIOD	EPOCH	HOW LONG AGO	DURATION
CENOZOIC	QUATERNARY	RECENT	0-1	1
		PLEISTOCENE		
	TERTIARY	PLIOCENE	1-12	11
		MIOCENE	12-28	16
		OLIGOCENE	28-40	12
		EOCENE	40-60	20
		PALEOCENE		
MESOZOIC	CRETACEOUS		60-130	70
	JURASSIC		130-155	25
	TRIASSIC		155-185	30
PALEOZOIC	PERMIAN		185-210	25
	UPPER CARBONIFEROUS		210-235	25
	LOWER CARBONIFEROUS		235-265	30
	DEVONIAN		265-320	55
	SILURIAN		320-360	40
	ORDOVICIAN		360-440	80
	CAMBRIAN		440-520	80
PROTEROZOIC	PRECAMBRIAN		520-2100+	1600+

Fig. 5.4. The major divisions of geologic time and their approximate dates and durations. As is customary in geological series, the most ancient period is seen at the bottom, and the most recent at the top, corresponding to the positions which would be occupied by rocks of those ages in a continuous undeformed series. The numbers indicate millions of years. More recent estimates indicate slight increases in these figures.

racy. The 500 species of gymnosperms are insignificant in relation to the probable error in the estimate of 200,000 angiosperms. For practical purposes the figure of 295,500 known species may therefore be rounded off at about 300,000. It is possible that when all the species of plants in the world are known the figure may approach half a million.

SOME GEOLOGICAL BACKGROUND

Under all known natural conditions, uranium decomposes at a uniform rate, forming lead which differs slightly in weight from ordinary lead. The length of time required for a given quantity of a radioactive element to diminish by half is known as its **half-life.** The half-life of ordinary uranium is calculated at 4.498 billion years. On the assumption that the rate of radioactive decomposition has been as constant in the past as now, the age of any uranium-bearing rock can be calculated by the uranium-lead ratio, and similar ratios are used for other radioactive elements. The oldest rocks which have been dated by this method appear to be about 2.8 billion years old, but calculations based on deep-sea deposits indicate that the earth as a whole is about 4.5 billion years old. Meteors which may owe their origin to the same cataclysm which produced the earth are also dated at about 4.5 billion years. Geologists divide the history of the earth into a number of periods and eras,

each millions of years long. Sedimentary rocks from each, except the most ancient eras, bear characteristic fossils of plants and animals, so that an experienced geologist can often recognize the geologic position of a rock by the fossils it contains. Recent rocks contain fossils more or less readily identifiable with modern species or genera of plants and animals. Older rocks contain progressively fewer fossils which can be identified with modern organisms, and a progressively larger proportion which cannot. The more complex kinds of plants and animals disappear one by one from the fossil record of older rocks. Rocks formed prior to the Cambrian geologic period, which began about 550 million years ago, usually contain no definite fossils, although they sometimes bear traces of some of the simplest kinds of organisms. The fine, scattered particles of carbon found in many pre-Cambrian rocks are believed to be derived from the bodies of bacteria and other minute organisms.

SUGGESTED READING

Bailey, L. H., *How Plants Get Their Names,* Macmillan, New York, 1933, 209 pp. A simple, clearly written discussion of scientific names.

Jackson, B. D., *Linnaeus,* Witherby, London, 1923, 416 pp. A well-written biography.

Moore, Ruth, "Dating the Past," *Brittanica Book of the Year,* 1960, pp. 40–52. A fascinating, scientifically accurate, popular account.

CHAPTER 6

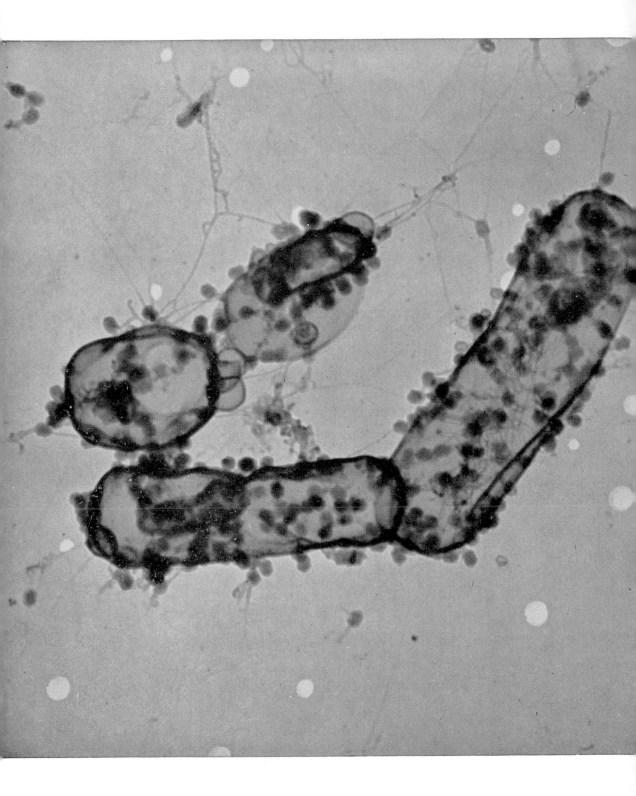

SCHIZOPHYTA. *Unicellular or thalloid plants, sometimes with some differentiation of cells, but without differentiated tissues; nucleus of relatively simple structure, lacking a nucleolus and usually lacking nuclear membrane, generally dividing amitotically; mostly asexual, but sometimes with parasexual processes. Two classes, the Schizomycetes and Cyanophyceae, plus the viruses, of uncertain taxonomic status.*

Class

Schizomycetes

BACTERIA

CHAPTER 6

HISTORY AND DEFINITION

Bacteria were first observed by Leeuwenhoek in pepper infusions which he prepared in 1676. His drawings of bacteria from his own teeth, made in 1683, include examples of the three common shapes currently recognized in bacteriological classification. Early microbiologists did not usually distinguish the bacteria as a group from other microorganisms, and the term *animalcule* (or its equivalent in other languages) was rather generally applied to all unicellular organisms and some very small multicellular ones. The name *Bacterium* was introduced for a particular genus by the German biologist Christian G. Ehrenberg (1795–1876) in 1828, and the names *Spirillum* and *Spirochaeta* first appeared in his classification of "infusion animalcules" published in 1838.

The bacteria were first recognized and defined as a group by the German botanist

◄

Escherichia coli, **the human colon bacillus, being attacked by bacteriophage. (×70,000.) (Electron micrograph courtesy of T. F. Anderson.)**

Karl Wilhelm von Naegeli (1817–1891), who proposed the name *Schizomycetes* for them in 1857. Another German botanist and bacteriologist, Ferdinand Cohn (1828–1898), who presented a comprehensive study of the then known kinds of bacteria in 1872–1875, is often called the Father of Bacteriology. The same title is also often bestowed on Pasteur, especially because of his work on the pathogenic (disease-causing) bacteria.

Bacteria may be defined as schizophytes which do not contain phycobilin pigments, and which either do not contain chlorophyll or do contain chlorophyll but do not release oxygen as a result of photosynthesis. About one third of the kinds of bacteria are visibly pigmented (not necessarily with chlorophyll). The remainder are apparently colorless, although many of them contain small quantities of colored enzymes, such as the cytochromes. Most bacteria are unicellular, but some form simple or branched filaments, or even nonfilamentous colonies of coherent cells. Most kinds have a definite cell wall which is usually nitrogenous. Bacteria store food reserves in a number of forms, including droplets of fat, granules of volutin (apparently a nucleoprotein), and especially granules of various kinds of polysaccharides; some of these latter resemble (or may actually be) glycogen; others resemble or may be starch. Reproduction is ordinarily accomplished by cell division, which is apparently amitotic. Some forms produce spores. Exchange of genetic material has been reported for a number of kinds of bacteria. In at least some cases the process is parasexual rather than truly sexual; i.e., genetic material is exchanged without the formation of a zygote. Recent evidence indicates that exchange sometimes occurs through a protoplasmic bridge between contiguous cells.

DISTRIBUTION

Bacteria are very widely distributed, on and beneath the surface of the earth, in fresh water and in the sea, on and in other organisms, and on the dust particles which float in the air. They do not generally occur inside normal, healthy cells of other organisms, but otherwise they are usually found wherever food is available to them. Almost all naturally occurring organic compounds can be used as food by one or another kind of bacteria, and some can derive energy through oxidation of inorganic substances. Many bacteria require free oxygen; others can use it or grow anaerobically without it; others are obligate anaerobes. Some bacteria live and grow at temperatures as high as 75°C.

CLASSIFICATION

In sexually reproducing organisms, species are usually interbreeding or potentially interbreeding populations which can be distinguished morphologically from other such populations. Neither the concept of interbreeding populations nor the concept of morphologically recognizable species is readily applicable to the bacteria. Bacteria which are morphologically similar may be physiologically so different that they must be regarded as separate species. Among the pathogenic bacteria, a single physiological difference, caused by a single gene mutation, may be of critical importance in determining the effect of the bacterium on the host and vice versa. The fact that bacterial populations consist of very large numbers of individuals increases the likelihood that mutants may be produced. Because of these problems, the definition of species in the bacteria is unusually difficult, and there are wide differences of opinion as to the total number of species in the class. More than 1000 species of bacteria are usually accepted, and many others have not yet been characterized.

Nearly all species of bacteria can be fitted into one or another of eleven orders, as indicated in the key given in the appendix. One of these, the Eubacteriales, makes up more than half the class, and it is usually the Eubacteriales and Pseudomonadales which are intended when reference is made to "bacteria" without further qualification.

GENERAL MORPHOLOGY AND CYTOLOGY

INTRODUCTION

Most bacteria are unicellular, the cells having one of three more or less definite shapes: (1) spherical, (2) rod-shaped, and (3) spiral or corkscrew-shaped. Spherical bacteria (Fig. 6.1) are called **cocci** (sing., coccus); rod-shaped (Fig. 6.2) bacteria are called **bacilli** (sing., **bacillus**), or merely **rods**; and corkscrew-shaped (Fig. 6.3) bacteria (except the spirochaetes) are called **spirilla** (sing., **spirillum**). The shape of the bacterial cell is a useful taxonomic character, but it does not by itself divide the bacteria in three wholly natural groups. The Eubacteriales range from spherical to rod-shaped, and all three shapes are found in the Rhodobacteriales. Cocci vary from about 0.2 to 4 microns in diameter; bacilli and spirilla usually resemble cocci in diameter, but are longer, sometimes as much as 40 microns. Cells of some of the sulfur bacteria are as much as 60 microns long and 25 microns thick. Some of the spirochaetes are even longer, up to 500 microns, but are still very slender.

THE CELL WALL

The cell wall of bacteria generally consists of two layers, the outer layer commonly being the thicker. The wall is usually nitrogenous; it was once thought to be composed largely of chitin, but recent studies indicate that proteins and protein-like compounds called *polypeptides* (both formed by chemical linkage of amino acid

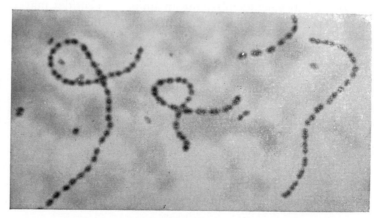

Fig. 6.1. *Streptococcus lactis*, the sour-milk bacterium. (×1700.) (Copyright by General Biological Supply House, Inc., Chicago.)

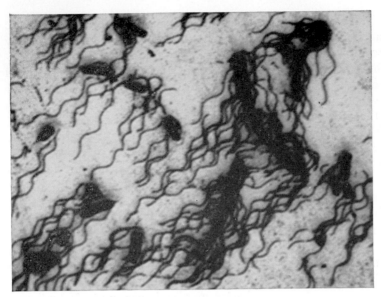

Fig. 6.2. *Salmonella typhosa,* the cause of typhoid fever. Note the long flagella. (× 8500.) (Copyright by General Biological Supply House, Inc. Chicago.)

molecules) are usually the principal constituents. A small proportion of lipid is usually associated with the proteins and polypeptides, perhaps as a cementing substance, and the resulting wall layers have no evident interior structure. Various polysaccharide constituents are also frequently associated with the other wall constituents, and in a few cases the wall is composed largely of cellulose arranged into micelles, just as in higher plants.

Hexose amines are also found in the bacterial cell wall. They differ from hexose sugars, such as glucose, in having an amine group (i.e., a small nitrogen-containing group, such as NH_2) substituted for one or more of the hydroxide (OH) groups of the sugar. Chitin is formed by polymerization of a particular type of hexose amine in a straight chain, just as cellulose is formed by polymerization of glucose molecules in a straight chain. The particular hexose amine which has been recovered from bacterial cell walls is the one from which chitin is formed; but in those bacteria which have been carefully studied by

modern methods the individual hexose amine molecules do not appear to be combined into chitin.

The cell wall is often surrounded by a thick gelatinous sheath. This may form a discrete capsule surrounding the cell or may dissolve into the medium as slime or mucus. Typically the gelatinous sheath is composed of polysaccharide, with different polysaccharides being produced by different kinds of bacteria, though in some bacteria the capsule is proteinaceous instead. Phospholipids, iron compounds, and polypeptides may also occur in the sheath. In many of the Chlamydobacteriales, or sheathed bacteria, the sheath encloses a whole filament but does not separate the individual cells of which the filament is composed.

FLAGELLA

Many of the bacteria are nonmotile. Many others swim by means of one, two, or several slender, thread-like or whip-like projections, known as **flagella**, which are generally longer than the breadth of the cell. The flagella commonly have a rotary motion, and a rate as high as 40 revolutions per second has been calculated in some instances.

A bacterial flagellum usually consists of a single proteinaceous fibril, which in some species has been demonstrated to be composed of a sheath and a core. The flagellum passes through the cell wall and usually terminates in a basal granule in the outer part of the cytoplasm. In some bacteria several distinct flagella are loosely aggregated and function as one, and in a few species a single flagellum, with a single basal granule, is composed of several strands, each comparable to the usual single flagellum. No bacteria are known to have the complex type of flagellum, with two central and nine peripheral strands, which is typical of flagellated cells in other groups of organisms.

As noted in the discussion of those groups, the beggiatoas, spirochaetes, and myxobacteria have means of locomotion other than flagella.

CYTOPLASM

The cytoplasm of bacteria is less highly organized than the cytoplasm of higher plants. It contains various kinds of granules, including polysaccharide food reserves, but mitochondria and plastids are absent. There is no central vacuole. RNA is regularly present. A magnesium salt of a particular type of RNA often occurs in a layer just within the cell wall. Bacteria which have this layer adsorb and retain a stain devised by the Danish physician Hans C. J. Gram (1853–1938), and are said to be Gram-positive. Bacteria which do not take Gram's stain are said to be Gram-negative. The actinomycetes and many of the eubacteria (including most of the spore formers) are Gram-positive; the other orders are generally Gram-negative. Most fungi are also Gram-positive. Some other chemical characteristics of various kinds of bacteria appear to be correlated with the reaction to Gram's stain.

THE NUCLEUS

The gelatinous sheath of most bacterial cells retards the penetration of most stains and other chemicals used in cytological studies, and chemical treatment which renders the sheath more readily permeable is also likely to disorganize the protoplasm. For this reason, as well as be-

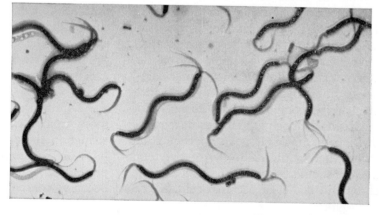

Fig. 6.3. *Spirillum* sp. (×1700.) (Copyright by General Biological Supply House, Inc., Chicago.)

Class Schizomycetes: Bacteria 83

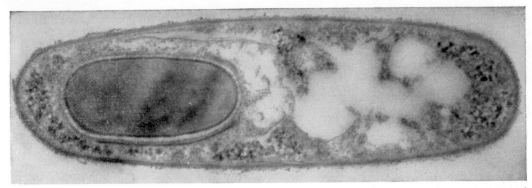

Fig. 6.4. *Bacillus cereus.* Electron micrograph of thin section, showing spore formation. (×44,000.) (Courtesy of George B. Chapman.)

cause of their small size, bacteria were long thought to have no nucleus.

More refined techniques, dating particularly from about 1937, make it possible to demonstrate the existence in the bacterial cell of a body which usually divides at about the same time as the cell, and which takes a stain that is commonly used as a test for DNA, the essential nuclear constituent. Sometimes this chromatin body divides well before the division of the cell, so that the cell contains two or more such bodies of apparently identical composition. The existence of these DNA-containing bodies has now been demonstrated in so many kinds of bacteria that they can reasonably be expected to occur also in the kinds of bacteria which have not been carefully studied in that regard. These bodies are essentially without interior structure, as far as present studies show. There is no clear indication of the differentiated chromonemata, nucleolus, nuclear membrane, and nuclear sap, which are familiar components of the nuclei of organisms belonging to other taxonomic divisions or phyla. It is an open question as to whether the definition of the term *nucleus* should be expanded to include the chromatin bodies of bacterial cells. There-

fore bacteria do or do not have a nucleus, according to how broadly the term is defined. In any case, there is some reliable mechanism for the regular and orderly transmission of hereditary characteristics to daughter cells, since characteristics of a particular bacterial species remain about as constant as they do in higher organisms. In this text the chromatin bodies of bacteria are called nuclei, following common bacteriological practice.

SPORES

Many bacteria produce thick-walled resting cells which are highly resistant to such unfavorable environmental conditions as drought and extremes of heat and cold. Although they may not be really comparable to the spores of other kinds of organisms, these resting cells are generally called **spores,** or more specifically, **endospores.**

During the formation of a bacterial spore from a vegetative cell, there is a change in the nature of some of the proteins of the protoplasm, and most of the protoplasmic contents other than water become concentrated into a relatively small mass around which a thick new wall is formed (Fig. 6.4). In some cases the nucleus is transformed into a ring just within the spore wall. The volume of the spore is commonly about $\frac{1}{4}$–$\frac{1}{10}$ that of the vegetative cell from which it is formed. Most of the water remaining in the spore is probably bound (by hydrophilic colloids or otherwise) so that it is not available as a medium for chemical reactions. Metabolic activities slow down to a rate at which they cannot be detected, and, in at least some cases, they evidently stop altogether—a notable exception to the general principle that continuous metabolism is characteristic of all life. Spores of bacteria have been sealed in containers at a high vacuum at the temperature of liquid helium ($-269°$– $-271°$C) without losing their power to give rise to normal, vegetatively active cells.[1] Resistance of spores to drought is doubtless similar to their resistance to cold, relating to dehydration and suspension of normal metabolic activities.

Many bacteria can also withstand temperatures far below freezing while still in the vegetative state. In such cases, most of the bacterial population dies at or soon after the time of freezing, but those individual cells not immediately killed may persist more or less indefinitely, although they are not quite so cold-resistant as spores.

Heat resistance in spores is probably due to a combination of three factors: (1) an inherently high resistance of the enzymes of the spore to destruction by heat; (2) the effect of dehydration, limiting the possibility of chemical reaction between different molecules; and (3) the demonstrated effect of some lipids and other protoplasmic substances in decreasing the susceptibility of enzymes to degeneration by heat.

The physiological conditions which initiate the process of spore formation are not clearly understood. In at least some cases it appears that the presence of glucose within the cell tends to inhibit the change from vegetative to spore proteins, and when the supply of glucose becomes unusually low (corresponding to an insufficient food supply) a mechanism is triggered which leads to the change of vegetative proteins to spore proteins and eventually to the formation of a spore. The traditional concept of sporulation as a response to unfavorable conditions is in a general sense correct, but it has not yet been possible to identify the discrete factors concerned.

When suitable conditions for growth

[1] A similar state of "suspended animation" has recently been induced in cells of higher organisms (e.g., bull sperm) by quick freezing and drying.

Fig. 6.5. *Bacillus cereus.* Electron micrograph of a thin section, showing a germinating spore. ($\times$29,000.) (Courtesy of George B. Chapman.)

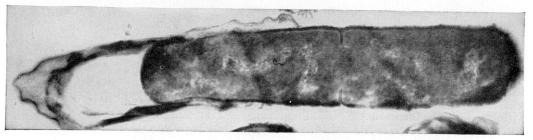

are re-established, the spore germinates, either immediately or after a necessary period of rest. **Germination** is a general term applied to the resumption of growth by any spore, seed, or other propagule after a period of dormancy. The spore swells, the old wall splits, and the vegetatively active cell, with its own new wall, is released (Fig. 6.5). A single vegetative cell (representing the complete organism) usually gives rise to only a single spore, and the germination of a spore gives rise to only a single vegetative cell. Therefore spores of unicellular bacteria are not reproductive bodies in the usual sense. In this respect ordinary bacterial spores differ from most other bodies generally called spores.

Some of the actinomycetes and sheathed bacteria, in which the filaments might well be considered to be multicellular organisms, form spores of a quite different types which are more distinctly reproductive bodies. These spores, called **conidia** or conidiospores, are produced one after another by the differentiation and separation of the terminal cell of a filament. Each conidium can germinate and give rise to a new filament or system of filaments. Conidia are also produced by many fungi. A few of the actinomycetes produce groups of spores in sporangia at the ends of the filaments, much as do the Phycomycetes (a class of fungi). A **sporangium** is a case or container in which spores are borne. Some bacteria also produce very small flagellated reproductive cells, comparable to the zoospores of algae, by repeated division of the protoplast within the wall of a single cell.

REPRODUCTION

Bacteria ordinarily reproduce by means of cell division. The cell appears merely to become constricted into two cells, and the process is commonly referred to as **fission**, binary fission, or simple fission. "Simple fission" is more complex than casual observation would suggest, however. Very often a transverse double membrane develops, from the margins toward the center, before the visible fission occurs (Fig. 6.6). The wall is then deposited between the two layers of the membrane, progressing from the outside to the center.

Growth of the daughter cells in both unicellular and filamentous forms is com-

Fig. 6.6. *Bacillus cereus*. Electron micrograph of thin section of dividing cell. (×50,000.) Note the partition developing from the margins toward the center. The attenuated dumbell in the middle is a "nucleus" in process of division. The cell evidently has other nuclei as well. (Courtesy of George B. Chapman and James Hillier.)

monly concentrated near the end that bears the new transverse wall. When studied by present-day techniques, the nucleus generally seems to divide merely by constricting into two parts, just as less refined techniques seem to show the whole cell dividing by merely constricting into two parts. The validity of some recent claims that certain bacteria have a rudimentary spindle and as many as three chromosomes during cell division remains to be confirmed.

Under favorable conditions, bacterial cells may divide as often as once every 20 minutes. Starting with a single cell, such a rate of reproduction would give 2 cells in 20 minutes, 4 cells in 40 minutes, 8 cells in 1 hour, 64 cells in 2 hours, 512 cells in 3 hours, 4096 cells in 4 hours, 32,768 cells in 5 hours, 1,073,741,824 cells in 10 hours, and more than 4,000,000,000,000,000,000,000 cells in 24 hours. This figure may also be expressed in a more convenient mathematical form as 4×10^{21}. If the same rate of increase could be maintained for about three days, the volume of bacteria would be greater than that of the earth. Competition for space and/or nutrients soon limits the rate of bacterial reproduction in any particular instance, even if other factors remain favorable, but the potentiality for rapid increase to exploit a food supply is obviously enormous.

SEXUALITY

Typical sexual processes, involving fusion of gametes (and their nuclei) to form a zygote, followed eventually by reduction division, have not yet been demonstrated in the bacteria. It is abundantly clear, however, that some kinds of bacteria do exchange genetic material. Processes, such as those in some bacteria, which transfer genetic material without nuclear fusion and reduction division, are sometimes called parasexual processes.

Sexuality has been more intensively investigated in *Escherichia coli* (an inhabitant of the human colon) than in any other bacterium. When two strains of this species which differ in several characters are grown in the same culture, types which recombine their characters in various ways occur far too frequently to be explainable as chance mutants. Recently it has been discovered that the transfer of genetic material occurs through a slender tube, called a conjugation tube, that is formed between the two cells (Fig. 6.7). Present evidence indicates that the transfer is in one direction only; the donor cell has two nuclei, and one of these is modified into a slender thread (comparable to a chromonema?) which flows through the tube into the other cell. The subsequent history of the transferred nucleus is not yet clear, but the cell which receives it gives rise to a variety of recombinant types in the next several divisions.

Transfer of genetic material in the bacteria does not always involve a conjugation tube. Star-shaped clusters of four to seven cells of *Agrobacterium tumefaciens*—the causative agent of crown gall— are often seen, and careful staining shows that the nuclear material of all the cells is concentrated in the area of contact. The cells remain rather firmly attached for several days and then separate spontaneously. Some of the virus particles which attack bacteria apparently carry bacterial genic material from one bacterial cell to another; this phenomenon is known as transduction. Sexuality in bacteria is being

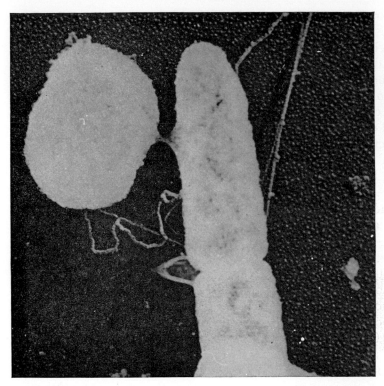

Fig. 6.7. *Escherichia coli.* Electron micrograph showing two strains in conjugation. The more elongate individual at the right is also in process of fission. In this instance the genetic material passes only one way. The cell at the right continues to divide, without showing any influence from the other cell. The progeny of the cell at the left show a variety of types recombining the characters of the two cells in conjugation; and new recombinant types continue to be formed for a number of generations before each line becomes stabilized. (×7000.) (Courtesy of T. F. Anderson, E. L. Wollman, and François Jacob.)

actively investigated by a number of students, and a better understanding will doubtless be achieved in a few years.

ABSORPTION OF FOOD

Some bacteria require only inorganic nutrients, but the majority require organic compounds of one sort or another. Of these, some require only an organic energy source, such as glucose, and can manufacture all the other organic compounds they need. Others require one or more organic compounds in addition to those used as a source of energy. A few kinds of bacteria require such a complex organic environment that it has not yet been possible to culture them outside the living cells which they parasitize. Some bacteria which manu-

facture their own carbohydrates from inorganic materials still require some organic compounds, especially nitrogenous compounds, from an external source.

The more complex organic compounds, such as proteins and polysaccharides, which are used by many bacteria, must be digested before they can be absorbed. Digestion is accomplished by enzymes which the bacteria release into the surrounding medium. Such enzymes are sometimes called **exoenzymes,** to distinguish them from **endoenzymes,** which are retained in the cell. All living cells contain endoenzymes, but among plants the production of exoenzymes is chiefly confined to things such as bacteria and fungi, which absorb food from their surroundings. The ability of some bacteria to cause certain diseases rests on their capacity to digest living tissues. Some of the more virulent toxins produced by bacteria, however, are by-products of their metabolism, rather than digestive enzymes.

SOME TERMS DESCRIBING THE NUTRITION AND ECOLOGY OF ORGANISMS

An organism which makes its own food from raw materials is said to be **autotrophic.** Autotrophic organisms are either plants or stand on the borderline between plants and animals, and their nutrition is therefore said to be **holophytic.** Organisms which do not make their own food are said to be **heterotrophic.** Heterotrophic organisms may obtain their food by eating (ingesting) it or by absorbing it. Organisms which eat their food are either animals or are on the borderline between plants and animals, and their mode of nutrition is therefore said to be **holozoic.** Some heterotrophic plants which absorb their food use dead organic matter and are said to be **saprophytes.** Others obtain their food from living organisms and are said to be **parasites.** The organism that provides food for a parasite is called the host. The term *parasite* is also applied to animals which are so much smaller than their hosts that the depredations of any one individual seldom cause very serious harm. The term *host* is also commonly extended to cover any organism which provides "lodging," i.e., a place of habitation, for another organism. No sharp line can be drawn between parasites and saprophytes. Some of the "saprophytic" wood-rotting fungi utilize only the nonliving parts of their host and grow just as well on a log as on a living tree; yet they may bring about the death of living cells of the host, so that

they might with some reason be called parasites.

Some kinds of organisms, including many bacteria, are either parasitic or saprophytic, according to the circumstances. An organism which is usually parasitic, but which has the power (the faculty) of becoming a saprophyte under some circumstances, may be referred to as a **facultative saprophyte.** An organism which is usually saprophytic, but which has the power of becoming a parasite under some circumstances, may be referred to as a **facultative parasite.** A parasite which cannot live in any other fashion is said to be an **obligate parasite,** and a saprophyte which cannot live in any other fashion is said to be an **obligate saprophyte.** Most parasitic bacteria can be grown on nonliving media and, from a laboratory standpoint, are therefore facultative saprophytes. The term *facultative saprophyte* is also applied to autotrophs which can live as saprophytes.

When two different kinds of organisms spend much or all of their lives in close physical association, deriving mutual benefit, they are said to have a **symbiotic relationship,** and each of the two organisms is a **symbiont.** The term *symbiosis* is sometimes expanded to include all permanent close physical associations between two different kinds of organism. Symbiosis from which both symbionts benefit is then called **mutualism,** or **mutualistic symbiosis;** and symbiosis from which one symbiont benefits, to the detriment of the other, is called **antagonistic symbiosis,** which would include most cases of parasitism. A close physical relationship between two different kinds of organism, in which one kind is benefited while the other is neither distinctly benefited nor harmed, is called **commensalism.** A plant which grows attached to some larger plant, without deriving nourishment from its host, is called an **epiphyte.**

All these different terms, except holozoic, may be used to describe some bacteria, or the relationships between some bacteria and other organisms.

THE NITROGEN CYCLE

INTRODUCTION

The elements used by plants go through a cycle of chemical changes as they are absorbed, used, and then restored to a form in which they can again be absorbed. The nitrogen cycle (Fig. 6.8), in which bacteria play several important roles, is an interesting and delicately balanced cycle that is commonly studied in beginning botany courses.

Most plants absorb nitrogen from the soil principally in the form of nitrate (NO_3^-) ions, although they can also absorb ammonium (NH_4^+) ions. The plants use the nitrogen in the formation of proteins and other compounds, such as nucleic acids. Animals which eat the plants digest and reassemble these proteins to form their own proteins.

Since nitrate ions are continually being removed from the soil by green plants, the supply of nitrates would eventually be exhausted if there were no way of replenishing it. Neither the elaborated nitrogenous compounds formed by plants and animals nor the nitrogenous wastes excreted by animals are directly available for re-use by most green plants. The conversion of nitrogen from proteins and other nitrogenous compounds into the form of nitrates involves several steps and is due in large part to the activities of bacteria, although some of the earlier stages are also carried on by fungi.

AMMONIFICATION

The nitrogenous compounds of both plant and animal bodies and the nitrogenous wastes excreted by animals serve as a food supply for many different kinds of bacteria (and fungi) which cause decay.

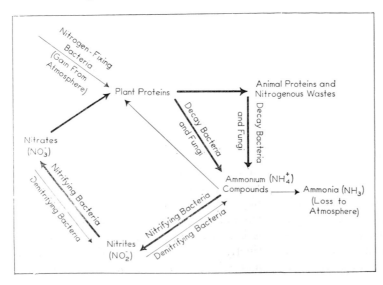

Fig. 6.8. **Principal features of the nitrogen cycle.**

Ammonia (NH_3) is produced as a result of the decay. Some of the ammonia escapes into the air and is lost to the cycle, but most of it reacts immediately with water to form ammonium hydroxide (NH_4OH), and various ammonium salts are derived from the ammonium hydroxide without the intervention of bacteria.

Remains of higher plants are usually relatively poor in nitrogen and rich in carbohydrates such as cellulose. When these plant remains are used as food by the bacteria, all the nitrogen is needed for the production of microbial cell material. The carbohydrates supply enough energy so that all the nitrogen can be assimilated, but some of the carbohydrate is oxidized in the process, so that the ratio of carbohydrate to nitrogen is slightly decreased. Another organism may then feed on the first organism and also on the remaining carbohydrate. It assimilates all the nitrogen and oxidizes more carbohydrate, again decreasing the ratio. This continues until the energy supply is insufficient to permit assimilation of all the nitrogen, and the protein is used for energy. Protein compounds consist essentially of carbohydrate derivatives with amine groups attached. When protein is used for energy, the amine group is split off as ammonia, and the carbohydrate derivative is then oxidized. Thus ammonification occurs when there is more organic nitrogen than can be assimilated. Plowing stubble under does not increase the nitrogen available to green plants until the stubble has decomposed.

NITRIFICATION

Ammonium ions can be absorbed directly by most plants and used as a source of nitrogen. However, ammonium compounds, when dissolved in water, readily produce some gaseous ammonia (NH_3) which tends to escape into the air and be lost to the cycle. Oxidation of ammonium compounds to the more stable nitrates is brought about exclusively by the activities of several kinds of bacteria. The first step, in which ammonium compounds are used and nitrites (NO_2^- compounds) are produced, is carried on especially by *Nitrosomonas*, a very short, flagellated, aerobic rod. The further oxidation of nitrites to nitrates is due chiefly to *Nitrobacter*, a very short, nonmotile aerobic rod. *Nitrobacter, Nitrosomonas*, and other bacteria which oxidize inorganic nitrogen compounds are called **nitrifying bacteria**. Energy is released in the oxidation of these nitrogen compounds, and some of this energy is used by the nitrifying bacteria in the manufacture of their own food from raw materials. The nitrifying bacteria are thus autotrophic. Instead of using light as a source of energy for food manufacture, as do most autotrophs, they use the energy released in the oxidation of inorganic nitrogen compounds. Instead of being photosynthetic, they are **chemosynthetic** or, more precisely, **chemoautotrophic.**

DENITRIFICATION

There are several factors which increase the complexity of the nitrogen cycle. We have noted that nitrogen may be lost to the cycle by the escape of gaseous ammonia into the air. A number of kinds of bacteria bring about denitrification, a change essentially opposite to nitrification. Sometimes the denitrification proceeds to the formation of nitrous oxide (N_2O) or free nitrogen, which escapes into the air and is lost to the cycle.

The denitrifying bacteria are facultative or obligate anaerobes; they extract oxygen

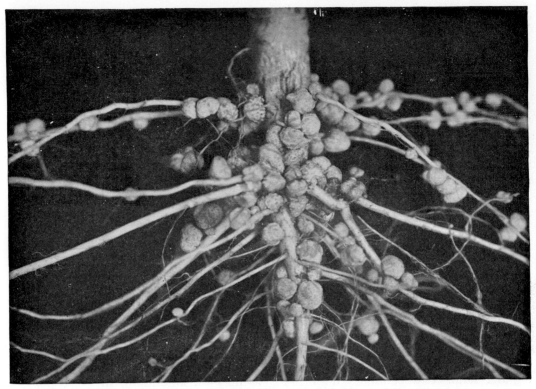

Fig. 6.9. Roots of soybean, showing bacterial nodules. (Courtesy of the Nitragin Co., Inc.)

from nitrates or nitrites, rather than using atmospheric oxygen. Essentially what happens is that the oxygen from the nitrates or nitrites is used to oxidize the hydrogen of organic foods, forming water as one of the end products. More energy is released in the oxidation of the hydrogen than is used in separating the oxygen from the nitrates or nitrites, so that there is a net transfer of energy into the metabolic system of the bacteria. Most denitrifying bacteria use atmospheric oxygen, if it is available in sufficient quantity, and carry on denitrification only under conditions of oxygen shortage. Denitrification is favored by poor aeration of the soil, and nitrates may eventually disappear from water-logged soils.

NITROGEN FIXATION

Some of the bacteria and some of the blue-green algae differ from all or nearly all other organisms in their ability to use atmospheric nitrogen. Some of the nitrogen-fixing bacteria, as they are called, are saprophytes which live in the soil; others are symbionts which live in the roots of some higher plants, especially legumes.

The two most important genera of free-living (i.e., nonsymbiotic) nitrogen-fixing bacteria are *Azotobacter* and *Clostridium*. *Clostridium* is an anaerobic, spore-forming rod. *Azotobacter* is an aerobic, non-spore-forming large rod which often appears so short as to be almost a coccus. *Azotobacter* is morphologically rather similar to some of the blue-green algae, such as *Chroococcus* and *Gloeocapsa*, but lacks photosynthetic pigments.

Many plants of the family Leguminosae, including clover, beans, peas, lupines, vetch, and alfalfa, develop characteristic swellings, called **nodules** (Fig. 6.9), on their roots. Some of the cells of these nodules are inhabited by bacteria belonging to the genus *Rhizobium*, an aerobic, non-spore-forming rod (in culture), the cells of which usually exhibit bizarre, irregular shapes when growing in the nodule. The development of the nodule is apparently stimulated by growth-promoting substances produced by the bacteria. Invasion by the bacteria occurs near the tip of the root, and some evidence suggests that each nodule ordinarily arises at a point where a branch root would otherwise be produced.

Different strains of *Rhizobium* differ greatly in the amount of nitrogen which they fix, and the same strain may vary according to the species of legume it inhabits. Nodules inhabited by the more effective strains tend to be pink, due to the presence of a special type of hemoglobin called leg-hemoglobin. The function of the hemoglobin is obscure, as is, indeed, the whole mechanism of nitrogen fixation.

Some nitrogen compounds produced by the nodule bacteria become available to the host plant for the formation of protein and other nitrogenous compounds, but the details of the process are not yet understood. Ammonia, or some compound which readily yields ammonia, is probably the primary nitrogen compound produced by *Rhizobium* and *Azotobacter*, but not by *Clostridium*. The fixation of nitrogen in the nodules depends on the symbiotic relationship between the bacteria and the host; neither of the two symbionts is able to use atmospheric nitrogen in the absence of the other.

A number of other kinds of plants bear root nodules resembling those of legumes, and some of these are inhabited by bacteria which resemble *Rhizobium*. The nodules on the roots of alder (*Alnus*) apparently contain nitrogen-fixing bacteria,

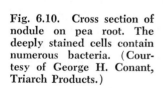

Fig. 6.10. **Cross section of nodule on pea root. The deeply stained cells contain numerous bacteria. (Courtesy of George H. Conant, Triarch Products.)**

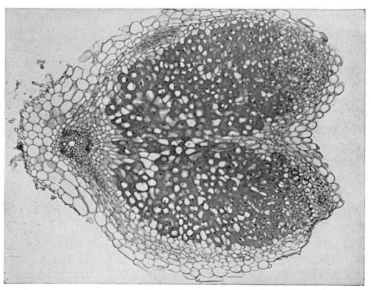

Class Schizomycetes: Bacteria 93

Fig. 6.11. Field of soybeans: at left, inoculated with nitrogen-fixing bacteria; at right, uninoculated. (Courtesy of the Nitragin Company, Inc.)

although these nodules have not been so carefully studied as those of legumes. Probably some of the root nodules of other plants will also prove to be effective in nitrogen fixation.

The free-living nitrogen-fixing bacteria are very widespread in the soil, being absent mainly from highly acid soils, and it is probably a safe assumption that they are already present in any natural soil capable of supporting them. The symbiotic nitrogen-fixing bacteria are also widely distributed in nature, but no one strain can inhabit all different kinds of legumes, and it is often advisable to dust legume seeds with the proper bacteria before planting, especially if the particular crop has not

previously been grown in the area (Fig. 6.11). The legume can grow in the absence of the bacteria, but then it has no special value as a soil builder.

Leguminous crops are frequently grown in rotation with other crops as a means of restoring nitrogen compounds to the soil. If the crop itself is harvested and carried away, there may be little or no benefit to the soil, because the amount of nitrogen left in the roots may not exceed the amount of nitrogen absorbed from the soil and removed with the crop. Therefore the crop is frequently plowed under; it is then spoken of as green manure. This practice improves soil texture by adding humus as well as adding nitrogen.

The principal steps in the nitrogen cycle are these: (1) Nitrates are absorbed by plants and used in the manufacture of proteins and other organic nitrogen compounds. Some of the proteins produced by plants are consumed by animals and used in the formation of their own proteins. (2) Plant and animal proteins (and other nitrogenous compounds) and nitrogenous wastes are used as a source of food by decay bacteria and fungi, resulting in the formation of ammonia and ammonium compounds. (3) Ammonium compounds are oxidized to nitrites by *Nitrosomonas* and other bacteria. (4) Nitrites are oxidized to nitrates by *Nitrobacter* and other bacteria.

SULFATE-REDUCING BACTERIA

Wherever organic matter and sulfates occur together in the absence of air, sulfate-reducing bacteria are likely to be found. These are slightly curved, motile rods which make up the genus *Desulfovibrio*. They produce hydrogen sulfide (H_2S) from sulfates (SO_4^- compounds) and other oxygen-containing sulfur compounds, and use the oxygen in the respiration of organic foods. Like the denitrifying bacteria, which reduce nitrates and nitrites, they obtain more energy by respiration than they use in extracting oxygen from other compounds. *Desulfovibrio* commonly occurs in subterranean petroleum deposits as well as in the more ordinary bacterial habitats. Sea water and most other salt waters contain sulfates, and the characteristic odor of tidal flats and salt marshes is due in large part to the H_2S produced by *Desulfovibrio*. Hydrogen sulfide reacts readily with certain iron compounds to form black ferrous sulfide (FeS), and the characteristic black mud of marine inlets, for which the Black Sea is supposed to have been named, gets its color largely from ferrous sulfide formed in this way.

FERMENTATION

Each of the elements used by plants goes through a cycle of greater or lesser complexity, in which the element occurs over and over again in the same chemical combinations but is continuously converted from one to another. Some of these cycles are as complex as the nitrogen cycle. Others, such as the carbon cycle, are relatively simple. Some of the carbon in plant bodies is used directly by animals in the formation of their own protoplasm, and some of this animal protoplasm is again used by other animals in the formation of their own protoplasm; but sooner or later these carbon compounds are used in respiration, either by the plants which produced them, or by animals, or by the bacteria and fungi (and occasionally other organisms) which cause decay.

Typically the carbon is immediately released as carbon dioxide, an end product of respiration. Some bacteria and fungi, however, do not completely respire the carbon compounds which serve as their foods. They bring about a partial decomposition of the food, which releases some of the energy of the food and results in the formation of some carbon dioxide, but which also results in the formation of another carbon-containing end product that can be further respired (by some other organism) with release of energy.

The type of respiration which has as one end product a substance that still contains chemically bound energy which can be released by respiration is called **fermentation.** Fermentation may be either aerobic (free oxygen being used) or anaerobic (no free oxygen being used), although, as noted in Chapter 3, some plant physiologists would now apply the term only to anaerobic respiration. Many kinds of plants can carry on anaerobic respiration for a time under conditions of oxygen shortage and then aerobically respire the partly broken-down products of anaerobic respiration when oxygen again becomes available. It is only some of the fungi and bacteria which regularly carry on fermentation and form an end product that can be further respired by some other kind of organism.

One of the best-known fermentation processes is alcoholic fermentation, which is carried on by yeasts and will be discussed in Chapter 15. Another common fermentation is carried on by lactic acid bacteria, a diverse group which includes both cocci and bacilli, but which are all Gram-positive, nonmotile, and non-spore-forming. All lactic acid bacteria form lactic acid as an end product of respiration. A chemical equation to express a typical set of reactions is:

$$C_6H_{12}O_6 \rightarrow 2\ CH_3CHOHCOOH$$
simple sugar   lactic acid

$$+\ energy.$$

Some of the lactic acid bacteria, such as species of *Streptococcus* and *Lactobacillus*, commonly occur in silage, sauerkraut, and milk; the souring of milk and the sourness of silage and sauerkraut result from their activity. Some parasitic bacteria, such as *Pneumococcus*, also produce lactic acid as an end product of respiration, although

they are not usually called lactic acid bacteria. Lactic fermentation also occurs in animal muscles, but here the lactic acid is eventually oxidized to form carbon dioxide and water, whereas it is an end product of respiration of the lactic acid bacteria.

Another fermentation process, acetification, is the formation of acetic acid from alcohol by vinegar bacteria (*Acetobacter*). The process may be represented as:

$$C_2H_5OH + O_2 \longrightarrow CH_3COOH + H_2O$$
alcohol   acetic acid

$$+\ energy.$$

Acetic acid is the essential constituent of vinegar. Commercial vinegar is produced by allowing vinegar bacteria to act on wine, beer, cider, or other liquids containing alcohol.

BACTERIA AND DISEASE

Before about 1850 bacteria were not generally suspected of causing disease. In 1850 two French workers noted large numbers of microscopic rods in the blood of cattle which had died from anthrax. Later it was shown that these rods, now known as *Bacillus anthracis*, are living organisms and are regularly present in infected animals. Final proof of the bacterial cause of anthrax was obtained in 1876 by the German physician and bacteriologist Robert Koch (1843–1910), who was able to obtain the bacteria in essentially pure culture and to cause the disease by injecting these bacteria into the bloodstreams of cattle. Several years earlier Pasteur had for practical purposes demonstrated the bacterial nature of the pebrine disease of silkworms, but his experiments did not rigidly eliminate the possibility of some other interpretation.

Fig. 6.12. Robert Koch (left) and Ferdinand Cohn (right), two of the "fathers" of bacteriology. (Courtesy of the New York Academy of Medicine.)

The first definite proof that a disease may be caused by bacteria is therefore generally attributed to Koch.

Another of Koch's important contributions to bacteriology was the use of gelatin (1881) as a solid substrate which lends itself to the cultivation of pure cultures derived from single individual bacteria. It is attacked by relatively few kinds of bacteria, and it can be used as a carrier for whatever nutrients are desired. Two years later one of Koch's assistants replaced gelatin with agar, a polysaccharide product of certain algae, that is attacked by still fewer bacteria than is gelatin and can be incubated at higher temperatures. Agar is still widely used for the cultivation of bacteria, although a medium of silica gel is now sometimes used when strict control of all potential nutrients is desired.

Some of the diseases caused by bacteria are diphtheria, gonorrhea, leprosy, pneumonia, plague, scarlet fever, syphilis, tetanus, tuberculosis, typhoid fever in man, fire blight of pears, crown gall of many plants, and soft rot of potatoes and fruits. Botulism is caused by one of the most powerful known poisons, produced by *Clostridium botulinum*, a spore-forming anaerobic bacillus. The organism thrives on meat and other high-protein foods (such as peas and beans) in the absence of air, and the spores often survive the temperatures used in home canning. Fortunately, the poison itself is readily destroyed by heat, and it is therefore generally recommended that all home-canned high-protein foods be boiled for 10 or 15 minutes before they are used or even tasted. The temperatures used in commercial canning of high-protein foods are high enough to destroy the spores of *C. botulinum*, and

Class Schizomycetes: Bacteria 97

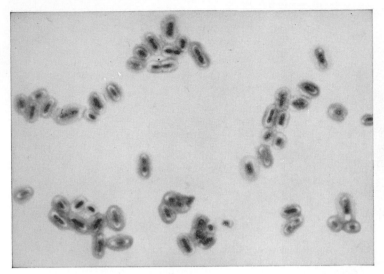

Fig. 6.13. *Klebsiella pneumoniae*, one of the causes of pneumonia. ($\times$1700.) (Copyright by General Biological Supply House, Inc., Chicago.)

prior to two cases in 1963 it had been many years since commercially canned foods had been known to cause any deaths from botulism in the United States.

BACTERIA AS HUMAN SYMBIONTS

Escherichia coli, formerly called *Bacterium coli* and *Bacillus coli*, is a regular inhabitant of the lower intestinal tract of man and other vertebrates. About 40 per cent of human feces consists of bacteria, mainly *E. coli*, and the presence of *E. coli* in milk, water, or food is used as an index of fecal contamination. *E. coli* has commonly been considered chiefly a commensal, occasionally a pathogen. It is now known, however, that *E. coli* and other intestinal bacteria synthesize considerable quantities of some of the B vitamins and release these into the intestine. These bacteria may therefore be properly regarded as normally being symbionts rather than mere commensals. The destruction of the bacterial flora of the colon by vigorous dosage with certain antibiotic drugs sometimes

causes functional disturbances which suggest that the usefulness of these organisms in human physiology is not limited to the production of known vitamins.

CHEMOSYNTHETIC (CHEMOAUTOTROPHIC) BACTERIA

We have noted that the nitrifying bacteria use, in the formation of their own food, some of the energy released by the oxidation of nitrogen compounds. The iron bacteria are another group of chemosynthetic autotrophs. They facilitate the oxidation of iron, and apparently use in food production some of the energy that is thereby released. One such oxidation may be represented as follows:

$$4\ FeCO_3 + O_2 + 6\ H_2O \longrightarrow$$
ferrous carbonate

$$4\ Fe(OH)_3 + 4\ CO_2 + energy.$$
ferric hydroxide

Some iron bacteria can oxidize manganese

as well as iron as a source of energy. There are two general types of iron bacteria. *Gallionella*, a unicellular curved rod belonging to the Eubacteriales, is widely distributed in iron-bearing waters. It produces a characteristic twisted ribbon of ferric hydroxide that is held together by some cement. *Sphaerotilus* and some other genera of iron bacteria belong to the Chlamydobacteriales; they have sheathed filaments which produce flagellated, motile cells resembling zoospores. Each such motile cell develops into a new filament, often attached laterally to an older filament, so that a seemingly branched filament is formed. The sheath becomes impregnated with ferric hydroxide, presumably due to chemical activity of the bacteria. *Sphaerotilus* is generally found where both iron and organic matter are present, and, even though it probably makes some of its own food, it requires an organic source of nitrogen for growth. It is frequently found in sewage-disposal plants and in polluted streams. The cell colonies or filaments of *Sphaerotilus* and other chlamydobacteria approach the status of multicellular organisms. *Crenothrix polyspora*, a relative of *Sphaerotilus* that often grows abundantly in water pipes, shows some differentiation of the cells that make up the filament, and conidia are released from the tip of the filament. Each of these conidia can germinate and eventually produce a whole new filament.

There are two groups of autotrophic sulfur bacteria, one chemosynthetic, the other photosynthetic. The chemosynthetic sulfur bacteria are colorless and utilize in the manufacture of their food some of the energy released in the oxidation of sulfur. Some of the chemical processes relating to the sulfur may be represented as follows:

$$2 H_2S + O_2 \longrightarrow 2 S + 2 H_2O + \text{energy}$$
hydrogen sulfide

$$2 S + 2 H_2O + 3 O_2 \longrightarrow$$
$$2 H_2SO_4 + \text{energy.}$$
sulfuric acid

Some of the chemosynthetic sulfur bacteria, such as *Thiobacillus*, are small, motile single cells. Some others, such as *Hillhousia*, are very large single cells, as much as 60×25 microns. The unicellular chemosynthetic sulfur bacteria are considered to belong to the Eubacteriales. Some other chemosynthetic sulfur bacteria, such as *Beggiatoa*, are filamentous, the filament consisting of a series of disk-shaped cells with the flat sides in contact. Filaments of *Beggiatoa* somewhat resemble those of the blue-green alga *Oscillatoria*, and they wave back and forth in similar fashion. *Thiospirillopsis*, another filamentous, colorless genus of sulfur bacteria, also has an oscillatorioid motion and is morphologically very similar to the genus *Spirulina* of the Oscillatoriaceae. The filamentous sulfur bacteria have sometimes been regarded as colorless derivatives of the blue-green algae, but it should be noted that they resemble some undoubted bacteria (and differ from the blue-green algae) in oxidizing sulfur as a source of energy for the manufacture of food.

PHOTOSYNTHETIC BACTERIA

Bacteria belonging to the Rhodobacteriales differ from the Eubacteriales in being photosynthetic, containing chlorophyll and associated carotenoid pigments. They vary in color from green (green bacteria) to more often purple, red, or brownish (all usually called purple bacteria). The yellowish carotenoid pigments of the green photosynthetic bacteria are masked by the chlorophyll, whereas among the remainder of the order the chlorophyll is masked by the abundant carotenoids. As many as ten different carotenoid pigments may be present in a single cell. Bacterial chlorophyll has minor chemical differences from the chlorophyll of other plants, and the chlorophyll of the green bacteria is different from that of the purple and red bacteria. Both types of bacterial chlorophyll differ from the chlorophyll of other plants[2] and from each other in the wavelengths of light which they use most effectively in photosynthesis.

All bacterial photosynthesis differs from all other photosynthesis in not liberating oxygen. Many photosynthetic bacteria use sulfur compounds in the photosynthetic process. If carbohydrate is, for convenience, represented by the generalized formula (CH_2O), some of the bacterial photosynthetic processes may be shown as follows:

bacteria can also carry on the following process:

$$CO_2 + 2\,H_2 + \text{light energy} \longrightarrow (CH_2O) + H_2O.$$

Various organic compounds, such as propyl alcohol, can also be used as raw materials for photosynthesis by many or all of the Rhodobacteriales. The order may be divided into two groups: (1) the Thiorhodaceae (purple sulfur bacteria) and Chlorobacteriaceae (green bacteria), which ordinarily accumulate sulfur as a result of photosynthesis but can (at least in some cases) dispense with sulfur and utilize organic compounds instead; and (2) the Athiorhodaceae (nonsulfur purple bacteria), which require organic compounds as raw materials for photosynthesis and do not generally use sulfur in the process. Some Athiorhodaceae can also live as saprophytes in the absence of light. The Rhodobacteriales thus span the gap between autotrophic and heterotrophic organisms.

$$2\,H_2S + CO_2 + \text{light energy} \longrightarrow (CH_2O) + 2\,S + H_2O,$$
hydrogen sulfide

$$2\,S + 3\,CO_2 + 5\,H_2O + \text{light energy} \longrightarrow 2\,(CH_2O) + 2\,H_2SO_4,$$
sulfuric acid

$$4\,Na_2S_2O_3 + CO_2 + 3\,H_2O + \text{light energy} \longrightarrow (CH_2O) + 2\,Na_2S_4O_6 + 4\,NaOH,$$
sodium thiosulfate   disodium thiosulfate   sodium hydroxide

$$Na_2S_2O_3 + 2\,CO_2 + 3\,H_2O + \text{light energy} \longrightarrow 2\,(CH_2O) + 2\,NaHSO_4.$$
sodium thiosulfate   sodium bisulfate

The first two of the foregoing reactions are the commonest. Granules of elemental sulfur accumulate in the cytoplasm as a result of the first reaction and are eventually used in the second. In some cases selenium can substitute for sulfur in the process. Some photosynthetic sulfur

The Thiorhodaceae are typically autotrophic, but they can also use organic compounds in photosynthesis. The Athiorho-

[2] A species of the bacterial genus *Chlorobium* is reported to contain a chlorophyll with an absorption spectrum very similar to that of chlorophyll *a*, one of the characteristic chlorophylls of higher plants.

daceae, but not the Thiorhodaceae, also generally require certain organic compounds other than those used in photosynthesis.

Some of the commoner genera of the Thiorhodaceae are *Thiopedia*, *Thiothece*, and *Thiospirillum*. The first two of these are spherical to very shortly rod-shaped; the last is a spirillum. *Rhodopseudomonas*, with rod-shaped to spherical cells, and *Rhodospirillum* are the only genera of the Athiorhodaceae; both are common in stagnant water and mud.

ACTINOMYCETES

The Actinomycetales, commonly called actinomycetes, are an order of bacteria that resemble fungi in their filamentous, branching structure. The filaments of actinomycetes are much more slender than those of fungi, being not more than about 1.5 microns in diameter, as contrasted to 3 microns or more in most fungi. The nuclei of actinomycetes, so far as known, are of bacterial nature. In some actinomycetes the filaments eventually break up into individual cells. In others the system of filaments remains intact, and conidia are produced at the ends of the branches, just as in many fungi. *Actinomyces* belongs to the former group, *Streptomyces* to the latter. The lumpy jaw disease of cattle is due to *Actinomyces bovis*. *Streptomyces* is abundant in the soil and is responsible for the characteristic odor of freshly turned earth. Several antibiotic drugs are obtained from species of *Streptomyces*: streptomycin from *S. griseus*, streptothricin from *S. lavendulae*, chloromycetin from *S. venezuelae*, aureomycin from *S. aureofaciens*, and terramycin from *S. rimosus*. The nature and biological significance of antibiotics are discussed in Chapter 15.

Like some of the sheathed bacteria, some of the actinomycetes are more nearly multicellular organisms than mere colonies of unicellular individuals. The actinomycetes have sometimes been considered to be fungi, but they are connected by a series of intermediate forms to undoubted bacteria; moreover, they find no evident allies among the fungi. The family Mycobacteriaceae, which includes the causative organism of tuberculosis (*Mycobacterium tuberculosis*), is more or less transitional between the Actinomycetales and Eubacteriales.

SPIROCHAETES

The Spirochaetales are an order of unicellular bacteria characterized by their spiral shape and the lack of a definite cell wall. They vary in length from about 4 to 500 microns, the larger ones being far longer than any other unicellular bacteria. They move by flexion of the entire body, and some of them have flagella as well. Although the protoplasm is technically naked, in that it lacks a cell wall, it is bounded by a definite, flexuous, living, proteinaceous membrane. *Treponema pallidum* (Fig. 6.14) one of the smaller spirochaetes, is the cause of syphilis. *Treponema pertenue*, the cause of yaws, is so similar to *T. pallidum* that the two can be distinguished only by the diseases which they produce, and the two diseases confer reciprocal immunity. Infectious jaundice is caused by another spirochaete, *Leptospira icterohemorrhagicae*. *Treponema dentatum* and *Borrelia buccale* are normal inhabitants of the human mouth, and at least the latter of these two spirochaetes can also invade oral and respiratory lesions.

The spirochaetes have sometimes been

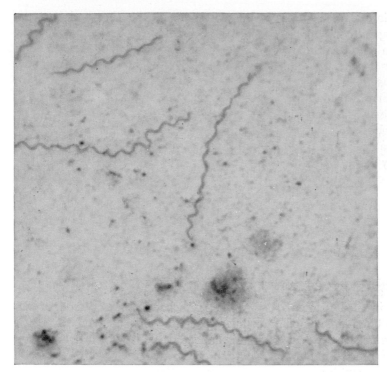

Fig. 6.14. *Treponema pallidum,* the cause of syphilis. (×3000.) (Copyright by General Biological Supply House, Inc., Chicago.)

considered to be protozoa, but they have no apparent relatives in that group. Their similarity (at least in form) to some of the spirillum type of bacteria is obvious. Their nuclear structure has not been adequately studied, but presumably they resemble bacteria in this respect also. At least the complex type of nucleus which characterizes nearly all organisms except the schizophytes has not been demonstrated to exist in the spirochaetes.

MYXOBACTERIA

The Myxobacteriales resemble the spirochaetes in being elongate slender cells without definite walls, but the myxobacteria are straight or merely flexuous and are either nonmotile or move slowly in an obscure fashion that probably involves protoplasmic streaming. They seem to flow or creep along the surface of the substrate. Most of them are saprophytic, but a few are parasites. An outstanding feature of the myxobacteria is their tendency to form colonies in which the individual cells are held together by a gelatinous gum. Most myxobacteria are red, but some are orange, yellow, green, or colorless. The green pigment is not chlorophyll, and the plants are not photosynthetic. The myxobacteria are widely distributed in soils, particularly lowland agricultural soils. Many of them can use chitin and cellulose as food. They often form visible "fruiting bodies" (Fig. 6.15), the upper or outer parts of which eventually break up into individual spores. In the nature of their fruiting bodies as well as in the absence of a typical cell wall, the myxobacteria are suggestive of the myxomycetes, a group of fungi, but the two groups are probably not closely allied.

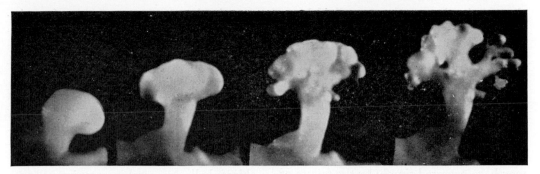

Fig. 6.15. *Chondromyces crocatus*, a member of the Myxobacteriales, showing developing fruiting bodies at 12-hour intervals. (× about 65.) (Photographs by E. A. Wheaton; courtesy of J. T. Bonner.)

ECONOMIC IMPORTANCE

Bacteria are an integral part of the balance of nature and play a particularly important role in the nitrogen cycle. The rotting of meat and other foods, which is caused chiefly by bacteria and which, of course, represents an economic loss, is merely one aspect of the necessary nitrogen cycle, by which organically bound nitrogen is restored to a form in which it can be used by green plants. Bacteria are normal inhabitants of the digestive tracts of animals. No mammal is known to produce an enzyme which attacks cellulose, and the ability of horses, cattle, and other herbivores to digest the cellulose which makes up so much of their diet is due to the presence in their digestive tracts of certain bacteria and protozoa. Some termites also contain intestinal microorganisms (protozoa and bacteria) which hydrolyze cellulose. The relative importance of bacteria and protozoa as intestinal symbionts which permit the digestion of cellulose remains to be determined. Certain bacteria, notably *Escherichia coli*, are symbionts in the human lower intestine, where they produce significant amounts of some the B vitamins. Bacteria carry on a number of fermentative processes, including lactic acid fermentation, which results in the souring of milk, and acetification, which is used in the commercial production of vinegar. Bacteria cause many diseases of plants, man, and other animals, but from the standpoint of human economics the enormous damage which they cause through disease and decay is far outweighed by their value in the nitrogen cycle and as intestinal symbionts.

EVOLUTIONARY ORIGIN AND RELATIONSHIPS

The bacteria very probably represent the most primitive group of living organisms, a group from which all other kinds of organisms are eventually descended. The origin of the bacteria themselves is obscure. According to the most widely (but only tentatively) accepted hypothesis, organic matter was first formed by happenstance chemical reactions promoted by ultraviolet light and taking place in the fresh (not yet salty) water of the sea. In the absence of any destroying or consuming agent, the organic molecules very gradually accumulated, and reactions among them led to the formation of larger molecules. Electrochemical attractions might reasonably be expected to hold some of these molecules together as colloidal particles. When such an aggregation of molecules came to include the proper chemical compounds to promote the formation of additional such compounds from the less complex organic substances in the surrounding medium, the first organism came into being. Under this concept, the first organisms were heterotrophic. Increase in the number of such primitive organisms may have occurred simply by the failure of the mass to hold together as its volume increased.

As more and more of the previously formed organic molecules became incorporated into the molecule systems which represented the first organisms, a premium must have been placed on the ability to use less and less complex substances as raw materials, and finally on the ability to tap some new source of energy. If, as many students of the subject believe, the atmosphere at that time contained relatively little free oxygen, these organisms were probably anaerobic. Any new source of energy, therefore, probably would not involve free oxygen and thus would not resemble the chemosynthetic processes now carried on by the iron and sulfur bacteria. Free oxygen is used in these latter processes. The first new source of energy may possibly have been photosynthesis resembling that of modern bacteria, in which organic material is used and free oxygen is neither used nor released. Photosynthesis in which oxygen is released would, under such a hypothesis, be a later development when water served as the source of hydrogen for photosynthesis.

Aerobic organisms characteristically contain the cytochrome system of respiratory enzymes, which are chemically related to chlorophyll. Anaerobic organisms generally do not have the cytochrome system. According to a current hypothesis, it was not until a considerable supply of atmospheric oxygen had been built up by the newer type of photosynthesis that the cytochrome system, which uses free oxygen, was developed by modification of chlorophyll. All aerobic organisms would, under such a hypothesis, be derived eventually from photosynthetic anaerobes more or less similar to the present day photosynthetic bacteria.

SUGGESTED READING

Breed, Robert S., *et al.*, *Bergey's Manual of Determinative Bacteriology*, 7th ed., Williams & Wilkins, Baltimore, 1957, 1094 pp. The standard work on the classification of bacteria.

DeKruif, Paul, *Microbe Hunters*, Harcourt, Brace, New York, 1926; also published in a Pocket Book edition of 400 pp.

DeKruif, Paul, *Men Against Death*, Harcourt, Brace, New York, 1927, 363 pp. A sequel to *Microbe Hunters*, treating more recent investigators.

Eberson, Frederick, *Microbes Militant: A Challenge to Man, Ronald Press*, New York, 1948, 401 pp. An authoritative popular treatment of the bacteria, with particular reference to human diseases.

Thimann, Kenneth V., *The Life of Bacteria*, Macmillan, New York, 1955, 775 pp. An excellent text, emphasizing the biological rather than the medical or industrial aspects of bacteriology.

CHAPTER 7

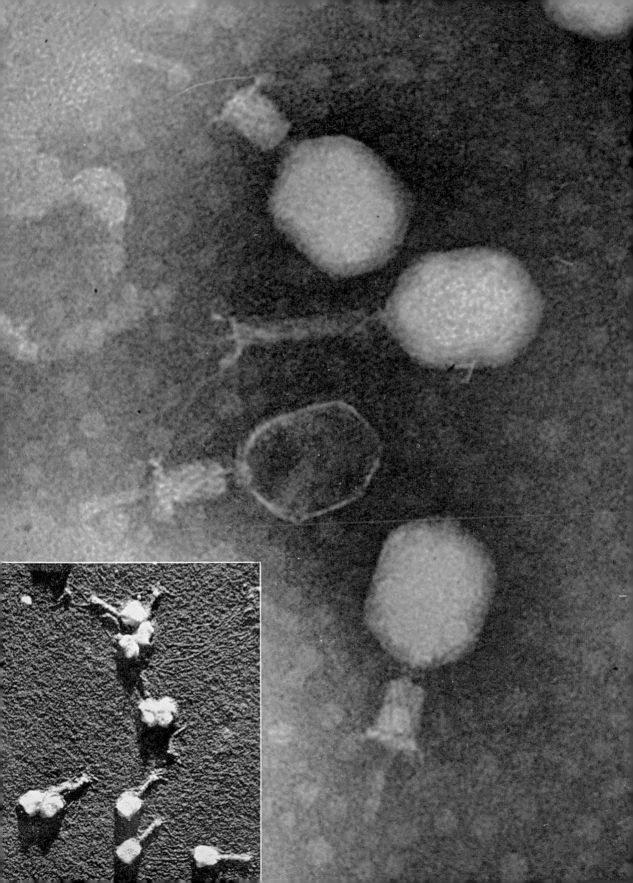

Viruses

◀

T₄ phage (×440,000). (Electron micrograph courtesy of T. F. Anderson.)
Inset: T₄ phage (×82,000). (Electron micrograph courtesy of R. C. Williams.)

HISTORY AND DEFINITION

During the latter part of the nineteenth century, after Koch's and Pasteur's demonstrations that some bacteria cause disease, a great deal of attention was devoted to determining the causative agents of particular diseases. In 1892 the Russian botanist Dmitri Iwanowski (1864–1920) reported the transmission of tobacco mosaic disease by means of sap that had been passed through filters that were supposed to retain all bacteria. Six years later foot and mouth disease of cattle was shown also to be caused by an agent which could pass through bacteriological filters, and similar reports for other diseases soon followed. Disease-causing agents which could pass through filters came to be called filterable viruses, the word **virus** being taken from Latin *virus*, a poison. As knowledge of the nature of these disease-causing agents has increased, it has become customary to speak of them merely as viruses, and it has come to be recognized that some of them may exist in the host without causing disease. As a preliminary working definition, viruses may now be characterized as submicroscopic or barely microscopic entities, capable of being introduced into living cells of particular kinds of organisms, and capable of reproducing (or being reproduced) only within such cells. Evidence which may later contribute to a more precise definition is discussed in the following pages.

STRUCTURE AND CLASSIFICATION

A typical virus particle apparently consists of a core of nucleic acid, partly or wholly surrounded by a sheath of protein. Our information about the physicochemical structure and behavior of viruses is so recent and pertains to such a relatively small percentage of the different kinds of viruses, that no generally accepted scheme of classification has yet been established. It is customary to speak of animal viruses, which inhabit vertebrates, arthropods, and many other animals; plant viruses, which inhabit angiosperms and probably other higher plants; and bacterial viruses (more commonly called **bacteriophages**, or **phages**), which inhabit bacteria. Some further groups may be recognized on morphological and chemical grounds, and doubtless a complete formal classification will eventually be achieved. For the present, however, it is customary to name each virus for the disease which it causes. Viruses have not been definitely observed in plants other than flowering plants and bacteria, but this may reflect a lack of study rather than a real absence.

Particles of both plant and animal viruses vary from spherical to slenderly rod-shaped, according to the kind of virus.

Some animal viruses are brick-shaped, and probably the same form will eventually be observed among plant viruses. Many of the bacteriophages are tadpole-shaped, with a more or less spherical "head" and a slender "tail" of equal or greater length. It is not known whether the tail has any function in locomotion, because the electron microscope cannot be used on living materials. The plant and animal viruses are generally assumed to be nonmotile. Some of the smallest viruses, such as the one which causes foot and mouth disease, are only about 0.01 microns in length, while some of the largest ones, such as the psittacosis virus, approach 0.5 microns.

The nucleic acid core of most plant viruses which have been studied consists of RNA; in bacteriophages and animal viruses it consists of DNA, or sometimes both DNA and RNA, or even (as in the polio virus) of RNA alone. It may be noted that some of the "plant viruses," such as the one causing aster yellows, are equally or more at home in the insects which transmit the disease and might therefore with some justification be considered to be "animal viruses."

In 1935 the American virologist W. M. Stanley (1904–   ) published a paper entitled "Isolation of a crystalline protein possessing the properties of tobacco mosaic virus." A number of other plant viruses have subsequently been crystallized, and crystals of tobacco mosaic virus have also been observed in living cells of the tobacco plant. Subsequent studies with the aid of the electron microscope have shown that the crystals of tobacco mosaic virus are composed of regularly arranged, slender, rod-shaped particles of the virus. In the chemically active, infectious state, the virus occurs in the form of these rods, which are about 0.3 microns long and 0.015

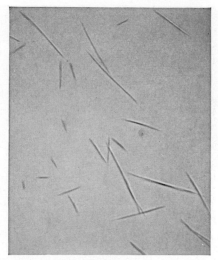

Fig. 7.1. Left, W. M. Stanley (1904–   ), American virologist, who was the first to "crystallize" a virus. Right, "crystals" of tobacco mosaic virus. (×675.) (Courtesy of W. M. Stanley.)

microns thick. The crystals of other viruses are likewise composed of individual virus particles, rather than being true crystals in the chemical sense.

The year 1955 was marked by three notable achievements of the Stanley team of virologists: (1) the polio virus became the first animal virus to be crystallized; (2) the RNA core was separated from the protein sheath of the rod particles of the tobacco mosaic virus, and the separated, individually inert parts were induced to reassemble into normal, potentially infectious virus particles; (3) the separated RNA core from one strain of tobacco mosaic virus was induced to combine with the separated protein sheath from another strain of the virus, giving a new strain different from any of those previously known.

REPRODUCTION

Studies of a number of different viruses, including representatives of all three major groups, indicate that new virus particles do not arise by division of existing particles but are formed directly by aggregation and organization of molecules within the protoplasm of the host cell. Instead of having a complete enzyme system of their own, viruses interact with the enzyme system of the host to bring about the formation of substances which become organized directly into new virus particles.

Among at least some bacteriophages, it is chiefly the DNA core of the virus particle which enters the host cell, and most of the inert protein sheath is left behind just outside the cell. Among some animal viruses in which complete particles (DNA core plus protein sheath) are introduced into the host cell, it seems probable that the DNA becomes dissociated from the protein sheath, just as in the bacteriophages, and that here too it is the chemical activity of the DNA of the virus in and with the protoplasm of the host cell which leads to the formation of new virus par-

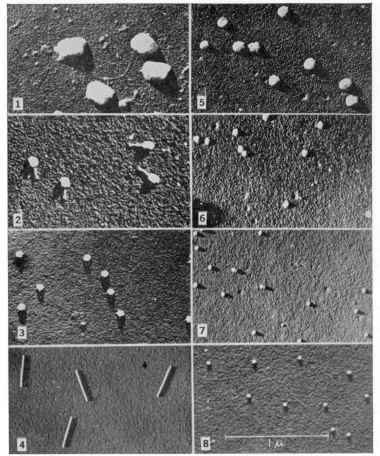

Fig. 7.2. Virus particles of various types. *1* (top left), vaccinia; *2*, T-2 bacteriophage, with tail; *3*, T-3 bacteriophage; *4*, tobacco mosaic; *5* (top right), influenza; *6*, rabbit papilloma; *7*, bushy stunt of tomato; *8*, polio. (All to scale indicated at lower right.) (Electron micrograph, courtesy of R. C. Williams and other members of the virus laboratory, University of California, Berkeley.)

ticles. A similar dissociation of the RNA core from the protein sheath may perhaps occur in some plant viruses, or the sheath itself may be incomplete, permitting the RNA to react with the protoplasm of the host cell without leaving the sheath.

If, as now seems likely, the formation of new particles directly in the protoplasm of the host cell (rather than by division of existing particles) proves to be characteristic of a very large proportion of the viruses, this manner of reproduction may come to be used as an important taxonomic criterion of the group. Supposed

viruses which prove to reproduce by fission may then be classified as bacteria instead of viruses.

MUTABILITY, AND THE NATURAL ORIGIN OF NEW STRAINS

The fact that the virus responsible for a particular disease may exist in several or many slightly different strains is due to mutation. It is clear that spontaneous mutations in viruses occur, and the frequency of mutation can be increased by exposure to X rays or other known mutagens. It seems entirely probable that mutations in viruses are similar in nature to the gene mutations which occur in cellular organisms.

Some bacteriophages have been shown to be able to produce new strains under essentially natural conditions by recombination of the characters of existing strains. In order for this to occur, two different but related strains of phage must infect the same bacterial cell. The new phage particles produced in the bacterial cell will then be of several different types, some resembling the original phage particles, others having various combinations of the characters of the original particles. There is no evidence that anything physically resembling a sexual process occurs, but the results are similar to those of sexual reproduction in that new and different combinations of existing characters are produced.

DISTINCTION FROM BACTERIA

The distinction between the viruses and the bacteria is partly arbitrary, but it also marks a real difference in the level of organization of the organisms or particles under consideration. The limit of resolving power of conventional microscopes and the size of the pores in the finest ordinary bacteriological filters both nearly coincide with the size of the smallest organisms which carry on the vital metabolic proc-

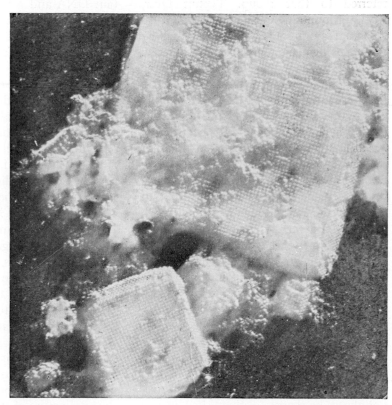

Fig. 7.3. Electron micrograph of crystal of tobacco necrosis virus. (Courtesy of R. Markham, K. M. Smith, and R. W. G. Wyckoff.)

esses within their own bodies and which can be cultivated on nonliving media.

Individual organisms of the bacterial family Rickettsiaceae are about at the lower size limit for bacteria and about at the upper limit for viruses, being commonly about 0.6×0.3 microns. They have not yet been cultivated outside living cells, and for that reason, as well as because of their small size, they have often been considered to be viruses. Observations with the electron microscope show that they have a definite cell wall surrounded by capsular material, just as in other bacteria, and that they reproduce by fission, just as do other bacteria. Rickettsia-type organisms evidently do not differ essentially from the bacteria, and they may now be referred to that group. Typhus fever, Rocky Mountain spotted fever, and Q fever are among the diseases caused by organisms belonging to the Rickettsiaceae.

The vaccinia (viruses such as those causing smallpox and cowpox) are relatively large for virus particles (commonly about 0.3 microns long and nearly as thick), and the mature particle evidently has at least a partial enzyme system within the limits of some sort of membrane. The evidence suggests that these constituents become at least partially disassociated during the reproductive stage in the host cell, however, and that new virus particles are formed de novo rather than by division of existing particles. It seems proper, therefore, to continue to consider the vaccinia as large viruses rather than small bacteria.

DISTINCTION FROM NORMAL PROTOPLASMIC CONSTITUENTS

We have noted that the viruses may not always be sharply distinguished, at one extreme, from bacteria. It is just as difficult, at the other extreme, to distinguish viruses from normal components of the host cells. In many cases a virus is more or less **latent** (i.e., it exists and reproduces but causes no detectable harm) in a particular host and causes a recognizable disease only when introduced into some other kind of host. Several different kinds of plants and animals have been demonstrated to contain cytoplasmic particles of approximately virus size which multiply or are multiplied in the cells containing them, and which affect the physiological reactions of the host cells without causing anything which could be called a disease.

The kappa granules of some races of *Paramecium aurelia* (a protozoan) contain DNA and govern the formation of a chemical substance that is poisonous to strains lacking kappa granules. Kappa granules can be introduced under properly controlled conditions into individuals of some nonkappa strains, and they reproduce (or are reproduced) in the new host. Thus kappa granules, which are usually considered to be normal protoplasmic constituents of the cells which contain them, are potentially infectious, and they scarcely seem to differ from true viruses.

The virus which causes potato paracrinkle is a regular inhabitant of the King Edward potato plant, in which it is transmitted from one generation to the next through the tubers, and causes no symptoms. A susceptible variety of potato may acquire the disease by being grafted to the King Edward potato. The disease is transmitted only by grafting and is otherwise unknown. Within the King Edward potato, this virus might well be considered to be a normal constituent of the cytoplasm; with some other varieties of potato, the viral nature of the particles can scarcely be questioned. As a practical matter, minute, noncellular particles which reproduce and cause harm in any particular kind of host are considered to be viruses, regardless of the number of hosts in which they may be latent.

A virus which causes a disease in one organism may beneficially affect some other kind of organism. The work of the American virologist Karl Maramorosch (1921–) on corn leaf hoppers is especially instructive in this regard. This leaf hopper normally lives only on corn (maize) or its near relative, teosinte. Deprived of its normal food, it will feed on other plants, but it soon dies. However, if it feeds on China aster plants that are infected with Aster yellows virus, its host range is tremendously expanded. Not only does it thrive on the sick asters, but thereafter it can attack many other hosts, including such dissimilar ones as carrots and rye. Healthy China aster plants now also become fit food for the leaf hopper. Its ability to live on corn and teosinte is unimpaired, and it suffers no obvious ill effects from the virus.

The increased host range is due to infection of the leaf hoppers by the Aster yellows virus. Heat treatment which destroys the virus in the insect destroys also its ability to live on the unusual hosts. Neither the virus nor the expansion of the host range is transmitted to the next generation. If the virus were transmitted through the egg from one generation to the next, as is true of some other viruses inhabiting other kinds of organisms, it would become a normal and valuable cytoplasmic constituent of the species. Its viral origin could then be detected only if the insect happened to feed on a healthy China aster plant, giving it the yellows disease.

As yet we have no inkling of how the virus accomplishes its effect on the leaf hopper.

EVOLUTIONARY ORIGIN

There are two principal concepts as to the evolutionary origin of viruses. According to one concept they are simplified bacteria, which have gradually lost their structural and metabolic complexity as they have come to depend more and more on the host cell for the necessary enzymes as well as for food, so that they finally come to consist of merely a gene or gene group with some associated protein. According to the other concept they are cytoplasmic or nuclear particles which have somehow attained a separate individuality which permits them to be transferred from cell to cell and from organism to organism without loss of their vital properties. That is, they are genes, or plastids, or other protoplasmic structures which have escaped from the control of the metabolic system which brought them into being.

The evidence available does not permit the whole-hearted acceptance or complete rejection of either of these two concepts of the evolutionary origin of viruses. One difficulty to be faced under either concept is the manner of reproduction of virus particles. Bacteria reproduce by division of existing cells. Plastids and mitochondria, at least usually and perhaps always, likewise reproduce by the division of the existing structures or their recognizable precursors. The template function of existing genes in gene duplication suggests a way that virus molecules may govern the formation of more virus molecules, but the assembly of these new virus molecules into organized particles apparently does not require contact with existing virus particles. A further difficulty with the hypothesis of bacterial origin is that many viruses have a core of RNA, a usual cytoplasmic constituent, rather than DNA, the essential nuclear constituent.

It is possible that both concepts are partly correct and that viruses are of diverse origins. The vaccinia viruses, which have at least a partial enzyme system of their own, may well be derived from bacteria, in spite of their apparently nonbacterial mode of reproduction, and it would seem possible to derive some of the less complex animal viruses by reduction from types similar to the vaccinia. The RNA-containing viruses, on the other hand, may perhaps be more readily correlated with cytoplasmic constituents. It has also been pointed out that even some of the bodies which appear to be normal cytoplasmic constituents of the cells which contain them may have originated as bacteria which became highly modified and reduced in the course of achieving a symbiotic relationship with the host.

LIVING AND NONLIVING PROPERTIES OF VIRUSES

There has been some argument as to whether viruses should be considered to be living or nonliving. In their chemical composition they certainly resemble protoplasmic constituents. They must also be chemically active in protoplasmic fashion, since the mere physical presence of virus particles could scarcely stimulate the host

Fig. 7.4.   Resistant (left) and susceptible (right) varieties of tobacco, inoculated with tobacco mosaic virus. (Courtesy of Howard E. Haggsted, Agricultural Research Service.)

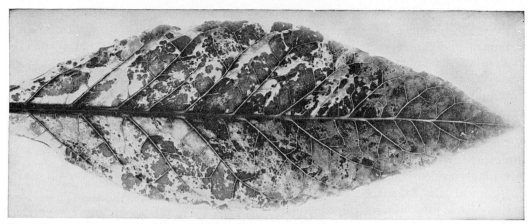

Fig. 7.5. A single leaf of tobacco showing characteristic symptoms of mosaic disease. (Photo by H. A. Allard, courtesy of the Agricultural Research Service.)

to produce new virus particles, in the absence of any chemical reaction between the virus particles and the protoplasm of the host cell. On the other hand, virus crystals separated from the host are chemically inert and can apparently be kept indefinitely without significant change. This seemingly suspended animation is perhaps not an insuperable barrier to the admission of viruses to the category of living organisms, inasmuch as spores of some bacteria and even other plants are now also believed to be able to go into an inert state without losing their vital properties.

Under either concept of their evolutionary origin, viruses are of a protoplasmic nature, and because of their essential similarity to protoplasmic systems or constituents they will doubtless continue to attract the attention of biologists. Whether they are themselves considered to be alive is less important than the recognition of their essential similarity to protoplasm or protoplasmic constituents. If viruses are considered to be alive, then the synthesis of new virus strains from separated, individually inert viral components must

be very close to the creation of new life.

ECONOMIC IMPORTANCE

The plant and animal viruses are economically important because of the diseases which they cause. Some of the diseases caused by plant viruses are aster yellows, potato leaf roll, rice stunt, sugar beet curly top, tomato bushy stunt, and a series of different mosaic diseases of such plants as beans, cucumbers, peas, peaches, sugar beets, sugar cane, tobacco, turnips, and wheat. The mosaic diseases are so named because they tend to inhibit chlorophyll production in a more or less definite pattern (often along the main veins) in the leaves of infected plants. Many plant viruses are transmitted by leaf hoppers, aphids, and other insects, in which they are often quite at home, multiplying without apparent damage to the insect host. Other virus diseases of plants are mechanically transmitted, usually through some point of injury. Plant viruses can also be transmitted by grafting.

Some of the diseases caused by animal viruses are dengue fever, several types of human and equine encephalitis, influenza, measles, mumps, polio, chickenpox, smallpox, the common cold, foot and mouth disease of cattle, rabies, hog cholera, distemper, psittacosis (parrot fever), myxomatosis of rabbits, and granulosis of butterflies and moths. Cold sores and warts are also caused by viruses, and it is becoming increasingly evident that a virus or virus-like element may be involved in human cancer. A large proportion of animal viruses are transmitted by contact, but some, such as the yellow fever virus and some of the encephalitis viruses, are transmitted by mosquitoes or other biting insects.

The degree of importance of bacteriophages in limiting the numbers of bacteria remains to be determined. Many of the phages are sufficiently adapted to their hosts that they are carried on from generation to generation in morphologically undifferentiated form, only occasionally maturing into definite phage particles which are liberated by death and rupture of the host cell. Like other viruses, individual kinds of bacteriophage frequently have a number of different hosts, being highly virulent to some, and causing but little damage to others.

SUGGESTED READING

Eberson, Frederick, *Microbes Militant: A Challenge to Man*, Ronald Press, New York, 1948, 401 pp. Includes two chapters on viruses.

Luria, S. E., *General Virology*, John Wiley & Sons, New York, 1953. 427 pp. A textbook.

Stanley, W. M., Isolation of a crystalline protein possessing the properties of tobacco-mosaic virus, *Science* 81:644–645. June 28, 1935. The classic paper which opened the way to an understanding of the nature of viruses.

Williams, Greer, *Virus Hunters*, Knopf, New York, 1959. An interesting popular treatment, at a somewhat higher level than *Microbe Hunters*.

CHAPTER 8

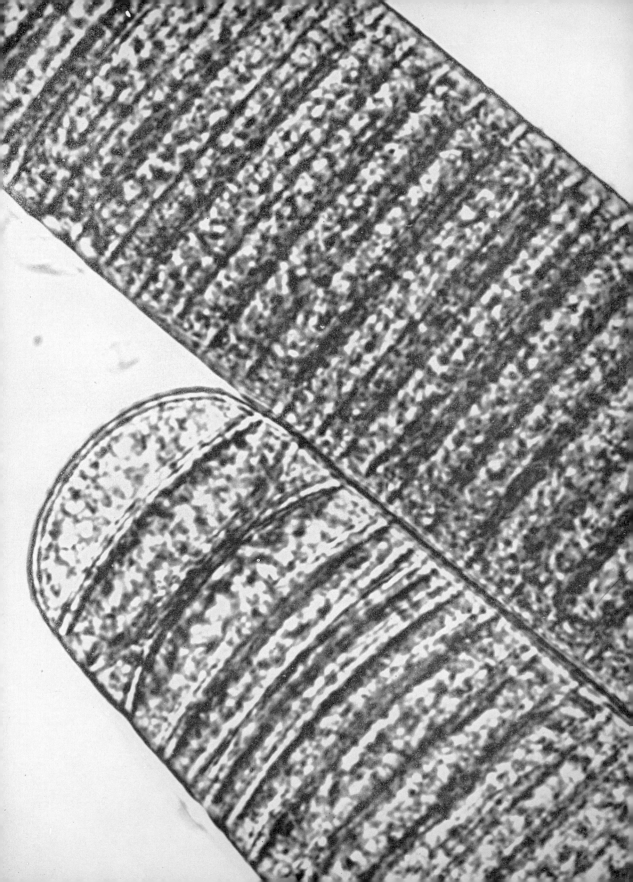

Class
Cyanophyceae

BLUE-GREEN ALGAE   **CHAPTER 8**

HISTORY AND DEFINITION

The term **algae** is applied to most of the chlorophyll-bearing plants other than those in which the zygote normally begins its growth and development as a parasite on the parent plant. A few colorless plants are included because of their similarity to undoubted algae, as are also a few plants in which the zygote does begin its growth as a parasite on the parent plant. The chlorophyllous bacteria are excluded from the algae by their unusual type of photosynthesis, as well as by their evident relationship to other bacteria. As so defined, the algae are mostly water plants and mostly relatively simple in structure, although some of the marine algae are large and structurally complex. Nearly all plants which float free in the ocean are algae; many of the plants inhabiting fresh waters and ocean shores are algae, but others are basically land plants which have returned to an aquatic habitat. Some algae do occur on land, especially in moist places, but

◀
Oscillatoria filaments (×2000). (Photomicrograph courtesy of George Schwartz.)

119

these are always small, simple organisms. Algae never have specialized water-conducting tissues, as do many land plants, and only a few of the larger marine algae have tissues comparable to the phloem (a food-conducting tissue) of many land plants. Any complete plant body which lacks specialized conducting tissues is called a **thallus,** particularly if it is multicellular but relatively simple in external form, not being divided into parts which resemble roots, stems, and leaves.

Gametes of algae are generally borne in unicellular gametangia, and never in structures resembling the multicellular gametangia of many of the land plants. A **gametangium** is any structure in which gametes are borne.

The algae have often in the past been considered to constitute a subdivision of a division Thallophyta, but that classification has been abandoned, and the algae are now considered to be a convenient artificial group rather than a natural taxon.

The definition of the algae in approximately the modern sense dates from a "natural" system of plants proposed in 1789 by the French botanist A. L. de Jussieu (1748–1836). In 1836 the algae were divided by the Irish botanist W. H. Harvey (1811–1866) into three groups which correspond fairly well to the red algae, brown algae, and green plus blue-green algae, as those groups are now understood. The blue-green algae were recognized as a group distinct from the green algae by the Swiss botanist Karl Wilhelm von Naegeli in 1853, although he did not propose a formal name. The oldest (1860) formal name for the blue-green algae is Myxophyceae, but the more descriptive name Cyanophyceae has been more generally adopted. The characteristic ending for names of algal classes is *-phyceae.*

Excluding bacteria, the unicellular and colonial organisms which move by means of flagella are commonly called **flagellates.** Most flagellates, even those with chlorophyll, were generally included with the protozoa (unicellular animals) until the German botanist Georg Klebs (1857–1918) pointed out, in 1883, that several groups of flagellates are related to different groups of undoubted algae. The lead provided by Klebs was worked out by another German botanist, Adolf Pascher (1887–1945) in a series of papers published principally from 1910 to 1931. The present-day classification of the major groups of algae conforms fairly closely to Pascher's concepts.

Some undoubted protozoa are allied to various groups of chlorophyllous flagel-

Fig. 8.1. Adolf Pascher (1887–1945), German botanist who made fundamental contributions to the classification of algae. (Photo courtesy of Einar Teiling.)

lates. No division of the flagellates into plant and animal groups has yet proved mutually acceptable to algologists and protozoologists, and it may be that no satisfactory separation is possible. The same organism may be treated as an alga by botanists and as a protozoan by zoologists. From a botanical standpoint, any organism which contains chlorophyll is necessarily a plant, and a coherent classification requires that some nonchlorophyllous organisms also be included with the plants because of their evident relationships.

The blue-green algae (Cyanophyceae) may be defined as Schizophytes which ordinarily possess chlorophyll and associated phycobilin pigments, especially the blue pigment phycocyanin, and which release oxygen as a result of photosynthesis. Phycobilin pigments, although recently discovered in the Cryptophyceae, are found chiefly in the Cyanophyceae and Rhodophyta (red algae). The red algae are almost always sexual and are often structurally complex, whereas the blue-green algae are apparently always asexual and are small and relatively simple in structure. Some blue-green algae are unicellular, but more often they occur as filaments or small colonies of various other shapes, in which the cells may or may not be all alike. They ordinarily have a definite wall which contains cellulose and hemicelluloses. The cell wall is surrounded by a gelatinous sheath that is generally composed of pectic compounds. Reproduction is accomplished by cell division, fragmentation, or spores. No motile reproductive structures of any sort are produced. Cyanophyceae differ from all other algae in having the chlorophyll and associated pigments in minute granules uniformly distributed throughout the peripheral part of the protoplast, rather than being localized in plastids.

DISTRIBUTION

Blue-green algae occur in fresh and salt water and in moist subaerial habitats throughout the world. They are more abundant in fresh than in salt water, and more abundant near the surface than at depths of more than a few feet. Sunny habitats which are covered by a thin film of water for prolonged periods usually harbor blue-green algae which become dormant during dry periods. Temporary pools are likely to contain more blue-green algae than any other sort, especially during the first few weeks. Many blue-greens occur at or just beneath the surface of the soil. They can also be cultured from soil samples taken at depths up to 50 cm or even 2 m, but it is believed that the cultures arise from dormant individuals or spores which have been washed down from the surface. Spray-dampened cliffs and dripping ledges tend to be especially rich in Cyanophyceae. They are also commonly present in and about hot springs, sometimes at temperatures as high as 85° Centigrade. The Red Sea is said to have been so named because of the abundance of *Trichodesmium*, a blue-green alga which is red.

Many blue-green algae occur in association with other organisms as epiphytes, commensals, symbionts, or parasites. Some of them live symbiotically with certain fungi, forming the associations known as lichens. Some are enslaved within the cells of other organisms, such as various fungi, protozoa, and other algae, providing food for the host cell while deriving no apparent benefit from the relationship. Such a condition is called **helotism.** A few colorless members of the family Oscillatoriaceae are mild parasites in the digestive tract of man and other animals.

CHARACTERISTICS

EXTERNAL MORPHOLOGY

Blue-green algae occur as single cells, as small cell colonies, and as multicellular filaments which are themselves sometimes aggregated into colonies. Cell colonies may be flat and only one cell thick, or spherical and hollow, or elongate and quasi-filamentous, or massive and cubical or formless. The sheaths of the individual cells may remain readily distinguishable, or they may become confluent so that the individual cells are merely embedded in a common gelatinous mass. The quasi-filamentous types are those in which the cells are arranged in a linear sequence but are separated by the sheath material. In truly filamentous blue-green algae the walls of most adjacent cells are in contact, rather than being separated by sheath material. The individual chain of cells in a filament is called a **trichome.** A filament is composed of one or sometimes several trichomes, enclosed in a common gelatinous sheath; sometimes the sheath is very thin or apparently absent. A trichome is usually only one cell thick, but in some genera it is several cells thick. The cells of a trichome may or may not be all alike.

MOTION

Blue-green algae have no evident means of locomotion, but some filamentous ones move nevertheless. The whole filament may move slowly forward and backward, either in a straight line or in a spiral, or the end of the filament may wave slowly back and forth. Students are not agreed about the mechanism of locomotion. One suggestion is that a gelatinous substance is excreted through the cell wall, in some cases from pores arranged in a definite pattern, and that the rapid swelling of this substance causes the filament to move. Another suggestion is that rhythmic waves of alternate expansion and contraction pass along the length of the filament.

CYTOLOGY

An individual cell of a blue-green alga (Fig. 8.2) consists of a protoplast, surrounded by a wall, which is usually enclosed in a gelatinous sheath. The wall contains pectic compounds and other hemicelluloses, plus some cellulose, whereas the sheath is usually composed wholly or largely of pectic compounds. The protoplast consists of two well-defined portions, a colorless **central body** and a pigmented

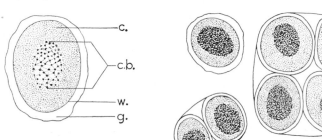

Fig. 8.2. Left: a single cell of a blue-green alga, showing parts: c., chromoplasm; c.b., central body; g., gelatinous sheath; w., cell wall. Right: *Gloeocapsa*, single cell and colonies. (×1000.)

outer region called the **chromoplasm.** The central body contains chromatin and is evidently of nuclear nature, but it is not usually bounded by a definite membrane, and there is no nucleolus. There is no central vacuole, although scattered small vacuoles are sometimes present. In at least some cases these are apparently gas bubbles rather than vacuoles of the type usually found in other plants. Cell division is in some cases apparently strictly amitotic, with the central body merely being constricted into two parts. In other cases apparent chromosomes and a poorly differentiated spindle may be formed. Cytokinesis is accomplished by the centripetal growth of a transverse membrane, sometimes accompanied by constriction or furrowing of the protoplast.

PIGMENTATION

Blue-green algae ordinarily contain chlorophyll, plus carotenoid and phycobilin pigments. Each minute color granule of the protoplast apparently bears pigments of all these types. The chlorophyll is always (so far as known) chlorophyll *a* only. Chlorophyll *a* is also the principal chlorophyll of the other groups of algae and of the higher plants, but these groups commonly contain other chlorophylls as well. The principal carotenoid pigment of the Cyanophyceae is β-carotene, just as in other algae. Two other carotenoid pigments, myxoxanthine and myxoxanthophyll, are usually also present in some quantity; these two pigments have not been found in other organisms. At least some of the blue-green algae also contain still other carotenoid pigments.

Phycobilin pigments are proteins, and, unlike chlorophyll and the carotenoid pigments, they are soluble in water and insoluble in the common fat solvents. Like the carotenoid pigments, the phycobilins evidently transfer some of the energy absorbed from light into the photosynthetic process. Phycobilin pigments are of two general kinds: **phycocyanins,** which absorb green, yellow, and red light, while transmitting blue; and **phycoerythrins,** which absorb blue-green, green, and yellow light, while transmitting red. The phycobilin pigments which occur in blue-green algae are identified by the prefix *c-*; the similar but not identical pigments in the red algae are identified by the prefix *r-*. Most Cyanophyceae contain the blue pigment *c*-phycocyanin; some also contain the red pigment *c*-phycoerythrin; and a few have *c*-phycoerythrin but lack *c*-phycocyanin.

Some pigments which are neither carotenoids nor phycobilins occur in the wall or sheath of some kinds of blue-green algae.

The typical color of the blue-green algae is just what the name suggests. Variations in the kinds and proportions of pigments in the different species also produce many other colors, including diverse shades of purple, red, yellow, brown, and blackish.

FOOD RESERVES

Blue-green algae commonly store food as small granules of carbohydrate in chemical combination with protein. Glycogen in animals often also occurs in combination with proteins, forming compounds known as glycoproteins, and the food granules of blue-green algae have also been considered to be glycoproteins. Recent work suggests that the carbohydrate fraction of these granules in blue-green algae may not be strictly identical with glycogen, and many algologists prefer the term **cyanophycean**

starch. Glycogen and the glycogen-like carbohydrates such as cyanophycean starch are similar to the amylopectin fraction of ordinary starch in that the molecule is composed chiefly of glucose units arranged in a branching chain.

REPRODUCTION

Reproduction in blue-green algae is accomplished by cell division, by fragmentation of colonies or filaments, and by spores.

There are two types of spores. One type, called an **akinete,** is formed by the enlargement of a single vegetative cell, accompanied by an increase in thickness of the wall. The mature akinete contains the entire protoplast of the original vegetative cell, and the wall of the original cell makes up part of the wall of the akinete. An akinete is a resting cell which carries the organism over a period of unfavorable conditions, and it usually germinates as soon as favorable conditions for growth are restored. The other type of spore, called an **endospore,** is formed by repeated division of a protoplast within a cell wall. The original cell wall thus comes to constitute a sporangium, i.e., a case or container in which spores are borne. The sporangium eventually breaks open, releasing the spores, which usually soon germinate. Both akinetes and endospores are nonmotile, and no motile reproductive structures of any sort are known in the class.

Many filamentous blue-green algae have occasional enlarged thick-walled cells in which the protoplasm degenerates into a colorless, homogeneous, viscous substance. These cells are called **heterocysts.** In an evolutionary sense they are probably modified spores, but they do not ordinarily function as such. In some blue-green algae heterocysts are apparently functionless; in others fragmentation of the filament usually occurs between two adjacent heterocysts or between a heterocyst and a vegetative cell. In some kinds of blue-green algae fragmentation of the filament occurs at special points where two vegetative cells are separated by a double-concave disk of gelatinous material. The disks are known as **separation** disks, and the segments of the filaments delimited by the disks are called **hormogonia** (singular, **hormogonium**). Segments of a filament delimited by heterocysts are also called hormogonia if the heterocysts mark the points at which fragmentation occurs. Fragmentation of colonies (as opposed to true filaments) of blue-green algae is usually a matter of chance disturbance, or of the failure of the gelatinous sheath to hold the larger colonies together.

No sexual processes of any sort are known among the blue-green algae.

NITROGEN FIXATION

Several genera of blue-green algae belonging to the family Nostocaceae, including *Nostoc* and *Anabaena*, resemble some of the bacteria in being able to use atmospheric nitrogen. Free-living (i.e., nonsymbiotic) nitrogen-fixing bacteria often occur in the gelatinous sheaths of *Nostoc* and other blue-green algae of the soil, using some of the sheath material as food, and it is therefore necessary to use bacteria-free cultures in determining nitrogen-fixing ability of the algae. The importance of blue-green algae as nitrogen fixers remains to be established, but it has been suggested that they play a prominent role in maintaining the fertility of rice paddies.

CARBONATE DEPOSITION

There is a complex chemical balance between dissolved carbon dioxide, carbonic acid (H_2CO_3) and dissolved bicarbonates in natural waters. Depletion of the dissolved carbon dioxide tends to cause the formation of insoluble carbonates from dissolved bicarbonates, as for example in the following equation: $Ca(HCO_3)_2 \longrightarrow CaCO_3 + H_2O + CO_2$. The use of dissolved carbon dioxide for photosynthesis by algae and other water plants, therefore, tends to cause precipitation of carbonates. The fact that some algae are much more prone than others in the same habitat to accumulate lime on or within their bodies suggests, however, that these calcareous algae also play a more direct role in the process. Many of these algae, especially certain blue-green, green, and red algae, probably extract carbon dioxide more or less directly from dissolved bicarbonates, leading to the deposition of such insoluble carbonates as calcium carbonate, magnesium carbonate, and calcium magnesium carbonate. The marl which accumulates at the bottom of some lakes and bogs is composed largely of calcium carbonate formed through the activities of green and blue-green algae, and the precipitation of calcium carbonate through the chemical activities of red, blue-green, and green algae in the geologic past is believed to have been an important factor in the formation of many or most limestone deposits.

THERMAL ALGAE

Most kinds of organisms do not long survive at temperatures higher than about 50°C. Some blue-green algae, like some of the bacteria, thrive at temperatures well above 50°. Blue-green algae are common inhabitants of hot springs throughout the world. In general, the species which inhabit hot springs are especially adapted to high temperatures and do not occur elsewhere. Some thermal blue-green algae in Yellowstone National Park live at a normal temperature of about 85°C and are regularly exposed to overflow waters at a temperature of about 90°C (nearly the boiling point, at that altitude). The brilliant colors of the formations at Mammoth Hot Springs and other hot springs and geysers in the Park are due chiefly to blue-green algae, which, as already noted, are not always blue-green. These algae also contribute to the deposition of calcium carbonate, silica, and other minerals in and around the springs and geysers, but under such conditions the minerals would be deposited even without algal action.

CLASSIFICATION

There are about 1500 known species of Cyanophyceae. These may be classified into three orders, the Chroococcales, Chamaesiphonales, and Oscillatoriales, on the basis of structure of the thallus and method of reproduction. A key to the orders is provided in the appendix.

REPRESENTATIVE GENERA

GLOEOCAPSA

Gloeocapsa (Fig. 8.2) commonly occurs on damp rocks. The individual cells are more or less spherical and are aggregated into amorphous colonies of less than 50 cells. The sheath is colored red, blue, violet, yellow, or brown by one or more pigments called gloeocapsin, and the sheaths of the individual cells retain their identity. Reproduction is by cell division and colony fragmentation.

POLYCYSTIS

Polycystis forms free-floating colonies and is often especially abundant in hard-water lakes. The cells are more or less spherical and form colonies of various shapes, commonly several hundred to a colony. The cells lie in a gelatinous common matrix of very watery consistency and do not have recognizable individual sheaths. Reproduction is by cell division and colony fragmentation.

Algae such as *Polycystis,* which are of microscopic or barely megascopic size and which float freely in water, being carried about by the currents and waves, are called plankton algae. The term **plankton** includes the plankton algae and the tiny aquatic animals of similar size which are also carried about by the water. Most divisions of algae include some plankton genera, and some divisions include more plankton than other types.

MERISMOPOEDIA

Merismopoedia (Fig. 8.8) occurs in lakes, ponds, and semipermanent pools. It forms free-floating colonies, one cell thick,

with the cells arranged in regular vertical and transverse rows. The colonies are rectangular to irregular in shape and may be composed of several hundred or only a few cells. Reproduction is by cell division and colony fragmentation.

SYNECHOCOCCUS

Synechococcus (Fig. 8.3) grows in a wide variety of habitats, including fresh and salt water, hot springs, and damp soil. It is one of the most common genera of thermal algae in Yellowstone National Park, occurring at temperatures up to 84°C. The broadly ellipsoid to cylindric cells, nearly or quite without a gelatinous sheath, occur singly or joined end to end in colonies of two to four. Reproduction is by cell division. The various species are blue-green to violet or rose red.

PLEUROCAPSA

Pleurocapsa (Fig. 8.4) includes both marine and fresh-water species. One species, *P. entophysaloides,* occurs in Great Salt Lake as well as in the ocean. *Pleurocapsa* has a multicellular thallus that is irregularly quasi-filamentous and forms a crust on the surface of the substrate. The filaments are branched, but the sheaths enclosing the branches tend to be coherent. Individual filaments penetrate the sub-

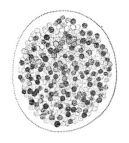 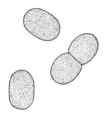 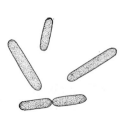

Fig. 8.3. Left: *Polycystis incerta.* (×450.) Center: *Synechococcus minervae.* (×2000.) Right: *Synechococcus vulcanus.* (×1000.) (*Synechococcus* spp. after Copeland.)

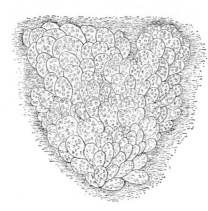
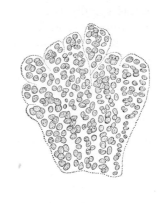

Fig. 8.4. *Pleurocapsa ento-physaloides.* Left: habit. (×65.) Right: detail. (×300.) (After Gardner.)

strate, providing anchorage. Reproduction is by the formation of endospores. Sporangia may resemble ordinary vegetative cells or may be distinctly larger, and they may be terminal on the filaments or scattered among vegetative cells. There may be as many as 50 or more endospores in a sporangium.

OSCILLATORIA

Oscillatoria (Fig. 8.5) is one of the commonest genera of algae and occurs in a wide variety of fresh-water and subaerial habitats, including hot springs. It forms well-defined, unbranched, cylindrical, uniseriate filaments that occur singly or irregularly interwoven in layers of indefinite extent. The gelatinous sheath, if present at all, is extremely thin. The individual cells vary from much shorter to evidently longer than broad. In some species the

cells are all about alike; in others the free surface of the apical cell is broadly convex, and sometimes the filament tapers near the end. Reproduction is by hormogonia delimited by separation disks. The filaments of *Oscillatoria* and some related blue-green algae wave slowly from side to side and sometimes also move very slowly from place to place.

Phormidium, a genus which differs from *Oscillatoria* chiefly in having a thin but definite gelatinous sheath, includes a number of thermal species as well as species that grow at ordinary temperatures. It is the most abundant genus of thermal algae in Yellowstone Park.

SPIRULINA

Spirulina (Fig. 8.5) is a plankton genus occurring more commonly in brackish and salt water than in fresh water. It

Fig. 8.5. Top: *Oscillatoria:* s, separation disk. (×1500.) Bottom: *Spirulina.* (×2800.)

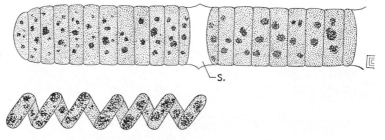

Class Cyanophyceae: Blue-Green Algae **127**

forms spirally twisted filaments less than
$\frac{1}{10}$ mm long, which are not divided into
separate cells. The central body extends
throughout the length of the filament,
which may be regarded as a single cell.
There is no gelatinous sheath. *Spirulina* is
very closely allied to *Arthrospira,* in which
the filaments have distinct cross walls that
are often so thin as to escape casual microscopic observation.

Nostoc

Nostoc (Fig. 8.6 and 8.7) occurs on
bare soil and in fresh water, either free-
floating or attached to submerged vegetation. Some species occur in the intercellular spaces of liverworts, the two plants
having little or no apparent effect on each
other. The cells of *Nostoc* form trichomes
which resemble the trichomes of ordinary

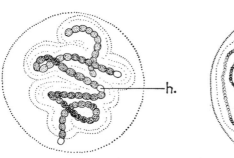
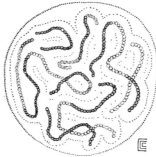

Fig. 8.6. *Nostoc,* two colonies: h., heterocyst. (Left,
×300; right, ×100.)

Fig. 8.7. *Nostoc,* section of part of a large colony. (Copyright by General Biological Supply House,
Inc., Chicago.)

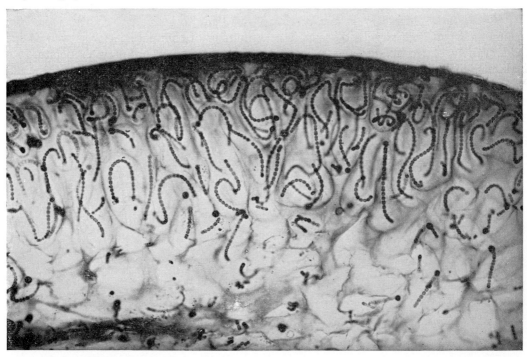

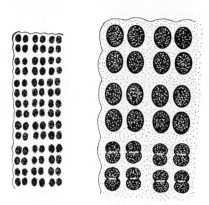
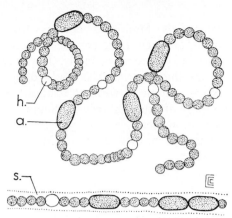

Fig. 8.8. Left: *Merismopoedia*, parts of colonies. (×300 and ×800.) Right: *Anabaena*, 2 spp. a., akinete; h., heterocyst; s., sheath. (Above, ×400; below, ×700.)

Fig. 8.9. *Stigonema*, g., gelatinous sheath; h., heterocyst. (×350.)

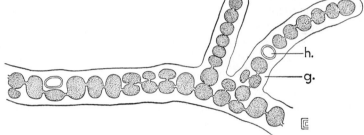

filamentous blue-green algae, except for being much contorted and twisted. These trichomes have individual sheaths and are aggregated into a rather firm, amorphous or globular colony with a common sheath. Mature colonies are readily visible to the naked eye and are often several centimeters thick. There are scattered heterocysts not much larger than ordinary vegetative cells. The trichomes often separate between a heterocyst and a vegetative cell, and thus a mature colony contains many trichomes. When the colony becomes mature many of the cells develop into akinetes.

ANABAENA

Anabaena (Fig. 8.8) occurs chiefly as free-floating colonies of filaments in lakes, ponds, and semipermanent pools. One species inhabits the aerial roots of some cycads, where it also harbors nitrogen-fixing bacteria. *Anabaena* is much like *Nostoc*, except that the gelatinous sheath is very watery, so that large colonies of definite form are not usually produced. The trichomes of *Anabaena* are sometimes contorted as in *Nostoc*.

STIGONEMA

Stigonema (Fig. 8.9) occurs on wet rocks, or less commonly on moist soil or in shallow water. It has branching filaments in which the main axis is at least partly multiseriate (i.e., more than one cell thick). The sheath surrounding the filament is firm, and colorless to tan, brown, or black. Heterocysts are often produced, akinetes more rarely. Hormogonia are produced near the ends of young branches, with or without relation to the position of the heterocysts. Some species have prominent intercellular connections suggestive of those seen in the red algae.

ECONOMIC IMPORTANCE

Except for the chemosynthetic bacteria, all organisms are directly or indirectly dependent on chlorophyll-bearing plants for their food. Animals either eat plants, or eat animals which eat plants, or eat animals which eat animals which eat plants, etc. Ultimately the plant is the source of the food. Land animals are dependent chiefly on land plants. Aquatic animals, including fish, are dependent chiefly on algae. All the classes of algae are ultimate sources of food for fish, but the blue-green algae are less important than some other groups, such as the diatoms and green algae.

The significance of blue-green algae in the fixation of nitrogen and in the deposition of carbonates and other minerals has already been noted.

If allowed to grow unchecked, algae often become so abundant in reservoirs as to give the water a bad taste. Some of the blue-green algae are particularly offensive. Most algae are much more susceptible to poisoning by copper than are human beings and most other organisms, and small quantities of copper sulfate are, therefore, often added to public water supplies during the summer.

FOSSIL FORMS

Fossils of the structurally less complex kinds of algae are often difficult to recognize clearly as such. Scratches, worm-borings, and inorganic formations resulting from chemical action have frequently been mistaken for fossil algae. Slender branching filaments which may be remains of blue-green algae are associated with the presumed bacterial remains of pre-Cambrian iron-ore deposits in Michigan and elsewhere. Blue-green algae are believed to have been involved in the formation of some pre-Cambrian limestones in Montana. Fossils which resemble *Nostoc* have been found in Cambrian rocks, and fossils which almost certainly represent blue-green algae are known from as far back as the Ordovician period. *Gloeocapsomorpha*, an Ordovician fossil named for its resemblance to *Gloeocapsa*, has definite cells aggregated into colonies held together by a matrix.

RELATIONSHIPS

The blue-green algae are undoubtedly derived from the bacteria. Both groups have a primitive type of nucleus, which is different from that of all other organisms. Neither group has been demonstrated to have typical sexual processes, although parasexual processes are known in some bacteria. Bacterial starch and cyanophycean starch, the characteristic carbohydrate reserves, are chemically similar, both resembling glycogen (animal starch). Both groups usually have the cells enclosed in a gelatinous sheath, although similar sheaths occur among some of the other algae as well. Certain blue-green algae and certain bacteria differ from all or nearly all other organisms in being able to use atmospheric nitrogen. Certain bacteria and certain blue-green algae thrive at temperatures far higher than can be withstood by cells of other organisms. Some chemosynthetic bacteria are so similar in appearance to the blue-green algae that some students have suggested that the organisms in question are more closely related to the Cyanophyceae than to the Schizomycetes. Many botanists believe that the close relationship between the bacteria and the blue-green algae should be reflected by putting the two classes together in a single division apart from all other plants, as is done in this textbook. Others, preferring to emphasize the differences between the two groups, consider the blue-green algae to make up a division Cyanophyta, containing a single class, the Cyanophyceae.

SUGGESTED READING

Tiffany, L. H., *Algae, the Grass of Many Waters*, Charles C Thomas, Springfield, Ill., 2d ed., 1958, 199 pp. A very readable popular account by a noted authority, emphasizing ecology, economic importance, and interesting and unusual algae.

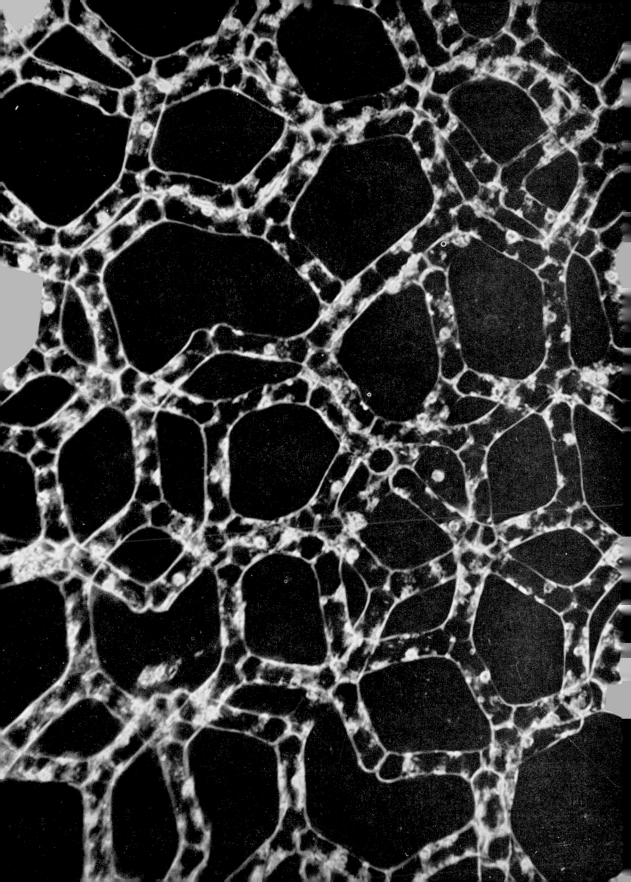

Division
Chlorophyta

GREEN ALGAE

Unicellular, multicellular, or coeno-cytic thalloid plants mostly without much differentiation of tissues, never with specialized conducting tissues; nuclei well developed, ordinarily dividing mitotically; chloroplasts (when present) grass-green, with chlorophyll a, chlorophyll b, and yellow carotenoid pigments occurring in about the same proportions as in the Embryophyta; flagella, when present, of the whiplash type and all alike; cell wall usually containing cellulose or sometimes callose, seldom absent; food reserves usually starch, sometimes partly or even wholly oils instead; reproduction sexual or asexual; gametangia (structures in which the gametes are produced) always unicellular, though sometimes surrounded by multicellular sterile jackets; zygotes physiologically independent of the parents. Two classes, the Chlorophyceae and Charophyceae.

◄ ─────────────────────────

Hydrodictyon reticulatum. (×600.) (Photomicrograph courtesy of Elsa H. J. O'Donnell.)

Chlorophyceae

HISTORY AND DEFINITION

The Chlorophyceae may be defined as Chlorophyta which do not have the gametangia surrounded by a sterile jacket of cells. The class was first recognized in approximately its present sense in 1863 by the German botanist Gottlob Ludwig Rabenhorst (1806–1881). The Chlorophyceae are by far the larger of the two classes of the Chlorophyta, and it is usually this class which is meant when "green algae" are spoken of without further qualification.

DISTRIBUTION

Green algae occur in fresh and salt water, and in many (mostly moist) sub-aerial habitats, including snowbanks. Many species are epiphytic, and a few are epizoic, being attached to such animals as turtles and sloths. A small proportion are

133

colorless, some being saprophytes, others being internal parasites of plants and animals. Only about 10 percent of the species are marine; these occur chiefly in shallow water along the seashore, often attached to rocks where they are exposed at low tide. A few species grow at depths of as much as 100 m in warm seas. The larger nonfilamentous forms are chiefly marine. Fresh-water species include both free-floating and attached forms and are often filamentous. *Chlamydomonas* often occurs in snowbanks at high altitudes or latitudes (as well as in other places) and is the commonest cause of red snow. The red color is due in this instance to one or more abundant carotenoid pigments called hematochrome, which are distributed throughout the cytoplasm and mask the green of the chloroplasts. Green algae such as *Trebouxia* are often associated with fungi to form lichens.

STRUCTURE

GENERAL MORPHOLOGY

Green algae may be unicellular, colonial, or multicellular, or they may have the

Fig. 9.1. *Chlamydomonas.* **Left: vegetative cell; cp., chloroplast; c.v, contractile vacuole; e, eyespot; f., flagellum; n., nucleus; py., pyrenoid; w., cell wall. (×1400.) Right: four cells produced by reduction division within the zygote wall.**

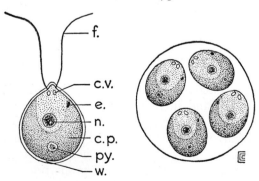

nuclei scattered in a continuous protoplast. Multicellular green algae may be filamentous, or may form thin, leaf-like thalli up to several inches across, or may have various other shapes. Frequently the cells are not all alike, but in any case the thallus lacks the complex differentiation of tissues which characterizes the vascular plants.

Unicellular flagellates such as *Chlamydomonas* (Fig. 9.1) are believed to represent one of the most primitive types of body organization among the algae. Evolutionary development of the algae from the motile unicell follows four principal lines: (1) loss of the cell wall and flagella and development of an amoeboid organization; (2) organization of the cells into a colony, without loss of motility; (3) loss of both motility and the capacity for vegetative cell division, although the capacity for nuclear division may be retained, so that a multinucleate protoplast is formed; and (4) loss of motility (except for reproductive cells), but retention of the capacity for vegetative cell division. The first of these tendencies is often associated with the loss of chlorophyll and further evolution along protozoan rather than algal lines. The second tendency has inherently limited possibilities, and the third has had only moderate success. The fourth tendency has infinite possibilities for variation. All these evolutionary tendencies occur among the Chlorophyceae.

The amoeboid tendency is only poorly developed among the Chlorophyceae. Some genera of the Volvocales lack a cell wall, and these genera with naked protoplasts include some which also lack chlorophyll. Some of the protozoan flagellates have probably been derived from such forms.

Colonies of flagellated green algae may

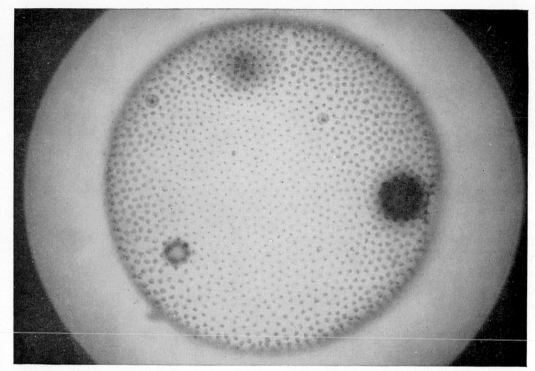

Fig. 9.2.   *Volvox* colony. (×200.) (Copyright by General Biological Supply House, Inc., Chicago.)

consist of small clusters of cells, or of a disk, but more often they form a hollow sphere (Fig. 9.2). In some cases the cells of a colony remain connected by plasmodesmata.

Plants which have the nuclei scattered in a continuous protoplast that is not divided into definite cells are said to be **coenocytic.** Coenocytic green algae have the protoplast bounded by a wall chemically and structurally similar to a cell wall. Many of the coenocytic green algae are filamentous, the filaments resembling those of multicellular green algae except for the absence of cross walls. Some other coenocytic green algae produce a complex, branching thallus several inches long. In some cases this thallus is externally differentiated into root-like, stem-like, and leaf-like parts. Such plants represent the

most complex of any coenocytic organisms.

A few green algae are transitional between the typical coenocytic and the typical multicellular types. These are filamentous plants with occasional cross walls and with a multinucleate protoplast between one cross wall and the next. The term *coenocytic* is often expanded to cover these transitional forms.

CELL WALL

The cell wall of green algae generally consists of two layers. The inner layer is firm and usually composed largely of cellulose; the outer layer is more gelatinous and consists of pectic substances. These pectic compounds are often produced continuously throughout the life of the cell, filtering out through the micelles of the

Division Chlorophyta: Green Algae   135

cellulose layer. The gelatinous sheath thus formed usually tends to dissolve into the surrounding water, the loss by solution commonly about balancing the new production. In a few green algae, such as *Oedogonium,* the outermost part of the pectic layer becomes impregnated with an insoluble substance (perhaps chitin) so that there is no loss by solution. Cells of multicellular green algae are separated by a middle lamella chemically more or less similar to the gelatinous sheath. The cellulose layer of the cell wall may itself be divided into two layers, corresponding more or less to the primary and secondary walls of the cells of higher plants. The cell walls of some green algae may also become impregnated with calcium carbonate, so much so that in some marine forms the whole plant is a greenish white.

Some of the unicellular flagellated green algae that lack a cell wall have the cell partly enclosed in a wall-like structure called a **lorica.** A lorica differs from a cell wall in that most of its surface is not in contact with the enclosed protoplast, the intervening space being filled with water or a watery gelatinous matrix, and also in that it usually does not completely enclose the cell. Often it is open at one end, through which the flagella project. Sometimes it is composed of two overlapping halves. A lorica generally contains no cellulose, and it is often impregnated with compounds of calcium and/or iron. Loricate cells are more common among the Chrysophyta than among the green algae.

Nucleus

The green algae have well-organized nuclei like those described in Chapter 3, with chromonemata, nuclear membrane, nuclear sap, and one or more nucleoli.

Nuclear division is ordinarily mitotic. The chromonemata are sometimes difficult to demonstrate between cell divisions, so that the chromosomes may seem to arise directly from the nuclear sap.

Chloroplasts and Food Reserves

Chlorophyll and the associated carotenoid pigments of green algae are normally borne in definite chloroplasts that are grass green in color. The chloroplasts may be one, two, several, or many in each cell. Their shape is usually constant in a given species or genus, but different genera show a wide variety of shapes. The single, massive, cup-shaped chloroplast seen in *Chlamydomonas* (Fig. 9.1) and many other flagellated green algae is believed to be a relatively primitive type.

Chloroplasts of the Chlorophyceae contain chlorophylls *a* and *b*, α- and β-carotene, and the xanthophylls lutein and neoxanthin. They usually also contain one or more additional carotenoids, but they have no other chlorophylls. Chlorophyll *a* is the principal chlorophyll, as in all other groups of algae and higher plants. β-carotene is usually the principal carotene, and lutein the principal xanthophyll, although some members of the order Siphonales have more α- than β-carotene, and more of several other xanthophylls than lutein. Lutein also occurs in the higher plants and in some other groups of algae.

In most green algae each chloroplast contains one or more specialized proteinaceous bodies called **pyrenoids,** on or around which starch accumulates. The actual photosynthesis evidently occurs on or in the chlorophyll-bearing part of the chloroplast, and the pyrenoid is merely a storage center. Some of the larger green algae lack pyrenoids and accumulate starch in leucoplasts, much as in the higher plants. Many green algae produce oils as well as starch, and a few produce oils *instead* of starch.

FLAGELLA

Flagella of green algae are attached at or near one end of the cell, when present, and are usually two or four in number, although uniflagellate and multiflagellate types are also known. The flagella of any one cell are alike. At the base of each flagellum, within the cell, there is a granule. The granules are connected by a transverse fiber, which is connected to a longitudinal fiber that extends nearly or quite to the nucleus. The flagella and these granules and fibers collectively constitute the **neuromotor apparatus.**

Flagellated cells of green algae usually have a small orange-red **eyespot** in the cytoplasm, typically near the base of the flagella. The eyespot is sensitive to light and probably affects the neuromotor apparatus. The eyespot is usually not found in vegetative cells of nonmotile green algae, but motile gametes and zoospores often have it. It is regarded as a modified plastid.

It has been noted on p. 83 that a bacterial flagellum usually consists of a single proteinaceous fibril. Flagella of other kinds of organisms, including green algae, are more complex, characteristically having a core of two strands surrounded by a group of nine peripheral strands (Fig. 9.3). All these strands are proteinaceous, but the nine outer strands are chemically different from the two central ones. Usually the central strands are longer than the outer strands and extend out beyond them. Flagella which are more or less round in cross section, without lateral appendages,

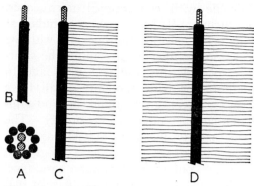

Fig. 9.3. Flagellar structure: *A,* cross section, showing two central and nine peripheral strands; *B,* whiplash type, without lateral appendages; *C,* pectinate type, with one row of lateral appendages; *D,* pinnate type, with two rows of lateral appendages.

are called the **whiplash** type. Only the whiplash type of flagellum is known in the green algae.

Flagella with slender lateral fibrils extending out from the central shaft are called the **tinsel** type. Carefully prepared and stained tinsel flagella appear to be flattened or band-shaped when studied at a level of magnification that does not distinguish the lateral fibrils from each other. Many flagellates have two dissimilar flagella, one whiplash, one tinsel.

Tinsel flagella may be further classified according to whether they have one or two rows of lateral fibrils. Those with only one row, like the teeth of a comb, are called the **pectinate** type (from Latin *pecten,* a comb). Those with two rows, one on each side, like the two rows of barbs on the shaft of a feather, are called the **pinnate** type (from Latin *pinna,* a feather). Both the pectinate and the pinnate types of flagella are probably derived (in an evolutionary sense) from the whiplash type.

The whiplash, pectinate, and pinnate flagellar types are distinguishable only with some difficulty at magnifications ob-

Division Chlorophyta: Green Algae 137

tainable with conventional microscopes. Enough flagella have now been studied at the higher magnifications possible with the electron microscope to confirm the structure of the three different types and to indicate the basic similarity of all three types in having a two-strand core and a differentiated nine-strand periphery. The flagella of organisms as different as algae, fungi, mosses, ferns, mollusks, frogs, and man all conform to this same basic type. This essential similarity of all flagella that have been carefully studied, thus far, other than those of bacteria, strongly suggests a real evolutionary relationship and a single common origin for all organisms (other than bacteria) which produce or consist of flagellated cells. Further observations with the electron microscope should materially aid in clarifying the taxonomy of the flagellates.

Vacuoles

Flagellated green algae generally have two (seldom more) small contractile vacuoles, commonly near the base of the flagella. The vacuolar contents are largely water but probably include waste materials as well. Each vacuole undergoes a forcible contraction followed by a slow distension. It is believed that the vacuolar contents are discharged from the cell and that the contractile vacuoles are excretory structures, although this interpretation is less certain than in the case of some protozoa that also have contractile vacuoles.

The nonflagellated genera of green algae usually lack contractile vacuoles and have a central vacuole similar to that described in Chapter 2. Sometimes there are several large vacuoles instead of only one, or the vacuole may be transversed by strands of cytoplasm. Some green algae,

notably some of those which are subaerial rather than aquatic, have no very evident vacuoles of any sort.

REPRODUCTION

Introduction

Some green algae are wholly asexual, some have only sexual reproduction, and others reproduce both sexually and asexually. Among the unicellular members of the group, cell division is also reproduction. Several types of spores are produced by different members of the class.

Spores

The commonest type of spore (in green algae) is the zoospore, a motile, flagellated cell which usually lacks a cell wall. The sporangium in which the zoospores are borne is usually derived from an ordinary vegetative cell; sometimes it is a specialized cell morphologically unlike other cells. The entire protoplast of the sporangium may be transformed into a single zoospore; more often the protoplast undergoes one or more mitotic divisions, leading to the formation of two to many (seldom more than 32) spores within the original cell wall.

Zoospores are commonly released through a pore which develops in the wall of the sporangium. The zoospore swims about for a period of a few minutes to 2 or 3 days, depending on the genus and species; 1 or 2 hours is a common time. It then retracts or loses its flagella and secretes a wall, becoming a vegetative cell. In multicellular or colonial types, the vegetative cell then undergoes a series of mitotic divisions to produce a new colony or organism. In many genera the zoospore settles on some solid object in the water before it changes into a vegetative cell and becomes cemented to the substrate by the pectic material of the new wall.

Zoospores are haploid or sometimes diploid. In addition to being borne in sporangia, they are sometimes formed by reduction division from a zygote, or by mitotic divisions from akinetes (see below). Zoospores of many genera of green algae are very similar to vegetative cells of *Chlamydomonas*, except for lacking a cell wall.

Another type of spore produced by many green algae is the **aplanospore**. Aplanospores are comparable to the endospores of the blue-green algae; they differ from zoospores in the absence of flagella and the presence of a definite cell wall. Like zoospores, they are borne in unicellular sporangia which may or may not resemble ordinary vegetative cells. Some aplanospores germinate also immediately, sometimes even before being liberated from the sporangium. Others undergo a period of rest before germination; when these have notably thick walls they may be designated as hypnospores. Some aplanospores have the same distinctive shape as the parent cell; these are known as autospores.

Some green algae also produce akinetes, similar to those of the blue-green algae. Akinetes may eventually develop directly into new plants; more often (in the green algae) the protoplast divides into a number of zoospores.

Sexual Cycle

The sexual cycle in green algae, as in other truly sexual organisms, involves alternating stages with n and $2n$ chromosomes. The $2n$ stage is brought about by fusion of gametic nuclei, and the n condition is restored by reduction division. In the simplest situation, as in some species of *Chlamydomonas* (a unicellular member of the Volvocales), ordinary flagellated vegetative cells act as gametes and fuse to produce a zygote. The zygote then undergoes reduction division to produce four spores which develop directly into unicellular vegetative plants (Fig. 9.1). Some other species of *Chlamydomonas* have a cycle which differs from the foregoing only in that the vegetative cells do not function directly as gametes; each vegetative cell instead gives rise by one or more mitotic divisions to 2, 4, 8, or 16 smaller daughter cells which are released from the wall of the parent cell and function as gametes.

One type of evolutionary advance from the situation in *Chlamydomonas* leads to the formation of a multicellular thallus from the zygote or from zoospores by a series of mitotic divisions. In many green algae mitotic division occurs only during the haploid stage, so that a multicellular haploid thallus may be produced, while the zygote remains the only diploid cell. In other green algae mitotic divisions may take place during both the haploid and the diploid stages of the life cycle, so that the complete sexual cycle consists of: (1) fusion of gametes to form a diploid zygote; (2) development of a diploid thallus by mitotic divisions; (3) production of haploid cells (typically zoospores) by meiosis affecting some or all the cells of the diploid thallus; (4) development of a haploid thallus from each zoospore by a series of mitotic divisions; and (5) formation of gametes within some or all of the cells of the haploid thallus.

The diploid and haploid thalli may be alike or different. When alike, they are said to be **isomorphic**; when different, they are said to be **heteromorphic**. If a single thallus produces both sperms and eggs, or isogametes which can fuse with each other to form a zygote, the alga is said to be **homothallic**. If eggs and sperms are borne on separate thalli, or if isogametes produced by one thallus cannot fuse with each other, the alga is said to be **heterothallic**.

Alternation of haploid and diploid (or *n* and *2n*) **generations**, such as in the foregoing cycle, is characteristic of the higher plants (subkingdom Embryophyta) as well as of many thallophytes. Because the reproductive body of the haploid (or *n* chromosome) generation is the gamete, it is customary to call this generation the **gametophyte**. Because the reproductive body of the diploid (or *2n* chromosome) generation is the spore, it is customary to call this generation the **sporophyte**. It should be noted that the spore itself, being the product of reduction division, is typically haploid and therefore represents the first step in the gametophyte generation.

The green algae show all conditions from typical isogamy (see Chapter 4) to pronounced heterogamy. It is sometimes useful to divide the heterogamous condition into **anisogamy** and **oögamy**. In anisogamy the two gametes which fuse are both motile but differ in size. In oögamy one gamete (the sperm) is small and motile, whereas the other (the egg) is larger and nonmotile. Isogamous and anisogamous green algae usually have gametangia that are morphologically undifferentiated from vegetative cells, and syngamy (fusion of gametes) occurs in the water, external to the parent plants. Oögamous green algae generally have gametangia that are morphologically different from each other and from vegetative cells, and syngamy occurs in the female gametangium. A male gametangium is called an **antheridium**, regardless of whether it is unicellular (as among the algae) or multicellular (as among the embryophytes). A female gametangium is called an **oögonium** when it is unicellular (as among the algae) and an **archegonium** when it is multicellular (as among the embryophytes).

Zygotes of many green algae develop a thick wall and go into a resting stage which may last from a few days to several months, depending on the genus or species. Such thick-walled zygotes are called **zygospores**. Zygospores ordinarily undergo reduction division immediately on germination, or even before, so that the zygospore itself is the only diploid cell in the life cycle. Several groups of green algae, in contrast, have thin-walled zygotes which germinate within a day or two after being formed; these develop mitotically into diploid thalli which eventually produce zoospores or gametes as a result of reduction division. Most of the green algae which produce zygospores occur in fresh water, and most of the green algae in which the zygote does not go into a pronounced resting stage are marine.

We have noted that in addition to the sexual cycle the green algae may produce zoospores which are not a product of reduction division and not a part of the sexual cycle. Many other kinds of plants which show a normal sexual cycle with alternation of gametophytic and sporophytic generations also have means to reproduce one or the other of these generations asexually.

CLASSIFICATION

There are about 6500 species of Chlorophyceae. These may be grouped into 12 orders, as indicated in the key given in the appendix.

REPRESENTATIVE GENERA

CHLAMYDOMONAS

Chlamydomonas (Fig. 9.1) is a large genus of unicellular flagellates occurring in standing fresh water, on damp soil, and on persistent snowbanks. Waters rich in ammonium compounds, such as barnyard pools, provide an especially favorable habitat for some species. The cells are spherical to subcylindric or pear-shaped and have a definite cellulose wall that in some species is enclosed by a gelatinous pectic sheath. There are two flagella and a well-developed eyespot. Most species have a pair of contractile vacuoles near the base of the flagella. There is no central vacuole, and the nucleus is often more or less central in position. Most species have a single cup-shaped chloroplast, which is often so large that it occupies most of the protoplast, usually at the opposite end from the flagella. Usually there is only one pyrenoid.

Asexual reproduction occurs by one or a series of mitotic divisions of the protoplast to form 2, 4, 8, or 16 (typically 4) daughter protoplasts within the wall of the parent cell. After the daughter protoplasts have each developed flagella and a wall, the wall of the parent cell ruptures or softens and the daughter cells are released. These daughter cells grow directly into mature vegetative cells; they have sometimes been called zoospores, but they differ from ordinary zoospores in having a cell wall.

When the plant grows on damp soil instead of in water, the daughter protoplasts sometimes remain in the gelatinous matrix formed by dissolution of the old cell wall and reproduce for generation after generation without forming flagella. Amorphous colonies of hundreds or thousands of cells in a common gelatinous matrix may be formed in this fashion, but as soon as the colony is flooded with water the individual cells develop flagella and are released from the matrix. These temporary colonies resemble the normal colonies of a related genus, *Palmella*, which produce *Chlamydomonas*-like flagellated cells only as reproductive bodies. Many different kinds of algal flagellates produce *Palmella*-like temporary colonies of nonmotile cells under certain conditions.

Most species of *Chlamydomonas* are isogamous, although the gametes are often chemically differentiated. The chemicals which result in the mutual attraction of gametes have been studied, but they have not yet been fully analyzed. Ordinary vegetative cells of many species can function as gametes under proper conditions. The protoplasts of the fusing cells may or may not escape from the enclosing wall before fusion.

The zygote has four flagella, and remains motile for several hours, or in some species for as much as two weeks, before losing the flagella and developing a thick wall. Often the zygote continues to manufacture food and to grow during the "resting" stage. In most species the starch reserves of the zygote are eventually changed into oils, and considerable quantities of a diffuse red carotenoid pigment (hematochrome) are produced.

Eventually the protoplast of the zygote undergoes reduction division, producing four haploid protoplasts within the zygote wall. Usually these immediate products of reduction division acquire walls and are released by rupture of the zygote wall, developing flagella immediately after liberation. Each then matures directly into a vegetative cell. Sometimes the immediate products of reduction division undergo further mitotic divisions before liberation, so that 8, 16, or 32 "zoospores" are produced within the wall of the zygote.

VOLVOX

Volvox (see Figs. 9.2, 9.4), is a colonial flagellate that occurs in temporary and permanent pools of fresh water. The colonies are spherical to ovoid, hollow, only one cell thick, and composed of 500 to 60,000 cells. The individual cells are very similar to cells of *Chlamydomonas*. In at least some species the protoplasts of the cells are connected by well-developed cytoplasmic strands, and the colony might better be considered a multicellular organism. All the cells of a young colony are alike. As the colony matures, some of the cells lose their flagella and increase to as much as ten times the diameter of ordinary cells. These enlarged cells, often

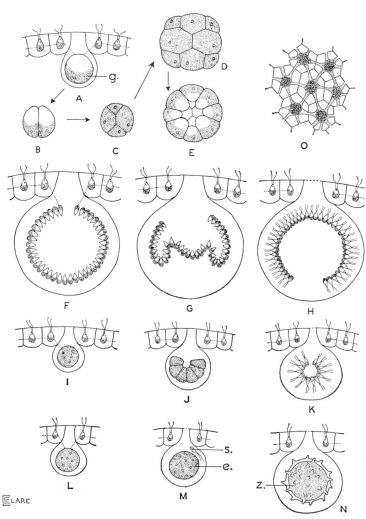

Fig. 9.4. *Volvox. A–H*, stages in the asexual formation of a new colony; *I–K*, stages in the development of sperms; *L–N*, stages in the development of the egg and formation of the zygote; *O*, detail of tangential section of colony, showing prominent cytoplasmic connections between adjacent cells; e., egg; g., gonidium; s., sperm; z., zygote.

called **gonidia,** are reproductive cells. Each gonidium becomes depressed below the surface of the colony and then develops along sexual or asexual lines, according to the season.

During the spring and most of the summer reproduction is asexual. The gonidium undergoes a series of mitotic divisions, producing a pouch-shaped cluster of cells that forms an invagination in the surface of the parent colony. While still enclosed within the parent colony, and within the gelatinous sack that originally contained the gonidium, the young colony turns inside out by progressive invagination from the interior end. Shortly after this inversion the individual cells develop flagella. Eventually the new colony escapes through the opening at the surface of the parent colony. Usually several asexual generations occur during a single season.

Late in the season asexual reproduction gives way to sexual reproduction. Sexual reproduction is oögamous and is homothallic or heterothallic according to the species. Some gonidia develop directly into eggs. Others produce clusters of biflagellate sperms. The cluster of sperms escapes through a pore at the surface of the parent colony and is attracted to the egg by chemical stimuli. When the sperm cluster nears an egg the sperms separate. Fertilization occurs while the egg is still retained just beneath the surface of the parent colony.

The fertilized egg develops a thick wall and goes into a resting state. The resting zygote is colored orange-red by the hematochrome pigment which it develops. The zygotes are liberated by death and decay of the parent colony and usually do not germinate until the following spring. The first division of the zygote is meiotic. In some species the four cells produced in meiosis become the first four cells of a new colony. In others a single haploid zoospore is formed, and presumably three of the nuclei formed in meiosis degenerate. The zoospore then develops into a new colony by a series of mitotic divisions.

ULOTHRIX

Ulothrix (Fig. 9.5) is a genus of green algae occurring in fresh water, often in flowing streams. The cells are cylindrical, longer or shorter than thick, and are united end to end in uniseriate, unbranched filaments of indefinite length. In some species the filament has a gelatinous sheath; in others it does not. All cells are alike except that the basal one is slightly modified into a holdfast. Each cell has a large central vacuole and a single large, thin chloroplast that forms a broad band partly or wholly encircling the protoplast. The chloroplast has one or several pyrenoids.

Asexual reproduction usually occurs by the formation of quadriflagellate zoospores. The whole protoplast of a cell may be changed into a zoospore, but more often 2 to 32 zoospores are formed by mitotic divisions of a protoplast within the original cell wall. The zoospores usually escape through a pore which develops in the cell wall. After swimming about for a period of several hours to several days, the zoospore settles down, loses its flagella, and becomes a holdfast cell from which a new filament is produced by a series of mitotic divisions. Some species produce two different kinds of zoospores that differ from each other in size, position of the eyespot, and duration of the free-swimming stage.

Asexual reproduction may also occur by the formation of aplanospores. The whole protoplast of a cell may round up

Division Chlorophyta: Green Algae   143

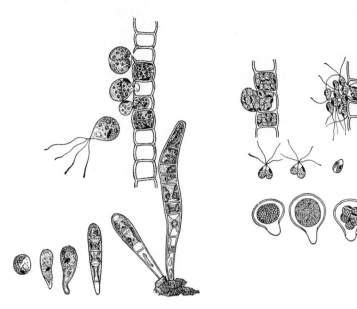

Fig. 9.5. *Ulothrix.* Top left: formation of zoospores; bottom left: germination of zoospore to form a new filament; top right: formation and escape of gametes; middle line, right: conjugation of gametes; bottom right: germination of zygotes with formation of zoospores. (From W. H. Brown, *The Plant Kingdom*, 1935; courtesy of Ginn & Company, Boston.)

and secrete a new wall, or zoospores which fail to be liberated from the parent cell may lose their flagella and secrete a wall. Each aplanospore gives rise to a new filament by a series of mitotic divisions, sometimes germinating even before being liberated from the parent cell.

Sexual reproduction is isogamous. The gametes are biflagellate and have an eyespot. *Ulothrix* is heterothallic; i.e., gametes produced by a single filament do not fuse with each other. Any two gametes which fuse with each other are morphologically alike but chemically different. The zygote soon loses its flagella, secretes a thick wall, and goes into a "resting" stage during

which it continues for some time to carry on photosynthesis and accumulate food reserves. The zygote is the only diploid cell in the life cycle, its first nuclear division being meiotic. The zygote gives rise to 4 to 16 zoospores or aplanospores, each of which develops into a new filament.

PLEUROCOCCUS

Pleurococcus (Fig. 9.6) is one of the commonest genera of green algae. It forms a thin green coating on tree trunks, stone walls, flower pots, etc., usually in shaded or protected sites, and it also occurs in fresh water. It has been shown to be able

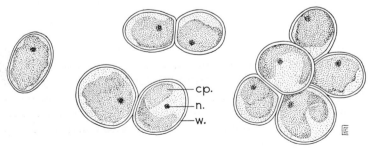

cp.
n.
w.

Fig. 9.6. *Pleurococcus:* cp., chloroplast; n., nucleus; w., cell wall. (×1700.)

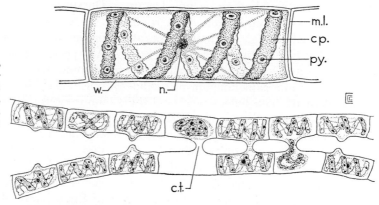

Fig. 9.7. *Spirogyra.* Top, vegetative cell: cp., chloroplast; m.l., middle lamella; n., nucleus; py., pyrenoid; w., cell wall. (×400.) Bottom, two filaments conjugating: c.t., conjugation tube.

to absorb water from moist air. The side of the tree that is the most protected from evaporation usually has the thickest coating of *Pleurococcus.*

Pleurococcus is nonmotile and typically unicellular. There is a well-developed cellulose wall and no gelatinous sheath. Solitary cells are spherical to ellipsoid. Sometimes the cells do not separate after division, and small colonies are formed. When growing in water, *Pleurococcus* sometimes forms irregularly branched filaments of as many as 50 or more cells. Each cell has a single large, thin chloroplast near the wall, usually without pyrenoids. There is no evident vacuole. Reproduction is exclusively by cell division. *Pleurococcus* is usually considered to be a reduced and modified derivative of *Ulothrix*-like ancestors.

Pleurococcus has often been known under the name *Protococcus,* but it has been shown that the latter name does not properly apply.

SPIROGYRA

Spirogyra (Figs. 9.7, 9.8) is a common green alga in ponds and streams. The cells are cylindrical, one to several times as long as thick, and are united end to end

in uniseriate, unbranched filaments of indefinite length. Usually the cells are all alike, but sometimes some of them develop slender projections which help to anchor the filament to the substrate in running water. The cell wall consists of two layers of cellulose and an outer layer of pectose; the pectose also forms the middle lamella between adjacent cells. Each cell has a large central vacuole, and one or two (seldom several) ribbon-shaped spiral chloroplasts that extend the whole length of the cell. The chloroplast has several pyrenoids. The nucleus, with a sheath of cytoplasm, is often suspended in the central vacuole by cytoplasmic strands extending from near the pyrenoids.

Asexual reproduction sometimes occurs by fragmentation of the filaments into single cells or few-celled bits. In at least some cases, the fragmentation is preceded by conversion of the middle lamella from pectose to soluble pectin. Spores are seldom formed. These are always nonmotile and are derived from the whole protoplast of a cell without division.

Sexual reproduction is isogamous, in the sense that the gametes are morphologically alike, although their behavior is different. Conjugation usually involves two different filaments, which come to lie side by side even though there is no obvious means of locomotion. Usually all cells are potentially gametangia, although not all may so develop. Each gametangium generally forms a bulge in the wall opposite a similar bulge in a gametangium of the adjacent filament. The bulges meet and the wall between them disappears, so that there is a **conjugation tube** leading from one cell to the other. The protoplast of each cell then shrinks by expulsion of water and becomes a nonflagellated gamete. One of these gametes flows through the tube in an amoeboid manner, and fusion follows. In some species of the related genus *Zygnema*, both gametes are motile and syngamy occurs in the conjugation tube.

In both *Spirogyra* and *Zygnema*, the zygote develops a thick wall and goes into a resting stage which commonly lasts through the winter. Chlorophyll disappears during the resting stage, and most of the starch is changed into oil. Germination of the zygote is preceded by reduction division. Three of the four haploid nuclei formed in meiosis degenerate, so that each filament is derived from a single haploid cell.

DESMIDS

Algae belonging to the family Desmidiaceae are called desmids (Fig. 9.9). All species occur in fresh water, especially in somewhat acid water. Most desmids are unicellular, but some form filaments or amorphous colonies. Each cell generally has a median constriction, dividing it into two halves called **semicells** that are connected by an **isthmus.** The semicells have various distinctive shapes, according to the genus and species. The cell wall consists of three layers, the inner of cellulose, the middle of cellulose that is impregnated with pectic compounds and often also with iron salts, the outer of a gelatinous pectose sheath. The two inner layers have pores that are commonly arranged in a pattern. The pores are filled with pectic gelatinous materials, and changes in the volume of these materials are related in some way to a jerky movement of the cells. The nucleus lies at the isthmus of the cell. Cytokinesis results in separation of the semicells, each of which later develops a duplicate half. Spores are seldom formed and are always nonmotile.

Sexual reproduction in desmids is

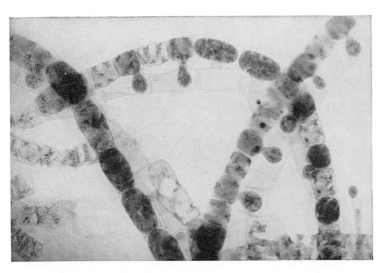

Fig. 9.8. *Spirogyra,* conjugating (Copyright by General Biological Supply House, Inc., Chicago.)

isogamous, with amoeboid, nonflagellated gametes. Typically two cells come to lie in a common gelatinous envelope, each cell breaks open at the isthmus, and the two protoplasts emerge into the envelope and fuse. Some filamentous species develop a conjugation tube like that of *Spirogyra*. The zygote develops a thick wall and goes into a resting state. The first division of the zygote is meiotic; often three of the four nuclei produced in meiosis degenerate.

OEDOGONIUM

Oedogonium (Fig. 9.10) occurs in small permanent ponds and slow streams, often as an epiphyte on larger aquatic plants. The cells are cylindric and are joined end to end in uniseriate, unbranched filaments of indefinite length. The cell wall consists of three layers, the inner of cellulose, the middle of pectose, and the outer chiefly of chitin or a chitin-like substance. The basal cell is differen-

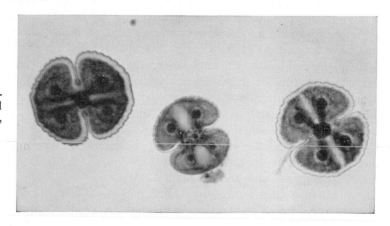

Fig. 9.9. *Cosmarium*, a desmid. (Copyright by General Biological Supply House, Inc., Chicago.)

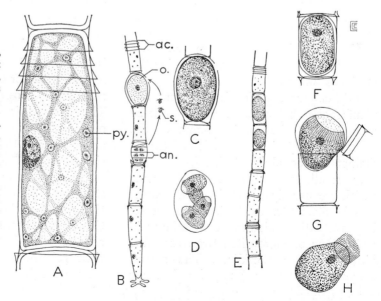

Fig. 9.10. *Oedogonium. A,* vegetative cell of filament (×500); *B,* part of filament, with reproductive structures (×85); *C,* oögonium, with included zygote (oöspore) (×170); *D,* zygote germinating to produce four zoospores (×170); *E,* part of filament, with zoosporangia (×85); *F,* zoosporangium; *G,* zoospore escaping from zoosporangium; *H,* zoospore; a.c., apical cap; an., antheridium; o., oögonium, with egg included; py., pyrenoid; s., sperm.

tiated into a holdfast, and the gametangia are visibly different from vegetative cells. Each vegetative cell has a large central vacuole and a single reticulate chloroplast which extends the whole length and circumference of the cell. The chloroplast has many pyrenoids. Due to a complex process which accompanies mitosis, many cells of a filament have one or more narrow concentric girdles of hemicellulose at one end, forming a characteristic **apical cap.**

Asexual reproduction occurs by the formation of zoospores, aplanospores, or akinetes. Zoospores are borne only in cells that have an apical cap. The entire protoplast of the cell becomes a single zoospore that bears a ring of rather short flagella near one end and seldom has an eyespot. The cell wall breaks open about at the junction of the apical cap with the rest of the wall, liberating the zoospore. After an hour or so, the zoospore settles down, retracts its flagella, and secretes a wall. A new filament is then formed by a series of mitotic divisions. The basal cell in the first division becomes modified into a holdfast and does not divide again. Any of the other cells of the filament may divide. The basal cell further differs from the other cells of the filament in not developing the chitinous outer wall.

Sexual reproduction is oögamous, the plants being heterothallic or homothallic according to the species. Some of the heterothallic species have male and female filaments of equal size. Other species have very small, few-celled, male filaments which are usually epiphytic on the larger female filaments. Antheridia are shorter than vegetative cells and are often borne in series. One or more often two sperms are borne in an antheridium. The sperms somewhat resemble zoospores but are smaller and have fewer and often longer flagella—these still borne in a ring near one end. Oögonia are obviously swollen and larger than vegetative cells. Each oögonium contains a single large egg with abundant food reserves and no large vacuole. The sperm is attracted to the egg by a chemical stimulus and enters the oögonium through a pore near one end.

The fertilized egg develops into a thick-walled zygote which is eventually liberated by decay of the oögonial wall. The zygote often remains in a resting condition for a year or more. Four zoospores are formed when the zygote germinates. Germination is preceded by reduction division, and the zygote is the only diploid cell in the life cycle. Each zoospore gives rise to a new filament, as previously described.

Ulva

Ulva (Figs. 9.11, 9.12), the sea lettuce, is a common alga along ocean shores between high and low tide. The thallus consists of a holdfast and a blade. Plants are often broken loose by the tide, and may be washed up on the shore. The blade is an irregular sheet two cells thick and several inches or even a foot or more long, superficially suggestive of a lettuce leaf. The holdfast is a cluster of **rhizoids** at one end of the blade. The rhizoids are filaments that are divided by occasional cross walls into multinucleate segments. (The term *rhizoid* is applied to any structure which resembles a root in position and function but lacks the complex tissues of the roots of higher plants.) The cells of a blade are all about alike, and their gelatinous sheaths are confluent to form a tough gelatinous matrix. Each cell has a single large, often cup-shaped chloroplast with a single pyrenoid. There is no large vacuole.

The sexual cycle includes an alternation of similar diploid (sporophytic) and haploid (gametophytic) generations. Many of the cells near the margin of a haploid thallus become gametangia in which 32 or 64 biflagellated gametes are produced by a series of mitotic divisions. The gametes are liberated through a terminal pore in a nipple-like protrusion that develops on the gametangium at the surface of the thallus. Syngamy occurs in the water. Most species are isogamous, but a few are anisogamous. The species which

have been investigated are all heterothallic; gametes produced on one thallus do not fuse with each other.

The zygote formed by fusion of biflagellate gametes has four flagella. It soon settles down, loses its flagella, and secretes a wall. It germinates within a day or so thereafter and eventually produces a diploid thallus by a series of mitotic divisions. One of the two cells formed in the first division develops into a rhizoid; the other eventually develops into the blade. At an early stage in its development the blade resembles an ordinary filamentous green alga.

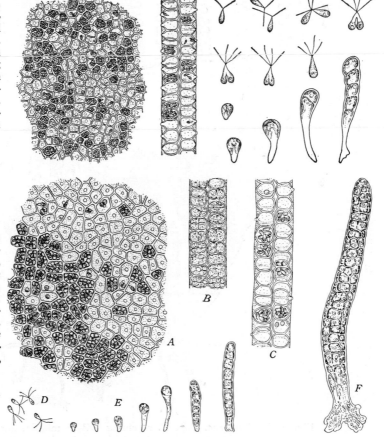

Fig. 9.11. *Ulva.* Left, surface view of part of haploid thallus, showing gametangia. Center, cross section through haploid thallus, showing gametangia. Right, stages in conjugation, and germination of the zygote. (From W. H. Brown, *The Plant Kingdom,* 1935; courtesy of Ginn & Company, Boston.)

Fig. 9.12. *Ulva.* A, surface view of part of diploid thallus, showing sporangia; B, C, sections through diploid thallus, showing sporangia; D, zoospores; E, F, germination of zoospores and development of new haploid thallus. (From W. H. Brown, *The Plant Kingdom,* 1935; courtesy of Ginn & Company, Boston.)

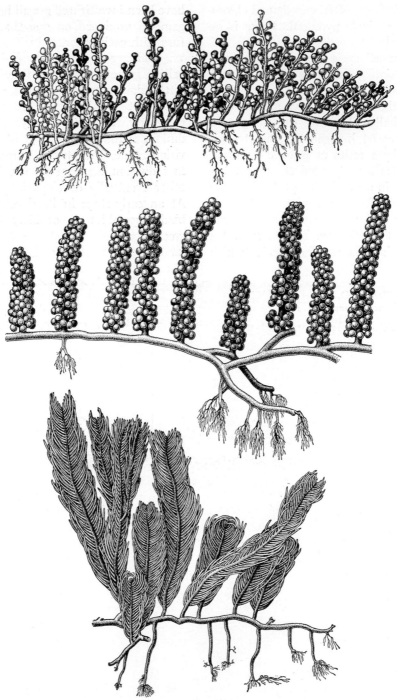

Fig. 9.13. *Caulerpa*. Top, *C. racemosa* (×½); middle, another form of *C. racemosa* (×1); bottom, *C. sertularioides* (×1). (From W. H. Brown, *The Plant Kingdom*, 1935; courtesy of Ginn & Company, Boston.)

The mature diploid thallus is similar to the mature haploid thallus. Many of the cells near the margin of the diploid thallus become sporangia which resemble the gametangia of the haploid thallus. The first division of the protoplast of the developing sporangium is meiotic; 32 or 64 quadriflagellate haploid zoospores are produced by a series of subsequent mitotic divisions. Each zoospore develops into a haploid thallus in the same way that a zygote develops into a diploid thallus.

In some species a gamete which fails to fuse may function as a zoospore and develop into a haploid thallus. Otherwise, accidental fragmentation is the only means of asexual reproduction.

CAULERPA

Caulerpa (Fig. 9.13) is a coenocytic genus of green algae occurring in warm seas, sometimes at depths of as much as 75 m. The thallus is commonly several inches or more in length and is divided into parts which superficially resemble roots, stems, and leaves. The protoplast is continuous, with many scattered nuclei and no division into separate cells. The nuclei are diploid. There are many discoid chloroplasts, without pyrenoids. Vegetative reproduction occurs by abscission of fragments of the thallus.

Sexual reproduction is isogamous, with biflagellate gametes that have a well-developed eyespot and a single chloroplast. Most species are heterothallic. Formation of gametes is preceded by reduction division in the nuclei of a small part of the protoplast, which may be in either the stem-like or the leaf-like part of the thallus. The quadriflagellate zygote soon loses its flagella, secretes a wall, and then gradu-

Fig. 9.14. *Acetabularia crenulata*, natural size, near Bermuda. (New York Botanical Garden photo.)

ally develops into a mature diploid thallus with scattered nuclei.

ACETABULARIA

Acetabularia (Fig. 9.14), the mermaid's wineglass, is another coenocytic genus of green algae, also occurring in warm seas. The mature thallus is 2–10 cm tall, depending on the species. It consists of a system of rhizoids, one or more erect stalks, and usually a single whorl of branches at the top, these forming a cap up to about 1 cm wide. The original zygotic nucleus enlarges to about 20 times its diameter but does not divide until the thallus is nearly mature. It then divides amitotically (according to report) into a number of nuclei which may undergo subsequent mitotic divisions. The whole protoplast is continuous, and many of the nuclei migrate into the apical whorl of branches. The part of the protoplast in each branch then differentiates into uninucleate segments which secrete individual walls. Each such cyst becomes a gametangium, in which numerous biflagellate isogametes are eventually produced after a series of nuclear divisions. The last nuclear division before differentiation of the gametes is meiotic.

Thalli of *Acetabularia* and many of its relatives become strongly encrusted with lime and contribute to the formation of marine limestone deposits.

FOSSIL FORMS

Fossils which probably represent some of the larger green algae are known from as far back as the Cambrian period. Forms which are clearly identifiable with the order Dasycladales (to which *Acetabularia* belongs) are abundantly represented in calcareous deposits of most of the geologic periods from the Ordovician to the present. *Rhabdoporella*, a small, slender, unbranched form from Ordovician deposits, may be near the ancestral prototype of the order.

ECONOMIC IMPORTANCE

Like the blue-green algae, the green algae are important as an ultimate source of food for aquatic animals (especially in fresh water), in the formation of limestone deposits, and as contaminants which give a bad flavor to water supplies. Some of the green algae are involved in the formation of coral reefs, but the coralline red algae are more important in this regard. The waterbloom which sometimes forms on the surface of reservoirs, lakes, and ponds in the summer is composed largely of planktonic green and blue-green

algae. Green algae are also important inhabitants of oxidation ponds in sewage-treatment plants, providing through photosynthesis the oxygen necessary for rapid decomposition of the sewage by bacteria.

RELATIONSHIPS

The Chlorophyceae are thought to be derived eventually from the photosynthetic bacteria, as are also the Cyanophyceae. Possibly a single group of photosynthetic bacteria developed the capacity to use water as a source of hydrogen and release free oxygen in photosynthesis, and the Chlorophyceae and Cyanophyceae diverged from this proto-algal stock which contained chlorophyll *a* as the principal chlorophyll and β-carotene as the principal carotene. Probably all the other groups of algae except the Rhodophyta and Cyanophyceae are derived eventually from the Chlorophyceae, as is also the whole subkingdom Embryophyta. The Chlorophyceae also appear to be directly ancestral to some of the Protozoa, and eventually so to all of them.

Unicellular flagellates such as *Chlamydomonas* have been regarded as among the most primitive members of the Chlorophyceae, perhaps not much different from the ancestral prototype of the class.

Charophyceae

The Charophyceae, or stoneworts, may be defined as Chlorophyta in which the gametangia are surrounded by sterile jackets. The thallus is multicellular, consisting of a system of rhizoids and an erect axis, commonly several inches long, with regularly arranged whorls of short branches. A single much-enlarged cell extends from

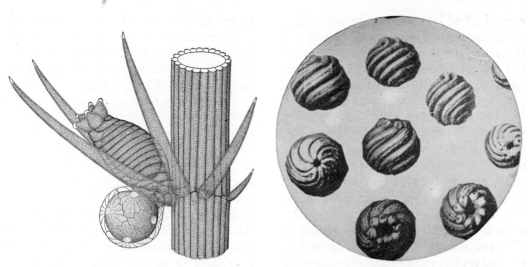

Fig. 9.15. *Chara.* Left, branch showing a large ellipsoid oögonium and below this a rounded anther-idial cluster. (×35.) (From W. H. Brown, *The Plant Kingdom,* 1935; courtesy of Ginn & Company, Boston.) Right, Paleozoic fossil charoids (×15.) (Courtesy of R. E. Peck.)

Fig. 9.16. *Chara.* Left, whole plants, about twice natural size. Right, a single branch with an oögonium and an antheridial cluster. (×30.) (Copyright by General Biological Supply House, Inc., Chicago.)

one whorl of branches to the next. Sometimes the central axis consists merely of a succession of such cells; in other cases the central cell of the axis is surrounded by a single layer of smaller cells. The gametangial jackets are one cell thick.

Cells of Charophyceae have cellulose walls which often become impregnated with lime. The cells near the tips of the main "stem" and branches are uninucleate and without conspicuous vacuoles. These cells, and particularly the apical cell of the main axis, undergo repeated mitotic divisions. Cells of the mature region are relatively large, have a well-developed central vacuole, and often have several irregular nuclei which have been formed by amitotic division of the original nucleus of the cell. There are numerous small chloroplasts. Food reserves are starch.

Sexual reproduction is oögamous. The gametangia (Fig. 9.15) are usually borne on the branches of the thallus, the oögonia and the antheridial clusters often being adjacent. Each oögonium contains a single large egg and is surrounded by a single layer of elongate, spirally wound cells. The cells of the oögonial sheath separate from each other near the tip of the oögonium to form five small slits which allow access of the sperms to the oögonium. The antheridia are arranged in clusters of complex structure; each cluster is surrounded by a sheath of eight sterile cells. Each antheridium produces a single elongate, biflagellate sperm. (Some botanists prefer to call each antheridial cluster an antheridium, which they compare to the multicellular antheridia of higher plants.) The zygote secretes a thick wall and undergoes a resting period of several weeks. The first division of the zygote is meiotic, and

three of the nuclei soon degenerate. Neither zoospores nor any other sort of spore is produced by Charophyceae. Vegetative reproduction sometimes occurs by the formation of special buds.

Fossil Charophyceae, readily recognizable by the characteristic structure of the oögonial sheath, are known from as far back as the Devonian period. All members of the class, including the fossils, are placed in a single order, the Charales. The two most common genera are *Chara* (Fig. 9.16) and *Nitella*. In *Nitella* the central axis of the thallus is only one cell thick; in *Chara* the axial cell is usually surrounded by a layer of smaller cells. *Chara* is one of the most prominent marl-forming algae. It sometimes becomes a serious weed in fish hatcheries. The class otherwise has little economic significance beyond providing a little food for aquatic animals.

Stoneworts occur in fresh (especially calcareous) or brackish quiet waters, submerged and attached to the bottom. Superficially they more nearly resemble higher plants than the familiar kinds of fresh-water green algae. Their relationship is clearly with the Chlorophyceae, of which they are an isolated, highly modified offshoot. Their distinctness from other green algae has long been recognized, and some botanists would even establish a separate division, the Charophyta, for them.

SUGGESTED READING

Smith, G. M., *Fresh-Water Algae of the United States*, 2d ed., McGraw-Hill, New York, 1950, 719 pp. A taxonomic treatment, with many illustrations. The green algae take up about half the book.

CHAPTER 10

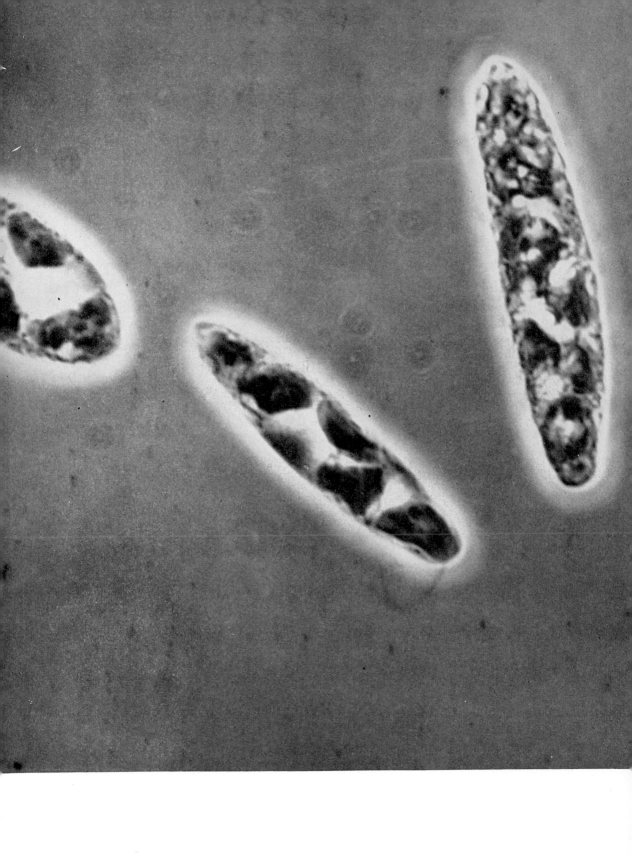

Division
Euglenophyta

*Mostly unicellular flagellates with a gullet and without a wall, or seldom colonial, nonmotile, and with a noncellulose wall, but still with a gullet; flagella one or two, seldom more, **equal** or more often unequal, pectinate; nuclei well developed, dividing mitotically; chloroplasts, when present, grass-green, with chlorophylls a and b, β-carotene, and several xanthophylls; food reserves mostly paramylum, a starch-like carbohydrate; largely or wholly asexual; reproducing by cell division. A single class, the Euglenophyceae.*

◄

Euglena gracilis. (×2500.) (Photomicrograph courtesy of Elsa H. J. O'Donnell.)

HISTORY AND CHARACTERISTICS

The euglenoids were first recognized as a group by Ehrenberg in 1838. Nearly all of the 400 to 500 species are unicellular flagellates which lack a cell wall. The outer part of the protoplast is differentiated into a fairly firm, but usually flexible, often striated layer called the **pellicle** or **periplast**. A few genera have a firm gelatinous lorica, which contains no trace of cellulose. The cells characteristically have a distinct **gullet** formed by invagination of the cell tip. The opening of the gullet is called the **cytostome**; the enlarged cavity at its base is called the **reservoir;** and the narrow passage connecting the reservoir to the cytostome is called the **cytopharynx.** Most often there are only one or two flagella, but sometimes there are three or more. The flagella are sometimes equal, more often unequal, and all are of the pectinate type. They are attached near the base of the reservoir and extend out through the cytopharynx and cytostome. Near the base of the gullet

157

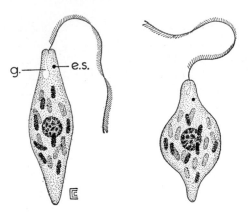
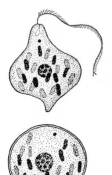

Fig. 10.1. *Euglena.* Varying shapes assumed by a single cell; e.s., eyespot; g., gullet. The cell at the lower right is in a resting stage, with a definite wall and without a flagellum. (×500.)

there are one or more contractile vacuoles which eventually discharge their contents into the reservoir and disappear. New contractile vacuoles are formed by fusion of smaller vacuoles. The cell may or may not have an evident eyespot.

Chloroplasts are present or absent and may or may not have pyrenoids. They have the same chlorophylls as the Chlorophyceae (*a* and *b*), plus β-carotene, and several unidentified xanthophylls. Nutrition varies from autotrophic to saprophytic or holozoic. Some of the chlorophyllous forms are apparently wholly autotrophic, but others require vitamin B_{12} or an organic source of nitrogen. The chlorophyllous species, or most of them, can live saprophytically when deprived of light, but those which have been carefully studied apparently do not usually ingest significant quantities of food through the gullet. Some forms are facultatively saprophytic or holozoic, ingesting small food particles through the gullet as well as absorbing dissolved foods. A few members of the group are internal parasites of amphibia and invertebrates. Food reserves are largely **paramylum**, an insoluble carbohydrate which can be hydrolyzed to glucose, but which does not respond to the usual tests (such as the iodine test) for starch.

Reproduction is ordinarily by cell division, which is mitotic. Reports of sexual reproduction have not convinced most algologists. Cells of some genera may go into a resting stage and secrete a wall consisting of an unidentified carbohydrate.

REPRESENTATIVE GENERA

EUGLENA

The most characteristic genus of the class is *Euglena* (Figs. 10.1, 10.2), which occurs in both fresh and salt water (including Great Salt Lake), but is commonest in "fresh" water that is rich in organic matter, such as in barnyard pools. The cells have a flexible pellicle and change shape freely while they swim, varying from slenderly cigar-shaped to pear-shaped. There are usually numerous discoid to band-shaped chloroplasts. There is a single long flagellum and usually an eyespot. Thick-walled resting cells are frequently produced.

COLACIUM

Nearly all members of the Euglenophyceae are placed in the order Euglenales, typified by *Euglena*. The genus *Colacium* (Fig. 10.3), consisting of two species, is so

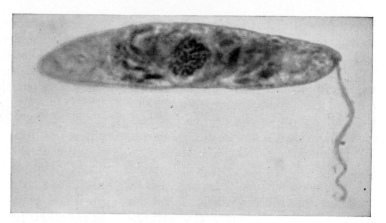

Fig. 10.2. *Euglena.* (× about 1000.) (Copyright by General Biological Supply House, Inc., Chicago.)

different from the other genera that it is placed in a distinct, unifamilial order, the Colaciales. The cells of *Colacium* have a gullet, but they are nonmotile and are enclosed by a firm, gelatinous wall. One end of the wall is prolonged into a stalk by which the cell is attached to the body of one or another kind of zooplankton. Often the cells occur in colonies which have a common stalk. The cells have well-developed chloroplasts and do not parasitize the host. The gullet is not functional. Vegetative cells lack flagella, but the protoplast

of a cell may escape from the wall as a uniflagellate, euglenoid zoospore which soon settles down and secretes a new gelatinous wall.

RELATIONSHIPS

The Euglenophyceae are interesting because they form a well-defined, coherent group poised on the border between the plant and animal kingdoms. *Colacium* is surely a plant; *Euglena* could with some

Fig. 10.3. Left: *Colacium;* e.s., eyespot; g., gullet. (×1200.) Right: *Euglena*, anterior end in section, showing flagellum, gullet, and eyespot. (*Euglena*, From W. H. Brown, *The Plant Kingdom*, 1935; courtesy of Ginn & Company, Boston.)

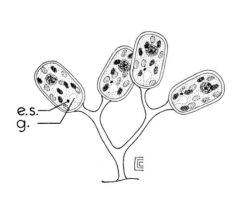

e.s.
g.

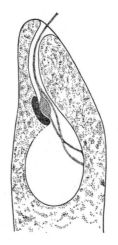

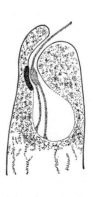

justice be regarded as either a plant or an animal, depending on the point of view; and the holozoic genera are surely animals.

The euglenoids have variously been treated as an order of the Protozoa, as an order of the Chlorophyceae, as a class of the Chlorophyta, or as a division Euglenophyta. Divisional status for the group was first proposed by Pascher in 1931. Any relationship with the Chlorophyceae is probably through some unicellular flagellates of the latter class which resemble *Chlamydomonas* except in lacking a cell wall, although probably no living member of the Chlorophyceae is directly ancestral to the euglenophytes. The principal changes necessary to develop euglenoids from such forms would be the formation of a gullet, a change in the nature of the food reserves from starch to paramylum, and the development of the pectinate type of flagellum.

The Euglenophyta may be considered as a group which diverged from relatively primitive members of the Chlorophyceae in the direction of the Protozoa. Some undoubted protozoa probably had euglenoid ancestors. It is purely a matter of opinion and convenience whether the euglenoids should be assigned to the plant or the animal kingdom. If assigned to the plant kingdom, they cannot readily be referred to any other division and must, therefore, constitute a division Euglenophyta.

We shall see that each of several major groups of algal flagellates has given rise to protozoan types by loss of chlorophyll and assumption of a holozoic mode of nutrition. Just as botanists need to include all chlorophyllous flagellates in order to have a coherent picture of the evolutionary history of plants, so do zoologists need to include these same groups in order to trace the various groups of Protozoa to a common ancestry.

SUGGESTED READING

Gojdics, Mary, *The Genus Euglena*, University of Wisconsin Press, Madison, 1953, 268 pp. The structure and classification of *Euglena*, with many illustrations.

CHAPTER 11

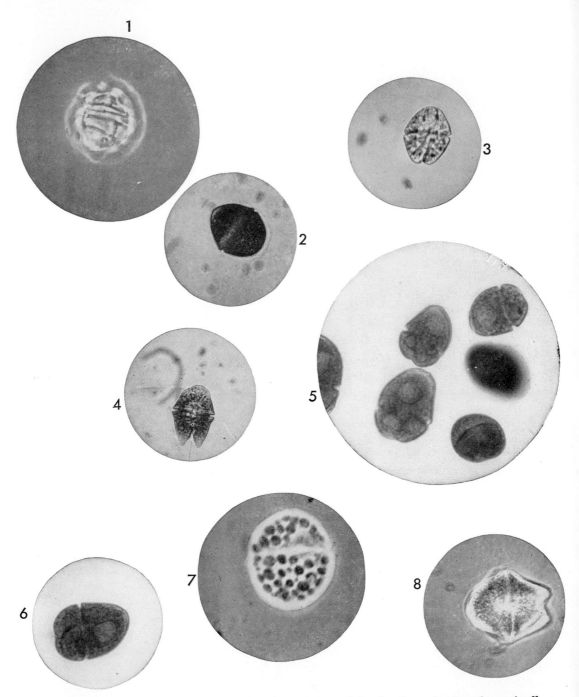

Miscellaneous dinoflagellates: (1) *Gonyaulax*, an armored dinoflagellate, showing plates of cell wall (×450); (2) *Peridinium* (×225); (3) *Gymnodinium* (×450); (4) *Gymnodinium* (×450)— note the trailing flagellum; (5) *Katodinium* (×350); (6) *Katodinium* (×450); (7) *Glenodinium*, showing chloroplasts (×900); (8) *Gyrodinium* (×400). (Photomicrographs courtesy of John Lee and John J. A. McLaughlin.)

Division Pyrrophyta

Mostly unicellular flagellates, the non-motile forms unicellular, colonial, or filamentous, and producing zoospores which resemble vegetative cells of motile genera; nucleus well developed, dividing mitotically, the chromonemata often moniliform (constricted at intervals like a string of beads); chloroplasts (when present) mostly golden-brown to yellowish-green, containing chlorophyll a, chlorophyll c, β-carotene, and typically with a unique series of xanthophylls—peridinin, dinoxanthin, neodinoxanthin—and often also other pigments; motile cells with two more or less dissimilar flagella, one often whiplash, the other at least frequently pectinate; cell wall, when present, usually of cellulose and often consisting of two valves, or divided into interlocking plates, or both; food reserves mostly starch or starch-like, sometimes oils; reproduction chiefly asexual, rarely sexual and isogamous. Three classes, the Cryptophyceae, Desmophyceae, and Dinophyceae.

THE PYRROPHYTA were first proposed as a division by Pascher in 1914.

CRYPTOPHYCEAE

The Cryptophyceae are pyrrophytes in which the flagella are only slightly dissimilar and the chromonemata are not evidently moniliform. The flagella are attached in a groove or a distinct gullet, usually at or near one end of the cell. They have been described as narrowly ribbon-shaped, but examination with the electron microscope shows that they are at least sometimes of the pectinate type. The cells are asymmetrical and somewhat compressed. A few genera have a cellulose wall, and one has a lorica; the others have the cells bounded by a flexible periplast. Cryptophyceae occur in both fresh and salt water, sometimes in fresh water that is rich in organic matter. Some genera lack chloroplasts and are saprophytic or holozoic. The Cryptophyceae were first recognized as a natural group by Klebs in 1892.

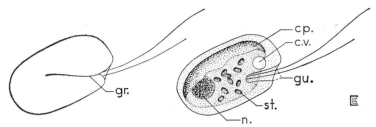

Fig. 11.1. *Cryptomonas.* Left, surface view; right, internal; cp., chloroplast; c.v., contractile vacuole; gr., groove, gu., gullet; n., nucleus; st., starch granules. (×1100.)

Very recently it has been shown that several genera of cryptomonads contain the phycobilin pigments phycoerythrin and phycocyanin. This is the only known occurrence of these pigments in groups other than the Cyanophyceae and Rhodophyta. It will be recalled that the phycobilins of the Cyanophyceae differ slightly from those of the Rhodophyta, and those of the Cryptophyceae likewise differ slightly from those of the other two groups. These cryptomonads contain chlorophyll *c* in addition to chlorophyll *a*, just as do the dinoflagellates, but they lack the characteristic xanthophylls of the latter group.

Cryptomonas (Fig. 11.1), a fresh-water genus, may be taken as representative of the class. Its cells are slightly compressed, more or less elliptic, and bounded by a firm periplast which has an evident longitudinal groove. Two slightly unequal flagella are inserted in a gullet near one end of the cell. The gullet is a simple in-

vagination of the periplast, lined with small spindle-shaped cavities of uncertain function called **trichocysts.** A single contractile vacuole lies alongside the gullet and empties into it. There are one or two large, thin, flattened chloroplasts which are usually yellowish to olive green. Granules of starch are scattered in the cytoplasm or associated with pyrenoids on the chloroplasts. There is no central vacuole. Reproduction is by mitotic cell division. Prior to dividing, a cell becomes immobile and surrounded by mucilage.

Only a few genera and well under 100 species of Cryptophyceae are known, and most of these are rare. Most (or, by some botanists, all) of the genera are included in a single order, the Cryptomonadales. Several of these genera form temporary palmelloid colonies of nonmotile cells, as described under *Chlamydomonas.* In one genus, *Phaeoplax* (Fig. 11.2) such colonies are more or less permanent, and the

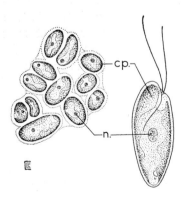

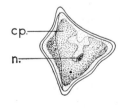

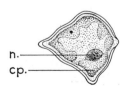

Fig. 11.2. Left, *Phaeoplax*, colony (×1300) and zoospore (×3500): cp., chloroplast; n., nucleus. Right, *Tetragonidium*, two views (× 900): cp., chloroplast; n., nucleus.

temporary motile cells are regarded as zoospores. Some algologists establish for this genus a separate order (Phaeoplacidales), which bears the same sort of morphologic and presumably phyletic relationship to the Cryptomonadales that the order Tetrasporales of the green algae bears to the Volvocales.

In the genus *Tetragonidium* (Fig. 11.2) the cells are solitary, nonmotile, and provided with a cellulose wall. The cells do not divide vegetatively, and reproduction is by the formation of biflagellate zoospores which resemble vegetative cells of the Cryptomonadales. Some algologists establish for this genus a separate order (Tetragonidiales), which bears the same morphologic and presumably phyletic relationship to the Cryptomonadales that the Chlorococcales of the green algae bear to the Volvocales.

DESMOPHYCEAE

The Desmophyceae are Pyrrophyta in which the chromonemata are **moniliform** (regularly constricted so as to resemble a string of beads) and the two flagella are attached at one end of the cell, which has neither a groove nor a gullet. The flagella tend to differ in position and movement, but they are not otherwise very different as seen under conventional microscopes. Their detailed structure remains to be elucidated. The cell wall, when present, consists of two longitudinal valves or halves that are not subdivided into definitely arranged plates.

The Desmophyceae were first recognized as a natural group by Pascher in 1914. The class contains only about half a dozen genera and 30 species, all rare, and mostly marine. Motile genera without a wall, including *Desmomonas*, are placed in the order Desmomonadales. Motile genera with a wall, including *Exuviaella* and *Prorocentrum*, are placed in the order Prorocentrales. *Desmocapsa*, nonmotile and with a wall, is placed in the order Desmocapsales.

Exuviaella (Fig. 11.3) may be taken as representative of the Desmophyceae. The cells are solitary, slightly compressed, and have two apical flagella. One flagellum projects forward and propels the cell

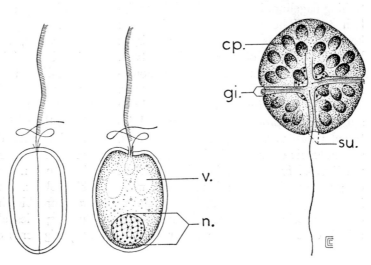

Fig. 11.3. Left, *Exuviaella:* surface view and in section; n, nucleus; v., vacuole. (× 1000.) Right, *Gymnodinium:* cp., chloroplast; gi., girdle; su., sulcus. (×1500.)

through the water; the other undulates at right angles to the propulsive flagellum and causes the cell to rotate during its progression. The cell wall is composed of cellulose and consists of two longitudinally apposed valves, with a pore at the flagellar end. Several noncontractile vacuoles sometimes occur near the flagellar end of the cell, but there is no large central vacuole. There are two large, thin, brownish chloroplasts, with or without pyrenoids. Small droplets of oil and minute granules of presumed starch occur on the pyrenoids and scattered in the cytoplasm. Reproduction is by mitotic cell division. Each of the two daughter cells retains one of the two valves of the parent cell and forms a new valve opposite the old one.

DINOPHYCEAE

The Dinophyceae are pyrrophytes in which the two flagella are inserted in a transverse or spiral groove (the **girdle**), with one flagellum trailing and the other lying in the groove. Usually the groove more or less completely encircles the cell. The trailing flagellum is apparently of the whiplash type. The transverse flagellum has been described as ribbon-shaped and is, at least sometimes, of the pectinate type. The chromonemata are distinctly moniliform. Often the cell has a definite eyespot.

The class includes photosynthetic autotrophs, saprophytes, external and internal parasites of fish and other animals, and holozoic organisms which ingest small particles of food. Some individuals are at once autotrophic and holozoic, both making and ingesting food. A large majority of the species are unicellular flagellates, called **dinoflagellates.** Genera with non-

motile vegetative cells produce zoospores which resemble vegetative cells of motile genera.

Most Dinophyceae occur in the ocean, especially in the warmer regions. They often become so numerous as to color the sea water bright yellow to red. Some species of *Noctiluca, Gymnodinium, Peridinium*, and other genera of dinoflagellates are luminous in the dark, and when the individuals are very numerous the sea glows at night. This phosphorescence of sea water can be caused by a wide variety of plankton organisms, both plant and animal, but dinoflagellates are by far the most common cause.

The Dinophyceae were first recognized as a natural group by Ehrenberg in 1838. There are about 1000 species, a fact which makes them by far the largest class of the Pyrrophyta. The class may be divided into eight orders, of which only three, the Gymnodiniales, Peridiniales, and Dinophysidales, are represented by large numbers of species.

Gymnodinium (Fig. 11.3) may be taken as representative of the dinoflagellates which lack a wall. The cell is bounded by a firm periplast with a fixed shape. The girdle encircles the cell in a loose spiral, the separated ends of the spiral being joined by a longitudinal furrow called the **sulcus.** The ribbon-like transverse flagellum is inserted at the junction of the sulcus with the upper end of the girdle; the whiplash trailing flagellum is inserted farther down in the sulcus, often near the lower end of the girdle. Most species have numerous small golden-brown chloroplasts. Sometimes the chloroplasts are more bluish or greenish, or wanting. Some species also have abundant (often red) pigments distributed through the cy-

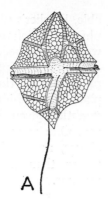

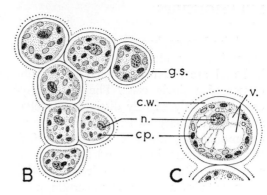

Fig. 11.4. A, *Peridinium*. (×500.) B, *Dinothrix*, filament, stereoscopic view; C, *Dinothrix*, cross section of a single cell; cp., chloroplast; c.w., cell wall; g.s., gelatinous sheath; n., nucleus; v., vacuole.

toplasm and masking the plastids. According to the species, the organisms are autotrophic, saprophytic, holozoic, or at once autotrophic and holozoic, both making and ingesting food. Reproduction is usually by cell division. Sometimes the cell goes into a resting stage and secretes a wall. The protoplast of the cell may emerge from its wall and return directly to the vegetative state, or several zoospores may first be formed within the wall.

The armored dinoflagellates, such as *Peridinium* (Fig. 11.4), have a more or less *Gymnodinium*-like protoplast surrounded by a wall that usually contains cellulose, consisting of a definite number of plates arranged in a definite pattern. One of these plates encircles the cell at the region of the girdle, dividing the remainder of the wall into two parts, each composed of several plates. The flagella emerge through small pores in the wall. One flagellum trails; the other lies in the groove at the region of the girdle. Nearly all armored dinoflagellates are photosynthetic, forming starch as a reserve food. Some also evidently ingest food particles by an undetermined means, which may perhaps involve extrusion of part of the protoplast between the plates of the cell wall.

ECONOMIC IMPORTANCE

The dinoflagellates are one of the most important ultimate sources of food for fish and other animals in the warmer parts of the ocean.

The sporadic red tides on the coast of Florida are caused by *Gymnodinium brevis*, and other dinoflagellates of this and other genera cause similar phenomena elsewhere. The red tides caused by *G. brevis* kill large numbers of fish and other marine animals, and some other species of this and other genera of dinoflagellates have similar effects, although still others are apparently harmless, even when sufficiently abundant to color the water. The cause of the mortality to marine animals is not yet fully understood, but it is believed that some poison is liberated into the water either as a by-product of metabolism or as a product of the decay of dead cells. The depletion of the supply of dissolved oxygen in the water through respiration by the dinoflagellates at night may be responsible for some of the difficulty, but if this were the sole cause one would not expect such pronounced differences in the amount of damage done by comparable quantities of different species.

RELATIONSHIPS

The Desmophyceae and Dinophyceae are universally admitted to be closely allied and are often considered to be subclasses of a single class. The Cryptophyceae, with only slightly dissimilar flagella, and with ordinary rather than moniliform chromonemata, are less highly modified than the Desmophyceae and Dinophyceae and have often been excluded from the Pyrrophyta as a group of uncertain position. They resemble the Pyrrophyta in producing starch, in at least sometimes having pectinate flagella, in having chlorophyll c, and in the predominance of carotenoid pigments in the chloroplasts, although the carotenoids are not the same ones. Until more information, particularly on the chemistry of the pigments, becomes available, Pascher's suggestion that the Cryptophyceae be referred to the Pyrrophyta may well be followed.

The Pyrrophyta, like the Euglenophyta, are on the borderline between the plant and animal kingdoms and have doubtless given rise to some of the Protozoa. One or more genera in each of the classes, nevertheless, are distinctly plants rather than animals or borderline organisms.

SUGGESTED READING

Johnson, Frank H. (Ed.), *The Luminescence of Biological Systems*, Am. Assoc. Adv. Science, Washington, 1955. A symposium which includes two chapters on luminous dinoflagellates.

CHAPTER 12

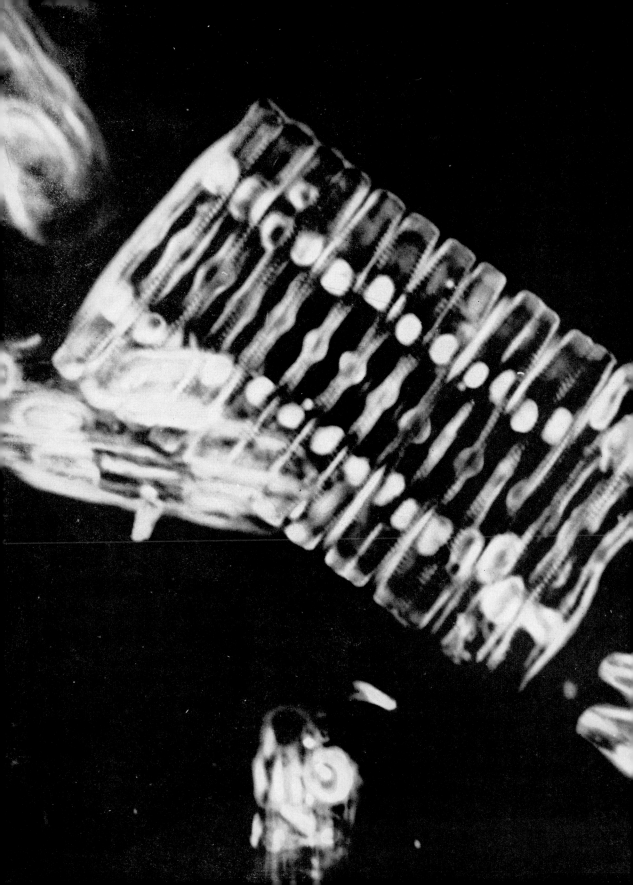

Division
Chrysophyta

Plants unicellular, colonial, or filamentous, the cell walls, when present, seldom containing appreciable quantities of cellulose, often silicified, very often of two overlapping halves; flagella, when present, usually two and dissimilar, one whiplash, one pinnate; nucleus dividing mitotically; chloroplasts, when present, mostly yellowish-green to golden-brown, lacking the characteristic xanthophylls of the Pyrrophyta; food reserves leucosin and/or oils, rarely starch; often produce statospores, which are unique to this division. Four classes, the Chloromonadophyceae, Xanthophyceae, Chrysophyceae, and Bacillariophyceae.

THE BASIC similarities among the Xanthophyceae, Chrysophyceae, and Bacillariophyceae were first pointed out by Pascher, who in 1914 proposed the division Chrysophyta to cover these classes. The Xanthophyceae and Chrysophyceae are closely allied classes, evidently derived from flagellates of chlorophycean nature. The Bacillariophyceae are more isolated, and some phycologists would establish a separate division for them. The distinctive features which mark the Bacillariophyceae are, however, wholly compatible with a relationship to the Chrysophyceae and Xanthophyceae. A fourth class, the Chloromonadophyceae, treated in this text as a doubtful member of the Chrysophyta, was regarded by Pascher and many later algologists as a group with uncertain affinities.

Chloromonadophyceae
(Chloromonads)

The Chloromonadophyceae are unicellular, flagellated chrysophytes which or-

◀

Fragilaria, a colonial diatom. (×1800.) (Photomicrograph courtesy of Elsa H. J. O'Donnell.)

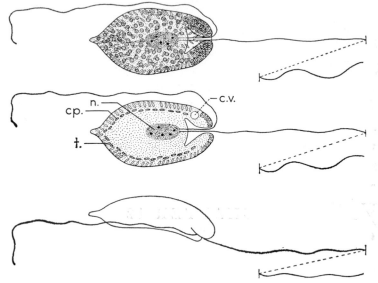

Fig. 12.1. *Gonyostomum semen.* Above, stereoscopic view. Center, cross section: cp., chloroplast; c.v., contractile vacuole; n., nucleus; t., trichocyst. Below, surface view only, from the side. (×500.) (After Drouet and Cohen.)

dinarily lack a cell wall. Chloroplasts, when present, are numerous, discoid, and bright-green to yellowish-green; the pigments have not been analyzed. Food reserves occur as minute drops of oil. Reproduction is by cell division. The flagella are attached at or near one end of the cell. The swimming flagellum projects forward and is probably of the tinsel type; the trailing flagellum, of the whiplash type, is so slender and lies so close to the body of the cell that it is easily overlooked. A reservoir lies just beneath the flagella, and one or more contractile vacuoles lie close to the reservoir. The nucleus occupies a more or less central position, and there is no evident central vacuole. Although the cells are usually naked and motile, they sometimes go into a temporary nonmotile stage in which they round up, lose their flagella, and secrete a gelatinous wall. Sometimes the cells divide while in this encysted condition, producing temporary palmelloid colonies.

The chloromonads were first recog-

nized as a natural group by Klebs in 1892. There are only a few genera and species; most or all of these are placed in a single family, the Vacuolariaceae (Chloromonadaceae), which makes up the order Chloromonadales.

Gonyostomum (Fig. 12.1), a freshwater genus, may be taken as representative of the family, order, and class. The cells are compressed, more or less ovate to nearly circular in outline, and bounded by a flexible periplast. The chloroplasts are a distinctive bright green. Many slender trichocysts lie just within the periplast. The trichocysts are perhaps a defense mechanism; under certain conditions they produce or become long threads of slime that project from the cell.

The systematic position of the Chloromonadophyceae is somewhat doubtful and will perhaps remain so until their pigments are carefully analyzed and their flagellar structure ascertained. The Cryptophyceae (Pyrrophyta) and the Xanthophyceae (Chrysophyta) have been suggested as possible allies. The original definition of the class Xanthophyceae (under another name) included the Chloromonadales as an order. Because they have neither starch nor cellulose and have not been demonstrated to possess the characteristic dinophycean xanthophylls, it seems unwise to refer the chloromonads to the Pyrrophyta at this time. On the other hand, there is nothing in the available evidence to controvert their being considered a near-basal group in the Chrysophyta, allied to the Xanthophyceae.

The chloromonads are of little economic importance. Like other algae, they contribute directly or indirectly to the food supply of aquatic animals.

Xanthophyceae (Yellow-green algae)

HISTORY AND DEFINITION

The genera of algae with yellow-green chloroplasts and lacking starch were segregated as an order of the Chlorophyceae by the Italian botanist Antonino Borzi (1852–1921) in 1889. In 1899 the Finnish botanist Alexander F. Luther pointed out that these genera also differ from typical green algae in the nature of the flagella. He elevated the yellow-green algae to the status of a class, under the name Heterokontae, but the later name Xanthophyceae (1930) is now generally preferred as being more in accord with standard nomenclatural principles.

The Xanthophyceae are Chrysophyta with yellowish-green chloroplasts that contain chlorophylls *a* and sometimes *e*, β-carotene, and a single unnamed xantho-

phyll. Chlorophyll *e* is not known to occur in any other group of plants. The cell wall, when present, consists of pectic compounds, often impregnated to some extent with silica; cellulose seldom occurs in appreciable amounts. Often the cell wall is composed of two overlapping halves, which fit together like the halves of a pillbox or medicinal capsule, but this construction can be demonstrated only by careful chemical treatment. In the multicellular filamentous genera, the halves of adjacent cell walls are joined back to back, so that in longitudinal section the wall of a filament seems to consist of a series of H-pieces, as illustrated in Fig. 12.2. Nuclei of the Xanthophyceae are so small that they are difficult to recognize in living cells; those which have been carefully investigated have the same structure as in most other plants. Food reserves of Xanthophyceae are usually leucosin, an insoluble carbohydrate. Sometimes oils are produced in addition to or instead of leucosin. Flagella, when present, are two, dissimilar, and attached at one end of the cell. The longer flagellum is pinnate, the shorter one whiplash.

CLASSIFICATION

There are about 400 species of Xanthophyceae. Most of them occur in fresh water or in subaerial habitats, but a few are marine. Most of the theoretically possible types of body organization discussed under the green algae occur in the Xanthophyceae, although some types are represented by only a few members; there are, for example, but few flagellates. The amoeboid types are commonly at once autotrophic and holozoic, both making and ingesting food. The class may be divided into six orders, of which the Heterococcales have more genera and species than the other orders combined.

REPRESENTATIVE GENERA

BOTRYDIOPSIS

Botrydiopsis (Fig. 12.2) is a widely distributed genus occurring on moist soils, seldom in any great abundance. The cells are solitary and spherical, with a thin wall composed of pectic compounds. Mature cells have numerous disk-shaped, evenly spaced chloroplasts. The cells do not di-

vide vegetatively. Sexual reproduction is unknown in the genus.

Zoospores are formed by repeated mitotic division of the protoplast within the wall of the parent cell. Young, relatively small cells may produce as few as four zoospores; older, larger cells may produce more than 200. The zoospores have two unequal flagella, one whiplash, one pinnate, and they usually have only one or two chloroplasts. Each zoospore soon loses its flagella and develops directly into a vegetative cell. Under some circumstances aplanospores (lacking flagella, and with a wall) are produced instead of zoospores. Aplanospores sometimes develop directly into vegetative cells, just as do zoospores;

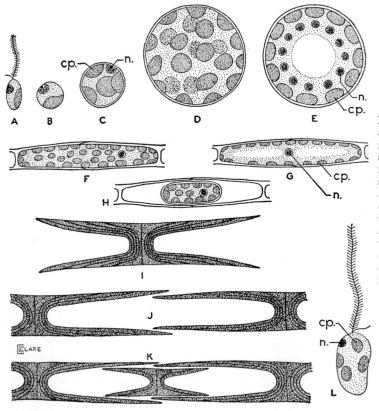

Fig. 12.2. *A–E, Botrydiopsis arhiza.* A, zoospore; *B–D,* growing vegetative cells, stereoscopic view: E, multinucleate vegetative cell, in section. (×750.) *F–L. Tribonema, F, G,* vegetative cells, in stereoscopic and sectional view. (×500.) *H,* aplanospore. (×500.) *I–K,* wall structure and formation of new walls. (×750.) *L,* zoospore: cp., chloroplast; n., nucleus. (×900.)

in other cases they form a thick wall and go into a resting state, after which the protoplast divides into a number of zoospores or aplanospores.

TRIBONEMA

Tribonema (Fig. 12.2) is a common filamentous alga of temporary pools and standing water, superficially resembling some of the green algae, except for a slight difference in color. The filament is unbranched and consists of a single row of cylindric or barrel-shaped cells joined end to end. Observation after careful chemical treatment shows that the wall of each cell consists of two halves, as described on p. 173. The cells are uninucleate and contain few to many discoid yellow-green chloroplasts, according to the species.

Asexual reproduction occurs by fragmentation of the filaments, or by the production of zoospores, aplanospores, or akinetes. Aplanospores are the most common type of spore. One or several ellipsoid aplanospores may be formed within the wall of the parent cell. Zoospores are more or less pear-shaped, with two dissimilar terminal flagella and two to several chloroplasts; they are usually borne singly in the cells. Both zoospores and aplanospores are liberated by disarticulation of the two halves of the wall of the parent cell. The wall of an aplanospore, like that of the parent cell, consists of two halves. A germinating aplanospore sheds its wall, and develops a new wall after elongating to become the first cell of a new filament. Zoospores, after swimming about for some time, settle down, lose their flagella, and develop a wall with a basal holdfast. After several divisions the terminal part of the filament

breaks away and continues to grow as a free-floating filament.

Sexual reproduction occurs by fusion of gametes which are initially similar and biflagellate. One of each pair of fusing gametes comes to rest and withdraws its flagella just before syngamy takes place. The first division of the zygote is probably meiotic.

VAUCHERIA

Vaucheria (Fig. 12.3) is a well-known genus occurring in fresh and salt water and on moist soil. The thallus is a sparingly branched coenocytic filament, sometimes several centimeters long, with a continuous protoplast and scattered nuclei. Terrestrial species sometimes have colorless rhizoids (root-like filaments) penetrating the soil. A well-developed central vacuole extends the length of the filament. The numerous, small, spherical to ellipsoid, yellow-green chloroplasts without pyrenoids occur in the outer layer of the cytoplasm, and the numerous, even smaller nuclei occur in the inner layer. Food reserves occur as small droplets of oil. The filament and its branches grow by terminal elongation. The wall is relatively thin and is composed of pectic substances.

Asexual reproduction occurs by the formation of zoospores, aplanospores, or akinetes. A zoosporangium is the swollen, club-shaped end of a branch, delimited from the rest of the branch by a cross wall. Each zoosporangium contains a single multinucleate zoospore, with numerous pairs of flagella of about equal length but probably dissimilar structure. The protoplast of the zoospore, unlike that of the mature filament, has the chloroplasts in the inner layer of cytoplasm and the nuclei in the outer layer. Each pair of flagella is associated with a nucleus just beneath it. The zoospore escapes through a pore formed by softening of the wall at the end of the sporangium. After swimming about for as much as half an hour, the zoospore settles down, retracts its flagella, and develops a wall. Germination follows immediately, with one to three filaments being produced by local distension of the wall.

In terrestrial species the protoplast of a sporangium often develops into a thin-walled aplanospore or a thin-walled akinete, or less often into numerous thin-walled aplanospores. Aplanospores are liberated by irregular rupture of the wall of the sporangium. Akinetes may become

detached from the filament or may germinate in place. Sometimes the whole protoplast of the filament of terrestrial species may divide into a series of thick-walled aplanospores. These may give rise directly to new filaments or may divide to form cells which pass through an amoeboid stage before developing into new filaments.

Sexual reproduction is oögamous. Most species, including all the fresh-water and terrestrial ones, are homothallic; both types of gamete are borne on the same filament. Antheridia and oögonia (Fig. 12.4) are commonly borne on adjacent short lateral branches. The antheridium is delimited by a transverse wall in the branch and

Fig. 12.3. *Vaucheria.* **Life cycle, sexual at right, asexual at left. (From W. H. Brown, *The Plant Kingdom*, 1935, courtesy of Ginn & Company, Boston.)**

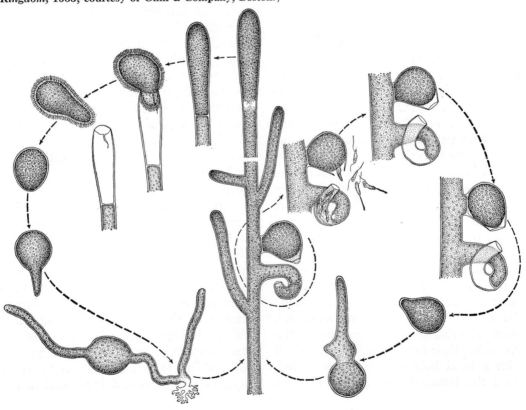

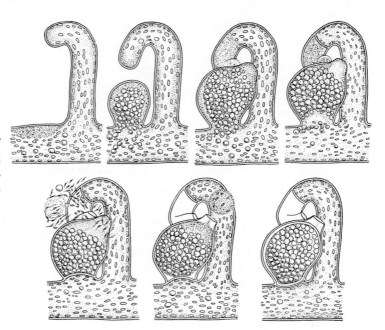

Fig. 12.4. *Vaucheria*. Details of sexual structures. (From W. H. Brown, *The Plant Kingdom*, 1935, courtesy of Ginn & Company, Boston.)

is commonly recurved, so that the branch is hook-shaped. Numerous uninucleate, terminally biflagellate sperms are produced in each antheridium. The flagella are of nearly equal length but dissimilar structure, one being whiplash, the other pinnate. The oögonium is a bulge or short thick branch delimited from the rest of the filament by a transverse wall. It is at first multinucleate, but before the cross wall is formed all but one of the nuclei either degenerate or migrate back into the body of the filament, according to the species. The sperms are released through a pore which develops by softening of the wall at one end of the antheridium. They reach the egg through a similar pore in the oögonium. The zygote formed by fusion of the sperm and egg develops a thick wall and goes into a resting state. After several months it germinates directly into a new filament, with the first division of the zygotic nucleus probably being meiotic.

ECONOMIC IMPORTANCE

The yellow-green algae are of little economic importance. Like the other algae they are an initial link in the plant-to-fish food chain, but they are much less abundant than some of the other classes.

Chrysophyceae (Golden algae)

HISTORY AND CHARACTERISTICS

The Chrysophyceae, or golden algae, which were first clearly recognized as a coherent group by Klebs in 1892, are chrysophytes with golden-brown chloroplasts and without a highly silicified wall. Usually there are only one or two chloroplasts in a cell. These contain chlorophyll *a*, β-carotene, fucoxanthin, lutein, and perhaps other xanthophylls. Fucoxanthin is otherwise found only in the diatoms and brown algae, both of which contain a

Fig. 12.5. Statospores of various sorts.

chlorophyll (chlorophyll *c*) and several xanthophylls that are unknown in the Chrysophyceae. Food reserves are leucosin and/or oils.

Most flagellated and amoeboid forms of golden algae have a naked protoplast, but some are partly enclosed by a lorica, and others have a cell wall composed of pectic materials or sometimes cellulose. The walls of nonmotile genera are sometimes divided into two overlapping halves. The cell wall, or the otherwise naked protoplast, often bears thin siliceous scales which vary in shape according to the species.

Flagellated forms usually have two (rarely three) flagella, one whiplash, the other pinnate. Some forms are uniflagellate, with only the pinnate flagellum. Often there are one or more contractile vacuoles at the base of the flagella.

Motile unicellular forms reproduce by cell division. Nonmotile forms produce zoospores with one or two flagella of dissimilar structure and unequal length. Usually only one zoospore is borne in a cell.

Many of the genera, both motile and nonmotile, produce a type of spore found only in the Xanthophyceae, Chrysophyceae, and Bacillariophyceae, called the statospore (Fig. 12.5). These are spores with the wall composed of two usually very unequal overlapping halves. The silicified, or more often unsilicified, smaller half forms a plug closing a pore in the highly silicified larger half of the wall. Statospores are formed singly within vegetative cells. The larger half of the wall forms around a differentiated central part of the protoplast, including the nucleus. The excluded peripheral cytoplasm sometimes degenerates, or sometimes it flows into the developing spore through the pore before the plug is formed. Germination of a statospore is preceded by separation or dissolution of the plug. The protoplast may emerge directly through the pore—or may first divide into two or four zoospores.

Sexual reproduction in the Chrysophyceae is apparently rare. It is isogamous in the known examples.

Fossils which have been identified as belonging to this class are known from marine deposits of Cretaceous and later ages.

CLASSIFICATION

There are about 300 species of Chrysphyceae; a large proportion of them occur in fresh water, but marine forms are not uncommon. Most of them are unicellular or merely colonial, but there are a few filamentous types as well. More than half the species are flagellated, and some others are amoeboid. The amoeboid types are commonly at once autotrophic and holozoic, both making and ingesting food.

Amoeboid and flagellated Chrysophyceae which fail to develop chloroplasts can scarcely be distinguished from true protozoa, and doubtless some of the protozoa are derived from this group.

The taxonomy of the Chrysophyceae is not yet well understood; a conservative treatment, recognizing six orders, is presented in the appendix.

REPRESENTATIVE GENERA

CHROMULINA

Chromulina (Fig. 12.6) is a fresh-water plankton genus with solitary, uniflagellate cells of various shapes. Near the base of the flagellum there are one or more vacuoles and sometimes also an eyespot. There are one or two broad, thin chloroplasts which rarely contain pyrenoids. There is neither a cell wall nor a central vacuole. Food reserves accumulate as leucosin and, to a lesser extent, oils. Reproduction is by

longitudinal cell division. Several species produce statospores.

CHRYSAMOEBA

Chrysamoeba (Fig. 12.6) is an amoeboid fresh-water plankton genus which sometimes has a temporary flagellated stage. In either case there is no cell wall. The cells are uninucleate, and solitary or temporarily united in colonies. There are one or two broad thin chloroplasts that may or may not have pyrenoids. Leucosin is a food reserve. In addition to making food by photosynthesis, *Chrysamoeba* ingests solid particles of food. Reproduction is by cell division; statospores are also formed.

In the amoeboid state the cells have numerous short, sharply pointed cytoplasmic projections (**pseudopodia**) radiating in all directions. The flagellated state is achieved by the retraction of the pseudopodia, the assumption by the protoplast of an ovoid shape, and the protrusion of a

Fig. 12.6. Left, *Chromulina.* (×1500.) Right, *Chrysamoeba:* cp., chloroplast; c.v., contractile vacuole; e.s., eyespot; n., nucleus. (×1000.)

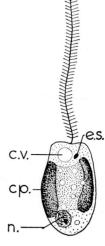

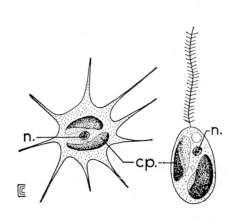

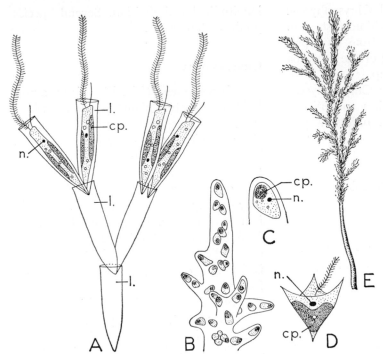

Fig. 12.7. A, Dinobryon. (×1000.) B–E, Hydrurus: B, tip of filament; C, same, enlarged; D, zoospore; E, whole plant; cp., chloroplast; l., lorica; n., nucleus.

long flagellum, near the base of which a contractile vacuole develops. Neither cell division nor statospore formation occurs in the flagellated state.

DINOBRYON

Dinobryon (Fig. 12.7) is a fresh-water plankton genus in which the cells are partly enclosed by a lorica. The lorica is shaped more or less like a hollow cone, closed at the pointed end, and is reported to contain cellulose and also to be somewhat impregnated with silica. The protoplast is spindle-shaped to conical or ovoid, bounded by a firm periplast, and is usually attached to the lorica only by a short cytoplasmic stalk at the base. There are two distinctly unequal flagella, one or more contractile vacuoles, and usually an evident eyespot. Food reserves are chiefly leucosin.

There are one or two broad thin chloroplasts. In addition to making food by photosynthesis, *Dinobryon* also ingests small particles of food. Reproduction is by longitudinal cell division. Often one or both daughter cells become attached near the mouth of the old lorica before secreting a new lorica, so that branched colonies are formed. Some species also produce statospores. Sexual reproduction by fusion of isogametes appears to have been clearly demonstrated in one species.

HYDRURUS

Hydrurus (Fig. 12.7) is a colonial genus of fast mountain streams. The cells are ovoid, or angular by compression, and are embedded in a firm, much branched, common gelatinous sheath, forming a tough, greenish-brown, penicillately branched coating on the rocky stream bottom. Large colonies may be as much as 3 feet long and contain hundreds of thousands of cells. Each cell contains several vacuoles and a single large chloroplast with an evident pyrenoid.

Colony reproduction is by zoospores and statospores. Zoospores are formed directly from young cells near the tips of the smaller branches. They are tetrahedral, with a single long flagellum on one face. Statospores are developed from individual cells in special short-branched gelatinous stalks borne on the branches of the colony.

ECONOMIC IMPORTANCE

The golden algae, like other algae, are an initial link in the plant-to-fish food chain, and some of the marine species, especially the silicoflagellates (Siphonotestales) are sufficiently abundant to be important in that regard. Otherwise the Chrysophyceae have very little economic significance.

Bacillariophyceae (Diatoms)

HISTORY AND DEFINITION

The Bacillariophyceae, or **diatoms**, are unicellular or loosely colonial algae with a silicified wall composed of two halves which fit together like the halves of a petri dish or pillbox. They further differ from all other Chrysophyta in that the vegetative cells are diploid rather than haploid. The distinctiveness of the diatoms from most other algae was soon recognized, although early students usually confused them with the desmids, a group of green algae with

the cells medially constricted into two similar halves. The diatoms were first clearly differentiated from the desmids in 1833 by the German algologist Friedrich Kützing (1807–1893), who in 1844 published a monographic treatment of the group.

DISTRIBUTION

Diatoms are common in both fresh and salt water, particularly in temperate or cool regions. In fresh-water ponds and lakes they tend to be more numerous in the spring and fall than during the hot summer months. They make up a large proportion of the vegetable plankton of the ocean. Many of them also occur attached to rocks or aquatic plants, and some are found in subaerial habitats. An ample supply of dissolved silicates tends to favor the growth of diatoms, but at least some species can be cultured in a silicon-free medium, where they produce unsilicified cell walls.

STRUCTURE

The diatom cell has a well-developed central vacuole and one or more variously shaped chloroplasts. Sometimes the nucleus is suspended in a broad band of cytoplasm that passes through the vacuole. The chloroplasts are typically golden-brown or somewhat yellowish and bear chlorophylls *a* and *c*, β-carotene and ε-carotene, fucoxanthin, neofucoxanthin, diatoxanthin, and diadinoxanthin. ε-carotene, diatoxanthin, and diadinoxanthin are known only in diatoms. A few species lack chloroplasts and live as saprophytes. Food reserves of diatoms are chiefly oils, and often also leucosin.

The cell wall is very complex and has

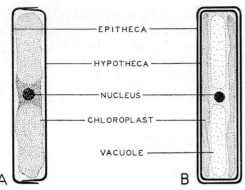

Fig. 12.8. A typical pennate diatom. A, side view; B, top view.

forations, so that a distinct pattern is formed. The pattern follows one of two general types. In the **centric** diatoms (Fig. 12.11), it tends to be radially symmetrical from a central point. In the **pennate** diatoms (Fig. 12.8), there is a longitudinal (commonly bilaterally symmetrical) pattern arranged on both sides of a central or offset longitudinal strip called the **axial field.** Often the axial field is traversed by a complex longitudinal slot, the **raphe.** The raphe is a passageway through the wall, often V-shaped in cross section, with the separated parts of the wall being aligned like the tongue and groove of floor boards. The raphe is usually interrupted at midlength by a channeled thickening of the wall, the central nodule, and is sometimes also marked by a similar thickening at each end.

Pennate diatoms with a raphe are often motile, the movement being alternately forward and backward in the direction of the long axis. The cytoplasm extends through the raphe and is in direct contact with the water along the **outer fissure** (the outer arm of the V, in cross section). The cytoplasm flows along the outer fissure from one end of the raphe to the other, and friction with the water causes the cell to move in the opposite direction to the cytoplasmic current. There is an opposing cytoplasmic stream flowing along the **inner fissure** of the raphe, the two streams constituting an essentially continuous circuit. Tiny whirling currents set up in the water at the ends of the raphe by the cytoplasmic

received a great deal of study because of the taxonomic usefulness of small variations in its structure. The outer of the two overlapping halves of the wall is called the **epitheca,** and the inner the **hypotheca.** Each half consists of a flat or convex plate, called the **valve,** and a lateral band, at right angles to the valve, called the **connecting band,** or **cingulum.** The connecting band may be compared to an open hoop having a small gap between the approximated ends. The matrix of the wall consists largely of pectin or a pectin-like substance, without cellulose. On this is deposited a layer of hydrated silica, chemically similar to opal. Often the whole cell, or colonies of cells, are embedded in a watery gelatinous substance, which is at least sometimes composed largely of pectic acid.

The siliceous material of the valves is deposited as a continuous sheet, often with spiny processes or appendages, and with regularly arranged thin spots or per-

Fig. 12.9. Wall structure of a pennate diatom.

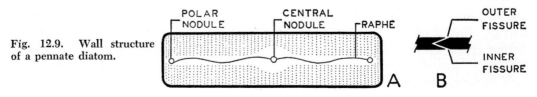

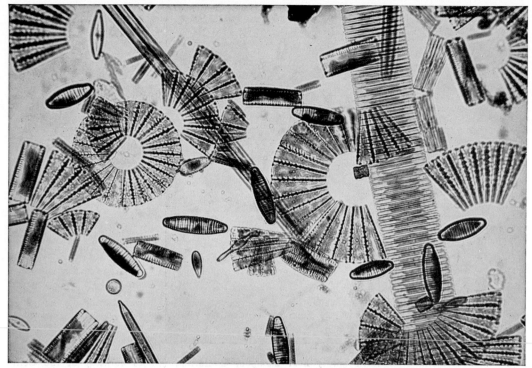

Fig. 12.10.   Mixed diatoms. (Courtesy of E. J. Kohl, Lakeside Biological Products, Ripon, Wis.)

streaming probably also contribute to the motion of the cell.

REPRODUCTION

Asexual reproduction of diatoms occurs by cell division. Division is mitotic, and each of the two daughter cells retains one of the two halves of the original cell wall. Each cell then produces a new half which fits into the older half. Thus, of the two daughter cells, one is the same size as the parent and the other is slightly smaller. Repeated cell division therefore leads to a gradual diminution in the average size of the descendants of an original cell.

Restoration of diatom cells to the maximum size for the species involves a sexual process leading to the formation of a particular type of "spore" (actually a zygote) called an **auxospore.** Vegetative cells of diatoms are diploid. The first step leading toward auxospore formation is reduction division. Thereafter the process varies in detail according to the kind of diatom, but it commonly involves release of the protoplast from the cell wall, restoration of the diploid condition (usually by syngamy), enlargement of the naked diploid protoplast, and finally the formation of a new wall around the now mature auxospore. The auxospore wall is composed of two halves which are smooth or variously ornamented, but in any case unlike the walls of the vegetative cells. The germinat-

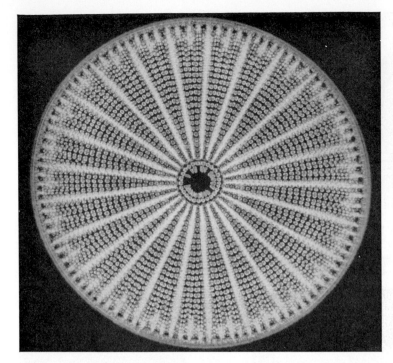

Fig. 12.11. *Arachnoidiscus,* a centric diatom. (Copyright by General Biological Supply House, Inc., Chicago.)

Fig. 12.12. Diatomaceous earth quarry near Lompoc, California. (Photo courtesy of the Celite Division, Johns-Manville Corporation.)

ing auxospore usually divides mitotically into two vegetative cells, each of which produces a complete new wall composed of the usual two parts.

In the pennate diatoms reduction division commonly leads to the formation of only one or two usually amoeboid gametes, the other nuclei degenerating. The gametes are not released until the two cells come to lie side by side in a common gelatinous envelope. The gametes which fuse are often alike; sometimes, on the contrary, they are of different sizes, or one may be amoeboid while the other is immobile.

In the centric diatoms syngamy is frequently oögamous. From 4 to 128 uniflagellate or biflagellate sperms are produced by some cells, while other cells produce each a single egg. These sperms were called microspores before their function was understood.

In both the pennate and the centric diatoms, typical syngamy is sometimes dispensed with, and two of the nuclei formed by reduction division in a single cell fuse to form a new diploid nucleus of the developing auxospore.

Many centric diatoms produce statospores apparently similar in origin and essentials of structure to those of the Chrysophyceae. The wall of the statospore is distinctly different in detail from that of the vegetative cell in which it is produced.

CLASSIFICATION

The diatoms, with perhaps as many as 10,000 living species, are probably the largest single class of algae. They may be divided into two well-marked orders, which have already been referred to as the pennate and the centric diatoms. The contrasting characters of the two orders are given in the appendix.

ECONOMIC IMPORTANCE

PLANKTON

It has already been noted that diatoms make up most of the vegetable plankton of the cooler parts of the ocean. They are, therefore, the most important ultimate source of food for fish and other marine animals in these regions. Their importance in fresh-water lakes is proportionately less, inasmuch as green and bluegreen algae are often more abundant there than the diatoms.

DIATOMACEOUS EARTH

The siliceous part of the cell wall of diatoms is scarcely affected by the death and degeneration of the rest of the cell, and diatom shells therefore tend to accumulate at the bottom of any lake or sea in which diatoms live. When other sediments are very slight, deposits consisting almost wholly of diatom shells may be formed. Such deposits, especially those which have been preserved from the geologic past, are called diatomaceous earth. A soupy diatomaceous ooze is now accumulating at the bottom of Klamath Lake in southern Oregon, and in some other freshwater lakes, but the most important deposits of diatomaceous earth are of marine origin. Oil wells in the Santa Maria oil fields of California pass through a layer of marine diatomaceous earth about 3000 feet thick. Near Lompoc, California, surface beds of marine diatomaceous earth several miles across and over 700 feet thick are being exploited by quarrying (Fig. 12.12).

The oldest fossil diatoms of thoroughly authenticated date come from the early part of the Cretaceous period, but most diatomaceous earth formations are of Late Cretaceous or later age. All Late Cretaceous genera are still represented by living species, and some Late Cretaceous species are apparently identical with modern ones.

The most important commercial use of diatomaceous earth is in filtration of liquids, particularly in sugar refineries. Small quantities of powdered diatomaceous earth added to a sugar solution will retain the suspended impurities from the solution when the mixture is forced through a filter. Some other uses of diatomaceous earth are as a fine abrasive (as in silver polish, and, at least in the past, in toothpaste), as an additive to paint to increase the night visibility of signs, and as an insulating material, especially in blast furnaces and other high-temperature installations. At temperatures of over 1000°F, diatomaceous earth is a more effective insulator than asbestos.

SUGGESTED READING

Smith, F. G. Walton, and Henry Chapin, *The Sun, the Sea, and Tomorrow*, Scribner, New York, 1954, 210 pp. The sea as a potential source of food, energy, and minerals. Informative, without requiring a technical background.

CHAPTER 13

Division Phaeophyta

BROWN ALGAE

CHAPTER 13

Plants multicellular, composed of branching filaments, or more complex; cell wall with an inner cellulose layer and a gelatinous outer pectic layer usually of algin; motile cells generally with two dissimilar lateral flagella, one whiplash, one pinnate; nucleus dividing mitotically; chloroplasts mostly brownish, containing chlorophylls a and c, β-carotene, fucoxanthin, and other xanthophylls; food reserves chiefly laminarin (a soluble carbohydrate), sometimes mannitol or fats. Three classes, the Isogeneratae, Heterogeneratae, and Cyclosporae.

HISTORY

The brown algae were first recognized as a distinct group by W. H. Harvey, who in 1836 segregated them as a subclass Melanospermeae of a class Algae. Later (1881) the brown algae were raised to the status of a class under the name Phaeophyceae, and modern algologists generally consider them to constitute a division, Phaeophyta (Wettstein, 1901). The three major groups of brown algae (Isogeneratae, Heterogeneratae, and Cyclosporae), based primarily on the life cycle, were first clearly recognized in 1933 by the Swedish phycologist Harald Kylin (1879–1949).

DISTRIBUTION AND STRUCTURE

There are about 1500 species of brown algae, nearly all of them marine. They are especially common along and near the seashore in the cooler parts of the world, both in the intertidal zone and wholly sub-

◀
Fucus vesiculosus, a common brown alga. (×2.)
(Photo by W. H. Hodge.)

189

merged. Some brown algae are microscopic and filamentous, but most of them have a larger, more complex thallus, ranging from a few inches to more than 150 feet long. The larger forms are usually complex in structure, with several different kinds of cells.

The gelatinous outer pectic layer of the cell walls of brown algae is commonly algin, which is wholly or largely the calcium salt of alginic acid, an organic acid with the approximate formula $(C_6H_8O_6)_n$. The inner layer of the cell wall consists largely of cellulose. There are one to more often several or many variously shaped, often discoid chloroplasts in each cell. The chloroplasts bear chlorophylls a and c, β-carotene, fucoxanthin, and other xanthophylls. Vegetative cells usually contain many small vacuoles, or occasionally a large central vacuole. The nucleus contains one or more nucleoli and divides mitotically. A number of clear vesicles containing a substance called fucosan are usually aggregated about the nucleus. Fucosan has many of the properties of tannin and is believed to be a metabolic waste product. The commonest food reserve is laminarin, a soluble polysaccharide composed of about 16 or 20 linked glucose units. Laminarin is known only in brown algae. Mannitol (a 6-hydrogen alcohol which can be oxidized to yield the hexose sugar mannose) and fats are also frequently found.

TISSUES

In unicellular and colonial organisms, every cell is capable of carrying out all the functions of the organism. Some of the smaller multicellular organisms also have all the cells essentially alike, but one of the most basic evolutionary tendencies,

among both plants and animals, is toward the differentiation and specialization of the cells of which an organism is composed. The groups of cells with similar or related functions which make up a complex multicellular organism are called **tissues**. Tissues in which all the cells are essentially alike are called **simple** tissues. Tissues in which different kinds of cells contribute to a common function are called **complex tissues**. A tissue or group of tissues which makes up a morphologically (and usually functionally) distinct part of an organism is called an **organ**. Sometimes the term *organ* is loosely applied also to single cells which are sharply differentiated in structure and function. Many of the brown algae contain differentiated tissues, and some of them are composed of recognizably distinct stem-like, root-like, and leaf-like organs. The terms *stem*, *root* and *leaf* are properly reserved for characteristic organs of the vascular plants, which have several different kinds of tissues, including specialized water-conducting and food-conducting tissues. The term **rhizoid** is used for root-like structures of relatively simple composition, and the terms **stalk** or **stipe** are used for any stem-like structure on which some other structure is borne, without regard to the anatomical composition.

Most tissues are specialized for one or another function, or sometimes two or more functions, the cells having a characteristic form and structure according to the function. Tissues composed of relatively unspecialized cells, in the brown algae and elsewhere, are called **parenchyma**. Parenchyma cells are usually rather thin-walled, seldom much, if at all, longer than wide, living when functional, and typically have a well-developed central vacuole. The walls of adjacent parenchyma cells are commonly in close contact over a large part of their surface, but there are generally intercellular spaces, just as there are spaces among the potatoes in a bag or among particles of soil. Most photosynthetic tissues are parenchymatous. Often it is useful to distinguish more than one kind of parenchymatous tissue in a single plant.

The thalli of many brown algae consist chiefly of parenchyma. Parenchyma cells in the brown algae differ from parenchyma cells of most land plants in usually lacking intercellular spaces and central vacuoles. The intercellular spaces that might otherwise exist among the parenchyma cells of brown algae are commonly filled by the gelatinous algin which makes up the outer layer of the cell wall.

One of the ways in which the more complex kinds of plants differ from the more complex kinds of animals is that in plants, but not in animals, cell division is carried on chiefly or wholly by cells specialized for that function. A tissue characterized by cell division is called a **meristem,** or a meristematic tissue. Meristematic cells, like parenchyma cells, are thin-walled and usually not greatly elongate. They differ from most parenchyma cells in lacking a central vacuole. In brown algae meristematic cells differ from parenchyma cells chiefly in function, as both types commonly lack the central vacuole.

The brown algae present all degrees of variation from a condition (especially in some of the genera with uniseriate, branching filaments) in which any cell may divide, to a condition in which cell division is largely restricted to meristematic tissues or solitary apical meristematic cells. The meristematic tissues may be apical, lateral (forming a layer around the outside of the thallus), or intercalary (inserted between nonmeristematic tissues). Often the branches, regardless of how many cells

thick the basal part may be, terminate in a uniseriate filamentous tip in which any cell (but especially the basal cells) may divide. Growth by means of such apical filaments or tips of filaments is said to be **trichothallic.**

LIFE CYCLE

The sexual cycle in two of the three classes of brown algae (the Isogeneratae and Heterogeneratae) includes a distinct alternation of sporophytic (diploid) and gametophytic (haploid) generations, both generations being multicellular and physiologically independent. The sporophyte generation is initiated by fusion of gametes, and the gametophyte generation is initiated by reduction division leading to the formation of spores.

The sexual sporangium (i.e., the meiosporangium, in which reduction division occurs) is produced on the sporophyte and begins its development as an ordinary uninucleate vegetative cell with $2n$ chromosomes. The cell enlarges and its nucleus undergoes meiosis, producing four nuclei each with n chromosomes. Usually these nuclei then undergo one or more further mitotic divisions, so that the developing sporangium contains from 4 to 128 haploid nuclei. This multinucleate protoplast then generally cleaves into uninucleate naked protoplasts without cell walls. Each such uninucleate protoplast within the sporangium usually develops into a biflagellate zoospore. The flagella are lateral in position and dissimilar, one being pinnate, the other whiplash. In some genera the spores do not develop flagella and are therefore called aplanospores. The spores are liberated into the water by rupture of the sporangial wall. Each of these sexual spores (either zoospores or aplanospores) develops into a mature gametophyte by a series of mitotic divisions.

The gametangia borne on the gametophyte are unicellular and often clustered into groups of definite external form, but neither the individual gametangia nor the clusters are surrounded by specialized sterile cells. Isogamous and anisogamous brown algae regularly have the gametangia in definite clusters, and in the anisogamous forms the two types of clusters are morphologically different. Oögamous brown algae always have solitary, unicellular oögonia, whereas the antheridia may be solitary or clustered according to the taxonomic group.

The entire protoplast of any gametangium (except in the Cyclosporae) becomes transformed into a single gamete. Isogametes, anisogametes, and sperms are ordinarily biflagellate, just as the zoospores. Eggs lack flagella and are nonmotile. In some oögamous orders the eggs are released into the water; in others the eggs are merely extruded from the oögonia, to which they remain attached. Isogametes which fail to fuse sometimes develop into new gametophytes, as may also unfertilized eggs and the larger of the two types of anisogametes. The development of unfertilized gametes into mature individuals is a phenomenon found in many different kinds of plants and animals and is called **parthenogenesis.**

Sporophytes of many brown algae produce clusters of asexual sporangia which resemble the gametangial clusters of gametophytes. Each sporangium in such a cluster produces a single biflagellate zoospore which differs from sperms or isogametes in having $2n$ chromosomes and in developing directly into a new sporophyte without a sexual process. Thus the sporophyte generation may be reproduced repeatedly, generation after generation, by means of these asexual or neutral zoospores. The clusters of asexual sporangia form such distinctive structures, differentiated from the vegetative body of the sporophyte, that it has been customary to call the whole cluster a sporangium, and before the life cycles were understood it was customary to refer to both the sporangial clusters and the superficially similar gametangial clusters as plurilocular sporangia.

The Cyclosporae differ from all other brown algae in that the gametophyte generation is nearly eliminated from the sexual cycle. The thallus is diploid with one-celled gametangia in which the primary nucleus undergoes reduction division.

The Cyclosporae are all oögamous. In the oögonium each of the 4 nuclei produced in meiosis divides mitotically, but some of the resulting nuclei often degenerate, so that 1, 2, 4, or 8 eggs may be borne in the oögonium. Each of the 4 nuclei resulting from reduction division within an antheridium usually undergoes several mitotic divisions, so that a considerable number (typically 64) of sperms are borne in an antheridium. Fertilization takes place free in the water after both types of gametes have been liberated from the gametangia.

It has been pointed out that the gametangia of the Cyclosporae are comparable to the unicellular sporangia of the other brown algae, and that, by comparison with other brown algae, the gametes of the Cyclosporae might be considered to be spores which function directly as gametes instead of developing into typical gametophytes. Thus the gametophyte (or n chromosome) generation in the Cyclosporae consists only of the gametes themselves and their immediate precursors within the gametangia. This condition is essentially the opposite of that seen in many green algae, in which the gametophyte makes up most of the life cycle, and the zygote is the only $2n$ or sporophyte stage in the life cycle.

ECONOMIC IMPORTANCE

In the past brown algae have sometimes been used directly as fertilizer and have been burned for the potassium and iodine which can be recovered from the ash. These uses have been largely discontinued because economic changes have made them unprofitable.

The larger species of brown algae, particularly the kelps, are harvested as a major source of food by the Japanese and as a source of the colloidal gel algin in Europe and America. Algin is used as a stabilizer or as a moisture retainer in a wide variety of commercial products, including ice cream, cake frosting, paint, and various pharmaceuticals; it is also used in the processing of natural and synthetic rubber latex.

Although the brown algae contribute directly or indirectly to the food supply of fish and other marine animals, they are not nearly so important in this regard as some of the plankton algae, such as diatoms and dinoflagellates.

RELATIONSHIPS

The brown algae form a well-marked division not very closely related to the other algae. A common ancestry with the Chrysophyta is suggested by the flagella; flagellated cells in both divisions characteristically have two flagella, one whiplash, one pinnate. Among the algae the pinnate flagellum is largely or wholly restricted to these two divisions.

The pigmentation of the brown algae suggests a relationship to both the Chrysophyta and the Pyrrophyta. All these groups have an excess of carotenoid pigments over chlorophylls, as compared to the Chlorophyta. Chlorophyll c is known only in the Phaeophyta, Chrysophyta, and Pyrrophyta. Fucoxanthin, the principal xanthophyll of the brown algae, occurs also in the Chrysophyta but is unknown among the Pyrrophyta.

The sum of the evidence indicates that the brown algae originated from a prechrysophytan stock after the pyrrophytan line had already diverged from the ancestors of this same stock.

The three classes of brown algae seem to form a simple evolutionary series. The Isogeneratae, with similar gametophytes and sporophytes that are usually small and filamentous, are clearly the basal group in the division. The Heterogeneratae are apparently derived from the more primitive members of the Isogeneratae by elaboration of the sporophyte without significant change in the gametophyte; and the Cyclosporae seem to be derived from the Heterogeneratae by reduction of the gametophyte. The Cyclosporae form a well-defined and clearly natural group.

Algologists are not agreed as to the naturalness of the distinction between the Isogeneratae and Heterogeneratae. Some competent students maintain that the Heterogeneratae consist of two or more parallel groups independently derived from the Isogeneratae, and that the present classification, therefore, cuts across the evolutionary relationships rather than following them.

The fossil record is hardly useful in determining relationships of the brown algae. Fossils more or less resembling *Fucus* and other Phaeophyta occur in rocks of various ages back to the early Paleozoic, but these cannot be certainly placed in any of the classes now recognized, and they provide no hint of the ancestry of the group.

Isogeneratae

CLASSIFICATION

The Isogeneratae are brown algae that have an isomorphic alternation of generations, the gametophyte and sporophyte being essentially similar in size and appearance. There are five orders, as indicated in the key given in the appendix.

REPRESENTATIVE GENERA

ECTOCARPUS

Ectocarpus (Fig. 13.1) is a cosmopolitan genus of many species, commonly found growing epiphytically on larger brown algae along the seashore. The thallus is a sparingly to profusely branched filament, usually one cell thick, with a prostrate, attached basal part (or a mere holdfast) and an erect free part. Any cell may divide. The sporophyte bears two kinds of sporangia on short lateral branches, but often not both at the same time. The asexual sporangia are relatively small and occur in dense clusters of several hundred, each such cluster forming what is usually called a plurilocular sporangium. The protoplast of each sporangium of the cluster becomes a single biflagellate neutral (i.e., asexual) zoospore which has $2n$ chromosomes like the parent filament and

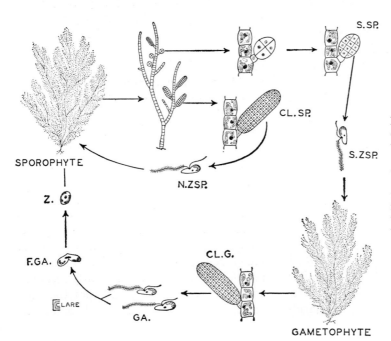

Fig. 13.1. *Ectocarpus.* **Life cycle; sporophyte and gametophyte** ($\times\frac{1}{3}$); **cl.g., cluster of gametangia** ($\times200$); **cl. sp., cluster of neutral sporangia** ($\times200$); **f.ga., fusion of gametes; ga., gametes; n.zsp., neutral zoospore; s.sp., sexual sporangium; s.zsp., sexual zoospore.**

which develops directly into a new sporophytic filament by a series of mitotic divisions.

The sexual sporangia are relatively large and commonly occur singly at the ends of short lateral branches. Usually 32 or 64 biflagellated zoospores with the reduced number of chromosomes are produced in a sexual sporangium. Each such sexual zoospore develops into a gametophytic filament by a series of mitotic divisions.

The gametangia occur at the ends of short lateral branches in clusters which closely resemble the clusters of asexual sporangia. A single biflagellate gamete is produced in each unicellular gametangium of the cluster. Fusion of two similar gametes produces a zygote with 2n chromosomes, from which a new sporophytic filament is developed by a series of mitotic divisions. Gametes which fail to fuse sometimes act as spores and develop parthenogenetically into normal gametophytes.

DICTYOTA

Dictyota (Fig. 13.3) is widely distributed in the warmer parts of the world. The thallus is repeatedly and dichotomously branched, sometimes as much as a foot long, with flattened, ribbon-shaped branches that often all lie in the same plane. It is attached to the substrate by a discoid or more elongate holdfast. Growth is restricted to the tips of the branches, each of which has an apical meristematic cell. The cells produced from the apical cell usually undergo several more divisions before maturing into vegetative cells, but only the apical cell remains permanently meristematic.

The sexual sporangia are loosely aggregated on the surface of the thallus but

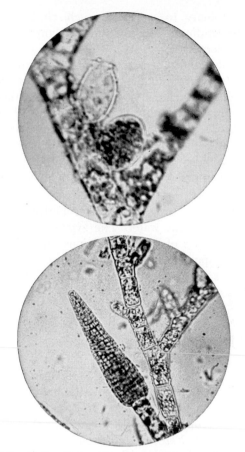

Fig. 13.2. *Ectocarpus.* Top, with sexual sporangia, one of which has already discharged its spores. (×600.) Bottom, with a cluster of gametangia. (×250.) (From Harold Bold, *Morphology of Plants*, Harper, 1957.)

retain their individual identity. Four naked, nonflagellated spores (therefore aplanospores) with the reduced number of chromosomes are produced in each sporangium. Two of these develop into male gametophytes, and two into female gametophytes. Asexual spores are not produced. The gametophytes are morphologically similar to each other and to the sporophytes. The individual unicellular antheridia (male gametangia) are borne in definite clusters of several hundred cells, and it has been customary to call each such cluster an antheridium. These compound antheridia are loosely grouped at the surface of the thallus and surrounded by a cup-like, open outgrowth from the thallus, called an involucre. Each cell of the compound antheridium produces a single sperm. The oögonia are loosely clustered but retain their individual identity; each cluster of unicellular oögonia is surrounded by a poorly developed involucre. The protoplast of each oögonium is released into the water as a single large egg. Fertilization occurs in the water. The zygote develops by a series of mitotic divisions into a mature sporophyte. Unfertilized eggs sometimes develop parthenogenetically into female gametophytes.

Heterogeneratae

The Heterogeneratae are brown algae with a heteromorphic alternation of generations. The gametophyte is always a microscopic branching filament, often resembling *Ectocarpus*, whereas the sporophyte is larger, usually of macroscopic size, and often structurally complex. The kelps, constituting the order Laminariales, are

the largest and anatomically most complex of all algae. Five orders of Heterogeneratae may be recognized. See the key given in the appendix.

REPRESENTATIVE GENERA

DICTYOSIPHON

Dictyosiphon (Fig. 13.3) occurs in the cooler regions along the seacoast, including both coasts of North America. The mature sporophyte is commonly several inches long, with a slender cylindrical central axis and a number of lateral branches which are again branched and rebranched in similar fashion. Each branch tip has a meristematic apical cell which sometimes gives rise to a terminal hair just before cessation of growth. Mature branches are solid or hollow, several cells thick, with colorless, elongate interior cells and nearly isodiametric outer cells that contain chloroplasts.

The sporangia are embedded just beneath the surface of the thallus; they are unicellular and much larger than the adjoining vegetative cells. The primary nucleus of the sporangium undergoes meiosis,

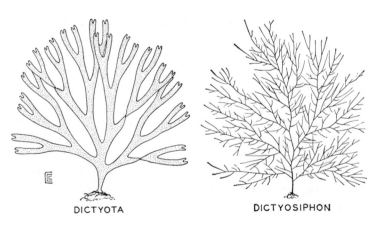

DICTYOTA

DICTYOSIPHON

Fig. 13.3. *Dictyota.* (×½.) *Dictyosiphon.* (×½.)

and the resulting biflagellate zoospores have the reduced number of chromosomes. The zoospores develop into *Ectocarpus*-like filamentous gametophytes, with the gametangia arranged in linear series of 2 to 12 terminating short, lateral branches. Each gametangium produces a single biflagellate gamete. The gametes are released into the water, and zygotes are formed by the fusion of morphologically similar gametes. The germinating zygote first develops a uniseriate filament, from which a branch with the more typical structure of the mature sporophyte is later produced. Unfertilized gametes sometimes germinate parthenogenetically and develop into new gametophytes.

LAMINARIA

Members of the order Laminariales are called **kelps.** *Laminaria* (Fig. 13.4), the type genus, occurs on both coasts of North America as well as elsewhere in the world, often in the intertidal zone. The mature sporophyte is commonly at least a foot long, often much longer, and is divided into three distinct parts, the holdfast, stipe, and blade. The holdfast, which anchors the plant to the substrate, is a solid disk, or more often a system of forking, root-like branches. The stipe, superficially similar to the stem of land plants, is erect, unbranched, and cylindrical to somewhat flattened. It is terminated by a single blade which may or may not be vertically cleft into several segments. Growth is due largely to an intercalary meristem at the junction of the stipe and blade. Both the blade and stipe increase continuously in length, but a mature blade commonly wears away at the tip as fast as new cells are formed at the base. The blade commonly stops growth in late summer and

Fig. 13.4. *Laminaria saccharina* in Nova Scotia. (New York Botanical Garden photo.)

disintegrates in the fall. The new blade which replaces it often begins to develop before the old one is wholly disintegrated.

A cross section of a mature stipe shows three concentric regions which do not usually have sharp boundaries. The central portion, called the **medulla,** consists of slightly separated vertical filaments, among which are interwoven transverse and diagonally ascending **connecting filaments,** which arise as lateral branches from some of the vertical filaments. Some of the vertical filaments have numerous cross walls. Others are composed of elon-

Division Phaeophyta: Brown Algae **197**

gate cells with expanded ends. These elongate cells evidently serve in the vertical conduction of food. In some related, larger genera, such as *Macrocystis* (Fig. 13.5), the giant kelp, which sometimes reaches a length of 150 feet, the end walls of adjacent cells in such filaments are perforated so as to resemble the sieve plates of food-conducting tissues in land plants.

Surrounding the medulla is a **cortex** consisting of radially arranged, vertically elongate cells, the outer members of which continue to divide throughout the life of the plant. In many species there is a network of mucilage ducts in the cortex. The mucilage is produced by groups of secretory cells at the surface of the duct. The outermost layer of the stipe forms a compact epidermis generally two cells thick, composed of small cubical cells with numerous chloroplasts.

The blade is anatomically rather similar to the stipe. The cells of the cortex are mostly isodiametric, rather than elongate, and decrease progressively in size toward the usually single layer of epidermal cells. Both the epidermis and the outer cortical cells usually contain chloroplasts.

The only reproductive organs produced by the sporophyte are numerous, more or less club-shaped, single-celled sporangia borne on both surfaces of the blade and intermingled with more slender sterile hairs. The nucleus of the sporangium divides meiotically, and the 4 resulting cells divide again three or four times to produce 32 or 64 biflagellate zoospores, each with the reduced (haploid) number of chromosomes. Each zoospore develops into a microscopic filamentous gametophyte, the female gametophytes being less branched and having longer cells than the male.

Fig. 13.5. Above: *Macrocystis pyrifera*, fragment of plant. This kelp, common along the Pacific coast of North America, reaches a length of several hundred feet, probably greater than that of any other organism. (×⅕.) (New York Botanical Garden photo.) Below: Root-like holdfast of a kelp. (Photo by W. H. Hodge.)

Half the zoospores from any one sporangium produce male gametophytes; the other half produce female. One-celled antheridia are borne singly on short lateral branches of the male gametophyte. The protoplast of each antheridium develops into a single sperm with two dissimilar lateral flagella. Any cell of the female gametophyte may become an oögonium bearing a single egg. The egg is extruded through a pore at the apex of the oögonial wall but remains attached. Oögonia formed from intercalary (as opposed to apical) cells of a filament develop a lateral protuberance through which the egg is extruded. The sperm swims to the egg, and the zygote resulting from gametic union develops by a series of mitotic divisions into a mature sporophyte.

Cyclosporae

The Cyclosporae are brown algae in which the spores produced in the unilocular sporangia function directly as gametes. The thallus is diploid, the only haploid cells in the life cycle being the spores (or gametes) and their immediate precursors after meiosis within the sporangia (or gametangia). The gametophyte generation has been so reduced that there is no free-living, multicellular gametophyte. The spores (or gametes) are of two types, gametic union being oögamous. Sporangia (or gametangia) are born in special cavities called **conceptacles**; these may be scattered over the surface of the thallus, but more often they are borne only on the inflated tips (called **receptacles**) of the branches. There is only one order, the Fucales, which has about 40 genera and 350 species.

REPRESENTATIVE GENERA

Fucus

Fucus (Figs. 13.6, 13.7) is a common alga of the intertidal zone along rocky shores in the Northern Hemisphere, less commonly occurring in coastal salt marshes. The thallus commonly has a discoid basal holdfast, from which arises a buoyant, dichotomously branched axis several inches or a foot or more long. The branches are flattened and ribbon-like, with a more or less evident midrib. The structure of the branches is rather similar to that of *Laminaria*, with a central medulla of elongate, laterally more or less separated cells interwoven with connecting filaments, this surrounded by a parenchymatous cortex, and the whole enclosed by a single layer of epidermis. The epidermis is more or less permanently meristematic and is sometimes called a meristoderm. Growth in length is due to an apical meristematic cell on each branch. The central cells of the medulla are fairly closely compacted, with numerous connecting filaments, so as to form a midrib. Some species, such as the common *Fucus vesiculosus*, have bladder-like, air-filled cavities scattered along the branches.

The tips of the mature branches are inflated and marked by numerous globose cavities, called **conceptacles** (Fig. 13.9), which have a small external opening (the **ostiole**) and are lined with specialized cells forming a fertile layer. The inflated branch tip is called a receptacle, although this term is used in a quite different sense in the flowering plants. Slender filaments, called **paraphyses**, are produced from many cells of the fertile layer. The tips of some of the paraphyses extend out through the

Fig. 13.6. *Fucus*, growing on rocks along the coast near New York City. (New York Botanical Garden photo.)

Fig. 13.7. *Fucus*. (×⅔.) (Photo by W. H. Hodge.)

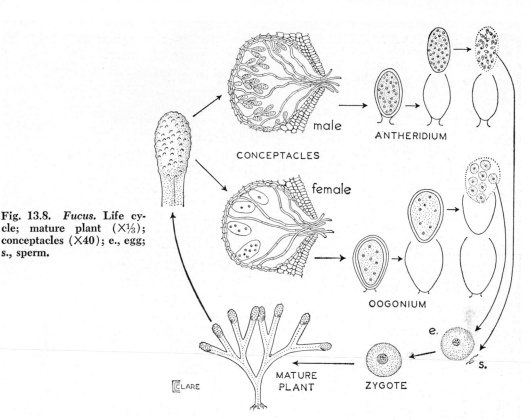

Fig. 13.8. *Fucus*. Life cycle; mature plant (×⅓); conceptacles (×40); e., egg; s., sperm.

ostiole of the conceptacle. Unicellular antheridia are borne either on short branches of the paraphyses or on short single-celled stalks arising directly from the fertile layer. The primary nucleus of the antheridium undergoes a reduction division, followed by a series of usually 4 mitotic divisions, so that typically 64 sperms are produced. The sperms, as in all brown algae, are laterally biflagellate, the anterior flagellum being pinnate.

According to the species, oögonia may be borne in the same conceptacles as the antheridia, in different conceptacles on the same plant, or on different plants. An oögonium arises from the fertile layer of the conceptacle on a short stalk cell. The primary nucleus of the oögonium undergoes meiotic division, and the four result-

ing nuclei each divide mitotically, so that eight eggs are borne in the mature oögonium.

The oögonial wall consists of three layers. Swelling of the innermost layer breaks open the outermost layer, and the cluster of eggs, still contained in the inner and middle layers, passes out through the ostiole, probably being forced out by expansion of gelatinous material in the conceptacle. Continued swelling of the inner layer bursts the middle layer, and the eggs eventually float off through the now watery inner layer.

The antheridial wall has two layers. The inner layer swells, rupturing the outer layer, and the included mass of sperms is extruded through the ostiole into the water, after which the sperms are released by

Division Phaeophyta: Brown Algae 201

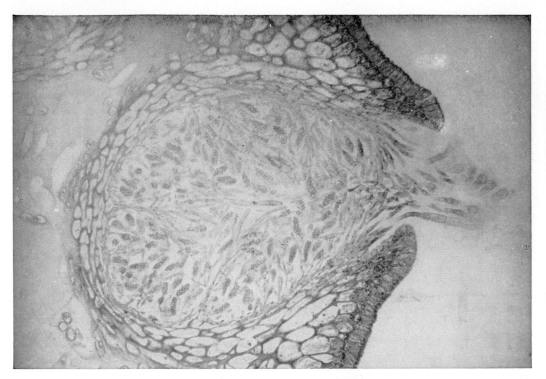

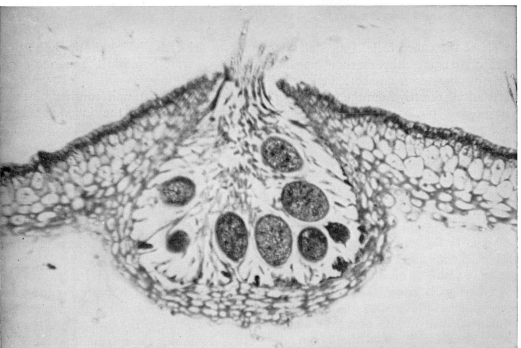

Fig. 13.9. *Fucus.* Conceptacles, cross section. Above, male; below, female. (×100.) (Copyright by General Biological Supply House, Inc., Chicago.)

the progressive softening of the inner layer. Fertilization takes place free in the water. The zygote soon germinates and develops into a mature sporophyte by a series of mitotic divisions.

SARGASSUM

Sargassum (Fig. 13.10) is a chiefly tropical and subtropical genus, occurring both attached alongshore and free-floating in the open ocean. The Sargasso Sea, a large area in the Atlantic Ocean between the West Indies and Africa that is relatively little affected by ocean currents, gets its name from the abundance and conspicuousness of plants of this genus. The sporophyte is larger and more complex than that of *Fucus,* commonly several feet long, and is divided into stem-like and leaf-like portions, with specialized fruiting branches. The sexual cycle is much like that of *Fucus,* except that all but one of the eight nuclei in the oögonium degenerate, leaving a single large egg. The free-floating species of *Sargassum* reproduce asexually by the detachment of fragments which float away and develop into new plants, never producing sexual structures.

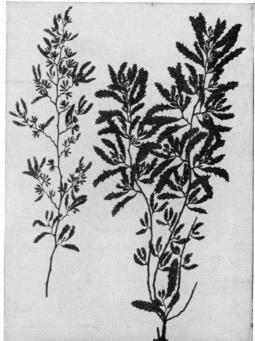

Fig. 13.10. *Sargassum.* Above, S. *hystrix,* left, and an unidentified species, right; below, S. *platycarpum,* left and right. (New York Botanical Garden photo.)

SUGGESTED READING

Chapman, V. J., *Seaweeds and Their Uses,* Methuen & Co., London, 1950, 287 pp. A factual rather than a popular treatment.

Guberlet, M. L., *Seaweeds of the Ebb Tide,* University of Washington Press, Seattle, 1956, 182 pp. A semipopular treatment, with many black and white illustrations.

Smith, G. M., *Marine Algae of the Monterey*

Peninsula, Stanford University Press, Stanford, 1944, 622 pp. A taxonomic treatment, useful over a much wider area than the title suggests. Many black and white illustrations.

Taylor, William Randolph, *Marine Algae of the Northeastern Coast of North America,* 2d ed., University of Michigan Press, Ann Arbor, 1957, 509 pp. A taxonomic treatment with many illustrations.

Division Rhodophyta

RED ALGAE

Plants multicellular or rarely unicellular, the thallus often branched and externally complex, but without much differentiation of tissues; commonly sexual, with male and female gametes, but without flagellated cells of any sort; cell wall with cellulose and pectic compounds; nucleus dividing mitotically; chloroplasts with chlorophyll a and usually chlorophyll d (unique to this division), α- and β-carotene, lutein, r-phycoerythrin, and sometimes r-phycocyanin; food reserves usually stored as cytoplasmic granules of floridean starch, the complex soluble sugar floridoside sometimes also being produced. Two classes, the Bangiophyceae and Florideophyceae.

◄

Dasya peaicellata, a common red alga from the northeast coast of the United States. (×3.) (Photo by W. H. Hodge.)

HISTORY

The red algae were first clearly recognized as a distinct group by W. H. Harvey, who in 1836 segregated them as a subclass Rhodospermeae of a class Algae. Later (in 1855) the red algae were raised to the status of a class, under the name Rhodophyceae, and modern algologists generally consider them to constitute a division, Rhodophyta (Wettstein in 1901). The most important early contributions to our knowledge of the structure and classification of the red algae were made by C. J. Friedrich Schmitz in two papers published in 1883 and 1889. Recognition of the two major groups of red algae (here called the Bangiophyceae and Florideophyceae) dates from his work. The present-day arrangement of the orders of Florideophyceae is based on Schmitz' work, as modified and developed especially by Kylin and his students in a series of papers published from 1923 to 1932.

Fig. 14.1. Harald Kylin (1879–1949), Swedish phycologist, outstanding recent student of the red algae. (Courtesy of the Botaniska Laboratoriet, Lunds Universitet, Sweden.)

DISTRIBUTION

There are about 3500 species of red algae, the vast majority of them marine; only about 200 species occur in fresh water. Red algae occur in all oceans but are commonest in tropical and warm-temperate regions, especially in the Southern Hemisphere. The marine species are almost always attached rather than free-floating; typically they are attached to rocks or other inorganic substrate, but frequently they are epiphytic on other algae, or parasitic on other red algae. Some species occur in the intertidal zone; many others are wholly submerged, at depths of up to 200 meters. Red algae occur at greater depths than any other photosynthetic organisms.

STRUCTURE

The red algae are nearly all multicellular, forming well-developed, often complexly branched thalli which are typically composed of compacted or distinct filaments, without much differentiation of tissues. The cell wall consists of an inner layer composed largely of cellulose, and an outer layer of pectic compounds. In the large class Florideophyceae, the cross wall formed between two sister cells in mitosis is imperfect, with a large central pore or pit. Studies with the electron microscope show that in some species the cytoplasm is continuous from one cell to another through the pore, but in other species the pore is closed (and the cytoplasm interrupted) by a thin membrane. In addition to these primary pits between sister cells, similar secondary pits often develop by dissolution of the wall between adjacent cells which were derived from different mitotic divisions. The pit connections evidently function in the transfer of food and other substances from one cell to another.

Some species of red algae have uninucleate cells, whereas others are multinucleate. The nucleus, although usually small and inconspicuous, has a well-developed nucleolus and nuclear membrane. The chromonemata are often difficult to demonstrate, at least by ordinary methods. Nuclear division is mitotic.

There are one to many chloroplasts in a cell. Solitary chloroplasts often have a central colorless proteinaceous body which is considered to be a pyrenoid, but in this instance the pyrenoid does not serve as a center for starch accumulation. The chloroplasts of those species which have been investigated contain chlorophylls a and usually d, α- and β-carotene, lutein, and probably other xanthophylls, r-phycoerythrin, and often r-phycocyanin. Chlorophyll *a* is the principal chlorophyll, and β-carotene is the principal carotene. Chlorophyll *d* is unique to the red algae. The chloroplasts often contain only a small amount of chlorophyll as compared to the amount of phycobilin pigments.

The phycobilin pigments produced by red algae are designated by the prefix *r-* to distinguish them from the similar but not strictly identical pigments of the blue-green algae, which are designated by the prefix *c-*. The phycobilin pigments, like the carotenoids, absorb light energy and transmit some of it into the photosynthetic process. Phycoerythrin absorbs reasonably well throughout the green part of the spectrum, with its absorption peak near the boundary of green and yellow. Only green light penetrates very far through water, the other wavelengths being practically all screened out within a few meters. Red algae which grow in the lower part of the intertidal zone or wholly submerged in the ocean have abundant phycoerythrin and usually little or no phycocyanin, but those from the upper intertidal zone and from fresh water commonly have a considerable amount of phycocyanin in addition to the phycoerythrin and thus do not have the characteristic red color of the deep-water species.

The carbohydrate reserves of red algae usually accumulate as small cytoplasmic granules of floridean starch, a substance which turns red or reddish violet when treated with iodine. Floridean starch is similar to, but apparently not identical with, glycogen and the amylopectin fraction of ordinary starch. Many red algae accumulate the soluble sugar floridoside in addition to floridean starch. A molecule of floridoside is believed to consist of one molecule of galactose combined with one molecule of glycerol. Galactose is a simple sugar having the same empirical formula as glucose, but with the atoms somewhat differently arranged. Both floridean starch and floridoside are unique to the red algae.

LIFE CYCLE

The structures associated with sexual reproduction in the red algae are so different from those of other algae that a special terminology has been developed to describe them. The male gametes are nonmotile and are called **spermatia** (sing., **spermatium**). The cell in which a spermatium is produced is called either an antheridium, as in other algae, or more often a spermatangium. Each spermatangium produces a single spermatium. The liberated spermatium has a delicate wall or membrane. The female gametangium, comparable to the oögonium of other algae, is called a **carpogonium**. Usually one end of the carpogonium is prolonged into a slender, filamentous appendage called a **trichogyne**. Typically the carpogonium has only one nucleus, which lies in the basal region, but sometimes there is a nucleus in the trichogyne as well. The spermatia are liberated into the water from the spermatangia and are carried passively about. The trichogyne is the receptive part of the carpogonium. A spermatium which lodges against a trichogyne fuses with it, and the male nucleus moves down through the cytoplasm of the trichogyne to the female nucleus at the carpogonial base, where the actual nuclear fusion takes place. Often the carpogonium is associated with some

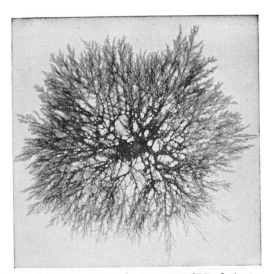

Fig. 14.2. Some common red algae. Top, *Phycodrys rubens*, from the Atlantic coast of North America and Europe; bottom left, *Microcladia coulteri*, from the Pacific coast of the United States; bottom right, *Polysiphonia harveyi*, from the northeast coast of the United States. (All × about ½.) (New York Botanical Garden photos.)

specialized cells to form a recognizable unit called the **procarp.**

The steps following fertilization vary in different groups of red algae. In the more primitive of the two classes, the Bangiophyceae, the first division of the zygotic nucleus is probably meiotic, and the zygote gives rise directly to 4 or more (up to 64) nonmotile spores called **carpospores.** Each carpospore usually develops directly into a new gametophyte. Many of the Bangiophyceae reproduce asexually by spores that are either borne singly in sporangia or are formed by direct metamorphosis of vegetative cells. Bangiophyceae which reproduce asexually may or may not have the sexual cycle also.

In the larger and more advanced of the two classes of red algae, the Florideophyceae, the sexual cycle is more complex, and except in one order (Nemalionales) meiosis is usually preceded by one or more mitotic divisions of the zygote nucleus. Fertilization is followed by the production of specialized filaments, called **gonimoblast filaments.** These arise either directly from the carpogonium, or more often from one or more **auxiliary cells** into which the zygotic nucleus or some of its descendants have migrated. The migration into an auxiliary cell takes place through a specialized filament which grows out from the carpogonium and connects to an adjacent or more or less distant cell. The auxiliary cell may send out secondary connecting filaments through which the descendants of the zygotic nucleus migrate to other auxiliary cells. The original haploid nucleus of the auxiliary cell migrates to the edge of the cytoplasm and takes no part in further developments. The gonimoblast filaments are multicellular and often branched. The mass of gonimoblast filaments is called the gonimoblast. The

visible unit formed by the gonimoblast and associated cells of the parent gametophyte is called the **cystocarp.** The cystocarp wall is not part of the gonimoblast. In many of the Nemalionales, the first division of the zygotic nucleus is meiotic, and the gonimoblast is therefore haploid; in other Florideophyceae the gonimoblast is diploid.

Each cell of a gonimoblast filament, or only the terminal cell or cells, matures into a sporangium called a **carposporangium.** Each carposporangium releases one or four naked **carpospores.** In those red algae in which the gonimoblast is haploid, the carpospores are haploid and are borne singly in the carposporangia. After being released from the carposporangium, a haploid carpospore germinates to form a new gametophyte. Red algae with a diploid gonimoblast may produce haploid or diploid carpospores. In the former case, meiosis occurs in the carposporangium, and each carpospore after release from the carposporangium germinates to form a new gametophyte. Diploid carpospores are borne singly in the carposporangium. After being released from the carposporangium, a diploid carpospore develops into a diploid thallus called a **tetrasporophyte.**

A tetrasporophyte is usually very similar to the gametophyte in appearance. A mature tetrasporophyte bears a number of sporangia. Each of these usually bears four spores and is called a **tetrasporangium;** the included spores are **tetraspores.** A young tetrasporangium generally has a single diploid nucleus that undergoes meiosis to produce four haploid nuclei, which become the nuclei of the tetraspores. After being released from the tetrasporangium, these tetraspores germinate and develop into new gametophytes. It has been suggested that some of the more complex

Division Rhodophyta: Red Algae **211**

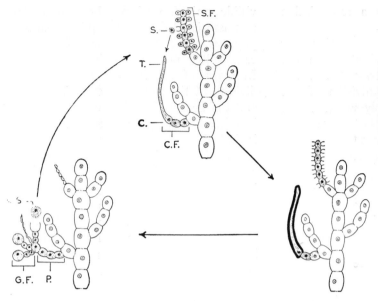

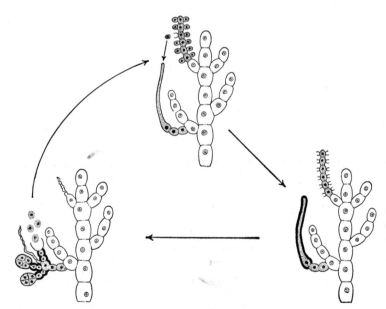

Fig. 14.3. Life cycles of red algae (diagrammatic), showing progressive postponement of meiosis. Diploid cells are shown in heavy outline. C., carpogonium; C.F., carpogonial filament; CS., carpospore; G.F., gonimoblast filament; P., placental cell; S., spermatium; S.F., spermatial filament; T., trichogyne. (Adapted from G. M. Smith, *Cryptogamic Botany*. Courtesy McGraw-Hill Book Co., Inc., New York.)

types of life cycle in the red algae have evolved from simpler ones by postponement of meiosis, a progressively larger number of mitotic divisions being intercalated between fertilization and reduction.

CLASSIFICATION

The red algae may be divided into two classes, the Bangiophyceae and Florideophyceae. The Bangiophyceae have until recently usually all been referred to a sin-

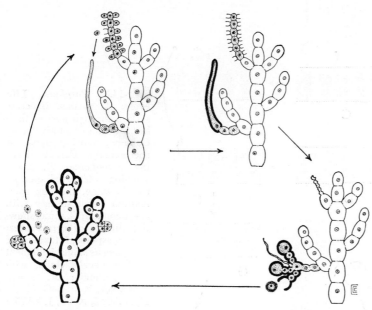

gle order, the Bangiales. Some modern students of the group prefer to recognize several orders instead, but for our purposes the traditional treatment will suffice. The Florideophyceae are customarily divided into six orders, largely on the details of the life cycle. The characteristics of the classes and orders are given in the appendix.

REPRESENTATIVE GENERA

ASTEROCYTIS

Asterocytis (Fig. 14.4) is a widespread fresh-water genus of the Bangiophyceae, rarely collected in the United States. The thallus is a branching filament with typically ellipsoid cells placed end to end. Each cell is enclosed by a gelatinous sheath distinct from the gelatinous sheath which encloses the whole filament. Within each cell there is a single, central, bright blue-green, star-shaped chloroplast with a central pyrenoid. Cell division is intercalary and at right angles to the long axis of the cell. Sexual reproduction is unknown in the genus. Asexual reproduction occurs by the formation of akinetes, or more often by the liberation of the protoplast of a vegetative cell as a naked asexual spore. After lodging in a suitable place, the spore forms a wall and divides mitotically to form a new filament.

Fig. 14.4. *Asterocytis.* (× 500.)

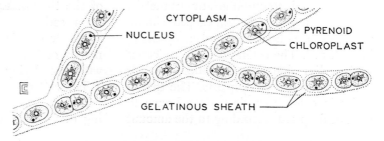

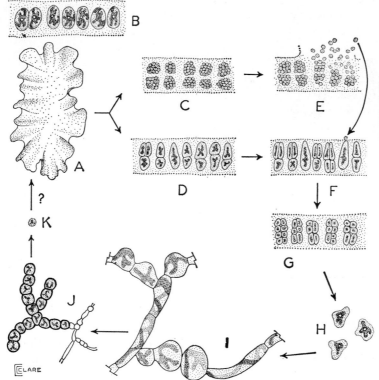

Fig. 14.5. *Porphyra*. Life cycle: *A*, thallus; *B*, cross section through part of thallus, showing vegetative cells; *C*, same, showing masses of spermatangia; *D*, same, showing carpogonia; *E*, same, showing release of spermatia; *F*, same, showing spermatium about to fuse with carpogonium; *G*, same, showing clusters of carpospores; *H*, carpospores; *I*, filament of *Conchocelis* stage; *J*, filament of *Conchocelis* stage, with monosporangia; *K*, monospore. (A, ×⅗; B–G, ×125; H, ×350; I, ×600; J, ×175.)

PORPHYRA

Porphyra (Fig. 14.5) is a marine genus of the Bangiophyceae, commonly found on rocks in the intertidal zone on both coasts of North America as well as in the Old World. The thallus is a flat or convoluted sheet, one or two cells thick and several inches to several feet across. It is attached to the substrate by a basal holdfast. The cells of the thallus are cubical to broadly ellipsoid and are embedded in a very tough common gelatinous matrix. There are one or two star-shaped chloroplasts, each with a large central pyrenoid, in each cell. The small and inconspicuous nucleus lies alongside the chloroplast, or between the two chloroplasts. The thallus varies in color from deep olive brown to pink or deep red, according to the amount and proportions of pigments in the chloroplasts. The pink and red species contain relatively more phycoerythrin and less phycocyanin than the olive-brown ones and occur lower in the intertidal zone.

Spermatangia and carpogonia are borne at the margins of the thallus on the same or on different individuals, according to the species. Spermatangia are produced in masses of 16, 32, 64, or 128, which lie just within the gelatinous matrix of the thallus. Each such mass is formed by a series of mitotic divisions from a single vegetative cell. The gelatinous matrix of the thallus shrinks considerably with the drying exposure between tides. When a thallus with mature spermatangia is flooded by the incoming tide, the swelling of the gelatinous matrix squeezes the male cells out into the water. The spermatia are carried about by the water, and some of them lodge against carpogonial portions of thalli.

Some of the vegetative cells near the margin of the thallus undergo minor modification to become carpogonia. A mature carpogonium is ellipsoid, with a small protuberance at one or both ends. The protuberance, which commonly reaches the surface of the matrix, may be regarded as a rudimentary trichogyne. In some cases the carpogonium does not reach the surface of the thallus, and the male nucleus is delivered to it through a tube which grows out of the spermatium. In any case, the spermatial nucleus migrates into the carpogonium and fuses with the carpogonial nucleus. The zygote then divides repeatedly to form 2, 4, 8, 16, or 32 carpospores. It has been claimed that the first division of the zygote is meiotic, but this has not yet been definitely established.

The naked carpospores are extruded from the thallus in the same manner as spermatia. After a few days in which it creeps about very slowly in an amoeboid manner, a carpospore rounds up, forms a wall, and undergoes a series of divisions to form a branching filament. It has only recently been recognized that these filaments are stages in the life cycle of *Porphyra*. The filamentous stage of *Porphyra umbilicalis* is a shell-boring alga that has previously been known as *Conchocelis rosea*. Filaments of the *Conchocelis* stage produce sporangia that each contain a single spore; and recent studies suggest that each of these spores develops into a gametophytic thallus of the ordinary *Porphyra* type.

NEMALION

Nemalion (Fig. 14.6) is found attached to rocks in the middle of the inter-

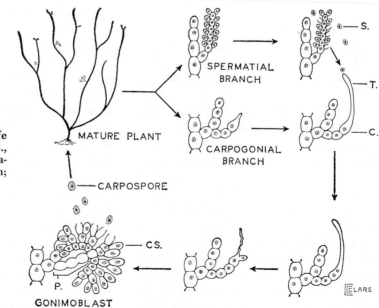

Fig. 14.6. *Nemalion.* **Life cycle: C., carpogonium; CS., carposporangium; P., placental cell; S., spermatium; T., trichogyne.**

MATURE PLANT

SPERMATIAL BRANCH

CARPOGONIAL BRANCH

S.

T.

C.

CARPOSPORE

GONIMOBLAST

P.

CS.

tidal zone. The reddish-brown mature thallus is several inches long and irregularly and sparsely branched; each branch is cylindrical, somewhat wiry in appearance, and composed of compacted filaments. The core of a mature branch is made up of intertwined longitudinal filaments composed of elongate cells without chloroplasts. This colorless central axis is enclosed by a sheath of short, densely branched, radially spreading filaments which commonly terminate in long slender hairs. Most cells of the lateral filaments are barrel-shaped, with a single stellate (star-shaped) chloroplast that has an evident pyrenoid. The cross wall between adjacent cells of any filament is imperfect, with a distinct pit connection.

Spermatangia and carpogonia are produced on the same plant, but not always at the same time. An ordinary vegetative cell terminating one of the lateral filaments divides repeatedly to form a chain of four to seven cells which become the spermatangial mother cells. Each of the spermatangial mother cells generally produces four radially arranged spermatangia. Each spermatangium contains a single uninucleate spermatium, which is eventually liberated by rupture of the spermatangial wall.

The one to five (typically three) cells of a carpogonial filament are produced by successive divisions from an intercalary cell of one of the lateral filaments of the thallus. The lateral filament thus appears to be bifurcate, with one of its two tips being carpogonial filament. The terminal cell of the carpogonial filament becomes the carpogonium, which is tipped by a well-developed trichogyne. When a spermatium lodges against the trichogyne, the walls separating the two dissolve at the point of contact. The spermatial nucleus divides, and one or both of the daughter nuclei are delivered to the trichogyne. One of the daughter nuclei moves down into the body of the carpogonium and fuses with the carpogonial nucleus.

The first division of the zygotic nucleus is meiotic. A horizontal cross wall is formed in the carpogonium between the first two nuclei formed by the reduction division. The nucleus in the lower of the two cells does not divide again, and eventually it disintegrates. The nucleus in the terminal cell divides again, and one of the daughter nuclei moves out into a protuberance which eventually becomes delimited by a cross wall. This latter cell becomes the initial of a gonimoblast filament. Several additional gonimoblast initials are produced in the same fashion by the terminal cell. Each of these gonimoblast initials develops by a series of mitotic divisions into a short, compactly branched, gonimoblast filament, and the apical cell of each of the branches eventually enlarges to become a carposporangium. Meanwhile the cross walls separating the lower cells of the carpogonial filament from each other dissolve, as does also the lower wall of the lower of the two carpogonial cells. The resulting elongate cell which connects the cystocarp (the collection of gonimoblast filaments and the upper carpogonial daughter cell from which they are developed) to the vegetative portion of the thallus is often called the **placental cell.**

Each carposporangium ruptures at the tip and releases a single naked carpospore. Thereafter a new carposporangium may be produced within the wall of the old one by proliferation from the cell beneath, and this process may be repeated several times during the summer. The whole thallus dies and disintegrates in the fall. The naked

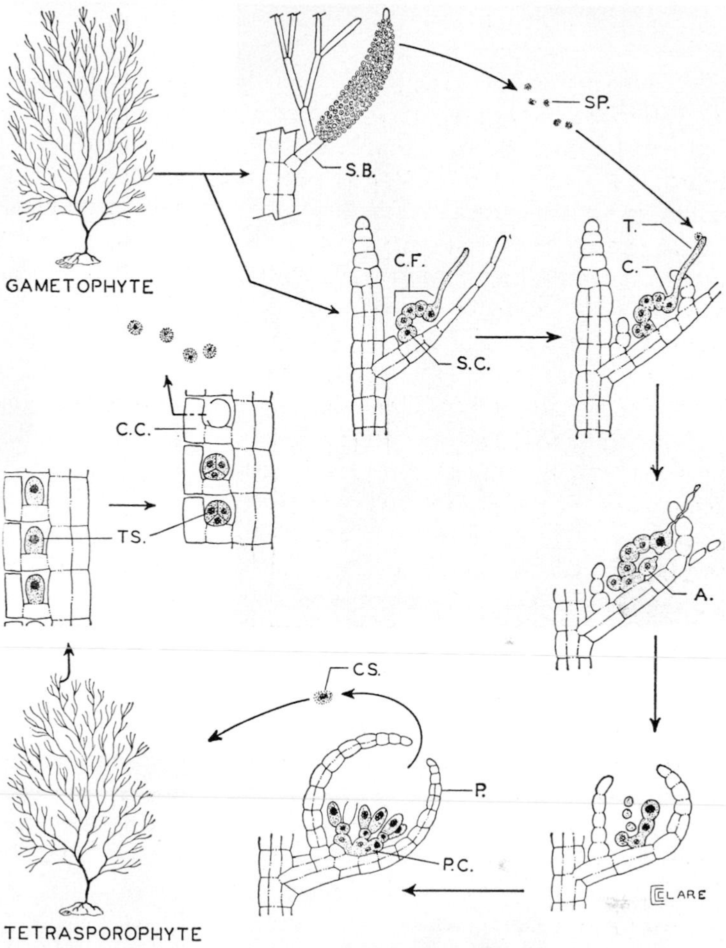

Fig. 14.7. *Polysiphonia.* Life cycle: A., auxiliary cell; C., carpogonium; C.C., cover cell; C.F., carpogonial filament; CS., carpospore; P., pericarp; P.C., placental cell; S.B., spermatial branch; S.C., supporting cell; SP., spermatium; T., trichogyne; TS., tetraspore.

carpospore attaches itself to the substrate and develops a wall. By a series of mitotic divisions a sparingly branched filament is formed, and the plant passes the winter in this filamentous stage. The characteristic mature thallus is produced in the spring by further growth and development from the overwintering filament.

POLYSIPHONIA

Polysiphonia (Figs. 14.7, 14.8) is a common genus in the intertidal zone on both coasts of North America and else-where. The reddish or pinkish thallus is commonly several inches long and delicately much branched, forming beautiful and artistically appealing patterns. A cross section of a mature branch shows an axial cell, surrounded by four or more pericentral cells. The pericentral cells are derived by mitotic division from the axial cell. All cells are uninucleate, and there are evident pit connections between adjacent cells. The pericentral cells, at least, contain numerous small chloroplasts. Both the axial and the pericentral cells are elongate and slender. Older branches of some species

Division Rhodophyta: Red Algae 217

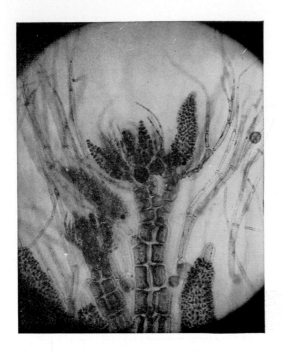 

 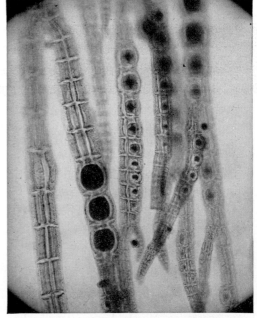

Fig. 14.8. *Polysiphonia*. Top, left and right, spermatangial clusters. Bottom left, cystocarp with enclosed gonimoblast; bottom right, tetraspores. (Photomicrographs, all copyright by General Biological Supply House, Inc., Chicago.)

develop an outer layer of small cells external to the pericentral cells.

Younger parts of the branches bear scattered **trichoblasts.** These are specialized branches, initially uniseriate, dichotomously branched one or more times, and with little or no pigmentation. Some trichoblasts are sterile, but others bear male or female gametangia. An individual gametophyte is usually or always unisexual.

One of the first two branches of a male trichoblast will produce spermatangia, but the other branch usually forks repeatedly without bearing spermatangia. The fertile branch of a male trichoblast is structurally somewhat like an ordinary vegetative branch with an axial filament surrounded by pericentral cells. Each pericentral cell cuts off one or more spermatangial mother cells on its outer face, and each of these bears one to four spermatangia, according to the species, on its outer surface. The resulting spermatangial branch, which is barely or scarcely visible to the naked eye, is covered all around with spermatangia. When magnified, its appearance casually suggests that of an irregular ear of corn. Each spermatangium ruptures to release its single spermatium, after which a new spermatangium is sometimes developed from the spermatangial mother cell within the wall of the old spermatangium.

The female trichoblasts are more modified and reduced than the male. The main axis is five to seven cells long, and the two basal cells give rise to surrounding pericentral cells. One of the pericentral cells in the upper tier becomes the supporting cell which gives rise to a curved, four-celled, carpogonial filament. The terminal cell of this filament becomes the carpogonium, with a definite trichogyne.

The supporting cell also gives rise to two short sterile filaments.

Fertilization takes place in the usual manner after the spermatia have been carried to the trichogynes by water currents. The supporting cell then produces on the upper lateral surface a new daughter cell which lies near the base of the carpogonium and becomes the auxiliary cell. A tubular connection is established between the auxiliary cell and the base of the carpogonium, and a diploid nucleus, formed by mitotic division of the zygote nucleus, migrates into the auxiliary cell. A densely compacted mass of gonimoblast filaments grows out from the auxiliary cell, and meanwhile the supporting cell, the auxiliary cell, and the cells of the sterile branches from the supporting cell fuse to form an irregular placental cell. The carpogonial filament itself withers and does not contribute directly to the formation of either the placental cell or the gonimoblast filaments. After fertilization a rim or cup of tissue arising from the pericentral cells of the trichoblast, grows out around the supporting cell and its derivatives. By the time the gonimoblast is mature, this cup has become a vase-like enclosing pericarp (or cystocarp wall) with a small opening at the tip. The term pericarp is used for an entirely different, although vaguely analogous, structure in angiosperms.

The cells of the gonimoblast filaments are diploid and uninucleate. The terminal cell of each of these filaments becomes a carposporangium which liberates a single diploid carpospore.

A carpospore grows and develops by a series of mitotic divisions into a tetrasporophyte which vegetatively resembles a gametophyte. The tetrasporangia are borne singly within the branches, adjacent to the axial filament and internal to a pair of cover cells. The tetrasporangium, the cover cells, and one or two other cells associated with the tetrasporangium all arise by a series of mitotic divisions from a single pericentral cell which is smaller than the other pericentral cells in its tier. Usually tetrasporangia are developed in several successive tiers, forming a row. The young tetrasporangium contains a single diploid nucleus which undergoes meiosis to produce four haploid nuclei, which become the nuclei of the four tetraspores. The two cover cells bow apart to release the tetraspores after the tetrasporangium breaks open. A tetraspore has the haploid number of chromosomes and develops by a series of mitotic divisions into a gametophyte.

CORALLINE ALGAE

The coralline algae, constituting the family Corallinaceae of the order Crypto-

nemiales, are marine red algae in which the thallus becomes strongly calcified. Such genera as *Lithothamnion* and *Porolithon* are important contributors to the growth of coral reefs. The algae commonly grow closely intermingled with coral animals, which are also heavily calcified. The life cycle of the coralline algae is more or less similar to that of *Polysiphonia*, with a number of differences in detail.

FOSSIL FORMS

The coralline algae have been active reef builders in the geologic past as well as in recent times, and fossils which are identified as representing the modern genus *Lithothamnion* are known from as far back as the Triassic period. Other fossils which very probably represent calcareous red algae are abundantly represented in strata of Ordovician to Jurassic age.

Fig. 14.9. *Gonolithon strictum*, a coralline red alga from the Bahama Islands. (About natural size.) (New York Botanical Garden photo.)

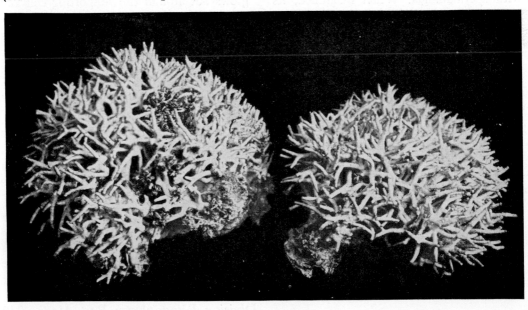

Fig. 14.10. *Chondrus crispus*, the Irish moss. (About natural size.) (Copyright by General Biological Supply House, Inc., Chicago.)

ECONOMIC IMPORTANCE

Red algae are economically important as the source of the colloids agar and carrageenin. Prior to World War II, agar was produced almost entirely in Japan, from the genus *Gelidium*. During and after the war, a number of other genera, occurring on both coasts of North America and on the coasts of Australia and South Africa, have also been used as a source of agar. Agar is widely used as a culture medium for bacteria (see Chapter 6), as a bulk producer in laxatives, and as a stabilizer or filler in various commercial foods.

Chondrus crispus (Fig. 14.10), the "Irish moss," is the traditional source of carrageenin, which has properties different from those of agar and algin. Irish moss is harvested on the coasts of northern Europe, New England, and the Maritimes, and colloids very similar to carrageenin are now obtained from other red algae elsewhere in the world. Carrageenin is extensively used as an emulsifying and stabilizing agent, as, for example, in chocolate milk.

Porphyra is used for food in the Orient, both as a prime ingredient of soup and as a flavoring for other foods. The

Division Rhodophyta: Red Algae 221

plant is cultivated on tidelands in Japan and is harvested annually.

The role of red algae in the formation of coral reefs has already been discussed. Red algae also have some significance as the original producers of the food on which marine animals directly or indirectly depend, but, like the brown algae, they are much less important in this regard than the diatoms and dinoflagellates.

RELATIONSHIPS

The red algae are so different from all other algae as to be taxonomically rather isolated; their only likely relatives are the blue-green algae. The red algae and blue-green algae are alike in having phycobilin pigments, which are not known in other organisms (except some members of the Cryptophyceae). They are also similar in the complete absence of flagellated cells. Furthermore, floridean starch, the characteristic carbohydrate reserve of the red algae, is chemically allied to cyanophycean starch, the characteristic carbohydrate reserve of the blue-green algae. The red algae differ from the blue-green algae in the presence of a nucleus, in having definite plastids, in having chlorophyll d in addition to chlorophyll a, in the usually more complex structure of the thallus, and in being usually sexual, often with a very complex life cycle. All these features may be regarded as evolutionary advances over the condition in the blue-green algae. The sexual processes in the red algae are so different from the sexual processes of other algae that a separate origin of the sexuality in red algae seems quite possible.

The Florideophyceae are the more advanced of the two classes of red algae, and if this class were the only one known, the relationships of the group might be questionable. The Bangiophyceae, however, are less highly modified, and some of the genera which have blue-green chloroplasts and lack sexual processes are very suggestive of the Cyanophyceae. The evidence indicates that the blue-green algae are ancestral to the Bangiophyceae and that the Florideophyceae are derived from the Bangiophyceae.

CHAPTER 15

Lepiota americana, a common mushroom. (×2.) This genus contains both edible and poisonous species, as well as species which are poisonous to some people and harmless to others. (Photo by Hugh Spencer, from National Audubon Society.)

◀

Division Fungi CHAPTER 15

Unicellular to multicellular or acellular plants with well-defined, mitotically dividing nuclei, without chlorophyll and without vascular tissue, typically more or less filamentous, with or without cross walls, less often distinctly unicellular, and sometimes plasmodial, or some of the filaments sometimes compacted into structures of definite macroscopic form but usually without much differentiation of tissues; walls of the cells or filaments mostly chitinous, sometimes of cellulose; food reserves typically glycogen; gametangia, when present, "unicellular," though often with many nuclei. Four classes, the Myxomycetes, Phycomycetes, Ascomycetes, and Basidiomycetes, plus the Fungi Imperfecti, a group in which the life cycle has bypassed the stages which permit assignment of the organism in one of the other classes. The Myxomycetes are here considered to constitute a subdivision Myxomycotina; the other classes collectively make up the subdivision Eumycotina.

Fungus (pl., **fungi**) is a Latin word, originally applied to mushrooms, the meaning of which has gradually been expanded to cover molds, yeasts, and all other organisms which seem to be related to the mushrooms. The fungi constitute part of one of the 24 classes of plants recognized by Linnaeus in the *Species Plantarum.* It has been estimated that there are more than 40,000 known species of fungi, and that at least as many more, perhaps twice as many, remain to be discovered. More than 75,000 species are listed in the *Sylloge Fungorum,* but many of these names represent inadvertent redescriptions of previously known species. The *Sylloge Fungorum* is an index, originally prepared by the Italian mycologist Pier Andrea Saccardo (1845–1920), in which an attempt is made to reprint in a standardized form all the original descriptions of species of fungi, with a reference to the original publication of each. The first complete set of *Sylloge Fungorum* occupied eight volumes, which were published serially from 1882 to 1889. Seventeen supplements have since been issued. The most recent and probably the last of these appeared in 1931.

Subdivision Myxomycotina: Myxomycetes

DEFINITION AND VEGETATIVE FEATURES

The Myxomycetes, or **slime molds,** are fungi which in part or all of the "vegetative" stage are amoeboid and usually holozoic, consisting of a mass of protoplasm in which the nuclei are not separated by cell walls. The characteristic "vegetative" or assimilative body of most slime molds is called a **plasmodium,** (Fig.

15.1) although it has been shown that the usual definition of a plasmodium (a naked, multinucleate mass of protoplasm not divided into separate cells) does not strictly apply. The mass of protoplasm seems on casual observation to be naked, but careful studies have shown that it is bounded by a flexible gelatinous wall or covering distinct from the proper protoplast. If this wall is ruptured, some of the protoplasm tends to flow out in a fashion that has been roughly compared to bleeding.

The plasmodium, as we shall continue to call it, is thin, colored or colorless, and often several inches across. It moves in an amoeboid manner, flowing slowly across or through the substrate and ingesting bacteria and other small organic particles. The limiting membrane is evidently very thin at the advancing front,

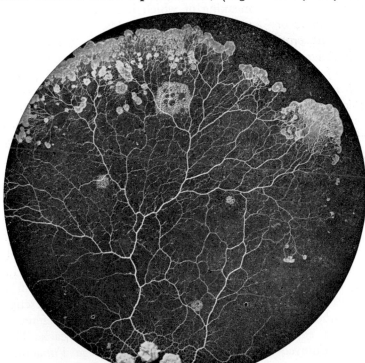

Fig. 15.1. Plasmodium of a myxomycete (*Physarum*). (Much enlarged.) (Copyright by General Biological Supply House, Inc., Chicago.)

and food particles are engulfed in an amoeboid manner. The lining of a food vacuole is part of the original exterior surface of the plasmodium. Farther back from the tip, the wall becomes thicker and more readily demonstrable as a separate structure. The protoplast flows forward within the wall, while the wall itself remains stationary. Consequently the old wall is left behind the advancing plasmodium as a slime trail which soon degenerates or decays. The chemical nature of this wall has not been established. Waste particles are left behind with the slime trail. The plasmodium also contains contractile vacuoles which presumably have an excretory function.

DISTRIBUTION AND HISTORY

The Myxomycetes are common but inconspicuous inhabitants of dead wood and other vegetable remains, and of the dung of herbivorous animals, often spending most of their lives within the substrate and emerging only when about to produce sporangia. They were first recognized as a natural group in 1829 by the Swedish mycologist Elias Magnus Fries (1794–1878), who is considered to be the father of systematic mycology. Fries considered the Myxomycetes to be a group within what we now call the class Basidiomycetes. Four years later another botanist elevated them to a rank coordinate with the other major groups of fungi, and the status of the slime molds as a group distinct from the other fungi has been essentially unchallenged since that time. Many students have even regarded them as animals, under the name Mycetozoa, rather than as fungi. The relationships of the Myxomycetes are discussed on p. 285. The greatest contribution to our understanding of the morphology and taxonomy of the group was made by the Polish mycologist Josef Rostafinski (1850–1928) in a monograph published in 1874.

LIFE CYCLE

The typical myxomycete life cycle (Fig. 15.2) is as follows: The spore wall ruptures to release one or, less often, two naked, biflagellate cells called **swarm spores** or **swarm cells.** The flagella are both of the whiplash type and are unequal, one often being so short as to be easily overlooked in ordinary microscopic preparations. These swarm cells move and ingest food particles in an amoeboid fashion; in at least some cases they also absorb soluble food material. Several mitotic divisions may or may not occur; the resulting cells all become separated. Eventually the swarm cells become more rounded and retract their flagella.

The **myxamoebae,** as these modified cells without flagella are called, usually enlarge and undergo several mitotic cell divisions, after which the separated individual myxamoebae act as gametes and fuse in pairs to form zygotes. Sometimes swarm cells fuse to form zygotes without going through the nonflagellated, myxamoeboid stage; in some other instances, the cells released by a germinating spore are nonflagellate myxamoebae, so that there is no flagellated stage. The zygote grows and undergoes a series of mitotic nuclear divisions without becoming differentiated into separate cells, thus forming a plasmodium. Individual zygotes or plasmodia may also fuse with one another, without subsequent nuclear fusion, so that the nuclei of a mature plasmodium may

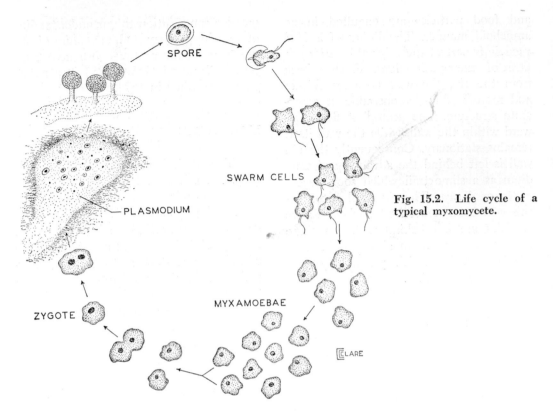

SPORE

SWARM CELLS

PLASMODIUM

ZYGOTE

MYXAMOEBAE

CLARE

Fig. 15.2. Life cycle of a typical myxomycete.

have been derived from a number of different zygotes.

Eventually the plasmodium heaps itself up somewhat and produces a number of short erect branches which develop into sporangia. The sporangia vary in length from less than 1 mm to fully 1 cm, and compound clustered sporangia formed by some species may be as much as 10 cm across. Often the sporangium is borne on a definite stalk. A sporangium with its stalk (if any) is called a fruiting body (Figs. 15.3, 15.4). A thin, very often calcified wall, called the **peridium**, surrounds the sporangium. The peridium often contains cellulose. A network of slender vacuoles is formed within the developing sporangium, and this network is often augmented by slender invaginations

of the peridium. The mature sporangium contains a network of fibrous, often calcified strands, called the **capillitium** (Fig. 15.4) which is formed by deposition from the surrounding protoplasm into the vacuolar network. The vacuolar network of the young sporangium seems to be the direct precursor of the capillitium of the mature sporangium.

The nuclei within the developing sporangium undergo reduction division, and a very large number of spores, each with the haploid number of chromosomes, is formed by cleavage of the protoplast. Sometimes there is a central column, the **columella**, which does not develop into spores. Each spore is surrounded by a definite wall, which in various species has been reported to contain cellulose,

Fig. 15.3. Myxomycete fruiting bodies, on dead wood. Left, *Lycogala epidendrum* (×½); right, *Trichia floriformis* (about natural size). (New York Botanical Garden photos.)

Fig. 15.4. *Stemonitis* fruiting bodies. Left, on wood (×3); right, part of capillitium, after discharge of spores (×100). (Copyright by General Biological Supply House, Inc., Chicago.)

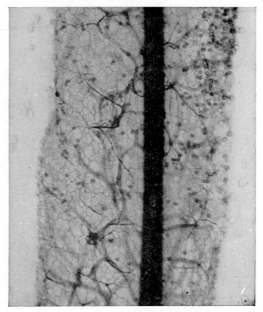

chitin, or neither of these substances. The capillitium regulates the release of the spores, preventing all of them from being discharged at once. Any part of the plasmodium which is not used up in the formation of spores and sporangia may return to "vegetative" activity, sometimes after going through a resting stage.

TAXONOMY

As here defined, the Myxomycetes consist of 8 orders and perhaps 500 species. Most of the species are encompassed in four orders, the Liceales, Trichiales, Stemonitales, and Physarales. These four orders are the typical Myxomycetes. With or without the addition of the Ceratiomyxales, an evidently but less closely allied order, these are often considered to constitute a subclass, the Myxogastres. The remaining three orders, the Acrasiales, Labyrinthulales, and Plasmodiophorales, are excluded by some mycologists from the Myxomycetes entirely. The Plasmodiophorales resemble some of the simple Phycomycetes in some respects and are sometimes referred to that class, although the flagella of the swarm cells of *Plasmodiophora* are both of the whiplash type, as in other Myxomycetes, instead of one being whiplash and one pinnate, as in biflagellate Phycomycetes.

The Acrasiales, consisting of only about 20 species, are particularly interest-

Fig. 15.5. *Dictyostelium discoideum,* a member of the Acrasiales. Naked cells aggregating to form a plasmodium-like body. (× about 1500.) (Courtesy of J. T. Bonner.)

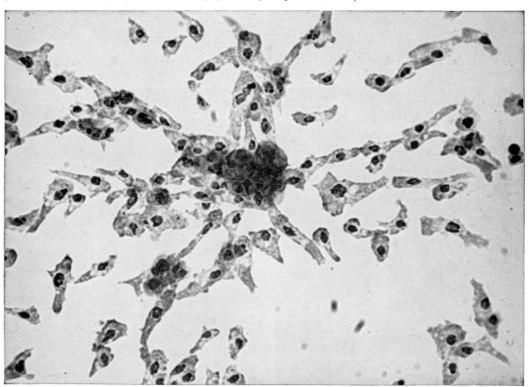

ing because of their relatively primitive structure as compared to more typical Myxomycetes. The individual naked cells which aggregate (Fig. 15.5) to form the vegetative body retain their identity throughout, or until immediately before the formation of spores, and the basal cells of the "plasmodium" sometimes develop cellulose walls at the time the upper cells are sporulating. The "sporangia" lack the peridium and capillitium characteristic of most other Myxomycetes, and it might be questioned whether the term *sporangium* can properly be used, because the clusters of spores are not enclosed in a case or container. Those who consider the Myxomycetes to belong to a division or subdivision apart from the true fungi sometimes elevate the Acrasiales, Plasmodiophorales, and Labyrinthulales to the status of classes, coordinate with the class Myxomycetes, and this may ultimately prove to be the most acceptable treatment. A synoptical key to the eight orders here recognized is given in the appendix.

ECONOMIC IMPORTANCE

The Myxomycetes are of relatively little economic importance. They contribute to the carbon and nitrogen cycles, etc., by using particles of organic matter as food, but they also consume bacteria, which play a similar role in these cycles. Some of the taxonomically peripheral genera are parasites of other plants. Clubroot of cabbage is caused by *Plasmodiophora brassicae*, and *Labyrinthula macrocystis* is believed to be the cause of the wasting disease of *Zostera marina*, a coastal marine seed plant which is much used as food by waterfowl.

Subdivision Eumycotina

The fungi other than the Myxomycetes constitute a coherent group which may be considered to represent a subdivision, the Eumycotina, as contrasted to the subdivision Myxomycotina for the Myxomycetes. The Eumycotina have definite walls which are usually chitinous, less often composed largely of cellulose. Fungus chitin is not strictly identical with insect chitin; the formula $(C_{22}H_{54}N_4O_{21})_n$ has been suggested for fungus chitin. Most Eumycotina are more or less filamentous; a small proportion are unicellular and uninucleate or have a multinucleate nonfilamentous protoplast. A single fungus filament is called a **hypha.** Most hyphae are branched, and a mass of branching hyphae is called a **mycelium.** Many parasitic fungi produce special short hyphae, called **haustoria,** which enter the cells of the host and absorb nutriment. The term *haustorium* is also applied to organs of similar function but different structure produced by some other kinds of parasitic plants. Many fungi also produce relatively short hyphae which penetrate the substrate and serve to anchor the external mycelium. Such hyphae are called **rhizoids,** a general term applied to any structure which performs some of the functions of a root (especially anchorage) but is anatomically rather simple, consisting of only one or a few cells, or part of a cell.

The Eumycotina, like the bacteria, commonly release exoenzymes into the surrounding substrate. Different kinds of fungi produce different kinds of exoenzymes, and a very large proportion of the naturally occurring organic substances can be used as food by one or another kind of fungus. Food materials which have been more or less completely digested by the action of these enzymes are absorbed by the fungus. Absorbed food which is not immediately used is stored in the cytoplasm in a variety of different chemical forms, the form often being influenced by the original nature of the food. The most common reserve carbohydrate among the fungi is glycogen. The alcohol mannitol is also frequently found. Starch is sometimes found associated with the cell walls. Many fungi store food as minute droplets of oil.

The sexual cycle is extremely varied among different fungi, with nuclear fusion often being delayed until long after the gametic nuclei have been brought together in the same protoplast. The actual union of nuclei is referred to as **karyogamy**, and the fusion of protoplasts which precedes karyogamy is called **plasmogamy**. The first division of a fusion nucleus is usually meiotic, with exceptions especially among various Phycomycetes and some of the yeasts. The structures associated with nuclear fusion and reduction division provide some of the most consistent guides to systematic relationships within the fungi, and the stage in which these structures are produced is called the **perfect** stage. When nuclear fusion and meiosis are well separated in the life cycle, the stage associated with nuclear fusion is considered to be the perfect stage. Often a fruiting body of definite macroscopic size and form is produced at the perfect stage. A fruiting body is, theoretically, composed of closely compacted hyphae, but the compaction is often so thorough that a more or less parenchymatous tissue is formed.

Reduction division usually leads directly, or after only one or a few intervening mitotic divisions, to the formation of spores. Many fungi have life cycles in which several different kinds of spores are produced. Spores which are produced immediately or very soon after meiosis are, in this text, designated as **sexual spores,** in contrast to the **asexual spores** which are not associated with reduction division. These two terms, although not at all new, are not accepted by all botanists, and some authors (particularly those who would restrict the application of the term *sex* to distinctly male and female structures or organisms) prefer the terms **meiospore** and **mitospore.**

Spores of the Eumycotina are usually nonmotile and are provided with a definite wall, except among some Phycomycetes, which have naked spores with one or two flagella. When two flagella are present, one is of the whiplash type and the other of the pinnate type, in contrast to the Myxomycetes, in which both flagella are of the whiplash type.

The term **conidium** (or gonidium) has often been used to apply to any asexual spore in the fungi, or elsewhere. (The spelling with the *c* rather than the *g* is almost universally used by mycologists.) Among the fungi, conidia are usually produced by the differentiation and abscission of a hyphal tip, and often the same hypha cuts off a series of conidia one after another. Any hypha on which conidia are produced may be called a **conidiophore,** especially if it is visibly different from hyphae which do not produce conidia. Many fungi produce more than one kind of conidium, or they produce conidia of such distinctive type as to warrant a distinctive name. Mycologists do not generally use the term *conidia* for spores produced in sporangia, even though such spores in the Phycomycetes are sometimes strictly asexual.

Eumycotina: Phycomycetes

DEFINITION AND HISTORY

The Phycomycetes are fungi which are typically coenocytic and usually more or less filamentous, and in which the perfect stage, usually consisting of a zygospore or an oöspore, is not borne on a definite fruiting body. Ordinarily the only cross walls in the mycelium are those which delimit the reproductive structures. Most Phycomycetes produce numerous spores in a sporangium, unlike nearly all other Eumycotina. Many Phycomycetes also produce flagellated gametes or zoospores; flagellated cells are unknown in other Eumycotina. The Phycomycetes were first recognized as a coherent group in 1873 by the German mycologist Heinrich Anton De Bary (1831–1888). The name Phycomycetes means algal fungi, and this translation of the scientific name is sometimes used as an English name for the group.

DISTRIBUTION AND TAXONOMY

Phycomycetes occur as parasites of a wide variety of terrestrial and aquatic plants, insects, and aquatic animals, and also as saprophytes wherever suitable organic remains are found. They are more likely to occur on vegetable than on animal matter, and they do not ordinarily attack wood.

It has been estimated that there are about 1300 known species of Phycomycetes. Disregarding a few small aberrant groups of doubtful affinities, they may be classified into nine orders, as indicated in the appendix. Four of these orders, the

Fig. 15.6. Left, Elias Magnus Fries (1794–1878), Swedish mycologist, the father of systematic mycology. Right, Heinrich Anton De Bary (1831–1888), German mycologist, who worked out the life cycle of *Puccinia graminis* and made many other important mycological contributions. (Photos courtesy of the Department of Plant Pathology, Cornell Unversity.)

Chytridiales, Saprolegniales, Peronosporales, and Mucorales, are discussed in this chapter. It is customary to arrange the orders into two groups, the Zygomycetes (orders Mucorales and Entomophthorales) and Oömycetes (all other orders) without implying a precise taxonomic status for these groups.

CHYTRIDIALES

The chytrids (Fig. 15.7) are among the simplest fungi in structure. They are all either aquatic or dependent on water for their dispersal. The zoospores and motile gametes of a given species are all alike in appearance, and in many cases they are interchangeable in function. They are naked, uninucleate, and provided with a single posterior whiplash flagellum. Two cells which would otherwise function as zoospores may unite isogamously to form a zygote, or sexual fusion of the two cells may be delayed until after the zoospores have settled down on the surface of the

host and lost their flagella, or even until after these cells have entered a cell of the host. Thereafter the sexual and asexual cycles are, at least in most cases, essentially similar, except that the first division of the zygotic nucleus is a reduction division which sometimes leads directly to the formation of zoospores.

Many chytrids are intracellular parasites, but some are saprophytes or parasites which remain attached to the surface of the host or substrate and extract nourishment by means of haustoria or rhizoids which penetrate the host cells or the substrate. The infecting fungus cell, be it zoospore or zygote, soon develops a definite wall, which is usually chitinous but sometimes contains cellulose in addition or instead. Among those chytrids which are intracellular parasites, the growing parasitic fungus cell may remain essentially spherical or ellipsoid, or it may send out a number of short, branching hyphae which have been called rhizoids. Some kinds of chytrids, especially those which are not wholly intracellular, develop a small coeno-

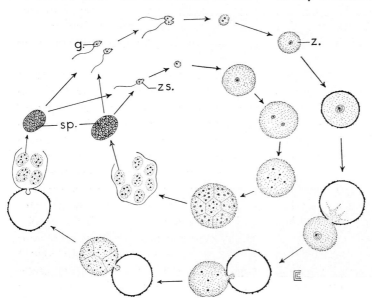

Fig. 15.7. Life cycle of a monocentric chytrid: g., gamete; sp., sporangium; z., zygote; zs., zoospore.

cytic mycelium with scattered swollen areas, each such swelling being comparable to the individual cell of simpler forms. The two types are referred to as **mono-centric** and **polycentric chytrids,** according to the number of swollen areas which make up the major part of the body of the fungus.

The nucleus divides repeatedly as the cell (or mycelium) enlarges, and eventually the protoplast of the cell (or of the individual center of a polycentric mycelium) becomes segmented into a very large number of uniflagellated, naked swarm cells, or into a smaller number of uninucleate or few-nucleate cells, each provided with its own wall. In the latter case, the individual cells thus formed may be wholly included within the wall of the original parent cell, or more or less exserted from it. After a series of further nuclear divisions, the protoplast of each of these cells becomes segmented into a large number of uniflagellate naked swarm cells. Thus, in some chytrids the original cell or individual center of the mycelium develops directly into a sporangium, whereas in others a number of sporangia are formed within or from the original cell or center. The swarm cells function as zoospores or as isogametes, according to the species and the circumstances. There are many chytrids in which only the asexual cycle, with the swarm cells acting as zoospores, is known; but more careful study will doubtless show that some of these also have the sexual cycle.

The mature sporangium, or cluster of sporangia, commonly occupies most or all of the space enclosed by the cell wall of the host, the host protoplast previously having died and been largely used by the fungus. Rupture of the cell wall of the host releases the sporangia or the individual swarm cells, which escape from the sporangium through a local softening of the wall or through a lid like a trap door, known as an operculum.

Most chytrids are of little economic interest. *Synchytrium,* a genus of monocentric chytrids without rhizoids, frequently parasitizes vascular plants. One species, *S. endobioticum,* causes the wart disease of potatoes.

SAPROLEGNIALES

The Saprolegniales, or **water molds,** occur most commonly in fresh water, but many of them inhabit moist soil. They are saprophytes living on dead plant or animal remains, or they are facultative or obligate parasites of algae, fish, and various small aquatic animals, or occasionally they are parasites of the roots of vascular plants. They have a well-developed mycelium, the walls of which generally contain appreciable quantities of cellulose. The larger hyphae commonly have a well-developed central vacuole. Most of the mycelium develops within the substrate, the external mycelium being chiefly reproductive in function.

A sporangium is formed at the tip of each of many external hyphae and becomes delimited from the remainder of the hypha by a partition. The hypha which terminates in a sporangium may be termed a **sporangiophore.** The multinucleate protoplast of the sporangium becomes segmented into numerous uninucleate zoospores which usually have two anterior flagella, one whiplash, the other pinnate. The zoospores escape through the softened tip of the sporangium, or through a lateral protuberance. After the sporangium has opened, the basal partition may arch

Fig. 15.8. A minnow infested with *Saprolegnia*. (New York Botanical Garden photo.)

upward and become the distal wall of a new sporangium which becomes delimited by another basal cross wall; or a new sporangium may be produced on a short ascending lateral branch which develops near the tip of the sporangiophore.

The **primary zoospores** are usually more or less pear-shaped. They swim about for some time and eventually settle down and develop a wall. After a few minutes or hours the protoplast usually escapes from the wall as a **secondary zoospore.** The secondary zoospore is typically kidney-shaped, with the two flagella inserted in a longitudinal groove a little forward of the middle. The pinnate flagellum is directed forward, the whiplash backward. The secondary zoospore eventually settles down and develops a wall, after which it germinates by the outgrowth of a slender hypha. There are several variations on this pattern of spore development in various species, the most extreme being one in which the spores develop walls while still enclosed in the sporangium and germinate thereafter without going through a flagellated stage.

Some water molds produce thick-walled conidia in chains at the ends of the individual hyphae. These conidia undergo a resting period before each one germinates to produce a new hypha and eventually a mycelium. Some of the forms which produce conidia apparently lack the usual sexual cycle.

Sexual reproduction involves the formation of antheridia and oögonia, usually apically to individual hyphae or short hyphal branches. The oögonium enlarges, rounds up, and becomes delimited from its stalk by a cross wall. Most of the nuclei in the oögonium degenerate, and one to several large uninucleate eggs are formed. When there is only one egg, some of the protoplasm of the oögonium often fails to become incorporated into the egg and remains for some time as a covering of **periplasm.**

Antheridia and oögonia are borne on the same or different mycelia, according to the species. The antheridium is a slightly enlarged hyphal tip which sooner or later becomes delimited by a basal cross wall. It is at first multinucleate, but most of the nuclei eventually degenerate. The antheridium grows toward the oögonium, and, after contact has been established, a further outgrowth from the tip of the antheridium, called the conjugation tube, penetrates the oögonial wall and delivers a single sperm nucleus to the egg. If there are several eggs in the oögonium, the conjugation tube may branch and deliver a sperm nucleus to each.

The fertilized egg secretes a thick wall and goes into a resting stage, at which time it is known as an **oöspore.** Fusion of the sperm and egg nucleus in the oöspore is usually delayed for some time, often until shortly before germination. The first nuclear division of the germinating oöspore is believed to be meiotic. In some species the hypha growing from the germinating oöspore develops into an extensive mycelium of the usual type, eventually producing sporangia; in others the sporangium is quickly produced on a small mycelium. Unfertilized eggs sometimes develop parthenogenetically into oöspores.

Water molds contribute to the carbon and nitrogen cycles, etc., in the same manner as the decay bacteria, but otherwise they are of relatively little economic importance. Some species cause occasional root rots in higher plants, and species of *Saprolegnia* (Fig. 15.8) are a common pest on fish eggs and young or injured fish in hatcheries.

PERONOSPORALES

The Peronosporales are closely related to the Saprolegniales and are evidently derived from them. They differ from the Saprolegniales in being mostly terrestrial rather than aquatic, mostly parasitic (often obligately so) rather than saprophytic, in regularly having only a single egg, with periplasm, in the oögonium, and they differ especially in that the structure which in the Saprolegniales remains attached to the mycelium and develops into a sporangium is in the Peronosporales generally released from the tip of the hypha as a conidium. A conidium of the Peronosporales often germinates directly to produce a new mycelium, as do the conidia of most other fungi, but, if it falls into the water, it commonly produces zoospores similar to the secondary zoospores of the Saprolegnales. The conidium of the Peronosporales is thus a modified sporangium which to some extent partakes of the characters of typical sporangia and typical conidia. The sexual cycle of the Peronosporales is essentially similar to that of the Saprolegniales, except as noted above.

Pythium is a genus more or less intermediate between the Saprolegniales and the Peronosporales, but it is usually placed in the latter order. Most of its species inhabit the soil and are facultatively saprophytic or parasitic. *Pythium* regularly produces sporangia which may or may not be deciduous, but which in either case usually germinate by the formation of numerous zoospores; rarely if ever does the sporangium behave as a true conidium and germinate directly to form a new hypha and eventual mycelium. *Pythium* is one of the most important causes of damping off, a fungus rot that is very destructive to seedlings.

Phytophthora infestans (Fig. 15.9), another member of the Peronosporales, is the cause of late blight of potatoes. Originally native to the Andes of South America, as is the potato itself, the fungus has now become generally distributed wherever potatoes are grown. The first severe outbreak of the disease in the cultivated crop occurred in 1845 and resulted in a crop failure over much of Europe and eastern North America. The great Irish famine of 1845–1846 resulted from this crop failure,

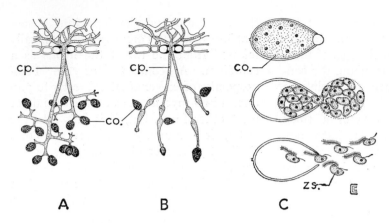

Fig. 15.9. Downy mildews: A, *Plasmopara; B, C, Phytophthora;* co., conidium; cp., conidiophore; zs., zoospore.

for potatoes were then the principal staple food of most of the population of Ireland.

The conidia of *P. infestans* are borne on specialized conidiophores which emerge from the leaf of the potato plant through characteristic small openings called stomates (see Chapter 26). The conidium is released into the air and is wind-borne. Subsequently, according to the environmental conditions, it may function as a sporangium and produce zoospores, as in most species of *Pythium*, or it may germinate directly, thus functioning as a true conidium. There is a minor technical difference in the process by which zoospores are developed from a sporangium in *Pythium* and *Phytophthora*, but otherwise certain species of the two genera are very similar.

There are many parasitic Peronosporales which, like *Phytophthora infestans*, produce conidia apically on specialized hyphae that typically extend out into the air through the stomates of the leaf of the host. These external hyphae are often so numerous as to make the leaf surface finely downy. Such members of the Peronosporales, and the diseases they cause, are known as **downy mildews.**

One of the most important downy mildews is the downy mildew of grape, caused by *Plasmopara viticola* (Fig. 15.9). The conidiophores of this species are much branched toward the tip and produce a single conidium at the end of each ultimate branch. The fungus is native to eastern North America and usually causes only minor damage to native American species of grape, but it is highly virulent to the common European species. It was introduced into Europe shortly before 1878 with American grapes which had been brought in because of their resistance to the insect parasite *Phylloxera. Phylloxera*, also of American origin, had earlier become a serious pest in European vineyards.

Prior to the introduction of the downy mildew disease, French grape growers had sometimes applied a mixture of copper sulfate and lime to vines nearest the roadsides in order to discourage casual pilferage. The mixture is poisonous and looks it. Later it was noticed that vines to which this mixture had been applied were much less affected by downy mildew than those not so treated. The celebrated **Bordeaux mixture** of copper sulfate and lime, which is still widely used to control fungus diseases, was established in 1883 as a result of experiments inspired by this discovery.

Albugo (Fig. 15.10), another genus of the Peronosporales, causes the diseases known as white rusts. Many kinds of plants are affected, especially members of the mustard (crucifer) family. The conidiophores are densely aggregated to form a mass which breaks through the epidermis of the host and becomes visible as a raised whitish sorus. A **sorus** is any cluster of sporangia or externally produced spores, in the fungi or elsewhere, especially if the cluster is large enough to be visible to the naked eye. Each conidiophore of an *Albugo* sorus cuts off numerous successive conidia from the tip. The conidia are distributed by the wind and germinate either directly or through the production of zoospores, according to the species and the conditions. Unlike the other rust diseases, which are caused by Basidiomycetes, the white rusts are seldom of much economic importance.

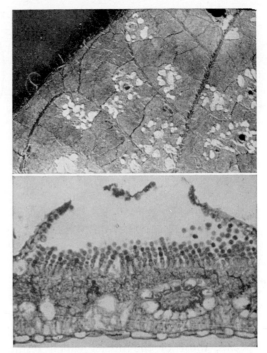

Fig. 15.10. *Albugo* (white rust) on *Amaranthus*. Top, part of leaf, showing sori; bottom, cross section of leaf and sorus (×100). (From Harold Bold, *Morphology of Plants*, Harper, 1957.)

MUCORALES

The Mucorales are a common group of terrestrial (rather than aquatic) saprophytes or facultative (seldom obligate) parasites which are vegetatively rather similar to the Saprolegniales. They usually have an extensive, coenocytic mycelium within the substrate, and a smaller aerial reproductive mycelium. The wall is usually or always chitinous. The asexual sporangia borne on the aerial mycelium produce numerous spores, each with its own wall and without flagella.

Sexual reproduction is of a special type apparently derived from that of the Saprolegniales. Two hyphal tips, usually of different mycelia, enlarge and come into

contact. A multinucleate terminal part of each tip is delimited from the rest of the hypha by a septum. Each such terminal part of a hypha is considered to be a gametangium. The wall separating the two gametangia dissolves, and the two protoplasts fuse. Karyogamy may follow immediately or may be delayed for some time. Usually the two gametangia involved in the sexual process are similar in size and form, but sometimes they are slightly unequal, and rarely they are strongly unequal.

The multinucleate protoplast resulting from the fusion of the contents of the two gametangia develops a thick wall and goes into a resting stage. This thick-walled resting cell is called a zygospore, although it is not strictly comparable to the zygo-

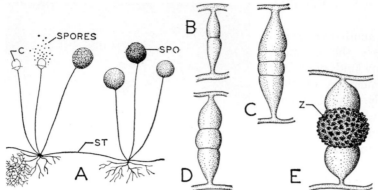

Fig. 15.11. *Rhizopus sto-lonifer*, the common bread mold. *A*, aerial mycelium, with a part of the internal mycelium (×35); *B–E*, stages in sexual reproduction; c., columella; spo., sporangium; st., stolon; z., zygospore. (*B*, ×125; *C–E* × 85.)

spores of algae such as *Spirogyra*. Sooner or later many of the nuclei of the zygospore fuse in pairs, one nucleus of each pair presumably having been derived from one gametangium, and the other from the other. The nuclei that fail to fuse usually degenerate, and, in at least some species, most of the nuclei which result from fusion also degenerate without developing further.

The first division of the diploid nuclei in the zygospore commonly occurs at or before the time the spore germinates and is a reduction division. One or more of the nuclei formed by reduction undergo repeated mitotic divisions during and/or after the germination of the spore. On germination the spore usually produces a short hypha on which is borne a sporangium with many spores, similar to the ordinary asexual sporangia and spores.

Rhizopus stolonifer (*R. nigricans*) (Fig. 15.11), the common bread mold, has been more thoroughly studied than other members of the Mucorales and may be taken as a typical example. Although it is generally saprophytic, the species is a rather weak facultative parasite and will grow, for example, on strawberry fruits.

The ordinary asexual spores are produced in sporangia and are air-borne. Under suitable conditions of moisture and temperature, the spore germinates to produce a hypha which penetrates the substrate and produces an extensive internal mycelium.

After usually a few days of growth within the substrate, the mycelium produces some hyphae which return to the surface to form an aerial mycelium that is, of course, connected to the internal one. Sporangiophores (hyphae that bear sporangia) are commonly borne in small clusters, and the base of each cluster is connected to one or more other clusters by strong lateral hyphae which are called **stolons** because of their casual resemblance to the more complex stolons of higher plants (see Chapter 24). The sporangia (Fig. 15.13) are globose, with very numerous spores borne between the limiting outer wall and the central sterile columella. The sporangium breaks open rather irregularly, releasing the spores. The columella and often the remnants of the sporangial wall remain attached to the sporangiophore. This asexual cycle can be repeated indefinitely.

Sexual reproduction (Fig. 15.12) occurs only when mycelia of two different strains, known as the plus and minus strains, come into contact. Any individual of the plus strain will mate with any individual of the minus strain, but two individuals of the same strain will not mate with each other. All individuals of the species, as far as is known, belong to one or the other of the two strains. The names applied to the two strains reflect a slight difference in the size and vigor of the types originally studied. Different individuals of both strains are now known to vary in size and vigor, however, and a mycelium can be identified as belonging to the plus or the minus strain only by its mating behavior. Among some other fungi which show a similar heterothallism without any evident morphological differentiation, any two strains which will mate are called plus and minus, and the decision as to which

strain shall be called plus and which minus is strictly arbitrary.

Sexual reproduction in *Rhizopus* proceeds in the fashion already described for the order. Many of the nuclei in the zygospore fuse, but all except one of the fusion nuclei degenerate. This single functional diploid nucleus undergoes reduction division at or shortly before the time of germination of the zygospore. All but one of the four nuclei formed by reduction degenerate, and all the nuclei of the new sporangium are derived eventually by mitotic divisions from this single functional haploid nucleus. The spores produced in a sporangium, being genetically identical, are either all plus or all minus. The sporangium and the spores it contains are similar in structure and function to the ordinary asexual spores and sporangia.

Fig. 15.12. *Rhizopus stolonifer,* showing stages in zygospore formation. (Copyright by General Biological Supply House, Inc., Chicago.)

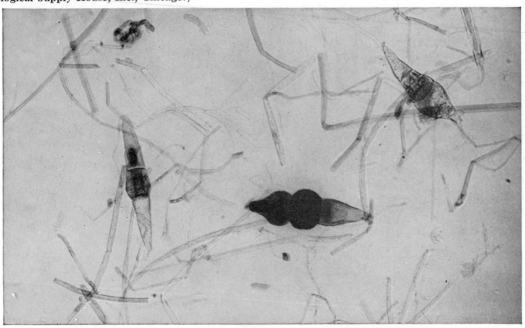

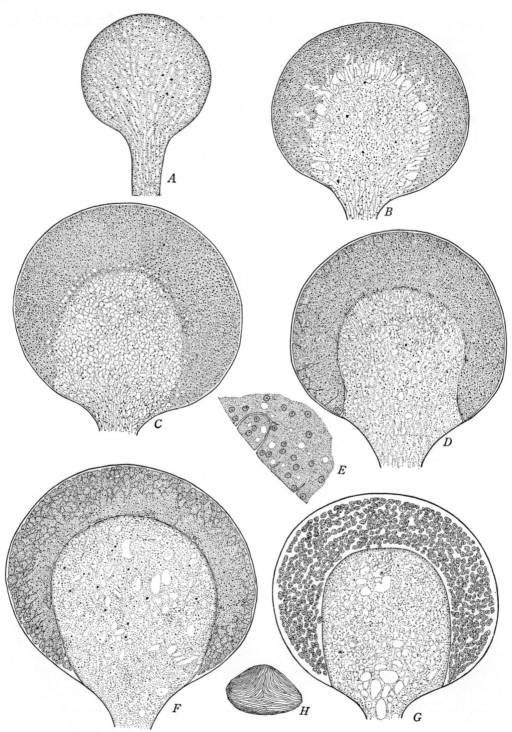

Fig. 15.13. *Rhizopus stolonifer.* Development of the sporangium. *E*, enlarged segment of *D*, showing cleavage furrows starting at the margin of the sporangium; *H*, a spore. (Much enlarged.) (From W. H. Brown, *The Plant Kingdom*, 1935; courtesy of Ginn & Company, Boston.)

Eumycotina: Ascomycetes

DEFINITION

The Ascomycetes are fungi in which the sexual spores (ascospores) are usually few and definite in number (typically eight) and are produced within a sporangium called an **ascus**. The term *ascus* is derived from the Greek word *askos*, meaning bladder, sac, or container, and the Ascomycetes are often called sac fungi. The Ascomycetes are mostly filamentous, with chitinous walls, only rarely with appreciable amounts of cellulose. The filaments are generally septate, but the segments delimited by the septa often contain several or many nuclei, and each septum commonly has a central opening through which cytoplasm and often nuclei may pass.

Many Ascomycetes reproduce asexually by conidia that are successively cut off from the ends of conidiophores, and only seldom carry on sexual reproduction. A conidium germinates directly to form a new hypha and eventually a mycelium, instead of giving rise to zoospores as in some Phycomycetes.

HISTORY

The Ascomycetes were first recognized as a coherent group by the Czech mycologist August Corda (1809–1849) in 1842, only 5 years after the ascus itself was defined by the French mycologist Joseph Henri Léveillé (1796–1870). The greatest contribution to our knowledge of the morphology and taxonomy of the class was made by two amateur French mycologists, the brothers Louis René Tulasne (1815–1885) and Charles Tulasne (1816–1884), in a series of papers published from 1861 to 1865.

SEXUAL CYCLE

Except for some relatively simple forms, such as the yeasts, the sexual cycle (Fig. 15.14) in Ascomycetes usually conforms more or less closely to the following pattern:

One or several adjacent cells or multinucleate segments at the end of a hypha of the vegetative mycelium become differentiated as an **ascogonium** which is usually somewhat broader than an ordinary vegetative hypha. Usually a slender prolongation, called a **trichogyne**, grows out from the end of the ascogonium. The ascogonium may be compared to the oögonium of some Phycomycetes, except that it does not contain differentiated eggs. Specialized apical segments of the hyphae of the same, or usually a different, mycelium act as antheridia. The trichogyne grows to the antheridium, and the walls between them dissolve. The nuclei of the antheridium then pass through the trichogyne into the body of the ascogonium, where they become paired with the ascogonial nuclei, without fusion. Sometimes the antheridial hypha itself grows to the ascogonium, and nuclei are transferred from the antheridium to the ascogonium without the intervention of a trichogyne. The nuclei of the ascogonium may even become paired without the introduction of nuclei from any other source. In such cases the trichogyne and antheridium may be formed but fail to function fully, or they may be completely lacking.

After one or more nuclei are paired in the ascogonium, several filaments, called

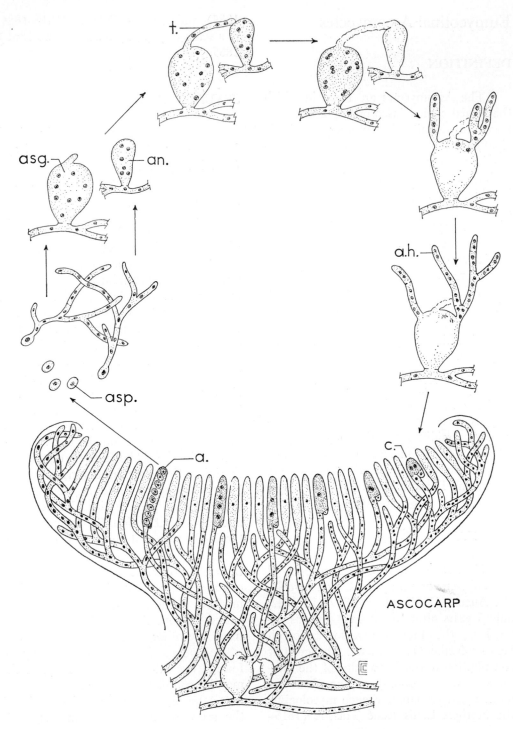

Fig. 15.14.   Life cycle of a typical ascomycete: a., ascus; an., antheridium; asg., ascogonium; asp., ascospore; a.h., ascogenous hypha; c., crozier; t., trichogyne.

ascogenous hyphae, usually grow out of the ascogonium. The ascogenous hyphae do not generally absorb food from the substrate, being dependent instead on the vegetative mycelium. Some or all of the nuclei of the ascogonium move into the ascogenous hyphae, and usually a number of mitotic divisions take place, but the nuclei remain paired. The ascogenous hyphae usually branch repeatedly and sooner or later develop septa. The segments nearer the ascogonium are often multi-nucleate, but each terminal segment contains only a single pair of nuclei.

Coincident with the growth of the ascogenous hyphae there is usually developed a very compact mycelium originating directly from the vegetative mycelium, which comes to surround the group of ascogenous hyphae, and slender hyphae, originating from or in the same way as this compact mycelium, become intermingled with the ascogenous hyphae. This compact mycelium usually has a definite form and structure, according to the genus and species. Together with the included ascogenous hyphae and eventual asci, it is known as the **fruiting body.** The fruiting body of an Ascomycete may also be called an **ascocarp.**

Usually the development of the tip of the ascogenous hypha, prior to the differentiation of the asci, follows a particular pattern leading to the formation of a characteristic hook or **crozier** (Fig. 15.15) which is apparently homologous with the clamp connections of the Basidiomycetes. The terminal cell curves back on itself like a hook, and the pair of nuclei lie in the bend. Both nuclei divide mitotically, so that four nuclei are present. Cross walls are then formed, leaving two nuclei (one daughter nucleus from each of the two original nuclei) in the bend, one nucleus

in the cell at the tip of the hook, and one in the cell cut off at the base of the hook. The binucleate cell at the bend of the hook enlarges to form an ascus. The uninucleate cells at the tip and base of the hook may or may not fuse and then elongate to form a new hook and ascus, etc.

The two nuclei in the developing ascus fuse to form a diploid nucleus. The diploid nucleus then undergoes reduction division, producing four haploid nuclei. Usually each of these undergoes a single further mitotic division, so that there are eight nuclei (and ultimately eight ascospores) in the ascus, but sometimes further mitotic divisions ensue, and an extreme number of more than 1000 ascospores has been recorded in one species.

After the nuclei in the ascus have ceased to divide, the cytoplasm surrounding each nucleus becomes differentiated from the remainder of the cytoplasm of the ascus, and each resulting aggregate of nucleus and cytoplasm develops a wall and becomes an ascospore. Some of the cytoplasm of the maturing ascus does not become incorporated into any of the spores and remains for a time as **epiplasm.** Eventually the epiplasm usually degenerates, although it sometimes apparently contributes to the formation of the outer wall layer of

Fig. 15.15. Development of croziers and asci; a, young ascus.

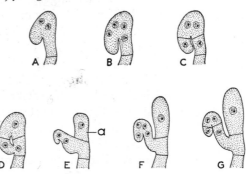

each ascospore. The inner wall layer of each ascospore is secreted wholly by the enclosed spore protoplast. This method of spore differentiation, in which some of the cytoplasm of the ascus is excluded from the spores as epiplasm, is one of the most characteristic features of the Ascomycetes.

TAXONOMY AND DISTRIBUTION

Ascomycetes occur as saprophytes and parasites (chiefly of plants and of insects) in terrestrial habitats throughout the world. Only a few are aquatic, but these include both fresh-water and marine species.

The form and structure of the fruiting body furnish some of the most useful criteria in the classification of the Ascomycetes. If the fruiting body is relatively amorphous, with one or more cavities in which asci are borne, it is called a **stroma.** There may also be a stroma at the base of the more characteristically developed part of the fruiting body. A fruiting body that is completely closed at maturity, with a definite, usually more or less spherical shape and a differentiated outer layer, is called a **cleistothecium.** A fruiting body which differs from a cleistothecium in having a narrow opening (the **ostiole**) is called a **perithecium.** Perithecia are often flask-shaped. Sometimes individual perithecia are embedded within a larger stroma but still have a wall differentiated from the rest of the stroma. The term *perithecium* is often loosely used to include cleistothecia and formerly was also applied to the ascogenous cavities in the stroma of Ascomycetes in which the wall of the cavity is not differentiated from that of the stroma. A fruiting body in which the layer of developing asci is exposed nearly or quite from the beginning is called an **apothecium.**

Many mycologists would extend this term to include fruiting bodies of the type found in the Hysteriales, which open at or shortly before maturity.

Asci are often borne in a distinct layer, intermingled with sterile hyphae, covering part of the surface of the fruiting body. Such a layer of asci and sterile hyphae is called a **hymenium.** In apothecia and some perithecia, the intermingled sterile hyphae are free at the tip and are called **paraphyses.** In other perithecia, perithecium-like cavities, and cleistothecia, the sterile hyphae are usually attached to the fruiting body at both ends and are called **pseudoparaphyses.** The paraphyses and pseudoparaphyses of Ascomycetes arise from the vegetative mycelium, as noted on p. 245, rather than from the ascogenous hyphae.

It is customary to segregate the yeasts and some other Ascomycetes which do not have definite fruiting bodies as a small subclass Hemiascomycetes. The remainder of the class, in which definite fruiting bodies are formed, has recently been divided into two subclasses, the Euascomycetes and Loculoascomycetes, on the structure of the asci and fruiting bodies.

It is also customary to arrange the orders of Euascomycetes and Loculoascomycetes into three convenient groups, without implying any taxonomic status. Those with permanently closed fruiting bodies (cleistothecia and cleistothecium-like stromata) are called Plectomycetes; those with fruiting bodies that open at maturity (perithecia, or stromata with embedded perithecia or perithecium-like cavities) are called Pyrenomycetes; and those with wide-open fruiting bodies (apothecia) are called Discomycetes.

It has been estimated that there are 15,000 known species of Ascomycetes.

Nearly all these can be placed in one or another of 18 orders, as indicated in the key given in the appendix.

REPRESENTATIVE GROUPS

Yeasts

Ascomycetes that are more or less distinctly unicellular and produce solitary asci are called **yeasts** (Fig. 15.16). They make up a large part of the order Endomycetales, also called Saccharomycetales. Asexual reproduction occurs by cell division. Some yeasts, called fission yeasts, divide into two equal cells, in much the same way as other unicellular plants, but most of them divide into two initially unequal cells by a process known as **budding**. A small projection or bud develops on a cell, the nucleus divides mitotically, and one of the daughter nuclei moves into the bud. The bud continues to enlarge, although the opening between it and the parent cell remains small. Eventually the opening is closed by a double partition, and the two cells separate from each other. Under favorable conditions for rapid growth, the initiation of new buds may so far precede the maturation and separation of previously formed buds that small, branching, temporary colonies are formed, with constrictions marking the points at which the cells will later separate.

The typical sexual cycle in yeasts involves the fusion of two equal or unequal uninucleate cells, followed almost immediately by nuclear fusion. The resulting cell, which may properly be called a zygote, enlarges and becomes an ascus. The diploid nucleus undergoes meiosis, after which the four resulting haploid nuclei may mature directly into ascospores, or they may first divide mitotically so that eight ascospores are produced in the ascus.

There are several variations on this general pattern. Sometimes one or more mitotic cell divisions intervene between sexual fusion and the maturation of each of the resulting cells into an ascus. In some cases the ascospores themselves fuse in pairs within the ascus, so that the ordinary vegetative cells are diploid. Any such diploid vegetative cell may, under proper conditions, develop into an ascus with ascospores which again fuse within the ascus to produce diploid cells.

There are a number of fungi which are similar to ordinary yeasts except in the absence of the sexual cycle. Although technically referable to the Fungi Imperfecti rather than to the Ascomycetes, these organisms are usually classified with the yeasts because of their evident relationship. Yeasts may thus be divided into two convenient groups, the sporogenous yeasts, which have the sexual cycle and produce ascospores as well as reproducing vegetatively, and the asporogenous yeasts, which lack the sexual cycle and reproduce only vegetatively. Some sporogenous yeasts have been known to give rise to asporogenous strains by mutation. There are also a few yeast-like imperfect fungi which may be related to the Basidiomycetes.

Yeasts are economically important chiefly because of the fermentation which many of them carry on, releasing alcohol and carbon dioxide as end products. The equation for alcoholic fermentation of glucose is $C_6H_{12}O_6 \longrightarrow 2\ C_2H_5OH + 2\ CO_2$ + energy. Only a relatively small proportion of the energy bound up in glucose is released in this process, and many kinds of organisms (including man) can use alcohol as a source of respiratory energy. Although there are a number of other or-

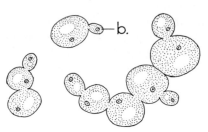
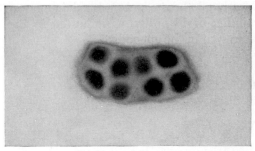

Fig. 15.16. Yeast. Left, baker's yeast, *Saccharomyces cerevisiae;* b., bud. (×2000.) Right, ascus and ascospores of *Schizosaccharomyces octosporus.* (Copyright by General Biological Supply House, Inc., Chicago.)

ganisms which, at least sometimes, carry on alcoholic fermentation, the economically important alcoholic fermentations are carried on almost exclusively by yeasts.

The common cultivated yeast, *Saccharomyces cerevisiae*, exists in a number of races which vary in physiological characteristics. The baker's yeasts are strains of S. *cerevisiae* in which further growth is inhibited when alcohol reaches a concentration of 4–5 per cent. The carbon dioxide produced by the yeast causes the dough to rise, and the texture of the finished product (e.g., bread) is due to the numerous small bubbles of carbon dioxide formed by fermentation. Alcohol is merely a by-product in the baking of bread and evaporates into the air during baking. The common

brewer's yeasts are strains of S. *cerevisiae* in which growth continues until the alcohol reaches a concentration of 14–17 per cent. Higher concentrations of alcohol are obtained only by distillation. Other species of *Saccharomyces* and related genera are used in the brewing of such beverages as sake, ginger beer, Jamaica rum, pulque, and some kinds of wine.

POWDERY MILDEWS

The **powdery mildews** are a group of obligate parasites belonging to the order Erysiphales. They parasitize the leaves and to a lesser extent other aerial organs of flowering plants. Usually the mycelium is largely external, with numerous haustoria

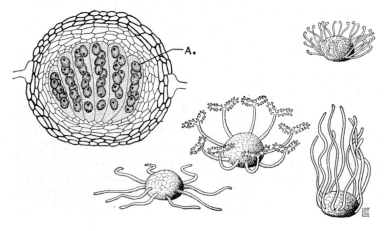

Fig. 15.17. Cleistothecia of powdery mildews; a., ascospore. Left, in section. (×300.) Others, external. (×85.)

that penetrate chiefly the surface layer of cells of the host. Asexual reproduction is by conidia which are commonly borne in chains at the ends of unbranched conidiophores. The powdery appearance for which the group is named is due largely to the numerous conidia.

Sexual reproduction of powdery mildews may involve the production of recognizable ascogonia and antheridia, with a single male nucleus being introduced into the ascogonium directly from the antheridium, or nuclear transfer may take place between two similar hyphae that are not visibly different from ordinary vegetative hyphae. Some species are homothallic, others heterothallic. The fruiting body is a small, usually black, more or less spherical cleistothecium that is usually well under 1 mm thick and barely visible to the naked eye. Often the cleistothecium has some simple or branched hyphal appendages which may be longer than the diameter of the body of the cleistothecium (Fig. 15.17). The function of these appendages is dubious, but their structure furnishes a useful taxonomic character. The cleistothecium contains from 5 to 30 asci which arise in one or more tufts from the base.

Erysiphe cichoriacearum has a very wide host range, and conidia from a single mycelium may infect many different hosts belonging to families of flowering plants that are not closely related. *Erysiphe graminis*, the powdery mildew of grasses, consists, on the other hand, of many morphologically indistinguishable races which are restricted to particular species groups, genera, or groups of genera of grasses. Powdery mildews damage small grains wherever these are grown throughout the world, but they are relatively unimportant as compared to the smuts and rusts. The culti-

vated European species of gooseberry are highly susceptible to a powdery mildew which is native to North America but causes only negligible damage to the North American species, and the common cultivated European grape is likewise susceptible to another powdery mildew to which the North American species are habituated.

ERGOT

Ergot is a disease of rye, barley, wheat, and other grasses, caused by several species of *Claviceps*, especially *C. purpurea*. The genus belongs to the order Sphaeriales. The fungus attacks the inflorescence of the grass, particularly the developing ovaries,

Fig. 15.18. Ergot on crested wheat grass. (Courtesy of G. W. Fischer, Department of Plant Pathology, Washington State University.)

Fig. 15.19. Ergot, showing fruiting bodies on the sclerotium. (X4.) (Courtesy of the Department of Plant Pathology, Cornell University.)

which would otherwise mature into the grains. The mycelium is relatively compact and dense, and develops largely within the ovary, eventually filling and destroying it. Conidia are produced on very numerous short conidiophores. The conidia are distributed both by wind and by insects, which are attracted by a copious sweetish exudate produced by the fungus.

The developing mycelium maintains the same general form as the unaffected grains and eventually becomes a conspicuous blackish-violet body somewhat larger, or at least longer, than the normal grains (Fig. 15.18). These bodies are called ergots. The ergots may also be called by the more general term **sclerotium**, which applies to any very dense, more or less parenchymatous body of modified mycelium, other than a true fruiting body. Sclerotia are usually resting bodies with a good supply of stored food, as is true of the sclerotia of *Claviceps*.

After overwintering, the ergot sends out a number of fruiting bodies (Fig. 15.19), each consisting of a stalk up to 1 inch long and an enlarged, spherical, stromatic head. The slender perithecia are embedded in the stromatic head (Fig. 15.20), only the ostioles reaching the surface. Paraphyses are intermingled with the asci. Eight elongate, slender ascospores are borne in each ascus. The ascospores are distributed by the wind, and infection of the host takes place only at flowering time.

Ergot contains a powerful alkaloid which has several physiological effects, notably the constriction of the capillaries. It also causes uterine contractions and is used medically as an abortifacient and as an aid in childbirth. Poisoning from ergot has evidently occurred in years of heavy infestation ever since grain first began to be ground into flour. Heavily ergotized grain is not now usually milled, but a severe local outbreak of acute ergotism occurred in France as recently as 1952. Chronic ergotism, due to the cumulative effect of ingesting small amounts of ergot over a period of time, results in a dry rot and eventual loss of extremities, such as fingers and toes, because of insufficient circulation. Acute ergotism causes violent hallucinations, especially of fire, as well as spasms and other nervous disturbances, and is often fatal.

The order Sphaeriales, to which ergot belongs, includes many other fungi which cause serious plant diseases. Among these diseases is chestnut blight, caused by *Endothia parasitica*, which was introduced from the Orient about 1904 and has almost exterminated the American chestnut.

NEUROSPORA

Neurospora is a saprophytic mold belonging to the order Sphaeriales. It characteristically produces numerous pink or orange conidia and is sometimes called pink bread mold. The perithecia are oval or pear-shaped, and .01–.02 inch thick. In the early 1930's the American mycologist Bernard O. Dodge (1872–1960) pointed out the usefulness of *Neurospora* as a tool for basic genetical studies, and many stu-

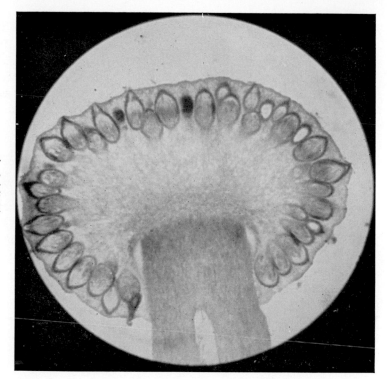

Fig. 15.20. Ergot, long section through fruiting body, showing perithecia. (Courtesy of the Department of Plant Pathology, Cornell University.)

dents have followed his lead. *Neurospora* is easily cultured and reproduces rapidly. The vegetative mycelium is haploid, as in other Ascomycetes. It produces four, or more often eight, ascospores in each ascus, according to the species, and these are arranged in a row. One of the great advantages of using an Ascomycete for genetic study is that nuclear fusion and reduction division occur within the ascus, leading to the formation of a limited number of spores which utilize all the nuclei formed in meiosis. By careful micromanipulation each one of these spores can be individually removed from the ascus and separately cultured. Such precision is obviously impossible in dealing with diploid organisms such as the higher plants and animals, in which for a number of reasons the nuclei produced in a single meiosis cannot be

followed through to maturity. The use of *Neurospora* in genetic experiments is further discussed in Chapter 35.

PEZIZALES

The Pezizales are a group of chiefly saprophytic Ascomycetes in which the fruiting body is an apothecium and the ascus opens by a distinct lid (the **operculum**). In *Peziza* (Fig. 15.21) and some other genera the apothecium is cup-shaped, often with a short basal stalk, and the hymenium lines the inner surface of the cup. The hymemium (Fig. 15.22) consists of very numerous cylindric to slightly club-shaped asci, intermingled with paraphyses. Each ascus contains eight ascospores in a single row. The remainder of the fruiting body is soft and rather parenchymatous.

Fig. 15.21.   *Peziza* ascocarps. (Courtesy of the Department of Plant Pathology, Cornell University.)

Fig. 15.22.   *Peziza.* A bit of the hymenium, spread out to show asci and paraphyses. (Much enlarged.) (Courtesy of the Department of Plant Pathology, Cornell University.)

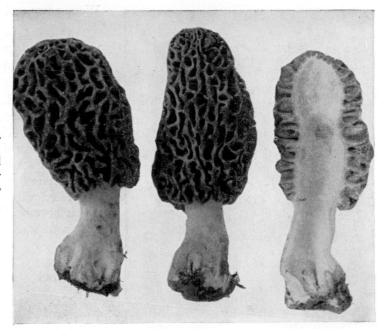

Fig. 15.23. Morel (*Morchella*) fruiting bodies. (Slightly less than natural size.) (Courtesy of the Department of Plant Pathology, Cornell University.)

The ascocarp in *Peziza* ranges from about 2 cm to as much as 30–40 cm across. Some related genera have smaller, but otherwise rather similar, fruiting bodies. In *Morchella* (Fig. 15.23), the common morel, the fruiting body is commonly about 10 cm long, with a thick stalk and a very deeply and characteristically wrinkled cap; the hymenium forms the surface layer of the cap. Morels are considered great delicacies by mycophagous gourmets.

The process by which nuclei are transferred from one hypha to another varies widely among different members of the Pezizales. Some species follow the standard ascomycetous pattern, with the nuclei passing from the antheridium to the oögonium (ascogonium) through a trichogyne, but there are all gradations from this condition to one in which nuclei are transferred from one hypha of ordinary appearance to another.

TUBERALES

The fruiting body of the Tuberales is a shallowy subterranean modified apothecium up to several centimeters across. The hymenium is completely covered by a more

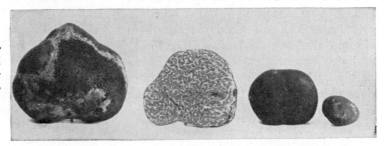

Fig. 15.24. Truffles (*Tuber nitidum*). (About natural size.) (Courtesy of the Department of Plant Pathology, Cornell University.)

Fig. 15.25. *Xylaria polymorpha*, a wood-rotting ascomycete; fruiting bodies. (×½.) (Courtesy of the Department of Plant Pathology, Cornell University.)

or less parenchymatous tissue formed by compaction and elaboration of the ends of the paraphyses, and often the hymenium itself is so much convoluted and modified as to lose its identity as a continuous layer. The Tuberales are evidently derived from the more usual types of Discomycetes, and a series of connecting forms exists. The cytological details of the life cycle have not been worked out. Some species of the genus *Tuber*, occurring in rather open forests (especially oak woods) of southern Europe, are known as **truffles** (Fig. 15.24) and are frequently eaten. Truffles are commonly gathered with the aid of pigs or dogs which have been trained to seek them out by the odor.

WOOD-ROTTING ASCOMYCETES

Many Ascomycetes, especially members of the family Xylariaceae (Fig. 15.25) of the order Sphaeriales, share with some Basidiomycetes the ability to use wood as a source of food. The fruiting body of the Xylariaceae is usually small (seldom much over an inch wide), often bright red or black, and consists of a stroma with numerous embedded perithecia. Prior to the production of perithecia, the young stroma is covered with a layer of conidiophores which bear conidia. Details of the sexual cycle mostly remain to be worked out.

LICHENS

Many Ascomycetes and a few Basidiomycetes are commonly found in symbiotic association with one or another species of green or blue-green algae. Such fungus-alga combinations are known as lichens. *Trebouxia* is an alga very often found in lichens. *Trebouxia* is vegetatively rather similar to *Pleurococcus* and has often been confused with it. The algae that occur in lichens usually also occur alone, but nearly all the lichen fungi are restricted to their lichen occurrence. For this reason, and because the form and structure of the lichen thallus are governed largely by the fungus rather than the alga, the rules of nomenclature provide that the name of a lichen is that of its fungal component.

Lichens have long been taken as a standard example of true symbiosis, in which both symbionts benefit from the association. It is clear that the fungus benefits, since it is wholly dependent on the alga for food, but it is not always equally clear that the alga benefits. Some lichens grow in dry places where algae alone could not survive, but some others occur side by side with the algal component, such as *Trebouxia*. Experimental work suggests that some lichen fungi produce substances which stimulate or are necessary to the growth of the included algae. It is evident that in an evolutionary sense lichens originated through helotism, or enslavement of the algal component by the fungus, but in at least some lichens the association has developed into true, mutualistic symbiosis. The student of history may see some parallels between the history of slavery in some human societies and the probable evolutionary history of lichens.

Lichens commonly form thin thalli up to several inches or even several feet long or across. A section through a typical lichen thallus shows a peripheral layer of compact mycelium, and an internal region of more scattered hyphae among which are interspersed cells, filaments, or cell colonies of an alga. Some hyphae of the fungus generally also penetrate the substrate as rhizoids, serving as an anchor and in the absorption of minerals. The fungus sometimes produces haustoria which penetrate and eventually kill some of the enslaved algal cells, but more often a hyphal branch tip merely becomes closely appressed to the algal cell, without entering it. Doubtless, in at least some cases, included algal

Fig. 15.26.   Crustose lichens on a tree trunk. (About natural size.) (Photo by W. H. Hodge.)

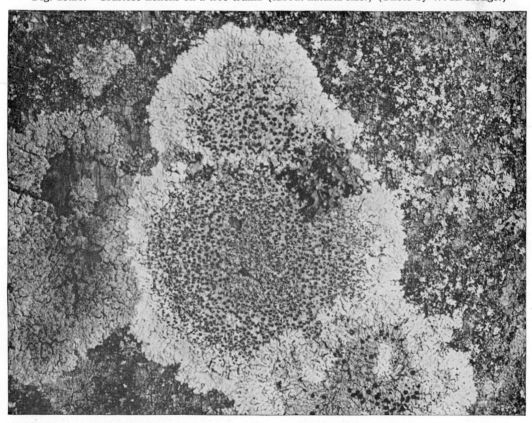

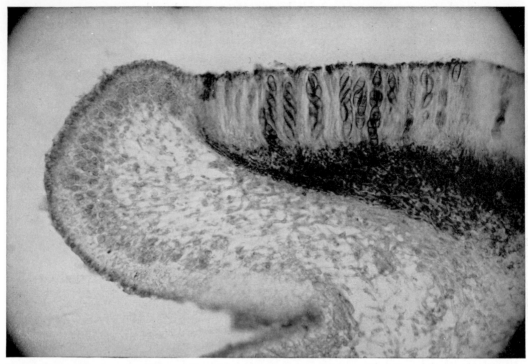

Fig. 15.27. Ascocarp of a lichen (*Physcia*) in long section. (Enlarged.) (Copyright by General Biological Supply House, Inc., Chicago.)

cells which have died are digested and used by the fungus.

It is convenient and customary to divide lichens into three groups according to the external appearance of the thallus, although there is no sharp distinction between these groups, and this classification bears no relation to the taxonomic position of the fungi and algae involved. Lichens which form a crust closely appressed to the substrate are called **crustose** lichens (Fig. 15.26); lichens with a more leaf-like thallus, usually attached to the substrate by a relatively smaller portion, are called **foliose** lichens; and lichens which are more or less bushy-branched are called **fruticose** lichens. A cross section of a foliose lichen usually shows a single layer or zone of algae near the upper surface of the thallus;

a similar section through a fruticose lichen shows the alga-bearing portion as a complete ring between the wholly fungal core and the wholly fungal periphery of the thallus.

Crustose lichens often occur on bare rocks and are also found as epiphytes on tree trunks and elsewhere. Foliose and fruticose lichens do not occur in such dry habitats as do many of the crustose lichens. The importance of lichens as pioneers on bare rock surfaces is discussed in Chapter 37. Trees in dense forests, especially of the Pacific states, often have epiphytic, slenderly branched, fruticose lichens up to several feet long hanging from their branches. These belong to the genera *Usnea* (Fig. 15.28) and *Alectoria* and are called old-man's-beard lichens; they have also been confused with Spanish moss, a superficially similar, highly modified flowering plant of the southeastern United States. *Usnea* and *Alectoria* have no rhizoids and are wholly dependent on rain and wind for raw materials.

Several lichens have some direct economic importance. Reindeer moss, an important forage plant in arctic regions, is a fruticose lichen (*Cladonia*, Fig. 15.28) rather than a true moss. A product obtained from European species of *Evernia*, a fruticose lichen commonly known as oak moss, is widely used as a stabilizer in perfumes. *Rocella*, another lichen, is the traditional source of litmus, a chemical which is red in acid solution and blue in alkaline solution.

The alga of a lichen usually reproduces solely by cell division, regardless of whether the alga has any other means of reproduction in the free state. The fungus carries on the normal sexual cycle, leading to the formation of fruiting bodies (Fig. 15.27) and spores. Many lichens produce conidia as well as sexual spores. Some lichenologists believe that the conidia of lichens are really sex cells, comparable to the spermatia of rusts, but this has not been satisfactorily demonstrated. The ascolichens constitute several different orders which are inserted individually in the synopsis of orders of Ascomycetes in the appendix. The basidiolichens consist of only a few species belonging to the order Agaricales, a large order of Basidiomycetes.

It is generally assumed that new lichen thalli are formed by capture of algal cells by the young mycelium which develops from a fungus spore, and it has been experimentally demonstrated that when artificially separated the two components can at least sometimes reassemble to form a normal lichen. Stages in the actual cap-

Fig. 15.28. Fruticose lichens. Left, *Cladonia verticillata,* fruiting; right, *Usnea florida,* with a crustose lichen at the lower left. (Both about ×2.) (Photos courtesy of H. H. Holliger.)

ture of an alga by a fungus to form a lichen have seldom, if ever, been observed in nature, however, except for a few species in which the algal colony is not wholly enclosed by the fungus.

Many lichens reproduce asexually as lichens (rather than as separated fungi and algae) by means of **soredia.** A soredium is a specialized small fragment of the lichen thallus, with a peripheral layer of mycelium enclosing a few cells of the alga. The soredium originates internally, grows out through the surface of the thallus, and becomes detached as a little ball which may be carried about by the wind or otherwise. On becoming lodged under favorable conditions, the soredium sends out rhizoids and develops directly into a new lichen thallus.

Lichens commonly become dormant during periods of drought and return to vegetative activity under proper conditions of temperature and moisture. The crustose lichens of bare rocks in dry regions exploit habitats in which neither the fungus nor the alga can grow alone. Although these lichens form spores, just as do other lichens, their actual reproduction probably occurs almost wholly by soredia.

Eumycotina: Basidiomycetes

DEFINITION AND VEGETATIVE CHARACTERS

The Basidiomycetes are fungi in which the sexual spores (basidiospores) are characteristically borne externally on a structure known as a **basidium.** Each basidium bears a small and usually definite number (typically four) of basidiospores, but sometimes additional basidiospores are formed after the first set has been released. The basidium is often more or less club-shaped, and the Basidiomycetes have frequently been called club fungi. In a few Basidiomycetes (notably some of the smuts), the basidium fails to produce basidiospores and germinates more or less directly, concomitant with meiosis, to form a new mycelium. Basidiomycetes, like Ascomycetes, are generally filamentous, with chitinous walls and with septa that have a central opening.

In addition to the manner in which the spores are borne, most Basidiomycetes differ from most Ascomycetes in developing an extensive vegetative mycelium with paired nuclei after nuclear transfer has taken place. Generally each segment of the hypha, as delimited by successive septa, has two nuclei, just as does the ultimate segment of an ascogenous hypha. One of these two nuclei is derived ultimately from one of the two hyphae or mycelia that were involved in the nuclear transfer, and the other from the other. The mycelium is thus physiologically diploid, although the individual nuclei are haploid. Such a mycelium, with two haploid nuclei of different origin in each segment or "cell," is said to be **dicaryotic.** A mycelium with uninucleate segments, or with multinucleate segments in which the nuclei are not associated in pairs, is said to be **monocaryotic.**

Hyphae of a large proportion of the Basidiomycetes are marked by **clamp connections** (Fig. 15.29) which bypass the septa. Usually there is only one clamp connection for each septum, but sometimes there are several. The clamp connection is evidently homologous with the crozier of Ascomycetes.

The usual function of the clamp connection is to permit the proper distribution of nuclei so that the dicaryotic condition

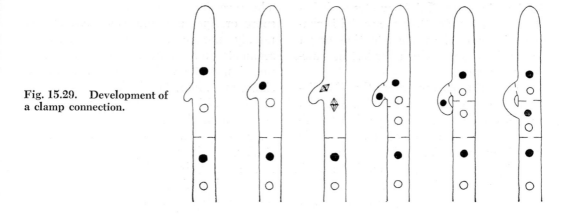

Fig. 15.29. Development of a clamp connection.

can be maintained when mitosis and the formation of a septum occur. Growth of the hyphae of a dicaryotic mycelium is largely apical. The nuclei are commonly so large, as compared to the diameter of the hypha, that they do not readily slip by each other. Nuclear division is typically preceded by the formation of a recurved pocket or bulge in the wall of the terminal segment of the hypha. One of the two nuclei in this segment is anterior to the pocket, the other posterior. The two nuclei approach each other, and the one which had been upper or anterior takes a position about at the mouth of the pocket. Both nuclei then divide mitotically, and one of the daughter nuclei from the anterior nucleus is formed in, or migrates into, the pocket. The hyphal tip, exclusive of the pocket, now contains three nuclei in a more or less linear arrangement, the two lower ones being the daughter nuclei of the original lower nucleus. Two partitions are now formed. One delimits the pocket, with its single included nucleus, from the main body of the hypha; the other is formed in the main hypha just below the pocket, between the two daughter nuclei of the original lower nucleus. At this stage the terminal segment of the hypha is di-

caryotic, with two nuclei, whereas the segment just beneath it (the penultimate segment) has only one nucleus. The tip of the pocket by this time, or shortly thereafter, comes into contact with the penultimate hyphal segment, and the walls between them dissolve. The nucleus from the pocket migrates into the penultimate hyphal segment, restoring this segment to the dicaryotic condition. The structure which began its development as a simple pocket or bulge has now become a clamp connection bypassing the newly formed septum. Both the septum in the main hypha and the septum delimiting the clamp connection from the apical segment are incomplete, with a central perforation through which the cytoplasm and sometimes the nuclei can pass.

Basidiomycetes in which the hyphae are relatively broad, as compared to the size of the nucleus, often lack clamp connections. In these forms there is enough room in the hypha so that the two dividing nuclei may lie side by side, the spindles being oriented with the hyphal axis. After mitosis has occurred, a septum is laid down between the two sets of daughter nuclei, and the dicaryotic condition is maintained. The existence of clamp connections in some Basidiomycetes with hyphae much broader than the nuclei is generally interpreted as the retention of an ancestral character which has lost its functional necessity.

Like the Ascomycetes, the Basidiomycetes often produce conidia. Conidia formed on monocaryotic mycelia are uninucleate. Conidia formed on dicaryotic mycelia are sometimes binucleate and dicaryotic, and sometimes uninucleate. Uninucleate conidia give rise to monocaryotic mycelia. Some Basidiomycetes, especially the rusts, produce more than one type of conidium, and these are often given distinctive names.

HISTORY

The basidium was discovered by Léveillé in 1837, and the group we now call the subclass Homobasidiomycetes was recognized as a natural taxon in 1842 by Corda. The existence of the smuts and rusts (the major part of the present subclass Heterobasidiomycetes) as a natural group was recognized as early as 1821 by Fries. The basidium of the smuts and rusts is somewhat different from that of the Homobasidiomycetes, however, and it was not until 1887 that all these organisms were brought together as a major group of fungi by Narcisse Patouillard (1854–1926), French pharmacist and mycologist.

SEXUAL CYCLE

Like the Ascomycetes, the Basidiomycetes have a variety of ways in which the nuclei may become paired, but usually follow a more stable pattern in the formation of sexual spores after nuclear fusion.

The mycelium produced from a basidiospore or from a uninucleate conidium is usually monocaryotic with uninucleate segments. In homothallic species pairing of nuclei may take place entirely within a single mycelium, but in heterothallic species the pairing must involve two different strains. Some heterothallic Basidiomycetes have only two differentiated mating strains, as in many Phycomycetes and Ascomycetes, but others have several or many such strains, each of which can mate with several others. The mechanism preventing selfing in these latter forms has been compared to an incompatibility mechanism in flowering plants; some mycologists object to the use of the term *heterothallism* for this condition.

A common method of nuclear transfer is for two ordinary monocaryotic hyphae to come into contact, after which the walls between them dissolve and the nucleus from one of the cells passes into the other cell. A dicaryotic mycelium may then be derived directly and solely by growth from this cell, or the existing mycelium may be converted to the dicaryotic condition by migration and mitotic divisions of the proper nuclei. Sometimes two uninucleate conidia, or two basidiospores, fuse to produce an initial dicaryotic cell from which the dicaryotic mycelium is derived.

Many Basidiomycetes produce more or less specialized conidia, variously called pycniospores, spermatia, or oidia, which, after transfer to a hypha of another strain, donate the single conidial nucleus to a cell of the receptor mycelium, thus initiating the dicaryotic stage. In at least some cases, these sex cells can also function as ordinary conidia, according to the circumstances. Oidia and spermatia (pycniospores) are often surrounded by or associated with a nectar that attracts insects, and the insects serve as unwitting agents of dissemination. Basidiomycetes which produce oidia or spermatia may also in many cases exchange nuclei directly between hyphae of different mycelia, as in other members of the class.

The fruiting body (basidiocarp) of a Basidiomycete is entirely a product of the dicaryotic mycelium. The basidia may or may not be borne in a definite hymenium, and the paraphyses sometimes found intermingled with the normal basidia are usually suppressed basidia rather than being homologous with the paraphyses of the Ascomycetes. Some Basidiomycetes produce basidia without the formation of a definite fruiting body.

Nuclear fusion occurs in the young basidium, which at this stage may be called the **probasidium.** In the subclass Heterobasidiomycetes the probasidium is commonly a spore which often has thick walls and goes through a resting period before developing into a mature basidium. Such spores are called **teliospores.** Teliospores sometimes consist of two or more cells, each cell representing a probasidium. The mature basidium of teliosporic Basidiomycetes generally consists of the **hypobasidium,** representing the remains of the teliospore cell, and the **epibasidium,** the structure produced by germination of a teliospore cell. In the Homobasidiomycetes development of the probasidium generally continues without interruption until the basidiospores are produced.

Meiosis generally occurs in the enlarging basidium. After meiosis there may or may not be a formation of septa which divide the basidium into uninucleate segments. Typically the mature basidium of the Heterobasidiomycetes is septate, whereas that of the Homobasidiomycetes lacks septa. The basidiospores originate as projections from the basidium in a manner that has been roughly compared to budding in yeasts. Typically the four nuclei produced in meiosis move out into the four basidiospores, leaving the body of the basidium without nuclei. Sometimes two nuclei degenerate and only two basidiospores are formed. Often the original nucleus of the developing basidiospore divides mitotically, so that the mature basidiospore is binucleate. The smuts (order Ustilaginales of the Heterobasidiomycetes) differ from other Basidiomycetes, among other respects, in that (1) the four nuclei produced in reduction division commonly undergo one or more mitotic divisions while still in the basidium, and (2) a single basidium often produces successive crops of four basidiospores.

Basidiospores are sometimes sessile (without a stalk) on the basidium, but often they are borne on specialized, apically very slender stalks called **sterigmata** (singular, **sterigma**). Basidiospores are very often discharged into the air, where they may float for long distances before settling down and germinating. In other cases they germinate more or less in place, and wind distribution is effective only for other types of spores.

A basidiospore typically germinates directly to produce a new monocaryotic mycelium, which eventually becomes a dicaryotic mycelium, as previously described. Among many Heterobasidiomycetes, however, a basidiospore often gives rise instead to a single conidium, which may be borne on a stalk resembling the sterigmata of the basidium. This is known as germination by **repetition.** A conidium formed by repetition may germinate directly to form a new mycelium or may give rise to another, smaller conidium by repetition, etc. Many mycologists call the basidiospores of Heterobasidiomycetes **sporidia** and apply this same term to the conidia which they produce by repetition.

DISTRIBUTION AND TAXONOMY

Basidiomycetes occur as saprophytes and parasites (chiefly of vascular plants) in terrestrial habitats throughout the world. There are very few, if any, aquatic forms.

The structure of the basidium and of the fruiting body are among the most important characters by which the orders of Basidiomycetes are distinguished. Among the Homobasidiomycetes, the orders with a closed fruiting body and without a definite hymenium at maturity are often collectively called the Gasteromycetes, as opposed to the Hymenomycetes, which have definite hymenial layers more or less exposed to the air. The part of a gasteromycetous fruiting body in which the basidia are borne is called the **gleba,** and this term is also applied to the ascus-bearing part of the closed fruiting body of the Tuberales (Ascomycetes). The outer layer of a gasteromycetous fruiting body, surrounding the gleba, is called the **peridium.** The Gasteromycetes are now considered to be merely a group of convenience, without formal taxonomic status, which probably relate to the Hymenomycetes at several different points. The Hymenomycetes, as now restricted, form the single large, natural order Agaricales, which is sometimes divided into two or more orders. Originally the term Hymenomycetes was applied to hymenial Ascomycetes as well as Basidiomycetes.

It has been estimated that there are about 15,000 known species of Basidiomycetes. These may be conservatively grouped into ten orders, although some mycologists prefer to divide some of the orders, such as the Tremellales and Agaricales. A synoptical key to the orders is given in the appendix.

REPRESENTATIVE GROUPS

Rusts

The **rusts** (other than the white rusts discussed on p. 239) constitute the order Uredinales, a large group of obligate parasites. Individual species of rusts may have a very wide or a very limited range of hosts. Some rusts can complete their life cycle on a single kind of host, but others require two often quite different kinds of host to complete the full sexual cycle. The former group are said to be **autoecious,** the latter **heteroecious.** The full life cycle of a typical rust (Fig. 15.30) is as follows:

The basidiospores are carried about by the wind. Any basidiospore which lands on a susceptible host germinates and develops a monocaryotic mycelium within the tissues of the host. After a time the mycelium produces a number of specialized conidiophores in pockets which open to the surface of the host. Each such pocket is called a **spermogonium** and has also been called a **pycnium.** Each conidiophore in the spermogonium cuts off a series of specialized uninucleate conidia, which are by different botanists called **spermatia** or **pycniospores.** A sugary slime of fragrant nectar is secreted in the spermogonium and serves to attract insects. The spermatia tend to stick to the visiting insects and are carried about by them.

The mycelium may or may not produce special **receptive hyphae,** more or less comparable to the trichogyne of some ascomycetes. Often these receptive hyphae extend out through the opening of the spermogonium. Usually there are two mating strains in each species, comparable to the plus and minus strains of *Rhizopus*, but each strain produces both spermatia and receptive hyphae. On coming into contact with a hypha of the opposite strain, a spermatium unites with the hypha to form an initial dicaryotic cell. The dicaryotic stage may also be initiated by direct fusion of two hyphae from different mycelia, if these come together, or by fusion of two spermatia of opposite type. The spermatia are thus a means of increasing the likelihood of contact between the plus and minus strains. A spermatium which fails to come into contact with a hypha or spermatium of opposite type may germinate to produce a new monocaryotic mycelium.

As used in the red algae and as technically defined, the term *spermatium* denotes a nonmotile male gamete. It has been pointed out that the spermatia of rusts are not truly comparable to male gametes, inasmuch as two spermatia of opposite sign may unite. Many botanists, therefore, prefer the terms *pycnium* and *pycniospore* to *spermogonium* and *spermatium*. Objection might also be raised to calling rust spermatia spores, however, since their usual function is more nearly gametic. The diversity among living organisms is too great to permit precise and easy definition of many descriptive terms, and the concepts developed for one group may be difficult or impossible to apply in another. Except for being produced in definite cavities, the spermatia of rusts appear to be essentially similar to the bodies which in the Homobasidiomycetes are called oidia.

The initial dicaryotic cell gives rise directly or indirectly to a dicaryotic mycelium, and within a few days numerous small, characteristically cup-like structures, called **aecia,** are formed. The wall of the aecium contains both monocaryotic and dicaryotic hyphae. Each aecium contains a number of conidiophores which cut off successive specialized conidia, called **aeciospores.** The aeciospores are binucleate and dicaryotic. They are carried about by the wind, and only those which land on the proper host survive and produce an infection. Aeciospores of autoecious rusts infect the same general kind of host on which they were produced (within the limits of the host range of the rust), but aeciospores of heteroecious rusts can survive only on a particular *different* kind or group of related kinds of host.

Typically the hypha produced by a germinating aeciospore enters the host through one of the stomates (see Chapter 26) on a leaf or stem, but sometimes the new hypha dissolves its way into the host instead. The dicaryotic mycelium produced in the new host from the aeciospore is seldom as extensive as the monocaryotic mycelium produced from a basidiospore. Usually two different kinds of spores are produced, at different times, from this dicaryotic mycelium. Short hyphae arise from a usually rather small, somewhat parenchymatous, mycelial mass just beneath the epidermis of the host. These hyphae rupture the epidermis and become visible as a definite sorus on which **uredospores** are borne. Each hypha of the sorus is two-celled. The terminal cell matures as a uredospore; the basal one elongates as a stalk. Uredospores are binucleate, dicaryotic, and usually yellow to orange-red. They are released into the air and infect only the same general kind of host as that on which they are produced. The uredospores of any particular rust have the same host range (one or more related species) as the aeciospores.

The mycelium produced from a germinating uredospore is essentially similar to that produced by a germinating aeciospore, and under proper conditions the uredospore stage may be repeated several times or even indefinitely. Sooner or later, however, the dicaryotic mycelium formed from a uredospore or aeciospore usually gives rise to another kind of spore, the **teliospore.** A **uredosorus** (on which uredospores are borne) may be transformed into a **teliosorus** (on which teliospores are borne), with both types of spore present during the transitional time, or new teliosori may be formed. Teliospores may be unicellular or composed of more than one cell. Sometimes they are borne on a stalk, like uredospores, sometimes not. They are usually thick-walled and often black. The teliospore often lies dormant for some time (frequently over a winter) before germinating. Each cell of a teliospore gives rise to a septate epibasidium on which the four basidiospores are borne. The nuclear phenomena associated with the development of the epibasidia have been discussed on p. 261.

Some rusts complete their life cycle without going through all the stages just described. Any or all types of spores, except basidiospores and teliospores, may be omitted, and in some cases the teliospores are produced in aecia and resemble the aeciospores of other rusts except in function. There are also some imperfect fungi, usually regarded as rusts, that produce only uredospores, or only aeciospores.

Most autoecious rusts are of relatively little economic importance, but the heteroecious rusts cause some of the most destructive of all plant diseases, from an economic standpoint. Perhaps the most important single plant disease is the **stem rust of wheat,** variously called red rust or black rust, according to the stage in which it is observed. The uredospores and uredosori are rusty red, and the teliospores and teliosori are black. The stem rust of wheat is caused by *Puccinia graminis,* a heteroecious rust composed of a number of physiologic races, in which one host is a barberry, typically the cultivated European barberry, *Berberis vulgaris,* and the other host is one or another kind of grain or other grass. The spermatia and aecia are produced on the barberry, and the uredospores and teliospores on the grass (Fig. 15.30).

The basidiospores, formed in the spring, are carried about by the wind and infect barberry leaves, developing a monocaryotic mycelium which produces spermogonia (Fig. 15.31) on the upper leaf surface. The spermogonia, which are barely, if at all, visible to the naked eye, contain spermatia and a sweet liquid that attracts insects. The insects unwittingly transfer the spermatia in moving from one spermogonium to another. Special receptive hyphae extend out through the mouth of the spermogonium, and often also through the stomates, or between the epidermal cells of the barberry leaf.

When a spermatium touches a receptive hypha of the opposite sexual strain, the spermatium fuses with a cell of the hypha. Probably the receptive hyphae are no more receptive in a physiological sense than any other hyphae of the monocaryotic mycelium, but it is the receptive hyphae with which the spermatia are most likely to come into contact. After plasmogamy has occurred, the spermatial nucleus is apparently passed down through the hypha from one cell to another, until it reaches a hyphal cell near the lower surface of the

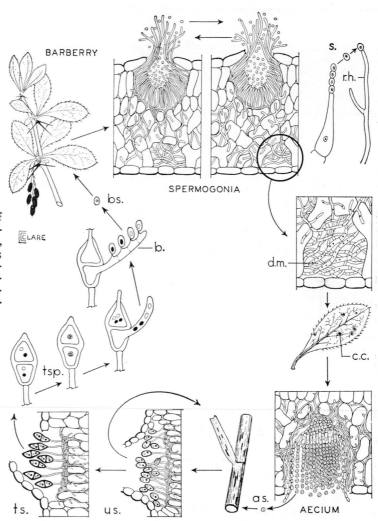

Fig. 15.30. Life cycle of wheat rust (*Puccinia graminis*); as., aeciospore; b., basidium; bs., basidiospore; c.c., cluster cups; d.m., dicaryotic mycelium; r.h., receptive hyphae; s., spermatium; ts., teliosorus; tsp., teliospore; us., uredosorus.

leaf which becomes the initial cell of the new dicaryotic mycelium. Probably the dicaryotic stage may also be initiated by fusion of hyphae from plus and minus mycelia if these come into contact, as is true in many other rusts.

Within a few days after initiation of the dicaryotic mycelium, clusters of aecia (often called cluster cups) appear on the lower surface of the barberry leaf (Fig. 15.31). The individual aecia are mostly less than 1 mm wide, but still readily visible to the naked eye. The aeciospores formed in the aecia are distributed by the wind, but effective distribution is strictly local, and long-distance transfer of viable aeciospores is seldom if ever accomplished. Aeciospores are infectious only to certain grasses. The race that affects wheat also affects some wild grasses.

The hypha produced by the germinating aeciospore enters the host through a

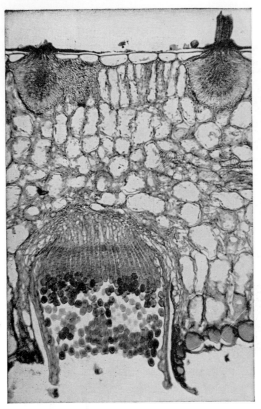

Fig. 15.31. Wheat rust, aecia and spermogonia on barberry leaf. (Courtesy of E. J. Kohl, Lakeside Biological Products, Ripon, Wis.)

long distances. The uredospore cycle may be repeated several times during the summer, with no other type of spore being produced. Later in the season, when the host is nearing maturity, some of the uredosori begin to produce teliospores instead of uredospores, thus becoming teliosori, and new teliosori are also formed directly from the mycelium within the host.

The teliospores (Fig. 15.32) are black and two-celled. They generally remain attached to the straw and do not germinate until the following spring. Each cell of the teliospore is a probasidium. The probasidium germinates to form an epibasidium, which is enlarged at the base into a hypobasidium bounded by the old spore (probasidium) wall. The epibasidium, which has also been called a promycelium, is microscopic, elongate, narrow, and transversely partitioned into four cells. Each cell of the epibasidium gives rise to a single ellipsoid basidiospore on a sterigma. The basidiospore is obliquely set on the sterigma and is forcibly discharged at maturity. Two of the basidiospores on a given basidium represent the plus strain, and two the minus strain. These strains cannot be called male and female, since each produces spermatia and receptive hyphae, corresponding more or less to male and female structures. The basidiospores are infectious to barberry, but not to wheat or other grasses.

Puccinia graminis seldom does much damage to the barberry but is often very destructive to wheat and other grains. In parts of Europe the barberry was commonly believed to be harmful to wheat for hundreds of years before the German mycologist Heinrich Anton De Bary demonstrated the principle of rust heteroecism by working out the life cycle of *Puccinia graminis*

stoma of the stem or leaf sheath, and in 1–2 weeks the rusty-reddish uredosori appear on the stem, leaf sheaths, and basal part of the leaf blades. An individual uredosorus is narrow and 2–10 mm long. The uredospores are carried about by the wind and are infectious to the same range of hosts as the aeciospores. In wheat-growing areas the most abundant potential host is wheat, and it is therefore commonly said that the uredospores are produced on wheat and return to wheat. Uredospores are resistant to drying and may retain their viability for some time, with the result that they can be effectively distributed for

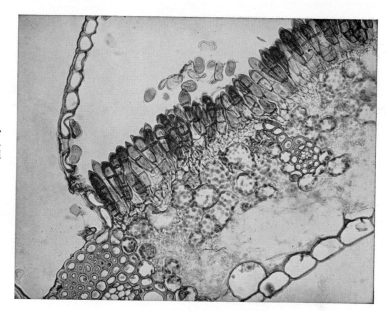

Fig. 15.32. Wheat rust, teliospores. (Courtesy of E. J. Kohl, Lakeside Biological Products, Ripon, Wis.)

(1864–1865). Inasmuch as the complete life cycle of the fungus requires the barberry as well as the grass host, it would seem that the disease could be eliminated by eradication of the barberry. This method of control has been highly successful in northern Europe, but much less so in the United States and some other parts of the world. The uredospores, which do not effectively survive the winter in cooler climates, survive very well in the southwestern United States, and carry the infection back to wheat, thus bypassing the barberry stages of the life cycle. New crops of uredospores carry the disease northward through the wheat belt of the Great Plains with the advancing season. The wheat-growing regions of northern Europe, on the other hand, are effectively cut off from warmer regions where the uredospores might survive, by the Pyrenees, the Alps, and related mountain masses.

Some cultivated varieties of wheat are far more resistant to rust damage than others, and a great deal of effort has been devoted to developing more resistant varieties by hybridization and selection. The intent is to combine in one variety all the other qualities desired, plus resistance to rust. The problem is tremendously complicated by the fact that the fungus exists in a number of minor races, and a wheat plant which is resistant to some of these may be susceptible to others. It is believed that elimination of the barberry is still a proper part of a control program in the United States, in combination with breeding for resistance, because the sexual stage of the life cycle cannot be completed without barberry. If the fungus reproduces only by uredospores, then new races, which might be able to infect previously resistant varieties of wheat, can arise only through relatively infrequent mutations, whereas if the full sexual cycle is allowed to take place new races can also be produced by recombination of existing genes.

Another important heteroecious rust

Fig. 15.33.   Left, white pine blister rust (*Cronartium ribicola*), aecial stage on white pine in Wisconsin; right, cedar-apple rust (*Gymnosporangium juniperi-virginianae*) on eastern red cedar. (Courtesy of the Department of Plant Pathology, Cornell University.)

is the white-pine blister rust, *Cronartium ribicola*. The spermogonia and aecia (Fig. 15.33) are borne on white pine (*Pinus strobus*) and other five-needled pines; the uredospores and teliospores on several kinds of currants and gooseberries (the genus *Ribes*), especially the black currant, *R. nigrum*. The aeciospores, which bring the infection from *Pinus* to *Ribes*, may be carried long distances, but the basidiospores, which bring the infection from *Ribes* to *Pinus*, are seldom effectively carried for more than about 1000 feet. Currants and gooseberries suffer relatively little from the disease, but pines are more seriously affected and often die. Eradication of susceptible species of *Ribes* from the vicinity of susceptible species of *Pinus* is an absolute control measure, but this is not easily accomplished, inasmuch as *Ribes nigrum*

has been commonly cultivated for its edible fruits, and other susceptible species of *Ribes* are widely distributed in the wild.

The cedar-apple rust, *Gymnosporangium juniperi-virginianae*, does not produce uredospores. The spermogonia and aecia are produced on apple trees (*Pyrus malus*), and the telia on *Juniperus virginiana*, the eastern American juniper or red cedar. The fungus causes the juniper to produce characteristic galls, often called cedar apples, that are commonly 1–2 inches thick. In the spring the gall gives rise to a number of teliosori which appear as gelatinous orange horns or slender projections commonly ¼ inch or more long (Fig. 15.33). The teliospores germinate in place to produce the basidiospores, which are forcibly discharged from the sterigmata. The disease does not usually travel far from either juniper to apple or apple to juniper, and here again local eradication of the alternate host has been used for control.

SMUTS

The **smuts** constitute the order Ustilaginales, a large group of fungi which in nature are obligate parasites of flowering plants, commonly affecting particularly the flowers and associated structures. The economically important smuts are mostly parasites of the cereal grasses, such as wheat, oats, rye, barley, and maize.

The smuts are related to the rusts, which they resemble in their essentially obligate parasitism, lack of definite fruiting bodies, production of teliospores, and often also in having a septate basidium. The smuts differ from the rusts in that the basidiospores of smuts are sessile on the basidium, without a sterigma, in the greater prevalence of blackish teliospores, and in the total absence of spermatia, aeciospores, and uredospores. The only spores produced by smuts are teliospores (always), basidiospores (usually), and conidia (frequently). Smuts are always autoecious, never having alternate hosts as do many rusts.

A large proportion of smuts differ from most or all other Basidiomycetes in that the four nuclei formed by reduction in the developing basidium do not directly become the primary nuclei of the basidiospores. Each such nucleus, instead, commonly undergoes one or more mitotic divisions within the basidium after meiosis, and some or eventually all of these nuclei subsequently migrate out into the basidiospores, which are often produced in successive crops of four. Sometimes the basidium fails to produce basidiospores at all, and the individual cells of the basidium germinate to produce new hyphae; or the teliospore may even produce one or more new hyphae without forming a distinct basidium.

Ustilago maydis, the common corn (maize) smut, causes large boils or tumors, often several inches across, on any rapidly growing, more or less meristematic part of the corn plant, frequently on or about the ears (Fig. 15.34). The unicellular, black teliospores germinate at or near the surface of the soil and typically produce an epibasidium that is transversely divided into four cells. Each cell of the epibasidium produces a sessile basidiospore somewhat resembling a yeast bud. The basidiospore may be released directly into the air or may germinate in place to produce a sessile conidium similar to itself. The basidium commonly produces successive crops of basidiospores in the same position, and when all these remain attached for some time, a branching mycelium with chains of basidiospores and similar intercalated conidia may be formed.

Sooner or later the basidiospores and conidia are released into the air. A spore which lands on a growing part of a susceptible corn plant germinates and forms a mycelium that spreads through the tissues of the host. The mycelium is both intercellular and intracellular, passing through and between the cells and producing haustoria which enter the host cells. The presence of the mycelium results in the formation of a tumor, which is at first covered by a definite whitish membrane. Many cells of the mycelium develop into teliospores, and the membrane of the tumor is ruptured, exposing the sooty spore mass.

The dicaryotic stage may be initiated

Fig. 15.34. Smuts. Left, *Ustilago maydis* on an ear of corn, showing the tumors still covered by the membrane. (Courtesy of the Department of Plant Pathology, Cornell University.) Right, *Ustilago tritici*, the loose smut of wheat. (Courtesy of G. W. Fischer, Department of Plant Pathology, Washington State University.)

early or late, and, according to the circumstances, may arise from fusion of spores, fusion of hyphae from different mycelia which come into contact, or, rarely, fusion of adjacent cells of the same hypha or mycelium. The species is heterothallic, and dicaryotization by fusion of cells from the same mycelium does not usually lead to the production of teliospores.

The only effective control for corn smut, other than breeding for resistance, is to avoid planting corn in infected soil. If the smut boils are removed and destroyed before they release their spores, the chance of infection is minimized. Crop rotation is a useful part of such a program of sanitation.

Ustilago tritici, the **loose smut of wheat**, is one of the more important smuts.

Infection takes place at the time of flowering. The unicellular, black teliospores are carried about by the wind. A teliospore which lands on the stigma (see Chapter 30) of a young wheat flower germinates and produces a branching mycelium without forming a recognizable basidium, although the first division of the teliospore nucleus is meiotic. The dicaryotic stage may be initiated by fusion of hyphal cells from different mycelia which come into contact, or by nuclear transfer within a single hypha. The mycelium grows down into the ovary of the wheat flower and eventually enters the apical meristem (epicotyl) of the developing embryo in the grain. The mycelium then goes into dormancy while the grain matures.

When the grain germinates the fol-

Fig. 15.35. Harvest scene in a wheat field heavily infested with stinking smut, near Pullman, Washington, in 1956. The clouds of spores will infest fallow fields for miles around. (From G. W. Fischer and C. S. Holton, *Biology and Control of the Smut Fungi*, 1957. Copyright Ronald Press, New York.)

lowing spring, the mycelium becomes active in the apical meristematic region but causes little or no evident damage until the new flowering spike is formed. The mycelium grows very vigorously within the developing flower spike, reducing it to a skeleton surrounded by a powdery mass of black teliospores which are released at about the time healthy plants come into flower (Fig. 15.34).

Some varieties of wheat are more resistant to smut than others. In susceptible varieties the disease may be controlled by immersing the grain in hot water for several minutes, after several hours of soaking at ordinary temperatures. The fungus mycelium is more sensitive to heat than is the embryo of the grain, especially after dormancy has been broken by the presoaking.

In the **covered** or stinking **smut of wheat**, caused by *Tilletia foetida* and *T. caries* (*T. tritici*), infection takes place as the seed is germinating, or directly thereafter. The fungus permeates the tissues of the host, often stunting its growth. When the flower spikes are produced, the grains,

or some of them, are replaced by masses of black teliospores. The chaff surrounding the grain is not much affected, hence the name **covered smut.** The name stinking smut comes from the foul odor given off by the smut bodies. The teliospores lie dormant over the winter and germinate the following spring, each producing a nonseptate epibasidium with a cluster of 4 to 12 narow, elongate, slightly curved, sessile basidiospores at the tip. These may germinate directly to form a new hypha which enters the host, or they may germinate by repetition, as in many other smuts, giving rise to conidia similar to themselves in form and function. The dicaryotic stage is often initiated while the basidiospores are still attached to the basidium. A conjugation tube is formed between two adjacent basidiospores, and the nucleus of one spore passes through the tube into the other spore to form an initial dicaryotic cell, which may germinate directly or by repetition. Two monocaryotic conidia may fuse in similar fashion.

Stinking smut is controlled by breeding for resistance and by chemical treat-

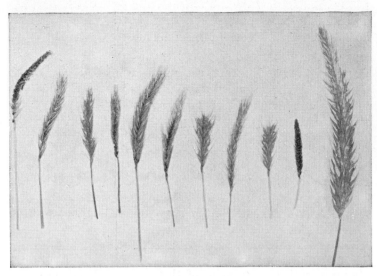

Fig. 15.36. Effect of different physiological races of one species of smut (*Ustilago bullata*) on *Hordeum brachyantherum*, the native American meadow-barley. Plants of *H. brachyantherum* from the same lot of seed were inoculated with smut spores collected from other kinds of grasses. The head at the right is normal; the others, from left to right, inoculated with smut taken from *Agropyron trachycaulum*, *A. cristatum*, *A. spicatum*, *Bromus mollis*, *B. marginatus*, *B. catharticus*, *B. vulgaris*, *B. anomalus*, *B. inermis*, *B. catharticus*. (From G. W. Fischer and C. S. Holton, *Biology and Control of the Smut Fungi*, 1957. Copyright Ronald Press, New York.)

Fig. 15.37. *Clitocybe brumalis*, a common mushroom. (Courtesy of the Department of Plant Pathology, Cornell University.)

ment of the seed to kill any teliospores which may remain on it.

MUSHROOMS AND TOADSTOOLS

Basidiomycetes which produce a definite fruiting body with a stalk and a cap are called **mushrooms** or **toadstools** (Figs. 15.37, 15.39). They belong to the order Agaricales, and some botanists would re- strict the application of that name to them alone. The hymenium is borne on the lower side of the cap, which is more technically called the **pileus**. Typically the lower side of the pileus is divided into many thin, more or less parallel, vertical plates, called **gills**, which radiate from the stipe to the margin of the pileus, and the hymenium covers the gills. Mushrooms and toadstools with gills are usually considered to make up a single family, the Agarica-

Fig. 15.38. *Amanita muscaria*, the fly amanite, a highly poisonous mushroom. Note the "death cup" at the base, found on many poisonous (and some edible) mushrooms. (Courtesy of the Department of Plant Pathology, Cornell University.)

ceae; members of this family are sometimes called agarics.

Agarics are mostly saprophytic, occurring especially in soil that is rich in organic matter, or on rotting logs or stumps, etc., but some are facultative parasites on the roots of trees and elsewhere, or they may be involved in mycorhizal associations (see p. 279). The vegetative mycelium is buried in the substratum and sends up fruiting bodies at irregular intervals of months or years, usually after soaking rains. A mycelium established at a single point tends to enlarge radially in all directions and to die out at the center with the depletion of the available food supply. Successive crops of fruiting bodies may thus be produced in successively larger rings, often called **fairy rings**, before environmental hazards break up the ring or change its shape. Puffballs often produce fairy rings in the same manner.

Many agarics are edible and are considered great delicacies, but others are extremely poisonous. Some species of *Amanita* (Fig. 15.38) are so virulent that a piece 1 cubic centimeter in size may be fatal, and there is no known antidote for

the poisonous principle of these species. Other species of *Amanita* are harmless; *Amanita caesaria* is so named because the emperor Nero was reputedly fond of it. Some kinds of mushrooms are poisonous to some people and harmless to others, and a few are poisonous only when consumed more or less concurrently with alcoholic beverages. Some poisonous amanitas have the stipe seated in a basal cup, commonly called the death cup, but some edible mushrooms have a similar cup, and some poisonous ones lack it. There is, in fact, no test, other than actual eating, which will distinguish all poisonous mushrooms from all edible ones, and this test is not conducive to the tester's longevity. It is, of course, possible to learn to recognize individual species which are edible and to learn also to recognize some of the notoriously poisonous species, but the chances of error are so great, and the possible results of error so serious, that people who are not competent mycologists are better advised to forego the consumption of wild mushrooms. The common field mushroom, *Agaricus campestris*, is widely cultivated, and at least in the United States only the cultivated specimens are used in commercial canning. Canned mushrooms may therefore be eaten safely.

Many nonbotanists apply the term *mushroom* to those agarics and related fungi which they believe to be edible, and the term *toadstool* to those which they believe to be poisonous. Because edibility is so difficult to determine safely, and because this criterion cannot be used to divide the agarics into taxonomically natural groups, most botanists prefer to use the terms interchangeably, or to use the term *mushroom* in a broad sense and relegate *toadstool* to popular usage.

The dicaryotic stage of agarics may be initiated in any of several ways. Monocaryotic mycelia of many species produce, at the surface of the substrate, conidia of a type usually called **oidia**. These may be distributed singly by the wind or may be borne in droplets of sticky liquid which attract insects. An oidium which comes into contact with a hyphal cell of the

proper type fuses with that cell, initiating the dicaryotic stage; otherwise, at least in some species, the oidium germinates to produce a new mycelium, in the manner of other conidia. The oidia of agarics are thus comparable in function to the spermatia of rusts. In addition to the fusion of an oidium with a hyphal cell, the dicaryotic stage may be initiated by fusion of hyphal cells of different, or even the same, mycelia. Heterothallic species, with two or more mating types, require the contact of mycelia or cells of different mating types, whereas in homothallic species the process may be completed within a single mycelium.

Once the initial dicaryotic cell has been formed, a new dicaryotic mycelium may develop from it by division, in the way described on p. 260, and, at least in many species, the existing mycelium is converted to a dicaryotic condition. In the latter instance the newly introduced nucleus in the dicaryon initial divides mitotically,

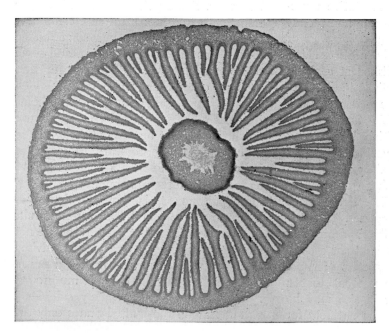

Fig. 15.39. *Coprinus* (a mushroom); cross section of fruiting body, showing stipe, gills, and cap. (Copyright by General Biological Supply House, Inc., Chicago.)

and one of the daughter nuclei passes through the pore in the partition into the adjoining cell, where it again undergoes mitosis, etc.

The fruiting bodies are produced only by dicaryotic mycelia, in quantities and at intervals controlled by the available food supply, moisture, temperature, and other factors. In many species the gills are exposed from the beginning. In others the margin of the pileus is at first recurved and is connected to the base of the stipe by a membrane called the **volva** or **veil.** At this stage the young fruiting body might at first be confused with the fruiting body of a more mature puffball, although the internal structure is different. Growth of the pileus and stipe ruptures the veil, which remains, in some species, as a cup surrounding the base of the stipe. Alternatively, or in addition to the primary veil, there may be a secondary veil, extending from the margins of the young pileus to a

level more or less midway along the stipe. The remnants of this secondary veil commonly persist as an **annulus** (little ring) around the stipe when the fruiting body is mature.

The gills (Fig. 15.40) on the lower side of the pileus are covered by the hymenium, which consists of a layer of very many basidia, either alone or intermingled with paraphyses, often also with some scattered, longer, firmly projecting cells which tend to hold the surfaces of the gills apart. The basidia are unicellular, commonly longer than thick, with four terminal, ellipsoid basidiospores obliquely set on the sterigmata. The four nuclei formed by reduction division within the basidium migrate into the basidiospores, of which they become the primary nuclei.

At maturity the basidiospores are forcibly discharged from the basidia, commonly for a distance several times their own length, and fall from between the gills

Fig. 15.40. *Coprinus* gill, showing basidiospores. (Copyright by General Biological Supply House, Inc., Chicago.)

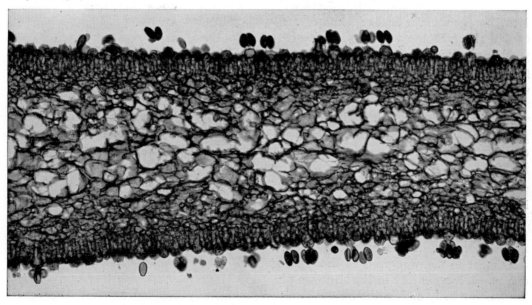

Fig. 15.41. *Hydnum imbricatum*, a tooth fungus (Agaricales, Family Hydnaceae). (×⅔.) (Courtesy of the Department of Plant Pathology, Cornell University.)

into the open air. The basidiospores are carried about by the wind, and under favorable conditions any basidiospore may germinate to produce a monocaryotic mycelium. The fruiting bodies die and decay soon after liberating their spores, but the vegetative mycelium which produced them generally lives on to produce successive crops of fruiting bodies and is potentially immortal.

BRACKET FUNGI

The **bracket fungi,** making up the family Polyporaceae of the order Agaricales, are similar in many respects to the Agaricaceae, differing chiefly in the structure of the fruiting body and in the greater tend-

ency to grow on wood. The fruiting body (Fig. 15.43) is usually a firm bracket on the tree or log within which the vegetative mycelium has developed. The lower surface of the bracket is covered with tiny pores that are often so small as to be barely visible to the naked eye. Each such pore is the external opening of a slender, usually vertical tube in the fruiting body, and the hymenium covers the internal surfaces of the tubes. Some genera of polypores produce perennial fruiting bodies, adding a new and larger layer on the lower side each year, so that the upper side shows a series of concentric arcs. There are several families of Agaricales (Figs. 15.41, 15.42) in which the hymenium is more prominently exposed than in the Agaricaceae and Polyporaceae, and one family, the Boletaceae, in which the fruiting body has the form of the Agaricaceae but the porous structure of the Polyporaceae.

Bracket fungi (Fig. 15.43) grow on both live and dead trees, or less commonly on organic matter in the soil; a few species are parasitic on other fungi. The species which grow on living trees typically attack directly only the dead cells of which the wood is largely composed, but the enzymes they produce may kill some of the living cells and ultimately contribute to the death of the tree. Bracket fungi often do serious damage to mature standing timber, and also to lumber which is kept moist or in contact with the ground. The author has even seen fruiting bodies attached to the

Fig. 15.42. *Clavaria pyxidata* (Agaricales). (X½.) (Courtesy of the Department of Plant Pathology, Cornell University.)

Fig. 15.43. *Polyporus squamosus*, a bracket fungus. (Courtesy of the Department of Plant Pathology, Cornell University.)

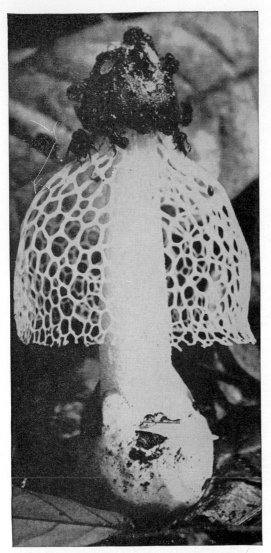

Fig. 15.44. *Dictyophora*, a stinkhorn fungus (order Phallales). Note the flies gathered on the malodorous gleba. (Photo by W. H. Hodge.)

The fruiting bodies of Basidiomycetes belonging to the family Lycoperdaceae of the order Lycoperdales are commonly called **puffballs** (Fig. 15.45). The Lycoperdaceae are much like the Agaricaceae in habitat, food supply, vegetative structure, and the manner in which the dicaryotic condition is achieved. They differ from the Agaricaceae chiefly in the structure of the fruiting bodies and position of the basidiospores. The fruiting bodies are usually more or less globose or depressed-globose, often tapering to a broad stalk-like base. The commoner species seldom exceed 2–3 inches in diameter, but a record specimen 4 feet across and 1 foot high was collected some years ago in New York. It has been estimated that such a specimen should contain about 1.6×10^{14} spores. Many species of puffballs are highly edible when young, and none is known to be poisonous, but a young puffball is so readily confused with a young mushroom that amateurs should beware.

A mature puffball consists of a compact outer layer called the **peridium**, enclosing a mass of looser, often more or less spongy mycelium, the **gleba**. The gleba consists of very numerous basidia and intermingled sterile hyphae, the latter forming the **capillitium**. The peridium and capillitium of the Lycoperdaceae are only vaguely and superficially similar to the peridium and capillitium of the Myxomycetes, being quite different in structure and origin. The basidia and basidiospores of the Lycoperdaceae resemble those of the Agaricaceae, except that the basidiospores of the Lycoperdaceae are symmetrically attached to the sterigma by one end, rather than being obliquely set, and are

wooden frame of a station wagon owned by one of his botanical colleagues in Georgia. The vegetative mycelium develops extensively in the substrate before fruiting bodies are produced, and the appearance of basidiocarps indicates that considerable decay has already occurred.

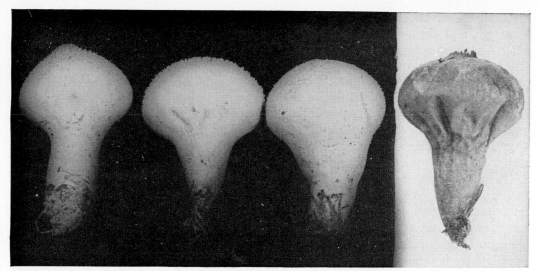

Fig. 15.45. *Lycoperdon prolatum,* a puffball. (Courtesy of the Department of Plant Pathology, Cornell University.)

merely released from the sterigma at maturity, rather than being forcibly discharged. At maturity the peridium tends to rupture, leaving one or more openings into the gleba, especially from the top. Wind or other disturbance causes the basidiospores to be discharged into the air, but the capillitium tends to restrict the number of spores which are discharged at any one time.

MYCORHIZAE

Many species of fungi enter into a symbiotic association with the roots of vascular plants, forming a structure known as a **mycorhiza.** This term is also extended to cover the products of somewhat similar associations between fungi and the underground gametophytes of *Lycopodium* and some other plants. Many members of the Boletaceae and Agaricaceae are mycorhizal, as are also the Tuberales (Ascomy-

cetes) and various other fungi. A large proportion of trees are mycorhizal, as are also most members of the heath and orchid families. Well-preserved fossil mycorhizae have been found in coal balls dating from the Lower Carboniferous (Mississippian) period. Mycorhizae are further discussed in Chapter 25.

Eumycotina: Fungi Imperfecti

Fungi of which the perfect stage is unknown are called Fungi Imperfecti, or Deuteromycetes. When the perfect stage of a fungus previously referred to the Fungi Imperfecti is discovered, the organism is transferred to the appropriate class. Often both the perfect and imperfect (asexual) stages of a fungus are discovered and named long before it is learned that both names apply to the same species. According to the rules of nomenclature, a name based on the perfect stage always takes precedence over one based on an imperfect stage, regardless of which name is the older. One reason for this is that species, genera, and higher groups which may be readily distinguishable in the perfect stage may be wholly indistinguishable in the imperfect stage, so that one name for an imperfect fungus may prove to apply to several different taxa when the perfect stages are discovered.

The imperfect genera *Aspergillus* and *Penicillium* (Fig. 15.46) may serve to illustrate the situation. Both are common genera, with many species that reproduce abundantly by conidia. In *Aspergillus* the conidiophore is swollen at the tip and covered with very numerous, short, radiating branches, each of which terminates in a chain of conidia. In *Penicillium* the conidiophore divides into two or more branches, each of which terminates in a chain of conidia. The common blue and green molds are mostly species of *Aspergillus* and *Penicillium*. The perfect stages have been found for only a small fraction of the species that have been placed in these two genera. The presently known per-

fect stages of *Aspergillus* prove to belong to three different genera, *Eurotium*, *Emericella*, and *Sartorya*, all of which belong to the family Eurotiaceae of the order Eurotiales of the Ascomycetes. The presently known perfect stages of *Penicillium* represent two genera, both of which belong to the Eurotiaceae. One of these, *Carpenteles*, had been known and described before its relationship to *Penicillium* was suspected. The other, *Talaromyces*, had not been previously known and was established to include some species which, in the imperfect stage, had been referred to *Penicillium*. According to the rules of nomenclature, the names which had been used for these species when only the imperfect stage was known should now be replaced by names based on the perfect stage, but the names *Aspergillus* and *Penicillium* are so well known that many botanists continue to use them, even for species whose perfect stage is now known. Even when those species for which the perfect stage has been discovered are removed to genera based on perfect stages, there remain many species of both *Penicillium* and *Aspergillus*

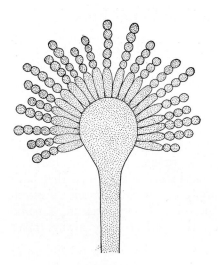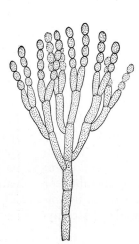

Fig. 15.46. Conidiophores and conidia of *Aspergillus* (left) and *Penicillium* (right). (×800.)

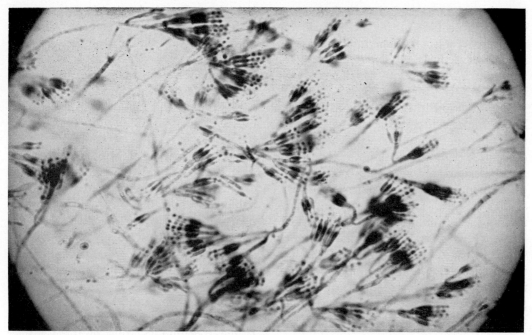

Fig. 15.47. *Penicillium* conidiophores. (Copyright by General Biological Supply House, Inc., Chicago.)

for which these latter names must be retained because the perfect stage has not yet been discovered.

In both *Aspergillus* and *Penicillium* the perfect forms so far discovered have proved to be closely related, even though they are referred to distinct genera. That is not always the case with other genera of Fungi Imperfecti. *Rhizoctonia* is a common and well-known imperfect genus with many species. One of these, *R. solani*, is a serious parasite of potatoes and a number of other plants. The perfect stage of *R. solani* is *Pellicularia filamentosa*, a member of the family Thelyphoraceae, order Agaricales, subclass Homobasidiomycetes. *Rhizoctonia crocorum*, another fairly important parasite, proves to be the imperfect stage of *Helicobasidium purpureum*, a member of the family Auriculariaceae, order Tremellales, subclass Heterobasidiomycetes. Thus species which had been referred to a single

genus on the basis of the imperfect stage prove to represent two different subclasses of Basidiomycetes. Genera of the Fungi Imperfecti are often spoken of as **form genera,** i.e., genera which are based on certain morphological characters but which do not necessarily represent natural groups of species.

A large proportion of the species which have been removed from the Fungi Imperfecti on discovery of the perfect stage prove to be Ascomycetes, but some, on the contrary, are Basidiomycetes. Conidial stages of Phycomycetes can usually be recognized and are commonly referred to the appropriate position in that class rather than being placed in the Fungi Imperfecti. Doubtless many of the approximately 10,000 species now referred to the Fungi Imperfecti will eventually be removed to other classes, but many others have probably lost the perfect stage completely. It is scarcely to be expected that perfect stages with macroscopic fruiting bodies will be discovered for such dermatophytes (skin-inhabiting fungi) as *Trichophyton gypseum* and *T. purpureum*, which cause athlete's foot.

In addition to causing plant diseases, Fungi Imperfecti cause several diseases of man. The dermatophytes, which are seldom more than a mere annoyance in temperate regions, are so vigorous and abundant in moist tropical regions as to be a serious menace. The San Joaquin Valley fever, a severe and often fatal illness which is sporadic in parts of California and elsewhere in the southwestern United States, is caused by *Coccidioides immitis*, an imperfect fungus. Some other imperfect fungi cause lung diseases with symptoms similar to those of tuberculosis.

ANTIBIOTICS

Any substance produced by a living organism, which under natural conditions tends to inhibit the growth of competing organisms, is called an **antibiotic**. Many fungi produce antibiotics which are particularly effective against bacteria. The first antibiotic to attract much attention was penicillin. The Scottish medical bacteriologist Alexander Fleming (1881–1955) noticed in 1928 that a species of *Penicillium* which occurred as a contaminant in a laboratory culture of *Staphylococcus* inhibited the growth of bacteria for some distance around and beyond the fungal mycelium. Obviously this effect could be achieved only by the release into the culture medium of some substance produced by the fungus. Fleming named this substance **penicillin** in 1929. Experimental work later demonstrated that penicillin

is highly effective in limiting the growth of many Gram-positive bacteria, although relatively harmless to most Gram-negative ones.

Penicillin was first used to treat a human illness in 1941, and the dramatically successful results soon led to its widespread use to combat a number of different bacterial diseases and infections, although the original patient suffered a relapse and died after the supply of the drug had been exhausted. Gonorrhea is particularly amenable to penicillin treatment, although penicillin-fast cases (i.e., cases which do not respond to treatment with penicillin) are now appearing with increasing frequency. The species of *Penicillium* observed by Fleming was *P. notatum*, but commercial penicillin (Fig. 15.48) is now obtained largely from the related species, *P. chrysogenum*. Neither of these species is known to have a perfect form. A synthetic product closely related to natural penicillin was placed on the market in 1959 under the name Syncillin.

The success of penicillin led to a widespread search for other antibiotics. Many fungi and actinomycetes have been shown to produce antibiotic substances, but most of these are unsuited to medicinal use because there is little or no margin between the therapeutic and the toxic dose. Medically useful antibiotics other than penicillin have come chiefly from the actinomycetes, especially the genus *Streptomyces* (See Chapter 6). Streptomycin, produced by *Streptomyces griseus*, is effective chiefly against Gram-negative bacteria, thus complementing the role of penicillin.

Fungi and bacteria are the only large groups of plants which regularly produce exoenzymes. The antibiotics which they produce are also released into the substratum. It has been suggested that these

Fig. 15.48. Production of penicillin. (Courtesy of Eli Lilly and Company.)

antibiotics are merely waste products comparable to the toxins produced by some of the pathogenic bacteria, but they also have a definite survival value for the organisms which produce them, in reducing the competition for the available food.

A number of vascular plants produce substances comparable to antibiotics through decay or solution from dead plant parts. Some intermediate products of decomposition of roots of many grasses are harmful to apple trees and some other plants; black walnuts exert similar harmful effects on some kinds of plants. Dead leaves of *Encelia farinosa*, a desert shrub of the southwestern United States, contain a water-soluble substance which is highly toxic to many other kinds of plants, and in nature this species is notable for the

fact that other kinds of plants are not generally found in its shelter.

Some substances are harmful to the organisms which produce them as well as to other organisms. It has already been noted that the concentration of alcohol which can be obtained by fermentation is limited by the degree of tolerance of the yeast to the alcohol which it produces. The decay products of peach roots have been shown to inhibit the growth of peach seedlings, and the tendency of some bunch grasses to die out from the center may be due to some similar phenomenon. There are all gradations and combinations in nature, from conditions in which some particular substance produced by an organism has a definite survival value in restricting competition, to conditions in which the waste product or decay product is distinctly harmful to the organism which gives rise to it.

Eumycotina: General Considerations

ECONOMIC IMPORTANCE

Fungi cause many serious diseases of plants, and also a few diseases of man and other animals. They are second only to the bacteria as agents of decay and are almost alone as the cause of decay of wood. As noted in the discussion of bacteria, decay is the means by which complex organic compounds are changed into simpler substances which can again be used as raw materials for plant growth. Some mushrooms, and other fungi such as truffles and morels, are used as food, and people often die as a result of mistaking poisonous mushrooms for edible ones. Lichens are significant as pioneers on bare rock surfaces, and many forest trees and other kinds of plants are dependent on mycorhizal associations for survival. Alcohol is obtained from yeasts, which are also important in the baking industry; and a number of other useful chemicals, including penicillin, are obtained from various kinds of fungi. Although fungi obviously cause enormous damage from a human standpoint, they are also an essential part of the balance of nature as it now exists.

METHODS OF CONTROLLING PLANT DISEASES

The most important general methods of controlling diseases of plants are breeding for resistance, spraying and other di-

rect treatment of the host, grafting on resistant stock, elimination of a necessary alternate host, and sanitation, including crop rotation. Most of these methods are used to control one or another disease caused by fungi. The importance of breeding for resistance against rusts and smuts has been mentioned, as have also the elimination of alternate hosts for some rusts and sanitation for some smuts. Breeding for resistance is particularly useful for annual crops, since new seed must in any case be planted each year. The use of Bordeaux mixture in controlling downy mildew of grapes has been mentioned. The outstanding example of a disease controlled by grafting on resistant stock is the *Phylloxera* disease of grapes. *Phylloxera* is a tiny insect, related to the aphids, which attacks the roots of grapes. It is native on American grapes, to which it usually causes relatively little damage. It is very destructive to European species of grape, however, and the vines in most European vineyards are now grafted on the roots of resistant American species.

RELATIONSHIPS

The relationships of the fungi have long been a matter of controversy. The coenocytic Phycomycetes closely resemble some of the coenocytic, filamentous, green algae, except in the absence of chloroplasts. The algal genus *Vaucheria*, in particular, has often been cited as probably related to the order Saprolegniales of the Phycomycetes. The proper position of *Vaucheria* in the Xanthophyceae rather than the Chlorophyceae has only rather recently been established, and in consequence the Chlorophyceae have in the past commonly been considered as probably ancestral to the

Phycomycetes. The Saprolegniales and some other Phycomycetes also resemble the Chlorophyceae (although not the Xanthophyceae) in having cellulose walls, whereas the walls of other fungi are generally chitinous.

In contrast to the Phycomycetes, the Ascomycetes are suggestive of the red algae in some respects. The trichogyne of the red algae has been compared with the trichogyne of the Ascomycetes, the gonimoblast filaments of the red algae with the ascogenous hyphae of the Ascomycetes, and the carposporangia of the red algae with the asci of the Ascomycetes. The central pore in the septa of ascomycetous filaments has likewise been compared with the pore in the wall between sister cells of rhodophycean filaments. These similarities have convinced many botanists that the Ascomycetes are, in fact, derived from the Rhodophyceae by loss of chlorophyll.

Nearly all students have agreed that the Basidiomycetes are derived from the Ascomycetes and that the basidium is a modified ascus. This view is strengthened by the fact that in some Basidiomycetes the developing basidiospore produces a wall of its own in ascomycetous fashion while still enclosed in the outer wall formed by the projection from the basidium.

The idea that the fungi are polyphyletic, being derived from two or more very different groups of algae, has never commanded universal botanical acceptance. Many botanists have believed that the similarities are so great and the gaps in the variability so small, that at least the Eumycotina must constitute an essentially natural group. The widespread presence of glycogen as the carbohydrate food reserve and of chitin as the wall material, in all classes of Eumycotina, tends to unite the Eumycotina and to separate them from all suggested algal ancestors, as does also the general tendency among the Eumycotina for karyogamy to be delayed until long after plasmogamy. The features of the Ascomycetes which have been used to suggest a relationship with the red algae can furthermore be at least as easily derived from the Phycomycetes, and the ascogonium can readily be interpreted as a modified phycomycetous oögonium. The author favors the view, which he also believes to be now the majority opinion among systematic mycologists, that the Eumycotina are an essentially natural group, and that the evolutionary sequence proceeds from Phycomycetes to Ascomycetes to Basidiomycetes.

The origin of the Phycomycetes is another question. There is abundant evidence to support the belief that the aquatic forms with flagellated zoospores are more primitive than the terrestrial forms without flagellated cells. It is not at all certain, however, that the primitive phycomycete was filamentous, as in the Saprolegniales. In spite of the similarity between *Vaucheria* and *Saprolegnia,* the view that the primitive phycomycete was a unicellular flagellate with two dissimilar flagella has much to recommend it. Since there is no very sharp distinction among the unicellular flagellates between plants (algae) and animals (protozoa), and since the protozoa are pretty clearly derived from chlorophyllous flagellates by loss of chlorophyll and subsequent evolution along holozoic lines, it does not seem necessary to try to decide whether a hypothetical unicellular flagellated ancestor to the present-day Phycomycetes was an alga or a protozoan.

The position of the Myxomycetes has been even more controversial than the relationships of the Eumycotina. The vegetative stage is quite animal-like, but the fruiting bodies are more plant-like, at least if the Eumycotina are considered to be plants. Although it has been customary to include the Myxomycetes among the fungi, many botanists have done so chiefly for convenience and out of respect for tradition, frequently with the comment that the group might better be referred to the animal kingdom. The Myxomycetes have no apparent close relatives, however, among undoubted animals, whereas they are connected to the Phycomycetes by such forms as the Plasmodiophorales. The Plasmodiophorales have variously been considered to be aberrant Myxomycetes, or aberrant Phycomyetes related to the chytrids. The recent discovery that the Plasmodiophorales and other Myxomycetes are alike in having two unequal whiplash flagella, unlike all known Phycomycetes, indicates that this order is properly placed with the Myxomycetes, but the suggestion of a relationship between the Myxomycetes and the Phycomycetes remains. The presence of naked flagellated cells in the life history of the Myxomycetes suggests that this class, like the Phycomycetes, is derived from a unicellular, flagellated ancestor. The fact that the two flagella of the Myxomycetes are similar in structure, even though of unequal length, suggests that the Myxomycetes may actually have originated independently of the Phycomycetes, in which the two flagella differ in structure. There it seems the matter must rest until more information becomes available.

In summary, the author adopts the following views about the relationships of the fungi: The Eumycotina are an essentially natural group. The Phycomycetes are probably derived from unicellular flagellates more or less on the borderline between the algae and protozoa, or possibly from filamentous coenocytic algae such as *Vaucheria* which produce biflagellated cells with dissimilar flagella during the reproductive stage. The terrestrial Phycomycetes without flagellated cells are derived from aquatic Phycomycetes with flagellated cells. The Ascomycetes are derived from the Phycomycetes, probably from forms similar to the present-day Saprolegniales and Peronosporales, and the ascogonium is homologous with the oögonium of these latter two orders. The Basidiomycetes are derived from the Ascomycetes, and the basidium is homologous with the ascus. The available evidence does not permit a firm conclusion regarding the relationship of the Myxomycotina to the Eumycotina. The similarity of the Plasmodiophorales of the Myxomycetes to the Chytridiales of the Phycomycetes in characters other than flagellar structure suggests that the Myxomycetes may indeed be related to the Phycomycetes, but the difference in flagellar structure suggests that the Myxomycetes may have been independently derived from a unicellular flagellated ancestor which had only the whiplash type of flagellum.

FOSSIL FORMS

The fossil record provides abundant evidence of the existence of fungi from the Devonian period to the present. Some of the oldest known fossils of vascular plants, from the Rhynie beds of Devonian age in Scotland, bear well-preserved fossil fungi which resemble the Phycomycetes in having nonseptate hyphae. Fossil leaves of Carboniferous and later ages often have small spots resembling the fruiting bodies of Pyrenomycetes, and leaves of Cretaceous and later ages have spots resembling the aecia, uredinia, and telia of rusts. Fossils of the larger fruiting bodies of fungi are very seldom found. Since the classification of fungi depends largely on the structure of the fruiting bodies and on microscopic details which are in any case not likely to be preserved, the fossil record provides but little evidence as to the phylogeny of the group.

SUGGESTED READING

Christensen, Clyde M., *The Molds and Man*, University of Minnesota Press, Minneapolis, ed. 2, 1961, 238 pp. A popular treatment by a noted mycologist.

Crowder, William, Marvels of the Mycetozoa, *National Geographic* 49:421–444, 1926. Includes striking pictures of slime molds.

Epstein, Samuel, and Beryl Williams, *Miracles from Microbes*, Rutgers University Press, New Brunswick, N. J., 1946. A popular account of the early antibiotics.

Large, E. C., *The Advance of the Fungi*. Holt, New York, 1940, 488 pp. A well-written account of the importance of fungi to man. No technical background is necessary.

Pratt, Robertson, and Jean Dufrenoy, *Antibiotics*, Lippincott, Philadelphia, 1949, 255 pp. Thorough and rather technical.

Ramsbottom, John, *Mushrooms and Toadstools*, Collins, London, 1953, 306 pp. An interesting, accurate account at the semipopular level, written by an outstanding botanist.

Smith, Alexander H., *The Mushroom Hunter's Field Guide*, University of Michigan Press, Ann Arbor, 1958, 197 pp. Includes many black and white photographs.

————, *Mushrooms in Their Natural Habitats*, 2 vols., Sawyer's, Portland, Oregon, 1949. The second volume contains a Viewmaster and 231 kodachromes.

Division Bryophyta

BRYOPHYTES

Plants with multicellular antheridia and archegonia, but without specialized conducting tissues such as xylem and phloem; sporophyte permanently attached to the gametophyte and partly or wholly parasitic on it. Three classes, the Anthocerotae, Hepaticae, and Musci.

◄

Conocephalum conicum, a liverwort belonging to the Marchantiales. (×4.) (Photo by John H. Gerard, from National Audubon Society.)

INTRODUCTION TO EMBRYOPHYTA

The classification of all plants into two primary groups, the Thallophyta and Cormophyta, was proposed by the Austrian botanist Stephan Ladislaus Endlicher (1804–1849) in 1836. Many botanists now use the term Embryophyta, as is done in this text, in place of Endlicher's name Cormophyta. The divisions Schizophyta, Chlorophyta, Euglenophyta, Pyrrophyta, Chrysophyta, Phaeophyta, Rhodophyta, and Fungi make up the subkingdom Thallophyta. The divisions Bryophyta, Psilophyta, Lepidophyta, Calamophyta, Filicophyta, Coniferophyta, Cycadophyta, and Anthophyta make up the subkingdom Embryophyta.

The divisions of Thallophyta are very diverse and have little in common, but their origin and interrelationships do not involve the Embryophyta. The divisions of Embryophyta, on the contrary, form a well-marked group with many morphological, anatomical, and physiological features in common, and it is clear that the Embryophyta are derived from the Thallophyta.

The pigments of the chloroplasts of embryophytes are chlorophylls *a* and *b*, β- and usually α-carotene, and several xanthophylls, generally including lutein, cryptoxanthin, and zeaxanthin. Chlorophyll *a* is the principal chlorophyll, β-carotene is the principal carotene, and lutein is the principal xanthophyll. The carotenes and xanthophylls, collectively called the carotenoid pigments, are masked by the more abundant chlorophylls. The most common carbohydrate reserve of the embryophytes is starch. The primary cell wall of embryophytes consists largely of cellulose. Flagellated cells of embryophytes have only the whiplash type of flagellum. In all these respects the Embryophyta resemble the green algae (Chlorophyceae), and the green algae are generally believed to be ancestral to the Embryophyta.

The embryophytes differ from the green algae and from most thallophytes in that the normal life cycle of the Embryophyta shows a well-developed alternation of generations in which the sporophyte always begins its development as a parasite on the gametophyte. The young sporophyte is called an **embryo.** The only thallophytes with a definite sporophyte attached to the gametophyte are some of the red algae, and these are so different from the embryophytes in other respects that no close relationship seems possible. We have noted that many thallophytes produce one or more kinds of asexual spores in addition to (or instead of) the sexual spores (meiospores) which are formed as a result of reduction division and are part of the normal sexual life cycle. The embryophytes regularly produce sexual spores by reduc-

tion division as part of the sexual life cycle, and they never produce any other sort of spore. Asexual reproduction, when it occurs among the Embryophyta, does not involve the formation of spores.

All the less highly modified divisions of the Embryophyta have multicellular antheridia and archegonia in which the gametes are borne. Except as noted in the Charophyceae, the gametes of the Thallophyta are borne in unicellular gametangia which may or may not be differentiated as antheridia and oögonia. The multicellular sexual structures of the Charophyceae do not resemble those of the Embryophyta.

All embryophytes except the bryophytes characteristically have specialized conducting tissues called xylem and phloem. Xylem, a water-conducting tissue, is wholly unknown in the thallophytes; and the only thallophytes which contain a tissue resembling phloem (a food-conducting tissue) are some of the brown algae. Sporophytes of some of the Bryophyta and nearly all the other Embryophyta have characteristic openings in the epidermis, called **stomates,** through which the internal tissues exchange gases with the atmosphere. A stomate is bounded by two specialized cells, called **guard cells,** which regulate the opening. The structure of the stomatal apparatus is discussed in Chapter 26. Stomates are unknown in the Thallophyta. A large proportion of the algae, and some fungi, are aquatic. The vast majority of embryophytes are terrestrial, and the Embryophyta are sometimes rather inaccurately spoken of as the **Land Plants.** A number of the characteristic differences between the Embryophyta and the Thallophyta are merely a reflection of the adaptation of the Embryophyta to a land habitat.

HISTORY

The bryophytes were first clearly recognized as a natural group by the British botanist Samuel Frederick Gray (1766–1828) in 1821, although the formal divisional name Bryophyta was not proposed until nearly half a century later. The two groups of bryophytes which Gray recognized, the Musci and the Hepaticae, had already been established by earlier botanists. Gray's contribution was to recognize the affinity between the two groups.

The name Musci is taken directly from the Latin word for moss, *muscus* (pl., *musci*). The Romans included under that name some things which are not now considered to be mosses. Linnaeus and his contemporaries did not distinguish between the true mosses and the club mosses (Lycopodiae), which are about as closely related as horses and sea horses. The present delimitation of the class Musci was established in 1782 by the German botanist Johann Hedwig (1730–1799), who is often called the father of bryology. The Hepaticae were first recognized as a group by the French botanist Antoine Laurent de Jussieu in 1789. Jussieu and his successors for more than a century included the Anthocerotae, or horned liverworts, with the Hepaticae. The Anthocerotae were first raised to the status of a class coordinate with the Hepaticae by the American botanist Marshall Avery Howe (1876–1936) in 1899.

CHARACTERISTICS OF BRYOPHYTES

The bryophytes are characterized by their life cycle, in which the sporophyte has no direct connection to the ground and is permanently dependent, wholly or in part, on the gametophyte for its nutrition. They are always small plants, seldom more than a few inches long and never rising more than a few inches above the surface of the substrate. The gametophyte is always photosynthetic and is generally larger and more conspicuous than the sporophyte, which often appears to be merely a stage in the reproduction of the gametophyte. Gametophytes of all land plants are inherently limited in size. In the bryophytes and related groups, the plant is still dependent on water as a medium in which the sperm swims to the egg, and therefore the sexual structures cannot be raised much above the level of the substrate. The sporophyte of bryophytes, being more or less dependent on the necessarily small gametophyte, is also inherently limited in size. Because of their small size, the bryophytes have no need for a

Fig. 16.1. Johann Hedwig (1730–1799), German botanist, the "father" of bryology.

specialized conducting system; if their ancestors ever had such a system, the bryophytes have lost it.

The sporophyte has the diploid ($2n$) number of chromosomes. It is typically an unbranched structure, attached to the gametophyte by a basal region called the **foot,** and producing spores in a terminal sporangium called the **capsule.** Usually the capsule is elevated above the foot on a slender stalk called the **seta.** In a few genera the sporophyte consists only of a capsule and its contents, the foot and seta being suppressed.

The spores are the direct products of meiosis. Since they have the reduced (haploid) number of chromosomes, the spores represent the first stage in the gametophyte generation. After being liberated from the capsule, the spores germinate and eventually give rise to green, photosynthetic gametophytes, which may be strictly thallose or may be divided into stem-like, leaf-like, and root-like parts. True roots, stems, and leaves of higher plants are sporophytic rather than gametophytic structures, and they regularly contain xylem and phloem, which are unknown in the bryophytes. The root-like organs of the gametophytes of bryophytes are called **rhizoids.** Rhizoids of the Anthocerotae and Hepaticae function principally or wholly as anchoring structures; in many of the Musci they appear to be effective in the absorption of water and minerals, as well as in anchorage. The stem-like and leaf-like organs of bryophytes are often loosely called stems and leaves, but they are more properly called **caulidia** (sing., *caulidium*) and **phyllidia** (sing., *phyllidium*).

The antheridia and archegonia of bryophytes are either microscopic or barely visible to the naked eye. They are borne on the same or different gametophytes, according to the species or genus. The archegonium is formed by a series of mitotic divisions from a primary archegonial cell. The first divisions are vertical, leading to a four-celled structure consisting of a single central axial cell and three peripheral jacket cells. Just before maturity the archegonium is a closed, flask-shaped structure, with a swollen base, called the **venter,** and a long, slender neck, capped by four **cover cells.** The venter of the archegonium is occupied by the large, naked egg cell. Immediately above the egg cell is the **ventral canal cell.** Above the ventral canal cell is a row of 4 to 15 or more **neck canal cells,** occupying the interior of the neck of the archegonium. The egg cell, the ventral canal cell, the neck canal cells, and the cover cells are derived by a series of mitotic divisions from the axial cell of the young archegonium. In the Hepaticae the jacket of the mature archegonium is derived wholly from the three jacket cells of the young archegonium. In some of the Musci some of the upper neck cells of the jacket are derived eventually from the axial cell, and the remainder of the jacket is derived from the original three jacket cells. In the Anthocerotae the lower cells of the venter are not derived from the archegonial initial at all; therefore some botanists would not consider these cells to be properly part of the archegonium. When the archegonium is mature, the cover cells spread apart or fall off, and the neck canal cells and the ventral canal cell disintegrate to form a mucilaginous mass.

The antheridium is formed by a series of mitotic divisions from an antheridial initial cell. Just before maturity the antheridium is an ellipsoid or spherical structure with a multicellular jacket one cell thick enclosing a central mass of cells called androcytes. Each androcyte changes into a slender, elongate, apically biflagellate sperm. The flagella are slightly unequal in length and are both of the whiplash type. The cell walls of the androcytes disappear during the metamorphosis into sperms, and at maturity the sperms lie in a viscous liquid. The antheridium then ruptures and the sperms swim about freely.

Although most bryophytes are terrestrial rather than aquatic, they are dependent on water for the transfer of the sperm to the egg. A film of water from dew or rain is ordinarily sufficient, and the splashing of raindrops doubtless aids in the transfer in some cases. The sperms are attracted to the archegonia by chemical stimuli. Entering the opening at the end of the neck of the archegonium, the sperm swims through the mucilaginous material of the neck canal until it reaches the egg in the venter of the archegonium.

Fusion of a sperm and an egg constitutes fertilization. Since it receives one full chromosome complement from each of the two gametes, the fertilized egg or zygote has the diploid ($2n$) chromosome number and constitutes the first step in the sporophyte generation. The zygote grows and undergoes a series of mitotic divisions to form a multicellular embryo that obtains its nourishment from the gametophyte. The embryo continues to grow and develops into a mature sporophyte which remains attached to the gametophyte. The developing and mature sporophyte may be wholly dependent on the gametophyte, or it may be green and manufacture some of its own food.

Anthocerotae (Horned Liverworts)

DEFINITION

The Anthocerotae, or **horned liverworts,** may be defined as bryophytes with thallose, dorsiventral gametophytes with embedded archegonia and antheridia, and with a **meristematic region** (i.e., a region characterized by continued cell division) near the base of the sporophyte. The term **dorsiventral** is a descriptive adjective applied to organisms which are more or less flattened, with the two flattened surfaces

Fig. 16.2. *Anthoceros* gametophytes. (×2.) (Photo courtesy of J. Proskauer.)

unlike. Human beings, for example, are dorsiventral. Both the presence of a meristematic region in the sporophyte and the embedded position of the sex organs of the gametophyte of the Anthocerotae are unique in the division. There are probably fewer than 50 valid species of Anthocerotae, all of which belong to the single order Anthocerotales. They occur in moist places throughout most of the world. *Anthoceros* (Fig. 16.2) is the most familiar genus in the temperate zone, the other genera being chiefly tropical.

THE GAMETOPHYTE

The gametophyte of the Anthocerotae is a dorsiventral thallus commonly an inch or more long or across, with numerous unicellular rhizoids on the lower (ventral) surface. The thallus is more or less lobed or divided and is sometimes dichotomously branched (i.e., the main axis is repeatedly forked into two more or less equal parts). Each branch or lobe has a single apical meristematic cell. The cells cut off from the apical cell usually divide a few more times before maturing into ordinary vegetative cells.

The vegetative cells of the main body of the gametophyte are all nearly alike, although the cells of the uppermost dorsal layer are commonly a little more regularly arranged than the other cells. There is no pronounced internal differentiation of tissues. The older parts of the thallus have scattered intercellular cavities that open to the ventral surface by narrow slits. These cavities are filled with mucilage and often contain colonies of the blue-green alga *Nostoc*. It has been reported that gametophytes without the algal colonies grow better than those which contain such colonies,

although the alga is presumably fully autotrophic.

The vegetative cells of the gametophyte usually contain a single large chloroplast each, although some cells of some genera have two to eight chloroplasts instead. Each chloroplast has a single large pyrenoid which gives rise to starch granules. The Anthocerotae differ from nearly all other Embryophyta in having pyrenoids, but these pyrenoids are not structurally identical with those of any of the algae.

The mature thallus often dies from behind about as fast is it grows in front, and when the progressive death reaches a fork in the thallus, the separated parts continue to grow as distinct individuals. Vegetative reproduction also occurs in some genera by means of marginal thickenings which develop a protective outer layer that enables them to survive periods of drought when the main thallus dies.

Most members of the class are homothallic, but some are heterothallic, with the antheridia and archegonia borne on separate individuals of slightly different appearance. Individuals of homothallic species often produce the antheridia before the archegonia. The antheridia and archegonia are embedded within the thallus.

The antheridia (Fig. 16.4) are borne singly or in small groups, on short stalks in mucilage-filled antheridial chambers. The antheridium (or group of antheridia), the stalk (or stalks), and the layer of cells covering the antheridial cavity are all formed by a series of mitotic divisions from a single antheridial initial cell at the upper surface of the thallus. The first division of this cell is parallel to the surface of the thallus, giving rise to an inner cell and an outer cell that soon become separated by a mucilage-filled cavity. By a series of further mitotic divisions, the outer cell develops into the cover of the antheridial chamber, and the inner cell develops into one or more antheridia and stalks. The cover of the chamber is one to several cells thick. Both the antheridial wall and the cover must rupture before the sperms can be released.

The archegonia (Fig. 16.4) are borne singly, and the jacket layer is not sharply differentiated from the surrounding vegetative tissue. The first divisions of the archegonial initial are vertical, giving rise to an axial cell surrounded by three jacket initials. The axial cell gives rise by a series of mitotic divisions to the egg, the ventral canal cell, the neck canal cells, and the four cover cells which become detached from the neck of the archegonium just before maturity. The jacket of the archegonium, formed by a series of mitotic divisions from the three jacket initials, surrounds the neck and possibly, or probably, the sides of the venter. The cells directly underlying the venter are ordinary vegetative cells not derived from the archegonial initial. Therefore they have often been considered not to be properly a part of the archegonium.

Fertilization takes place in the usual bryophytic fashion, with the sperms swimming freely in a film of water and being attracted to the egg by chemical stimuli.

THE SPOROPHYTE

The embryo sporophyte which develops by a series of mitotic divisions from the zygote is nutritionally dependent on the gametophyte. At the eight-celled stage the embryo consists of two tiers of four cells each. The four lower cells develop by a series of further mitotic divisions into a

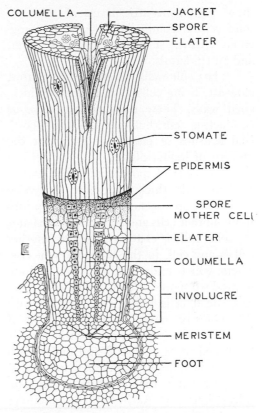

Fig. 16.3. *Anthoceros.* Part of sporophyte, in sectional and surface views, embedded in the gametophyte.

globose or invertedly hemispheric foot, which serves to anchor the sporophyte in the tissue of the gametophyte and through which nutriment and water are absorbed. At an early stage the lower cells of the foot have rhizoid-like projections, but these are wanting at maturity. No other bryophytic sporophytes bear anything resembling rhizoids. The four upper cells of the eight-celled embryo develop by a series of further mitotic divisions into the capsule.

Just before maturity the capsule is an erect, slender rod commonly 1 or 2 inches long and about the thickness of a pencil lead. A cross section through the capsule shows four concentric layers of tissue: a solid central columella, a layer of sporogenous tissue, a parenchymatous layer, and an epidermis.

The columella consists of narrow, elongate, living cells with somewhat thickened walls. These may perhaps serve as conducting cells, but they lack the specialized features of either the xylem or the phloem of higher plants.

The layer of sporogenous tissue is one to four cells thick. Alternate transverse tiers of the sporogenous tissue develop into **spore mother cells** and sterile cells or chains of cells called **elaters.** A spore mother cell is any cell, in the bryophytes or elsewhere, which undergoes reduction division to produce spores. Elaters are narrow, elongate, dead cells found intermingled with the spores of many bryophytes. Elaters of Hepaticae are single cells with spirally thickened walls; they coil and uncoil with changes in humidity, and their movement helps discharge the spores from the capsule. Elaters of Anthocerotae sometimes resemble those of the Hepaticae, but more often they have smooth or irregularly thickened walls; and they may be joined end to end in simple or branched chains of three to five cells. They are usually less responsive to moisture changes.

The parenchymatous tissue surrounding the sporogenous layer of the capsule contains chloroplasts and is photosynthetic. Species with the chloroplasts solitary in gametophytic cells have two chloroplasts in sporophytic cells; species with more than one chloroplast in gametophytic cells have more numerous chloroplasts in sporophytic cells, but fewer than twice as many.

The epidermis consists of regular, vertically elongate cells with the outer and lateral walls strongly cutinized. **Cutin** is a waxy material, characteristic of epidermal cells of the Embryophyta, which retards the evaporation of water. Most Anthocerotae have definite stomates with characteristic guard cells in the epidermis of the sporophyte. The epidermis of other species lacks stomates as well as other intercellular spaces.

During the early stages of development of the sporophyte, the embryo is covered by an upwardly growing sheath which develops from the jacket cells of the archegonium and the adjoining gametophytic tissue. Eventually the growing sporophyte breaks its way through the top of the sheath, which remains as an **involucre** at the base. The term *involucre* is applied to any structure which surrounds the base of another structure, without any implications as to the anatomical nature or evolutionary origin. The involucre of the Anthocerotae is roughly comparable to the calyptra of mosses and liverworts, which is derived wholly or mainly from the jacket of the archegonium.

The upper part of the capsule matures first and begins to open along one to four definite lines which extend progressively downward from near the top. The valves (longitudinal segments) of the capsule wall sometimes spread apart from the tip, but often they remain joined at the tip and merely bow apart below. The lower part of the capsule (just above the foot) is permanently meristematic, but the meristematic cells are not all alike, and the columella, sporogenous tissue, and jacket can be distinguished all the way to the base of the capsule. The Anthocerotae are the only bryophytes with a persistently meristematic region in the sporophyte.

The sporophyte continues to grow as long as the gametophyte remains vegetatively active, elongating from the base and opening from above. Although the sporo-

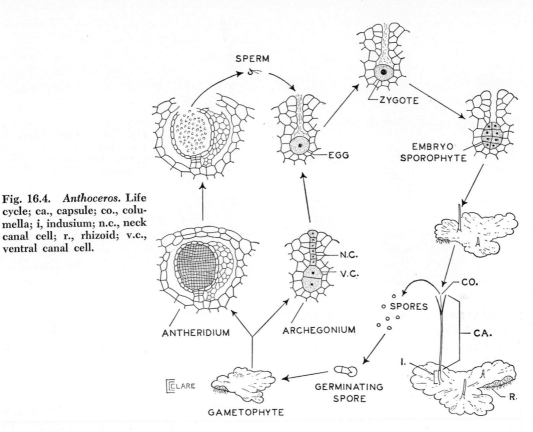

Fig. 16.4. *Anthoceros.* Life cycle; ca., capsule; co., columella; i, indusium; n.c., neck canal cell; r., rhizoid; v.c., ventral canal cell.

SPERM

ZYGOTE

EGG

EMBRYO SPOROPHYTE

N.C.

V.C.

CO.

SPORES

ANTHERIDIUM

ARCHEGONIUM

CA.

I.

ELARE

GERMINATING SPORE

R.

GAMETOPHYTE

phyte is green and evidently carries on some photosynthesis, it is basically dependent on the gametophyte. Sporophytes experimentally detached from the gametophyte may live for months, but they grow only very slowly.

The Anthocerotae differ from the Hepaticae, with which they have often been classed, in the relatively large, chlorophyllous, complex sporophyte which commonly has three features never found in sporophytes of the Hepaticae: (1) a columella; (2) a meristem; (3) stomates and a vestigial aerating system. These latter two features, at least, are presumably inherited from ancestors with larger and more complex sporophytes. The modified stomates on the lower side of the gameto-

phytes of some Anthocerotae likewise may be vestiges from a more complex ancestral gametophyte with functional stomates.

Hepaticae (Liverworts)

DEFINITION

The Hepaticae, or **liverworts,** may be defined as bryophytes in which the gametophyte is ordinarily dorsiventral, with superficial antheridia and archegonia, and in which the sporophyte has neither stomates, nor a meristematic region, nor a columella. Both the Anthocerotae and the Musci usually have a columella. The capsule of liverworts usually contains elaters

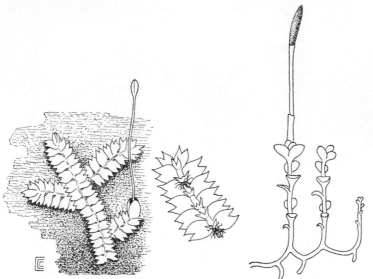

Fig. 16.5. *Lophocolea*, a leafy liverwort. (Left, ×3; center, from beneath, ×6.) *Calobryum*. (Right, ×1½.)

as well as spores. The gametophyte may be strictly thallose or may be differentiated into a caulidium with attached phyllidia. In either case (except in one small order) the gametophyte is attached to the substrate by rhizoids, and these are always unicellular. The antheridia and archegonia always originate from single superficial cells, but they may become more or less enclosed by growth of the surrounding tissues.

OCCURRENCE

Liverworts occur in moist places throughout the world but are most abundant in the tropics. They grow in swamps and bogs, on wet rocks and cliffs, on soil or rotting logs in dense woods, and as epiphytes on the bark and leaves of trees. A few species are found floating or submerged in water, and some others are found in sites which are alternately wet (or moist) and dry. The whole gametophytic thallus may go into a dormant state, returning to vegetative activity when proper conditions are restored, or only the apical

tissues may survive, the remainder of the thallus succumbing to the drought.

CLASSIFICATION

There are about 5000 species of Hepaticae, distributed among five orders. All but a few hundred of these species belong to the Jungermanniales, a cosmopolitan group, and most of the remainder belong to the Marchantiales and Metzgeriales. The very small order Calobryales, with only four species, is transitional toward the mosses in some respects. The recently described genus *Takakia*, from British Columbia and Japan, may prove to constitute a distinct order related to the Calobryales. The orders are characterized in the appendix.

REPRESENTATIVE GENERA

PORELLA

Porella (Fig. 16.6) is one of the commonest genera of leafy liverworts in the

United States. Unlike many other Hepati-cae, it is not limited to moist habitats but often occurs as a pioneer on dry rocks or as an epiphyte on the bark of trees, particularly in the southeastern United States.

The gametophyte is olive or dull green, up to about 10 cm long, and 2–4 mm wide, with a very slender, freely branched caulidium, and with well-de-veloped, relatively broad phyllidia. The phyllidia of the two dorsolateral rows are deeply and unequally bilobed, with a com-paratively large and broad, spreading dorsal lobe, and a much smaller, ventrally placed lobe lying parallel and adjacent to the lower side of the caulidium. There is a single median ventral row of phyllidia which somewhat resemble the ventral lobes of the dorsolateral phyllidia, so that super-ficially the plant appears to have three parallel rows of ventral phyllidia. The for-ward margin of each dorsolateral phyllid-ium overlaps the rear margin of the adja-cent phyllidium. This arrangement tends to channel drainage water toward the ven-tral surface of the gametophyte, where some of it is retained for a long time in tiny pockets that are bounded on the lower side by the ventral lobes of the dorsolat-eral phyllidia. Rhizoids are borne in clus-ters on the caulidia at the bases of the ventral phyllidia. They are unicellular, smooth-walled, and all about alike. There is little or no differentiation of tissues in the caulidia and phyllidia, and the phyl-lidia are only one cell thick. The oil bodies are minute and numerous in each cell. As in other leafy liverworts, there is a single meristematic apical cell on each branch.

Leafy liverworts which grow in moister habitats than *Porella* generally do not have ventral lobes on the dorsal phyllidia, and often the phyllidia overlap in reverse man-

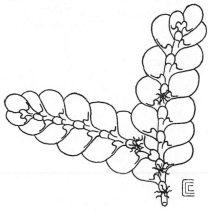

Fig. 16.6. *Porella*, a leafy liverwort; above, top view; below, bottom view, showing rhizoids. (×5.)

ner, with the forward margin underlying rather than overlying the rear margin of the adjacent phyllidium.

Antheridia of *Porella* are borne in the axils of slightly modified phyllidia on spe-cial antheridial branches which are other-wise not much different from the sterile branches. The **axil** of a leaf or phyllidium is the position or place at the point of the angle formed by the insertion of the leaf (or phyllidium) on the stem (or caulid-ium). A structure which is axillary thus lies between the stem (or caulidium) and the base of the leaf (or phyllidium). Each

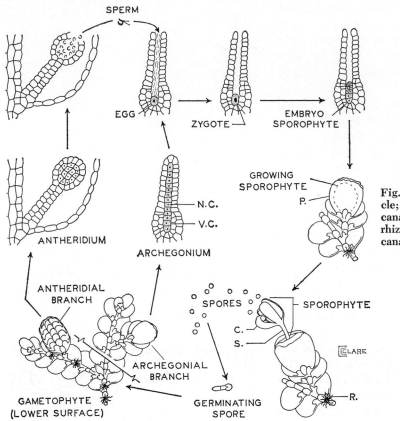

SPERM

EGG

ZYGOTE

EMBRYO
SPOROPHYTE

ANTHERIDIUM

N.C.

V.C.

ARCHEGONIUM

GROWING
SPOROPHYTE

P.

Fig. 16.7. *Porella.* Life cycle; c., capsule; n.c., neck canal cell; p., perianth; r., rhizoid; s., seta; v.c., ventral canal cell.

ANTHERIDIAL
BRANCH

ARCHEGONIAL
BRANCH

GAMETOPHYTE
(LOWER SURFACE)

SPORES

C.

S.

SPOROPHYTE

CLARE

R.

GERMINATING
SPORE

antheridium develops from a single superficial antheridial initial cell. The antheridia are globose and are borne on definite stalks.

The archegonia are borne at the tips of special archegonial branches, the apical cell functioning as the archegonial initial. The two or three dorsolateral phyllidia nearest the archegonium are laterally fused to form a cup-shaped perianth surrounding the archegonium. The term *perianth* is more generally used for the enclosing outer parts of flowers of the Anthophyta and is applied here only by analogy. The archegonium has a relatively stout neck and not much enlarged venter. The jacket of the venter and the lower part of the neck be-

come two cells thick before fertilization.

Fertilization takes place in the usual bryophytic fashion. The venter of the archegonium enlarges with the growth of the young sporophyte, forming a calyptra, but eventually the seta of the sporophyte elongates and the capsule ruptures the calyptra and is exerted beyond the perianth. The seta of *Porella* does not become nearly so long as that of many other genera of the Jungermanniales. The jacket of the capsule is more than one cell thick; at maturity it opens along four longitudinal lines, releasing the spores. The spores are distributed by wind, and under proper conditions they germinate to form new gametophytes.

MARCHANTIA

Marchantia (Fig. 16.8), a common and widely distributed genus in temperate regions, is the liverwort most commonly studied in general botany courses, although it is a rather highly specialized type, hardly typical of the class as a whole. The gametophyte is a flat, ribbon-shaped, dichotomously branched thallus commonly 2–3 inches long and well under 1 inch wide, with a thickened midrib along each branch. There is a transverse row of meristematic apical cells in a notch at the end of each branch. The cells cut off from the apical cells may undergo several further divisions before becoming mature cells of one or another sort, but only the apical cells remain permanently meristematic.

The lower side of the thallus bears two or more rows of multicellular scales and two kinds of rhizoids. Some of the rhizoids have smooth walls; others have internal projections from the walls. The smooth-walled rhizoids penetrate the soil as agents of anchorage and possibly absorption. The tuberculate-walled rhizoids grow parallel to the lower surface of the thallus on top of the soil. It has been suggested that they tend to channel surface water inward from the margins of the thallus by capillary action, thus helping to distribute the supply of water to all absorptive parts of the thallus.

The thallus (Fig. 16.9) is divided into a thin, upper, chlorophyllous layer and a thicker, lower, colorless layer. The colorless part consists largely of more or less isodiametric parenchyma cells, except for the

Fig. 16.8. *Marchantia.* Left, male; right, female. (Copyright by General Biological Supply House, Inc., Chicago.)

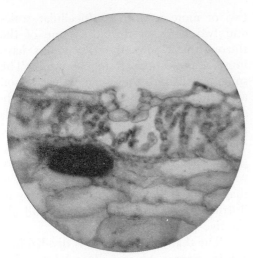

Fig. 16.9. *Marchantia*. Cross section of thallus, showing air pore, photosynthetic tissue, and colorless layer, with an oil cell (the dark body). (From Harold Bold, *Morphology of Plants*, Harper, 1957.)

midrib. The cells of the midrib are elongate and have locally thickened walls. The epidermis covering the upper surface of the thallus is chlorophyllous and is visibly marked off into small polygons, each with a central pore. Each pore opens below into a separate air chamber which is bounded all around by a layer of chlorophyllous cells. The partitions between the air chambers are mostly only one cell thick and consist wholly of chlorophyllous cells. Short, simple or branched, chlorophyllous filaments of one to several cells each extend upward into the air chamber from its floor. *Marchantia* is believed to be derived from leafy liverworts similar to the Jungermanniales, and it has been suggested that the upper epidermis and the partitions between the chambers represent the highly modified, incurved and fused dorsolateral phyllidia.

The pore opening into an air chamber is bounded by a ring of nonchlorophyllous cells arranged in three or four vertical tiers to form a barrel-like structure. The cells of the lowermost tier surrounding the pore change shape with changes in turgor. Under conditions of water deficiency, a basal flange from each of these cells extends out into the pore, constricting or closing the opening. The narrowing or closing of the pores tends to minimize the evaporation of water from internal tissues during dry periods, but the mechanism is evidently much less efficient than the stomatal apparatus of the sporophytes of higher plants. The two mechanisms are merely analogous rather than homologous; they have no phyletic relationship to each other.

Stomates of higher plants and the analogous structures of *Marchantia*, are evolutionary responses to the same problem: how to permit the exchange of gases necessary for photosynthesis without subjecting the plant to injurious or fatal desiccation when water uptake fails to balance the loss by transpiration. **Transpiration** is the evaporation of water from the living cells of a plant. A rate of water uptake which would be sufficient under ordinary circumstances might be insufficient on an especially hot, dry day; and a rate of transpiration which could be sustained under ordinary conditions might be too much if the soil is drier than usual. Therefore any mechanism which permits the access of air to photosynthetic cells under ordinary conditions, while restricting or preventing that access under conditions of excessive transpiration, has survival value.

Vegetative reproduction in *Marchantia* commonly occurs by death of the older parts of the thallus, leaving the separated branches as independent plants. Adventitious branches may also be formed on the ventral surface of the thallus, followed by death and decay of the connecting tissues. The term **adventitious** is applied to any structure, in the bryophytes or elsewhere, which arises from mature tissues, or from tissues that would not ordinarily be expected to produce such a structure.

The thallus of *Marchantia* also bears on its upper side some small open cups, each of which contains several vegetative reproductive bodies called **gemmae**. A gemma develops by a series of mitotic cell divisions from a single superficial cell of the floor of the cup. At maturity the gemma is just large enough to be readily visible to the naked eye. It is multicellular, more or less discoid, several cells thick at the middle, but only one cell thick at the margin. There is a shallow median indentation on each of the two lateral margins, with a row of apical cells in each indentation. Most cells of the gemma are chlorophyllous, but some are colorless. The gemma is attached to the floor of the cup by a short, one-celled stalk. Discharge and swelling of mucilage from club-shaped

mucilage cells intermingled with the gemmae breaks them from their stalks and forces them out of the cup. Gemmae which lodge in a suitable place develop rhizoids from some of the colorless cells, and the apical cells in the two notches begin to grow and divide in the usual way. The original tissues of the gemma eventually decay, leaving two thalli growing in opposite directions.

Archegonia and antheridia of *Marchantia* are usually borne on different gametophytes. The antheridia (Fig. 16.10) are borne at the top of a special upturned branch called an **antheridiophore**, and the archegonia are likewise borne on an **archegoniophore**. The antheridiophore is expanded at the top to form a shallowy eight-lobed disk, commonly about ¼ inch wide, that bears numerous antheridia. Each antheridium originates from a single superficial cell, but the surrounding tissues grow up around it, so that at maturity the an-

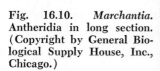

Fig. 16.10. *Marchantia.* Antheridia in long section. (Copyright by General Biological Supply House, Inc., Chicago.)

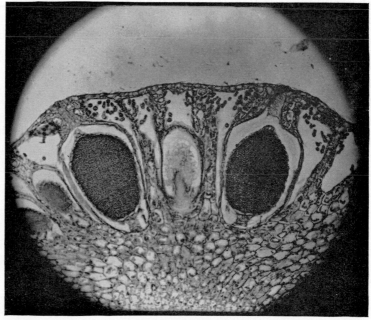

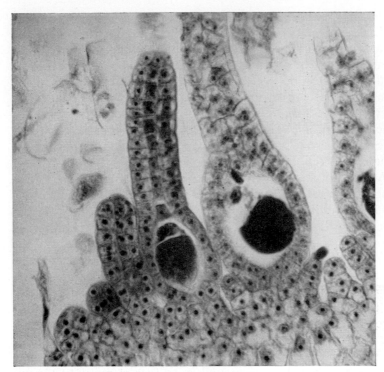

Fig. 16.11. *Marchantia.* Archegonium in long section. (Copyright by General Biological Supply House, Inc., Chicago.)

theridium is enclosed in an antheridial chamber connected to the surface by a narrow opening.

The young archegoniophore is expanded at the top to form a shallowy eight-lobed disk, and a radial row of several microscopic archegonia extends toward the tip of each lobe. Each archegonium (Fig. 16.11) develops from a superficial cell of the disk. Just before fertilization it has a long slender neck and an enlarged venter occupied by the egg. The disk of the archegoniphore is only slightly raised above the thallus when fertilization occurs. Fertilization takes place in the usual bryophytic way, with the sperms swimming through a film of water and being attracted to the egg by chemical stimuli. Splashing of raindrops often aids in the distribution of the sperms.

After fertilization the archegoniophore continues to grow, commonly reaching a length of about an inch. Meanwhile the disk expands and the margins become inflexed, so that the archegonia are directed downward, and a series of stout cylindrical processes a few millimeters long develop from the disk. These appendages (rays) radiate outward from the center and droop beyond the margins of the disk. After the margins of the disk have become inverted, a flange of tissue grows out along each side of each row of archegonia, forming a hanging, curtain-like involucre. The tissue adjoining each archegonium also grows out around the archegonium to form a thin sheath open at the end. The archegonium itself enlarges and undergoes a series of mitotic cell divisions, and the lower part becomes several cells thick. The enlarged archegonium is called the **calyptra**. The young sporophyte is thus successively enclosed by the calyptra, the sheath surrounding the calyptra, and the involucre which veils the row of archegonia (calyptrae).

The fertilized egg, or zygote, has $2n$ chromosomes and marks the first step in the sporophyte generation. The zygote undergoes a series of mitotic divisions to produce a pendent multicellular sporophyte (Fig. 16.12) a few millimeters long, composed of a foot, seta, and capsule. The cells of the seta elongate considerably and rather suddenly as the sporophyte approaches maturity, and the mature capsule, after having ruptured the calyptra, is exserted shortly beyond the sheath and involucre. The foot, seta, and capsule all contain chloroplasts, but the sporophyte makes only a small proportion of the food it uses. The water and most of the food used by the sporophyte are absorbed from the gametophyte through the foot.

The wall of the capsule is only one cell thick. At maturity it splits lengthwise from the tip into an indefinite number of segments. All the interior cells of the capsule generally develop into either spores or elaters. The elaters, which are differentiated before the spore mother cells are formed, are very long, slender cells, dead at maturity, with spirally thickened walls; they coil and uncoil with changes in moisture, helping to expel the spores after the capsule has opened.

Each spore mother cell in the capsule undergoes reduction division to produce a tetrad of spores. The spores have the haploid number of chromosomes and mark the first step in the gametophyte generation. A spore which lodges in a suitable place germinates to produce an irregular filament of several cells. A cell at the tip of the filament then begins to function as an apical cell, eventually producing a new gametophytic thallus.

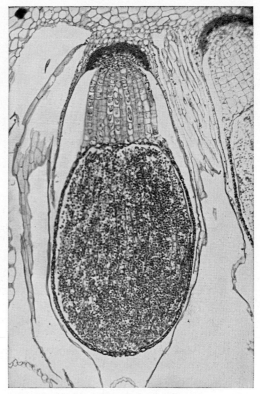

Fig. 16.12. *Marchantia.* Sporophyte in long section. (Courtesy of George H. Conant, Triarch Products.)

Musci (Mosses)

DEFINITION

The Musci, or **mosses**, are bryophytes in which the spore gives rise to a filamentous or thallose **protonema** (from Greek *protos*, first, and *nēma*, thread), which in turn gives rise to one or more **gametophores** that have well-developed, mostly equal phyllidia more or less spirally and symmetrically arranged around a caulidium. The protonema is usually a transitory stage that dies after the gametophores have become established. The gametophore is ordinarily the conspicuous and

Fig. 16.13. *Polytrichum*, the hairy-cap moss. (Somewhat less than natural size.) (Copyright by General Biological Supply House, Inc., Chicago.)

persistent part of the moss plant. It superficially resembles a small leafy stem, but it lacks xylem and phloem. The phyllidia generally originate in three (seldom two) rows, corresponding to the three cutting sides of the apical cell, but further growth of the caulidium often obscures the arrangement. Rhizoids of mosses are uniseriate, multicellular filaments with diagonally slanting cross walls. They are borne on the protonema and usually also (except in *Sphagnum*) on the gametophores, serving as agents of anchorage and absorption. The protonema and gametophores have chloroplasts and make their own food; both have *n* chromosomes and belong to the gametophyte generation.

The sporophyte may or may not contain chlorophyll, but it is always at least partly dependent on the gametophyte for its nutrition. The capsule of the moss sporophyte is usually more complex than that of other bryophytes, with a larger proportion of sterile tissue. It usually has a central columella, which may or may not reach the tip of the capsule. There are no elaters.

OCCURRENCE

Mosses occur in a wide variety of terrestrial or subaquatic to occasionally fully aquatic habitats, from the tropics to the polar regions, but they are especially common as pioneers on bare rock or on earth surfaces in moist regions. Many of them are found as epiphytes on the bark of trees, although the "moss" of tree trunks more often consists largely of algae such as *Pleurococcus*. Shingle roofs in moist regions often develop a coating of mosses, especially just below the end of each row of shingles.

CLASSIFICATION

There are three well-defined groups of mosses. These have traditionally been treated as three orders, the Andreaeales, Sphagnales, and Bryales. The Andreaeales and Sphagnales are relatively small and homogeneous groups; the Bryales are more varied and have many more species. Many modern bryologists prefer to consider these three groups as subclasses, the Andreaeobrya, Sphagnobrya, and Eubrya. the Eubrya are then divided into a number of closely related orders. For our purposes the traditional classification, as presented in the following key, will suffice.

1. Columella not reaching the summit of the capsule; sporophyte becoming elevated on a pseudopodium of gametophytic tissue, without a prominent seta; protonema broadly thallose; capsule never with an operculum fringed by a peristome
   2. Capsule opening along four longitudinal lines; caulidium not differentiated into a cortex and central cylinder; mature gametophores with numerous rhizoids along their length; cells of the phyllidia all chlorophyllous, not of two markedly contrasting types; generally several gametophores formed from each protonema   **1. Andreaeales**
   2. Capsule opening by a lid; caulidium differentiated into a cortex and central cylinder; mature gametophores without rhizoids; cells of the phyllidia of two strongly contrasting types, one with chlorophyll, one without; only one gametophore formed by each protonema   **2. Sphagnales**
1. Columella reaching the summit of the capsule and attached to it; sporophyte commonly with an elongate seta, not borne on a gametophytic pseudopodium; protonema generally filamentous, seldom broadly thallose; capsule generally opening by a lid (operculum), with a specialized peristome, or sometimes opening irregularly; mature gametophores with rhizoids at the base, or scattered along prostrate branches   **3. Bryales**

BRYALES

The Bryales consist of some 14,000 species and make up the bulk of the Musci. They occur in a wide variety of climates and habitats on all continents. They differ from other mosses in ways which have been summarized in the foregoing key.

THE GAMETOPHYTE

A spore of a member of the Bryales usually germinates to produce a filamentous, branching protonema (Fig. 16.15) which resembles a filamentous green alga. The protonema lies on the surface of the substrate and sends down occasional branches which penetrate the surface as rhizoids. The rhizoids differ from the rest of the protonema in having small or no chloroplasts, in having slanting rather than directly transverse cross walls, and in having a brownish rather than colorless cell wall. The differences are a direct response to the environment: parts of rhizoids exposed at the surface have large chloroplasts and resemble the rest of the protonema. The body of the protonema, exclusive of the rhizoids, is often called the **chloronema.** Eventually some of the older cells of the chloronema produce erect lateral branches, each of which, after a series of mitotic divisions, differentiates a meristematic apical cell and develops into a gametophore. The lower part of the gametophore soon produces rhizoids which act as anchoring and absorbing organs, and the protonema then generally dies.

The phyllidia of the gametophore vary in structure, according to the genus and species. Typically they are one cell thick except for a slightly thickened midrib of elongate, thick-walled cells that lack chlor-

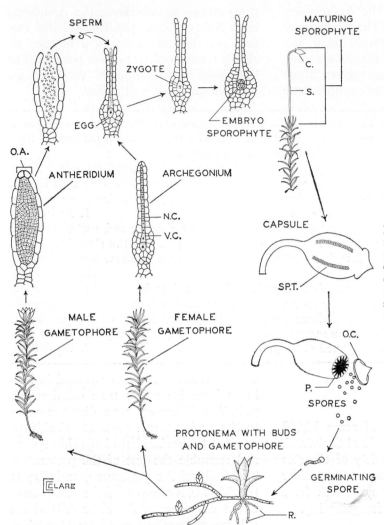

SPERM

ZYGOTE

MATURING
SPOROPHYTE

C.

S.

EGG

EMBRYO
SPOROPHYTE

O.A.

ANTHERIDIUM

ARCHEGONIUM

N.C.

V.C.

CAPSULE

SP.T.

Fig. 16.14. Life cycle of a
moss; c., capsule; n.c., neck
canal cell; o.a., operculum
of the antheridium; o.c., operculum of the capsule; p.,
peristome; r., rhizoid; s., seta;
sp.t., sporogenous tissue; v.c.,
ventral canal cell.

MALE
GAMETOPHORE

FEMALE
GAMETOPHORE

O.C.

P.

SPORES

PROTONEMA WITH BUDS
AND GAMETOPHORE

GERMINATING
SPORE

CLARE

R.

oplasts. Sometimes there is no midrib and the cells are all alike. In some genera such as *Polytrichum*, the hairy-cap moss, the phyllidium has a relatively broad central band which has many closely set, thin, longitudinal photosynthetic ridges several cells high and one cell thick arising from the upper surface.

The caulidium is differentiated into an epidermis, a cortex, and a solid central cylinder. The epidermis is one to several cells thick and contains chloroplasts. The cells of the cortex usually have chloroplasts when young but not at maturity. The central cylinder consists of vertically elongate cells that are narrower than the cortical cells and often have thick walls. A band of similar elongate cells often connects the central cylinder to the midrib of the phyllidium. It has been thought that these elongate cells of the midrib and central cylinder serve in the conduction of water;

but this is not borne out by experimental studies, and their main function seems to be mechanical strengthening.

Some kinds of mosses have the gametophores differentiated into prostrate and erect branches. The prostrate branches periodically give rise to additional erect branches, and after the prostrate branch dies its erect offshoots persist as separate plants. Many mosses also produce small multicellular gemmae on the phyllidia or caulidia. After becoming detached, these gemmae develop into new gametophores. Rhizoids of either the protonema or the gametophore may produce globular gemmae of 20 to 30 colorless cells attached to the rhizoid by a several-celled stalk. These generally remain dormant unless and until they become detached from the rhizoid, after which they may develop into gametophores.

The archegonia and antheridia are borne in clusters at the tips of the branches or main axis of the gametophore. According to the species, the two types of sex organs are intermingled in a single cluster, or are produced in separate clusters on the same branch, or on separate branches of the same gametophore, or on different individuals. Often they are intermingled with multicellular hairs called paraphyses. Both antheridia and archegonia originate from superficial cells of the caulidium and are borne on short erect stalks. The venter of the archegonium is not much thicker than the long, slender neck.

One or more cells at the top of the jacket of the antheridium (Fig. 16.16) are differentiated as a lid or **operculum**. The cells of the operculum are larger than other jacket cells, with thicker walls and more transparent protoplast. When a mature antheridium is moistened, it absorbs water, and the resulting internal pressure forces

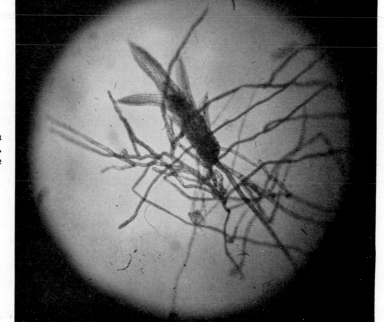

Fig. 16.15. Moss protonema with young gametophore. (Courtesy of Frances Wynne Hillier.)

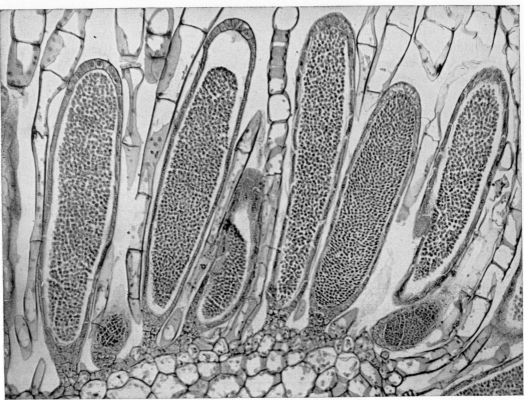

Fig. 16.16. Antheridia of *Mnium affine*, a moss. (Courtesy of E. J. Kohl, Lakeside Biological Products, Ripon, Wis.)

off the operculum, releasing the sperms. The antheridium does not usually open without being moistened. Fertilization takes place in the usual bryophytic way, with the sperms swimming actively in water and being attracted to the egg by chemical stimuli.

The archegonium (Fig. 16.17) enlarges somewhat with the growth of the embryo sporophyte, and is thenceforth called the calyptra. Growth of the calyptra is soon outpaced by that of the sporophyte, and the severed upper part of the calyptra remains perched atop the sporophyte until the capsule is nearly mature. Often this severed part of the calyptra continues to enlarge for some time, and in genera such

as *Polytrichum*, the hairy-cap moss, it forms a very prominent cap. In some mosses the cells of the archegonium stalk begin to divide after fertilization takes place, so that the developing embryo seems to migrate down into the stalk area, and the calyptra is then derived largely by continued division from the stalk cells, with the neck and side walls of the archegonium forming only the top of the calyptra.

THE SPOROPHYTE

The mature sporophyte consists of a basal foot, a slender, more or less elongate seta sometimes as much as several inches long, and a terminal capsule 1 to several millimeters long in which the spores are borne. The foot is anchored in the gametophore and serves to absorb food and water. Usually the seta has a differentiated central strand more or less similar to that of the gametophore.

The capsule (Fig. 16.18) generally contains several different tissues. Often the basal part has a spongy photosynthetic layer with large intercellular spaces, surrounding a solid sterile core, and enclosed by a colorless epidermis with well-developed stomates of the type found in vascular plants. The spores originate from a layer of sporogenous tissue commonly two cells thick which surrounds the solid central columella. The columella, which extends from the base to the top of the capsule, may or may not have chloroplasts. The tissue surrounding the sporogenous layer is several cells thick and often has chloroplasts. The epidermis consists of thick-walled cells, commonly with scattered stomates. The amount of food manufactured by the sporophyte varies with the species and the conditions, but the sporophyte is always at least partly dependent on the gametophyte and never has its own connection to the ground.

The capsule usually has a well-defined lid, or operculum, delimited at the base by a ring (annulus) of thin-walled epidermal cells. The cells of the annulus and the lower internal cells of the operculum shrivel and dry as the capsule matures, so that the operculum is shed from the capsule. The mouth of the capsule is then surrounded by a **peristome** (Greek, literally, around the mouth) commonly consisting of two rings of teeth which project inward from the margin and often close the opening. In dry weather the teeth bend outward and permit the discharge of spores; in wet weather they bend inward and re-

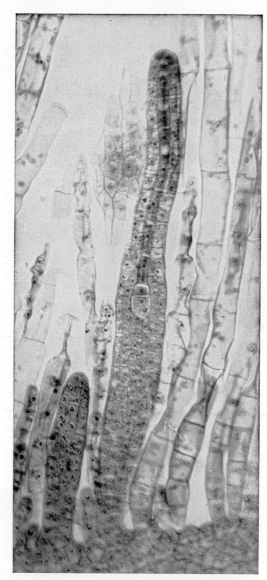

Fig. 16.17. Archegonium of *Mnium affine*, a moss. (Courtesy of E. J. Kohl, Lakeside Biological Products, Ripon, Wis.)

tain the spores. The original abscission of the operculum is probably caused partly by these hygroscopic movements of the teeth of the peristome.

In a few genera of Bryales, the capsule has no operculum and no peristome. In

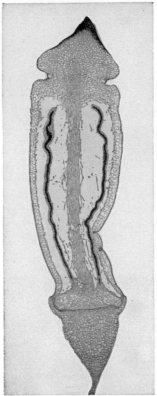
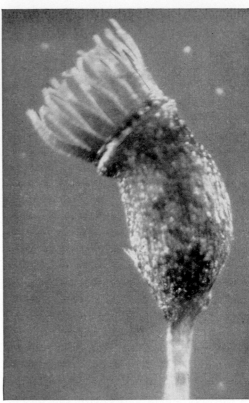

Fig. 16.18.   Left, capsule of *Polytrichum*, in long section. (Courtesy of E. J. Kohl, Lakeside Biological Products, Ripon, Wis.) Right, capsule of *Dicranella varia*, a moss, showing prominent peristome. (× about 75.) (Courtesy of Herbert Holliger.)

Fig. 16.19.   *Schistostega osmundacea*, a cave moss with lens-like cells which concentrate the available light on the single chloroplast of each cell. (Courtesy of Robert Giesy.)

these the capsule may split lengthwise, crosswise, or irregularly, but not in four definite lines as in the Andreaeales. In genera without an operculum, the columella often disappears before the capsule is mature.

ANDREAEALES

The Andreaeales, or **granite mosses,** consist of a single family, the Andreaeaceae, with only two genera. *Andreaea* has a little over 100 species, whereas *Neuroloma* has only one. The plants are largely restricted to arctic or alpine regions, where they grow exclusively on acid or siliceous rock, such as granite. The mature gametophore is brownish or blackish, owing to a diffuse pigment which more or less masks the chlorophyll. The essential characters of the group have been indicated in the key to the orders of mosses on an earlier page.

SPHAGNALES

The Sphagnales, or **peat mosses,** consist of a single family, the Sphagnaceae, which contains only the genus *Sphagnum*, with about 300 species. *Sphagnum* (Fig. 16.20) is common in moist or wet places in cool-temperate or arctic regions that are low in calcium, often forming extensive sphagnum bogs. The chemical activities of *Sphagnum* tend to increase the acidity of the surrounding water, through a colloidal absorption process that results in the breakdown of salts and release of the corresponding acids. Calcium evidently interferes with this process and hinders or prevents the plant from establishing the acid conditions necessary for optimum growth.

Decay proceeds very slowly under sphagnum bog conditions, and, as growth of the gametophores continues from above, the remains of the lower parts of the gametophores and of associated plants of other kinds accumulate as **peat.** In Ireland and some other northern countries, peat is used for fuel after being dug and allowed to dry for several months. The record of major vegetational changes over periods of thousands of years can often be deciphered by identification of the pollen grains of other plants preserved at successive depths in a peat bog. Many individual sphagnum bogs have been in existence since the close of the Pleistocene glaciation.

A germinating spore of *Sphagnum* gives rise to a short, few-celled filament. The terminal cell of the filament soon begins to function as an apical meristematic cell with two lateral cutting faces, leading to the formation of a small, flat, thallose protonema one cell thick. Some of the marginal cells of the protonema remain actively meristematic, and the protonema soon tends to become irregularly lobed. Any marginal cell may give rise to a new filament which develops into a new protonema. Rhizoids are usually restricted to the posterior end of the protonema.

A *Spaghnum* protonema gives rise to a single gametophore, which develops from marginal cells near the rear. The gametophore has an apical meristematic cell with three lateral cutting faces, and each cell cut off by the apical cell develops by a series of further divisions into a phyllidium and part of the caulidium. Every fourth phyllidium generally subtends a group of axillary branches. Some axillary branches droop; others are more or less erect and resemble the main shoot on which they are borne. As the older parts of the gametophore die and decay, the

Fig. 16.20. *Sphagnum squarrosum,* showing gametophores and sporophytes. (Courtesy of Frances Wynne Hillier.)

branches become separated from each other and continue to grow as independent, closely massed plants. The gametophores do not have rhizoids.

The caulidium is more or less strongly differentiated into a central cylinder and a surrounding cortex. The cells of the central cylinder are smaller and often have thicker walls than the cortical cells. The phyllidia are one cell thick and are usually composed of two very different kinds of cells in a regular pattern. Some of the cells are long and narrow and contain chloroplasts. Others are somewhat longer and much broader, with spirally thickened walls and without living contents. A cross section of the phyllidium shows regularly alternating chlorophyllous and colorless cells. The colorless cells absorb water and release it only gradually under conditions

of drought. It is because of this water-retaining capacity that *Sphagnum* is commonly used to pack the roots of live plants for shipment. Often some of the cortical cells of the caulidium develop spirally thickened walls and function in the same way as the colorless cells of the phyllidia.

The archegonia and antheridia of *Sphagnum* are borne at or near the tips of short branches on the same or different gametophores, according to the species. The antheridial and archegonial initials are superficial cells of the caulidium, and the apical cell itself commonly becomes one of the archegonial initials. Sex organs of both types are borne on definite stalks. Fertilization takes place in the usual bryophytic way.

After fertilization the venter of the archegonium enlarges to form a calyptra that encloses the sporophyte until it is nearly mature. At maturity the sporophyte consists of a broadly ellipsoid capsule surmounting a basal foot. The foot is embedded in a gametophytic pseudopodium which commonly elongates to a length of 1 to several millimeters as the sporophyte approaches maturity, raising the capsule shortly above the surrounding phyllidia.

The capsule is commonly 2–3 mm long and has a central columella that does not reach the tip. The jacket of the capsule is several cells thick and contains chloroplasts until near maturity. The outer layer of the jacket commonly has poorly developed and scarcely functional stomates of the type found in higher plants. As the capsule matures, the walls of the superficial cells of the jacket become strongly thickened, except for a ring of cells which remain thin-walled and mark off a definite operculum. At maturity the now blackish capsule dehisces (opens along a predetermined line) explosively, often shooting the operculum and spores several inches into the air. The sporophyte and associated structures then soon shrivel and degenerate. The gametophores, on the other hand, are perennial and live indefinitely. Because of their early degeneration, the sporophytes of *Sphagnum* are much less often seen than those of other mosses.

Concluding Remarks on Bryophytes

ECONOMIC IMPORTANCE

The bryophytes are economically less important than some other groups of plants. They are frequently pioneers on exposed surfaces that have little or no other vegetation, and their role as soil builders in the long process by which a bare rock surface becomes covered with soil is discussed in Chapter 37. *Sphagnum* was once widely used for surgical dressings. The use of *Sphagnum* for packing plants for shipment has been noted earlier, as has also the use of peat for fuel.

FOSSILS

Fossils of bryophytes are rather rare, probably because of the delicate nature of the plant bodies. Most of the fossils are too fragmentary to permit close comparison with existing genera, but the mosses can be traced back as far as the Upper Carboniferous period, and the liverworts to the Upper Devonian. The fossils do not tend to connect the bryophytes with any other division.

One of the best-known fossil genera of bryophytes is *Naiadita*, which is well represented in some Triassic and Jurassic deposits. All parts of the gametophyte are known, including rhizoids, caulidia, phyllidia, archegonia, and antheridia. The sporophyte consists of a small globular capsule borne on a presumably gametophytic stalk. *Naiadita* is generally regarded as a liverwort, but the arrangement of equal phyllidia in a spiral around the caulidium is also suggestive of mosses.

RELATIONSHIPS

Most botanists are agreed that the bryophytes are related to the vascular plants, particularly the psilophytes, and that both the bryophytes and the vascular plants are derived from the green algae. Some of the evidence on which these conclusions are based is summarized in the opening paragraphs of this chapter.

It has traditionally been thought that the bryophytes represent a more or less direct link between the green algae and the vascular plants, and that the evolution of the land plants from the green algae follows a course of progressive elaboration of the sporophyte accompanied by reduction of the gametophyte. The more general view today is that the bryophytes are derived from the green algae through prepsilophyte ancestors in which both the gametophyte and the sporophyte were green and physiologically independent. These concepts are further discussed in Chapter 17. One of the most convincing bits of evidence pointing to the derivation of the bryophytes from ancestors with more complex sporophytes is the presence of stomates on many bryophytic sporophytes in which they have little or no functional importance. The stomatal apparatus is a complex evolutionary adaptation to the need of a land plant for access of air to internal photosynthetic tissues, without excessive evaporation during periods of water deficiency. It is not likely that such a mechanism would arise in advance of the need.

None of the three classes of bryophytes can be considered directly ancestral to any of the others. Regardless of which view is taken as to the evolutionary history of the group, each class is advanced in some features and more primitive in others. There has probably been an evolutionary progression from erect gametophytes bearing three rows of equal phyllidia, to dorsiventral gametophytes with the ventral row of phyllidia reduced or wanting, to strictly thallose gametophytes without phyllidia. The thallose gametophyte of the Anthocerotae is thus interpreted as among the most "advanced" in the division, whereas the sporophyte is the least reduced and therefore the most primitive in the division. Even if the older viewpoint is accepted and the sporophyte of the Anthocerotae is considered to be an advance toward the condition of the vascular plants, the presence of pyrenoids in the chloroplasts of the Anthocerotae is still a primitive character not shared by other bryophytes.

SUGGESTED READING

Conard, H. S., *How to Know the Mosses and Liverworts*, Wm. C. Brown, Dubuque, Iowa, 1956, 226 pp. A profusely illustrated key to the commoner bryophytes of North America.

CHAPTER 17

Division
Psilophyta

PSILOPHYTES

Vascular plants without roots, the sporophyte consisting of a branching stem with or without leaves, the leaves microphylls; gametophyte and sporophyte physiologically independent of each other at maturity; antheridia and archegonia multicellular. A single class, the Psilotae.

Introduction to the Vascular Plants

The divisions Psilophyta, Lepidophyta, Calamophyta, Filicophyta, Coniferophyta, Cycadophyta, and Anthophyta make up a large group characterized by the presence of specialized conducting tissues in the sporophyte. These divisions are often collectively called the **vascular plants.** The gametophytes of vascular plants are always small, inconspicuous bodies which are scarcely more than stages in the reproduction of the larger and more conspicuous sporophyte. The vascular plants clearly constitute a natural group, and some botanists consider them to form a single large division, the **Tracheophyta.** Other botanists prefer to recognize several divisions of vascular plants, as is done in this text. The two points of view do not reflect any fundamental conflict of ideas on relationship. Those who object to placing all vascular plants in a single division merely be-

◄
Psilotum nudum. (Slightly less than natural size.)

319

lieve that such a classification minimizes the differences within the group, and that so large and varied a division is hardly comparable to the other recognized divisions of plants.

The specialized conducting tissues of vascular plants are called **xylem** and **phloem.** Both xylem and phloem are usually complex tissues, with two or more kinds of cells. Xylem, the water-conducting tissue, is characterized by the presence of elongate, thick-walled cells called **tracheids.** Tracheids are dead at maturity, without living contents. They give strength or rigidity to the plant and serve to conduct water and minerals. They have a well-developed secondary wall with a high proportion of lignin, a complex substance whose chemical structure is not fully understood.

At any given level in a stem, the xylem which matures first is called **protoxylem,** and that which matures later is called **metaxylem.** Protoxylem generally matures while the surrounding cells of other types are still immature and have not reached full length. The secondary wall of a protoxylem cell is deposited in a series of rings or in a spiral, allowing the cell to stretch with the growth of the surrounding tissues. The secondary wall of a metaxylem cell is usually deposited in a network, or in a continuous sheet with scattered holes or **pits.** The wood of trees and shrubs consists of xylem, but the strands of xylem in the stems of herbaceous plants are not usually called wood. The structure of xylem is more fully discussed in Chapters 23 and 24.

Phloem, the food-conducting tissue, is characterized by elongate, thin-walled, living cells called **sieve elements.** The protoplast of a mature sieve element lacks a nucleus. Each sieve element is usually in contact with one or more normal parenchyma cells or specialized companion cells, and the cytoplasm of the adjacent cells is connected by plasmodesmata. It is believed that the nucleus of the adjoining cell functions for the protoplast of the sieve element as well. The sieve elements are connected to each other by groups of perforations in the wall, and the cytoplasm is continuous through the perforations, forming large, or very large, plasmodesmata. Each group of perforations is called a **sieve area.** In the more advanced vascular plants, successive sieve elements are joined end to end to form a **sieve tube,** and the sieve areas are concentrated in **sieve plates** which mark the ends of the individual sieve elements. The bark of trees and shrubs consists of phloem, but the strands of phloem in the stems of herbaceous plants are not called bark. The structure of phloem is more fully discussed in Chapters 23 and 24.

In the most primitive kinds of vascular plants, such as some fossil psilophytes, the sporophyte consists of a dichotomously branched axis which is considered to be a stem. In more advanced kinds of vascular plants, the sporophyte is differentiated into three principal kinds of organs, the **root,** the **stem,** and the **leaf.** In their typical forms, the root is the underground part of the plant, the stem is the aerial axis (including the branches), and the leaves are the flattened, photosynthetic appendages of the stem. The leaves and stem together are often called the **shoot,** as opposed to the root. Roots, stems, and leaves usually differ anatomically from each other, and specialized organs of various sorts can usually be classified as modified roots, stems, or leaves by their anatomy.

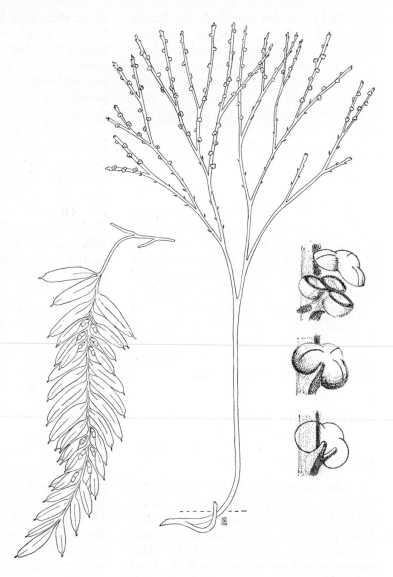

Fig. 17.1. *Tmesipteris*, left (slightly less than natural size). *Psilotum*, center (slightly less than natural size), and right (enlarged to show structure of sporangia).

Psilophytes

CLASSIFICATION AND DISTRIBUTION

There are only three living species of Psilophyta, but numerous fossils of Silurian and Devonian age are also referred to this division. The living psilophytes are *Psilotum nudum*, *Psilotum complanatum*, and *Tmesipteris tannensis*. *Tmesipteris* is confined to Australia and some of the Pacific Islands, but *Psilotum* is widespread in tropical and subtropical regions of both hemispheres. *P. nudum* extends as far north as South Carolina. *Psilotum* and *Tmesipteris*

(Fig. 17.1) together constitute the family Psilotaceae, the only family of the order Psilotales. The fossil psilophytes belong to several families which make up the order Psilophytales. The Psilotales and Psilophytales together make up the class Psilotae, the only class of the division Psilophyta.

HISTORY

The living psilophytes were long recognized as anomalous types which do not fit well into any other group of plants. After the discovery of numerous ancient fossils apparently related to *Psilotum* and *Tmesipteris*, it became evident that these genera are the remnant of what was once a large and dominant group. The psilophytes, living and fossil, were first treated as a distinct division in 1923 by the British botanist D. H. Scott (1854–1934).

CHARACTERISTICS

THE SPOROPHYTE

The sporophyte is the conspicuous generation in the psilophytes, the gametophytes being subterranean and very small. The sporophyte has a branched, green, photosynthetic stem which in the living species is seldom over a foot high. Most fossil forms were of comparable size, but some were as much as 10 feet tall. The branching is usually dichotomous, but sometimes it is more or less distinctly sympodial (i.e., one of the two branches of a pair continues as a segment of the zigzag main axis, while the other is smaller and lateral). The underground part of a psilophyte stem may be slightly differentiated from the aerial part, but any underground branch may turn up at the end and become a normal aerial branch. A more or less horizontal underground stem, in the psilophytes and elsewhere, is called a **rhizome.**

The stem (Fig. 17.2) is differentiated into an epidermis, a cortex, and a **central cylinder.** The central cylinder consists largely or wholly of xylem and phloem. Typically the xylem makes up a solid core, but sometimes it is a tube or sheath enclosing a core of parenchymatous tissue called **pith.** The phloem forms an interrupted or complete ring surrounding the xylem. The **cortex,** which surrounds the central cylinder, usually consists largely of parenchyma, although there may be some thick-walled strengthening cells. In the aerial part of the stem, the outer layer of the cortex has chloroplasts and carries on photosynthesis. The cortex is sometimes separated from the central cylinder by a distinct layer, one cell thick, called the **endodermis.** The epidermis, which forms the outermost layer of the stem, is covered by a layer of cutin and bears scattered stomates. In the living genera, at least, the growing tip of each branch has a single meristematic apical cell with three cutting faces. Cells cut off from the apical cell divide one or more times before maturing into the different kinds of cells which make up the sporophyte.

The stem may or may not have leaves. The leaves are always small and consist largely of photosynthetic tissue surrounded by a cutinized epidermis, with or without stomates. Sometimes there is a definite unbranched midvein, connecting through the cortex to the central cylinder and consisting of xylem and phloem surrounded by a more or less differentiated sheath. Leaves of this type are called **microphylls.** The nature of microphylls is further discussed in Chapter 20.

The sporangia are generally terminal on the branches. In fossil psilophytes they are borne on ordinary vegetative branches, but in the living species they are on specialized, very short branches which are subtended by leaves, so that the sporangia may appear to be axillary (i.e., in the axils). Reduction division takes place within the sporangium, and the spores have the reduced number of chromosomes. Each spore mother cell gives rise to a tetrad of spores.

THE GAMETOPHYTE

Gametophytes of fossil psilophytes are unknown. Gametophytes of living psilophytes are small, subterranean bodies which lack chlorophyll. They get their food through a mycorhizal association with a phycomycetous fungus. The Phycomycetes are the only fungi known to have existed in the Devonian period, when the psilophytes were abundant. The Ascomycetes and Basidiomycetes, which furnish the usual mycorhizal fungi for seed plants, do not appear in pre-Carboniferous deposits.

The antheridia and archegonia of psilophytes are borne on the same gametophyte (Fig. 17.3) and are multicellular. The archegonium is flask-shaped, with a short broad neck; the antheridium is subglobose or hemispheric. The sperms, which have numerous whiplash flagella, swim to the archegonium through a film of water and pass down through the neck of the archegonium to the egg in the same way as the sperms of bryophytes.

DEVELOPMENT OF THE EMBRYO

Fusion of a sperm and an egg constitutes fertilization. The fertilized egg, or zygote, has $2n$ chromosomes and is the first cell of the sporophyte generation. The first division of the zygote is at right angles to the long axis of the archegonium. The lower of the two cells formed in the first division gives rise, by a series of further mitotic divisions, to the foot; the upper cell gives rise to the shoot. The foot absorbs nourishment from the gametophyte and passes it on to the developing shoot. The first branches of the shoot are often horizontal and develop below the ground as rhizomes, but the characteristic aerial branches are soon produced. The underground part of the shoot becomes infected with a mycorhizal fungus, and it may become self-sustaining through this association even before the tip reaches the surface.

When the shoot has become established as an independent plant, a layer of cells is formed separating it from the foot. This layer is called an **abscission layer** because the disintegration of its cells detaches the shoot from the foot. Abscission layers which separate one organ from another occur in many kinds of vascular plants.

The gametophyte may persist for some time after the sporophyte has become established, but sooner or later the gametophyte dies and degenerates.

PSILOTUM

THE SPOROPHYTE

Psilotum may be taken as a representative example of the Psilophyta. The

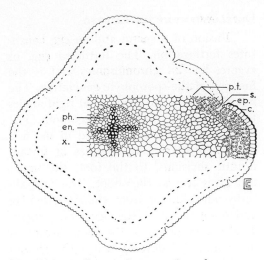

Fig. 17.2. *Psilotum.* Cross section of stem: c., cuticle; en., endodermis; ep., epidermis; ph., phloem; p.t., photosynthetic tissue; s., stomate; x., xylem.

mature sporophyte is a more or less dichotomously branched stem with very small and inconspicuous scattered leaves. The xylem forms a solid central core in the stem. In cross section the xylem appears to be irregularly star-shaped, with generally five or six radiating arms. The cells at the tips of the arms mature first, and those toward the center progressively later. The xylem cells are all vertically elongate, tapered toward the ends, thick-walled, and dead when functional. The radiating arms of xylem, as seen in a cross section of the stem, consist largely of protoxylem with annular or spirally thickened tracheids. **Annular tracheids** are tracheids with the secondary wall consisting of a series of separate rings. The core of the xylem consists of metaxylem with merely pitted tracheids. Tracheids of this type, as seen in *Psilotum,* are not much different from the elongate, thick-walled, strengthening cells found in many other parts of vascular plants. Thick-walled strengthening cells other than xylem cells are generally

called **sclerenchyma** cells. Elongate, narrow sclerenchyma cells are called **fibers** or sclerenchyma fibers.

The tissue immediately surrounding the xylem of the stem of *Psilotum* consists of thin-walled, vertically elongate, living cells with slanting end walls. This tissue is generally considered to be phloem, although sieve areas have not yet been demonstrated in it. Sieve areas have been seen in the related genus *Tmesipteris.* Phloem functions in the transport of food.

The xylem and phloem together constitute the central cylinder or **stele.** A solid stele, such as that of *Psilotum,* is called a **protostele.**

The stele of the aerial branches of *Psilotum,* like most other protosteles, is surrounded by an **endodermis.** The endodermis is a sheath consisting of a single layer of cells that are closely set, without intercellular spaces. In cross section the endodermis appears to form a ring. The radial walls of endodermal cells of *Psilotum* and other plants have prominent thickenings, called **Casparian strips,** that are often impregnated with a waxy substance called suberin. The endodermis evidently functions in regulating the passage of water and solutes between the cortex and the stele. Diffusion through the radial walls of the endodermal cells is inhibited by the Casparian strips, and the passage of water and solutes through the endodermis is thus subjected to the control of the protoplast of the cell. The nature and function of endodermis are further discussed in Chapter 25.

Most of the cortex of *Psilotum nudum* consists of colorless angular cells so closely packed as to lack evident intercellular spaces. The outer two to five layers of cortical cells of aerial branches are vertically elongate, thin-walled, and more loosely set, with intercellular spaces. These cells have numerous small chloroplasts. The cortical cells just within the photosynthetic layer have strongly thickened walls, but this thick-walled layer passes gradually into the thin-walled tissue which makes up most of the interior of the cortex.

The epidermis consists of a single layer of cells with a thick **cuticle.** A cuticle is a layer of cutin. The only intercellular spaces in the epidermis are the stomates, which in *P. nudum* occur mainly in the grooves between the longitudinal ridges of the stem. The underground branches of the stem are not cutinized and lack stomates.

The leaves of *Psilotum* are mere small, pointed scales about 1 mm long, irregularly scattered along the aerial branches of the stem. The epidermis is cutinized and lacks stomates. The interior tissue of the leaf consists of chlorophyllous cells similar to those of the stem. The leaves have no vascular tissue, but in *P. complanatum* a **leaf trace** extends from the stele through the cortex to the base of the leaf. A leaf trace is the vascular supply for a leaf, from the point where it leaves the stele to the point where it enters the leaf. In *Tmesipteris* the leaves are larger than in *Psilotum*, commonly about 1 cm long, with stomates in the epidermis and with a definite midrib of xylem surrounded by phloem.

The sporangia of *Psilotum* are borne in groups of three at the ends of very short lateral branches. The three sporangia of a cluster begin their development as separate bodies, but they are joined at maturity. Each such cluster of sporangia, terminating a short lateral branch, is subtended by a minute, deeply bifid leaf. As the sporangium approaches maturity, the internal tissue becomes differentiated into irregular clusters of cells with dense cytoplasm, scattered through a mass of cells with more watery cytoplasm. The cells with dense cytoplasm undergo repeated mitotic divisions and eventually give rise to the spore mother cells. The other cells divide slowly and finally disintegrate into a slimy mass at about the time the spores are formed. Each spore mother cell undergoes reduction division, producing a tetrad of spores. At maturity each sporangium opens along a longitudinal line of dehiscence that is marked by relatively small, thin-walled jacket cells.

The Gametophyte

A germinating spore gives rise by a series of mitotic divisions to a colorless, irregularly cylindrical gametophyte a few millimeters long. There are numerous scattered rhizoids, each of which is merely an extension from a single superficial cell. The internal cells of the gametophyte are densely filled with mycorhizal fungus filaments, but the outer several layers are largely fungus-free. A central strand of tracheids has been observed in some individuals but is not usually present. A single meristematic apical cell has been identified in both *Tmesipteris* and *Psilotum*.

The antheridia and archegonia are borne on the same gametophyte, as in all Psilotales. The antheridium forms a dome-shaped protrusion from the body of the gametophyte. The antheridial initial is a superficial cell of the gametophyte. Its first division gives rise to an outer cell, the jacket initial, and an inner cell, the primary androgonial cell. By subsequent mitotic divisions, the primary androgonial cell gives rise to the sperms, and the jacket initial gives rise to the wall of the protruding part of the antheridium. The wall

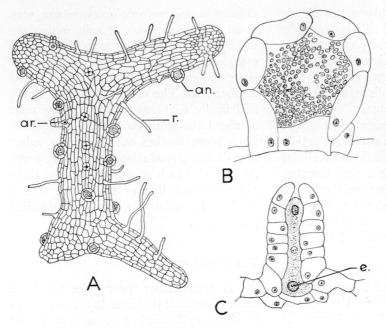

Fig. 17.3. *Psilotum. A,* gametophyte (×20); *B,* antheridium, long section (×175); *C,* archegonium, long section (×175); an., antheridium; ar., archegonium; e., egg; r., rhizoid.

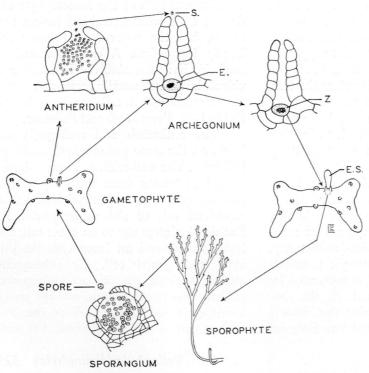

Fig. 17.4. Life cycle of *Psilotum:* e., egg; e.s., embryo sporophyte; s., sperm; z., zygote.

ANTHERIDIUM

ARCHEGONIUM

GAMETOPHYTE

SPORE

SPORANGIUM

SPOROPHYTE

of the basal part of the antheridium is formed by ordinary cells of the gametophyte. A single opercular cell at the center of the outer face of the jacket of the antheridium disintegrates, leaving an opening through which the sperms escape.

The archegonial initial cell of *Psilotum* is also a superficial cell of the gametophyte. The outer of the two cells formed in the first division gives rise to the neck of the archegonium, and the inner cell gives rise to the egg and the canal cells. The neck of the developing archegonium projects beyond the outer surface of the gametophyte, but most of the projecting part falls off before fertilization. The wall bounding the venter of the archegonium is formed largely by ordinary cells of the gametophyte. Fertilization and the subsequent development of the sporophyte follow the pattern described for the Psilophyta on p. 323.

FOSSILS

INTRODUCTION

The first fossil psilophyte to be discovered was *Psilophyton* (Fig. 17.5), which the Canadian geologist John W. Dawson (1820–1899) named in 1859 for its resemblance to *Psilotum*. Dawson's drawing was a reconstruction based on several separated fragments, and for many years the accuracy of the reconstruction was doubted. More than half a century later, in 1913, a series of extraordinarily well-preserved fossils of primitive vascular plants was discovered in rocks of Middle Devonian age near Aberdeen, Scotland—the now famous Rhynie beds. After these fossils became known, the skepticism regarding *Psilophyton* was dissipated, and an

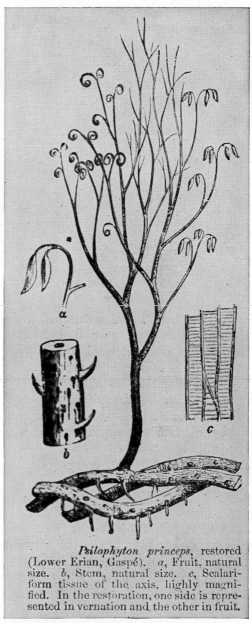

Psilophyton princeps, restored (Lower Erian, Gaspé). *a*, Fruit, natural size. *b*, Stem, natural size. *c*, Scalariform tissue of the axis, highly magnified. In the restoration, one side is represented in vernation and the other in fruit.

Fig. 17.5. *Psilophyton,* **as reconstructed by Dawson.**

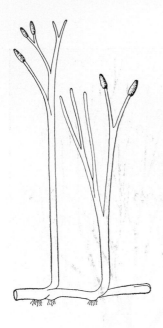
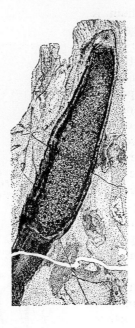

Fig. 17.6. *Rhynia major*. Left, habit. (×⅓.) (After Kidston and Lang.) Right, fossil sporangium. (× about 5.) (From Kidston & Lang.)

order Psilophytales was established to include all fossils of general psilotalean character. Other fossils referable to the Psilophytales have subsequently been found in rocks of Middle Silurian to Late Devonian age in various other parts of the world, and it is evident that the psilophytes were a prominent, or even a dominant, part of the land vegetation of the time.

Rhynia

Perhaps the most important genus of the psilophyte fossils is *Rhynia* (Fig. 17.6), because it so nicely fulfills the qualifications of an ancestral prototype for all vascular plants. The sporophyte consists of a dichotomously branched axis, with a horizontal rhizome and erect, aerial branches several inches or a foot high. The rhizome is basically similar in structure to the aerial branches, but it differs in bearing clusters of slender, unicellular rhizoids

which evidently acted as absorbing structures. Sporangia are borne singly at the tips of some of the aerial branches, and there are no leaves.

The aerial stem has a small central strand of xylem consisting of annular tracheids. The xylem is surrounded by a layer, four or five cells thick, of elongate, thin-walled cells which are considered to be phloem, although no sieve areas have been observed. The phloem is surrounded by a large cortex, without any intervening endodermis. Most of the cortex consists of more or less spherical cells with good-sized intercellular spaces, but the outer few layers of cortical cells are larger and more angular, without evident intercellular spaces except just beneath the stomates. The internal part of the cortex is believed to have been a photosynthetic tissue. The epidermis is a layer of cutinized cells with scattered stomates.

The sporangia are up to ½ inch long

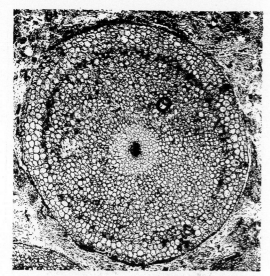

Fig. 17.7. *Rhynia major.* Cross section of stem. Xylem, phloem, two layers of cortex and epidermis may be seen. (× about 13.) (From Kidston & Lang.)

and are nearly cylindrical, tapering slightly toward the tip. The jacket of the sporangium is several cells thick and indehiscent. The sporangial cavity lacks a columella and contains many spores of about equal size. In some specimens the spores are grouped in tetrads, indicating that they are products of reduction division.

HORNEOPHYTON

Horneophyton (Fig. 17.8), another common fossil in the Rhynie beds, is basically similar to *Rhynia,* but the underground axis is short, thickened, without a vascular system, and there is a well-developed columella in the capsule.

ASTEROXYLON

Asteroxylon (Fig. 17.8), a psilophyte fossil now known from Devonian deposits in Germany as well as from the Rhynie

beds, is more complex than *Rhynia* and *Horneophyton.* The specimens from Germany differ somewhat from those of Scotland and are considered to represent a different species. *Asteroxylon* grew to about 3 feet high, and the stem had numerous small, thin, scale-like leaves about ¼ inch long. The core of xylem (Fig. 17.10), as seen in cross section of the stem, has several arms radiating from the center. The protoxylem is near the tips of the arms and consists of spiral tracheids or spiral and annular tracheids. The metaxylem consists wholly of spiral tracheids. The phloem forms a smooth sheath surrounding the xylem. The cortex has a dense inner layer and a dense outer layer, separated by a median layer with very large intercellular spaces. The intercellular spaces separate

Fig. 17.8. *Asteroxylon* and *Horneophyton* (*Hornea*). (From Kidston & Lang.)

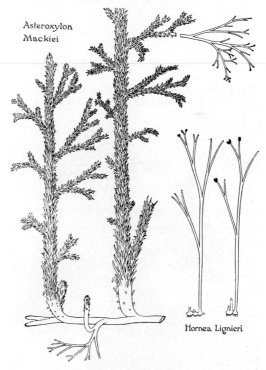

Asteroxylon Mackiei

Hornea Lignieri

Psilophyta: Psilophytes 329

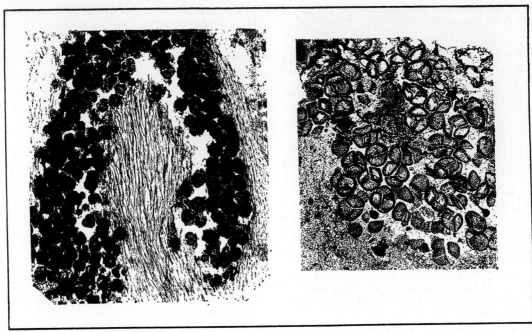

Fig. 17.9. *Horneophyton*. Left, spores around the columella; right, tetrads of spores. (From Kidston & Lang.)

Fig. 17.10. *Asteroxylon mackiei*. Left, cross section of the xylem (× about 35). Right, long section of the xylem (× about 225). (From Kidston & Lang.)

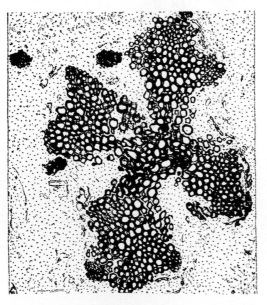

thin layers of tissue which connect the inner cortex to the outer cortex.

The leaves of *Asteroxylon* have no vascular tissue, but a small leaf trace extends from the tip of one of the radiating arms of xylem to the base of each leaf. The leaf trace passes diagonally upward through the cortex and has a layer of phloem surrounding a central strand of xylem.

The rhizome lacks rhizoids, but some of its branches are markedly slender and tend to extend downward into the substrate. These slender branches, which are repeatedly forked, doubtless functioned as anchoring and absorbing organs, although they can hardly be called roots.

The sporangia of *Asteroxylon* are small, only about 1 mm long, and are borne at the tips of leafless, slender, dichotomously forked branches. These fertile branches have not been found attached to the vegetative branches, but the two types of branch are so commonly associated, without any evidence that either of them belongs with some other kind of plant, that there is little doubt they are parts of the same plant.

RELATIONSHIPS

The psilophytes are the most primitive known group of vascular plants. All other groups of vascular plants, except possibly for some ancient and poorly known fossils, appear to be derived eventually from the psilophytes. Most botanists are agreed that the bryophytes are also related to the psilophytes and that the green algae are ancestral to all these groups. The development of the archegonium and the retention of the egg within it are seen as the natural corollary to the adoption of a land habitat. The sporophyte remains attached to the gametophyte, at least in its early stages of development, because there is nothing to cause their separation.

There are two opposing theories as to the nature of the green algal ancestors of the embryophytes and the general course of evolution of the embryophyte subkingdom. According to the **homologous theory** of land-plant evolution, the ancestor of the embryophytes was a green alga with isomorphic alternation of generations, i.e., the gametophyte and sporophyte were essentially similar. The primitive embryophyte is likewise believed to have had similar gametophyte and sporophyte generations; and from this type evolution proceeded in two directions. In one line the sporophyte became essentially parasitic on the gametophyte, losing much or all of its photosynthetic capacity and coming to be scarcely more than a stage in the reproduction of the gametophyte. The bryophytes represent this line of development. In the other line the sporophyte became the dominant generation, and the gametophyte was reduced, ultimately becoming merely a step in the reproduction of the sporophyte. The vascular plants represent this line of development.

According to the **antithetic theory** of

Fig. 17.11. *Asteroxylon mackiei.* Part of the epidermis, with stomates. (×200.) (From Kidston & Lang.)

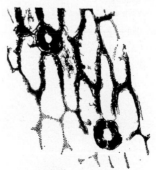

land-plant evolution, the ancestor of the embryophytes was a green alga in which the zygote was the only diploid or sporophytic cell. The sporophyte is regarded as an entirely new structure interposed between two gametophyte generations, and evolutionary advance consisted of progressive elaboration of the sporophyte and eventual reduction of the gametophyte. Under the antithetic theory, the bryophytes are regarded as a transitional step from the green algae toward the vascular plants.

At the time the antithetic theory was first proposed, the only green algae in which sexual reproduction was known had only a single diploid cell in the life cycle, but many genera with isomorphic alternation of generations are now known. Evidence from comparative morphology of the bryophytes furthermore suggests that the forms with very small sporophytes have been derived from ancestors with larger sporophytes. Although the antithetic theory was once widely accepted, the accumulation of evidence has favored the homologous theory, which has become more and more generally adopted.

Fritschiella, a terrestrial green alga with isomorphic alternation of generations and with some differentiation of tissues, has attracted attention as a plant having the potentiality of evolutionary development along the lines of the embryophytes, but there is still a considerable gap between this genus and any known embryophyte.

SUGGESTED READING

Dawson, J. W., On fossil plants from the Devonian rocks of Canada, *Geol. Soc. Lond. Quart. Jour.* 15:477–488. 1859. The classic paper on *Psilophyton.*

Kidston, R., and W. H. Lang, On old red sandstone plants showing structure, from the Rhynie chert beds, Aberdeenshire, Parts i–v. 1917–1921. *Trans. Roy. Soc. Edinb.* 51:761–784; 52:603–627, 643–680, 831–854, 855–902. The classic papers on psilophytes from the Rhynie beds.

CHAPTER 18

Division Lepidophyta

CLUB MOSSES
AND QUILLWORTS

Vascular plants with roots, stems, and leaves, the leaves microphylls; gametophyte and sporophyte physiologically independent of each other at maturity in all modern species, but the gametophyte small and inconspicuous; sporangia axillary or borne on the adaxial (upper) surface of the leaf near its base; leaves alternate or opposite, seldom whorled. A single class, the Lycopodiae.

HISTORY

The Lepidophyta were first recognized as a distinct division of plants by the American botanist Charles Edwin Bessey (1845–1915) in 1907. The studies leading up to this classification are discussed in Chapter 20.

CHARACTERISTICS

HABIT AND STEM

The sporophyte is the conspicuous generation in the lepidophytes, the gametophyte being small and often subterranean. Many lepidophytes of the Carboniferous and Permian geologic periods were trees, but all the modern (i.e., living) species are relatively small herbs with short or elongate, sometimes vine-like stems. Elongation of the stem is due to mitotic divisions of an apical cell or a group of apical cells which form an apical

◄

Lycopodium lucidulum, a club moss of eastern North America. (×2.) (Photo by Hugh Spencer, from National Audubon Society.)

335

Fig. 18.1. *Lycopodium.* (About natural size.) (Copyright by General Biological Supply House, Inc., Chicago.)

meristem. The stem is simple or more often branched. Branching is dichotomous to sympodial or essentially monopodial (i.e., the central axis essentially straight and not obviously developed by a succession of unequal dichotomies), according to the species, and the position of the branches bears no relation to the position of the leaves. The branches originate by

bifurcation of the apical meristem or apical cell, each of the two parts continuing to develop as the apical meristem or apical cell of a separate axis. The stem is usually differentiated into an epidermis, cortex, and central cylinder, and in some types it increases in thickness by secondary growth. The nature of secondary growth is discussed under the Lepidodendrales.

LEAVES

The leaves of lepidophytes are narrow and usually small, with a single unbranched midvein (rarely two veins) of vascular tissue. Anatomically they are microphylls. The place on a stem where a leaf is (or has been) attached is called a **node,** and the part of the stem between one node and the next is called an **internode.** Leaves are said to be **alternate** if only one is borne at a node, **opposite** if two are borne (usually on opposite sides of the stem) at a node, and **whorled** if three or more are borne at a node. The leaves of lepidophytes are usually alternate or opposite, seldom whorled. "Opposite" leaves of lepidophytes are often modified in position so that both are on the same side of the stem.

In all lepidophytes except the Lycopodiales, the leaf has a small appendage on the adaxial side (the side toward the stem, the upper side) a little above the base. This appendage is called a **ligule,** and lepidophytes are described as **ligulate** or **eligulate,** according to whether or not the ligule is present. If the leaves of lepidophytes originated by modification of some branches of a dichotomously branched stem system, as many botanists believe (see p. 378), the ligule may represent a vestigial branch. The term *ligule,* (from

Latin *ligula,* a little tongue,) is applied to several quite different structures in different groups of vascular plants.

Root

All divisions of vascular plants except the psilophytes ordinarily have the root clearly differentiated from the stem. Roots characteristically grow downward into the soil in response to the pull of gravity; i.e., they are positively geotropic. Most stems tend to grow upward, away from the pull of gravity; they are negatively geotropic. Stems generally bear leaves, usually in a more or less definite arrangement; they have nodes and internodes. Roots do not have leaves; they lack nodes and internodes. The growing point of a root ordinarily has a protective covering, the **root-cap.** The cells of the rootcap are constantly being sloughed off as the root grows through the soil and are replaced by new cells derived from the apical meristem. The growing point of a stem is generally hidden by the adjacent leaves which extend up around it, but there is no direct cover comparable to the rootcap. Certain other differences between roots and stems characterize most vascular plants, but these differences do not always hold true for lepidophytes and calamophytes.

The primary root, in the lepidophytes and in other plants, usually originates early in the development of the embryo sporophyte, but in lepidophytes it does not generally persist until the sporophyte is mature. Roots of the mature sporophyte of lepidophytes originate adventitiously from internal tissues of the stem, or from internal tissues of special stem-like organs called **rhizophores.** The growing point of the root pushes its way through the outer tissues of the stem or rhizophore and continues its growth into the soil. Roots of lepidophytes are often simple (unbranched), but sometimes they are dichotomously branched one or more times. The branches originate by simple bifurcation of the apical meristem, just as do the branches of the stem.

Sporangia

The sporangia of lepidophytes are borne singly in the axils of the leaves, or on the adaxial side of the leaf near the base. Leaves which bear or subtend sporangia are called **sporophylls.** The sporophylls of some lepidophytes and other plants are ordinary vegetative leaves. Other lepidophytes and many plants of other divisions have more or less modified sporophylls which are grouped into a terminal cone called a **strobilus.**

The ontogeny (individual development) of the sporangia of lepidophytes follows a characteristic pattern. A sporangium originates from a group of superficial cells, the sporangial initials, in or near the axil of a leaf. Each of these sporangial initials divides parallel to the surface, so that an inner layer and an outer layer of cells are formed. The cells of the outer layer give rise by further mitotic divisions to the jacket of the mature sporangium. The cells of the inner layer give rise by further mitotic divisions to the **sporogenous** (spore-producing) **tissue** which fills the interior of the sporangium. Ultimately many or all the cells of the sporogenous tissue act as spore mother cells and undergo reduction division to form spores. The spores have n chromosomes and are the first stage in the gametophyte generation.

A single layer (or two layers) of cells, the **tapetum,** lies between the jacket and the sporogenous tissue of the sporangium. The cells of the tapetum die and degenerate as the sporangium approaches maturity, and their contents are largely used up by the developing spore mother cells. The tapetum is said, therefore, to be a nutritive tissue. In some genera, the tapetum originates from the outer layer of sporogenous tissue of the young sporangium. In others it is derived largely from the inner layer of the developing jacket, which is two to several cells thick at maturity.

Vascular plants in which the development of the sporangia follows essentially the pattern found in the lepidophytes are said to be **eusporangiate.** The sporangia of the Calamophyta originate from single cells instead of from groups of cells, but the ontogeny is otherwise so much like that of lepidophytes that the calamophytes are also considered to be eusporangiate. Some filicophytes are eusporangiate like the lepidophytes, but most of them follow a different method of sporangial development (described in Chapter 20) and are said to be leptosporangiate.

Gametophytes

The gametophytes of the Lepidophyta are always small and inconspicuous, up to about an inch long in some of the Lycopodiales, even smaller and often microscopic in the other orders. In the Lycopodiales the spores of a given species are all about alike, and the antheridia and archegonia are borne on the same gametophyte. The Lycopodiales are therefore said to be **homosporous.** In the remaining orders of lepidophytes the spores are of two different types, borne in different spo-

rangia. These orders are said to be **heterosporous.** One of the two kinds of spores develops into a female gametophyte, which bears archegonia (or a single archegonium) but not antheridia; the other develops into a male gametophyte, which bears an antheridium but no archegonium.

The spores which develop into male gametophytes are microscopic, and a great many of them are borne in a sporangium. These spores are called **microspores,** and the sporangium in which they are borne is called a **microsporangium.** A sporophyll which bears or subtends a microsporangium is called a **microsporophyll.** A male gametophyte is often called a microgametophyte, although this term is not universally used.

The spores which develop into female gametophytes are relatively large, often about the size of a pinhead, and only a limited number are borne in a sporangium. These spores are called **megaspores,** and the sporangium in which they are borne is called a **megasporangium.** A sporophyll which bears or subtends a megasporangium is called a **megasporophyll,** and the female gametophyte is sometimes called a megagametophyte. The prefix *mega-* in the foregoing terms is sometimes replaced by the prefix *macro-.* Both mean "large," as opposed to *micro-,* which means "small."

The antheridium of lepidophytes is multicellular and is derived from a single antheridial initial cell. The pattern of cell division leading to the formation of the mature antheridium varies in the different genera of the group. The sperms are naked (without a cell wall) and have either two or many long flagella of the whiplash type.

The archegonium of lepidophytes originates from a single epidermal cell of the gametophyte, the archegonial initial.

The first division of the archegonial initial gives rise to an outer cell, the primary cover cell, and an inner cell, the central cell. By a series of further mitotic divisions, the central cell gives rise to the egg and one or more canal cells, and the cover cell gives rise to the neck of the archegonium. The neck (or at least the top of the neck) protrudes from the surface of the gametophyte, but the venter is embedded. As in the Psilotales and Anthocerotales, the cells bounding the venter of the archegonium are ordinary gametophytic cells which are not derived from the archegonial initial. As the archegonium approaches maturity, the canal cells disintegrate into a slimy mass, and the uppermost cells of the neck tend to spread apart and often partly disintegrate, so that the sperms have free access to the egg. The sperms are attracted to the egg by chemical stimuli and require a film of water in which to swim.

Embryo

Fusion of a sperm and an egg in the venter of the archegonium constitutes fertilization. The fertilized egg or zygote has $2n$ chromosomes and is the first cell of the sporophyte generation. The embryo sporophyte is derived from the zygote by a series of mitotic divisions. The precise pattern of development varies among and within the different orders, but the embryo usually has a well-developed foot which absorbs food from the gametophyte. Eventually the growing young sporophyte breaks through the tissues of the gametophyte, establishes its own connection with the ground, and goes on to develop into a mature sporophyte. The gametophyte may persist for some time after the sporophyte has become independent, but eventually it

dies and degenerates. Ordinarily a gametophyte gives rise to only a single sporophyte.

CLASSIFICATION

Classification of plants is usually based primarily on modern (i.e., living) species, and fossil forms are merely appended to the scheme. This is done for both theoretical and practical reasons. The modern forms are of inherently greater interest and importance from a human standpoint, and the gaps in variability, which are of fundamental significance in classification, would, of course, be largely eliminated if all organisms of the past as well as the present were considered. Furthermore, the characteristics which enable us to classify living plant species are often not preserved in the fossils. The modern representatives of several divisions, however, are mere vestiges of groups which were much more abundant and varied in past geologic eras. This is particularly true of the Psilophyta, Lepidophyta, Calamophyta, and Cycadophyta, and therefore fossil forms are given more importance in the classification of these divisions.

There are about 1200 modern species of lepidophytes, divided into four genera: *Lycopodium*, *Phylloglossum*, *Selaginella*, and *Isoetes*. *Lycopodium* and *Phylloglossum* belong to the family Lycopodiaceae, the only living family of the order Lycopodiales. *Selaginella* is the only modern genus of the family Selaginellaceae, which is the only living family of the order Selaginellales. *Isoetes* is the only modern genus of the family Isoetaceae, the only family definitely referable to the order Isoetales. (Another genus of Isoetaceae, *Stylites*, has recently been described, from the South American Andes, but it is not yet certain that it should be kept separate from *Isoetes*.) All these orders are represented by both modern and fossil forms. A fourth order, the Lepidodendrales, is known only from fossils. All the fossil lepidophytes which are sufficiently well preserved to permit formal classification are usually referred to one or another of these four orders. The orders are characterized in the appendix.

LYCOPODIALES

LYCOPODIUM

The genus *Lycopodium* (Figs. 18.1, 18.2) consists of about 600 species. The species are more numerous in warm climates than in cool ones, and more numerous in moist regions than in dry ones. Many tropical species are epiphytes with

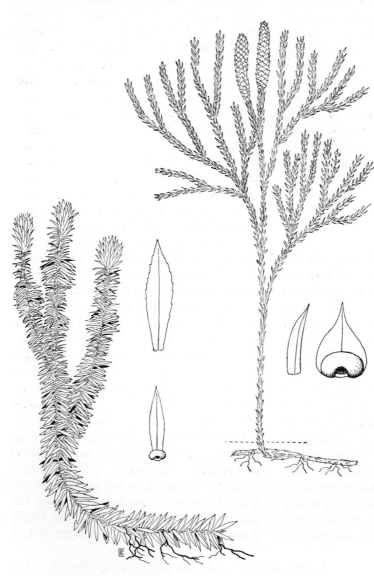

Fig. 18.2. *Lycopodium.* Left, *L. lucidulum* ($\times\frac{2}{3}$), with sporophyll and vegetative leaf ($\times$3). Right, *L. obscurum* ($\times\frac{2}{3}$), with sporophyll and vegetative leaf ($\times$4).

weak, drooping branches. *Lycopodium* and *Selaginella* are often called **club mosses,** although they bear no close relationship to the Musci. The name comes from the superficial resemblance of the sporophytes of many species of these two genera to large moss gametophytes, plus the club-like terminal strobilus. Some species of *Lycopodium* are also called ground pine or running pine, because of a very casual resemblance to pine twigs.

The species of *Lycopodium* are classified into two subgenera. In one subgenus the stem is erect or pendent and simple or dichotomously branched. In the other subgenus the stem is usually monopodially branched, with erect branches arising from a prostrate (and often subterranean) main stem. The erect branches are usually several inches to a foot high and are often annual (living only one year). The prostrate branches are commonly perennial (living several or many years) and of indeterminate length, continuing to grow at the tip and dying off behind. Individuals of these species are potentially immortal. When the main stem is subterranean its leaves are generally more or less reduced and without chlorophyll.

The growing point of the stem contains a group of apical initial cells, forming the apical meristem. The mature part of the stem (Fig. 18.3) is differentiated into an epidermis, cortex, and central cylinder. Some species have a well-defined endodermis between the cortex and the central cylinder. Just within the endodermis, and external to the xylem and phloem, is a parenchymatous tissue called the **pericycle.** The pericycle is usually three to six cells thick, as seen in cross section. The cortex may be wholly parenchymatous, or part of it may be composed of thick-walled, more or less sclerenchymatous cells. The epidermis is one cell thick and has well-developed stomates.

Some species of *Lycopodium* have a characteristic protostele, with the xylem forming a solid core that is more or less star-shaped in cross section. The protoxylem lies at the points of the star and consists of tracheids with annular or spiral secondary walls. The metaxylem consists largely of tracheids with the secondary wall laid down in a regular network, forming a pattern of the type described in Chapter 23 as scalariform. As seen in cross section, the phloem forms patches between the arms or points of the xylem core and is separated from the xylem by a narrow band of parenchyma. The phloem consists of intermingled parenchyma cells and sieve elements. The sieve elements are

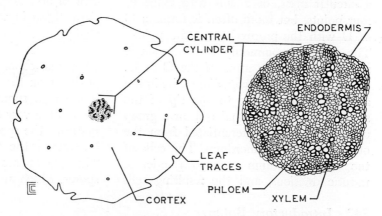

Fig. 18.3. *Lycopodium.* Left, cross section of stem. (×15.) Right, cross section of central cylinder of stem. (×60.)

CENTRAL CYLINDER

ENDODERMIS

LEAF TRACES

PHLOEM

CORTEX

XYLEM

tapered at the ends and have scattered sieve areas.

Other species of *Lycopodium* have a more complex stelar anatomy, which in cross section shows several isolated strands of xylem surrounded by or mingled with strands of phloem. This dissection of the stele bears no relation to the origin and position of the leaves, and the stele is not of the same type as the dissected steles of ferns and modern seed plants.

Roots of *Lycopodium* originate internally from the stem, most commonly from the pericycle, but sometimes from the endodermis. A group of pericycle cells becomes meristematic and functions as the apical meristem of a new root. The growing point of the root pushes its way out through the endodermis, cortex, and epidermis. After it has emerged from the stem, a root may remain simple or may be repeatedly branched; the branching is always dichotomous.

Many epidermal cells of *Lycopodium* roots have a long slender projection called a root hair. Root hairs absorb water and minerals; they may be regarded as a means of increasing the absorbing surface of the root.

The roots are differentiated into an epidermis, cortex, and central cylinder. As seen in cross section, the xylem may form a circular mass, or a star with three or four points, but more often it forms a C or U with the protoxylem at the points. The phloem commonly forms a single strand between the arms of the C or U.

The leaves of *Lycopodium* arise in the apical meristem, close to the tip of the stem. A young epidermal cell, or a group of cells, becomes differentiated from the others as a **leaf primordium.** The cells of the leaf primordium undergo a series of mitotic divisions, and the resulting cells

differentiate to form a new leaf. The leaves are narrow and seldom over an inch long. They are commonly broadest near the base, and are **sessile** (attached directly to the stem, without a stalk). Usually the leaves are alternate, but in some species they are opposite, or even whorled. When the leaves are opposite, the two leaves of a pair are often displaced so as to be on the same side of the stem.

The leaf has a single unbranched midvein which is continuous with the leaf trace that passes through the cortex and connects to the central cylinder. Near the base of the leaf the vein contains both xylem and phloem, the phloem beneath, but often the phloem does not extend to the leaf tip. The vein may or may not be surrounded by an endodermis. The tissue between the vein and the epidermis is **chlorenchyma** (parenchyma with chloroplasts), with or without evident intercellular spaces. The epidermis is cutinized and has stomates on one or both surfaces. Chloroplasts are usually present in the ordinary epidermal cells as well as in the guard cells of the stomates.

The sporophylls (Fig. 18.2) of some species of *Lycopodium* resemble ordinary vegetative leaves. In other species the sporophylls are shorter and relatively broader than the vegetative leaves, with little or no chlorophyll. Most species, especially those in which the sporophylls are obviously different from the vegetative leaves, have the sporophylls grouped into a terminal cone. In the axil of each sporophyll, or on the upper side near the base, is a single sporangium on a slender, or more often very short and broad, stalk. At maturity the sporangium dehisces along a line across the top, releasing the spores. The plants are homosporous, and the spores, which are distributed by the wind, are all essentially alike in form and size.

The spore germinates after a resting period of several days to several years, depending on the species. Young gametophytes have a single meristematic apical cell, but later there is an apical meristem of several cells. The mature gametophyte (Fig. 18.4) is small and inconspicuous, varying in size and shape according to the species. In some species it is about the size of a pinhead and lies on the surface of the ground. This type of gametophyte is green and photosynthetic and generally matures in a few months. In other species the gametophyte is partly or wholly subterranean, simple (often parsnip-shaped) or variously branched, and up to about an inch long, with several differentiated tissues but no xylem or phloem. The aerial part, if any, is generally green and photosynthetic, and the subterranean part commonly harbors a phycomycetous mycorhizal fungus from which some food is obtained. Gametophytes which are wholly subterranean are wholly dependent on the fungus for nourishment and sometimes take as long as 10 years to mature.

Antheridia and archegonia of *Lycopodium* are borne on the same gametophyte, near the apical meristem. The first division of the antheridial initial gives rise to an outer cell, the jacket initial, and an inner cell, the primary androgonial cell. The jacket of the mature antheridium is derived from the jacket initial, and the sperms are derived from the primary androgonial cell. The antheridium is commonly ellipsoid and embedded in the gametophyte, barely reaching the surface at one end. The jacket is only one cell thick, and a single cell at the surface end is an opercular cell which degenerates to form an opening through which the sperms escape. The sperms have two more or less equal whiplash flagella at one end.

Development of the archegonium (Fig. 18.5) follows the standard pattern for the division. The fertilized egg, or zygote, has $2n$ chromosomes and is the first cell of the sporophyte generation. The first division of the zygote is at right angles to the axis of the archegonium. The outer of the two cells formed in the first division enlarges and may undergo one or two subsequent divisions, forming a one- to three-celled **suspensor** which pushes the inner cell, called the embryonic cell, deeper into the tissue of the gametophyte. By a series of further mitotic divisions, the embryonic cell gives rise to the embryo and thus eventually to the whole mature sporophyte.

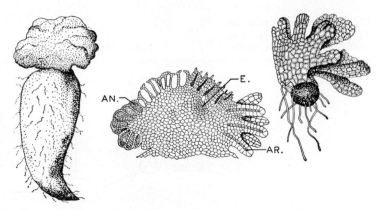

Fig. 18.4. *Lycopodium* gametophytes. Left, *L. complanatum.* (×12.) (After Bruchmann.) Center, long section of aerial part of *L. complanatum,* showing antheridia (an.), archegonia (ar.), and an embryo sporophyte (e.). (×20.) (After Bruchmann.) Right, *L. cernuum.* (×35.) (After Traub.)

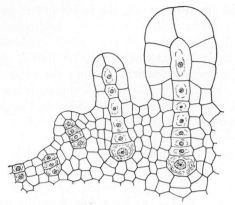

Fig. 18.5. **Development of the archegonium of** *Lycopodium selago.* (After Bruchmann.)

The embryo regularly has a well-developed foot which absorbs food from the gametophyte, but the structure and development of the remainder of the embryo vary according to the species. Often there is an early differentiation of a primary root, a primary stem, and a primary leaf, all joined at the foot. The primary leaf is

often called the **cotyledon.** After the enlarging embryo breaks through the surrounding tissue of the gametophyte, the root grows downward into the soil and the cotyledon and stem grow upward into the air. Later on new roots originate from internal tissues of the stem, and the primary root disintegrates.

Fossils

Fossils essentially similar to *Lycopodium* are referred to the genus *Lycopodites.* *Lycopodites* is known from deposits extending from the Upper Devonian period to the present. One of the oldest known fossils of vascular plants—older than those of the Rhynie beds—is *Baragwanathia,* from Middle Silurian strata of Australia. *Baragwanathia* resembles some modern species of *Lycopodium* that do not have a differentiated strobilus, differing in being a little larger (the stem com-

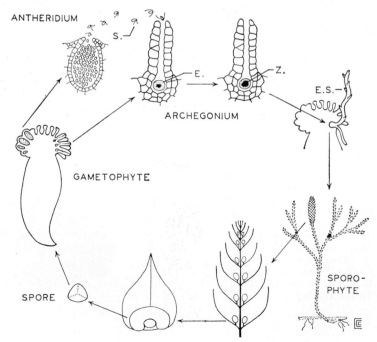

Fig. 18.6. **Life cycle of** *Lycopodium:* **e., egg; e.s., embryo sporophyte; s., sperm; z., zygote.**

monly 1–2 cm—sometimes 6.5 cm—thick),
and particularly in that all tracheids have
merely annular thickenings. There are a
number of other Paleozoic fossils more or
less similar to *Lycopodium*, including some
which may be transitional toward the
Lepidodendrales.

SELAGINELLALES

Selaginella

The only modern genus of the Selaginellales is *Selaginella*, with about 500
species. Species of *Selaginella* (Fig. 18.7)
are mostly rather similar to *Lycopodium*
in appearance, though often smaller, and
both genera are called club mosses. The
genus is cosmopolitan, but most of its
species occur in moist tropical regions.
Branching of the stem, as in *Lycopodium*,
may be dichotomous or sympodial to
monopodial. Often there is an indefinitely
elongated underground stem, the rhizome,
from which more or less erect lateral
branches arise. The growing point sometimes has an apical meristem, as in *Lycopodium*, but more often there is a single
well-defined apical cell. The epidermis of
the stem is one cell thick and lacks
stomates. As in *Lycopodium*, the central
cylinder may be a simple protostele or may
be variously modified, but it does not resemble the steles of more advanced groups
of vascular plants. Often the stele is dissected into several separate strands, each
with its own xylem, phloem, pericycle,
and endodermis.

The phloem of *Selaginella* is similar
to that of *Lycopodium*. The xylem of
some species of *Selaginella* resembles that
of *Lycopodium*, but in other species some
of the tracheids are modified to form more

efficient conducting structures, called
vessels. A vessel of *Selaginella* consists of
a series of more or less cylindrical tracheid-
like elements placed end to end, with the
end walls perforated. Vessels are found in
several other groups of vascular plants,
notably the Anthophyta, and are further
discussed in Chapter 23.

The endodermis of the stem is usually highly modified and is recognizable as
such only by its position and by the
characteristic Casparian strips on the radial
walls of the cells. The cells of the endodermis are much elongated in the direction of the radial axis of the stem and are
separated by very large intercellular spaces.
As a result the stele appears to be suspended in a very large central cavity, being
connected to the cortex only by the ribbon-like individual endodermal cells.
These highly modified endodermal cells
of *Selaginella* are called **trabeculae**.

Most species of *Selaginella* have
characteristic slender, leafless branches
from which the roots originate. These
branches, called **rhizophores**, develop from
superficial tissues in the angle of a dichotomy of the stem. They are root-like in
that they lack leaves and are positively
geotropic, but they are stem-like in that
they originate externally and lack a rootcap. The organization of the central cylinder resembles that of roots but is also
similar to that in the less modified types
of central cylinder found in stems of other
plants. There has been much argument
as to whether rhizophores are roots, stems,
or organs *sui generis* (of their own kind).
Such controversy misses the fact that the
fundamental and convenient classification
of plant organs as roots, stems, and leaves
cannot be expected to work perfectly
among the more primitive kinds of vascular plants, in which the differences among

Lepidophyta: Club Mosses and Quillworts 345

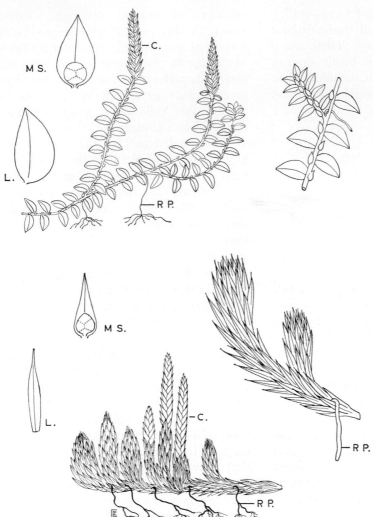

Fig. 18.7. *Selaginella,* two species; habit (×2); branches (×4); sporophylls and vegetative leaves (×10, above and ×6 below); c., cone; l., leaf; ms., megasporophyll; rp., rhizophore.

these organs have not become wholly stabilized.

The rhizophores are simple or occasionally branched, and the branching is dichotomous. The roots originate from internal tissues of the rhizophores, usually near the tip. Like other roots, the roots of *Selaginella* have a rootcap. A cross section of the small stele generally shows a single mass of xylem alongside a single mass of phloem. The roots are sparingly branched, and the branching is dichotomous.

The leaves of *Selaginella* are microphylls much like those of *Lycopodium*, differing in the presence of a small membranous outgrowth, the ligule, on the upper (adaxial) side near the base. The chlorenchyma cells of the leaf contain each a single, large, cup-shaped chloroplast or several smaller chloroplasts. Each

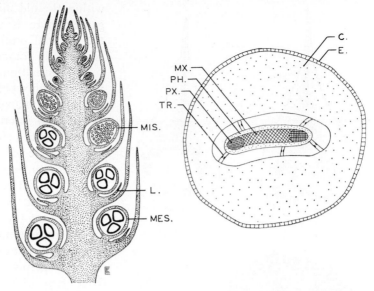

Fig. 18.8. *Selaginella*. Left, long section of cone (×15); right, cross section of stem (diagrammatic) (×30); c., cortex; e., epidermis; 1., ligule; mes., megasporangium; mis., microsporangium; mx., metaxylem; ph., phloem; px., protoxylem; tr., trabecula.

chloroplast contains several pyrenoids which are associated with the formation of starch grains. *Selaginella*, *Isoetes*, and the Anthocerotae are the only embryophytes with pyrenoids.

The more primitive species of *Selaginella* have spirally arranged, alternate leaves, as do many species of *Lycopodium*. More often the stem has basically opposite leaves, which are displaced so as to form four rows, two rows on the upper surface and one row along each margin. The leaves of the marginal rows are distinctly larger than those of the upper rows.

The sporophylls of *Selaginella* are much like the vegetative leaves and are always borne in terminal cones. The axis of the cone may continue to elongate, however, producing ordinary vegetative leaves in the region beyond the strobilus. The sporophylls are often arranged in four distinct vertical rows, forming a four-sided strobilus. Each sporophyll bears a single sporangium on the adaxial surface near the base, or the sporangium may be in the axil of the sporophyll.

The sporangia (Fig. 18.9) are of two types. The megasporangium contains one to four relatively large, thick-walled megaspores. The wall of the megasporangium often encloses the megaspores so closely that their outline governs the shape of the sporangium. The microsporangium contains many microspores, which are much smaller and thinner-walled than the megaspores. The megasporophylls and microsporophylls are similar in appearance and are usually borne in the same strobilus, the microsporophylls commonly above the megasporophylls.

The megasporangia and microsporangia are basically similar in structure. The jacket layer and the sporogenous tissue are differentiated early in the development of the sporangium. The jacket is two cells thick at maturity. The tapetum is a single layer of cells just within the jacket. At maturity the sporangia open in an apical slit, more or less as in *Lycopodium*, but the dehiscence is more violent and tends to expel the spores forcibly.

The microsporangium contains a large

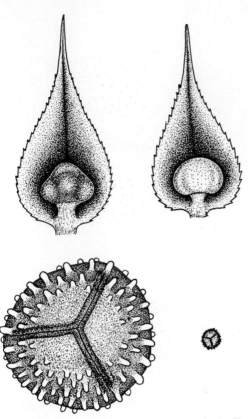

Fig. 18.9. **Sporangia and spores of *Selaginella*.**
Upper left, megasporophyll with megasporangium
containing four megaspores (×20); upper right,
microsporophyll with microsporangium (×20);
lower left, megaspore (×100); lower right, microspore (×100). (From W. H. Brown, *The Plant
Kingdom*, 1935; courtesy of Ginn & Company,
Boston.)

number of potential microspore mother
cells. Some of these degenerate just before
maturity, but most of them undergo reduction division, each producing a tetrad of
microspores. The microspores have *n*
chromosomes and represent the first step
in the male gametophyte generation. Development and maturation of the male
gametophyte results from a number of
mitotic cell divisions without any increase
in size, and the mature male gametophyte
(Fig. 18.10) is largely or wholly contained

within the old microspore wall. The male
gametophyte is not photosynthetic, and
the original protoplast of the microspore
is the only source of nourishment.

Germination of the microspores commonly begins before they are shed from
the microsporangium and continues with
little or no interruption after they are released. Just before maturity the male
gametophyte consists of a multicellular
antheridium and a single additional cell,
the **prothallial cell**. The prothallial cell is
considered to be a vestige of the vegetative body of the gametophyte. The jacket
of the antheridium is one cell thick; often
it consists of exactly eight cells. The numerous sperms in the antheridium each
have two whiplash flagella at one end.
As the gametophyte nears maturity, the
spore wall ruptures, exposing one end of
the antheridium. The jacket cells soften
and degenerate when moistened, or concurrently with spermatogenesis, allowing
the sperms to escape.

The megasporangium of *Selaginella*
contains a considerable number of potential megaspore mother cells. Usually all
but one of these degenerate. The remaining megaspore mother cell undergoes reduction division, generally producing a
tetrad of megaspores. Sometimes one or

Fig. 18.10. **Male gametophyte of *Selaginella
kraussiana*. (×1400.) (After Stagg.)**

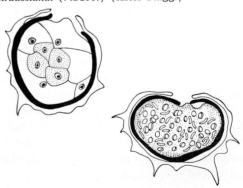

348   *Introductory Botany*

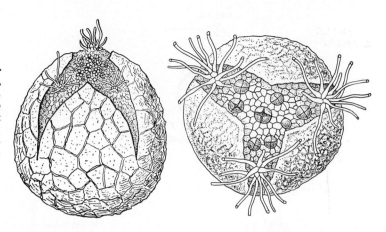

Fig. 18.11. Female gametophytes of *Selaginella*. Left, side view of *S. kraussiana*. (× about 50.) Right, top view of *S. martensii*. (× about 125.) (After Bruchmann.) Note the archegonia, distinguishable by the four neck cells.

more of the megaspores does not develop to maturity, so that the megasporangium has less than four megaspores. The megaspores have *n* chromosomes and represent the first step in the female gametophyte generation.

The megasporangium opens and the megaspores usually fall out, but sometimes they remain loose in the sporangium throughout the development of the female gametophyte. Development and maturation of the female gametophyte result from a number of mitotic cell divisions without much increase in size. The protoplast becomes multinucleate, and partitions are then formed, beginning at the top. The megaspore wall eventually ruptures at one end, and the top of the mature gametophyte (Fig. 18.11) protrudes. The exposed part of the gametophyte often becomes green and may develop rhizoids, but the amount of food made is relatively small. The main source of nourishment of the female gametophyte is the original protoplast of the magaspore, including its stored food.

The female gametophyte generally produces several archegonia, but fertilization of the egg in one of these seems to inhibit further development from other archegonia. As in *Lycopodium*, the zygote gives rise to a suspensor and an embryo. The embryo has a primary root and a short stem with two opposite leaves (the cotyledons) near the tip. At the tip of the stem, between the cotyledons, is the apical cell or an apical meristem. Usually there is a foot forming a bulge about at the point where the base of the stem meets the top of the root. Except for the foot, the embryo bears a striking resemblance to the embryo of a dicotyledonous flowering plant, but the similarity is probably due to parallel evolution instead of close relationship.

FOSSILS

Heterosporous fossils resembling *Selaginella* are referred to the genus *Selaginellites*. *Selaginellites* is known from deposits as far back as the Upper Carboniferous period. Some species have 4 megaspores in a sporangium, as in *Selaginella*; others have from 16 to 24 megaspores.

One of the most interesting fossils belonging to the Selaginellales is *Miadesmia*, (Fig. 18.13) from Carboniferous deposits. *Miadesmia* is vegetatively rather similar to *Selaginella* but differs in having the

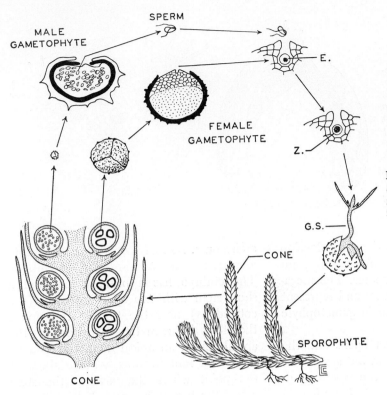

SPERM

MALE GAMETOPHYTE

E.

Z.

FEMALE GAMETOPHYTE

G.S.

CONE

CONE

SPOROPHYTE

CONE

Fig. 18.12. Life cycle of *Selaginella*: e., egg.; g.s., germinating sporophyte; z., zygote.

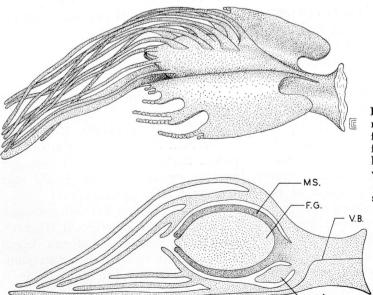

MS.

F.G.

V.B.

L.

Fig. 18.13. *Miadesmia* sporophyll with seed; above, surface view; below, in section; f.g., female gametophyte; l., ligule; ms., megasporangium wall; v.b., vascular bundle. (×25.) (Redrawn from Benson.)

megaspore retained within the megasporangium. The mature female gametophyte is closely enveloped by the megasporangium, only the tip being exposed by a small opening that develops in the megasporangium wall. The megasporangium itself is loosely enveloped, except for an apical opening, by an outgrowth from the surface of the megasporophyll. The whole megasporangium with its included female gametophyte is shed intact from the megasporophyll. At this stage the megasporangium of *Miadesmia* is comparable in some respects to the seed of modern seed plants. In modern seed plants, however, the female gametophyte is *completely* enclosed within the megasporangium, and the sperms are usually delivered to the egg through a special outgrowth (the pollen tube) of the male gametophyte which grows through the megasporangial wall. In fossil "seed plants" belonging to the Lepidophyta, the sperms evidently reached the egg in the normal pteridophyte fashion —by swimming through a film of water— and no structure comparable to a pollen tube was necessary. Some botanists, therefore, object to the usual botanical practice of calling these megasporangia seeds.

LEPIDODENDRALES

The Lepidodendrales are a group of fossil lepidophytes known from the Upper Devonian to the Permian period. They are similar to *Selaginella* in being heterosporous and in having ligulate leaves, but they differ in being much larger, commonly of tree size. In the Selaginellales and Lycopodiales, the tissues of the mature sporophyte are derived directly by maturation of cells produced from the apical meristem or apical cell. New apical meristems may arise adventitiously from internal tissues of the stem, commonly giving rise to roots, but it is still true that, with minor exceptions, all meristematic cells are associated with apical meristems. The Lepidodendrales commonly have, in addition to the normal apical meristems, a layer of persistent meristematic tissue between the xylem and the phloem of the stems and roots. This **lateral** (as opposed to apical) **meristem** is called a **vascular cambium.** In plants with vascular cambium, the cambium typically forms a complete ring as viewed in cross section of the stem or root, but in the Lepidodendrales the ring is often incomplete. Cambium produces new xylem on the inner side of the ring and new phloem on the outer side. Normally a cambium layer is only one cell thick. When a cambium cell divides, one of the two daughter cells remains a cambial cell, while the other usually matures into either a xylem cell or a phloem cell, depending on its position. Tissues derived from cambium are called **secondary tissues,** in contrast to **primary tissues,** which are derived directly from the apical meristem. Growth resulting from cambial activity is called **secondary growth.** The structure and function of cambium are further discussed in Chapter 23.

In addition to the vascular cambium, the Lepidodendrales commonly have another lateral meristem in the cortex. The **cork cambium,** or **phellogen,** as this meristem is called, produces cork cells on its outer surface and relatively unspecialized cells on its inner surface. The structure and function of phellogen are further discussed in Chapters 23 and 24. When the term *cambium* is used without qualification, it usually refers to the vascular cambium rather than to the phellogen.

The leaves of the Lepidodendrales are long and narrow, sometimes more than 6 inches long, and usually with a single unbranched midvein. Anatomically they are microphylls, as contrasted to the megaphylls of true ferns, which are described in Chapter 20. The leaves of the Lepidodendrales were deciduous, i.e., they fell away from the stem some time after reaching maturity. The older parts of stems are commonly covered with characteristic scars marking the positions of former leaves.

The rhizophore system of the Lepidodendrales is unique. The stem, which is

Fig. 18.14. *Lepidodendron,* as reconstructed by Dawson.

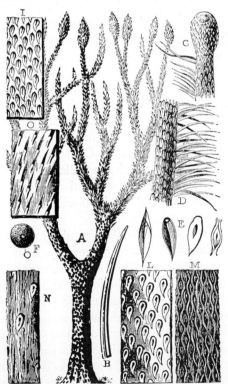

FIG. 43.—*Lepidodendron corrugatum,* Dawson, a tree characteristic of the Lower Carboniferous. A, Restoration. B, Leaf, natural size. c, Cone and branch. D, Branch and leaves. E, Various forms of leaf-areoles. F, *Sporangium.* I, L, M, Bark, with leaf-scars. N, Bark, with leaf-scars of old stem. o, Decorticated stem (*Knorria*).

unbranched for some distance above the ground, breaks up at the base into four large branches which undergo repeated dichotomies as they spread outward. The true roots originate endogenously (i.e., from internal tissues) from these branches. The roots are slender and commonly less than a foot long. They generally have a relatively large central cavity; a small excentrically placed stele lies next to the cortex adjoining one side of the cavity. In this feature the roots of the Lepidodendrales resemble those of the modern genus *Isoetes.* The branches from which the roots of the Lepidodendrales originate are anatomically much like the stems, and, like the stems, they have well-developed secondary growth. These branches are usually called rhizophores, and they have been compared to the more slender rhizophores of *Selaginella.*

One of the commonest genera of the Lepidodendrales is *Lepidodendron* (Fig. 18.14). Large specimens reached a height of well over 100 feet. The straight, tall trunk is dichotomously branched above to form a broad rounded crown. The leaves are narrow, commonly several inches long, and arranged in a close spiral. The older parts of the trunk are covered with closely set, spirally arranged scars marking the position of leaves which have fallen.

Lepidodendron does not have seeds, and the female gametophytes of at least some species are rather similar to those of *Selaginella.* Some members of the Lepidodendrales have seeds of the type described in *Miadesmia.* These have not been found organically attached to the sporophytes, but seeds of the type known as *Lepidocarpon* possibly belong with sporophytes of the type known as *Lepidophlois. Lepidophlois* is vegetatively much like *Lepidodendron,* the most ob-

Fig. 18.15. *Lepidodendron* stumps on Stigmarian bases; sandstone casts at Victoria Park, Glasgow. (Crown copyright reserved. Geological Survey photograph reproduced by permission of the Controller H. M. Stationery Office.)

vious differences lying in the shape of the leaf scars.

Another common genus of the Lepidodendrales is *Sigillaria*. The leaf scars of *Sigillaria* are arranged in vertical rows, and the rows are often separated by longitudinal ridges on the stem. The trunk of *Sigillaria* is commonly unbranched and sometimes several feet thick. The leaves are long and grass-like and are borne in a large cluster at the top of the trunk. These leaves are sometimes more than 3 feet long, and some of them have two parallel veins instead of the usual single midvein found in other lepidophytes.

The rhizophore system of *Sigillaria* is apparently indistinguishable from that of *Lepidodendron* and a number of other genera of the Lepidodendrales. When they are found alone, without the remainder of the sporophyte, these rhizophore systems are given the generic name *Stigmaria*. *Stigmaria* (Fig. 18.15) is a good example of what, in paleobotany, is called a **form genus**. A single name is necessarily used to cover fossil structures of a particular

type, although it is realized that these are merely detached parts belonging to several genera which differ in other respects.

ISOETALES

ISOETES

Isoetes (Fig. 18.16), the **quillwort,** is the only modern genus of the Isoetales. There are about 80 species, some 20 of which occur in the United States. They grow in permanent or ephemeral ponds and lakes, slow streams, and swampy places, where they are submerged for part or all of the year.

The sporophyte has a short, thickened base called the **stock.** The stock is as broad as or broader than high, commonly 1–2 cm broad, and bears both the leaves and the roots. The leaves are slender, commonly 5–50 cm long, and clustered in a close spiral on the upper part of the stock. The sporophylls are similar to the other leaves.

Lepidophyta: Club Mosses and Quillworts 353

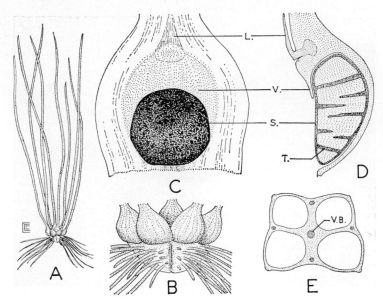

Fig. 18.16. *Isoetes. A,* habit (×⅜); *B,* rhizophore, with roots and leaf bases (×3); *C,* sporophyll, inner surface view at base (×10); *D,* sporophyll, side view in long section at base (×10); *E,* cross section of leaf (×20); l., ligule; s., sporangium; t., trabecula; v., velum; v.b., vascular bundle.

The roots arise endogenously from the lower part of the stock.

The stock usually has two or three rather deep vertical furrows that make it two- or three-lobed. Otherwise it is externally rather simple, but internally it is quite complex. There is a meristematic region in a small depression at the top of the stock, but vertical growth proceeds only very slowly. There is a thick, parenchymatous cortex and a small stele that commonly has a central core of xylem consisting of tracheids intermingled with parenchyma. The upper part of the stele is more or less cylindric, and the xylem is surrounded by a thin sheath of phloem. The lower part of the stele is flattened and spade-shaped in two-lobed stocks, with the two edges aligned with the furrows. In three-lobed stocks, the lower part of the stele is three-lobed in cross section, and the phloem lies in three strands alternating with the lobes or arms of the xylem. One of the three xylem lobes is broader than the others and probably consists of two

fused lobes. It is thought that the ancestors of *Isoetes* had a four-lobed stock with four radiating arms of xylem in the lower part. The three arms of xylem in the lower part of the stock are directed toward the three external furrows rather than toward the lobes. There is a persistent meristematic region at the outer edge of each of the lobes of the stele, internal to the furrows of the stock.

The leaves of *Isoetes* originate from the apical meristem at the top of the stock, and the leaf traces connect to the cylindrical upper part of the stele. The roots originate from the lower part of the stock, just internal to the furrows, and their vascular supply connects to the radiating arms of the stele.

The proper morphological interpretation of the stock has been much disputed. The most generally accepted view is that the upper part is a true stem and the lower part a highly modified rhizophore more or less comparable to the rhizophores of the Lepidodendrales.

The central cylinder of *Isoetes* is not delimited by an endodermis, but it is surrounded by a peculiar sort of cambium *external* to the phloem. On the inner side this cambium produces a small amount of poorly differentiated secondary vascular tissue which in some species has been reported to contain both tracheids and sieve elements. On the outer side the cambium produces parenchyma. The outer tissues of the cortex are pushed farther and farther to the outside as the cambium continues to produce new tissues from within. In at least some species the outer tissues die and degenerate concurrently with the formation of new parenchyma by the cambium, so that the cortex eventually comes to consist wholly of secondary tissue derived from the cambium.

The roots of *Isoetes* are slender and commonly less than an inch long, either unbranched or with occasional dichotomies. They arise internally from the meristematic region at the lobes of the stele in the rhizophore part of the stock and break their way to the surface in the furrows. Continued growth of the internal tissues of the rhizophore pushes the roots farther and farther out from the center of the furrow, and new roots continue to appear in the furrow. Growth of the roots is due to an apical meristem which is protected by a rootcap.

The root has a small stele and an irregular cortex. The stele is placed well to one side of the center of the root, and the central cortical cells soon degenerate, leaving a large cavity near one side of the stele. The stele contains a single strand of xylem alongside a single strand of phloem and is surrounded by a well-defined endodermis.

The leaves of *Isoetes* are elongate, slender, and more or less cylindrical, with a flattened broader base. There is a small ligule on the inner side about at the top of the flattened part. A single vascular bundle runs the length of the leaf, which is anatomically a microphyll. The cylindrical part of the leaf contains four large, longitudinal air cavities spaced around the vascular bundle, so that in cross section the leaf tissue forms a circle enclosing a cross. The air cavities are interrupted by frequent transverse partitions. Often the peripheral tissue of the leaf contains four longitudinal strands of sclerenchyma, one adjoining each of the four thin partitions between the air cavities. The leaf has a well-defined epidermis, and, when it develops in the air rather than in the water, it contains definite stomates.

The leaves of *Isoetes* are usually annual, a new crop being produced each year. The outermost leaves often do not bear sporangia. The next inner leaves generally bear megasporangia, the next inner ones microsporangia, and the innermost ones bear rudiments of sporangia. The megasporangia and microsporangia are very much alike except for the kind and number of spores they contain, being more or less ellipsoid and commonly about ¼ inch long. The sporangium is more or less embedded in the flattened basal part of the leaf, on the inner side, and is usually partly, or even wholly, covered by a flap of leaf tissue called the **velum.** The interior of the sporangium is incompletely and irregularly divided by a series of transverse or slanting plates or bars called **trabeculae.** *Trabecula* is merely a Latin word meaning little beam, and the trabeculae of an *Isoetes* sporangium have nothing to do with the trabeculae of a *Selaginella* stem.

The sporangia of *Isoetes* are of the usual eusporangiate type, and the trabeculae represent modified potentially sporogenous tissue. A tapetum, one or two cells thick, is formed from the outer cells of the sporogenous tissue. The microspores are very small and numerous, and as many as a million of them may be borne in a single microsporangium. The megaspores are larger, up to about 1 mm thick, and 50 to 300 of them are borne in a megasporangium. As in other embryophytes, the spores are the immediate products of reduction division and are the first step in the gametophyte generation. The sporangia are indehiscent, and the spores are liberated only by the decay of the sporangial wall.

The spores may germinate as soon as they are released, or they may remain dormant for months. The male gametophyte takes about 2 weeks to mature and completes its development while still enclosed within the microspore wall. It (the male gametophyte) consists of an antheridium plus a single prothallial cell. The prothallial cell is considered to be an evolutionary vestige of the vegetative body of the gametophyte. Just before maturity, the antheridium consists of four jacket cells which collectively enclose the four central cells. Each of these central cells matures into an elongate, naked sperm with numerous, long, whiplash flagella. The jacket cells and the prothallial cell die and disintegrate as the sperms are maturing, and the microspore wall ruptures irregularly, releasing the sperms.

The female gametophyte of *Isoetes* generally takes 3–4 weeks to mature. Like the female gametophyte of *Selaginella*, it is multicellular and is largely enclosed within the megaspore wall, which cracks open at one end. Usually some rhizoids protrude from the opening, but there is no photosynthetic tissue, and throughout its development the female gametophyte is dependent on the food originally stored in the megaspore. Several archegonia are

formed at the exposed end of the gametophyte, developing in the same way as in other lepidophytes. Fertilization takes place in the usual way for the division.

The embryo of *Isoetes* differs from that of *Lycopodium* and *Selaginella* in lacking a suspensor. After a series of mitotic divisions, the embryo becomes a three-lobed structure, the three lobes representing the foot, the primary root, and the cotyledon (primary leaf). The root and the cotyledon break through the tissue of the gametophyte and grow in opposite directions, the root downward, the leaf upward. The region where the root joins the cotyledon, opposite the foot, eventually develops into the stock of the mature sporophyte, giving rise to new leaves and roots. By the time the sporophyte has become established as an independent plant, the cells of the female gametophyte have mostly disintegrated and the food from them has been absorbed by the foot.

FOSSILS

Fossils resembling *Isoetes* are known from the Lower Cretaceous period to the present and are referred to the genus *Isoetites*. A well-known Triassic fossil, *Pleuromeia* (Fig. 18.17), is more or less intermediate between the Isoetales and the Lepidodendrales and has been referred by different authors to each of these orders. *Pleuromeia* has numerous slender vegetative leaves on a stout, unbranched, erect stem up to about 2 m tall. The leaves are several inches long, in the same size range as many modern species of *Isoetes*. The sporophylls are very short and broad and are borne in a terminal strobilus.

The rhizophore of *Pleuromeia* is of particular interest because it suggests how the rhizophore of *Isoetes* may have been derived from that of the Lepidodendrales. The rhizophore of *Pleuromeia* is a massive, laterally four-lobed structure on which the stem is seated and from which numerous roots originate. Each of these four lobes presumably represents one of the four branches of the stigmarian system of the Lepidodendrales. If two of these lobes were partly fused into one, the rhizophore would have about the same shape as the primary vascular system of the *Isoetes* rhizophore. The lobes of the *Isoetes* rhizophore result from overgrowth of tissues between the meristems which lie at the tip and lower edge of each xylem arm, so that the meristems come to lie under the hollows rather than under the lobes of the rhizophore. The lobes of the *Pleuromeia* rhizophore, therefore, probably correspond to the sinuses between the lobes of the *Isoetes* rhizophore, but the point of the comparison is that it is possible to see how the rhizophore of *Isoetes* could be derived from that of *Pleuromeia*. The shortening of the stem, so that the stem and rhizophore form a single structure, as in *Isoetes*, would be an easy final step. It is not contended that *Pleuromeia* is directly ancestral to *Isoetes*, however, especially because of the difference in the sporophylls.

ECONOMIC IMPORTANCE

The modern lepidophytes are of very minor economic importance. They furnish a little forage for wild animals. Some species of *Lycopodium* are used in Christmas decorations, and a few species of both *Lycopodium* and *Selaginella* are occasionally grown for ornament. *Selaginella lepidophylla* (Fig. 18.18), a species of dry regions from Mexico to Peru, is often sold under the name of resurrection plant. In

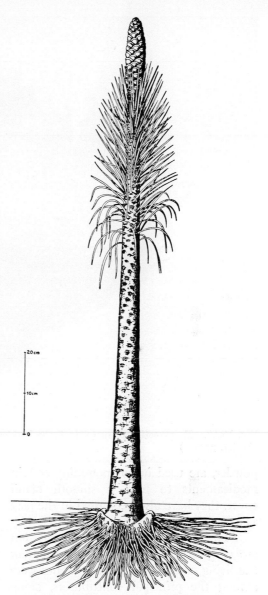

Fig. 18.17. *Pleuromeia*, as reconstructed by Hirmer.

very dry weather the plant is dormant and forms a tight gray-brown ball, but when the supply of moisture is restored, it unrolls to form an attractive green plant. The spores of *Lycopodium*, sold as lycopodium

Fig. 18.18.   Resurrection plant (*Selaginella lepidophylla*). (About natural size.) (New York Botanical Garden photo.)

powder, are used in compounding certain medicaments to form a smooth bland cover; they have also been used in the past as a flash powder.

The extinct members of the division are of greater economic importance than the living ones. The Lepidodendrales were among the principal contributors, along with the Calamophyta, to the vegetable deposits of the Carboniferous period which became transformed into coal. Cannel coal, which burns with a bright and nearly smokeless flame, is derived largely from the spores of Lepidodendrales and Calamophyta.

RELATIONSHIPS

The lepidophytes are evidently derived from the psilophytes, from which they differ in having true roots, in regularly having a distinct midvein in the leaf, and in the consistently axillary or foliar position of the sporangia. The sporangia of some psilophytes might be interpreted as axillary, but more often in that group they are distinctly terminal. The presence of roots in the lepidophytes is doubtless an evolutionary advance over the rootless condition of the psilophytes, as is also the position of the sporangia. Probably the sporangia became axillary by shortening the sporangium-bearing branch, and the placement of the sporangium on the adaxial surface of the leaf is a further modification. Whether the vascularization of lepidophyte leaves is an advance over the mostly nonvascularized leaves of the psilophytes is an open question (discussed in Chapter 20), but, in any case, the leafless kinds of Psilophytes, such as *Rhynia*, must have preceded any psilophytes or lepidophytes with leaves.

The modern species of *Lycopodium* which lack a well-defined strobilus are apparently not far removed from the ancestral prototype of the Lepidophyta. The leafy shoots of *Baragwanathia*, one of the oldest known fossils of vascular plants, closely resemble the leafy shoots of this group of *Lycopodium*, although there are some minor anatomical differences.

The Lycopodiales, Selaginellales, and Lepidodendrales are all obviously related. The Lycopodiales, which are homosporous and have eligulate leaves, are the least removed from the ancestral psilophytes and are obviously the most primitive of the three orders. The Selaginellales, which are heterosporous and have ligulate leaves, seem to be derived from early Lycopodiales. The Lepidodendrales are a further development from presumed early Selaginellales, from which they differ in their larger size and usually well-developed secondary growth. Fossils which recognizably represent the Selaginellales do not extend as far back in geological time as the Lepidodendrales, but this may merely reflect the incompleteness of the known fossil record.

The Isoetales are rather isolated from the other three orders of the division, although their ligulate leaves and heterospory link them to the Selaginellales and Lepidodendrales. The possible derivation of the Isoetales from the Lepidodendrales has been discussed on pp. 356–357.

SUGGESTED READING

Bower, F. O., *Primitive Land Plants*. London, 1935, 727 pp. Textbook style.

Division Calamophyta

HORSETAILS AND
SCOURING RUSHES

Vascular plants with roots, stems, and leaves; gametophyte and sporophyte physiologically independent of each other at maturity, but the gametophyte small and inconspicuous; stems jointed and longitudinally striate; leaves whorled, those of modern species microphylls; sporangia borne on more or less strongly modified sporangiophores which are arranged in whorls in a terminal strobilus. A single class, the Equisetae.

Young fertile shoots of the common horsetail, *Equisetum arvense.* (×2.) **(Photo by Hugh Spencer, from National Audubon Society.)**

HISTORY AND CHARACTERISTICS

The Calamophyta were first formally recognized as a distinct division by Bessey in 1907. The events leading up to this classification are discussed in Chapter 20.

The sporophyte is the conspicuous generation of the Calamophyta, the gametophyte being a small thallus seldom over 1 cm wide. Both generations are photosynthetic and physiologically independent at maturity. Many Calamophytes of Carboniferous time were trees, but all the modern species are smaller plants, seldom much over 1 m tall and without secondary thickening.

All modern calamophytes belong to the single genus *Equisetum*. The fossil forms referred to the Calamophyta include some plants rather similar to *Equisetum*, some others which appear to be transitional to the psilophytes, and some which represent a line of development quite different from *Equisetum*. All these forms have whorled leaves, and nearly all have distinctly jointed stems that are longitudinally striate. The sporangia are borne on **sporangiophores** that are arranged in whorls on a terminal strobilus. The possible homology of the sporangiophores with leaves is not very evident in most members of the group (including all the modern species), and the term *sporophyll* is therefore avoided.

CLASSIFICATION

It has been customary to refer all calamophytes to a single class, here called the Equisetae; the name Sphenopsida has also been used. Two of the orders, the Equisetales and Calamitales, are obviously related to each other and surely belong to one and the same class. Two other orders, the Hyeniales and Sphenophyllales, are so different from the Equisetales and from each other that they would probably be treated as distinct classes if they were represented by modern species.

All living calamophytes belong to the order Equisetales. Most of the fossils can be referred to this or one of three other orders, the Hyeniales, Sphenophyllales, and Calamitales, as indicated in the appendix.

EQUISETALES

EQUISETUM

There are about 20 species of *Equisetum* (Fig. 19.1), widely distributed throughout most of the world, except Australia. Most of them occur in wet places, or in shallow water from which the stems emerge, but some grow in ordinary well-drained soil. The epidermal cells of the stem contain appreciable amounts of silica,

and the species with relatively firm stems were used in pioneer communities for scouring pots and pans, whence the name **scouring rush.** The common name **horsetail** is also often used, especially for the species with branching stems. As we have noted, all modern members of the Equisetales belong to the genus *Equisetum*.

THE SHOOT

The stem of *Equisetum* is green and photosynthetic, less than an inch thick, and seldom much over 1 m tall. It is conspicuously jointed, with a whorl of small narrow leaves at each joint. The basal part of each internode is meristematic, and increase in length is brought about by the activity of these intercalary meristems as well as by the apical cell at the stem tip. The meristematic tissue consists of soft, thin-walled cells, and the stems can readily be pulled apart at the nodes. The stem is longitudinally ribbed and grooved, with the ribs and grooves tending to alternate in successive internodes. Each leaf is directly aligned with a rib of the internode beneath it. When the number of ribs in successive internodes is the same, as is usually the case, each leaf also lies over a groove in the internode above it.

The leaves are usually less than an inch long, and the members of each whorl are joined by their lateral margins to form a sheath around the stem. The tips of the leaves are usually free from each other, so that the sheath is toothed at the apex. Each leaf has a single, unbranched midvein and is anatomically a microphyll. The leaves have little or no chlorophyll and seem to be mere vestigial structures whose only significant function is to protect the intercalary meristems of the stem.

Branches of the stem of *Equisetum*

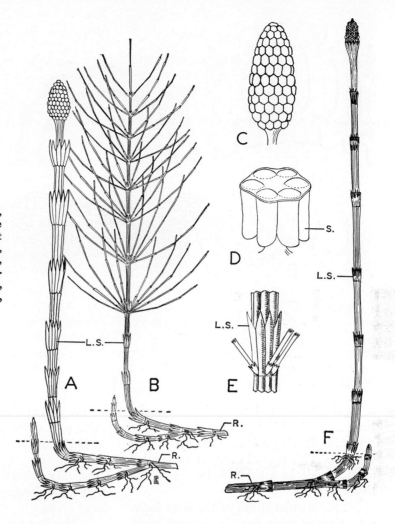

Fig. 19.1. *Equisetum. A–E, Equisetum arvense: A,* fertile shoot (×1); *B,* sterile shoot (¼); *C,* strobilus (×2); *D,* sporangiophore (×20); *E,* part of stem (×3). *F, Equisetum hiemale* (×¼); l.s., leaf sheath; r., rhizome; s., sporangium.

arise from small branch primordia which alternate with the leaves at the surface of the stem at each node. The branch primordia, like the leaves themselves, are derived from the apical cell of the stem. A branch primordium may give rise immediately to a branch with its own apical cell, or it may remain dormant for some time before developing, or it may never develop beyond the primordium stage. The branches break their way through the basal part of the leaf sheath, so that on casual inspection they seem to be borne just beneath the leaves. The branches are generally smaller than the main stem from which they arise, with fewer leaves in each whorl.

The stem is differentiated into an epidermis, cortex, endodermis, and central cylinder. All tissues are derived directly from the apical cell or from the intercalary meristems; there is no secondary thickening. The stele consists of a large, parenchymatous, central pith surrounded by

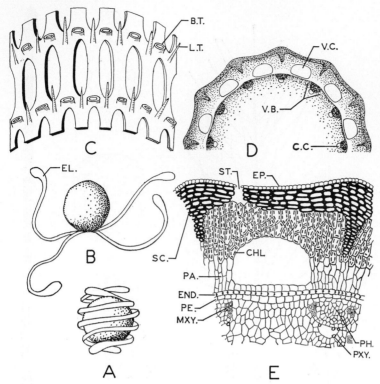

Fig. 19.2. *Equisetum. A, B,* spore, with elaters wrapped around and spread out (× 175); *C,* diagram of vascular anatomy of the stem; *D,* cross section of part of stem (×7); *E,* detail of cross section of part of stem (×35); b.t., branch trace; c.c., carinal canal; chl., chlorenchyma; end., endodermis; ep., epidermis; lt., leaf trace; mxy., metaxylem; pa., parenchyma; pe., pericycle; ph., phloem; pxy., primary xylem; sc., sclerenchyma; st., stomate; v.b., vascular bundle; v.c., vallecular canal.

a regularly arranged network of vascular tissues. Most of the pith usually soon degenerates, leaving a large central cavity in the stem. This central cavity is interrupted at each node by a thin diaphragm of firm tissue.

The vascular tissue of the stem forms a continuous transverse ring at each node, and these nodal rings are connected by distinct vascular bundles running the length of the internodes. Each vascular bundle lies under (centripetal to) one of the external ridges of the stem. The tissue between adjacent vascular bundles is usually parenchymatous. The protoxylem of a vascular bundle, as seen in cross section, consists of a few annular or spiral tracheids on the inner side of the bundle. Several layers of parenchyma cells intervene between the protoxylem and the remainder

of the vascular tissue of the bundle. The outer part of the bundle consists of a mass of phloem, with a few metaxylem tracheids at each side. The phloem is composed largely or wholly of elongate sieve cells that have slanting end walls and scattered sieve areas.

The leaf traces depart from the lower edge of the nodal ring, just at the top of each vascular bundle of the stele, and the ring is continuous above the trace. Since they depart from the bottom of the ring, rather than from the top, the leaf traces are believed to bear no causal relationship to the gaps between the vascular bundles of the succeeding internode. The branch traces alternate with the leaf traces at the nodal ring. Each branch trace departs from the nodal ring as a small cylinder of vascular tissue, enclosing a pith. The pith enclosed by the branch trace is continuous with the pith of the main stem, forming a **branch gap** in the vascular tissue of the nodal ring.

In addition to the central cavity, the stem generally has two rings of longitudinal cavities, called the **carinal canals** and the **vallecular canals.** A small carinal canal lies just internal and immediately adjacent to the primary xylem of each vascular bundle. A usually larger vallecular canal lies in the cortex just under each groove of the stem, alternating with the vascular bundles but closer to the surface. The vallecular canals are filled with air and evidently serve to aerate the submerged parts of the stem. The carinal canals and the central cavity often contain water, however.

The pericycle of the stem of *Equisetum* generally consists of a single layer of cells forming a sheath just external to the vascular bundles and just internal to the endodermis. Sometimes there is a second endodermis delimiting the pith from the vascular part of the stele, and in some species each vascular bundle is ensheathed by its own endodermis, there being then no barrier between the cortex and the pith.

The cortex is anatomically complex, containing sclerenchyma, chlorenchyma, and simple parenchyma. The sclerenchyma commonly forms a column just internal to each ridge of the stem, and sometimes a smaller column just internal to each groove, and often the columns are laterally joined at intervals to form a network. The cortical sclerenchyma forms the principal supporting tissue of the stem. The outer part of the cortex, other than the sclerenchyma, consists of thin-walled cells that have chloroplasts. This chlorenchyma is the principal or only photosynthetic tissue of the plant. The inner part of the cortex consists of colorless parenchyma, sometimes with intermingled sclerenchyma.

The cells of the epidermis have highly silicified walls, often with well-developed and regularly arranged external projections, so that the epidermis is minutely rough to the touch. The stomates are usually confined to the groove between the ridges.

The aerial stems of *Equisetum* arise as branches from a rhizome that creeps along beneath the surface of the ground. The rhizome is anatomically rather similar to the aerial stems, except that it often lacks the prominent cavities. The aerial stems of some species are annual, dying down each year; in other species they are perennial, lasting through several years. In the common species *E. arvense* the aerial stems are of two types. The fertile stems, which arise early in the spring, are only a few inches tall, unbranched, soft, and without chlorophyll. They soon produce a terminal cone and then wither and die. The sterile vegetative stems, which persist throughout the season, arise from the rhizome after the fertile stems have begun to wither. They are a foot or so tall, much branched, green, and photosynthetic.

THE ROOT

The roots of *Equisetum* are slender and rather short, seldom over an inch long, with or without a few lateral branches. The roots originate endogenously at the nodes of the rhizome and subterranean parts of the aerial branches. Growth of the root is due to a well-developed apical cell that is covered by a root-cap. The central cylinder is a small protostele. In cross section the xylem forms a solid, more or less star-shaped central mass of tracheids, with the protoxylem at the

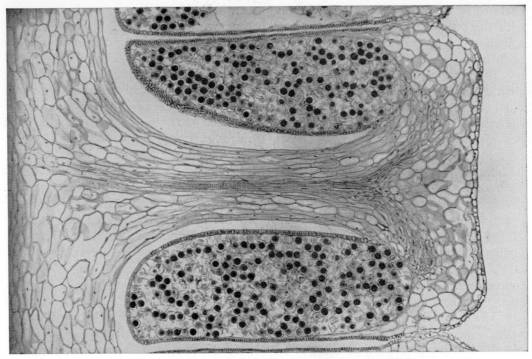

Fig. 19.3. *Equisetum.* Part of strobilus in long section, showing sporangiophore and sporangia. (Copyright by General Biological Supply House, Inc., Chicago.)

points. The phloem lies in separate strands between the arms of xylem. The roots lack a pericycle, and the vascular tissue is directly surrounded by an endodermis which is unusual in being two cells thick. Branch roots, when present, originate endogenously from the inner layer of the endodermis. The inner part of the cortex is parenchymatous, but the outer part consists of thick-walled cells at maturity. Many epidermal cells produce root hairs.

LIFE CYCLE

The sporangia of *Equisetum* are borne on sporangiophores (Fig. 19.3) that are grouped into a terminal cone commonly one to several centimeters long. The sporangiophores are arranged in successive whorls on the axis of the cone, in the same way as the leaves on the vegetative part of the stem. Each sporangiophore has a basal stalk and an expanded, usually hexagonal cap at right angles to the stalk. The caps of adjacent sporangiophores fit more or less closely together.

Each sporangiophore has five to ten sporangia attached to the lower side of the cap in a ring around the stalk. The sporangia are more or less cylindric and commonly 2 to several millimeters long. *Equisetum* is considered to be eusporangiate, although the pattern of sporangial development differs in detail from that of other eusporangiate plants. All the sporogenous tissue and the upper part of the jacket are derived from a single sporangial initial, but the lower part of the jacket is derived from surrounding cells of the sporangiophore.

The tapetum of the sporangium is irregular and generally several cells thick, the outer cells being derived from the jacket of the sporangium, and the inner from the sporogenous tissue. About a third of the potential spore mother cells degenerate more or less concurrently with the tapetal cells, and the remaining spore mother cells undergo reduction division to form tetrads of spores.

The spores (Fig. 19.2) have *n* chromosomes and are the first cells of the gametophyte generation. Four long, slender bands with slightly enlarged tips are attached at a common point to each spore. These bands are called **elaters**, although they are quite unlike the elaters of liverworts. Under moist conditions the elaters are spirally wound around the spore, but when dry they extend out from it and add to its buoyancy in the air. When the spores are mature, the jacket of the sporangium, now only one or two cells thick, dehisces along a single longitudinal line, and the uncoiling of the elaters helps to expel the spores from the sporangium.

The spores are all alike in appearance, but there may be a functional difference, at least in some species. In the common species *E. arvense*, it has been reported

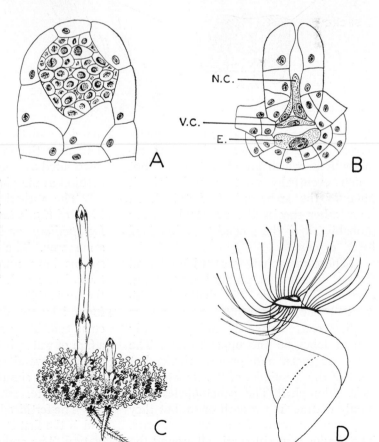

Fig. 19.4. *Equisetum.* **A**, antheridium, long section. (×250.) **B**, archegonium, long section. (×400.) (After Jeffrey.) **C**, gametophyte with young sporophytes. (× about 5.) **D**, sperm (×3000) (after Sharp); e., egg; n.c., neck canal cell; v.c., ventral canal cell.

N.C.
V.C.
E.

Calamophyta: Horsetails and Scouring Rushes 367

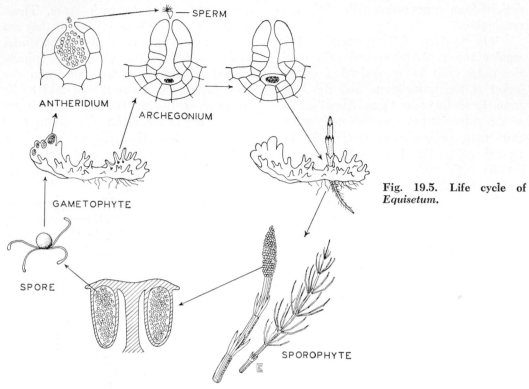

ANTHERIDIUM

SPERM

ARCHEGONIUM

GAMETOPHYTE

Fig. 19.5. Life cycle of *Equisetum.*

SPORE

SPOROPHYTE

that half the spores produce male gameto-phytes, while the other half produce ga-metophytes which are at first female but which eventually produce antheridia if none of the archegonia is fertilized. In some other species the gametophytes are probably all of the second type described for *E. arvense.*

The gametophyte is a cushion-shaped thallus, varying from pinhead size to 1 cm, or rarely 3 cm wide. The thallus has rhi-zoids on the lower surface and numerous small, erect, flattened and irregularly shaped lobes on the upper surface. The lobes are green and photosynthetic, but most of the remainder of the gametophyte lacks chlorophyll. The gametophytes com-monly mature in a month or so, but they may continue to live for as long as 2 years. The thallus is meristematic all around the

margin, and the gametangia, which origi-nate near the margins, may come to be distributed over much of the surface of the cushion as marginal growth continues.

The antheridia and archegonia (Fig. 19.4) of *Equisetum* are much like those of *Lycopodium* and develop in about the same way. The naked, spirally twisted sperms have numerous whiplash flagella toward one end. The sperms escape from the antheridium through a small opening formed by the disintegration of an oper-cular cell. They swim to the egg through a film of water, being attracted by chemical stimuli. Several sporophytes may develop more or less simultaneously from the same gametophyte.

The fertilized egg has 2n chromosomes and is the first step in the sporophyte gen-eration. The embryo which develops from the fertilized egg has a foot, a primary root, and a primary shoot, but it differs from the embryo of most lepidophytes in lacking a suspensor. The foot absorbs food from the body of the gametophyte and passes it on to the remainder of the embryo. The primary root forces its way down through the body of the gametophyte into the soil, and the shoot pushes up through the archegonium into the air. The first leaves are usually borne in a whorl of three or four, united into a sheath, and are much like the mature leaves.

The primary stem does not generally develop more than 10 or 15 internodes. A branch develops from one of the basal nodes, and from this branch, or from one of its successors formed in the same way, a branch which develops into a rhizome is eventually produced. The ordinary aerial stems of the mature sporophyte arise as branches from the rhizome.

Fossils

Fossils essentially similar to *Equisetum* are referred to the genus *Equisetites* and are known from as far back as the Upper Carboniferous period. Some other fossils are apparently transitional between the Equisetales and Calamitales.

CALAMITALES

The Calamitales (Fig. 19.6) are fossils that resemble *Equisetum* except for their larger size, well-developed secondary thickening, and different cone structure. The cone has whorls of sterile appendages alternating with the whorls of sporangiophores. Large plants possibly reached a height 100 feet, with a stem 2 feet thick; but a height of 20 to 30 feet was probably

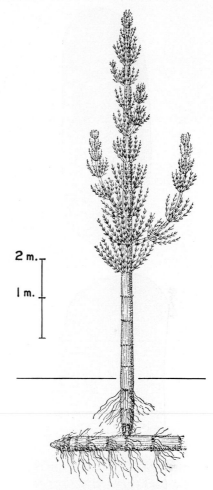

Fig. 19.6. *Calamites*, reconstruction.

more common. The stem is longitudinally ribbed, with the ribs sometimes alternating in successive nodes as in *Equisetum*, and sometimes directly superposed. Internally the stem is usually hollow, as in *Equisetum*, with solid diaphragms at the nodes. Vallecular canals are lacking, but there are carinal canals as in *Equisetum*. The primary vascular structure resembles that of *Equisetum*, but there is also a well-developed layer of secondary xylem composed largely of tracheids. A cork cam-

Fig. 19.7. Calamophyte fossils. Top, *Sphenophyllum*; bottom, *Annularia*. (× about ⅔). (Courtesy of the Chicago Natural History Museum.)

bium, similar to that described for the Lepidodendrales, produced a layer of corky tissue toward the outer part of the cortex, forming a protective outer covering on the mature parts of the stem. The roots also show some secondary thickening, and they at least sometimes have a double layer of endodermis as in *Equisetum*. The leaves are small and narrow, not more than about an inch long, and sometimes more or less connate as in *Equisetum*, but their structure indicates that they were photosynthetic.

The Calamitales are known from the Late Devonian to the Early Permian period and were abundant throughout the Carboniferous. There are numerous species, with considerable differences in detailed morphology. Some species were distinctly heterosporous, but no seed-bearing forms are known. The plants were readily fragmented, and it is often difficult to match up parts that have been separately preserved as fossils. A number of different generic names have been applied to calamitean fossils representing various parts of the plant, but in the broad sense they are sometimes all referred to the genus *Calamites*. If the plants existed today, so that they could be more thoroughly studied and compared, they would doubtless be classified into several different genera.

SPHENOPHYLLALES

Although they are clearly calamophytes, the Sphenophyllates represent a line of development quite different from the Equisetales and Calamitales. Features which cause the Sphenophyllales to be referred to the Calamophyta are the jointed, longitudinally ribbed stem, whorled leaves, and terminal strobilus. The stem, leaves, and strobilus are all anatomically unlike *Equisetum*, however.

The stem, which reaches a maximum thickness of about 1 cm, has a solid protostele. In cross section the xylem forms a usually triangular core, with the protoxylem at the points. Both secondary xylem and phloem and secondary outer protective tissues are present in some quantity.

The leaves are mostly less than an inch long, more or less wedge-shaped or fan-shaped, and toothed or cleft from the tip. The single vein which enters the leaf is dichotomously branched, with one of the ultimate branches directed to each terminal tooth or lobe.

The cone usually bears a number of whorls of leaf-like appendages, and the members of each whorl are often joined by their margins to form a more or less cup-like structure. Axillary to these appendages, and often more or less adnate to the upper surface, is a sporangiophore, which is usually branched, with two or more terminal sporangia. Less often the sporangiophores alternate with the subtending appendages instead of being directly superposed.

The most common genus of the Sphenophyllales is *Sphenophyllum* (Fig. 19.8), which covers the whole known life span of the order. It is found in rocks of Late Devonian to Triassic age, being most abundant in the Upper Carboniferous and Early Permian. No modern descendants of the Sphenophyllales are known.

HYENIALES

The Hyeniales are calamophytes which appear to be transitional toward the psilophytes. There are two genera, *Hyenia* and *Calamophyton* (Fig. 19.9), both from

Fig. 19.8. *Sphenophyllum*, reconstruction. (×about ⅓.) (Courtesy of the Chicago Natural History Museum.)

rocks of Middle Devonian age. The leaves in both genera are whorled, and in *Calamophyton* the young stems are distinctly jointed. The height of the plants is uncertain, but they were evidently not very large; the stems are up to about 1 cm thick, and branch systems 20 cm long have been found. The leaves are up to an inch long, in some species dichotomously several times branched, in others merely notched or bifid at the tip.

The stem in *Hyenia* and *Calamophy-*

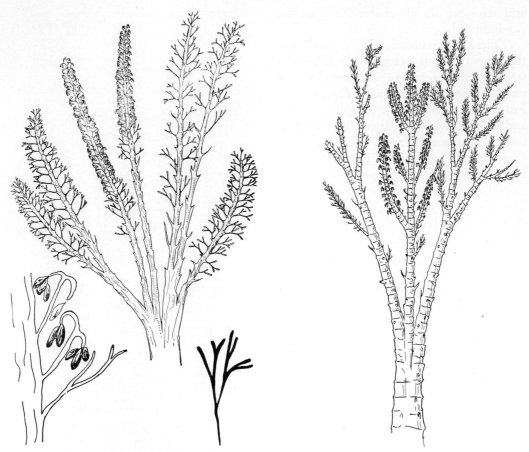

Fig. 19.9. *Hyenia* (left) and *Calamophyton* (right). (After Krausel and Weyland; courtesy of Ginn & Company, Boston.)

ton is irregularly and more or less dichotomously branched, with some of the dichotomies often so close together that the branching appears to be digitate (like the fingers of a hand). In this respect the Hyeniales differ from other members of the division, in which branches arise at the nodes of a continuing main axis and are usually whorled. Fertile stems or branches of the Hyeniales terminate in a lax strobilus with whorled sporangiophores. Each sporangiophore is apically bifid, with the two branches recurved and bearing sporangia at the tip. In *Hyenia* each branch has

two or more sporangia, but in *Calamophyton* each branch has only one sporangium. The stem anatomy and underground structure of the Hyeniales are scarcely known, although a stout rhizome has been described for one species of *Hyenia*.

ECONOMIC IMPORTANCE

The modern calamophytes are economically insignificant. *Equisetum arvense* is mildly poisonous to livestock but is seldom eaten in sufficient quantities to cause serious trouble. The Calamitales were among the most abundant plants of the Carboniferous period, at least in swampy areas, and were, therefore, important contributors to the deposits of vegetation which later became transformed into coal.

RELATIONSHIPS

The Calamophyta are generally believed to be derived from the Psilophyta. *Hyenia*, which has dichotomously branched unjointed stems, is placed with the calamophytes because of its whorled leaves and sporangiophores, the presence or absence of roots in the genus being as yet uncertain. The sporangiophores of *Hyenia* and *Calamophyton* are of particular interest. On the one hand, they resemble the fertile branch tips of *Psilophyton*; on the other, they seem to be homologous with the leaves that are borne lower down on the stem. The sporangiophores of *Equisetum*, which do not resemble leaves, could readily enough be derived from sporangiophores of something like *Hyenia*. The leaves of many fossil calamophytes are dichotomously branched, like stems, or have a dichotomously branched vein system.

The inference to be drawn from these facts is that both the leaves and the sporangiophores of the Calamophyta are modified branch stems. The Sphenophyllales represent a line in which the members of a more or less extensive branch system were laterally coalesced to form a flat leaf blade with dichotomous venation. The Calamitales and Equisetales represent a line in which the leaves were reduced to simple unbranched appendages, and these appendages later became joined by their margins to form the characteristic nodal sheaths. The nature and evolutionary origin of leaves are further discussed in Chapter 20.

The Calamitales and Equisetales are closely related and are sometimes placed in a single order Equisetales. The Equisetales do not extend so far back in the fossil record as the Calamitales, but this may well be because of the fragmentary nature of the record. It is generally believed that the Equisetales are reduced derivatives of the Calamitales, but the possibility cannot yet be excluded that the Equisetales are the more ancient group, from which the Calamitales were a temporarily successful offshoot that died out without descendants.

Division Filicophyta

FERNS

CHAPTER 20

Vascular plants with roots, stems, and alternate leaves, the leaves megaphylls, the central cylinder of the stem generally with leaf gaps; gametophyte and sporophyte physiologically independent of each other at maturity, but the gametophyte small and inconspicuous; sporangia numerous, borne on the leaves, or on modified appendages of the leaves. A single class, the Filices.

◄

Part of a leaf of *Cyathea arborea*, a West Indian tree fern. (Photo by W. H. Hodge.)

HISTORY

One of the most obvious distinctions in the plant kingdom is that between the seed-bearing plants, or **phanerogams,** and the non-seed-bearing plants, or **cryptogams.** The stamens (microsporophylls) and ovules (young seeds) of seed plants obviously represent male and female reproductive structures, whence the name phanerogam (from Greek *phaneros*, visible, and *gamos*, marriage). The method of reproduction of cryptogams (from Greek *kryptos*, hidden) is not so immediately evident.

The life cycles of *Equisetum, Isoetes, Selaginella,* and many mosses and ferns were first worked out by the German botanist Wilhelm Hofmeister. The book presenting his results, published in 1851, is a landmark of botanical history. Hofmeister did not fully understand the processes of gametic union and meiosis, with the associated changes in chromosome number, but he knew that the sperm stimulates the egg to develop into the new sporophyte,

375

Fig. 20.1. *Dryopteris marginalis*, a fern. (New York Botanical Garden photo.)

and he is responsible for the concept of **alternation of** sporophytic and gametophytic **generations.**

For more than three-quarters of a century after Hofmeister's work, it was customary to refer all vascular cryptogams to a single division, the Pteridophyta. The name comes from *Pteris*, a genus of ferns, plus the Greek ending, *-phyta*, meaning plants. *Pteris* is also the classical Greek word for a fern. The ferns (Fig. 20.1) make up by far the largest group of pteridophytes (vascular cryptogams), and the other pteridophytes have often been called fern allies. The "fern allies" are treated in this text as the divisions Psilophyta, Lepidophyta, and Calamophyta.

In 1902 the American botanist Edward Charles Jeffrey (1866–1952) pointed out that on anatomical grounds the vascular plants fall into two fundamental groups. One of these groups, including the ferns and the modern seed plants, tends to have relatively large leaves with a branching vein system. Very often the leaf is divided into basal stalk, or **petiole,** and an expanded **blade.** Except among a few of the more primitive ferns, the departure of the leaf trace leaves a gap in the primary vascular tissue of the central cylinder. This gap, called a **leaf gap** (Fig. 20.2), is filled with parenchyma, connecting the parenchyma of the pith with the parenchyma of the cortex. A segment of the vascular cylinder separates from the remainder of the stele and actually becomes the vascular supply of the leaf. Leaves of the type associated with leaf gaps are called **megaphylls.** Jeffrey suggested the name Pteropsida for the group of vascular plants characterized by megaphylls and leaf gaps, but he did not indicate the precise taxonomic rank to be assigned to the group.

The second of the two fundamental groups pointed out by Jeffrey has relatively small, narrow leaves with a single, unbranched midvein, and the leaf is not differentiated into a blade and petiole. The departure of the leaf trace does not disturb the continuity of the stele; an extra strand of vascular tissue is merely attached to the stele, and there are, therefore, no leaf gaps. Leaves of this type are called **micro-phylls**. Jeffrey suggested the name Lycopsida for the group of vascular plants characterized by microphylls.

Although all microphylls are small, not all megaphylls are large. Such small-leaved plants as firs, pines, and junipers, for example, have definite leaf gaps in the stele, and the leaves are therefore considered to be megaphylls. It is believed that megaphyllous plants with small leaves had ancestors with larger leaves.

Botanists are now agreed that Jeffrey's group Lycopsida should be divided into three: the Lycopsida proper, or Lepido-phyta; the Psilopsida, or Psilophyta; and the Sphenopsida, or Calamophyta. The taxonomic rank at which these groups should be received is not agreed upon. Some botanists consider them to be three divisions, as in this text; others treat them as three of the classes of a single comprehensive division of vascular plants, the Tracheophyta.

Some botanists still consider the Pteropsida to form a proper division or class, but evidence is accumulating that the conifers, which have been included in the group, originated independently from the psilophytes. In this text the plants which have been referred to the Pteropsida are treated as four divisions: the Filico-phyta, the Cycadophyta, the Conifero-phyta, and the Anthophyta.

The Filicophyta, or **ferns,** were first recognized as a distinct division by Bessey in 1907. Bessey used the name Pterido-phyta for this group, but that name has so generally been used in a broader sense (to include all vascular cryptogams) that the name Filicophyta is preferable when the ferns are treated as a division. The term *pteridophytes* is still useful to refer to the vascular cryptogams (including also the fossil seed plants among the Lepido-phyta), just as the term *algae* is useful for thallophytes with chlorophyll *a*, but neither the algae nor the pteridophytes are now generally regarded as proper *taxonomic* groups.

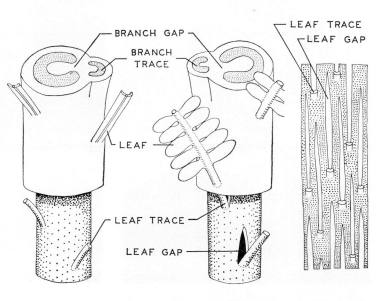

Fig. 20.2. Structure of lycopsid (left) and pteropsid (right center) shoots. (Adapted from Jeffrey.) Far right, part of the vascular system of *Osmunda*, a typical fern. (Adapted from Lachmann.)

BRANCH GAP

BRANCH TRACE

LEAF TRACE

LEAF GAP

LEAF

LEAF TRACE

LEAF GAP

It is now widely believed that the ancestral prototype of the vascular plants was a form in which the sporophyte consisted of a dichotomously branched leafless stem, much as in some of the fossil psilophytes. Megaphylls are considered to be modified branch stem systems. Some of the fossils which tend to support this conclusion are discussed on pp. 390–391. The microphylls of the Calamophyta are now also considered to be modified branch stem systems, not essentially different in origin from megaphylls. In all modern calamophytes, each leaf has become reduced to the equivalent of a single short branch.

Botanists are not agreed as to the evolutionary origin of the microphylls of the Lepidophyta and Psilophyta. An idea which at one time commanded wide acceptance is that they are mere emergences from the surface of the stem, comparable to enlarged epidermal hairs or scales, and that the development of a midvein is merely an evolutionary response to the enlargement of this emergence to a photosynthetically significant size. A more recent suggestion which has gained increasing support is that in these groups, also, the microphyll is a modified short branch stem and that the midvein is homologous with the central cylinder of the stem.

A comprehensive theory of the origin of all leaves by modification of branch stems or branch-stem systems has been developed by the German botanist Walter Zimmermann (1892–   ). Zimmermann calls the ultimate branches of a dichotomously branching stem **telomes**, and his theory is called the **telome theory**. Although some aspects of the telome theory are still highly controversial, its basic concepts are becoming rather generally ac-

Fig. 20.3 Left, Wilhelm Hofmeister (1824–1877), German botanist, who discovered alternation of **generations. Right, Walter Zimmermann (1892–**), **German botanist, author of the telome theory.**

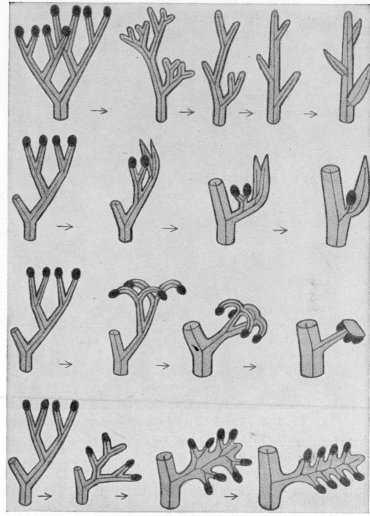

Fig. 20.4. Origin of leaves, sporophylls, and sporangiophores, according to the telome theory. Starting with a dichotomously branching stem with terminal sporangia, we derive, *top row*, the lepidophyte leaf; *second row*, the lepidophyte sporophyll; *third row*, the calamophyte sporangiophore; and *bottom row*, the fern leaf with marginal sporangia.

cepted. It provides a logical explanation of the evolutionary relationships among the pteridophytes.

OCCURRENCE

Ferns occur in a wide variety of habitats and climates, but most of them are found in shady rather than sunny places, in moist or wet rather than dry sites and climates, and in tropical or subtropical rather than in temperate or cold regions. No large part of the United States, even the desert regions, is wholly without ferns.

CHARACTERISTICS

General

The sporophyte is the conspicuous generation of the Filicophyta, the gameto-

Fig. 20.5. Tree ferns in the Colombian Andes. (Photo by José Cuatrecasas.)

phyte being a small thallus seldom over an
inch long. Both generations are physiologically independent at maturity. The sporophyte is always photosynthetic, and the
gametophyte is usually so, but the gametophytes of some kinds of ferns are subterranean, colorless, and mycorhizal, as in
Lycopodium; and in heterosporous ferns
the gametophytes are largely or wholly dependent on the food originally stored in
the spores. The fern sporophyte is ordinarily divided into roots, stems, and leaves.
A few ferns, such as the floating, aquatic
Salvinia, lack roots, but their rootless condition is believed to be secondary rather
than primitive; i.e., rootless ferns probably
had ancestors with roots.

HABIT AND STEM

Some ferns reach a height of more
than 60 feet, with a trunk nearly 2 feet
thick, although much of the thickness is
contributed by a covering of matted adventitious aerial roots. More often the stem
is represented only by a simple or branched
rhizome (underground stem) from which
the leaves arise. Apical growth of the stem
is brought about by an apical initial cell,
or by a group of apical initials forming an
apical meristem.

Branches of a fern stem characteristically originate by bifurcation of the apical
meristem or apical cell, each of the two
parts continuing to develop as the apical
meristem or apical cell of a branch. The

two branches may be essentially equal (dichotomous branching), or more often one branch may continue as the main stem to which the other is attached as a lateral branch (lateral branching). When the branching is lateral, the apical cell or meristem of the lateral branch commonly remains dormant for some time before resuming its meristematic activity, so that the branch actually originates well behind the tip of the main stem. Were it not for the transitional types, the developmental relationship of the lateral bud to the terminal one would be obscure.

In any given kind of fern, the branches of the stem generally arise in a particular position with respect to the leaves. When the stem branches dichotomously, a leaf is borne just beneath the dichotomy, evenly spaced between the two branches. When the stem branches laterally, the lateral branch generally arises alongside the leaf, or less often in the leaf axil, or even just beneath the leaf, according to the species.

Several different kinds of stele occur in ferns. It has already been pointed out that the most primitive type of stele is the protostele, in which a solid central core of xylem is partly or wholly surrounded by phloem. Protosteles are typically (and primitively) **exarch.** An exarch stele is one in which the protoxylem (first-formed primary xylem) is at the outside—commonly at the tips of the arms, as seen in cross section—and maturation of the **metaxylem** (later-formed xylem) progresses toward the center, so that the central cells of the stele, at any given level, are the last to mature. A protostele may also be **mesarch,** with the metaxylem developing both internally and externally to the protoxylem. Very young fern sporophytes frequently have protostelic stems, but the later-formed

parts of the stem of most kinds of ferns have a pith and are therefore not protostelic.

A stele in which the vascular tissue surrounds a central pith is called a **siphonostele.** The siphonostele is an evolutionary modification of the protostele, in which the central cells fail to mature into xylem, remaining as a parenchymatous pith instead. Siphonosteles may be exarch or mesarch, as in protosteles, but more often they are **endarch.** In an endarch siphonostele, the metaxylem is formed only external to the protoxylem, which lies next to the pith. The endarch condition is an evolutionary modification from the mesarch condition.

Siphonosteles of stems of plants belonging to the pteropsid group are interrupted by leaf gaps and branch gaps. A siphonostele in which the gaps are relatively short and well spaced, so that a cross section of the stem shows not more than one or two gaps, is called a **solenostele.** A siphonostele with more numerous and elongate gaps, so that the primary vascular tissue forms a ring of vascular bundles, is called a **dictyostele.** The dictyostele is the most common type of stele in the stems of ferns, and is also the characteristic type in the stems of cycads, conifers, and flowering plants. Transitional types between the solenostele and the dictyostele are not rare among the ferns, and the basal part of an otherwise dictyostelic stem is often solenostelic. In some ferns the dictyostele has become more or less strongly modified and can be interpreted only with difficulty.

The phloem in a fern stem typically lies just external to the xylem, either immediately adjacent to it or separated by a layer of parenchyma. In some fern stems there is a layer of phloem just internal to the xylem as well as just external to it, and the xylem of a vascular bundle may be completely surrounded by phloem. A siphonostele is said to be amphiphloic or ectophloic, according to whether the phloem lies on both sides of the xylem or only on the outside. Amphiphloic siphonosteles often have an inner as well as an outer endodermis.

The xylem of fern stems and roots usually consists largely of tracheids, often with some intermingled parenchyma cells. The tracheids are usually **scalariform** (i.e., the secondary wall forms an open network with ladder-like configurations), but sometimes they are **pitted** instead (i.e., the secondary wall is a continuous layer with scattered small openings). In a few genera, notably *Pteridium* (see p. 394), there are definite vessels.

The phloem of ferns consists largely or wholly of sieve cells with slanting end walls and scattered sieve areas. The stele of a fern stem may or may not be enclosed by an endodermis. When the endodermis is absent, the thin, parencyhmatous layer of pericycle just external to the phloem may be difficult to distinguish from the cortex. The cortex is partly or sometimes wholly parenchymatous, but usually it contains a considerable amount of sclerenchyma as well. Except among some of the Ophioglossales, there is usually no secondary thickening in either the stems or the roots of ferns.

ROOT

The root system of the mature fern sporophyte is entirely adventitious (i.e., the roots originate from the stem). The individual roots (Fig. 20.6) are rather small and fibrous, and simple or branched. Branches, when present, develop from in-ternal tissues, in the same way that the adventitious roots develop from the internal tissues (generally the pericycle) of the stem. The root usually has root hairs near the tip, but in some ferns it is mycorhizal and lacks root hairs. The apical meristem or apical cell is covered by a rootcap.

The roots of ferns, as of other vascular plants, are generally protostelic. The primary xylem usually forms a solid core, which in cross section shows a number of radiating arms or points. The protoxylem is at the tips of the arms, and maturation progresses inward. In a few ferns the central cells of the stele remain parenchymatous instead of differentiating into metaxylem.

As in the roots of most other vascular plants, the primary phloem of a fern root commonly forms a number of separate strands alternating with the radiating arms of primary xylem. Protosteles are said to be **monarch, diarch, triarch, tetrarch, pentarch,** or **polyarch,** according to the number of separate points or strands of protoxylem. Many fern roots, especially in the large family Polypodiaceae, are diarch, with only two protoxylem points, so that the xylem forms a flattened central strand bordered on each side by a strand of phloem. The central cylinder of a fern root is delimited by an endodermis, which is separated from the vascular tissues by a thin layer of pericycle.

LEAF

The leaves of ferns are usually divided into a basal stalk, or petiole, and an expanded blade. Typically the growing young blade unrolls from the tip, and the leaf is said to be **circinate.** Young leaves in which the blade has not yet unrolled, or has only begun to do so, are often called **fiddleheads**

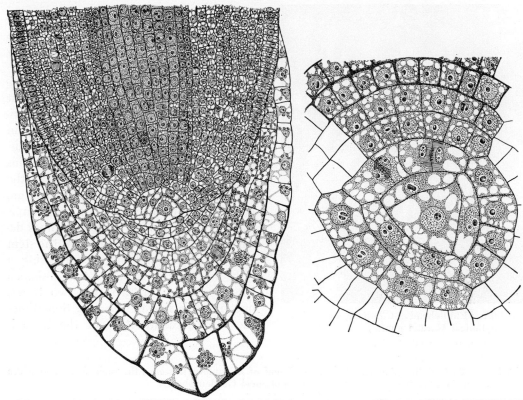

Fig. 20.6. Root tip of a fern, in long section (left) and cross section (right), showing the apical cell, rootcap, and young primary tissues of the root. (From W. H. Brown, *The Plant Kingdom*, 1935; courtesy of Ginn & Company, Boston.)

(Fig. 20.7). Fern leaves are often called **fronds,** but this term is also applied to very large leaves of gymnosperms and flowering plants. In a few genera, such as *Lygodium,* the leaf apex is persistently meristematic, and the climbing, freely branching leaf, resembling a stem with leaves, may become as much as 100 feet long.

The leaves of most ferns are **compound** (i.e., the blade is made up of several or many distinct parts of leaflets), but there are also many simple-leaved ferns, in which the blade is all in one piece. In most compound fern leaves, the petiole continues as the main axis or **rachis** of the leaf blade, and the primary segments or leaflets arise

as lateral branches from the rachis. Leaves of this type are said to be **pinnately compound** (from Latin *pinna,* a feather). Pinnately compound leaves in which the primary segments are again once or more times compound are said to be pinnately decompound, or the degree of dissection may be expressed by such terms as *bipinnately* or *tripinnately* compound. The primary lateral branches of a pinnately compound leaf are called **pinnae** (sing., **pinna**) or primary pinnae, and the ultimate segments, when the pinnae are themselves compound, are called **pinnules.** In some compound fern leaves, the leaflets or primary segments are all attached to the end

Fig. 20.7. Fiddlehead of *Cibotium*, a fern. (New York Botanical Garden photo.)

of the petiole at a common point, and the blade has no central rachis. Leaves of this type are said to be **palmately** or digitately **compound**.

The leaves of most ferns are anatomically more complex than those of most other pteridophytes. They characteristically have a branching vein system, in which the smaller branches are often distinctly dichotomous. The smaller veins sometimes form a network, so that the venation is reticulate, but often there are no such connections and the venation is open, or free. The leaf trace sometimes departs from the central cylinder of the stem as a miniature siphonostele enclosing a pith, but more often it is a trough-shaped vascular strand; or there are two traces, one on each side of the gap. Sometimes the vascular architecture of the trace is

Fig. 20.8. Part of the pinnately bicompound leaf of *Dryopteris filix-mas*, the male fern. The white dots are indusia, covering the sori. (New York Botanical Garden photo.)

more complex and difficult to interpret. In the petiole the leaf trace sometimes breaks up into several vascular bundles of various structure. The smaller branch veins of the leaves are generally rod-shaped, with the xylem on the upper side and the phloem on the lower.

The epidermis of fern leaves is generally cutinized and, except for the guard cells of the stomates, usually lacks chloroplasts. A number of species, especially of the Polypodiaceae (e.g., *Adiantum*, the maidenhair fern), have a chlorophyllous upper epidermis, however, with the chloroplasts of each cell concentrated in arm-like projections which extend down into the internal tissues of the leaf. The stomates are often confined to the lower epidermis.

The internal tissue of the leaf is composed chiefly of chlorenchyma, with interspersed veins. The internal chlorenchyma of a leaf (in ferns and other plants) is often called **mesophyll**. The mesophyll of fern leaves is sometimes differentiated into an upper and a lower part. The upper part, called the **palisade tissue**, palisade parenchyma, or palisade mesophyll, consists of elongate, parallel cells in which the long axis, as viewed in cross section of the leaf, is vertical (perpendicular to the epidermis).

The intercellular spaces in the palisade tissue are usually rather small. The lower part of the mesophyll, called the **spongy tissue**, spongy parenchyma, or spongy mesophyll, is composed of irregularly shaped cells with large intercellular spaces. Fern leaves with reticulate venation and with well-developed palisade and spongy layers of mesophyll are anatomically very similar to the leaves of flowering plants, which are discussed in Chapter 26.

SPORANGIA

The sporangia of ferns are generally borne on the leaves, or on appendages associated with the leaves. The sporophylls are in most cases ordinary vegetative leaves, but not infrequently the sporophyll is more or less modified and not photosynthetic. Numerous sporangia are borne on each sporophyll, and, except in the Ophioglossales, the sporangia of modern ferns are generally aggregated into distinct groups called **sori** (sing., **sorus**). A typical sorus is about the size of a pinhead, but it may be larger or a little smaller, and adjacent sori may be more or less confluent. In most modern ferns, the sori are borne on the lower (abaxial) surface of the sporophyll,

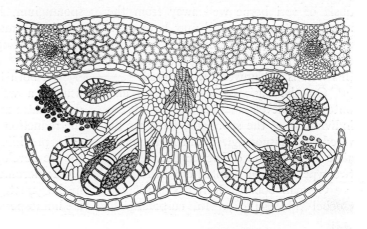

Fig. 20.9. Cross section of part of a fern leaf, showing a sorus with its indusium. (From Transeau, Sampson, and Tiffany, *A Textbook of Botany*, Harper, 1953.)

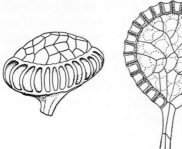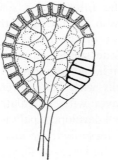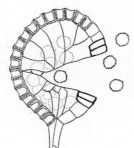

Fig. 20.10. Two types of leptosporangia. Left, with annulus complete; center and right, with annulus interrupted by the stalk, and with prominent lip cells.

often at the tips of some of the ultimate veinlets. Less often the sporangia are truly marginal, or (in the Ophioglossales) borne on a "fertile spike" which projects from the upper side of the leaf. The brown dots which can frequently be seen on the lower side of fern leaves are sori.

A young sorus is usually covered by a thin protective membrane called the **indusium.** The shape and structure of the indusium vary in different kinds of ferns, and the differences furnish a number of useful taxonomic characters. When the sori are borne near the margin of the leaf, the margin is often inrolled and modified to form a single common indusium for a whole row of sori, or individual bits of the margin may be modified to form separate indusia. It has been suggested that the indusia of sori borne well away from the margin of the sporophyll may have originated by enlargement and concrescence of epidermal hairs surrounding the sorus, but this view is not universally accepted.

On the basis of the structure and ontogeny (developmental history of the individual) of the sporangia, ferns are divided into **eusporangiate** and **leptosporangiate** groups. The difference between the two types was first pointed out in 1880 by the German botanist Karl Eberhardt von Goebel (1855–1932). In eusporangiate

ferns the sporangium develops from a group of sporangial initial cells. The jacket layer is more than one cell thick at maturity, and there is no highly specialized mechanism of dehiscence. There is a large and indefinite number of spores in each sporangium.

In leptosporangiate ferns the sporangium (Fig. 20.10) develops from a single sporangial initial cell. The jacket layer is only one cell thick at maturity, and dehiscence is usually due to hygroscopic changes in a group of thick-walled cells which commonly form a partial or complete ring, the **annulus.** Tensions which develop within the annulus cause the sporangium to break open at a definite point or line marked by thin-walled cells. Some leptosporangiate ferns have numerous spores in each sporangium, but more often there is a relatively small and definite number of spores, ranging from 16 to 64 in different species.

In both types of sporangium there is usually a well-developed tapetum which degenerates more or less concurrently with the reduction division of the spore mother cells, providing an additional food supply for the developing spores. The spores have n chromosomes and represent the first step in the gametophyte generation. Most ferns are homosporous, but both the modern and the fossil representatives of the group include some heterosporous forms.

GAMETOPHYTE

The gametophyte of ferns and other pteridophytes is often called a **prothallus** (Fig. 20.11). The prothallus varies in form and structure in different kinds of ferns, but it is always small and inconspicuous. In the eusporangiate ferns it is several or many cells thick and often comparatively massive, sometimes 1 inch or even 2 inches long. In the leptosporangiate ferns the most common type is a thin, flat, more or less heart-shaped, green thallus, seldom as large as the little fingernail. A prothallus of this type is only one cell thick, except for a slightly thicker median strip extending back from the notch. Rhizoids, antheridia,

and archegonia are borne on the under side of this median strip, the archegonia usually being closer to the notch than are the antheridia. Growth of fern gametophytes is brought about largely by an apical cell, or a row of apical cells. In the heart-shaped type, the apical cell or cells lie in the notch.

The archegonium (Fig. 20.13) is more or less flask-shaped, with a usually protruding neck which, in the heart-shaped types, is often curved toward the rear of the prothallus. The neck may be relatively long or short, with two to ten tiers of cells, but there are usually only two neck canal nuclei. The neck canal nuclei may or may not be separated by a cross wall in the neck. As in other pteridophytes, the neck of the archegonium, the egg, and the canal cells originate from a single archegonial

Fig. 20.11. Fern gametophytes. (×5.) (Copyright by General Biological Supply House, Inc., Chicago.)

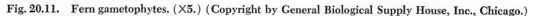

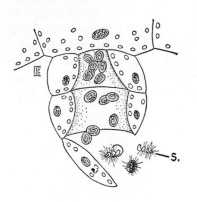

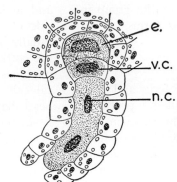

Fig. 20.12. Antheridium (left) and archegonium (right) of a fern, in long section; e., egg; n.c., neck canal nucleus; s., sperm; v.c., ventral canal nucleus. (X 500.)

initial, but the wall of the venter is composed of ordinary gametophytic cells not derived from the archegonial initial.

The antheridia (Fig. 20.12) are more or less globose. In the eusporangiate ferns the antheridia are sunken in the body of the gametophyte, only the upper or outer surface being exposed. When the sperms

Fig. 20.13. Fern archegonium, in long section. (From Harold Bold, *Morphology of Plants*, Harper, 1957.)

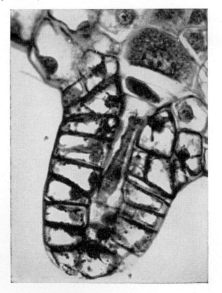

are mature, an **opercular cell** in the antheridium degenerates, leaving an opening through which the numerous (commonly several hundred) sperms escape. In the leptosporangiate ferns the antheridium projects from the surface of the gametophyte. A **cover cell**, corresponding to the opercular cell of the eusporangiate ferns, is pushed away from within by expansion of the antheridial contents when the sperms are mature. Leptosporangiate ferns usually have only about 32 sperms in each antheridium, but the number is sometimes as high as 100 or more. Sperms of both eusporangiate and leptosporangiate ferns are naked, coiled, and provided with more or less numerous whiplash flagella at one end. As in other pteridophytes, the sperms are attracted to the egg in the archegonium by chemical stimuli and require a film of water in which to swim.

EMBRYO

The fusion of an egg and a sperm in the venter of the archegonium constitutes fertilization. The fertilized egg has $2n$ chromosomes and is the first cell in the sporophyte generation. The developing embryo has a foot, a primary root, a primary stem, and a primary leaf. In most genera there is no suspensor. The foot absorbs food from the body of the gametophyte and passes it on to the remainder of the developing embryo. After the new sporophyte has become established as an independent plant, the gametophyte sooner or later dies and degenerates. In most leptosporangiate ferns growth and differentiation of the embryo proceed rapidly, and by the time the embryo has reached the eight-celled stage, two of the cells are destined to produce the foot, two the root, two the stem, and two the cotyledon. In the eusporangiate ferns growth and differentiation of the embryo proceed more slowly, and the embryo commonly becomes a massive, multicellular structure before the primordia of the different organs can be distinguished. In both eusporangiate and leptosporangiate ferns the primary root is short-lived, and is soon replaced by adventitious roots which typically originate from the pericycle of the stem.

CLASSIFICATION

There are nearly 10,000 modern species of ferns, of which the vast majority belong to the order Filicales. The modern ferns may be classified into five orders, some of which also have fossil representatives. Among the numerous fossil ferns and fern-like plants, three groups stand out as possibly warranting recognition as distinct orders. Others, mostly incompletely known fossils of general fern affinities, may not be properly referable to any of these orders. The eight orders of fossil and living ferns here recognized are characterized

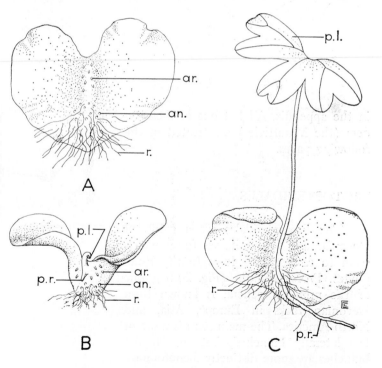

Fig. 20.14. Gametophytes and young sporophytes of a fern; A, lower side of gametophyte; B, side view of gametophyte with a very young sporophyte; C, gametophyte with slightly older sporophyte; an., antheridium; ar., archegonium; p.l., primary leaf; p.r., primary root; r., rhizoid. (×6.)

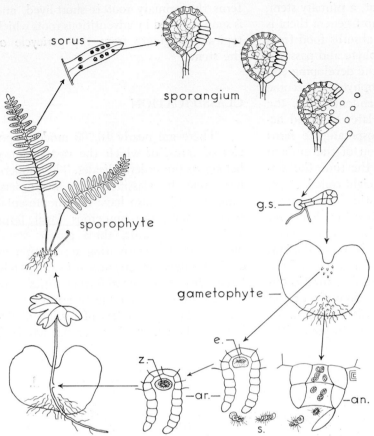

Fig. 20.15. Life cycle of a fern; an., antheridium; ar., archegonium; e., egg; g.s., germinating spore; s., sperm; z., zygote.

Fig. 20.16. *Protopteridium.* Sp., sporangia. (× 1⅔.) (After Halle.)

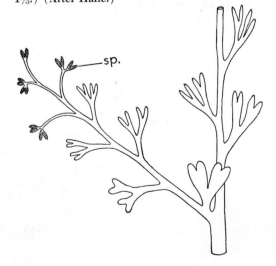

in the appendix. All but one of these orders (the Marattiales) are treated in the following pages.

PROTOPTERIDALES

The Protopteridales are a group of Devonian and Carboniferous fossils which seem to connect the ferns to the Psilophytes. *Protopteridium* (Fig. 20.16), one of the principal genera, is known from Devonian rocks in Europe, Asia, and North America. The main stem is more or less laterally branched, but the smaller branches are more distinctly dichotomous, and these dichotomous branchlets are commonly flattened. Some of the branchlets toward the tip of a lateral branch system often bear terminal sporangia. Such a lateral branch system is probably homologous with a sporangium-bearing leaf of a modern fern. The internal anatomy of *Protopteridium* is unknown, but some other fossils probably allied to *Protopteridium* have protostelic stems. It is not known whether any of the Protopteridales have true roots.

COENOPTERIDALES

The Coenopteridales are a large and varied group of fossil ferns known from Middle Devonian to Permian rocks. The leaves are pinnately dissected and, at least sometimes, circinate. In some members of the group, the primary and all succeeding segments of the leaf tend to lie in the same plane, as in modern ferns, and the vascular anatomy of the rachis is also suggestive of modern ferns. In others the vascular anatomy of the leaf rachis is more stem-like, and the segments of the leaf do not all lie in the same plane. *Etapteris* is a form genus of certain leaves of this latter group. The primary pinnae of *Etapteris* are borne alternately on opposite sides of the leaf rachis. Each primary pinna is immediately forked (dichotomously) into two secondary pinnae which lie at an angle to the plane of the primary pinnae. The secondary pinnae are divided into tertiary pinnae, and these often into quaternary pinnae, with pinnae of successive orders tending to lie in different planes.

The stems of the Coenopteridales are usually protostelic, sometimes with definite secondary thickening, and some members of the group evidently reached tree size.

Adventitious roots are borne on the stem of at least some species. The sporangia contain numerous spores and are borne terminally on some of the ultimate segments of the leaf, either singly or in small sori. Species with the leaf segments all in one plane and the sporangia borne in sori are much like modern eusporangiate ferns, except for the truly marginal rather than abaxial position of the sori, and even this distinction is not always clear. On the other hand, coenopterid ferns with the leaf segments in different planes are not much different from the Protopteridales and from the psilophytes.

OPHIOGLOSSALES

The Ophioglossales are a small order of modern ferns which retain a number of apparently primitive characters. There are only three genera, *Helminthostachys*, *Botrychium*, and *Ophioglossum* (Fig. 20.17). *Helminthostachys*, with only a single species, is confined to the Indo-Malayan region. *Botrychium*, with about 23 species, and *Ophioglossum*, with about 25, are cosmopolitan. *Botrychium* is often called the grape fern, from a casual resemblance of the fertile spike to a cluster of tiny grapes, and *Ophioglossum* is called adder's-tongue, from a fancied resemblance of the narrow, forked leaf blade of some species to a snake's tongue. No fossil members of the Ophioglossales are known.

The Ophioglossales differ from all other ferns in having the sporangia borne on a fertile spike which projects from the upper (adaxial) surface of the leaf near the junction of the blade and petiole. Superficially the fertile spike often seems to be a direct continuation of the petiole, whereas the leaf blade appears as a lateral

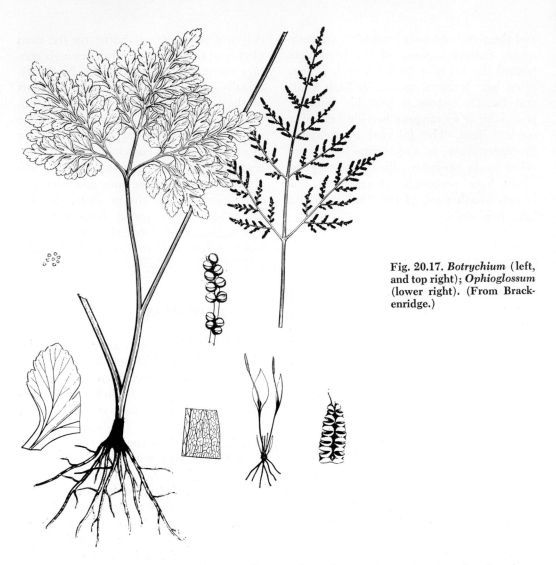

Fig. 20.17. *Botrychium* (left, and top right); *Ophioglossum* (lower right). (From Brackenridge.)

appendage to this petiole—fertile-spike axis. In *Ophioglossum* the fertile spike is unbranched, with a row of sporangia on each side; in *Botrychium* it is pinnately compound or decompound, with a sporangium at the end of each ultimate branch. The sporangia are eusporangiate, and a vascular bundle extends into the base of each. The number of spores in a sporangium ranges from about 1500 to about 15,000.

The morphological nature of the fer-tile spike in the Ophioglossales has been a subject of controversy. The prevailing opinion, founded partly on the vascular anatomy, holds that it generally represents the first pair of pinnae of the leaf, these two pinnae having become fused into one and assumed an erect position. In one species of *Botrychium*, the fertile spike is inserted in the middle of the blade, in a position where an ordinary pair of pinnae would be expected.

The leaves of the Ophioglossales differ from those of most other ferns in not being circinate, although the young leaf is often abruptly bent over near the middle. The leaf blades of *Botrychium* are otherwise more or less fern-like, being typically compound or decompound, with dichotomously branched, free veinlets. The leaves of *Ophioglossum* are usually simple or merely forked, and have reticulate venation. Most species of the Ophioglossales typically produce only one leaf each year.

The stems of the Ophioglossales are short, subterranean, and usually erect. They are basically siphonostelic, with mesarch or endarch xylem, and in *Botrychium* there is some secondary thickening. The plant body is soft and somewhat fleshy throughout, without the sclerenchyma commonly found in other ferns. The roots are strongly mycorhizal and usually lack root hairs.

Gametophytes of the Ophioglossales are mycorhizal and partly or wholly subterranean. They range from pinhead size to 1 inch or even 2 inches long and differ in shape from species to species. Some are simple and flattened; others are more or less cylindric, simple or branched; others are short and stellately branched. The antheridia and archegonia are borne on the same gametophyte. The antheridia are sunken in the body of the gametophyte and contain numerous sperms.

The embryo may or may not have a suspensor, according to the species. Growth of both gametophytes and sporophytes is slow. Development of the embryo into an independent sporophyte commonly takes a year or more, and the gametophyte often persists for some time after the sporophyte has become well established. Two or more sporophytes are sometimes produced from the same gametophyte.

The Ophioglossales clearly belong to the Filicophyta, but they are well set off from all other members of the division. In some of the respects in which they differ from other ferns, they are suggestive of the psilophytes.

ARCHEOPTERIDALES

The Archeopteridales are fossil ferns in which the sporangia are borne on the upper (adaxial) surface of the leaf. *Archeopteris*, the principal genus, is abundant and widely distributed in Late Devonian rocks and is also occasionally found in the Middle Devonian. *Archeopteris* is known principally from carbonized compressions of the leaves, which resemble those of modern ferns and are sometimes as much as 2 m long. The leaves are pinnately twice compound. Some of the pinnules are flattened, with dichotomous free venation. Others are narrower and bear sporangia on the upper side. The sporangia are either sessile (without a stalk) or are borne terminally on short, simple or dichotomously branched stalks. At least some of the species are distinctly heterosporous, with spores of very unequal size. The megasporangia and microsporangia are borne on the same leaf and are only slightly dissimilar in appearance.

FILICALES

All homosporous leptosporangiate ferns are referred to the order Filicales, and the vast majority of the species of the division belong to this one order. The Filicales are often called the true ferns.

The Filicales may be divided into three groups on the basis of the detailed

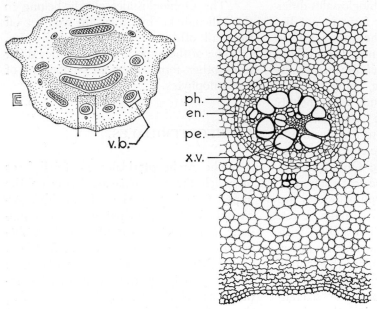

Fig. 20.18. *Pteridium* rhizome, in cross section; left (×6); right, a segment, as indicated (×60); en., endodermis; pe., pericycle; ph., phloem; v.b., vascular bundle; x.v., xylem vessel.

structure and ontogeny of the sporangia. Several small families have **simple sori** in which all sporangia develop simultaneously. Several other families have **gradate sori** in which maturation of the sporangia usually proceeds in regular succession from the center of the sorus to the margin. A single very large family, the Polypodiaceae, has **mixed sori** in which the sporangia mature at different times but in no simple pattern of sequence. The Polypodiaceae are a very heterogeneous group, and most pteridologists believe that they represent a number of end lines which have independently developed the technical characters that mark the family. None of the several attempts to divide the Polypodiaceae into smaller and more natural families has yet proved satisfactory; therefore, the family is customarily retained in the broad sense as a group of convenience. The Polypodiaceae are common in both tropical and temperate regions, and most familiar ferns of temperate regions belong to this family.

The common bracken fern, *Pteridium aquilinum*, is a cosmopolitan species of the Polypodiaceae that is often studied in general botany classes. Like the majority of members of the family, *Pteridium* lacks an aerial stem, and the leaves arise from a rhizome. The stele of a *Pteridium* rhizome is more complex than that of most ferns, being a highly modified dictyostele with two concentric dissected cylinders of vascular tissue. Both the inner and outer cylinders contribute to the vascular supply of each leaf. Each vascular bundle of the rhizome, as seen in cross section, contains a central mass of xylem, surrounded successively by phloem, pericycle, and endodermis. Some of the xylem cells are ordinary tracheids, but many of them are relatively large and have perforated end walls, so that a continuous passageway is provided from one cell to the next. A linear series of these modified tracheids is called a **vessel**, and the individual modified tracheid is a vessel segment. Vessels are very common in flowering plants (Anthophyta), but *Selaginella, Pteridium,* and a few other ferns are the only pteridophytes in which they are known.[1] In addition to the tracheids and vessels, the xylem of a vascular bundle of *Pteridium* usually contains some parenchyma cells.

The leaves of *Pteridium* are pinnately decompound, with the lowest pair of pinnae often much larger than the others. Anatomically they are much like the leaves of flowering plants, having well-developed layers of palisade and spongy mesophyll. The sori are borne in a row along the margin of each pinnule. The margin is turned under, and a small flap of tissue grows out above and below the row of sori, forming a continuous marginal indusium. The flap which corresponds to the lower epidermis of the leaf is hidden from view, so that the flap corresponding to the upper epidermis appears to be the complete indusium.

The sporangia of *Pteridium,* like those of most other leptosporangiate ferns, are nearly discoid, with slightly bulging sides, and each sporangium is borne on a slender stalk. The margin of the sporangium is formed by a single ring of cells, the annulus. As in other members of the Polypodiaceae, the annulus is interrupted at the stalk. In other families of the Filicales, the annulus is more obliquely set (with relation to the stalk) and usually forms a continuous ring.

Except for several (commonly about eight) cells nearest the stalk on one side, the cells of the annulus of *Pteridium* and other polypodiaceous ferns have conspicuously thickened walls. When the sporangium is mature, the cells of the annulus die and dry out, and the resulting hygro-

[1] Perforations also develop occasionally in the end walls between adjacent tracheids in species of *Equisetum,* and these rows of connected tracheids may also be interpreted as vessels.

scopic changes set up a tension, so that the annulus is like a curved spring. When the tension is great enough, the annulus breaks open between the two central cells of the row of eight, and the longer part of the annulus flips backward, rupturing the lateral walls of the sporangium and forcibly discharging the spores. The four central cells of the row are usually more or less differentiated from the cells on each end of the row and are often called the **lip cells.**

The gametophytes of *Pteridium* and most other polypodiaceous ferns are of the thin, heart-shaped type described on p. 387. Under favorable conditions the gametophytes mature in a few weeks, and they die as soon as the sporophyte has become well established.

Another family of the Filicales, the Cyatheaceae, is of interest because of the large proportion of tree ferns in the group. The family is confined to tropical and south-temperate regions, usually in humid forests. Several other families of the Filicales, including the Polypodiaceae, also have some arborescent genera. Stems of tree ferns are unbranched and usually erect, with a crown of very large, compound leaves. The stem has no cambium, and often it is covered over much of its length by short adventitious roots. Large tree ferns are as much as 20 m tall, with leaf blades 3–4 m long, borne on petioles of equal length. Fossil tree ferns that are probably related to the Cyatheaceae are known from rocks as far back as the Jurassic period.

MARSILEALES

The Marsileales are heterosporous, leptosporangiate ferns which grow in water or wet places and are rooted to the sub-

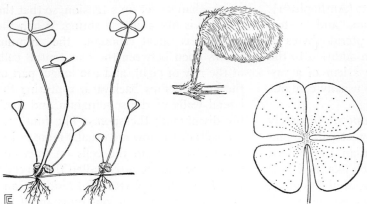

Fig. 20.19. *Marsilea vestita.* Left, habit (×⅜); top center, sporocarp (×4); lower right, leaf (×1).

strate. The sporangia are enclosed in modified folded leaves or leaf segments called **sporocarps,** and both types of sporangia (megasporangia and microsporangia) are borne in the same sporocarp. The order contains only a single family, the Marsileaceae. *Marsilea* (Fig. 20.19), the water clover, is the most familiar genus, with about 40 species distributed throughout most of the world. The leaves of *Marsilea* have a long petiole, and a flat, floating blade composed of four leaflets, all attached at nearly the same point (actually two closely set pairs), suggesting a four-leaf clover.

The spores of *Marsilea* remain viable for many years, and the sporocarps open only after decay. In addition to the sporangia, a sporocarp contains a considerable amount of gelatinous material. If a sporocarp is placed in water after a segment of the wall has been cut away, the gelatinous material expands and forces the sporocarp open. The spores germinate and the gametophytes mature while still embedded in this gelatinous mass.

The male gametophyte of *Marsilea,* which matures in less than 24 hours, consists of a prothallial cell and an antherid-

ium with 16 sperms. The prothallial cell, which is an evolutionary vestige of the body of the gametophyte, remains within the old wall of the microspore, but the antheridium protrudes. The female gametophyte consists of a very large basal cell and a small multicellular bulge containing an archegonium. The basal cell fills the old megaspore wall, and the remainder of the gametophyte protrudes from a small opening in the wall. The embryo develops rapidly after fertilization.

SALVINIALES

The Salviniales are heterosporous, leptosporanginate ferns which float on the surface of the water. The sporangia are enclosed in specialized appendages of the leaves, called sporocarps. A sporocarp contains numerous microsporangia, or a single megasporangium, but not both types. Male and female gametophytes are both very small and mainly enclosed within the spore wall.

The order contains a single family, the Salviniaceae, with two small genera, *Salvinia* and *Azolla.* *Azolla* has adventitious roots extending a short distance into the water, but *Salvinia* is rootless. In both genera the delicate, branching stem becomes a few inches long and is provided with small, simple to bifid or more or less dissected leaves. The stems are easily fragmented, and vegetative reproduction is accomplished in this way. The leaves of *Azolla* each contain a special chamber inhabited by *Anabaena azollae*, a blue-green alga. Experimental evidence suggests that the alga fixes atmospheric nitrogen and that the relationship is symbiotic. The universal occurrence of this single species of alga in the leaves of *Azolla* suggests that reproduction of this water fern may be chiefly vegetative, with long-distance dispersal being due to waterfowl.

Both *Salvinia* and *Azolla* are found in the United States and elsewhere in the world. Fossils of both genera are known from Cenozoic deposits only.

The Salviniales and the Marsileales have sometimes been grouped into a single order, but it is now believed that they are not closely related and that the similarities between them are due to parallel evolution. The sporocarps of *Salvinia* and *Azolla* are

Fig. 20.20. *Ceratopteris pteridoides*, a floating aquatic fern that is sometimes grown in aquaria in America; a closely related species is used for food in the Orient. (New York Botanical Garden photo.)

quite different from those of the Marsileales, and the detailed ontogeny of the sori of the two orders suggests that they are related to different groups within the Filicales.

ECONOMIC IMPORTANCE

Modern ferns are of relatively little economic importance. Some are grown for ornament, and others are used for Christmas decorations. The bracken, *Pteridium aquilinum*, is mildly poisonous to livestock but is seldom eaten in sufficient quantities to cause serious damage. The fiddleheads and young foliage of many species are edible. Leaves of *Athyrium esculentum*, a common Malaysian species, and *Ceratopteris thalictroides*, an aquatic species sometimes grown in rice paddies in the Orient, are used as raw or cooked green vegetables. Even bracken fiddleheads are fairly palatable, when properly cooked so

that the poisonous principle is eliminated, although they are seldom consumed except by people who wish to demonstrate the variety of things that can be eaten. A drug derived from the rhizomes of certain species of *Dryopteris*, especially *D. filix-mas*, the "male fern," is a standard anthelmintic used to expel worms, especially tapeworms, from the intestinal tract of man and other animals, although it is now often replaced by some of the newer synthetics.

Ferns contributed to the vegetable deposits of the Carboniferous period which were transformed into coal, but they were much less important in that regard than the lepidophytes and calamophytes.

RELATIONSHIPS

The ferns are evidently derived from the psilophytes, to which they are connected by such fossils as *Protopteridium*.

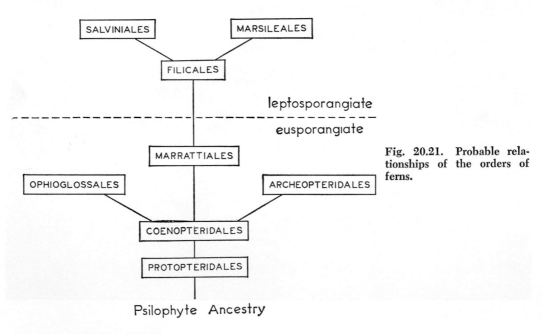

Fig. 20.21. Probable relationships of the orders of ferns.

Among modern ferns the Ophioglossales are the most primitive group, but they are not to be regarded as directly ancestral to any of the other orders. The Marattiales help connect the Ophioglossales to the Filicales, having some characters of one group and some of the other. The Filicales are the most advanced order of homosporous ferns; within the Filicales, the Polypodiaceae, with vertical annulus and mixed sori, are the most advanced types. The Marsileales and Salvineales are separate heterosporous derivatives from the Filicales. The heterosporous condition has evidently been separately achieved by a number of groups of vascular cryptogams, and some of the heterosporous fossil ferns, such as *Archeopteris*, relate to the eusporangiate rather than to the leptosporangiate homosporous ferns. Both the Cycadophyta and the Anthophyta are believed to be derived eventually from ancient heterosporous eusporangiate ferns.

SUGGESTED READING

Andrews, Henry M., Jr., *Ancient Plants and the World They Lived In*, Comstock, Ithaca, New York, 1947, 279 pp. A popularized treatment, with many illustrations and a minimum of technical terminology, written by a competent paleobotanist. It deals mainly with the vascular cryptogams and the gymnosperms.

Manton, Irene, *Problems of Cytology and Evolution in the Pteridophyta*, Cambridge University Press, New York, 1950, 316 pp. The application of cytological methods to the study of evolution of genera and species in the vascular cryptogams. The student without a background in genetics will be better able to understand this interesting but rather technical book after finishing Chapter 35 of this text.

Division
Cycadophyta

CYCADOPHYTES

CHAPTER 21

Vascular plants with roots, stems, and leaves, the leaves usually large and pinnately compound, the central cylinder generally with leaf gaps; seeds borne on scarcely to strongly modified megasporophylls which are often aggregated into a simple strobilus; ovules more or less exposed to the air at the time of pollination, the pollen generally landing at the micropyle; female gametophyte multicellular. A single class, the Cycadae.

◄

Encephalartos transvenosus, in Transvaal, Union of South Africa. Inset: cones of another species of *Encephalartos.* (Photos by W. H. Hodge.)

Introduction to the Seed Plants

The divisions Cycadophyta, Coniferophyta, and Anthophyta differ from all other plants, except some fossil lepidophytes, in the production of seeds. Even the lepidophyte seeds lack one of the essential features of the seeds of modern plants, as has been noted in Chapter 18.

All seed plants are heterosporous. The characters which distinguish seed plants from heterosporous cryptogams relate to the ontogeny of the male and female gametophytes and the embryo sporophytes. The megaspore of a seed plant is permanently enclosed within the megasporangium, and the female gametophyte which develops from the megaspore completes its development while still enclosed within the megasporangium wall. The developing female gametophyte is nourished by the enclosing sporophyte. The egg or eggs produced by a female gametophyte may or may not be associated with definite archegonia, but, in any case, they are enclosed within the megasporangium. The embryo sporophyte which develops from the fertilized egg characteristically begins its growth while still enclosed within the body of the female gametophyte.

The structure and function of the reproductive parts of seed plants were partly deciphered before the correlation of these parts with the reproductive structures of vascular cryptogams was understood. Some reproductive parts of seed plants, therefore, have names which do not reflect their homologies. The wall of the megasporangium of a seed plant is called the **nucellus.** The nucellus is enclosed by one or two additional layers of tissue, the **integuments.** The integuments have no obvious counterpart among heterosporous cryptogams, and their evolutionary origin is not clearly understood. The megasporangium, plus the enclosing integument or integuments, is called an **ovule.** There is a small opening through the integuments at one end of the ovule. In the less modified types of ovules, this opening, called the **micropyle** (from Greek *mikros*, small, and *pylē*, little gate), is at the opposite end from the stalk. At the micropylar end of the ovule the megasporangial wall (the nucellus) is generally well defined; at the other end it is often not clearly differentiated from the integuments.

The microspores of seed plants generally undergo one or more mitotic divisions before they are released from the microsporangium in which they are produced. At the stage in which they are shed from the microsporangium, the young male gametophytes are called **pollen grains.** The microsporangium itself is called a **pollen sac.** The nuclear divisions which occur in the development of pollen grains from microspores do not result in any significant increase in the volume of the protoplast, and the wall of the pollen grain is merely the matured wall of the microspore. The sperms of most seed plants (the cycadophytes are a notable exception) are delivered to the egg through an outgrowth from the pollen grain, called the **pollen tube.** There is no definite antheridium, and sooner or later the sperms are free in the cytoplasm of the pollen tube. The pollen tube digests its way through the tissue enclosing the female gametophyte and breaks open at the end, delivering the sperms.

The ripened ovule is called a **seed,** and the integuments of the ovule become the seed coat. The mature seed characteristically represents three successive generations: (1) the integuments and nucellus of the old sporophyte; (2) the femal gametophyte; and (3) the embryo sporophyte. The nucellus and the body of the female gametophyte may or may not be evident in the mature seed. The micropyle of the ovule is often visible as an imperfection in the mature seed coat.

The ovules and young seeds of flowering plants (Anthophyta) are characteristically enclosed within a structure called an **ovary,** and the flowering plants are therefore often called **angiosperms** (from Greek *angeion*, a vessel, or enclosing vessel, and *sperma*, seed). The ovules and young seeds of coniferophytes and cycadophytes are exposed to the air, and pollen grains can be carried directly to the micropyle. The coniferophytes and cycadophytes are therefore **gymnosperms** (from Greek *gymnos*, naked, and *sperma*, seed). This basic difference between the gymnosperms and angiosperms was first pointed out in 1825 by the Scottish botanist and natural scientist Robert Brown.

There are several other differences be-

Fig. 21.1. Left, Robert Brown (1773–1858), Scottish botanist and naturalist, who pointed out the distinction between gymnosperms and angiosperms. (Courtesy of the New York Botanical Garden.) Right, Charles J. Chamberlain (1863–1943), American botanist, outstanding student of the cycads. (Courtesy of Mrs. Charles J. Chamberlain.)

tween gymnosperms and angiosperms, and the gymnosperms were for many years considered to form a natural taxonomic group. The evidence now available casts serious doubt on this conclusion. The gymnosperms fall into two groups, the cycadophytes and coniferophytes, both of which can be traced as far back as the Devonian period in the fossil record, with no indication of any common ancestor short of the ferns or more likely the psilophytes. Modern students of the gymnosperms, therefore, treat the cycadophytes and coniferophytes as parallel groups which have independently achieved the seed habit. The term *gymnosperm* is still useful to describe plants in which the seeds are not enclosed in an ovary, just as the term *pteridophytes* is useful for vascular cryptogams, but the gymnosperms are no longer generally regarded as a proper *taxonomic* group.

Cycadophyta

HISTORY

The Cycadophyta were first treated as a separate division by Bessey in 1907. His proposal, at first generally disregarded, has received increasing acceptance during the past several decades. Students of the gymnosperms are now agreed that the cycadophytes form a group distinct from the coniferophytes, but botanists continue to differ as to how this distinction should be expressed in a taxonomic system.

CHARACTERISTICS

The cycadophytes are gymnosperms with more or less fern-like, usually large and pinnately compound leaves. The seeds are borne on scarcely to strongly modified megasporophylls which, in most modern species and some fossils, are aggregated into a simple terminal cone. The stem has a large pith, a well-developed cortex, and rather scanty vascular tissue. There is usually some secondary thickening, but the cortex remains a prominent part of the mature stem. The central cylinder is a siphonostele, usually with well-developed leaf gaps. The stem of modern species and many fossils usually appears to be unbranched.

CLASSIFICATION AND DISTRIBUTION

The modern cycadophytes are an evolutionary vestige of a group which was abundant and varied in Mesozoic and late Paleozoic times. The Paleozoic and Mesozoic forms evidently occurred over most of the world (possibly indicating a relatively uniform mild climate), but the modern species are wholly confined to tropical and subtropical regions. All cycadophytes, living and fossil, are referred to a single class, the Cycadae. All the modern species, and some of the fossils, belong to the order Cycadales. Most of the remaining cycadophytes can be placed in one or another of three additional orders, the Cycadofilicales, Caytoniales, and Bennettitales.

CYCADOFILICALES

The Cycadofilicales, also called **seed ferns** or **pteridosperms**, are fern-like plants with seeds (Fig. 21.2). They are known from rocks of Late Devonian to Jurassic age but are most abundant in the Carboniferous. The Devonian forms are referred here because of the anatomy of the stem and leaves, no seeds yet having been found in association with them. The leaves of pteridosperms resemble those of ferns, and most of the numerous fossil leaves which have caused the Carboniferous period to be called the Age of Ferns are actually pteridosperms. Pteridosperm leaves were evidently firmer than most fern leaves, however, and

Fig. 21.2. A seed fern, reconstructed.

the cuticle is much more resistant to alteration under chemical treatment than the cuticle of modern or fossil ferns.

Many pteridosperms were small trees, reaching a height of 30 feet or more, with an unbranched stem and a crown of large leaves, as in modern tree ferns. Others had climbing and more or less branched stems, with more scattered leaves. Shorter plants, both branched and unbranched, are also known. The primary vascular cylinder is a siphonostele, and the primary xylem is commonly mesarch. Usually there are well-developed leaf gaps, but, in some of the Devonian fossils referred here, the leaf trace is merely a branch from a strand of primary xylem that continues upward without interruption. The stem generally shows some secondary growth, but the proportion of secondary tissues is not high (Fig. 21.4). The tracheids of the secondary wood usually have bordered pits. The leaf trace consists of one or several strands. Often a strand which departs from the stele as a single trace forks into two before entering the base of the leaf. The roots are commonly slender and adventitious.

Seeds of many pteridosperms are well enough preserved to show the integument, the nucellus, and the female gametophyte, and some even show suggestions of archegonia. Yet no embryo has ever been found in a pteridosperm seed. The reason for this lack remains to be clarified. There is some indication that the nucellus may have degenerated before the female gametophyte matured, so that the sperms had direct access to the archegonia. The most characteristic position of the seeds is along the margins of the leaves, but in some Permian species they are on the leaf surface instead (either the upper or the lower surface, according to the species). The megasporo-

Fig. 21.3. Leaf impression of *Neuropteris rarinervis*, a seed fern of Carboniferous age. (From Kukuk.)

phylls (i.e., the seed-bearing leaves) are similar to ordinary vegetative leaves, or only slightly modified. The microsporophylls are pinnately compound or decompound, with several microsporangia on each pinna or pinnule, but they are often more different from the vegetative leaves than are the megasporophylls.

The stems, leaves, and seeds of pteridosperms are more often preserved separately than attached, and there are many form genera as a result. Some of the common form genera based on leaves are *Alethopteris*, *Neuropteris* (Fig. 21.3), and *Sphenopteris*. The leaf of a particular kind of pteridosperm was originally described in

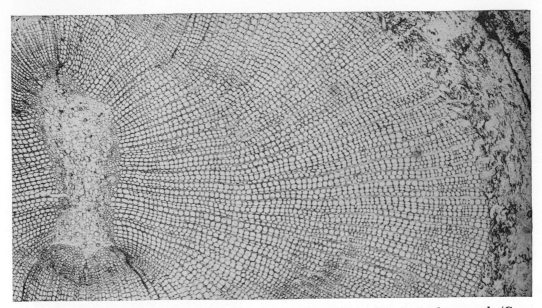

Fig. 21.4. *Callistoxylon*, the stem of a fossil seed fern, showing well-developed secondary growth. (Copyright by General Biological Supply House, Inc., Chicago.)

1828 as *Sphenopteris hoeninghausi*; the stem was described in 1866 as *Dadoxylon oldhamium*; the seed was later described as *Lagenostoma oldhamia*; the cupulate envelope partly enclosing the seed was described as a species of *Calymmatotheca*, the petiole as *Rhachiopteris aspera*, and the roots as *Kaloxylon hookeri*. Each of these parts, originally found detached, was later found attached to other parts of the plant; and all these names are believed to apply to the same species. The microsporophylls are perhaps also known, but they have not yet been found attached to the stem. The separate names here listed are still used to refer to the detached parts, partly as a matter of convenience, and partly because there is no assurance that the correlations which have been demonstrated are the only ones possible. Individual organs of different kinds of modern plants are sometimes so similar that they can scarcely be distinguished, and the chance for con-

fusion is considerably greater among the fossils.

CAYTONIALES

The Caytoniales (Fig. 21.5) are an unusual group of fossil cycadophytes that occur in rocks of Triassic to Cretaceous age. The stem is known only from fragmentary branched twigs. The leaves are fairly common fossils and have been known since 1828. They characteristically have a slender petiole and four more or less digitately arranged leaflets (actually two closely set pairs). A common species has narrowly elliptic leaflets about 2 inches long, with a midrib and a network of smaller veins. The microsporophylls are pinnately compound, with the microsporangia all on one side. The ovules are contained in small, nearly closed pouches, which are pinnately arranged along a short slender axis that is probably a modified megasporophyll. Each pouch holds a number of small ovules, from about 8 to about 30 in different species. These pouches were at first (1925) compared to the ovaries of angiosperms, and the Caytoniales were suggested as possible ancestors of the flowering plants. The resemblance is purely superficial, however, and the Caytoniales are now generally regarded as a pteridospermous offshoot that died out without leaving descendants.

BENNETTITALES

The Bennettitales are a group of fossil cycadophytes known from rocks of Triassic to Cretaceous age. They were evidently common during most of the Mesozoic era; and it is this group, more than the true cycads (Cycadales), which have caused the Mesozoic era sometimes to be called the Age of Cycads. The Bennettitales, often called **cycadeoids,** are an offshoot from the pteridosperms, characterized by their well-developed female cones with highly modified megasporophylls. The cones are commonly borne on short axillary shoots. Usually there is a group of microsporophylls toward the base of each fertile shoot, beneath the female cone (Fig. 21.6). The microsporophylls are pinnately compound, more or less spreading, and generally several inches long. Sometimes they are connate below to form a cup-like base. Most pinnae of a microsporophyll have a row of synangia along each side. Each synangium is composed of more or less numerous, partly fused microsporangia. The female cone terminates the fertile shoot; the cone axis bears numerous megasporophylls intermingled with sterile appendages which presumably represent modified megasporophylls that have lost their reproductive function. Each fertile

Fig. 21.5.   *Caytonia. A,* leaf (×½); *B,* base of leaflet (×3); *C,* microsporophyll (×12); *D,* seed pouch with two ovules (×9); *E,* megasporophyll (×1½). (All figures after T. M. Harris.)

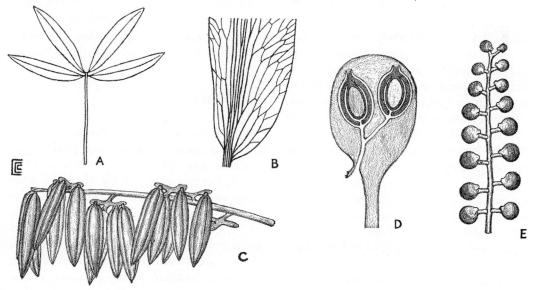

Fig. 21.6. *Cycadeoidea ingens*, a Mesozoic cycadophyte (Bennettitales); restoration showing pinnately compound microsporophylls surrounding the female cone. (Courtesy of the Chicago Natural History Museum.)

megasporophyll is narrow and undivided, with a single terminal ovule. The seeds are much like those of pteridosperms, except that they often contain embryos; the embryo has two cotyledons.

The stem of the Bennettitales is typically unbranched (except for the short fertile shoots) with a crown of leaves at the top. Sparsely branched forms are not uncommon, however, and a few are freely branched. Like other cycadophytes, the Bennettitales have a relatively large pith and cortex, and comparatively little xylem. The primary vascular cylinder is an endarch siphonostele with well-developed leaf gaps; the leaf traces pass directly through the cortex to the leaf. The leaves are generally large (sometimes as much as 10 feet long), of firm structure, and pinnately once compound, as in modern cycads. A few genera, such as *Williamsoniella*, have simple, strap-shaped, entire leaves. The roots of the cycadeoids, so far as known, are fibrous and adventitious, as in the pteridosperms.

It is generally agreed that the Bennettitales have no modern descendants.

CYCADALES

The Cycadales, or **cycads**, are cycadophytes with the microsporophylls simple and aggregated into a strobilus. There are 9 modern genera with about 65 species, all restricted to tropical and subtropical regions. *Zamia floridana* (Fig. 21.7), of Florida, is the only cycad native to the United States. Other species of *Zamia* occur from Mexico and the West Indies to northern South America. Fossil cycads are known from as far back as the Triassic. Cycads are often much like small tree ferns in appearance, with a simple trunk and a crown of pinnately compound leaves, but the leaves are much firmer than those of most ferns. The arborescent forms are usually called palms by non-botanists, and even in areas where tree ferns are well known, they are not generally called ferns.

Root

The primary root of a cycad seedling develops into a large main root which often becomes several or many feet long. Such a root is called a **taproot.** Some branches from the upper part of the taproot often grow upward to the surface of the ground, where they produce numer-

ous, short, thick, irregular branches. A zone in the cortex of these aerial roots is inhabited by a species of *Anabaena* (blue-green algae). The relationship is believed to be symbiotic, with the alga supplying nitrogen to the root, much as the symbiotic nitrogen-fixing bacteria supply nitrogen to the roots of legumes.

Stem

The stem of cycads is typically erect, unbranched, or with only a few small branches, and up to 10 feet or, in one species, even 60 feet tall. The leaves are borne in a crown at the top, and below this the stem is covered by an armor formed by the persistent petiole bases of dead leaves of previous years. The approximate age of the plant can be computed from the num-

Fig. 21.7. *Zamia floridana*, with female cones. (Photo by Gilbert Hughes III.)

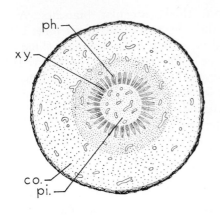

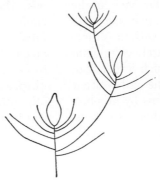

Fig. 21.8. *Zamia floridana.* Left, cross section of stem; co., cortex; ph., phloem; pi., pith; xy., xylem. (After Chamberlain.) Right, method of branching, the internodes shown much exaggerated. (After F. G. Smith.)

ber of leaf bases, the number of leaves in a crown, and the number of years' duration of a crown. On this basis some cycads are believed to be more than 1000 years old. Some species have a short, fleshy-thickened, underground stem instead of an aerial trunk. Most species have strictly terminal cones, and further elongation of the stem after a cone has been produced is usually due to growth from an axillary bud just beneath the cone. The apparently simple and unbranched stem of many cycads is, therefore, in a strict morphological sense, composed of a series of short axillary branches. Such a stem is said to be **sympodial.**

The stem of a cycad (Fig. 21.8) has a large pith and thick cortex, with relatively little xylem. The primary vascular cylinder is generally an endarch siphonostele, although seedlings and the cone axes tend to be mesarch. The secondary xylem consists largely of pitted tracheids, except in *Zamia* and *Stangeria*, which have fernlike scalariform tracheids instead. The phloem consists largely of sieve cells with scattered sieve areas and slanting end walls. Apical growth is due to the activity of an apical meristem, and the slight secondary thickening is due to a cambium. Sometimes there are several concentric rings of

vascular tissue, the rings being produced successively by new cambial layers which differentiate from the parenchymatous tissue of the cortex.

LEAVES

The leaves of cycads are firm and pinnately (in *Bowenia* bipinnately) compound. They are typically several feet long, ranging from a minimum of about 2 inches to a maximum of about 10 feet. The leaves of *Cycas* are distinctly circinate in bud; other genera vary from slightly to not at all circinate. The pinnae are often stiffly spine-tipped.

Usually several leaf traces enter each leaf. The traces spiral outward and slightly upward through the cortex, some of them often passing as much as halfway around the stem before entering the leaf. The leaf has a heavy cuticle and a thick-walled epidermis, with the stomates chiefly confined to the lower surface and commonly sunken in small pockets. Usually there is a thickwalled hypodermis just within the epidermis. The mesophyll usually consists of an upper layer of palisade tissue and a lower layer of compact spongy tissue. The vascular bundles are surrounded by a bundle sheath of thick-walled cells. The whole leaf anatomy is suggestive of that often found in plants of very dry habitats, as discussed in Chapter 27. Possibly the scantiness of the xylem necessitates compensating adaptations in the leaf structure to minimize damage from water loss.

DEVELOPMENT OF THE POLLEN

In contrast to the Bennettitales, the cycads are strictly **dioecious** (Greek, two-houses); i.e., the megasporophylls and microsporophylls are borne on separate individuals. The Bennettitales, with both types of sporophylls on the same plant, are **monoecious**. The microsporophylls of cycads are simple (i.e., not compound) and are aggregated into a simple strobilus. The microsporangia are borne on the lower side, often covering the whole lower surface, and usually numbering from 25 to about 1000. Development of the microsporangia follows the eusporangiate pattern, and there is a definite tapetum. A microsporangium contains numerous microspore mother cells, each of which undergoes meiosis to form a tetrad of microspores.

The microspores have n chromosomes and are the first cells in the male gametophyte generation. The wall of the microspore is composed of an outer layer called the **exine** and an inner layer called the **intine.** The first division of the protoplast within the wall of the ellipsoid microspore results in the formation of a small prothallial cell at one end and a larger cell occupying the remainder of the space. The prothallial cell is an evolutionary vestige of the vegetative body of the gametophyte. The larger of the two cells formed in the first division divides again, forming a small **generative cell** next to the prothallial cell, and a larger "**tube cell**" filling the rest of the space. At this stage the three-celled male gametophyte, now called a **pollen grain,** is shed from the microsporangium.

DEVELOPMENT OF THE OVULES

The megasporophylls (Fig. 21.10) of most cycads are aggregated into a compact

Fig. 21.9. *Zamia chigua,* in Colombia, with male cones. (Photo by José Cuatrecasas.)

Cycadophyta: Cycadophytes 411

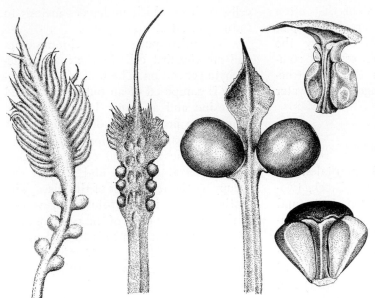

Fig. 21.10. Megasporophylls of living cycads. Left, *Cycas revoluta*, with young ovules; next, *Cycas circinalis*, with young ovules; third, *Cycas rumphii*, with seeds; upper right, *Dioon edule*, with seeds; lower right, *Zamia*, with seeds. (*Zamia* ×⅔; others × ⅓.) Note the gradual transition from the pinnately compound megasporophyll of *Cycas revoluta* to the more prevalent type in modern cycads, shown by *Dioon* and *Zamia*. (From W. H. Brown, *The Plant Kingdom*, 1935; courtesy of Ginn & Company, Boston.)

strobilus that ranges from about 1 inch to nearly 3 feet long. In *Cycas* the megasporophylls are only loosely clustered, and the distal part of each megasporophyll is more or less expanded and often pinnately cleft, whereas the proximal part (the part nearest the stem) bears a row of ovules along each side of the rachis. In other cycads the megasporophyll usually consists of a stalk and an expanded cap, with two ovules which lie alongside the stalk beneath the cap.

The ovule has a single, massive integument that is wholly distinct (above the base) from the well-developed nucellus. At the opposite end from the point of attachment to the megasporophyll, the integument is interrupted by a small opening, the micropyle. The integument does not fit closely around the upper (micropylar) end of the nucellus, and the space between them is called the **pollen chamber.** The ovule produces a single, large megaspore mother cell surrounded by the nucellus. The megaspore mother cell undergoes meiosis, giving rise to a single functional megaspore and two or three vestigial megaspores which soon degenerate and disappear.

FEMALE GAMETOPHYTE

The megaspore has n chromosomes and is the first cell in the female gametophyte generation. By a series of mitotic divisions, it gives rise to a multicellular gametophyte which is enclosed within the nucellus of the ovule. Formation of cell walls within the body of the female gametophyte is delayed until after a number of nuclear divisions has occurred, so that there is a **free-nuclear** stage in which numerous nuclei are scattered through a continuous mass of cytoplasm. Sometimes as many as 1000 nuclei are produced before any partitions are formed.

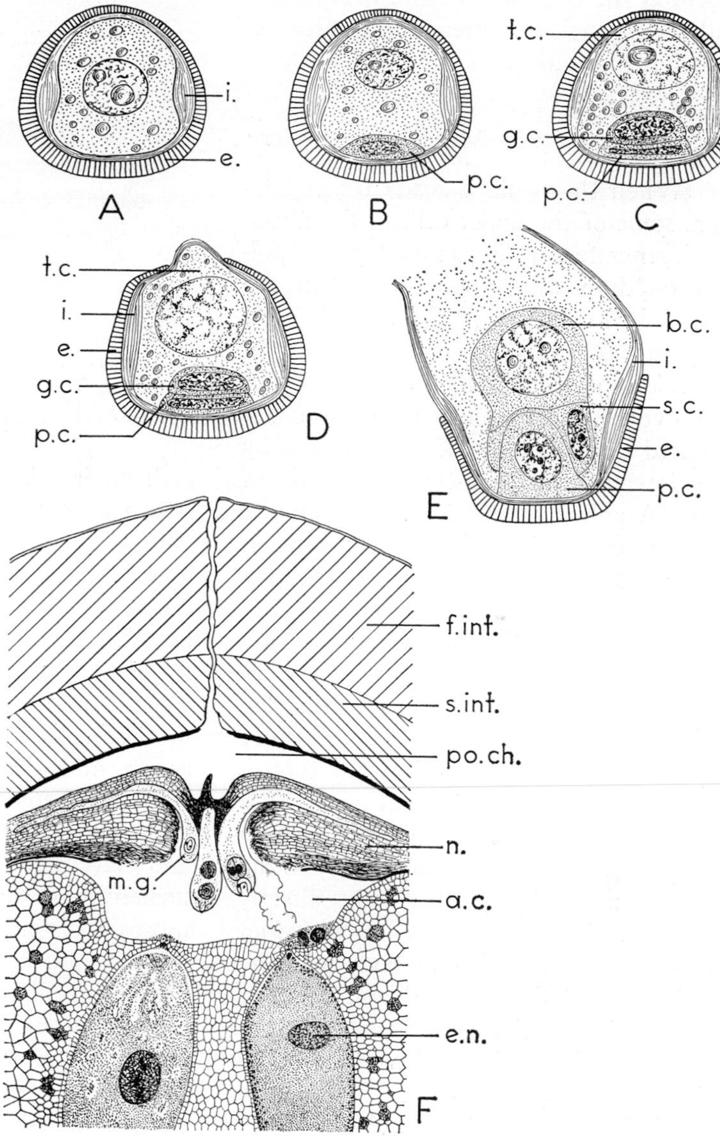

Fig. 21.11. Dioon edule.
A–E, development of pollen: A, microspore; B, two-celled stage; C, mature pollen grain; D, germinating pollen grain; E, lower part of developing pollen tube; F, long section of upper part of developing ovule at the time of fertilization; the pollen tube at the right has discharged its sperms, which with their surrounding cytoplasm lie near the top of the archegonium at the right; a.c., archegonial chamber; b.c., body cell; e., exine; e.n., egg nucleus; g.c., generative cell; i., intine; f.int., fleshy integument; s.int., stony integument; n., nucellus; m.g., male gametophyte; po.ch., pollen chamber; p.c., prothallial cell; t.c., tube cell; s.c., stalk cell. (A–E, × about 125; F, × about 20.) (All adapted from Chamberlain.)

The female gametophyte does not completely fill the nucellus at the micropylar end, and the resulting cavity is called the **archegonial chamber**. The archegonial chamber is separated from the pollen chamber by the nucellus. Exclusive of the ordinary gametophytic cells which line the "venter," the archegonium consists of only four cells: two neck cells, a very large egg, and a ventral canal "cell." The ventral canal cell is represented only by a nucleus which lies within the same mass of cytoplasm as the egg nucleus, and it (the ventral canal nucleus) often degenerates before fertilization.

MATURATION OF THE MALE GAMETOPHYTE

When the ovule is ready for pollination, some of the upper cells of the nucellus degenerate, forming a mucilaginous **pollination drop** which oozes out from the top of the micropyle. (**Pollination**, in gymnosperms, is the transfer of the pollen from the microsporangium to the micropyle of the ovule.) The pollen grains are distributed by the wind, and possibly also by the insects which customarily feed on them. A pollen grain which lands on the pollination drop is held there and is drawn down into the pollen chamber as the pollination drop dries and contracts.

On reaching the nucellus at the base of the pollen chamber, the pollen grain germinates, forming a **pollen tube.** The intine expands in a local area opposite (not adjacent to) the prothallial cell, rupturing the exine and pushing out as the wall of the pollen tube. The pollen tube grows slowly into the nucellus, tangentially to the female gametophyte rather than directly toward it. The generative cell soon divides to produce a **stalk cell** and a **body cell.** The prothallial cell, the stalk cell, and the body cell remain at the pollen-grain end of the gametophyte, the pollen tube proper being formed by enlargement of the tube cell of the pollen grain.

The pollen grain acts as a haustorium, producing digestive enzymes and absorbing food from the degenerating nucellar tissue around it. After several months, the upper end of the nucellus is so thoroughly destroyed that the pollen-grain end of the male gametophyte hangs loose in the

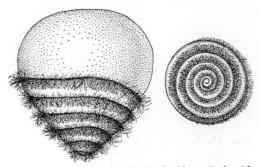

Fig. 21.12.   Sperm of *Zamia floridana*. Left, side view; right, end view of ciliate part. (×125.) (After Webber; from W. H. Brown, *The Plant Kingdom*, 1935; courtesy of Ginn & Company, Boston.)

archegonial chamber, suspended from the pollen tube, which is anchored in the less damaged, lateral tissue of the nucellus. The body cell of the male gametophyte divides at about this time into two sperm mother cells. The protoplast (or most of it) of each sperm mother cell matures into a sperm, and the original wall of the sperm mother cell breaks down, liberating the sperm into the cytoplasm of the pollen tube. The sperms (Fig. 21.12) are relatively large, frequently about 0.3 mm long, and have numerous whiplash flagella attached to a spiral band at one end. In most cycads only two sperms are produced by the pollen grain; but in *Microcycas* the stalk cell cuts off a succession of body cells, each of which produces 2 sperms, and 16 or more sperms are often present in a single pollen tube. The pollen-grain end of the gametophyte now swells and bursts, releasing the sperms and much of the rest of its contents into the archegonial chamber. Some of the cytoplasm of the egg also escapes into the archegonial chamber, and eventually the nucleus of the sperm reaches the nucleus of the egg.

Fusion of a sperm and an egg constitutes fertilization. More than one sperm may enter the cytoplasm of an egg, but only one sperm nucleus fuses with an egg nucleus. The fertilized egg has 2n chromosomes and is the first cell in the sporophyte generation. It gives rise, by a series of mitotic divisions, to the embryo of the seed. Walls do not form between the

nuclei of the embryo until 64 to 1000 or more nuclei have been produced. Before the formation of partitions, the embryo is said to be in the free-nuclear stage. Often several young embryos are produced in an ovule, but usually only one matures.

The embryo has a primary root, a primary shoot, and two cotyledons which are attached just below the primary shoot. The primary shoot of the embryo of a seed plant is called the **epicotyl**, or

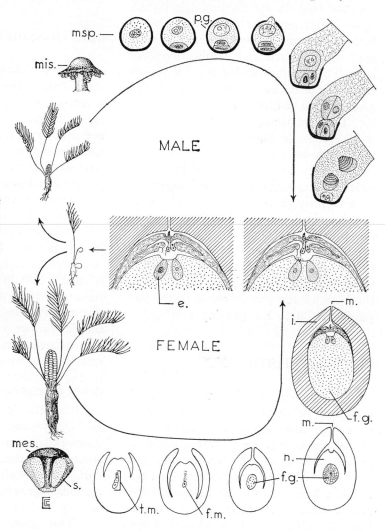

Fig. 21.13. **Life cycle of** *Zamia:* e., archegonium with fertilized egg; f.g., female gametophyte; f.m., functional megaspore; i., integument; m., micropyle; mes., megasporophyll; mis., microsporophyll; msp., microspore; n., nucellus; p.g., pollen grain; t.m., tetrad of megaspores.

plumule, and the primary root is called the radicle. The radicle of a cycad seed lies at the micropylar end and is attached to a long, tightly coiled suspensor which, at an earlier stage in the ontogeny of the seed, served to push the embryo down into the body of the female gametophyte. The embryo of the mature seed is embedded in the body of the female gametophyte, which is a food storage tissue.

The integument of the ovule becomes the seed coat. In cycads the single integument is differentiated at maturity into a fleshy, often red or orange outer layer, a hard middle layer, and a thin, dry inner layer. The nucellus persists as a dry, papery cap over the micropylar end of the female gametophyte, within the seed coat.

The cone usually disintegrates as soon as the seeds are mature, and germination follows immediately. The embryo elongates, and the radicle, protected by a hard outer coating called the coleorhiza, breaks its way through the seed coat. The stem remains short at first, but it soon gives rise to a first vegetative leaf which grows up into the air and becomes photosynthetic. The cotyledons remain largely within the seed coat, absorbing food from the body of the female gametophyte and passing it on to the growing seedling.

ECONOMIC IMPORTANCE

The modern cycads are not of much economic importance. They are often grown for ornament in warm regions, and *Cycas revoluta* is regularly cultivated in greenhouses for its attractive leaves, which are used in funeral wreaths and on Palm Sunday. Many cycads are poisonous, and *Dioön edule* is reported to cause serious losses of cattle in parts of Mexico. A special kind of flour, now called Florida arrowroot starch, is prepared from the thickened base of *Zamia floridana*, after the poisonous principle has been leached out.

The pteridosperms, which were common and widely distributed during the Carboniferous period, were among the most important contributors to the masses of decaying vegetation that became transformed into coal.

RELATIONSHIPS

The pteridosperms were evidently derived during the Devonian period from heterosporous, eusporangiate ferns that may not have been advanced much beyond the psilophyte stage. The position of the seeds in the more primitive pteridosperms —on short, stem-like stalks terminating the pinnae or pinnules of the leaves—is highly suggestive of the psilophytes. Although none of the known heterosporous fossil ferns seems to be directly ancestral to the pteridosperms, the well-known fossil *Archeopteris* shows that heterosporous ferns did exist in Devonian time. The retention of the female gametophyte within the megasporangium, forming a seed, is a simple further evolutionary step which, as we have seen, has occurred in other groups of heterosporous plants as well as in the pteridosperms. In addition to the production of seeds, the pteridosperms differ from the ferns in their firmer leaves and cuticle, and in the more or less well-developed secondary thickening of the stem. Both these characters are readily compatible with a fern ancestry, and secondary growth is not entirely unknown among the ferns themselves.

The groups Caytoniales, Bennettitales, and Cycadales can each be readily interpreted as derived directly from the pteridosperms, and each has advanced features which make it unlikely to be ancestral to any of the others. The seed pouches of the Caytoniales, which presumably represent modified pinnae of the megasporophyll, are quite unlike anything else in the division. The megasporophyll of the Bennettitales, which is unbranched and bears a single terminal ovule, can be derived by reduction from the multiovulate megasporophyll of the seed ferns but could hardly be ancestral to the cycad megasporophyll, which has lateral rather than terminal ovules.

The ontogeny of the stomatal apparatus in the Bennettitales is unlike that of other cycadophytes. The guard cells and two or four adjacent epidermal cells are all derived from a single initial cell of the epidermis. This type of stomatal apparatus, described as **syndetocheilic,** is otherwise found only in *Gnetum, Welwitschia,* and many angiosperms. In all other plants with stomates, only the two guard cells are derived from an initial cell, and the adjoining epidermal cells are sister cells of the stomatal initial and of other ordinary epidermal cells, rather than being sister cells of the guard cells. This type of stomatal apparatus, called **haplocheilic,** is considered to be more primitive than the syndetocheilic type, and it is not to be expected that a group with syndetocheilic stomates would be ancestral to a group with haplocheilic stomates. Possession of syndetocheilic stomates is no guarantee of relationship, however; this evolutionary advance, like many others, seems to have occurred more than once.

The cycads proper, with the simple microsporophylls aggregated into a compact strobilus, could hardly be considered ancestral to the Caytoniales or Bennettitales, which retain the branched microsporophylls of the pteridosperms.

SUGGESTED READING

Arnold, Chester, A., Origin and relationships of the cycads, *Phytomorphology* 3:51–65. 1953. A rather technical paper which many students may find of interest. The journal *Phytomorphology* contains an extraordinarily high proportion of important botanical papers, and the student may find other items of interest by browsing through the tables of contents.

Harris, T. M., The relationships of the Caytoniales, *Phytomorphology* 1:29–39. 1951. Technical but intelligible.

Division
Coniferophyta

CONIFEROPHYTES

CHAPTER 22

Vascular plants with roots, stems, and leaves, and with vigorous secondary growth, the pith usually small; leaves usually small and simple, never pinnately compound; central cylinder generally with leaf gaps; seeds generally borne on telome-like stalks, or on modified "ovuliferous scales," which are often aggregated into a compound strobilus; ovules more or less exposed to the air at the time of pollination, the pollen landing at the micropyle. Two classes, the Coniferae and Chlamydospermae.

HISTORY

The coniferophytes were first recognized as a distinct division by Bessey in 1907. The taxonomic history of the group is further discussed in Chapter 21.

CHARACTERISTICS

The coniferophytes are gymnosperms with usually freely branched stems, vigorous secondary growth, and mostly simple, usually small leaves. In some of the fossil Ginkgoales the leaves are dichotomously several times divided, but the pinnately compound leaves which characterize the cycadophytes are unknown among the coniferophytes. The primary vascular cylinder is a siphonostele, usually with well-developed leaf gaps, and the pith is usually small.

The seed-bearing organs of coniferophytes are variously modified but never distinctly leaf-like; probably they are modified telomes, or telome systems, which

◄

Giant sequoia, *Sequoiadendron giganteum*, in the Mariposa grove, Yosemite National Park, California. (National Park Service photo by Ralph H. Anderson.)

419

Fig. 22.1. Rudolf Florin (1894–   ), Swedish botanist, outstanding student of fossil coniferophytes.

have never been vegetative leaves. The female cones of modern species, when present, are of complex structure, unlike the simple cones of the cycadophytes. The organs on which the microsporangia are borne are usually called microsporophylls, although they may actually be modified telomes rather than proper sporophylls. In the Coniferae these so-called "microsporophylls" are grouped into a simple strobilus. In the Chlamydospermae both the male and female cones are compound. Other differences between the Coniferae and Chlamydospermae are discussed under the latter group.

Coniferae

CLASSIFICATION

There are nearly 400 living species of Coniferae; these may be classified into three orders, the Coniferales, Taxales, and Ginkgoales. A fourth order, the Cordaitales, is known only from fossils. A synoptical key to the orders is presented in the appendix.

CORDAITALES

The Cordaitales are a group of fossil coniferophytes known from rocks of Devonian to Permian age. They were tall trees, reaching a height of 100 feet or more and, judging from the abundance of the fossil remains, they must have formed large forests during the Carboniferous period. They show vigorous secondary growth, as do modern conifers, but the pith is usually larger, commonly 1–4 cm or even 10 cm thick. The secondary wood, which lacks resin canals, is suggestive of the modern genus *Araucaria* (Coniferales). The primary vascular cylinder is a more or less dissected endarch to mesarch siphonostele, usually with leaf gaps, but, in several Devonian and Lower Carboniferous fossils, the leaf trace originates as a branch from a strand of primary xylem that continues upward without interruption.

The leaves of the Cordaitales are long and rather narrow, undivided, and distinctly larger than in most modern conifers, sometimes as much as 1 m long. Numerous small, dichotomously branched veins run the length of the leaf, as in the modern coniferous genera *Agathis* and *Araucaria*.

The cones of the Cordaitales are borne on specialized slender branches commonly 10–20 cm long. Each such branch bears small, narrow, modified leaves (bracts) along its length, and in the axil of each bract is a small cone seldom much over 1 cm long. The cone bears narrow, spirally arranged appendages, some of which are fertile. The fertile appendages were at one time thought to be in the axils of the sterile ones, but in better preserved specimens they appear to be in the same spiral as the sterile ones. Each cone, and each cone-bearing branch, is exclusively male or exclusively female, as far as is known, but both types sometimes occur on the same tree. The microsporophyll bears one, two, four, or even six slender, terminal microsporangia, whereas the megasporophyll usually bears a single terminal ovule (rarely two).

The pollen grains are globular, with a large air cavity separating the intine from the exine over most of their area. The ovule has a single integument which is wholly distinct from the nucellus. The seeds are usually flattened, often heart-shaped, with a thin wing margin, evidently being adapted for wind distribution as are the pollen grains. Often the megasporophyll elongates so that the mature seed is exserted from the cone. Seeds containing definite embryos have not yet been found, although the body of the female gametophyte is frequently well defined.

The Devonian members of the Cordaitales are so classified because of the anatomy of the stem, their seeds or other reproductive structures being as yet unknown. Most of the common Carboniferous members of the order may be referred in the broad sense to the single large genus *Cordaites* (Fig. 22.2), although detached parts are often named under various form genera instead. The names *Cordaioxylon*, *Dadoxylon*, and *Mesoxylon* have been used for the wood, *Amyelon* for the root, *Cordaianthus* for the cones and associated structures, *Artisia* for pith casts, and *Cordaicarpus*, *Cardiocarpus*, *Mitrospermum*, and *Samaropsis* for the seeds. No post-Paleozoic fossils are definitely referred to the Cordaitales, but some of the Mesozoic

Fig. 22.2. Reconstruction of *Cordaites*. (Courtesy of the Chicago Natural History Museum.)

fossil wood called *Araucarioxylon* (Coniferales) would doubtless be considered cordaitalean if it were found in Paleozoic rocks instead.

CONIFERALES

DISTRIBUTION AND HABIT

The Coniferales are the largest group of modern coniferophytes, with about 300

Fig. 22.3. Pitch pine, *Pinus rigida;* mature tree in New York State. (New York Botanical Garden photo.)

species. They occur from the Arctic to the Antarctic Circle but are most common in temperate and cold-temperate regions, especially in the Northern Hemisphere, where they form extensive forests. *Pinus* (pine) (Fig. 22.3), with about 90 species, is the largest genus of the Northern Hemisphere. *Araucaria* is a common genus of the Southern Hemisphere; various species are called Chilean pine, Brazilian pine, Norfolk Island pine, and monkey puzzle. Some other familiar genera of the Northern Hemisphere are *Abies* (fir), *Cedrus* (true cedar, including cedar of Lebanon), *Juniperus* (juniper, "cedar"), *Larix* (larch), *Picea* (spruce), *Pseudotsuga* (*P. menziesii* is the Douglas fir), *Thuja* (*T. plicata* is the western red cedar), and *Tsuga* (hemlock) (Fig. 22.4).

Conifers are usually trees, less often shrubs, typically with **excurrent** branching (i.e., with a well-defined central axis and smaller lateral branches). Individual trees of *Sequoiadendron giganteum,* the California big tree or Sierra redwood, are the largest living things, reaching a height of about 300 feet and a diameter of about 35 feet near the base. The coast redwood (*Sequoia sempervirens*), of the coast ranges of northern California and adjacent Oregon, is even taller, up to 350 feet, although the total bulk is less because the trunk is more slender.

STEM (PRIMARY TISSUES)

Growth in length of the stem is due to an apical meristem which remains functional throughout the life of the plant. The apical meristem is covered by the adjacent leaves which extend up around it and protect it from injury. Usually the apical meristem is dormant for much of the year, and the leaves which subtend it during the dormant period are distinctly modified, relatively small, and closely set, forming a compact covering. The dormant meristem with its covering leaves (**bud scales**) is called a **terminal bud.** Branches originate by the segmentation of the apical meristem into terminal and lateral parts, each of the lateral parts becoming the apical meristem of a branch. Branches of the main stem are often whorled, but those of the primary branches are more often opposite; in any case they bear no positional relationship to the foliage leaves.

The primary vascular cylinder is an endarch siphonostele with well-developed leaf gaps. The primary xylem consists of tracheids with annular or spiral secondary walls. The primary phloem forms strands adjacent and immediately external to the primary xylem, separated only by a single layer of cells (the procambium) which eventually develops into the cambium.

The leaf gaps in the stele are filled with parenchyma tissue which connects the parenchyma of the slender pith with the parenchyma of the cortex. These parenchymatous connections between the pith and the cortex are called **medullary rays** or **pith rays.**

The cortex is generally more or less parenchymatous, and usually photosynthetic. Often it contains well-developed resin canals, of the type described on page 427. The epidermis is cutinized and has scattered stomates.

STEM (CAMBIUM)

The cambium forms a continuous layer, one cell thick, between the xylem and phloem of the stem (and also the root). It is a primary tissue, derived directly by differentiation from the apical meristem. The cambium is a meristematic layer, the function of which is to produce secondary tissues. Before it has produced any secondary tissues, the layer of cells which will mature into cambium is called the **procambium.** When a cambial cell divides, one of the two daughter cells remains a cambial cell, and the other develops directly, or after one or more subsequent divisions, into either a xylem cell (if internal to the cambium) or a phloem cell (if external to the cambium). In many conifers it is difficult to distinguish the permanent cambium from the newly formed adjacent cells which will divide one or more times again before maturing into xylem and phloem. Thus the cambium sometimes appears to be several cells thick.

STEM (SECONDARY WOOD)

The secondary xylem of conifers consists largely of tracheids and parenchyma cells (Figs. 22.5, 22.6). Often there are scattered resin cells as well. The tracheids are long and narrow (0.5–11 mm long),

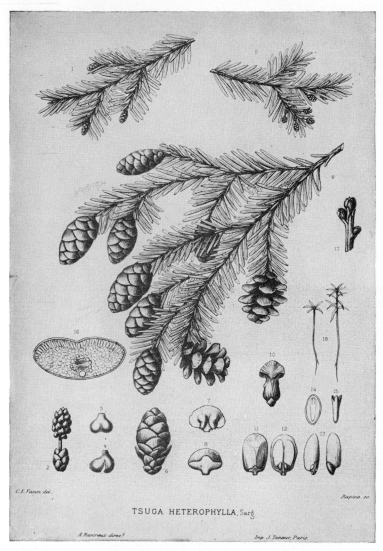

Fig. 22.4. Western hemlock, *Tsuga heterophylla.* A plate from *Silva of North America,* by Charles Sargent (1841 – 1927), outstanding American dendrologist and first director of the Arnold Arboretum, near Boston, Mass.

tapering at the ends. They have a lignified secondary wall with bordered pits. Like tracheids of other plants, the tracheids of conifers die at maturity and thereafter have a dual function: support and water conduction. The space enclosed by the walls of the tracheid, through which the water passes, is called the **lumen.**

The **bordered pits** of most conifers have a rather elaborate structure. Pits in adjacent tracheids are typically opposite each other. The secondary wall arches out over the pit cavity from all sides, forming a border around the pit aperture. The pit membrane which separates a pair of pits consists of the two primary walls and the middle lamella. The primary wall of each surface of the pit membrane has a lens-shaped thickening, the **torus,** which is commonly wider than the pit aperture

424 *Introductory Botany*

but does not reach the margins of the pit cavity. Between the edge of the torus and the margin of the pit cavity, the pit membrane is very thin and probably has small pores. The pits facilitate the passage of water from one tracheid to another, through the thin part of the pit membrane.

Most (in some species all) of the parenchyma cells of the xylem of conifers are arranged in ribbon-shaped bands which, in cross-sectional view of the stem, form lines radiating toward the outside. These bands are called **wood rays** or **xylem rays**. Some xylem rays are extensions of the medullary rays and reach all the way from the cambium to the pith. Others extend only part way from the cambium toward the pith and then stop. The ray cells of the secondary wood, like the tracheids, are formed by cell division

from the cambium. New rays are initiated from time to time, so that the number of rays is greatest next to the cambium, and least toward the pith. The lateral distance between the rays is thus maintained at a fairly constant figure (usually well under 1 cm) by the progressive insertion of new rays between the previously established ones.

A wood ray is one to several cells wide and 1–20 or even 50 cells high. The box-shaped cells of which it is largely composed have secondary as well as primary walls in the pines, firs, spruces, and their close allies, but only primary walls in junipers, cypresses, and the characteristic conifers of the Southern Hemisphere, such as *Araucaria*. The cell walls have only simple pits, without the prominent overarching borders and without the torus. Some of the cells at the margin of a ray

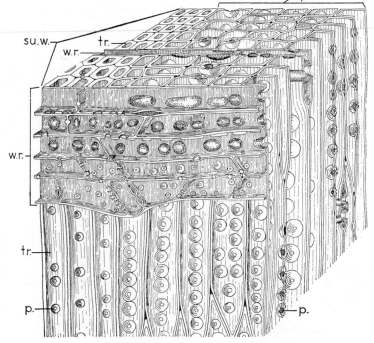

Fig. 22.5. *Pinus strobus;* a cube of secondary wood; p., pit; sp.w., spring wood; su.w., summer wood; tr., tracheid; w.r., wood ray. A wood ray crosses the block in the foreground; the base of another can be seen halfway back in the block. Note that the pits (appearing doughnut-shaped in surface view) are larger and more numerous in the spring wood than in the summer wood. Note also that the pits between the tracheids are all bordered, whereas many of the pits of the ray cells are simple. (×350.) (Redrawn from Coulter and Chamberlain, *Morphology of Gymnosperms*, 1910, courtesy of University of Chicago Press.)

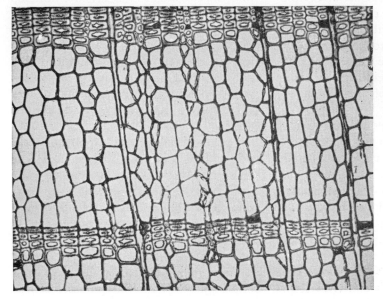

Fig. 22.6. Big tree, *Sequoiadendron giganteum;* cross section of a small part of the xylem, showing spring and summer wood and ray-parenchyma cells. Oldest wood is at bottom, youngest at top. Note how the spring wood (large cells) passes into the summer wood, which is abruptly succeeded the next year by spring wood. (Photo courtesy of E. J. Kohl, Lakeside Biological Products, Ripon, Wis.)

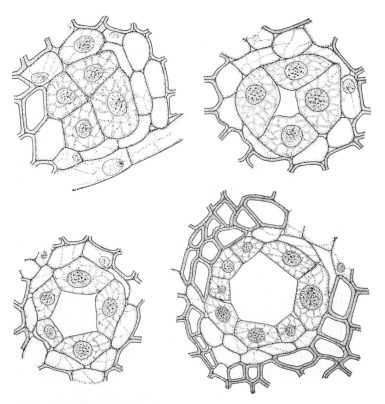

Fig. 22.7. Successive stages in the formation of a resin duct in pine. (×300.) (From W. H. Brown, *The Plant Kingdom*, 1935; courtesy of Ginn & Company, Boston.)

are often intermediate in structure between ray cells and ordinary tracheids. Such cells are called ray tracheids. Every tracheid is in contact with one or more parenchyma cells somewhere along its length, and these parenchyma cells may in some way be necessary for the continued functioning of the tracheids in water conduction.

The rays of many conifers contain horizontal resin ducts (Fig. 22.7) which originate by separation of the cells which come to border the duct. Resin ducts which originate in this way are said to be **schizogenous.** Often there are also vertical, schizogenous resin ducts which are not associated with the rays. The modified parenchyma cells which border the vertical resin ducts are often the only parenchyma cells of the xylem other than the ray cells.

In the conifers, as elsewhere, secondary tissues can usually be distinguished from primary tissues by the arrangement of the cells in regular radial rows, as seen in cross section of the stem or root. Each such row of cells is derived eventually from a single cambial cell.

Tracheids produced early in the spring, when moisture is abundant and growth is rapid, have relatively thin secondary walls and a large lumen, whereas those produced later in the season, when the water supply is usually more restricted and growth is slower, have thicker secondary walls and a smaller lumen. In some conifers the summer wood is sharply differentiated from the spring wood of the same year, and in others the spring wood fades gradually into the summer wood. In either case, there is generally a clear demarcation between the last-formed wood of one year, with very thick-walled tracheids, and the first-formed wood of the

next year, with relatively thin-walled tracheids. These annual growth layers, which appear as concentric rings when the stem is viewed in cross section, are called **annual rings.**

The thickness of an annual ring varies according to the kind of tree, its age, and the environmental conditions, especially the weather. In rapidly growing young trees they may be as much as 1 cm thick. In much of the western (especially southwestern) United States, where moisture is a very important limiting factor in plant growth, a thicker ring is produced in wet years than in dry years, and it is thus possible to discover something about the climate of the recent past. On the basis of tree rings, the drought during the middle 1950's is believed to have been the most severe to occur in parts of the southwestern United States for more than six centuries.

The age of a particular tree may be determined by counting the number of annual rings, although there is a possibility of error because of occasional false annual rings formed during unusual years in which the growing season may have been interrupted by a dry spell after which growth was resumed. False annual rings may often be detected by their failure to extend all the way around the stem, or by their incomplete differentiation from the next previous ring.

All woody plants have an inherently limited life span. Sooner or later growth slows down and the tree becomes more susceptible to attack by natural enemies, such as fungi and insects. Ages of 100–200 years are common among the conifers, and some species characteristically live much longer. The Sierra redwood, which has very few natural enemies, sometimes reaches an age of 4000 years, and trees of this age were long thought to be the oldest living things. More recently ring counts have established that some bristlecone pines (*Pinus aristata*) near timberline in the White Mountains of California are even older, up to 4600 years.

The parenchyma cells of the xylem remain alive and continue to function normally for some years after they are produced. The resin of resin ducts is formed by the parenchyma cells surrounding the duct. Resin has an antiseptic effect and tends to inhibit the growth of fungi that might otherwise attack the tree. When the tree is injured, the resin flows out over the injured surface, sealing it off from possible infection. A small amount of food is stored in the ray-parenchyma cells, which also carry on lateral conduction.

Sooner or later the metabolic activity of the parenchyma cells is modified, with the result that the tracheids become more or less impregnated with resinous substances, and the torus of each pit cavity tends to expand until it joins the surrounding secondary wall. Due to these changes, the tracheids lose their water-conducting function, retaining only the function of mechanical support. The parenchyma cells then die and their protoplasm degenerates.

The central core of xylem that has lost its water-conducting function is called **heartwood**, and the outer sheath of xylem which continues to conduct water and dissolved substances is called **sapwood**. The heartwood is generally darker in color than the sapwood, due to the resinous deposits, and the distinction is usually obvious to the naked eye. The boundary between the sapwood and heartwood is often irregular, extending several annual rings closer to the cambium at some points

than at others. The inner part of the sapwood is continuously transformed into heartwood as more sapwood is formed by divisions of the cambial cells. The heartwood thus constitutes a progressively expanding core, whereas the sapwood tends to remain about the same thickness throughout the life of the tree. Some of the Sierra redwoods have a layer of sapwood only 3–4 inches thick surrounding a core of heartwood many feet thick.

STEM (BARK)

The part of a woody stem external to the cambium is called the **bark**. In a young stem the bark includes phloem, cortex, and epidermis. As the stem expands in girth due to the activity of the cambium, the outer tissues are ruptured and eventually slough off, so that in an older stem the bark consists entirely of secondary tissues derived directly or indirectly from the cambium. The bark of mature parts of the stem is divided into a zone near the cambium, the live bark, in which most of the cells are living, and an outer zone, the dead bark, with no living cells.

The secondary phloem, formed by the cambium, consists of sieve cells, parenchyma cells, and sometimes also sclerenchyma cells. The sclerenchyma may consist of elongate fibers or short stone cells. Some of the parenchyma cells are intermingled with the sieve cells; others are grouped into rays which are usually continuous with the xylem rays (separated only by the cambium).

Every sieve cell is in contact with at least one parenchyma cell, and sometimes there is a regular arrangement of sieve cells and parenchyma cells suggestive of the sieve-tube–companion-cell structure of angiosperms, although the ontogeny is different (see Chapter 23). The sieve cells, like those of other vascular plants, lack a nucleus, and it is believed that the nucleus of the adjacent parenchyma cell serves in effect for the cytoplasm of the sieve cell as well. In any case, the parenchyma cells seem to be necessary to the continued functioning of the sieve cells. The parenchyma cells of the phloem, including the ray-parenchyma, also serve in the storage of food.

After the primary tissues of the young stem have matured and secondary tissues have begun to be produced, some of the parenchyma cells of the cortex or the phloem revert to a meristematic condition and begin to produce new tissues in much the same manner (but not the same kind) as the cambium. This new meristematic layer is called the **phellogen,** or **cork cambium,** after its most conspicuous product. The true cambium, which produces xylem and phloem, is often called the **vascular cambium,** to distinguish it from the cork cambium.

The first layer of cork cambium is often a nearly continuous sheet extending all the way around the young stem. It produces cork cells externally; internally it usually produces a tissue called the **phelloderm.** The cork cambium resembles the vascular cambium to the extent that one of the cells formed in each division remains a cambial cell, whereas the other cell, either internal or external to the cambium, loses its meristematic capacity and eventually develops into a mature cell (or cells) of another type. The cork cells are generally boxed-shaped and are characterized by the impregnation of their walls with a water-proofing substance called **suberin.** The cells are said to be suberized. The cork cells die on reaching maturity, and cork is a dead tissue. The cork layer formed by the cork cambium cuts off the water supply of all tissues external to it, and these tissues then die.

As more secondary phloem continues to be formed by the vascular cambium, new layers of cork are produced by successive phellogens which develop from the parenchyma of the secondary phloem, so that the live bark never becomes very thick. The dead bark increases in thickness as more and more live bark becomes dead bark, but this increase is eventually offset by the sloughing off of the outer layers of dead bark. The continued expansion of the stem causes the dead bark to split, and the pattern in which the bark splits and sloughs off is often characteristic of a particular genus or species.

The individual layers of phellogen, after the initial one, do not generally extend all the way around the stem; instead they commonly form small scales or bands which are arranged in an overlapping pattern. In a cross section of the stem, the cork layers produced by these phellogens often appear as pale tangential lines in the dead bark.

Root

The root system of conifers is usually derived from the primary root of the embryo, rather than being adventitious as in the ferns. Some conifers have a central taproot which penetrates deep into the soil; others have a more shallow root system with several subequal large branches. Growth in length of the root is due to the activity of an apical meristem, which is covered by a rootcap. Branch roots originate in the pericycle and push their way through the surrounding tissues into the soil.

The stele of a conifer root is an exarch

protostele with two to five protoxylem points, as seen in cross section, the number two being the common one in most genera except *Pinus*. As seen in cross section, the patches of primary xylem alternate with the patches of primary phloem; i.e., the strands of primary xylem and primary phloem are on alternate radii. There is a well-developed endodermis, and a parenchymatous pericycle usually several cells thick lies between the endodermis and the primary vascular tissues. This general structure is the most characteristic form

Fig. 22.8. Young needle cluster of *Pinus laricio*. The modified leaves which make up the bundle sheath are shown in black. (×9.) (From Chamberlain, *Gymnosperms*, by permission of the University of Chicago Press.)

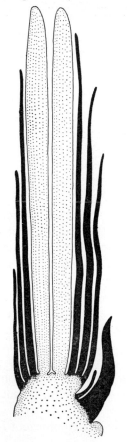

of the protostele, whether in roots or stems. The roots of all major groups of vascular plants (except the psilophytes, which have no roots) are usually protostelic, but only some of the more primitive vascular plants have protostelic stems.

Like the stem, the conifer root very often has resin ducts. The most common position of the resin ducts in the primary tissues is just external to the protoxylem ridges, but in *Abies* there is commonly a central resin duct in the metaxylem. The young root has a usually parenchymatous cortex and single layer of epidermis. Most conifers are mycorhizal, with relatively few (or no) root hairs, the absorbing surface of the root being in effect provided by the fungus.

Secondary tissues of the roots and stems are usually rather similar.

LEAVES

The leaves of conifers are always simple and usually very narrow, although some of the genera which occur chiefly in the Southern Hemisphere, such as *Agathis* and *Araucaria*, have relatively broad leaves with numerous subparallel, dichotomously branched veins. Typically the leaves are from ½ inch to several inches long and less than ⅛ inch wide. Such leaves are called needles. In most junipers, and in the various other native American conifers which are called cedars, as well as in some other genera, the leaves of mature plants are reduced to small green scales appressed to the twigs and covering them. The leaves, regardless of their size, are associated with well-developed leaf gaps in the stele and are thus anatomically megaphylls. The leaf trace consists of one bundle in some families, two in others.

Conifer leaves are typically alternate

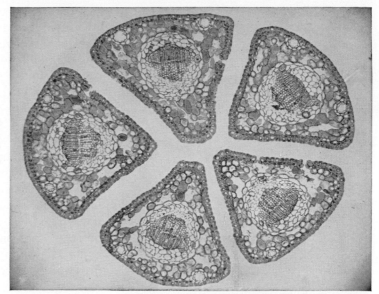

Fig. 22.9. *Pinus strobus* needles, in cross section. (Copyright by General Biological Supply House, Inc., Chicago.)

in a rather close spiral, less often opposite or whorled. In the larches, in the true cedar, and in some other genera, most of the leaves are borne on specialized, short spur shoots, although some of them are on the more elongate ordinary shoots. In *Pinus* these short spur shoots have become further specialized, and all the foliage leaves (except in seedlings) are borne on them. Each spur shoot of *Pinus* bears a bundle of one to five needles (Fig. 22.8). When there are two needles, they are attached opposite each other on the short axis, and when there are more than two needles they are whorled. The bundle is surrounded at the base by a **bundle sheath** consisting of several small leaves which are modified into thin, membranous scales wrapped around the spur shoot. The whole spur shoot with its attached needles is eventually deciduous.

Conifers produce some new leaves every year, but the duration of the leaves varies with the genus and species. In *Larix* and *Pseudolarix* they die and fall off after a single season, and the tree is bare during the winter. In *Taxodium* the leafy twigs of the season fall off in the autumn, and the tree is also bare in the winter. In other conifers the leaves of one year persist at least until the leaves of the next year are fully developed, and the tree is evergreen. Sometimes the leaves live as long as 10–15 years.

Conifer leaves are generally firm, with small, thick-walled epidermal cells and a thick cuticle. The stomates are typically sunken and are often borne in definite longitudinal bands. A hypodermis, consisting of one to three layers of small, thick-walled cells, often lies just within the epidermis. Leaves of the needle and scale types have one or two central vascular bundles, and often (e.g., *Pinus*, Fig. 22.9) the bundle or the two bundles collectively are surrounded by a well-defined endodermis with characteristic Casparian strips. The tissue between the endodermis and the bundle or bundles consists of parenchymatous or more or less lignified cells

Coniferophyta: Coniferophytes 431

Fig. 22.10. *Pinus resinosa;* young cone, enlarged. The awl-shaped structure at the lower left is a cluster of young needles, not yet expanded. (Photo courtesy of J. Arthur Herrick.)

and is called transfusion tissue. The part of the needle between the epidermis (or hypodermis) and the endodermis (or vascular bundle) consists largely or wholly of chlorenchyma, often with one or more schizogenous resin ducts. In broad-leaved conifers the chlorenchyma tends to be differentiated into an upper palisade layer and a lower spongy layer, suggesting the anatomy of the leaves of flowering plants.

Cones

The reproductive structures of conifers are borne in unisexual cones (strobili). Most genera are **monoecious,** with both kinds of cones borne on the same tree, but *Juniperus* and some other genera are **dioecious,** with male and female cones borne on separate trees.

The male cones are axillary or terminal on short branches. They generally mature the spring following the one in which they are differentiated from the apical meristem of the growing shoot. They are usually about 1 cm long or less, ranging up to 10 cm or more in some species of *Araucaria.* The microsporophylls are attached directly to the central axis of the cone in a close spiral or a series of whorls. The microsporangia are born on the lower (abaxial) surface of the microsporophyll, and range from 2 to about 15 in number, 2 being the most common number in the familiar genera of the Northern Hemisphere. Development of the microsporangium follows in general the eusporangiate pattern, as described for the ferns. There is a well-developed tapetum which is derived by differentiation of the inner cells of the jacket. The microsporangium contains numerous microspore mother cells, which undergo reduction division to produce tetrads of microspores. The microspores have n chromosomes and are the first cells in the male gametophyte generation. The most common n number in the conifers is 12.

The female cone is generally a compound structure, the ovules being borne not on the primary appendages (the **bracts**) of the cone axis, but on outgrowths (the **ovuliferous scales**) from the axils of the bracts. The ovules are mostly on the upper (adaxial) side of the ovuliferous scale, usually two per scale. In *Pinus* (Fig. 22.11) the bract is much shorter than the ovuliferous scale which it subtends, although it is readily visible when the cone has opened. In *Pseudotsuga* the bract is longer than the ovuliferous scale, but narrower and thinner. In *Araucaria* the bract is the principal cone scale, and the "ovuliferous scale" of other conifers is reduced to a mere "ligule" on the upper surface of the bract. (Technically, the ligule is the free tip of the ovuliferous scale, the base of this scale being fused to the bract.) In *Agathis* the ligule is obsolete, and the cone appears to be simple in structure like the male cones. The female cones of *Juniperus* and some related genera are small and superficially berry-like, with only a few small cone scales and these much thickened, but the basic morphology is the same as in other conifers.

The female cone of conifers is usually interpreted as comparable to the whole cone cluster of the Cordaitales, with each small cordaitalean cone having been reduced to a single ovuliferous scale in the axil of a bract. A number of fossils provide intermediate steps which bolster this interpretation.

The conifer ovule (Fig. 22.12) is essentially similar to the cycad ovule, consisting of a megasporangium plus an enclosing tissue, the integument. The integument fits closely around the megasporangium wall (the nucellus), except at the end opposite the stalk, and often these two tissues are fused toward the stalk end. At the end opposite the stalk, there is a cavity, the pollen chamber, between the nucellus and the integument. The pollen chamber opens to the surface via a passageway (the micropyle) through the integument. In several genera the ovule is more or less bent back on itself, so that the micropyle is fairly close to the stalk instead of at the opposite end from it.

The megasporangium follows the general eusporangiate type of development. There is a multilayered tapetum and a single, large megaspore mother cell. The megaspore mother cell undergoes meiosis, usually forming a linear tetrad of megaspores (Fig. 22.13). Sometimes one of the nuclei formed in the first division of the meiotic process fails to divide again, so that a row of three cells is formed instead of a row of four. Usually only one megaspore is functional, and the others soon degenerate. The megaspore has n chromosomes and is the first cell of the female gametophyte generation.

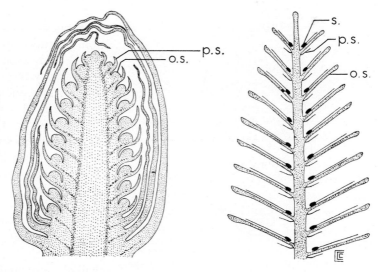

Fig. 22.11. Long section of young pine cone (left, ×20); mature pine cone (right, ×1), diagrammatic; o.s., ovuliferous scale; p.s., primary scale; s., seed.

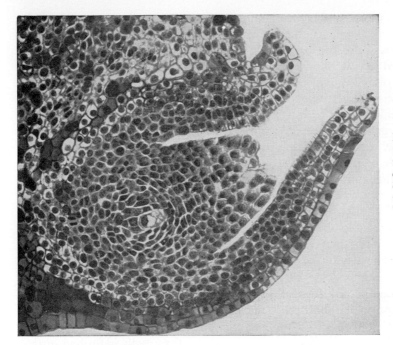

Fig. 22.12. Long section of young pine ovule, showing megaspore mother cell; micropyle and integuments ascending at the right. (Courtesy of George H. Conant, Triarch Products.)

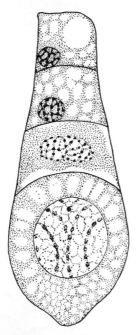

Fig. 22.13. Linear tetrad of megaspores in *Pinus laricio;* only the lowest megaspore functional. (×1000.) (After Ferguson.)

POLLEN

The microspore has a two-layered wall, the outer wall being called the **exine**, the inner the **intine**. Usually one or more nuclear divisions occur within the microspore wall before the young male gametophyte, now called the pollen grain, is shed from the microsporangium. In *Pinus* (Fig. 22.14) and some other genera, the exine bulges away from the intine to form two large air sacs, increasing the volume of the grain without changing its weight, thus contributing to its buoyancy and facilitating its distribution by the wind. All conifers are normally wind-pollinated, and some of them produce tremendous quantities of pollen.

The pollen grain of *Pinus* (Fig. 22.15) has two small cells, the prothallial cells, at one side; a somewhat larger cell, the generative cell, lies next to the prothallial cells; and a still larger tube cell occupies the remainder of the space enclosed by the wall of the pollen grain. In some genera of the Southern Hemisphere, there are several prothallial cells, and in some other familiar genera, such as *Juniperus*, *Thuja*, and *Sequoia*, there are no prothallial cells at all. In any case, the prothallial cells, when present, soon degenerate, and they play no part in the further development of the gametophyte; they are mere evolutionary vestiges of the vegetative body of the gametophyte.

FEMALE GAMETOPHYTE

The megaspore in the ovule gives rise by a series of mitotic divisions to the female gametophyte, which usually has several thousand cells. The tapetum of the ovule, sometimes called the spongy tissue (but not to be confused with the spongy tissue of angiosperm leaves) degenerates as the female gametophyte develops. There is always a free-nuclear stage in the early development of the female gametophyte, with the thin protoplast appressed to the well-defined megaspore wall, leaving a large central vacuole. Usually there are several hundred to a thousand or more nuclei before any walls are formed, and the developing cellular gametophyte gradually encroaches on the central cavity (the old central vacuole), eventually filling it.

The archegonia, usually several in number, are borne at or near the nucellar end of the gametophyte (i.e., the end where the nucellus separates the gametophyte from the pollen chamber). Each archegonial initial gives rise to a single large egg, a ventral canal cell (or nucleus), and from 2 to 25 neck cells. Typically there are eight neck cells in two tiers of four. There is no neck canal cell. The well-defined jacket of the archegonium is

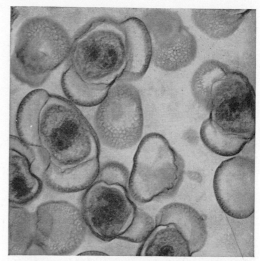

Fig. 22.14. Pine pollen, in cross section. (Copyright by General Biological Supply House, Inc., Chicago.)

derived by differentiation from ordinary vegetative cells of the gametophyte.

POLLINATION AND FERTILIZATION

When the ovule is ready for pollination, some of the cells of the nucellus degenerate, forming a mucilaginous **pollination drop** which reaches the orifice of the micropyle. Pollen grains which land on the pollination drop are drawn down into the pollen chamber as the drop dries up.

The pollen grain comes to rest on the nucellus, and a pollen tube is formed by an outgrowth from the side opposite the prothallial cells. The nucleus of the tube cell moves into the pollen tube and, if it has not already done so, the generative cell divides, forming a stalk cell (next to the prothallial cells) and a body cell. The body cell divides again, forming two sperms which are released into the pollen tube. The sperms do not have a well-defined cell wall, and often their cytoplasm, if any, cannot be distinguished

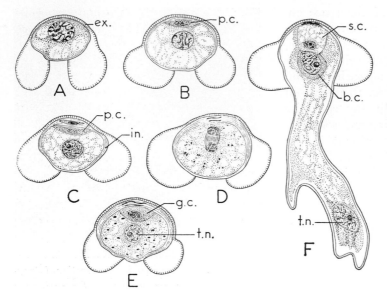

Fig. 22.15. Pollen development in *Pinus laricio*; b.c., body cell; ex., exine; g.c., generative cell; in., intine; p.c., prothallial cell; s.c., stalk cell; t.n., tube nucleus. (×500.) (After Coulter & Chamberlain, Morphology of Gymnosperms, 1910, courtesy of the University of Chicago Press.)

from that of the pollen tube. In any case they have no cilia or flagella.

The pollen tube continues to grow slowly through the nucellus, releasing digestive enzymes into the surrounding tissue and causing it to degenerate. After a period of a few weeks to more than a year, the pollen tube reaches the female gametophyte. The tip of the tube becomes turgid and bursts, discharging the sperms and much of the rest of its contents into or next to the egg. Fusion of a sperm and an egg constitutes fertilization. The fertilized egg has 2n chromosomes and is the first cell in the sporophyte generation.

Seeds and Seedlings

The fertilized egg gives rise to the embryo of the seed by a series of mitotic divisions. Usually there is a brief free-nuclear stage, with 4 to 64 nuclei being produced before any walls are formed.

The developing embryo has an elongate and usually coiled suspensor which pushes it deeper into the body of the female gametophyte. Later the suspensor tends to degenerate, commonly forming a mere small cap over the radicle of the embryo. In addition to the suspensor, the mature embryo consists of the radicle, the hypocotyl, the cotyledons, and the plumule (epicotyl). The **radicle** is the embryonic root. The **hypocotyl** is the transition region, just beneath the cotyledons, between the stem and the root. The **cotyledons** are embryonic leaves, and the epicotyl is the embryonic **shoot**. Most conifers have several cotyledons, but some have only two or three.

Conifer seeds very often have more than one embryo, although usually only one is fully developed. In some genera this condition of **polyembryony** is due to the fertilization and subsequent development of more than one egg; in others the two cells formed in the first division of the fertilized egg separate and develop independently into embryos. The two types of polyembryony might be compared to fraternal and identical twinning in human beings.

The mature embryo is embedded in the body of the female gametophyte, which is the principal food-storage tissue of the seed. The nucellus tends to degenerate as the seed ripens, but a vestige of it is often visible as a cap over the micropylar end of the gametophyte. The seed coat, developed from the integument of the ovule, is usually dry and firm and often extends out into a thin wing at one end of the seed, facilitating wind dispersal.

Conifer seeds are eaten by birds, squirrels, and other animals. The seeds of the piñon pine (*Pinus edulis* and related species) of the southwestern United States and northern Mexico are quite palatable; they are used for food by American Indians and can often be bought locally as "pine nuts." Some Old World species also have relatively large, palatable seeds.

The seeds of some conifers are shed as soon as they are ripe, and are ready to germinate immediately. Others require a rest period of weeks, months, or even years. The cones of some species, such as *Pinus contorta* (lodgepole pine) of the western United States and Canada, and *P. banksiana* (jack pine), its eastern coun-

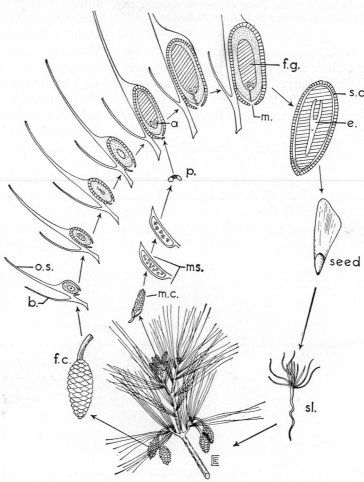

Fig. 22.16. Life cycle of *Pinus;* a., archegonium; b., bract (primary scale); e., embryo; f.c., female cone; f.g., female gametophyte; m., micropyle; m.c., male cone; ms., microsporophyll; o.s., ovuliferous scale; p., pollen grain; s.c., seed coat; sl., seedling.

Fig. 22.17. Fossil twig and leaves of *Metasequoia occidentalis*, from Oligocene deposits in Montana. (Courtesy of Herman F. Becker.)

the cotyledons remain enclosed within the seed coat for some time before it is pushed off. The cotyledons are generally green and much like ordinary small needles. The first true leaves (after the cotyledons) of all the needle-leaved and scale-leaved species have the needle form and are borne separately on the main shoot axis, regardless of their form and position in mature trees.

FOSSILS

The conifers are well represented as fossils from the Upper Carboniferous to the present. The Paleozoic conifer fossils, such as *Lebachia*, are vegetatively much like the modern forms, but their cones are intermediate to the cordaitalean type. Except in the structure of the female cones, the Araucariaceae are among the most primitive modern conifers, and fossil wood (*Araucarioxylon*) resembling that of *Araucaria*, from rocks of Mesozoic and more recent age, is very similar to that of the Paleozoic Cordaitales.

One of the common Cretaceous and Tertiary fossils of the Northern Hemisphere is *Metasequoia* (Fig. 22.17), a relative of *Sequoia*, *Sequoiadendron*, and

terpart, commonly remain on the tree for several or many years, opening only very slowly. After a forest fire, the cones release their seeds, and even-aged stands of these species usually indicate a previous fire.

The radicle of a germinating conifer seed elongates and pushes through the seed coat to form the primary root of the seedling, after which the hypocotyl elongates, carrying the seed coat, cotyledons, epicotyl, and the remains of the female gametophyte up into the air. The tips of

Fig. 22.18. Yew, *Taxus baccata;* a branch with berry-like seeds. (About half natural size.) (New York Botanical Garden photo.)

Taxodium (bald cypress). A modern *Metasequoia*, later named *Metasequoia glyptostroboides*, was discovered in southwestern China in 1941, and seeds were distributed to a number of botanical centers throughout the world. The trees, which are deciduous in the manner of *Taxodium*, are now being offered by some commercial nurseries in the U.S.A.

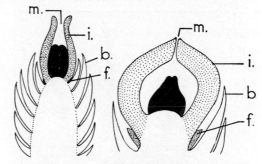

Fig. 22.19. Yew, *Taxus baccata;* young ovules in long section; b., bract; f., tissue from which the fleshy covering of the mature seed develops; i., integument; m., micropyle. (Left, X20; right, X15.) (After Hagerup.)

TAXALES

The Taxales differ from the Coniferales in having a well-developed fleshy covering surrounding the individual seeds, which are terminal or subterminal on short axillary shoots instead of being in definite cones. The ontogeny of the fleshy covering varies in different members of the order, but in any case it does not involve the integument. *Taxus* (yew) (Figs. 22.18, 22.19), with needle leaves much like those of many conifers, is the most familiar genus of the Northern Hemisphere. *Podocarpus* (plum yew), with the leaves often somewhat broader, and with the stalk enlarged into a fleshy receptacle just beneath the seed, is a large and widely distributed genus of the Southern Hemisphere. The structures associated with the ovule of *Podocarpus* can, with some difficulty, be interpreted as representing a reduced and highly modified cone. The Podocarpaceae are in this respect somewhat intermediate between the true conifers and the Taxaceae, in which latter the ovule is strictly terminal on a short axillary shoot that would not in any sense be considered a cone. Botanists are not agreed as to whether the Podocarpaceae should be included in the Taxales or the Coniferales.

Fossils probably allied to *Podocarpus* are known from the Jurassic period to the present. Pre-Tertiary fossils referable to the Taxaceae are very few; *Taxus jurassica*, from Jurassic rocks in England, appears to be a true *Taxus*, and *Palaeotaxus rediviva*, from Upper Triassic deposits in Sweden, is an evidently related form that also recalls the Cordaitales in some respects.

GINKGOALES

Ginkgo biloba (Fig. 22.20), the maidenhair tree, is the sole modern representative of a group which is well represented in the fossil record from as far back as the Permian period. The species became known to Western civilization through its cultivation about Buddhist monasteries in China, and it is doubtful that it now exists at all in a truly wild state.

Ginkgo is a medium-sized tree with more or less excurrent branching, although a few of its branches are often much larger than others. The stem and root are anatomically much like those of conifers, but the wood has mucilage cavities instead of resin ducts. Most of the leaves are borne on short spur shoots, although some are

Coniferophyta: Coniferophytes 439

Fig. 22.20. Maidenhair tree, *Ginkgo biloba*, in cultivation in New York City. (New York Botanical Garden photo.)

on the ordinary long shoots as well. The leaves, which fall off in the autumn, are fan-shaped, usually more or less notched or bifid at the tip, and commonly 2–3 inches long. The veins are dichotomously branched and free (without cross connections). There is a vague resemblance between the leaves of *Ginkgo* and the leaflets of the maidenhair fern (*Adiantum*), whence the name maidenhair tree.

The ovules are borne in pairs at the ends of slender stalks on a short spur shoot, but often one of the ovules aborts. The leaves of the spur shoots, especially the fertile spur shoots, tend to be less strongly notched than other leaves, or they lack the notch entirely. The ovule is seated on a well-defined collar at the end of the stalk, and some botanists have interpreted this collar as a reduced and modified sporo-

phyll. There is only one integument, but, as the seed ripens, this becomes differentiated into a fleshy outer layer, a stony middle layer, and an inner layer that is at first fleshy but eventually dry and papery.

Ginkgo is dioecious, with male cones much like those of conifers. The exine of the pollen grain has a large opening at the side opposite the prothallial cells, and the intine bulges out through this opening to form a pollen tube. The pollen tube grows into the nucellus, but, like that of the cycads, it acts solely as a haustorium. The pollen-grain end of the gametophyte slowly digests its way through the nucellus, as in the cycads, and eventually discharges the sperms into the archegonial chamber at the tip of the female gametophyte. The sperms, like those of cycads, have a spiral band of flagella (or cilia) at one end. The flagella have no present functional significance but are an evolutionary vestige from the pteridophyte ancestry in which the sperms swam from the antheridium to the archegonium.

The seeds (Fig. 22.21), which at full maturity smell like some of the riper varities of cheese, are esteemed in the Orient as food but are not acceptable to most Occidental palates. The male tree is, therefore, preferred in cultivation.

The similarities between *Ginkgo* and the cycads in the sperms and male gametophytes are believed to reflect a comparable degree of evolutionary progress, rather than a real relationship. In other respects the maidenhair tree is much more like the coniferophytes, and there is nothing in the fossil record to suggest convergence with the cycadophytes.

Fossils related to the maidenhair tree show a complete transition between the shallowly bilobed leaf of the modern species and leaves which are palmately to sub-dichotomously dissected into narrow seg-

Fig. 22.21.   Maidenhair tree, *Ginkgo biloba*. Left, seedling, with deeply cleft leaves; right, mature branch with a pair of naked fleshy seeds at the end of a stalk. (New York Botanical Garden photos.)

ments, with the more dissected types being progressively more prevalent in the older rocks. Even the modern *Ginkgo* often shows very deeply cleft leaves on seedlings (Fig. 22.21) and on vigorous young shoots. Undoubted relatives of the modern *Ginkgo* are known from as far back as the Permian period, and specimens from Devonian and Carboniferous rocks have sometimes also been thought to be of this affinity.

ECONOMIC IMPORTANCE

The Coniferae, particularly the Coniferales, are highly important to modern society, although perhaps not essential. They are the principal source of lumber for a wide variety of uses, from matches to construction timbers, and from shingles and siding to boxes and cedar chests. The western American species *Pseudotsuga menziesii*, the Douglas fir, is one of the most important timber trees in the world. Many species of *Pinus* are extensively logged, and various kinds of *Abies*, *Larix*, *Picea*, *Thuja*, and *Tsuga*, among others, are also much used for lumber in North America. In the Southern Hemisphere *Agathis* and *Araucaria* are similarly important.

Wood pulp for use in making paper is obtained from conifers as well as from some angiosperm trees, such as aspen and birch. Tremendous quantities of the rather small trees that make up the boreal spruce-fir forests are used in the production of newsprint. The smaller pines of southeastern United States are also coming into prominence for this purpose, now that a satisfactory process has been devised to remove the resin from the pulp and permit the production of a white paper. Much of the pulp used in the manufacture of rayon is obtained from spruce wood.

Crude turpentine is a mixture of resins obtained from certain pines and some other conifers. The tree is tapped by slicing into the bark, and the liquid exudate is collected in a cup attached to the tree. The mixture gradually solidifies when exposed to air. On distillation it yields oil of turpentine and a hard, amber-colored resin called rosin. Oil of turpentine is the principal solvent for most paints and varnishes and has some minor medical uses related to its stimulant, astringent, antispasmodic, and diuretic properties. Rosin is an ingredient of varnishes, paints, soaps, and a variety of other products; it is used on bowstrings and baseballs to increase surface friction, and in paper to impart gloss and water resistance. In the days of sailing ships, crude turpentine was extensively used in calking and waterproofing, and turpentine products are still known as naval stores. In the United States, the southeastern species *Pinus palustris* (longleaf pine), *P. caribaea* (slash pine) and *P. taeda* (loblolly pine) are the principal sources of crude turpentine.

Canada balsam, a resin obtained from *Abies balsamea* (balsam fir), has refractive properties similar to glass. It is used to join the lenses of optical instruments and as a combined mounting medium and seal for microscope slides.

Most of the ornamental evergreen trees and shrubs planted in the United States belong to the Coniferae. Various species of *Pinus, Picea, Abies, Tsuga, Thuja, Juniperus, Chamaecyparis,* and *Taxus,* among others, are familiar sights around homes throughout most of the United States, and well-formed individuals

of *Ginkgo biloba* are among the most beautiful of all specimen trees.

RELATIONSHIPS

The Coniferae can be traced all the way back to the Devonian period in the fossil record, but the pre-Carboniferous fossils show only vegetative parts, and there is a very considerable gap between the known fossil Coniferae and any possible ancestor. There is hardly any doubt that the Coniferae are eventually derived from the Psilophytales, but the nature of the connection is obscure. The evidence does not suggest any approach to the ferns or pteridosperms.

There is no indication of a compound or otherwise fern-like leaf in the Cordaitales. The *Ginkgo* leaf is a little more fern-like, but the fossil record suggests an independent origin of the *Ginkgo* leaf from a flattened, dichotomously branching stem, without any stage of pinnate arrangement, such as is shown by ferns.

The presence of leaf gaps in both filicophyte - cycadophyte - angiosperm line and the coniferophyte line, and the absence of leaf gaps among all other vascular plants, suggests the possibility of a relationship, but this character may not be so important as was once supposed. The evolutionary tendency for the primary xylem to break up into separate strands apparently permeates all groups of vascular plants. Some of the pteridosperms, as well as some of the Cordaitales, had dissected steles without leaf gaps, the vascular bundle continuing upward beyond the leaf trace without interruption. The anatomical structure here is comparable, although not identical in all details, with that of the Calamophyta, which also have dissected steles but no true leaf gaps.

The ovules of the Cordaitales and Ginkgoales, which represent the most primitive groups of Coniferae, are terminal on slender stalks, which are likely to be dichotomously branched and which give every evidence of being only slightly modified stems. The ovules of the pteridosperms, on the other hand, are borne on vegetative leaves, just as are the sporangia of most ferns.

The inference to be drawn is that the more primitive members of the Coniferae have been derived directly from the psilophytes, independently of the ferns and pteridosperms. Because of this apparent independence of the coniferophyte and cycadophyte lines, taxonomists are beginning to feel a necessity for breaking up the group Gymnospermae and recognizing the cycadophytes and coniferophytes as separate divisions.

The fossil record does not connect the Ginkgoales with the Cordaitales, and it is conceivable that the Ginkgoales were independently derived from the psilophytes. However, the evidence is also compatible with an early dichotomy of the coniferophytes into a cordaitalean and a ginkgoalean line. Parallel evolutionary development, which has repeatedly been shown to occur, is one of the greatest factors hindering the construction of a satisfactory taxonomic system. Yet the proper presumption is always that thoroughgoing structural similarities indicate an evolutionary relationship, unless there is evidence to the contrary. The Ginkgoales are therefore referred to the Coniferae, rather than being treated as a distinct division.

The Coniferales are evidently derived from the Cordaitales, as shown by their similarities in so many respects and by fossils which tend to bridge the differences between them. The Taxales are also derived from the Cordaitales, either directly or conceivably through the Coniferales, although here the fossil record is not decisive. The fleshy seeds of the Taxales do not indicate any relationship to the Ginkgoales, inasmuch as the ontogeny of the fleshy covering is quite different in the two groups.

Chlamydospermae

The Chlamydospermae (from Greek *chlamys*, a cloak or mantle) are a group of gymnosperms of doubtful taxonomic position. There are three genera, *Gnetum*, *Ephedra*, and *Welwitschia*. All three have often in the past been referred to a single order, the Gnetales, but the differences among them are so striking that most present-day students of the group prefer to place each genus in an order of its own.

The three orders of the Chlamydospermae—the Gnetales, Ephedrales, and Welwitschiales—have a number of technical features in common. They have vessels in the secondary wood; the cones of both sexes are compound; the ovules have two integuments, with at least the inner integument forming a very long micropylar tube; the leaves are opposite; the embryo has two cotyledons; and there are no resin canals. The xylem vessels and the compound male cones are not found in any other gymnosperms; the other characters mentioned (except the compound female cones) are more or less uncommon among other gymnosperms, but not unique.

Gnetum and *Welwitschia* further differ from all other gymnosperms in the ab-

Fig. 22.22. *Ephedra viridis* in Arizona. (Photo courtesy of J. Arthur Herrick.)

Fig. 22.23. *Ephedra viridis*. Left, twigs, with female cones. (Copyright by General Biological Supply House, Inc., Chicago.) Right, long section of ovule; a., archegonium; f.g., female gametophyte; i.i., inner integument; m., micropyle; o.i., outer integument (×25.)

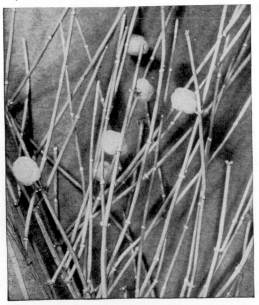
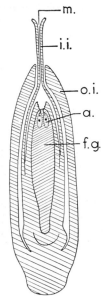

sence of an archegonium. In *Welwitschia* a specialized cell which is probably homologous with an archegonial initial functions directly as an egg. In *Gnetum* fertilization takes place while the female gametophyte is still in the free-nuclear condition, with one or more of the nuclei becoming associated with some differentiated cytoplasm and functioning as eggs.

Gnetum, Ephedra, and *Welwitschia* are so different in appearance that no relationship among them would at first be suspected. *Gnetum* (Fig. 22.24) is a woody vine, or sometimes a tree or shrub, with oval, entire, net-veined leaves—altogether like an angiosperm in general appearance. There are about 35 species, all tropical. *Ephedra* (Fig. 22.22), the source of the drug ephedrine, is a freely branched, low shrub with reduced, scale-like leaves and photosynthetic stems. There are about 35 species, mostly of arid regions such as the southwestern United States. The American species are often called Mormon tea or Brigham tea, reflecting an early use of the plant in beverages.

Welwitschia (Fig. 22.25) is one of the most bizarre plants in the world. The single species, *W. mirabilis,* is confined to deserts in southwest Africa. The plant has a very short, unbranched, woody main stem, sometimes as much as 4 feet thick, which is cushion-shaped or saucer-shaped and tapers rapidly to a very long taproot. There are only two leaves (after the cotyledons), and these persist throughout the life of the plant—perhaps 100 years. They are broadly strap-shaped, as wide as the stem, sessile, firm, and leathery, but they split readily between the parallel veins, becoming disheveled in age. The leaf is permanently meristematic at the base, dying away progressively from the tip, so that it seldom gets to be more than

Fig. 22.24. *Gnetum gnemon;* seedling at the University of Chicago. (Courtesy of the Chicago Natural History Museum.)

about 2 m long. The cones are borne on numerous slender, branching shoots that arise from the stem just above (centripetal to) the leaves.

The relationships of the Chlamydospermae have provoked a great deal of botanical investigation and controversy. They were at one time thought to be more or less directly ancestral to the angiosperms, but that idea has been generally abandoned. The ontogeny of the vessels is different from that of angiosperm vessels, and, in spite of the absence of archegonia in *Gnetum* and *Welwitschia,* the reproductive structures are difficult to homologize with those of angiosperms. In their

Fig. 22.25. *Welwitschia mirabilis;* habitat group at the Chicago Natural History Museum. (Courtesy of the Chicago Natural History Museum.)

simple leaves, well-developed secondary growth, and compound female cones, they are suggestive of the Coniferae, but they do not seem to be closely allied to any modern member of that group. The male and female cones of *Ephedra* have been considered to be homologous with the cone clusters of the Cordaitales, and the same interpretation might perhaps be extended to the somewhat different cones of *Welwitschia* and *Gnetum.* The best present guess is that the Chlamydospermae are highly modified descendants of the Cordaitales, but the absence of a significant fossil record conspires with the morphological isolation of the group to make such phylogenetic speculation hazardous.

SUGGESTED READING

Chamberlain, C. J., *Gymnosperms. Structure and Evolution,* University of Chicago Press, Chicago, 1935, 484 pp. The standard text.

Greguss, P., *Identification of Living Gymnosperms on the Basis of Xylotomy,* Trans. Mrs. L. Jocsik, Akademiai Klado, Budapest, 1955, 263 pp. plus 350 full-page plates showing sections of wood.

Kumlien, L. L., *The Friendly Evergreens,* Rinehart, New York, 1946, 1954, 237 pp. An abundantly illustrated book on conifers for cultivation.

Schulman, Edmund, and W. Robert Moore, Bristlecone pine, the oldest known living thing, *National Geographic 113*:355–372. 1958. Good *National Geographic* style.

Studhalter, R. A., and Waldo S. Glock, Tree growth, *Bot. Rev. 21*:1–188. 1955. Includes a discussion of dating by tree rings.

Introduction to Angiosperms; Tissues; Soil

CHAPTER 23

Anthophyta: Vascular plants with roots, stems, and leaves, the central cylinder with leaf gaps or with scattered vascular bundles; ovules enclosed in an ovary; female gametophyte reduced to a few-nucleate embryo sac without an archegonium; male gametophyte producing two naked sperms, one of which fuses with the egg to form the zygote, the other of which fuses with two nuclei (or the product of fusion of two nuclei) of the embryo sac to form a triple-fusion nucleus that is typically the forerunner of the endosperm of the seed. Two classes, the Monocotyledonae and Dicotyledonae.

◀

Tulip tree, *Liriodendron tulipifera*, a native of eastern United States. (Slightly larger than natural size.) *Liriodendron* belongs to the Magnoliaceae, one of the most primitive families of angiosperms. (Photo by F. E. Westlake, from National Audubon Society.)

INTRODUCTION TO ANGIOSPERMS

The Anthophyta, commonly called the **angiosperms** or **flowering plants**, are the most complex as well as the most familiar of all plants. The name angiosperm (from Greek *angeion*, vessel, and *sperma*, seed) refers to the fact that the young seeds are enclosed within a special structure, the ovary, instead of being exposed directly to the air, as in gymnosperms (from Greek *gymnos*, naked, and *sperma*, seed). The name Anthophyta (Greek *anthos*, flower, and *phyta*, plants) refers to the characteristic flowers which are associated with seed production. In its strictest sense, the term *flower* applies only to structures of angiosperms, although it is sometimes loosely used to cover analogous or otherwise more or less similar structures in other plants. Many angiosperms have large and showy flowers, but in others the flowers are small and inconspicuous. All the garden flowers and crops, the familiar broad-leaved trees and shrubs, the cereal grains and other

449

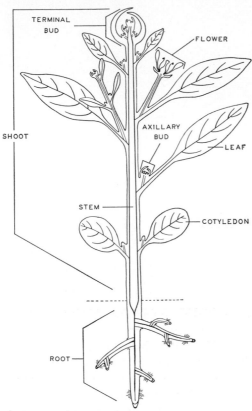

TERMINAL BUD

FLOWER

SHOOT

AXILLARY BUD

LEAF

STEM

COTYLEDON

ROOT

Fig. 23.1.   Diagram of the structure of a typical dicot. (Adapted from Sachs.)

grasses, and the ordinary garden and road-side weeds are angiosperms.

The two classes of angiosperms, the Monocotyledonae and Dicotyledonae, often referred to as **monocots** and **dicots,** usually differ in several respects, but no one of the differences is absolutely constant. The most consistent single difference is the one suggested by the names: in dicotyledons the embryo of the seed has two cotyledons (seed leaves), whereas in monocotyledons it has only one. The two classes are contrasted in Chapter 33, following the study of the structure and life cycle of angiosperms. Most of the characteristic features of the monocots are evo-lutionary modifications from the condition in dicots.

Because the angiosperms are the most common and familiar plants, botanical terminology tends to center around them. Many terms and concepts developed for the angiosperms are equally applicable to at least some other divisions of plants, especially to the other **vascular plants** (i.e., plants with a well-developed conducting system); but often the structures of plants in these other groups differ from those of angiosperms, and it is sometimes difficult to decide just how far the terms should be stretched.

In angiosperms and nearly all other vascular plants, the vegetative plant body, which has $2n$ chromosomes, customarily consists of three general kinds of parts, called roots, stems, and leaves. These may be considered the primary organs of the plant; other kinds of organs are modifications or appendages of these three. **Roots** are typically the organs which anchor the plant in the soil and absorb water and minerals. The **leaves,** which are typ-ically thin and flat, are usually the principal photosynthetic organs of the plant, although the stems are often also photo-synthetic. The **stems,** which are typically cylindrical and usually branched, display the leaves and the flowers and eventually the seeds. The stem and leaves are collectively called the **shoot.** Roots, stems, and leaves often have additional or different functions from those just listed, and they are sometimes so highly modified as to be recognizable only with difficulty. Sometimes one or another of these three basic organs is entirely absent. For example, the aquatic flowering plant bladder-wort (*Utricularia*) lacks roots, and *Wolffia*, a highly reduced floating aquatic, lacks both roots and leaves.

Angiosperms differ greatly in length of life. Plants which live only a single year are called **annuals;** plants which live two years are called **biennials;** and plants which live three or more years are called **perennials.** Typical annuals, such as corn and petunias, complete their life cycle in a single growing season; they come up from seed in the spring, mature within a few months or even weeks, and die. **Winter annuals,** such as winter wheat, come up in the fall and set seed the following year, but still complete their life cycle in less than 12 months.

Biennials usually do not flower the first year; during the second year they flower, set seed, and die. Often they grow vigorously the first year, storing food in the roots or elsewhere, and then draw on this reserve the following year, when seeds are produced. Carrots, parsnips, and turnips are familiar biennials with fleshy storage roots.

Perennials usually do not flower during the first year or so, but thereafter they commonly flower repeatedly, year after year. Some perennials, on the other hand, flower only once and then die. The century plant (*Agave americana* and related species), which commonly reaches an age of 10–25 years, is a notable example. Plants which characteristically flower only once are said to be **monocarpic.** The term is applicable to annuals and biennials, as well as to perennials which flower only once, but it is more often used in speaking of perennials.

TISSUES

INTRODUCTION

Angiosperms are multicellular plants, generally with several different kinds of cells, which are organized into groups called **tissues.** The cells of any one tissue have a common origin and function. Tissues in which all the cells are essentially alike are called **simple tissues.** Tissues in which different kinds of cells contribute to a common function are called **complex tissues.** Any group of tissues which collectively form an externally differentiated body is called an **organ.** The primary organs of the vegetative body of an angiosperm are, as noted above, the roots, stems, and leaves.

Some kinds of tissues occur in all three kinds of organs; others are usually more restricted. Such tissues as parenchyma, collenchyma, and sclerenchmya are defined largely by the nature of the cells of which they are composed; often these simple tissues are parts of complex tissues that contain several kinds of cells. Parenchyma, collenchyma, and sclerenchyma cells sometimes also occur singly in complex tissues of other types.

Tissues such as cortex, pericycle, and pith are defined by their position, regardless of the types of cells of which they are composed. These tissues are discussed in later chapters. Several tissues have both a characteristic position, or positions, and a characteristic structure. The most notable of these are epidermis, endodermis, meristem, xylem, phloem, and cork.

PARENCHYMA

Most tissues are specialized for one or another function, or sometimes two or more functions, the cells having a characteristic form and structure according to their function. Tissues composed of relatively unspecialized cells are called **parenchyma.** The wall of a parenchyma cell is usually thin, without a secondary layer,

Introduction to Angiosperms; Tissues; Soil 451

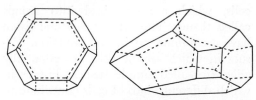

Fig. 23.2. Left, an orthic tetrakaidecahedron, the theoretically ideal shape of parenchyma cells. Right, an actual parenchyma cell from a dicot stem, showing an approach to the orthic tetrakaidecahedron. (After Matzke.)

and is usually composed largely of cellulose and pectic compounds. The cell is living when functional and generally has a well-developed central vacuole. Parenchyma cells vary in shape, but they are seldom much elongate; often they are more or less isodiametric, although this tends to overstate the case. Adjacent cells are usually in contact over only parts of their surface, leaving large or small intercellular spaces.

Closely packed parenchyma cells are generally polyhedral, with a number of flat surfaces. Ideally, they have 14 surfaces, with 8 hexagonal and 6 square faces, but this form, called the **orthic tetrakaidecahedron** (Fig. 23.2) is seldom precisely realized. Experiments with bubbles and compressed shot by the American botanist Edwin B. Matzke (1902–   ) and his students indicate that, under conditions of mutual pressure, the orthic tetrakaidecahedron is the most economical shape, with the lowest surface-volume ratio, if no interspaces are to be left among bodies which in the absence of pressure would be spherical and of equal size.

Parenchymatous tissues (Fig. 23.3) generally occur in all organs of a plant, and they carry on a variety of functions. The name itself (from Greek *para*, beside, and *en + chein*, to pour in) reflects the ancient concept of parenchyma as something which is figuratively poured around the other, more specialized tissues in the various organs. Morphologically, physiologically, and phylogenetically, parenchyma is the basic or fundamental type of tissue, and the other types may be considered as modifications of it. Often it is difficult to decide whether some slightly specialized or modified tissue should be called parenchyma or not, and sometimes the term is used with a qualification, as for example, "thick-walled parenchyma."

Parenchyma cells often have chloroplasts, and most photosynthetic tissues are parenchymatous. Sometimes it is useful to distinguish chlorophyllous parenchyma under the name **chlorenchyma**. Tissue which differs from ordinary parenchyma only in that the cells are much elongate is often called **plectenchyma**.

COLLENCHYMA

Collenchyma (Fig. 23.3) is a living tissue composed of more or less elongate cells with thick primary walls that consist largely of cellulose, along with the usual pectic compounds. The protoplast has a well-developed central vacuole, and the cytoplasm often contains chloroplasts. The cells are typically prismatic, but the more elongate types, which are sometimes as much as 2 mm long, taper at the ends. The thickening of the wall is usually unequally distributed, often chiefly in the angles of the cell. Collenchyma may or may not contain intercellular spaces. When it does, the walls adjoining the intercellular spaces are frequently the thickest. The term *collenchyma* (from Greek *kolla*, glue) refers to the characteristically glistening wall.

The principal function of collenchyma is mechanical strengthening. It is usually the first supporting tissue in young stems and leaves and is important in many mature ones as well. It is much less often found in roots. The cells combine considerable tensile strength with flexibility, and they can continue to grow after the wall has thickened; they are, therefore, ideally adapted to the support of growing organs.

SCLERENCHYMA

Sclerenchyma (from Greek *skléros,* hard) is a tissue composed of thick-walled cells whose sole or principal function is mechanical strengthening. The cells have a definite secondary wall that is often lignified, and they commonly lack living contents at maturity. In both these respects sclerenchyma differs from collenchyma, another strengthening tissue. Sclerenchyma is distinguished from xylem (a complex tissue composed largely of thick-walled, lignified, dead cells) by its function and position. Xylem is important in the conduction of water and minerals as well as in mechanical support, whereas sclerenchyma has no conducting function.

Sclerenchyma cells (Fig. 23.4) vary greatly in size and shape. Long slender ones are called **fibers**, a term also applied to long slender xylem cells. (Xylem fibers might, in fact, be considered as sclerenchyma cells, although the term is seldom so applied.) Short or irregular sclerenchyma cells are called **sclereids**, although there is no sharp distinction between the two types. Sclereids are sometimes also called **stone cells.** Sclereids of unusual shape which occur singly among cells of more ordinary type are often called **idioblasts.** Sclereids often occur as scattered cells in otherwise parenchymatous tissues, but fibers nearly always occur in organized groups. Collenchymatous or parenchymatous tissues sometimes become

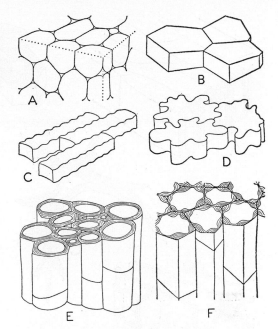

Fig. 23.3. Some types of tissues, showing only the cell walls or cell outline, without contents. A, parenchyma; B–D, epidermis; E, F, collenchyma.

sclerenchymatous in age; i.e., they develop secondary walls and thereafter tend to lose their protoplasts.

EPIDERMIS

Epidermis (Fig. 23.3) is the characteristic outermost tissue of leaves and of young roots and stems. In older roots and stems, especially of woody plants, the epidermis is often replaced by other tissues. Epidermis consists of cells which fit closely together, nearly or quite without intercellular spaces, except for the special type of intercellular space called the **stomate.** Stomates are found in the epidermis of most stems and leaves, but usually not in roots. Epidermal cells vary in shape, but the inner surface is usually flat, and the outer surface flat or bulged. The depth of

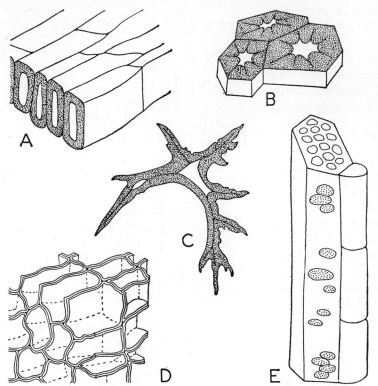

Fig. 23.4. Some types of cells. A–C, sclerenchyma cells, with the walls stippled: A, fibers; B, stone cells; C, an idioblast; D, cork cells; E, sieve tube and companion cells of phloem, the sieve tube showing a well-developed sieve plate at the end and some less well-developed lateral sieve areas.

the cell, from interior to exterior, is usually less than any other dimension, and the cells are therefore said to be tabular in shape. The epidermal layer is typically only one cell thick, and (except for the cells bounding the stomates) the cells are in most cases all about alike. Sometimes, however, the epidermis is two to several cells thick, or composed of two or more kinds of cells, or both.

Epidermal cells are usually living when functional. They have a well-developed central vacuole, and, except for the guard cells adjoining the stomates, they seldom have chloroplasts. The outer walls of epidermal cells of stems and leaves, but usually not of roots, are impregnated with a waxy material called **cutin;** and the cutin also forms a continuous layer, the **cuticle,** over the outer surface of the epidermis.

Even the inner walls are often cutinized and covered with cuticle where they abut on intercellular spaces. Cutin retards the passage of water and water vapor. Except for the cutin, the walls of epidermal cells are usually composed largely of cellulose and pectic compounds.

Epidermis of roots is chiefly an absorptive tissue, absorbing water and minerals used by the plant. Epidermis of stems and leaves is largely a protective tissue, usually providing some mechanical strength as well as inhibiting the evaporation of water from internal tissues. Sometimes it has other functions as well.

The stomates in the epidermis allow exchange of gases between the internal tissues and the atmosphere, at the same time permitting some evaporation of water. Each stomate is bounded by two specialized epidermal cells, the **guard cells.** Under conditions of water deficit and under certain other conditions, the guard cells become pressed closely together, closing the opening. The structure and function of the stomate–guard-cell apparatus are further discussed in Chapter 26.

When the epidermis appears to be more than one cell thick, only the outer layer is cutinized. It was formerly customary to admit only the outer layer as the epidermis and to call any adjacent layer of more or less similar nature a **hypodermis.** Nowadays plant anatomists prefer to speak of a several-layered epidermis, if all these layers arise in the same way, reserving the term *hypodermis* for epidermis-like internal layers whose ontogeny differs from that of the true epidermis. In this sense, only developmental studies can differentiate between a multilayered epidermis and an epidermis accompanied by a hypodermis.

The epidermis often bears small, unicellular, or multicellular appendages called **trichomes.** Trichomes in some species are small, flat scales, but more often they are slender hairs, from less than 1 mm to 2–3 mm long, seldom longer. Some trichomes are tipped with a sticky or greasy globule called a gland. A leaf or stem with trichomes on the epidermis is said to be **pubescent.** One without trichomes or other roughenings is **glabrous.** The kind, distribution, and to some extent the amount of pubescence tend to be reasonably constant within each species, and differences in pubescence can often be used as handy technical characters to distinguish related species. An extensive terminology has been developed to describe pubescence.

The function of pubescence is doubtful. In some plants, the trichomes are so stiff and bristly as to furnish some protection from grazing animals, and in others, such as nettles, the glandular tip of the trichome contains formic acid or some other irritant. A thick coating of pubescence, such as occurs in mullein (*Verbascum thapsus*), probably tends to reduce evaporation of water from the leaves, at least under some conditions. In the majority of cases, however, it requires a hopeful ingenuity to detect any probable function.

Many of the epidermal cells near the growing point of a root have slender projections called root hairs. Because of their distinctive structure and function (see Chapter 25), these are not considered to be trichomes. Trichomes do sometimes occur on roots as well as on aerial organs, however.

ENDODERMIS

The endodermis is a tissue which in angiosperms is largely confined to roots, although it often occurs in the stems of other kinds of vascular plants, and sometimes even in the leaves. Endodermis is discussed in Chapter 25.

MERISTEMS

In most animals and in many of the less complex kinds of plants, all or nearly all living cells can divide, and growth is diffuse. In angiosperms and other vascular plants, however, cell division tends to be more or less restricted to certain tissues which occupy particular places in the plant body. Any plant tissue characterized by cell division is called a **meristem.** Any stem, and each of its branches, is ordinarily tipped by a group of cells which make up the **apical meristem.** The main root and branch roots also have apical meristems. The apical meristem of a root might better be described as subapical, inasmuch as it is covered by a tissue called the rootcap. All tissues derived directly by differentiation from an apical meristem are called **primary tissues.** Mature primary tissues often retain some capacity for cell division, generally at a rate much slower than that in the apical meristem.

Increase in thickness of a stem or root, after the primary tissues have matured, is usually due to cell divisions from **lateral meristems** which lie within the stem or root, usually nearer to the surface than to the center. The most important lateral meristem is the vascular cambium, often called merely the **cambium.** The cells formed from the cambium mature into xylem and phloem, the characteristic conducting tissues of the plant. (Some primary tissues also consist of xylem and phloem.) Another kind of lateral meristem is the **phellogen,** or **cork cambium,** which produces cork and a parenchymatous tissue called phelloderm.

All tissues derived from lateral meristems are called **secondary tissues.** Many angiosperms, especially the monocots, lack a cambium and are composed wholly of primary tissues. Some tissues, such as the epidermis, are always primary tissues; others, such as phelloderm, are always secondary. Xylem and phloem may be either primary or secondary; the primary tissues of vascular plants characteristically include xylem and phloem, but these are also produced by cambial activity.

A third type of meristem, the **intercalary meristem,** is sometimes inserted between primary tissues in a position different from that of lateral meristems. The leaves of grasses, for example, commonly have an intercalary meristem at the base of the blade. Tissues derived from intercalary meristems are generally similar to those derived from apical meristems and are, therefore, considered to be primary tissues.

The characteristics of meristematic cells vary in different kinds of meristems and in different kinds of plants. Apical meristems typically consist of rather small, nearly isodiametric cells with thin cellulose walls, dense cytoplasm, rather large nuclei, and no central vacuole. The plastids are usually in the proplastid stage, and intercellular spaces are generally wanting. Cambium cells, on the contrary, are often much elongate, and they are more likely to be thick-walled than are the cells of an apical meristem.

Xylem

Xylem (Greek *xylon,* wood) (Fig. 23.5) is a complex tissue which functions in the conduction of water and minerals, and in mechanical support. The fundamental cell type of xylem is the **tracheid.** Tracheids are long, slender cells, tapered at the ends, with well-developed, lignified secondary walls, a well-developed lumen, and without living contents at maturity. The space enclosed by the wall of a cell, especially a dead cell, is called the **lumen.**

Tracheids are divided into several categories, according to the pattern of the secondary wall. Tracheids in which the secondary wall consists of a series of separate rings are called **annular tracheids;** tracheids in which the secondary wall tends to form a continuous spiral are called **spiral tracheids;** tracheids in which the secondary wall tends to be arranged in the form of the rungs and uprights of a ladder are called **scalariform tracheids;** those in which the secondary wall forms a continuous network are called **reticulate tracheids;** and those in which the continuous secondary wall is merely interrupted by small openings (pits) are called **pitted tracheids.** These several types grade into each other. In xylem elements other than parenchyma cells, the aperture by which the pit opens to the lumen is usually narrower than the basal part. Pits of this type are called **bordered pits.**

Annular and spiral tracheids can be stretched to some extent before breaking, and the first tracheids to mature near the growing points of stems and roots are usually of these types. In more mature tissues, the pitted tracheid is usually the most abundant type.

Evolutionary modification of the tracheid has proceeded in two opposite directions: (1) toward support at the expense of conduction, and (2) toward conduction at the expense of support. Cells exemplifying the former modification are called **xylem fibers;** those exemplifying the latter are called **vessel segments.** Xylem fibers are proportionately longer and more slender than tracheids, with a thick, merely pitted secondary wall and a small lumen. Fibers of more or less similar structure also often occur in other tissues but are not regarded as modified tracheids.

A series of vessel segments placed end to end constitutes a **vessel.** In its most typical form, a vessel may be compared to a series of barrels stacked end on end after the end walls have been knocked out. Vessel segments are usually broader and often shorter than tracheids, with a large lumen and often with a relatively thin secondary wall. The pattern in which the secondary wall is deposited undergoes the same vari-

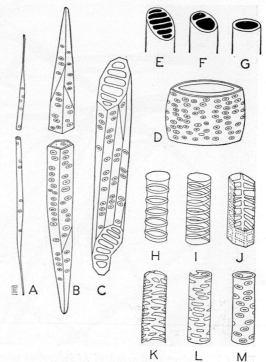

Fig. 23.5. **Xylem cells.** *A*, fiber; *B*, tracheid; *C, D*, vessel segments; *E–G*, ends of vessel segments, with progressively less obstructed opening; *H–M*, types of secondary thickening of xylem cells: *H*, annular; *I*, spiral; *J*, scalariform; *K*, reticulate; *L*, reticulate-pitted; *M*, pitted.

ation as in tracheids; and the same types are recognized. Vessels are often as much as several feet long, but they have complete end walls at the top and bottom.

Vessels are more effective conducting elements than tracheids, because water can move from one end of a vessel to the other without having to pass through a partition. There are all gradations between tracheids and vessel segments. Many vessel segments have slanting end walls with distinct perforations. The presence of these perforations in the end walls separating adjacent cells is the ultimate distinction between vessel segments and tracheids.

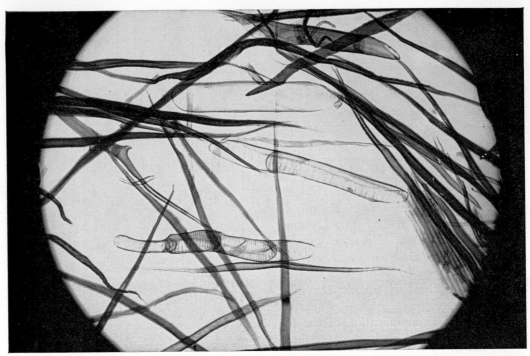

Fig. 23.6. Macerated wood of *Liriodendron tulipifera,* tulip tree, showing vessel segments and fibers. (Copyright by General Biological Supply House, Inc., Chicago.)

Tracheids, vessels, and fibers are all dead when functional. Xylem of stems and roots generally also contains some living cells. These are usually called parenchyma cells, although often they are not typical of parenchyma in all respects. The distribution of parenchyma cells in the xylem is discussed in later chapters, as is also the mechanics of water movement.

Phloem

Phloem (from Greek *phloos,* bark) is a complex tissue which functions in the conduction of food and other dissolved substances, including minerals. Phloem is usually associated with xylem in plant organs, and together these two tissues constitute the vascular system of the plant.

The fundamental type of cell in phloem is the **sieve element.** Sieve elements are long, slender, thin-walled cells which at maturity have cytoplasm and a central vacuole but no nucleus. The cytoplasm is continuous from one sieve element to another through clusters of perforations in the wall, called **sieve areas.** These connecting strands of cytoplasm might be considered to be much enlarged plasmodesmata. In angiosperms sieve elements are joined end to end to form **sieve tubes,** and the sieve areas tend to be concentrated on the slanting or transverse end walls of the sieve elements. These end walls with sieve areas are called **sieve plates** (Fig. 23.7). Among the angiosperms any sieve areas that may be present on the lateral walls of the sieve elements are usually poorly developed as compared to the sieve plates.

One of the characteristic features of sieve elements is the presence of a viscous, apparently proteinaceous slime. The slime originates in the cytoplasm, forming definite slime bodies during the growth and differentiation of the young sieve element, before the nucleus has disintegrated. Later the slime bodies lose their individuality, and the slime comes to lie largely in the central vacuole, also being associated in some way with the perforations in the sieve areas.

The primary cell wall of sieve elements is composed largely of cellulose, and usually there is no secondary wall. **Callose** is deposited on and around the sieve areas, often eventually closing off the perforations. Callose is chemically related to cellulose, but its precise chemical composition is unknown; it is recognized by its affinity for certain stains which have little or no effect on cellulose. Extensive accumulation of callose, forming a well-defined plug over the sieve plate, generally marks the end of the conducting activity of the sieve element. Thereafter the protoplasm tends to degenerate, and often the plug separates from the sieve plate and disappears.

Sieve elements are ordinarily interspersed with more or less modified parenchyma cells which retain a functional nucleus. The cytoplasm of these parenchyma cells is continuous with that of the associated sieve tubes by numerous small plasmodesmata, and it has been suggested that the nucleus of the parenchyma cell serves for the cytoplasm of the associated sieve element as well as for its own cytoplasm. In most angiosperms these parenchyma cells are rather highly specialized and have a direct ontogenetic relationship with the associated sieve elements. Modified parenchyma cells of this type are called **companion cells.** The sieve element and its associated companion cell(s) arise from the same individual meristematic cell. A single companion cell may extend the whole length of the sieve element, or there may be a vertical file of two to several companion cells next to each sieve element. The eventual death and degeneration of the protoplasm of the sieve element is usually correlated with the death and degeneration of the protoplast(s) of the associated companion cell(s).

In addition to the sieve tubes and companion cells, the phloem of angiosperms usually contains parenchyma cells and fibers, and sometimes other kinds of cells as well. The fibers are usually sclerenchymatous, with thickened, often lignified secondary walls, and without living contents at maturity; but phloem fibers with persistent protoplasts are also known.

The mechanics of movement of dissolved substances in the phloem are still in dispute, as noted in Chapter 29. It is obvious that the sieve tube acts as a sort of pipe line, and that the sieve plates are important in providing a passageway from one sieve element to the next; but in-

Fig. 23.7. **Sieve plate of squash (*Cucurbita maxima*), with the outlines of surrounding cells. (×100.) (From W. H. Brown,** *The Plant Kingdom,* **1935; courtesy of Ginn & Company, Boston.)**

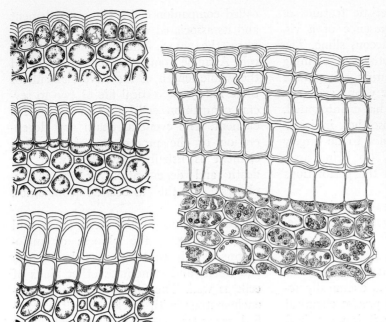

Fig. 23.8. Stages in the formation of cork in oleander (*Nerium oleander*). Upper left, epidermis and adjacent cortex; the exposed outer surface of the epidermal cell wall is much thickened in this species. Left center, the epidermal cells have elongated and divided to produce an internal layer of phellogen, next to the cortex. Lower left, the phellogen has produced a single layer of cork cells just beneath the epidermis. Right, the uppermost row of cells is epidermis, the next four rows are cork, and the sixth row is the phellogen. (×300.) (From W. H. Brown, *The Plant Kingdom*, 1935; courtesy of Ginn & Company, Boston.)

vestigators are not agreed as to the role of the cytoplasm in the process, the significance of the slime, or the propulsive force.

CORK

Cork (Fig. 23.8) is a waterproofing protective tissue, dead when functional, characterized by the suberization of the cell walls. The secondary wall consists largely of **suberin**, a waxy substance; the primary wall, originally composed chiefly of cellulose, tends to become impregnated with suberin as well. Cork cells are usually more or less prismatic; in cross sections of stems and roots, they often appear to be rectangular or box-shaped, but careful studies show that they tend to be tetrakaidecahedral, with an average of 14 surfaces. Cork is ordinarily a secondary tissue, derived from a particular kind of meristem called the phellogen or cork cambium; and

cork cells tend to be arranged in regular rows aligned with the cells of the phellogen, nearly or quite without intercellular spaces. Cork commonly occurs in the outer parts of woody stems and roots, forming or helping to form a protective outer covering after the epidermis has broken down.

LATICIFERS

Many plants have some specialized cells or ducts which contain **latex**, a colorless to more often white, yellow, or reddish liquid, often slightly viscous, characterized by the presence of colloidal particles of terpenes dispersed in water. Terpenes are a chemical family of hydrocarbons, including such substances as rubber, resins, balsams, essential oils, camphor, and carotenoids. The kinds and amounts of terpenes differ in the latex of different species, but rubber and resins are especially common. The latex of commercial rubber trees contains up to 50 per cent rubber. Latex also regularly contains dissolved salts and other dissolved or suspended substances such as sugar, proteins, fats, tannins, and alkaloids. Crystals and starch grains may also be present. Latex has been considered to be the cell sap of the latex cells, but it is often difficult to distinguish between the latex and the cytoplasm.

Latex in some plants occurs in cells much like ordinary parenchyma cells, but usually it occurs in elongate, slender tubes called **laticifers** (Fig. 23.9). Laticifers are **nonarticulate** or **articulate,** according to whether they consist of one or many cells. The end walls between the cells of articulate laticifers soon degenerate, so that a continuous tube is formed. Both types of laticifers are coenocytic, with numerous nuclei scattered through the cytoplasm. They occur in almost any tissue, often completely permeating the plant, but are most common in or near the phloem. Laticifers are commonly branched, and articulate laticifers often form an interconnecting system. The single multinucleate cell represented by a nonarticulate laticifer may extend throughout the whole length of the plant.

The function of laticifers is dubious. Many suggestions have been made, but none is backed by very substantial evidence. The most common interpretation is that they form an excretory system. Terpenes in particular appear to be nonfunctional by-products of cellular metabolism, particularly in young, growing tissues, and they are not known to be used again by the plant after they have been deposited in the laticifers. A difficulty with this interpretation, though perhaps not an insuperable one, is that the latex seems

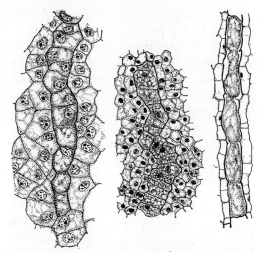

Fig. 23.9. Stages in the formation of an articulate laticifer in *Manilkara zapotilla*, the tree from which chicle (the essential ingredient of chewing gum) is obtained. (After Karling, from W. H. Brown, *The Plant Kingdom,* 1935; courtesy of Ginn & Company, Boston.)

to be formed directly within the laticifers, rather than being carried to them from other cells.

SOIL

COMPONENTS OF SOIL

The mantle of weathered mineral and organic matter that covers most of the land surface and supports plant growth is called **soil.** The upper layers of most soils contain 30–60 percent pore space which is filled with water and air. The ratio of water to air in the pore space varies from day to day. Soils with more than 80 percent (by weight) of the solid matter consisting of mineral particles (thus less than 20 percent organic matter) are called **mineral soils** and are much commoner than **organic soils,** which have more than 20 percent organic matter. A fair average of organic matter for a good mineral soil is 4–5 percent.

Soil is important to land plants as the primary source of water and minerals, and as an anchoring agent. Most plants also obtain oxygen for respiration of the underground parts from the soil. A soil which is too loose may not provide adequate anchorage, but too firm a consistency interferes with growth of roots. Mineral nutrition and water relations of angiosperms, as well as the nitrogen cycle, are taken up in other chapters of this text, therefore, only the more general aspects of the influence of soil on growth will be discussed here.

The size of soil particles has at least as much to do with the characteristics of the soil as does its chemical composition. The colloidal particles in particular (those less than about 0.001 mm thick) strongly influence the texture, water-holding capacity, and chemical activity of the soil.

Soil particles are classified, according to increasing size, as clay, silt, sand, and gravel. The distinctions among the classes are of course wholly arbitrary, and several different standards have been set up. The U.S. Department of Agriculture standard is: **clay**—particles less than 0.002 mm in diameter; **silt**—particles 0.002–0.05 mm in diameter; **sand**—particles 0.05–1 mm in diameter; **fine gravel**—particles 1–2 mm in diameter.

GENERAL CHARACTERISTICS AND TYPES OF SOILS

According to the proportions of the various sizes of particles, mineral soils can mostly be classified as sands, silts, clays, and **loams,** or the terms may be used in combinations such as sandy loam, silty clay, etc. The upper size limit of clay particles is only about twice that of colloidal particles, and much of the clay in soil is in colloidal form. These colloidal particles so strongly influence the nature of the soil that any soil with more than about 30 percent clay, by dry weight, is called a clay soil. Soils with more than 80 percent sand are sands, and soils with more than 80 percent silt are silts. Soils with other proportions of mineral particles, i.e., with less than 30 percent clay, less than 80 percent sand, and less than 80 percent silt, are loams. The mineral part of a typical loam is about half sand (by weight), and half silt and clay.

Clay soils have a high water-holding capacity and retain mineral nutrients well, but the pore spaces are so small that movement of water and air is impeded, and, if worked when wet, they may become practically impervious. Sandy soils, on the contrary, are well aerated and drain well. They are loose enough to permit easy cultivation and free passage of roots, but they do not have much capacity to hold water and mineral nutrients. Silt soils are uncommon and are intermediate between sand and clay. Loam soils are the best, combining the advantages and minimizing the defects of sands and clays.

Under natural conditions soils that are not too sandy or too high in clay tend to develop a porous, crumb-like structure which promotes aeration and drainage without interfering seriously with the capacity to retain enough minerals and water for plant growth. The **humus** in the soil is one of the most important factors contributing to the development and maintenance of the crumb structure. Humus is partly decayed organic matter in a colloidal state.

It is more resistant to decay than the plant and animal bodies and wastes from which it is derived, but it does gradually disintegrate. In tropical regions the rapid destruction of humus, especially when the bare soil is exposed to the sun, is one of the greatest impediments to soil fertility.

The colloidal nature of humus and much of the clay in the soil enables these particles to adsorb water and exchangeable mineral ions, which can then be taken up by plants; but humus is much more effective in this regard than clay. Unlike clay, humus also promotes the desirable crumb structure of the soil, and the addition of a small amount of humus often causes a disproportionate improvement in fertility.

Except in very dry climates, the upper part of the soil, called the A horizon, is subject to continual leaching of minerals and other solutes. Some of these, especially the iron and aluminum, accumulate in the next layer down, the B horizon. The A horizon, which is seldom over a foot thick and is more or less equivalent to the topsoil of common speech, has more humus than the B horizon and is usually a good source of both water and minerals for plant growth. Some of the roots generally also enter the B horizon, or subsoil, which continues to provide water during dry weather for some time after the upper soil has dried out. The B horizon is more compact than the A horizon, with less air space and less humus, so that penetration by the roots is more difficult, and the minerals present are less readily available. Sometimes there is a **hardpan** layer, 1 or more inches thick, in the B horizon, with an especially high concentration of iron and aluminum (and in dry soils calcium carbonate), and often with the interstices filled by fine clay particles which have washed down from above.

Plants growing in such a soil generally thrive better if the hardpan is broken, so that the roots can reach the moister soil below.

CORRELATION OF CLIMATE WITH SOIL TYPE

The nature of an uncultivated soil depends chiefly on the climate, the nature of the parent material, and the vegetation. Given sufficient time, the effect of the climate tends to overcome the other factors, and several broad climatic types of soils can be recognized. The characteristics of these soil types, in turn, influence the vegetation by favoring the growth of some kinds of plants as compared to others.

In the broadest sense, there are three general climatic types of soils in nonarid regions; **tundra** soils in the arctic, **podzolic** soils in temperate climates, and **lateritic** soils in the tropics. Tundra soils have an accumulation of organic matter over a sticky and compact bluish-gray subsoil; they are poorly drained and subject to severe frost heaving, often being underlain at no great depth by permafrost.

The most typical podzols, occurring in cold temperate regions, are characterized by severe leaching of iron, aluminum, calcium, magnesium, and other nonsiliceous minerals, leaving a sandy, infertile A horizon. Some of the iron and humus are deposited in the B horizon, but the other minerals are largely carried away. Organic remains decay slowly, and there is a surface covering of litter and partly decomposed organic matter. The whole soil profile is generally very acid, with pH values ranging from 3.5 to 4.5. In the United States typical podzolic soils are largely confined to northern New England, the northern Great Lakes region, and the higher Appalachians, but they are widespread in Canada and northern Eurasia. They are not very fertile and for the most part are best left uncultivated, as forest land.

Laterites, the typical soils of moist tropical regions, are characterized by leaching and loss of the siliceous minerals, and retention of iron and aluminum as oxides, so that the soil, especially in the B horizon, is a red or reddish clay of peculiar texture, which absorbs water easily and does not erode so rapidly as clay soils of temperate regions. Organic matter decays rapidly in tropical regions, and laterites contain but little humus. They are also low in exchangeable minerals, and lose their fertility rapidly under cultivation.

Most soils of the eastern United States are podzolic in the broad sense, but they diverge from typical podzol in the direction of laterite and are, in fact, more fertile than either typical podzol or typical laterite. The organic matter decays rapidly enough to provide a reasonable amount of humus, which is not so quickly destroyed as in tropical regions. Available minerals are more abundant than in either typical podzols or typical laterites. The red and yellow soils so common in the southeastern United States are intermediate between podzol and laterite but are usually classified with the podzols. Like the brown and gray-brown podzolic soils found farther north in the United States, they are much more fertile than typical podzols.

Soils of drier regions, such as those of most of the western United States, do not fit well into the podzol to laterite series and are classified into several types on bases which will not be discussed here. Leaching of soil minerals is not so pronounced in dry regions as in moist ones, and, in dry areas without good drainage, evaporation tends to concentrate the minerals near the surface of the soil. In extreme cases the minerals form a layer of alkali on top of the ground, and only plants with a very high osmotic potential can grow in such sites.

SUGGESTED READING

Black, C. A., *Soil-Plant Relationships*, John Wiley & Sons, New York, 1957, 332 pp. A textbook-level presentation, covering "some of the more important soil-plant relationships with emphasis throughout on soil as a substrate for plant growth."

CHAPTER 24

Angiosperms: Stems

INTRODUCTION

SOME EXTERNAL FEATURES

Stems are the organs of a plant on which the leaves are borne. They are usually more or less round in cross section, commonly tapering toward the tip. The leaves are usually arranged in a regular pattern. A place on the stem where a leaf is (or has been) attached is called a **node,** and the part of the stem between two successive nodes is called an **internode.** Often the stem is somewhat swollen at the nodes, sometimes so much so as to appear jointed. The point of the angle formed by the leaf or leafstalk and the upward internode of the stem is called the **axil** of the leaf. Normally each axil bears a bud, the **axillary bud,** which is capable of developing into a branch shoot. Even when the leaves are highly modified, or much reduced and inconspicuous, the axillary bud, marking the node, is often evident. It may be said that stems characteristically have nodes and

◀

White birch, *Betula alba.* (Photo by Eva Luoma, from National Audubon Society.)

Fig. 24.1. Long section of growing stem tip of *Elodea*. (Courtesy of E. J. Kohl, Lakeside Biological Products, Ripon, Wis.)

internodes, and that branch stems (of angiosperms) characteristically arise from axillary buds. Both these features are in contrast to those of roots.

APICAL GROWTH

The tip of the stem is ordinarily occupied by an apical meristem. In an actively growing stem, the apical meristem is protected by the developing young leaves which extend up and around it from below. As these leaves expand and spread away from the stem with increasing maturity, new young leaves are progressively formed by the apical meristem, and these

in turn protect the growing point for a time before they mature. The apical meristem and its protective leaves constitute the **terminal bud.**

The apical meristem of woody stems, especially in extratropical regions, is often dormant for much of the year, and the dormant meristem is usually covered and protected by some modified, small, firm leaves, the **bud scales.** When the apical meristem resumes its growth after a period of dormancy, the bud scales spread away from the growing point and fall off, typically leaving a ring of bud-scale scars around the twig. Twigs of many woody plants show successive rings of bud-scale scars marking the annual increments in length. There are all degrees of variation, from dormant buds that are merely covered by ordinary young leaves whose development is arrested, to the more common type in which the bud scales are distinctly different from ordinary leaves. Axillary buds of woody plants, as well as terminal buds, are commonly covered by bud scales.

Growth in length of the stem is due to cell divisions occurring in and near the apical meristem, followed by enlargement of the cells which do not remain meristematic. The apical meristem is thus constantly being carried upward or onward by the growth of the new cells it produces. The region just beneath the apical meristem, marked by rapid enlargement (especially elongation) of the cells, is called the **region of elongation,** or more precisely, the region of cell enlargement. The boundary between the apical meristem and the region of elongation is rather vague; some capacity for cell division is often retained even by mature primary tissues. Even within the meristematic region, where cell division is actively occurring, most of the cells are ultimately destined, after one or more divisions, to develop into parts of mature primary tissues. The relatively few cells in the apical meristem which remain more or less permanently meristematic are called the **initials.** In practice, the initials are often difficult to identify. Young, differentiating tissue, in the region of elongation and just behind the initials in the apical meristem of a stem or root, is classified as **protoderm, provascular tissue,** and **ground meristem,** according to whether it is destined to develop into epidermis, vascular tissue, or fundamental tissue (defined on p. 471).

In most angiosperms the apical meristem has a more or less differentiated outer

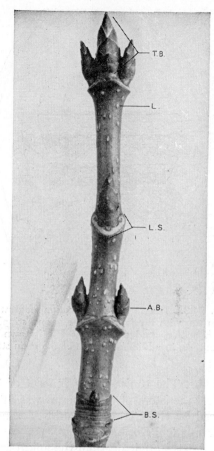

Fig. 24.2. Twig of sugar maple, *Acer sac-charum,* in winter after the leaves have fallen: a.b., axillary bud; b.s., bud-scale scars; l., lenticel; l.s., leaf scar; t.b., terminal bud. (New York Botanical Garden photo.)

part, the **tunica** (Latin, cloak), sheathing a central mass, the **corpus** (Latin, body). The tunica may be one to five layers thick. The cell divisions occurring in the tunica are mostly anticlinal (perpendicular to the outer surface), increasing the surface area without adding new layers. The individual layers of the tunica tend to retain their identity, and each has its own tier of initials. The corpus has only a single tier of initials, but division occurs in various planes, so that the whole mass increases in

Angiosperms: Stems 469

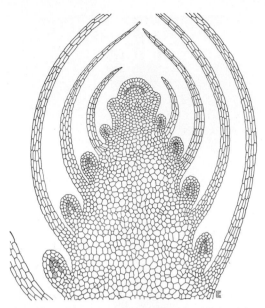

Fig. 24.3. Diagram of long section of growing stem tip, with the initials of the corpus stippled. Each axillary bud primordium has its own set of initials, in addition to those of the main stem.

volume. The tunica-corpus concept of the apical meristem of angiosperms was introduced by the German botanist Alexander Schmidt in 1924.

Leaves originate from the apical meristem of a stem, appearing first as mere bumps (the **leaf primordia**) on the apical meristem a little below the tip. The initiation of the leaf primordium may be due chiefly to localized cell divisions in the tunica, or in the outer part of the corpus, or both, depending on the species.

The axillary buds also originate from the apical meristem, usually after the formation of the subtending leaf primordia. Both the tunica and the corpus are usually involved, the proportions varying in different species. Sometimes the formation of the axillary bud is delayed so long that it develops from essentially mature primary tissues of the stem just above the leaf. Under some circumstances, especially af-

ter injury, adventitious buds are produced away from the axils. The term **adventitious** is applied to structures which originate from mature nonmeristematic tissues, especially if such a development would not ordinarily be expected.

Each axillary bud is potentially the terminal bud of a new branch shoot. Sometimes the bud continues its growth without interruption, developing immediately into a leafy branch or one or another kind of modified shoot (such as a flower). More often the bud becomes dormant after developing to a length of usually less than 1 cm. It may then remain permanently dormant, or it may sooner or later resume active growth, depending on the species and the environmental conditions. The number of axillary branches on a plant seldom represents more than a small fraction of the total number of axillary buds.

The dormancy or activity of the axillary buds is governed largely by hormones produced by the plant. Actively growing shoots commonly produce hormones which tend to inhibit the growth of axillary buds. If the shoot tip is cut off, interrupting the supply of the inhibitory hormone(s), one or more axillary buds usually begin to grow, forming a new shoot which in turn inhibits the development of other buds. The phenomenon is called **apical dominance.** Plant hormones are further discussed in Chapter 32.

ANATOMY

The nature and arrangement of the primary tissues of the stems of angiosperms vary in different groups, but nearly all have several features in common. They are bounded externally by an epidermis. They contain a network of longitudinal strands of vascular tissue, the **vascular bundles,** embedded in a usually parenchymatous matrix, the fundamental tissue. Each vascular bundle contains both xylem and phloem, commonly with the xylem toward the center of the stem and the phloem toward the outside.

Stems in which the primary tissues are similar in composition and arrangement often differ in the amount and distribution of secondary tissues. The anatomy of angiosperm stems is most conveniently studied under four headings: (1) herbaceous dicot, (2) woody dicot, (3) herbaceous monocot, and (4) woody monocot. Woody stems differ from herbaceous stems in the higher proportion of wood, i.e., hard tissue composed largely of thick-walled cells. In woody dicots, as in conifers, xylem is the principal or only woody tissue, and the terms *wood* and *xylem* are often used interchangeably. Much of the wood of woody monocots, however, is not xylem.

HERBACEOUS DICOT STEMS

GENERAL FEATURES

A cross section of a typical herbaceous dicot stem, before secondary growth has started, shows a central pith, successively surrounded by a ring of vascular bundles, a cortex, and an epidermis. All these are primary tissues or groups of tissues, formed by growth and maturation of cells derived from the apical meristem. The pith, the cortex, and the tissue separating the vascular bundles collectively constitute the **fundamental tissue.**

PITH

The pith is usually parenchymatous, with starch-forming leucoplasts (amyloplasts), but without chloroplasts. Sometimes, especially in age, it shows specialized

cells in which tannins or crystals of one sort or another are deposited, or some of the cells may be modified into sclereids or other specialized types. Resin ducts and/or laticifers are also present in some species.

Resin ducts, here mentioned in connection with the pith, may occur in any internal tissue of a stem, root, or even of a leaf. They are long, slender, intercellular spaces which become filled with resins and other substances suspended or dissolved in water. Resin ducts are **schizogenous** or **lysigenous,** according to their origin. Schizogenous resin ducts originate by the separation of adjacent cells, as described in Chapter 22. They are especially common in conifers but are also found in some angiosperms, being particularly frequent in members of the sunflower family (Compositae). The oil ducts found in many members of the carrot family (Umbelliferae) are of similar nature. Lysigenous resin ducts, which originate by the degeneration of rows of cells, are much less common.

The most common function of the pith is food storage. Often it loses all function and dies or degenerates, especially in the internodal regions, as the plant matures.

VASCULAR CYLINDER

The vascular bundles appear in cross section as separate units, but they actually fork and rejoin in a fairly regular pattern, forming a network in the shape of a hollow cylinder (Fig. 24.5). This cylinder, together with the pith it encloses, is called the **central cylinder,** or **stele.** The network of bundles alone is called the vascular cylinder. The spaces among the vascular bundles are filled with parenchyma, connecting the parenchyma of the pith with the parenchyma of the cortex. These inter-

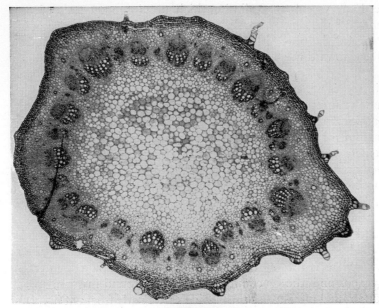

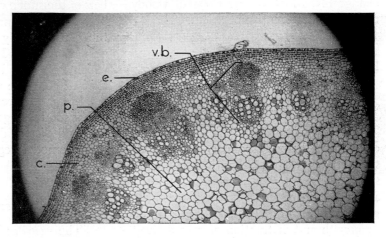

Fig. 24.4. Cross section of a sunflower stem. Left, the whole stem. (Courtesy of E. J. Kohl, Lakeside Biological Products, Ripon, Wis.) Below, a segment of the stem: c., cortex; e., epidermis; p., pith; v.b., vascular bundle, with the xylem toward the center and the phloem toward the outside. (Copyright by General Biological Supply House, Inc., Chicago.)

fascicular areas of parenchyma are called **medullary rays,** or pith rays. Often they are wider than the bundles themselves.

Some of the bundles diverge from the vascular cylinder and pass out through the cortex into the leaves. These are the **leaf traces.** Often there are three traces for each leaf, but in some species there are five or more, or only one. The place of the departing leaf trace in the vascular cylinder is taken by a new bundle formed by the fusion of branches from adjacent bundles on each side. There is, however, a parenchymatous gap between the departing leaf traces and the new vascular bundle of the stele above it. This is the **leaf gap.** The parenchyma of the leaf gap is continuous with that of the adjoining medullary rays. Nodes are said to be unilacunar, trilacunar, pentalacunar, or multilacunar, according to

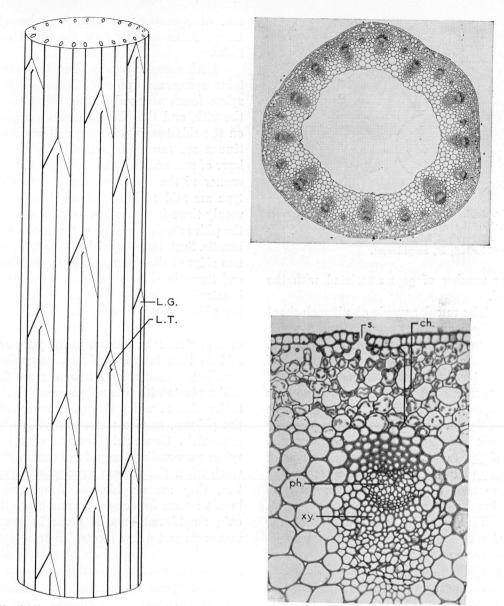

Fig. 24.5. Left: vascular anatomy of flax stem, showing the vascular bundles enclosing the pith: l.g., leaf gap; l.t., leaf trace. The nodes are unilacunar, with a single gap and a single trace for each leaf; the stem of flax is unbranched, and the branch traces do not develop. (Adapted from Esau.) Right: cross section of buttercup (*Ranunculus*) stem (above), and detail of same (below); ch., chlorenchyma; ph., phloem; s., stomate; xy., xylem. (Courtesy of E. J. Kohl, Lakeside Biological Products, Ripon, Wis.)

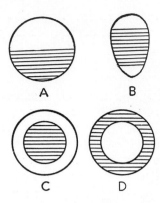

Fig. 24.6. Types of vascular bundles, in cross section, the xylem crosslined, the phloem clear. A, collateral; B, bicollateral; C, D, concentric; C, amphicribal; D, amphivasal.

the number of gaps associated with the leaf.

The vascular supply of a branch shoot usually begins as two **branch traces** which arise from the vascular bundles of the stele. Typically the branch traces flank the leaf trace (or the central leaf trace, if there is more than one) and depart from the stele so nearly at the same level as the leaf trace that the branch gap left by their departure is not differentiated from the associated leaf gap. In the most characteristic type of stele, each bundle, in its course up the stem, sooner or later becomes a leaf trace or branch trace.

Leaf gaps are characteristic of the steles of ferns, gymnosperms, and angiosperms. Among many ferns, the network construction of the vascular cylinder is clearly due to the leaf gaps and branch gaps formed in an otherwise tubular cylinder by the departure of segments as leaf traces and branch traces. In most dicots and gymnosperms, the actual leaf gaps form only a small part of the interfascicular areas, and the situation more nearly approaches that of an interconnected sys-

tem of potential leaf traces and branch traces. Steles of this type are called **eusteles.**

Each vascular bundle (Fig. 24.6) contains xylem and phloem. Typically the xylem forms a strand on the side toward the pith, and the phloem forms a strand on the side toward the cortex. These two tissues are usually separated by a single layer of procambium, the ontogenetic forerunner of the cambium. Bundles of this type are said to be **collateral.** Less commonly there is a strand of phloem next to the pith as well as on the outer side of the bundle. Such bundles, with the phloem on two sides of the xylem, are called **bicollateral.** Sometimes the inner strand of phloem is actually embedded in the outer part of the pith instead of being directly next to the xylem. Plants with bicollateral bundles, or with strands of phloem in the pith, are said to have **internal phloem.** Pumpkins, squashes, potatoes, and tomatoes are familiar plants with internal phloem. Vascular bundles in which the xylem surrounds the phloem, or vice versa, are said to be **concentric.** Concentric bundles with the xylem surrounding the phloem are **amphivasal;** when the phloem surrounds the xylem, they are **amphicribal.** Amphicribal bundles occur in many ferns and a few dicots; amphivasal bundles occur in many monocots and a few dicots. These several types of bundle are not always sharply differentiated, and transitional types occur.

The xylem nearest the pith matures first, and maturation (at any given level in the bundle) proceeds progressively toward the outside. Xylem which matures while the surrounding tissues are still elongating is called **protoxylem;** that which matures later is called **metaxylem.** Protoxylem vessels and tracheids usually have annular or spiral secondary thickenings, allowing some stretching, but by the time the surrounding tissues have matured, the protoxylem has usually been stretched so much that it becomes disorganized, and often it degenerates and disappears. Usually there is a considerable proportion of parenchyma in the protoxylem, and this parenchyma often survives and may become thick-walled in age. Metaxylem usually contains relatively little parenchyma, and it often has fibers as well as vessels and/or tracheids. In plants with little or no secondary growth, the metaxylem remains functional throughout the life of the stem.

Maturation of the sieve tubes in the phloem of a vascular bundle generally progresses from the outside toward the xylem. The sieve tubes of the **protophloem** mature while the surrounding tissues are still elongating, whereas those of the **metaphloem** mature thereafter. The sieve tubes of the protophloem function only briefly, and they often lack companion cells. The elongation of the surrounding tissues stretches the sieve tubes of the protophloem, and they usually degenerate more or less concurrently with the maturation of the metaphloem. Often the protophloem contains a high proportion of cells which mature more slowly and eventually develop into elongate fibers, so that there is a group of fibers on the cortical side of the vascular bundle. Bundles with such fibers are often called **fibrovascular bundles.**

Endodermis

In most herbaceous dicot stems, the vascular bundles abut directly on the cortex. In a few species, however, the cortex is delimited at the inner margin by a single layer of specialized cells without intercel-lular spaces, the **endodermis.** Endodermis is much more commonly found in roots than in stems, and its structure is discussed in Chapter 25. When the cortex is delimited by an endodermis, there are generally one or more layers of cells (typically parenchyma) between the endodermis and the vascular cylinder. These cells constitute the **pericycle.** In young stems without an endodermis, there is often a layer of cells, in the position of an endodermis, marked by the large and numerous starch grains. This starch sheath seems to be homologous with the endodermis, and it sometimes eventually becomes one.

Cortex

The cortex is usually parenchymatous, at least toward the inside; but toward the surface of the stem it often contains some collenchyma or sclerenchyma. These latter tissues, which help to support the stem, occur as individual vertical strands, or a network, or a complete sheath which sometimes forms a distinct hypodermis. Frequently some or all of the outer part of the cortical parenchyma bears chloroplasts and carries on photosynthesis. Food storage is another common function of the cortical parenchyma. Like other internal tissues of the stem, the cortex sometimes contains resin ducts or laticifers, according to the species.

Epidermis

The epidermis is the outermost tissue of an herbaceous dicot stem. It retards evaporation of water from internal tissues and furnishes some protection from mechanical injury and infection. The epidermis of stems generally has some stomates (discussed in Chapter 26), but usually not so many as the leaves.

Secondary Tissues

In some herbaceous dicot stems, the procambium remains parenchymatous or eventually matures into vascular elements, and there is no secondary growth. More often the procambium becomes a definite cambium which produces secondary tissues. The cambium may be restricted to the vascular bundles (fascicular cambium), or it may also extend from one bundle to the next (interfascicular cambium), forming a complete sheath. Typically the secondary tissues produced by the cambium are xylem and phloem, but in some species only the fascicular part of the cambium produces vascular tissue, the interfascicular part producing parenchyma instead.

Most cell divisions in the cambium are periclinal (parallel to the cambial surface). Of the two daughter cells formed in a division, one remains a cambial cell and the other usually matures directly or eventually into either a phloem cell (if external to the cambium) or a xylem cell (if internal to the cambium). Often these cells cut off from the cambium undergo one or more periclinal divisions before maturing into xylem or phloem, but only the cambium remains permanently meristematic. In a cross-sectional view of the stem, the cells of the secondary phloem, and especially of the secondary xylem, appear to be arranged in regular radial rows, in contrast to the less regular arrangement of the cells of the primary xylem and phloem.

Herbaceous dicots with an active cambium, such as the common sunflower, produce a considerable amount of secondary xylem by the end of the season, and in cross section the xylem forms a continuous broad band. If such stems lived through the winter and continued to produce secondary tissues year after year, they would be woody stems. In herbaceous stems, the cortex and epidermis usually retain enough capacity for cell division so that the increase in circumference caused by secondary growth does not damage the outer tissues; but in woody stems, cell division in the outer tissues usually does not keep pace with the increase in diameter caused by secondary growth, and the outer tissues are progressively ruptured and slough off. Herbaceous stems usually die down to the ground each year (especially in temperate and boreal regions), in contrast to woody stems, which live year after year. Woody stems either grow continuously or more often go into dormancy for part of the year (the winter, in temperate and boreal regions; the dry season, in many tropical regions) and resume growth when favorable conditions return. All these differences are subject to exceptions or difficulties in interpretation, however, and the distinction between woody and herbaceous stems is not at all absolute.

WOODY DICOT STEMS

General Features

The basic structure and organization of the primary tissues of a woody dicot stem are essentially similar to those of an herbaceous stem. On the average, however, woody stems have a more nearly continuous primary vascular cylinder, with narrower interfascicular areas. The cambium is a continuous layer, forming secondary xylem and phloem in the same way as in herbaceous stems.

Fig. 24.7. Sugar maple, *Acer saccharum*, at the New York Botanical Garden in winter, showing the characteristic deliquescent branching of angiosperm trees. The main stem melts away into a series of branches, instead of continuing as a definite central axis. (New York Botanical Garden photo.)

SECONDARY XYLEM

The secondary wood usually consists of tracheids, vessels, fibers, and parenchyma cells, or not infrequently of vessels, fibers, and parenchyma cells, without tracheids. Many (rarely all) of the parenchyma cells are arranged in ribbon-shaped bands which, in cross-sectional view of the stem, form lines radiating toward the outside. These bands are called **wood rays** or **xylem rays**. A wood ray is one to several cells wide and one to many cells high. Some of them are extensions of the medullary rays and reach all the way from the cambium to the pith. Others extend only part way inward from the cambium.

The ray cells of the secondary wood, like the other cells, are formed by division from the cambium. New rays are initiated by the cambium from time to time, so that the number of rays is greatest next to the cambium, and least toward the pith. The lateral distance between the rays is thus maintained at a fairly constant figure (usually well under 1 cm) by the progressive insertion of new rays between the pre-

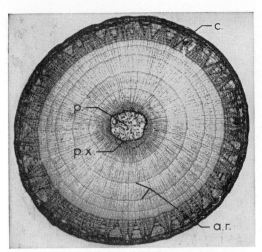

Fig. 24.8. Cross section of a five-year-old stem of basswood (*Tilia*): a.r., annual ring; c., cambium; p., pith; p.x., primary xylem. (Copyright by General Biological Supply House, Inc., Chicago.)

viously established ones at points progressively farther from the pith. Only rarely does the cambium fail to continue extending a wood ray once it has been established.

Most woody dicots have vertical parenchyma cells as well as rays. These are in contact with one another as well as with the tracheids, vessels, and fibers, and they form an interconnecting system with the rays. Each tracheid and vessel is in contact with one or more parenchyma cells somewhere along its length.

The cambium continues to produce secondary xylem and phloem year after year, so that the stem increases progressively in thickness. In tropical regions without a pronounced dry season, secondary growth is more or less continuous, but in regions with more marked seasonal differences, the cambium undergoes alternate periods of activity and dormancy.

Xylem cells produced in the spring, when moisture is abundant and growth is rapid, tend to be relatively large and thin-walled, with a large lumen. As the season progresses and the water supply diminishes, growth slows down, and the mature cells are smaller and thicker-walled. Usually there is an abrupt contrast between the last-formed xylem cells of one year and the first-formed ones of the next year. These annual growth layers, which appear as a series of concentric rings when the stem is viewed in cross section, are called **annual rings.** Annual rings vary from hardly visible to the naked eye to sometimes as much as an inch thick, but thicknesses of 1 mm to 1 cm are much more common. The age of a tree may be determined by counting the annual rings, although there is a possibility of error because of occasional false rings formed during unusual years when growth is interrupted by a dry spell and then resumed later in the season. False annual rings are frequently incomplete, extending only part way around the stem.

Sometimes there is an abrupt contrast between the spring wood and the summer wood of an annual ring. In **ring-porous** woods the vessels in the spring wood are larger and more numerous than those of the summer wood, whereas in **diffuse-porous** woods the vessels are more similar in size and more uniformly distributed (Fig. 24.10). As the student should by now expect, there are also transitional types. Even diffuse-porous woods may have the summer wood well differentiated from the spring wood of the same year.

The parenchyma cells of the xylem remain alive and continue to function normally for some years after they are produced. These functions include food storage, lateral conduction (in the rays), and possibly some service in keeping the tracheids and vessels functional in water conduction.

Sooner or later the metabolic activity of the parenchyma cells is modified, with the result that the other xylem cells are infiltrated with various organic substances such as oils, gums, resins, tannins, and aromatic and coloring materials. Due to these changes, the vessels and tracheids lose their conducting function, retaining only the mechanical function of support. The parenchyma cells then die and their protoplasm degenerates.

In many species the vessels and tracheids become blocked by **tyloses** concurrently with the other changes just mentioned. Tyloses are outgrowths from the adjoining parenchyma cells, which expand through the pit cavity and sometimes completely fill the lumen. Wood with tyloses is highly desirable for certain uses, e.g., watertight barrels.

The central core of xylem that has lost its water-conducting function is called **heartwood,** and the outer sheath which continues to conduct water and dissolved substances is called **sapwood.** The heartwood is generally darker in color than the sapwood, the difference being obvious to the naked eye. The boundary between the two is commonly irregular, extending several annual rings closer to the cambium at some points than at others. The inner part of the sapwood is continuously changed into heartwood as more sapwood is formed by divisions of the cambial cells. The heartwood thus constitutes a progressively expanding core, while the sapwood tends to remain about the same thickness throughout the life of the tree. A large tree may have a ring of sapwood only a few inches thick surrounding a core of heartwood several feet thick.

The eventual death of the xylem parenchyma cells and the associated change of sapwood into heartwood furnish another

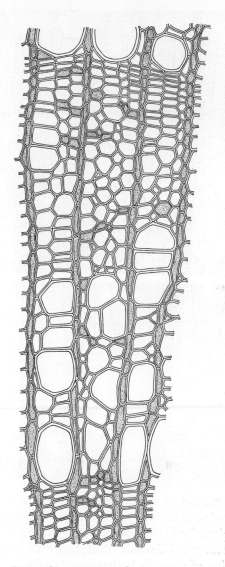

Fig. 24.9. Cross section of secondary wood of basswood (*Tilia*). Rows of narrow cells extending from top to bottom, wood rays; large, thick-walled openings, vessels; smaller, empty cells, fibers; cells with stippled contents, parenchyma. An annual ring ends with the small cells in the lower part of the drawing; another begins with the large vessels, and ends with the small cells near the top, just below the vessels of the next ring. (From W. H. Brown, *The Plant Kingdom*, 1935; courtesy of Ginn & Company, Boston.)

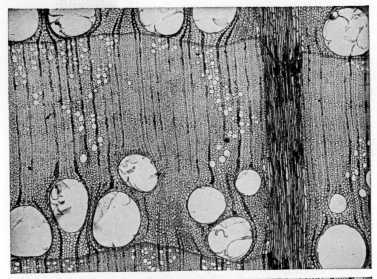

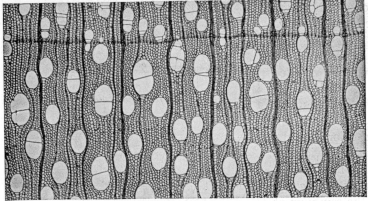

Fig. 24.10. Ring-porous wood of white oak (*Quercus alba*), above; diffuse-porous wood of river birch (*Betula nigra*), below. (Photos from the U.S. Forest Products Laboratory.)

example of the general principle that the nonmeristematic cells of a multicellular plant body do not have an unlimited life. The specialization of structure and function of the cells is always metabolically imperfect, and sooner or later metabolic imbalances and the accumulation of waste materials lead to death. Cells of the meristems largely avoid these difficulties by the constant production of new cells, so that the metabolic wastes are continuously distributed away from the meristem. Unicellular organisms commonly pass some of their wastes into the surrounding medium,

often by means of contractile vacuoles, but perhaps even unicells would not be potentially immortal were it not for the distribution of wastes resulting from cell division.

The appearance of lumber varies according to the direction in which it is cut (Fig. 24.11). Cross sections show concentric annual rings, with the rays forming lines at right angles to them. The vessels are often large enough to show as evident pores in a finer and denser matrix of tracheids, fibers, and parenchyma cells. In a lengthwise radial section (i.e., one cut

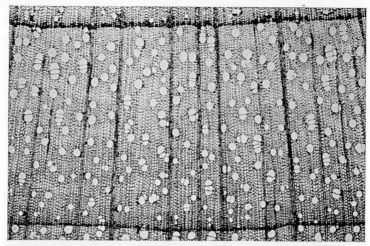

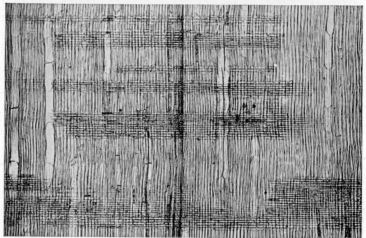

Fig. 24.11. Transverse, radial, and tangential sections of the wood of sugar maple (*Acer saccharum*). (Photos from the U.S. Forest Products Laboratory.)

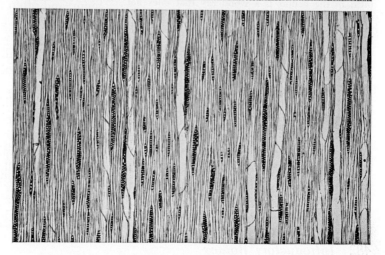

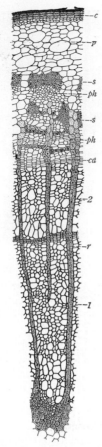

Fig. 24.12. Cross section of part of a two-year-old stem of tulip tree (*Liriodendron tulipifera*). Near each side is a wood ray extending to the pith; in the center is a wood ray that does not reach the pith; *1*, wood of first annual ring; *2*, wood of second annual ring; c., cork; ca., cambium; p., parenchyma; ph., phloem; s., sclerenchyma fibers of the phloem. (×60.) (From W. H. Brown, *The Plant Kingdom*, 1935; courtesy of Ginn & Company, Boston.)

along a radius of the stem) the annual rings appear as parallel vertical bands, and the wood rays appear as broad ribbons crossing them at right angles. The individual cells of the rays appear brick-shaped, with the long axis oriented with ribbon, whereas most other xylem elements are vertically much elongate. Quarter-sawed

lumber is sawed so as to obtain mostly radial and near-radial sections, after the log has first been cut into vertical quarters. In a lengthwise tangential section, the annual rings tend to form irregular figures. The tracheids, vessels, and fibers appear much the same as in radial section, and the rays also appear as vertical lines, parallel to the other xylem elements.

BARK

The part of a woody stem external to the cambium is called the **bark.** In a fairly young stem, this includes the epidermis, cortex, and primary phloem as well as the secondary phloem. In older stems, these tissues have generally been lost, and the bark consists wholly of secondary phloem plus the other tissues which have been formed in it.

The secondary phloem is often a very complex tissue, with more or less regularly arranged zones of sieve tubes, parenchyma cells, and fibers. As in the xylem, the parenchyma cells form horizontal rays and a more diffuse vertical system intermingled with the conducting elements. The phloem rays are generally continuous with the xylem rays, interrupted only by the cambium, and often some of them are notably wider than the others. A phloem ray and the xylem ray which adjoins it may collectively be called a **vascular ray.** The phloem fibers often form interconnected vertical strands, providing strength combined with flexibility.

The first phellogen usually differentiates during the first year, not long (if at all) after the vascular cambium becomes active. Typically some cortical parenchyma cells just beneath the epidermis become meristematic and begin to function as a phellogen, but in different species the phellogen may originate in any of the tissues external to the cambium. In birches, beeches, and some other trees, the phellogen forms a continuous sheath, but more often it is a series of overlapping concave scales. The phellogen and the tissues it produces are collectively called the **periderm.**

The phellogen functions in much the same way as the vascular cambium, except that the two tissues it produces are cork (externally) and **phelloderm** (internally). In some species the phellogen cuts off cells only toward the outside, and no phelloderm is formed. Cork is also called **phellem.** Cork cells, as we have noted, are suberized, and a layer of cork cuts off the water supply of all tissues external to it. These outer tissues die and finally slough off. The first layer of phellogen may persist and remain active for many years, as in beeches, but more often additional layers develop from parenchyma cells farther in, eventually in the secondary phloem, and the outer cork layers then also tend to slough off.

The part of the bark between the cambium and the innermost cork layer(s) contains both living and dead cells and constitutes the **live bark,** in which conduction of foods and other solutes occurs. The part of the bark from the inner edge of the innermost cork layer(s) to the surface contains only dead cells and constitutes the **dead bark,** which protects the inner tissues from mechanical injury and loss of water. The live bark is generally only a small fraction of an inch thick, but the dead bark of mature trees is often an inch or so thick, or even as much as one foot.

The continued increase in thickness of the tree, due to cambial activity, causes the dead bark to rupture and fall off. Eventually an equilibrium is reached, with the loss of dead bark from the outside about equaling the formation of new bark at the inside. The appearance of the bark of a mature tree depends in part on the duration of the initial phellogen, the size and shape of the initial and later phellogen layers, and the degree of cohesiveness of the cells making up the cork layers. The pattern is often distinctive, and many spe-

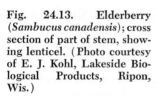

Fig. 24.13. Elderberry (*Sambucus canadensis*); cross section of part of stem, showing lenticel. (Photo courtesy of E. J. Kohl, Lakeside Biological Products, Ripon, Wis.)

Angiosperms: Stems 483

Fig. 24.14. Harvesting cork; inset, a bit of natural cork. (Courtesy of Armstrong Cork Company.)

cies can be recognized from the bark alone.

The dead bark of stems and roots is generally marked by scattered **lenticels** (Fig. 24.13). These are slightly raised areas of loosely arranged, nearly or quite unsuberized cells, formed largely by particular parts of the phellogen. Very often the lenticels arise just beneath the stomates. The lenticel phellogen, which is continuous with the ordinary phellogen, produces cells at a relatively rapid rate, and the lenticel becomes slightly raised above the general surface of the periderm. Lenticels are typically lenticular (like a double-convex lens) in external outline, whence the name. They are usually oriented vertically or horizontally on the stem, according to the species, and they vary from being barely visible to as much as 1 cm or even 1 inch long. In trees with deeply fissured bark, the lenticels are usually the bottom of the fissures. It is thought that the function of lenticels is to allow a slow exchange of gases between the internal tissues and the atmosphere.

Quercus suber, the cork oak, is the source of commercial cork. The tree is a native of the Mediterranean region where it is also extensively cultivated. The cork accumulates in a continuous sheath around the trunk, from which it is stripped in large sheets (Fig. 24.14) at intervals of about 10 years. Waterproof stoppers must be cut transversely to the lenticels, which extend all the way through the cork layer, from the phellogen to the surface, as visible, brown, powdery streaks.

HERBACEOUS MONOCOT STEMS

The herbaceous monocot stem typically has numerous small vascular bundles arranged in two or more rings, or scattered throughout the fundamental tissue. In the latter case there is neither a well-defined cortex nor a well-defined pith. The typical monocot stele, with polycyclic or scattered bundles, is called an **atactostele.** The fundamental tissue is usually parenchymatous, but often there is a collenchymatous or sclerenchymatous layer not far from the epidermis, and some of the vascular bundles may lie in this zone. The tissue just internal to the epidermis is often photosynthetic; not infrequently this chlorenchyma layer is interrupted at regular intervals by vertical strands of sclerenchyma fibers just beneath the epidermis.

Usually only a small part of the tissue of the monocot stem is formed directly from the apical meristem. A primary thickening meristem (Fig. 24.17), shaped like an inverted thimble, is continuous at the top with the small apical meristem. The leaf primordia and axillary buds originate from the apical meristem, but the thickening of the apical region of the stem is due chiefly to divisions in the cap of the

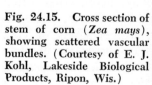

Fig. 24.15. Cross section of stem of corn (*Zea mays*), showing scattered vascular bundles. (Courtesy of E. J. Kohl, Lakeside Biological Products, Ripon, Wis.)

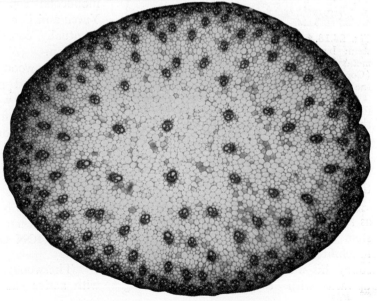

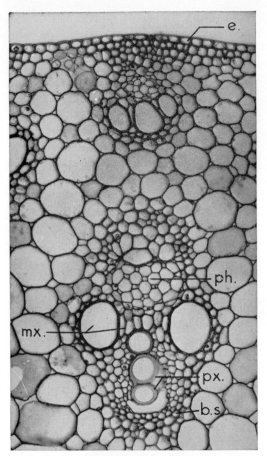

Fig. 24.16. Segment of cross section of corn stem: b.s., bundle sheath; e., epidermis; mx., metaxylem; ph., phloem; p.x., primary xylem. (Copyright by General Biological Supply House, Inc., Chicago.)

primary thickening meristem. Activity of this meristem decreases progressively in the region of elongation (corresponding to the sides of the thimble) and usually ceases in the region of maturation or in the mature region.

In a few herbaceous monocots, such as *Aloe* or *Sanseveria*, the thickening meristem continues to function more or less indefinitely. In the mature region of the stem, this meristem, which is continuous upward with the primary thickening

meristem, is called the cambium. Unlike the cambium of dicots, it does not pass through the individual vascular bundles. The cambium of monocots produces parenchyma and vascular bundles toward the inside, and usually only a small amount of parenchyma toward the outside. The vascular bundles of monocots are called **closed bundles** (i.e., closed to further growth), as contrasted to the **open bundles** which characterize most dicots.

WOODY MONOCOT STEMS

Woody monocot stems have scattered or polycyclic vascular bundles, just as do herbaceous ones. The tissue in which the bundles are embedded characteristically becomes collenchymatous or sclerenchymatous, however, instead of remaining largely parenchymatous. Some woody monocots, such as the palms, show little or no secondary growth, but others have a slow secondary growth of the type described above for some herbaceous monocots. Sometimes, as in species of *Yucca* and *Dracaena*, the secondary tissues eventually constitute the major part of the stem.

A few woody monocots develop a cork cambium and produce periderm in the same way as woody dicots. More often there is no definite phellogen, but scattered patches or distinct layers of cork are produced by the suberization of some of the cells near the surface of the stem, often after a series of preliminary cell divisions.

EVOLUTION OF STEM TYPES

The woody dicot stem, long-lived and with active cambium, is regarded as the

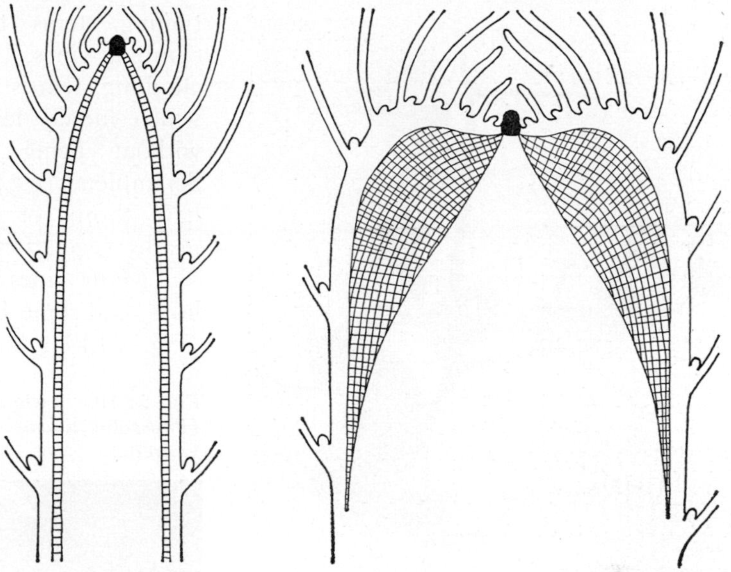

Fig. 24.17. Left, diagram of characteristic dicot stem, in long section, with the procambium crosslined. Right, diagram of characteristic monocot stem, in long section, with the primary thickening meristem crosshatched.

primitive type in flowering plants. The herbaceous dicot stem, short-lived and with less active or no cambium, is considered to be an evolutionary modification of the woody type. This change has occurred repeatedly in different groups of dicots. A few groups have reverted to the woody habit after having become herbaceous. The common sagebrush (*Artemisia tridentata*) of the western United States is a familiar woody plant that very probably had herbaceous ancestors.

The herbaceous monocot stem, with polycyclic or scattered vascular bundles and no fascicular cambium, is evidently derived from the herbaceous dicot type. The woody monocot stem is derived from the herbaceous one by a change of the fundamental tissue from parenchyma to collenchyma or sclerenchyma, associated with the persistence of the stem over a period of years. The wood of monocots is chiefly primary tissue, consisting of the vascular bundles together with the tissues in which they are embedded. The wood of woody dicots, on the other hand, consists of secondary xylem plus a little primary xylem. The vast majority of monocots are herbaceous, but the woody habit has been achieved in more than one group. The palms are the most familiar woody monocots, but some grasses (e.g., the bamboos) are rather woody, and the familiar Joshua tree (*Yucca brevifolia*) of the southwestern United States is a close relative of the lilies.

MODIFIED STEMS

THORNS

A fairly common type of modified stem is the **thorn,** as seen, for example, on hawthorns (*Crataegus*) (Fig. 24.18) and honey locust (*Gleditsia triacanthos*). Thorns differ from ordinary stems in that the terminal growth is limited; the apical meristem functions only briefly, after which it either sloughs off or matures into

Fig. 24.18. Twig of *Crataegus*, showing thorns (modified stems). (New York Botanical Garden photo.)

thick-walled, nonmeristematic cells. In the strictest sense, thorns, which are modified stems, should be distinguished from **spines**, which are modified leaves, and **prickles**, which are mere outgrowths from the surface of stems or leaves.

CLIMBING STEMS

The stems of many kinds of plants climb on other plants or on rocks and walls. All these stems have in common a persistent tendency to grow erect but have not sufficient strength to do so unassisted. Plants with climbing stems are called **vines** or **lianas**; the term *vine* is also applied to

trailing stems that otherwise resemble climbing vines. The least modified type of climbing stem is the rambler or scrambler, which merely leans on other vegetation, without being firmly attached to it. Scramblers (e.g., rambling roses) often have thorns or prickles which catch on nearby vegetation.

Many vines, such as morning-glories, hops, and some beans, have twining stems (Fig. 24.19). Some species twine clock-

Fig. 24.19. Twining stem of Lima bean (*Phaseolus limensis*). (Photo courtesy of T. H. Everett.)

wise, some counterclockwise, and some in either direction. The growing tip of any young stem, whether climbing or not, moves slowly in a more or less spiral course, due to inequalities in growth. This phenomenon is called **nutation**. The nutation of twining vines is exaggerated, and once the young stem touches some solid object the twining is strongly accentuated. The cells on the side that makes contact shorten somewhat, and those on the other side quickly elongate, so that the stem tends to curl around the supporting object. The physiological mechanism of twining is not well understood, but the immediate change after making contact with the support appears to be due largely to differences in turgor pressure of the cells, whereas the subsequent development involves differential growth. The initial reaction commonly takes only a few minutes, sometimes less than a minute.

Some vines have twining **tendrils,** although the main stem itself does not twine. Many tendrils are modified stems, but others are modified leaves or parts of leaves. In the common grape there is a tendril opposite each leaf. What appears to be the main axis of the stem is actually a succession of axillary branches (i.e., the stem is sympodial), and each tendril is really the terminal part of the stem from which the adjacent leaf and axillary shoot originated. Tendrils of Boston ivy (*Parthenocissus tricuspidata*) have expanded adhesive disks at the tip. Tendrils of this type tend to grow into small crevices of the supporting structure, enabling the vine to climb on vertical brick and stone walls as well as on tree trunks.

Poison ivy (*Rhus toxicodendron* and allied species) and some other vines produce numerous adventitious roots which adhere to the supporting surface and enable the plant to climb without twining. Adventitious roots are discussed in Chapter 25.

PHOTOSYNTHETIC AND SUCCULENT STEMS

Many ordinary herbaceous stems have some chlorenchyma toward the outer part of the cortex, supplementing the photosynthetic activity of the leaves. In a much smaller number of species, the leaves are very much reduced, and photosynthesis is carried on chiefly or wholly in the stem. In some of these plants, as, for example, the Scotch broom (*Cytisus scoparius*), the stem is not much modified and, except for its deep-green color, does not look very different from an ordinary stem. In others, such as *Colletia* (Fig. 24.20) and some of the cacti, some of the branches are strongly flattened and more or less leaf-like in appearance. Flattened, photosynthetic stems are called cladodes, or cladophylls.

Reduction of the leaves and transference of the main photosynthetic activity to the stem is often associated with the succulent habit. Succulent stems, such as those of cacti, have a high proportion of parenchymatous tissue, which resists desiccation because of the high concentration of certain colloids in the protoplasm and cell sap. Succulents are further discussed in Chapter 27.

STEMS AS PERENNATING AND REPRODUCTIVE STRUCTURES

Reproduction which does not involve sexual processes is called **vegetative reproduction.** Many angiosperms reproduce vegetatively as well as by forming seeds (which normally result from a sexual

Fig. 24.20. *Colletia cruciata*, with the branch stems modified into cladophylls. (New York Botanical Garden photo.)

process). Leaves, stems, and roots may all carry on vegetative reproduction in various kinds of plants, but stems are much more often involved than roots or leaves. All the individuals derived by vegetative reproduction from a single individual constitute a **clone**. Except for the possibility of mutations, all members of a clone are genetically identical. A few kinds of angiosperms have lost the power of sexual reproduction entirely and exist in nature only as clones.

A stem which creeps along the surface of the ground, sending down adventitious roots and producing new erect stems at intervals, is called a **stolon**. A very long, slender, nearly leafless stolon, such as that of the cultivated strawberry, is called a **runner**. The widely creeping, freely rooting stems of crab grass (*Digitaria sanguinalis*) might well be called stolons, although they do eventually turn up at the end.

A creeping **rhizome** is essentially similar to a stolon, except that it is underground. The leaves of rhizomes are generally much reduced and, of course, without chlorophyll, commonly appearing as mere small scales at regular intervals. The roots may originate chiefly at the nodes or may be scattered along the whole length of the rhizome.

Rhizomes may be relatively long and slender, as in Kentucky bluegrass and other sod-forming grasses, or thickened and fleshy, as in *Iris*. Some slender rhizomes have strongly thickened parts, especially at the end. These thickened parts are called **tubers**. The edible organ of the "Irish" potato (*Solanum tuberosum*, a native of northern South America), is a large tuber. Tubers have relatively little vascular tissue and a high proportion of parenchyma. The food stored in the parenchyma is used the following year to give the new plant a quick start.

A rhizome or stolon which is very short and produces a single new plant next to the parent plant is called an **offset**.

Rhizomes are commonly perennating structures as well as means of reproduction. The aerial stems of many herbs die down to the ground each fall and develop anew each spring from the rhizome. Often the rhizome is rather short, producing only one or a few aerial stems each year, and dying off behind as fast as it grows in front. Plants which perennate by rhizomes are potentially immortal.

A very short, stout rhizome is sometimes difficult to distinguish from a **caudex,** which is a short, more or less vertical (instead of horizontal) stem at or just beneath the surface of the ground, serving as a perennating organ from which new aerial stems arise each year. Some caudices have only adventitious roots, as do rhizomes, whereas others surmount a definite taproot.

Some kinds of plants, especially among the monocots, perennate by corms or by bulbs. A **corm** is a very short, stout, erect underground stem, as in the crocus or the gladiolus (Fig. 24.21), in which food is stored. Often it is broader than high. At the end of the growing season, the corm goes into dormancy, and the other parts of the plant usually die. The corm may be covered by one or more layers of leaf bases (the remains of the foliage leaves), but these are usually dead and dry, not serving as storage organs. At the beginning of the new growing season, the corm sends down adventitious roots, and the terminal bud (sometimes also some of the axillary buds) develops into the aerial flowering stem. As the season progresses, one or more new corms usually form from axillary buds of the old one, and it is these new corms which survive the winter.

A **bulb** differs from a corm in that the principal storage organs are the thickened leaves (bulb scales) which surround the short, erect stem. The bulb scales may be very short, and differentiated from the foliage leaves, as in tulips and onions, or they may be the thickened bases of ordinary leaves, as in daffodils. A new bulb may be produced each year, as in typical corms, or the same bulb may persist year after year, with the aerial flowering stems being produced from axillary buds. In non-botanical usage, the term *bulb* is commonly extended to cover corms as well as true bulbs.

ARTIFICIALLY INDUCED REPRODUCTION BY STEMS

LAYERING

We have noted that modified stems often act as organs of vegetative reproduction. Ordinary stems of many plants can also be encouraged to produce new plants. The simplest method of inducing reproduction by stems is called **layering**. Some of the branches of a tree or shrub are bent down to the ground, and the tip, or a section near the tip, is covered with moist soil. Adventitious roots develop from the covered part, and new aerial stems arise from some of the axillary buds. The new plant may then be severed from the parent and transplanted. Hazelnuts and black raspberries are often propagated by layering.

Natural layering also occurs in some kinds of trees, especially such conifers as spruces, hemlock, and arbor vitae, if some

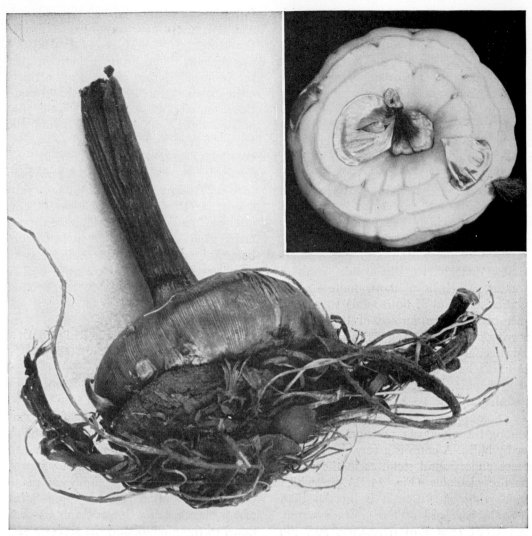

Fig. 24.21. *Gladiolus* corms. Below, side view of mature corm, with leaf bases, attached to the old corm of the previous year. Above, at right, top view, after the leaves have been stripped off. (New York Botanical Garden photo.)

of the lower branches happen to be held down against moist ground for a time.

CUTTINGS

Many kinds of plants, both woody and herbaceous, can be propagated by cuttings (Fig. 24.22). A small stem is merely cut off and the cut end placed in water or moist soil. Adventitious roots develop from the covered part, and a new plant is established. Willows are very easily propagated by cuttings, as is also the cultivated *Coleus.*

The formation of adventitious roots on a cutting can be encouraged by the application of indole-acetic acid, or any of several other chemicals, to the cut end. Indole-acetic acid is closely related to or identical with one of the normal growth-regulating substances produced by plants (See Chapter 32). Some other chemicals used to encourage rooting, such as carbon monoxide, are not apparently related to natural hormones, however.

GRAFTING

Most kinds of angiosperms can be reproduced by **grafting** (Fig. 24.23), but only the woody species are usually so treated. The cultivated varieties of most commercial fruit and nut trees are individual clones that are perpetuated by grafting. A twig (the **scion**) of one plant is transferred to the stem of another plant (the **stock**). Equivalent tissues of the scion and stock are juxtaposed, particular attention being paid to the cambium. The scion and stock are then bound firmly together and protected from evaporation while the living tissues have a chance to grow together. The cambium of the scion and stock must unite if the graft is to be successful. Water conduction through the graft is likely to be impeded to some extent until the healed cambium produces a continuous sheath of new xylem.

Fig. 24.22. Cuttings which have been rooted in moist sand. Left, *Buxus sempervirens* (boxwood); right, *Dieffenbachia seguine.* (Photos courtesy of T. H. Everett.)

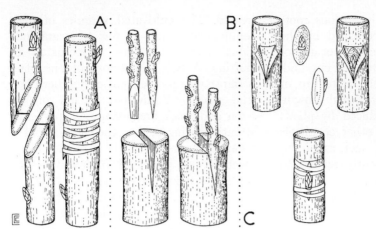

Fig. 24.23. Methods of grafting (*A*, *B*) and budding (*C*).

Customarily the stock is cut off just above the ground, while it is still rather small, and the scion is fitted to the cut end, so that little more than the root of a grafted tree represents the stock. The graft can also be made on a lateral branch, leaving most of the stock undisturbed; by making several such grafts one can grow several kinds of apples, for example, on one tree.

It is sometimes convenient to use merely a terminal or axillary bud, instead of a whole twig, as the scion. The base of the bud is inserted in a slit in the young bark of the stock. This type of grafting is often called **budding.**

Twigs of most woody angiosperms can easily be grafted onto other individuals of the same species. Grafts of gymnosperms, especially pines, are more difficult to make because of the resin which accumulates at the cut surface and hinders the union of the scion and stock. Grafts between different species of the same angiosperm genus are usually possible, and even different genera within the same family are often graft-compatible.

Often the scion is grafted onto a stock

of some other related species which has a more vigorous, or more disease-resistant, or otherwise more desirable root system. European grapes, for example, are customarily grafted to the roots of a related American grape, because of the much greater resistance of the latter to infestation by the root louse, *Phylloxera*. Almonds are commonly grafted onto peach stock, peaches on species of cherries, pecans and English walnuts on black walnuts, etc.

Lilacs are often grafted onto privet, a related genus which roots readily from cuttings. This graft is not always wholly successful, however. The cambium of the scion and the stock may fail to join perfectly, with the result that conduction of water through the graft is impeded, and the plants develop "graft blight" during periods of high evaporation.

The scion and the stock of a grafted plant tend to retain their individual characteristics, but they also exert some influence on each other. Hormones and other soluble substances pass freely back and forth. Atropine, an alkaloid produced by Jimson weed (*Datura*), accumulates in the fruits of tomatoes experimentally grafted to Jimson-weed stock. Dwarf varieties of various fruits are produced by grafting the regular varieties onto the stock of some smaller species. Dwarf apples, for example, are obtained by using quince as the stock. The grafted tree retains the relatively small, slow-growing root system of the quince, and growth of the top is therefore stunted.

SUGGESTED READING

Hottes, A. C., *How To Increase Plants*, A. T. DeLaMare, New York, 1949, 279 pp. A manual of technique, with detailed instructions.

Mahlstede, John P., and Ernest S. Haber, *Plant Propagation*, John Wiley & Sons, New York, 1957, 413 pp. A manual of practical instruction.

Angiosperms: Roots

CHAPTER 25

GENERAL CHARACTERISTICS

POSITION AND EXTERNAL MORPHOLOGY

Roots are the characteristic underground organs of angiosperms and most other vascular plants. In contrast to stems, which typically grow away from the direction of gravity, roots typically grow in the direction of gravity. Roots are therefore said to be **positively geotropic,** whereas stems are **negatively geotropic.** Tropisms (Greek, *tropos,* a turn) are further discussed in Chapter 32.

Like stems, roots are usually subcylindric, tapering toward the tip. Because their direction of growth is also influenced by pebbles and other obstructions in the soil, and often by differences in moisture and other conditions as well, roots are usually much more crooked than stems. This is particularly obvious in young slender roots; small kinks or bends may eventually be obscured as the root increases in thickness.

Unlike stems, roots do not bear leaves;

◄
Screwpine, *Pandanus,* showing large prop roots. (Photo by W. H. Hodge.)

therefore they lack nodes and internodes. Branches of angiosperm roots originate from internal tissues (as explained on p. 508) rather than from axillary buds as do branches of stems. There is some correlation between the position of the branch roots and the arrangement of the internal tissues, but there is nothing in the external structure to indicate the points at which the branches will appear.

The apical meristem of a root is covered by a special protective tissue, the **rootcap,** instead of being protected by young or modified leaves as in stems. The rootcap is typically less than 1 mm long, but in some free-floating aquatics, such as the water hyacinth (*Eichhornia crassipes*), it forms an elongate pocket more than 1 cm long. It has been suggested that the rootcap of *Eichhornia* protects the young tissues from attack by aquatic insects.

FUNCTIONS

The two principal functions of typical roots are **anchorage** and the **absorption** of water and minerals from the soil. Conduction of water and minerals upward to the stem, being an implicit corollary of absorption, is not always listed as a separate function. A third important function of many, but not all, roots is the **storage of food.** Other functions performed by vari-

ous types of specialized roots are discussed in the closing pages of this chapter.

TYPES OF ROOT SYSTEMS

The nature of the root system (Fig. 25.1) varies in different kinds of plants. Plants in which the primary root of the seedling eventually gives rise to most or all of the whole root system are said to have a **primary root system.** Plants in which most or all of the roots develop adventitiously from underground stems, or from the base of the aerial stems, are said to have an **adventitious root system.** Among plants with primary root systems, there are all variations from a **taproot system,** with a central taproot that is larger than any of its branches, to a **fibrous root system,** in which the primary root is quickly deliquescent into several or many roots all about the same size. Adventitious root systems are usually also fibrous, with the roots all slender. Most vascular cryptogams and monocots, as well as a considerable number of dicots (especially those with creeping rhizomes) have an adventitious root system. Many dicots and most gymnosperms, on the other hand, have a primary root system, of either the taproot or the fibrous type.

Different kinds of plants exploit different levels in the soil. Most cacti have

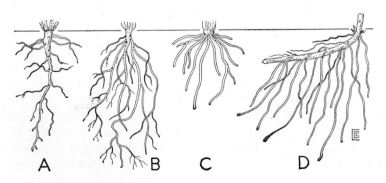

Fig. 25.1. Types of root systems. *A, B,* primary; *C, D,* adventitious: *A,* tap; *B, C, D,* fibrous.

very shallow roots, forming a densely branching fibrous system in the upper few inches of soil, sometimes for as much as 50 feet in all directions from the stem. The common sagebrush of the western United States (*Artemisia tridentata*) has a deep taproot as well as an extensive system of branches near the surface. The roots of grasses are usually rather shallow; most of the roots of the common lawn grasses are in the upper few inches of soil, and the dense sod which they form can be peeled in a layer only 3–4 inches thick. In a number of common crop plants, the principal development of the root system is at a depth of 3–5 feet, soil permitting. Few trees have root systems more than 10 feet deep, and many are much shallower, although cottonwoods are reported to penetrate more than 20 feet in some sites. Alfalfa has a very deep root system, often penetrating more than 20 feet or even as much as 50 feet, exploiting the water supply so vigorously that it may lower the water table and make subsequent cultivation of other crops difficult until the soil has had some years to recover.

The depth of penetration of roots is influenced by the nature of the soil and by other environmental conditions, as well as by their inherent tendencies. A hardpan or a layer of rock may block further growth. Soils saturated with water do not have enough oxygen to support the root growth of most plants, and roots do not generally descend below the lowest level to which the water table sinks during the growing season. Roots of hydrophytes (plants especially adapted to wet places or open water) are not checked by the water table, however. Conversely, roots of most plants will not grow through very dry soil, and the depth of root growth in dry regions may be governed in part by the depth to which the soil is moistened by rain. Some xerophytes (plants adapted to dry conditions) have very deep taproots, however, the roots penetrating many feet of dry soil before reaching a moister zone.

The development of the root system is also influenced by differences in the *amount* of water at different levels or in different areas of soil. The best development and most extensive branching of the roots generally occurs in soil which is moist but not saturated. Cultivated plants may be encouraged to develop relatively shallow or relatively deep root systems, according to whether they are watered frequently and lightly or less often and more heavily. Sewer pipes, furnishing a combination of abundant moisture and adequate aeration, provide a favorable habitat for root growth, especially of species adapted to moist or wet soils. Roots of trees often penetrate joints in the pipes and proliferate so extensively as to interfere with water flow. Willows and sycamores are notorious in this regard.

Competition with other plants influences both the lateral and vertical extent of root systems. This is especially evident when the competition comes from other individuals of the same species, which have similar needs and potentialities. Crop plants have deeper and less widespread root systems when crowded than when more widely spaced. The root systems of adjacent plants do overlap and intermingle, but the lateral spread of each tends to be checked by the desiccation of the soil brought about by the already established roots of the adjacent plants. Vertical development, exploiting areas not already occupied by roots of other plants, is thus encouraged. The same sort of response has been observed in tree plantations. The roots of isolated or widely

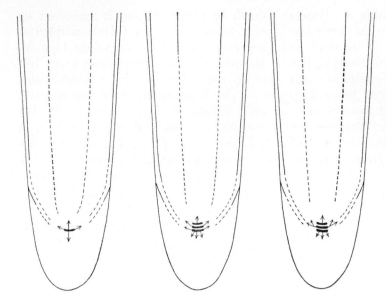

Fig. 25.2. Position of the initial cells in the apical meristem of roots of various types of angiosperms. (Adapted from Esau, *Plant Anatomy*, 1953; courtesy of John Wiley & Sons, New York.)

spaced trees, on the other hand, often extend far beyond the spread of the crown.

PRIMARY TISSUES

PRIMARY GROWTH

Growth in length of roots is governed by an apical meristem, much as in stems, although the detailed anatomy of the meristem is different. The apical meristem of roots is really *sub*apical rather than truly apical, being covered by a rootcap. The organization of the initials and other cells in the apical meristem varies in different kinds of roots (Fig. 25.2). In the simplest situation, shown by some ferns and other vascular cryptogams, there is a single apical initial, which gives rise to the rootcap as well as to the other primary tissues. Angiosperm roots usually or always have a number of initials. In some, such as the common onion (*Allium cepa*), there is a single layer of initials which gives rise

to both the rootcap and the other primary tissues. In many others there are two, or more often three, layers of initials, each layer giving rise to a particular part or parts of the root. The middle layer, in such meristems, produces new cells around its margin. In the commonest type (especially among the dicots) the layer farthest from the tip gives rise to the central cylinder, the next layer to the cortex, and the third to the rootcap and epidermis. In many monocots the distal layer of initials gives rise only to the rootcap. This layer and its immediate derivatives are then collectively called the calyptrogen (from Greek *kalyptra*, a cap).

The *rootcap* is composed of living parenchyma cells. The cells near its outer surface generally have mucilaginous walls. The mucilage apparently acts as a lubricant, easing the progress of the root tip through the soil. The outer cells of the rootcap are continually being sloughed off and lost, and the walls of the next layers of cells in turn become mucilaginous. The

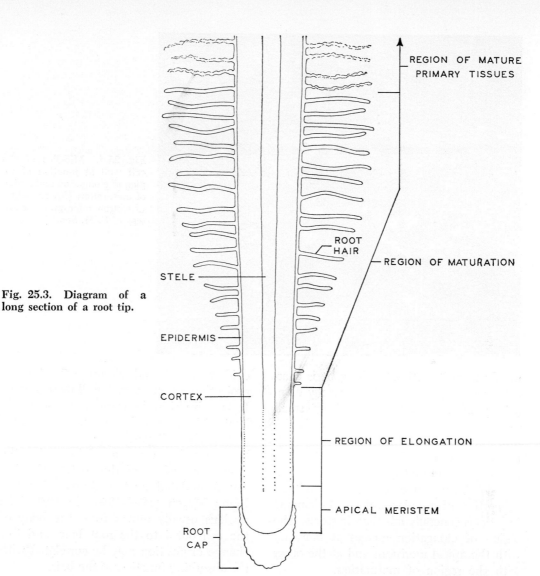

REGION OF MATURE
PRIMARY TISSUES

ROOT
HAIR

REGION OF MATURATION

STELE

Fig. 25.3. Diagram of a
long section of a root tip.

EPIDERMIS

CORTEX

REGION OF ELONGATION

APICAL MERISTEM

ROOT
CAP

sloughed off cells are at first commonly intact and turgid; it is the mucilaginous wall rather than a crushed or degenerating protoplast that furnishes the primary lubricant. The rootcap cells next to the developing young epidermis also have mucilaginous walls, permitting a sliding adjustment of position.

The primary tissues of the root are derived from the apical meristem by cell division and subsequent differentiation. The successive zones (Fig. 25.3) behind the apical meristem are: (1) the **region of elongation,** (2) the **region of maturation,** (3) the **region of mature primary tissues,** and (4) in many roots, the **region of secondary tissues.**

The *region of elongation* is usually only a few (1–10) mm long, in contrast to the same region in stems, which is com-

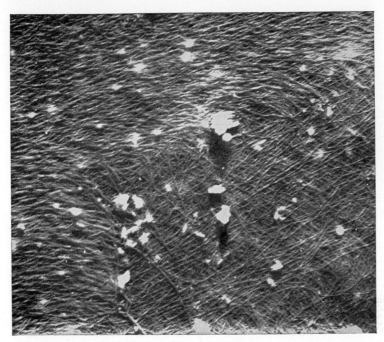

Fig. 25.4. Micelles of the cell wall at junction of region of elongation and region of maturation (lower right). (Electron micrograph, courtesy of F. M. Scott.)

monly several centimeters long. It is characterized by enlargement—especially elongation—of the cells. A relatively small number of cell divisions and the beginnings of differentiation of the various cell types also occur in this region. Only a few protoxylem and protophloem elements mature in the region of elongation, and the proportion of annular and spiral elements in roots is generally less than in stems. The region of elongation merges at one end with the apical meristem and at the other with the region of maturation.

The *region of maturation* is usually 1 to several centimeters long. Here the cells, having reached essentially full size, gradually assume their mature form and function. The region of maturation is often known as the **root-hair zone**, because of the characteristic **root hairs** (Fig. 25.5) borne by many of the epidermal cells. Each root hair originates as a bump on an epidermal cell and elongates to form a projection often several millimeters long. It is cylindrical in form, but commonly bent this way and that in its passage among the soil particles. Root hairs may be regarded as a means of increasing the absorbing surface of the root. This view was formulated by the German botanist Franz Meyen (1804–1840) in 1838. The nucleus usually moves from the body of the cell out into the root hair, and this change of position may be correlated with the absorbing function of the hair.

It is convenient to regard the beginning of root-hair formation as the dividing line between the region of elongation and the region of maturation. Certainly no significant elongation occurs after the root hairs have begun to form; if it did, they would be sheared off by the movement of the root through the soil. Root hairs may occur on all epidermal cells in the root-hair zone, or on only some of them, according to the species, and the cells on which they occur may or may not be otherwise obviously different from those on which they do not. Often there are several hundred root hairs for every square millimeter of the epidermal surface from which they originate.

Root hairs have a limited life span, often only a few days, seldom more than a few weeks. Sometimes they persist until the secondary tissues formed in the root cause the outer tissues to slough off, but often they degenerate even before the formation of secondary tissues. Even when they are present in the region of mature primary tissues, they have frequently become nonfunctional.

The formation of root hairs is governed partly by the environment, as well as by heredity. In water or in saturated soil they often do not develop at all. Mycorhizal roots (see pp. 514–517) usually have few or no root hairs.

ANATOMY OF PRIMARY TISSUES

In the zone of primary permanent tissues, before any secondary tissues have been formed, a cross section of a typical root (Fig. 25.6) shows a solid *stele*, surrounded successively by the *pericycle*, the *endodermis*, the *cortex*, and the *epidermis*. The xylem of the stele commonly forms a deeply ridged and grooved central strand. In cross section it tends to be roughly star-shaped, with several arms radiating from a common center. According to the number of these arms, the root is said to be diarch, triarch, tetrarch, pentarch, or poly-

Fig. 25.5. Left, development of root hairs in millet. (*Panicum miliaceum*). (×400.) Right, radish seedling, showing root hairs grown in moist air. (×1⅓.) (From W. H. Brown, *The Plant Kingdom*, 1935; courtesy of Ginn & Company, Boston.)

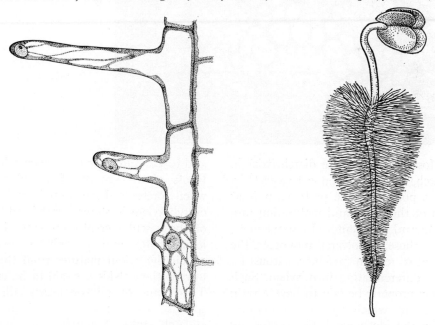

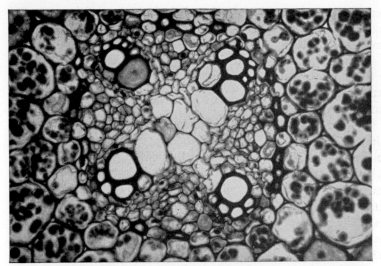

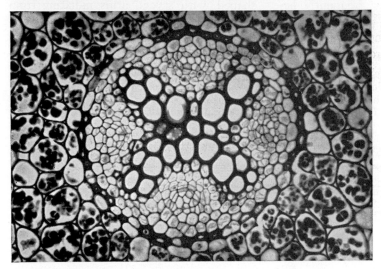

Fig. 25.6. Cross sections of buttercup (*Ranunculus*) root, showing central cylinder and part of the surrounding cortex. In the upper picture, the protoxylem is mature, but the metaxylem remains thin-walled. In the lower picture, representing a more mature stage, the metaxylem as well as the protoxylem is mature, and strands of phloem can be more clearly seen alternating with the arms of xylem. The cells of the cortex show numerous dark-stained starch grains. (Copyright by General Biological Supply House, Inc., Chicago.)

arch. Most dicot roots are diarch, triarch, or tetrarch, but many monocot roots (Fig. 25.7) are polyarch. The protoxylem is at the tips of the arms, and maturation progresses toward the center. In some roots, especially those of polyarch monocots, the central cells remain parenchymatous instead of differentiating into xylem. Such roots may properly be said to have a pith.

Steles in which the xylem matures from the outside toward the center are said to be **exarch,** or to have exarch xylem. Roots of all groups of vascular plants, when present, have exarch xylem, but exarch xylem in stems is restricted to some of the vascular cryptogams, especially the lepidophytes and psilophytes. Steles in which the xylem matures from the inside toward the outside are said to be **endarch.** The stems of all, or nearly all, angiosperms and most gymnosperms have endarch steles. **Mesarch** steles, with maturation progressing in both directions, occur chiefly among some of the ferns. Exarch steles with a solid core of protoxylem are called **protosteles.** The protostele is believed to represent the most primitive type of stele. Roots of all divisions of vascular plants (when present) tend to retain the protostelic structure, but stems of all but the more primitive groups have become more or less modified.

The primary phloem of the root forms a series of separate strands alternating with the ridges or arms of primary xylem. The protoxylem and the primary phloem are thus on *alternate radii*, instead of on the same radii as they are in stems. Vascular bundles containing both xylem and phloem, such as are regularly seen in stems, do not occur in most roots.

The phloem of roots ordinarily contains some parenchyma cells as well as sieve tubes and companion cells, and usually there are one or more layers of parenchyma between the phloem and the xylem. Some of these cells separating the phloem from the xylem may eventually mature into a cambium, or they may remain permanently parenchymatous, depending on the species. The parenchyma between the xylem and phloem, whether or not it later develops into a cambium, is called the **procambium.** Technically the term *procambium* applies to all the young, undifferentiated tissue of a root or stem which eventually develops into the vascular system; but it is most frequently used in speaking of the actual or potential forerunner of the vascular cambium.

The stele of a root is usually delimited by a definite endodermis. Usually there is a thin, parenchymatous layer, one or a few cells thick, between the endodermis and the vascular tissue; this is the **pericycle.** The pericycle is important chiefly

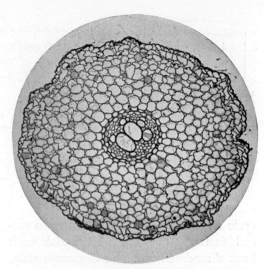

Fig. 25.7.   Cross section of an onion root, showing central cylinder, cortex, and epidermis. (Copyright by General Biological Supply House, Inc., Chicago.)

as the tissue in which branch roots commonly originate (see p. 508). Because of its close ontogenetic relation to the vascular tissue, the pericycle is usually considered to be the outermost layer of the stele; for a similar reason the endodermis is considered to be the innermost layer of the cortex. The endodermis has such a characteristic structure and distinctive probable function, however, that it is usually treated separately from the remainder of the cortex.

The endodermis (Fig. 25.8) forms a continuous sheath, one cell thick, without intercellular spaces. The cells are typically six-sided and nearly brick-shaped, with the longest axis vertical (parallel to the axis of the stele) and the intermediate axis tangential to the stelar surface. The tangential walls are usually bulged, so that the cell may look more nearly elliptical than rectangular in cross section.

The two tangential walls of an endodermal cell (those which abut on the peri-

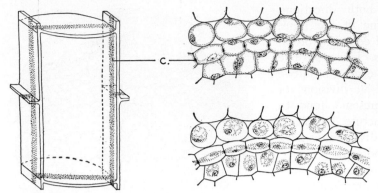

Fig. 25.8. Structure of the endodermis. Left, a single cell, showing only the wall. Top right, cross section of part of endodermis, with cortex above (outside) and pericycle below (inside). Bottom right, same as above, but with the cells plasmolyzed, showing the attachment of the cytoplasm to the Casparian strips; c., Casparian strip. (Adapted from Esau, *Plant Anatomy*, 1953; courtesy of John Wiley & Sons, New York.)

cycle and the cortex) usually have no special features, but the four radial walls have a modified area, the **Casparian strip,** which completely encircles the cell. Attention was first called to these strips in 1865–1866 by the German botanist J. X. Robert Caspary (1818–1887). The Casparian strip may be very narrow, or it may extend the whole width of the radial wall. Usually it is thickened, and whether thickened or not it is generally impregnated with a waxy substance similar to suberin. This substance may also be chemically allied to lignin, since it takes some of the same stains when sections are prepared for microscopic study; it has therefore been called lignosuberin.

The Casparian strips tend to inhibit the passage of water and solutes through the radial walls of the endodermal cells. In order to move between the stele and the cortex, substances must therefore pass through the tangential wall, into the cytoplasm, and out the other tangential wall. The movement of materials between the stele and the cortex is thus subjected to protoplasmic control. This may be of some significance to root pressure, as noted in Chapter 27. The cytoplasm of the cell tends to remain firmly attached to the Casparian strip, even when plasmolyzed

so that it shrinks away from the rest of the wall. This affinity is believed to have some functional significance, although the mechanism is obscure.

The degree of development of the Casparian strips differs markedly in different kinds of plants, and there is probably some chemical variation as well. Probably in some species they have lost whatever function they originally had.

In most dicots the root shows secondary growth and the endodermis is lost. In most plants without secondary growth, especially monocots, the endodermal cells eventually undergo further modification. A suberin layer is deposited over the entire inner surface of the wall, on the tangential as well as the radial faces, covering and often obscuring the Casparian strip. A thick cellulose wall is often then formed internal to the suberin layer, and this inner wall may become lignified.

At any given level in the endodermis these changes usually start opposite the phloem and progress gradually toward the protoxylem points. Often there is a stage at which the cells facing the phloem have become thick-walled, while the cells facing the protoxylem points remain thin-walled, with Casparian strips. Under such conditions the transfer of materials between the stele and the cortex is probably limited to these thin-walled **passage cells.** The passage cells may persist throughout the life of the root, or they may finally become thick-walled like the other endodermal cells.

The *cortex* of a root usually consists largely of parenchyma, often with some sclerenchyma as well, seldom with any collenchyma. The sclerenchyma frequently forms a complete cylinder near the epidermis, or just outside the endodermis. Laticifers or resin ducts are present in many species.

Many roots of gymnosperms and angiosperms, especially monocots, have a special type of hypodermis, the **exodermis,** forming a layer one to several cells thick just beneath the epidermis. The exodermis consists of living cells and is ontogenetically part of the cortex. Exodermal cells commonly have a suberin layer just inside the primary wall, and they often have a thick cellulose secondary wall which may become lignified. The exodermis of some species has Casparian strips like those of the endodermis, instead of a complete suberin layer. Often the development of an exodermis, or of a sclerenchymatous layer just beneath the epidermis, is followed by death and decay of the epidermis.

The *epidermis* of roots generally consists of a single layer of thin-walled, elongate, living cells without intercellular spaces. The formation of root hairs by epidermal cells has already been noted. Young epidermal cells with root hairs lack a cuticle. Older epidermal cells often develop a cuticle and may become thick-walled and even lignified as well. Frequently the outer wall is thickened or cutinized without any change in the other walls.

SECONDARY TISSUES

SECONDARY GROWTH

Roots of most monocots, except the woody species, lack secondary growth. Among dicots, secondary growth varies from vigorous to scanty or none. Dicot trees and shrubs regularly have woody roots with well-developed secondary growth. Perennial herbs with little or no secondary growth in the stems sometimes have woody roots; conversely, herbs, such as goldenrod (*Solidago*), with vigorous secondary growth in the stem, may have an adventitious root system in which there is little if any secondary growth. Adventitious roots in general seldom show significant secondary growth, except for the adventitious prop roots of some trees, such as banyan (*Ficus benghalensis*) and mangrove (*Rhizophora*).

Secondary growth in roots and stems is essentially similar. The cambium develops between the xylem and phloem, producing secondary xylem internally and secondary phloem externally. In roots the cambium internal to the primary phloem develops first, by differentiation of parenchymatous cells of the procambium. The vertical strips of cambium widen progressively by differentiation of procambial cells farther and farther toward the protoxylem points. Eventually the strips meet and join around the ends of the xylem arms, forming a continuous sheath. The cambial cells immediately adjacent to the protoxylem points are generally formed by division from the innermost (or only) layer of cells of the pericycle, rather than by a mere change in the activity of previously existing cells. The activity of the cambium internal to the primary phloem soon fills in the hollows between the ridges of primary xylem, and thereafter the xylem forms an essentially cylindrical core.

ANATOMY OF SECONDARY TISSUES

As compared to stems, the xylem of roots tends to have larger and more numerous vessels with thinner walls, as well as fewer fibers, more parenchyma, and more abundant rays. The phloem has less sclerenchyma and more storage parenchyma. The cambium opposite the protoxylem points commonly produces wide vascular rays. These differences between stems and roots are correlated with differences in their functions. More food is usually stored in roots than in stems, and the roots, being supported by the soil, have less need for strong supporting tissues.

Annual rings are usually less pronounced in roots than in stems, partly because the seasonal changes in environment to which the stem is subjected are buffered, for roots, by the soil. The soil beneath the surface does not get as hot as the air during summer, and the roots, being closer to the source of supply, are less subject to water deficit than stems. Long-lived woody roots develop a distinct core of heartwood surrounded by sapwood, just as in stems.

Most perennial roots, especially those with an active cambium, sooner or later develop a periderm. The cork cambium typically originates in the pericycle as a solid sheath, forming a continuous layer of cork, along with some internal phelloderm. All tissues external to the cork then die and decay. In many roots a single cork layer persists indefinitely. In others new phellogens are formed progressively farther into the secondary phloem, as in stems. The periderm of roots, like that of stems, has scattered lenticels. Environ-

mental conditions of the soil are conducive to rapid decay of dead tissues, and even long-lived woody roots seldom produce a thick bark like that of many stems.

BRANCH ROOTS

ORIGIN

Roots which originate as branches of other roots are called **secondary roots.** The primordia which give rise to secondary roots, unlike those which give rise to branches of stems, generally originate some distance behind the apical meristem, typically in the region of maturation. They may also develop in the mature region, and, in free-floating aquatics such as *Eichhornia*, they are sometimes formed in the region of elongation.

The root primordia nearly always originate internally, typically in the pericycle. Some cells of the pericycle become meristematic and by a series of divisions produce the apical meristem of a branch root. The endodermis sometimes also contributes to the formation of the new apical meristem, especially when this process occurs before the endodermal cells have matured and developed Casparian strips. The new apical meristem soon develops a rootcap, and the branch root (Fig. 25.9) pushes its way through the outer tissues of the root into the soil. It is not yet certain whether the branch root partly digests its way through the cortex, or whether the penetration is entirely mechanical. In mature roots, from which the pericycle has sloughed off, branches commonly originate in the cambium.

Adventitious roots borne on stems usually originate internally in much the same way as secondary roots. In young stems the root primordium commonly develops in the interfascicular parenchyma, i.e., the medullary rays. In older stems it may develop near the cambium in a vascular ray, or in the cambium itself. Stem-borne adventitious roots are restricted to the nodes in many species, but in others they occur along the internodes as well.

ARRANGEMENT

Branch roots are not so regularly arranged as leaves and axillary buds, and what arrangement there is tends to be obscured by the twisting and turning of the root as it grows through the soil. When plants are grown in water or loose soil, it can generally be seen that the secondary roots are in vertical rows. Triarch roots typically have three rows of branches, tetrarch roots typically have four rows, etc. Usually the branches are directly opposite the protoxylem points, but in grasses, sedges, rushes, and some other plants, they are opposite the strands of primary phloem instead. Diarch roots

sometimes have four rows of branches, one row a little to each side of protoxylem ridge.

NUMBER

The root system of an angiosperm or other vascular plant is ordinarily much branched, with numerous small ultimate branches. A single plant of rye (*Secale cereale*), after 4 months of growth in a box containing less than 2 cubic feet of soil, had nearly 14,000,000 roots and over 14,000,000,000 root hairs. The combined length of the roots was 387 miles, and of the root hairs about 6000 miles. The total surface of the root hairs was over 4000 square feet, and the total surface of the remainder of the root system more than 2500 square feet. A single cubic inch of soil in which blue grass (*Poa pratensis*) was growing has been estimated to have 1,000,000 root hairs and 65 square inches of root surface, with the root system making up 2.8 per cent of the volume of the soil.

The intricate branching and large

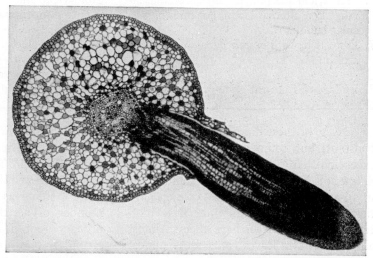

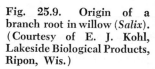

Fig. 25.9. Origin of a branch root in willow (*Salix*). (Courtesy of E. J. Kohl, Lakeside Biological Products, Ripon, Wis.)

surface area of the root system are significant both in anchoring the plant and in exploiting the supply of water and minerals in the soil. A concomitant result is that the soil itself is held in place. The value of a plant cover in minimizing soil erosion is well known.

REPLACEMENT

The smaller branches of the root system of perennials often die in the fall, being replaced by new branches the next year. These annual branches, which enable the plant to exploit the same soil year after year, are often called feeder roots. Without some such device, the root system would soon become inefficient, being forced either to grow farther and farther away from the base of the stem, or to so fill the soil with intricate branches that the absorbing parts would scarcely have room to operate. Perennials with creeping rhizomes meet this same problem in a different way, the rhizome and its adventitious roots eventually dying off behind, so that the plant gradually changes its position, migrating through the soil.

COMPARISON OF ROOTS AND STEMS

The outstanding differences between typical roots and typical stems of angiosperms are shown in the following table:

ROOTS	STEMS
1. Principal functions: anchorage and absorption	Principal functions: support and display of the leaves
2. Positively geotropic, underground	Negatively geotropic, aerial
3. Rootcap present	Rootcap absent
4. Leaves absent; no nodes and internodes	Leaves present, regularly arranged; nodes and internodes present
5. Branches originate internally, at irregular intervals	Branches originate superficially, from axillary buds
6. Protoxylem and primary phloem strands arranged on alternate radii, not forming vascular bundles	Protoxylem and primary phloem strands arranged on the same radii, forming vascular bundles
7. Protostelic, with exarch xylem and without a pith	Eustelic or atactostelic, with endarch xylem, and either with a pith or with the vascular bundles scattered
8. Endodermis present	Endodermis absent

None of these differences is absolutely constant, but some are more subject to exception than others. The first four listed differences hold for *typical* roots and stems in all groups of vascular plants which have these organs. Almost all roots have rootcaps, and stems never have them. Almost all stems have leaves, and roots almost never have them. The position, functions, and the response to gravity are less constant. There are many horizontal stems as well as horizontal roots, and many subterranean stems as well as a considerable number of aerial roots. Even when the primary root is strongly geotropic, the secondary ones may be much less so.

The last four listed differences hold for most angiosperms, but they are not necessarily true of other groups of vascular plants. The several anatomical differences between roots and stems have evolved gradually. Branching of lepidophyte roots is commonly dichotomous, like that of the stems. In their exarch xylem, as well as in the presence of an endodermis and the absence of a pith, roots of angiosperms resemble both roots and stems of the more primitive vascular plants. The usual absence of pith in roots is correlated with the regularly exarch (centripetal) differentiation of the xylem. As the root becomes more and more mature, the parenchymatous core is progressively reduced by the differentiation of its marginal cells into xylem elements, and the xylem thus comes to form a solid core. In many species, however, especially among the monocots, differentiation of the xylem elements does not proceed to the center, and there remains a parenchymatous pith. Angiosperm *stems*, on the other hand, are regularly endarch; even when the vascular bundles are scattered, the xylem nearest the center of the stem is generally the first to mature in each bundle.

ROOT-STEM TRANSITION

Inasmuch as the primary vascular tissues of roots are organized differently from those of stems, there must be a transition region (Fig. 25.10) in which these tissues are rearranged. Typically the transition occurs in the hypocotyl (the part of the axis between the top of the root and the cotyledon(s) of the seedling). In plants in which the cotyledons are never brought above the ground, the hypocotyl generally remains very short, and the transition

region then often extends through one or more internodes of the stem. Most monocots and a few dicots (e.g., *Pisum sativum*, the garden pea) are of this latter type.

The series of intermediate stages by which the rearrangement is accomplished differs in different species. Often the protoxylem ridges of the root are continuous with the cotyledonary traces, and the differentiation of metaxylem at progressively higher levels in these traces changes from strictly centripetal to centripetal in two diverging arms (the arms from the different protoxylem ridges no longer meeting in the center), to lateral in two diverging arms, to angularly centrifugal in two diverging arms, to centrifugal in a single mass (see Fig. 25.10). Concomitantly, the phloem strands between the xylem arms split and the separated halves become individually associated with the xylem strands to each side. Eventually the two phloem strands from opposite sides of the xylem strand meet and join directly centrifugal to the metaxylem, and a normal vascular bundle with exarch xylem is formed.

The cauline bundles may arise as branches of the cotyledonary bundles, or they may extend well down into the hypocotyl and have their own attachment. When the first cauline bundles differentiate very early, they may attach directly to the primary xylem and phloem of the hypocotyledonary axis, in the hollows between the xylem arms. At the lower end of such a bundle, the xylem matures first at the two sides, the direction of maturation thus corresponding to that in the two adjoining xylem arms. A shift in the position of the two protoxylem points of the bundle, resulting in their fusion at the inner edge of the bundle, is all that is

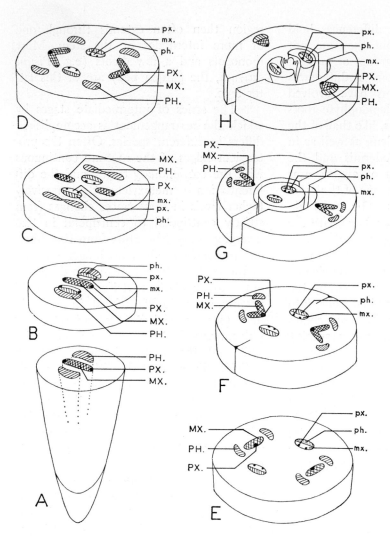

Fig. 25.10. Vascular anatomy of the root-stem transition region, from that of the root (*A*) to that of the stem (*H*), in a plant with diarch xylem in the root; mx., metaxylem; ph., phloem; px., protoxylem.

necessary to complete the transition in such types.

When the first cauline bundles do not differentiate until after secondary growth has already started in the hypocotyl, they may attach directly to the secondary tissues derived from the cambium. In any case the cambium of the root, the hypocotyl, and the stem is ordinarily continuous, and the formation of secondary tissues in these organs follows a common pattern.

MODIFIED ROOTS

Storage Roots

Most roots store some food as well as serving in anchorage and absorption. Carbohydrates, especially starch and sucrose, are the food usually stored. Sugar beets commonly contain 15–20 per cent sucrose.

One of the commonest types of modified root is the fleshy storage root (Fig. 25.11). Many biennials produce a fleshy storage taproot during the first year and use up the stored food the following year when flowers and seeds are formed. Carrots, beets, parsnips, turnips, and radishes are familiar examples, although some of these may be induced to mature the first year. In many plants with fleshy taproots, including carrots and beets, the fleshy structure includes the hypocotyl as well as the root proper, and the two parts can be distinguished only by careful anatomical study. The hypocotyl is the principal part of the fleshy structure of globe radishes.

Fleshy-thickened roots, or parts of roots, in an otherwise fibrous root system are called tuberous roots (Fig. 25.12), in reference to their superficial similarity to tubers. In plants such as water hemlock (*Cicuta*), a highly poisonous relative of the parsnip, tuberous roots are storage organs, without any reproductive function. In sweet potatoes (Fig. 25.13) and some other plants, however, they are reproduc-

Fig. 25.12. Tuberous roots of dahlia. (New York Botanical Garden photo.)

tive organs, producing adventitious stems from internal tissues the following year.

All storage roots have in common an abundance of parenchyma which is thoroughly permeated by vascular elements. In carrots the cortex is sloughed off in the normal way after the formation of a thin periderm, and there is a massive development of parenchyma in the xylem and phloem. In carrots grown under poor conditions, the woody nature of the central core is often quite apparent. In turnips and radishes the xylem parenchyma proliferates and differentiates scattered concentric vascular bundles. In sweet potatoes, the primary and secondary xylem are both highly parenchymatous, and anomalous cambia develop around individual vessels or groups of vessels, producing parenchyma-rich xylem centripetally and parenchyma-rich phloem centrifugally. Beets and sugar beets produce successive supernumerary cambia outside the normal vascular core; the concentric rings seen in cross section represent the growth layers formed by the successive cambia.

Fig. 25.11. Fleshy taproots of beet (left) and carrot (right). (New York Botanical Garden photos.)

Fig. 25.13. Tuberous root of sweet potato (*Ipomoea batatas*), producing roots below and adventitious stems above. (Photo courtesy of T. H. Everett.)

CONTRACTILE ROOTS

Many herbaceous perennial monocots and dicots, as well as some gymnosperms, have contractile roots. The bulbs of liliaceous plants are commonly drawn deep into the soil by contractions of successive sets of adventitious roots over a period of years. Roots of dandelions and other plants which have their leaves all or mostly at the ground surface contract year after year, so that the slight terminal growth of

the stem each spring does not bring the crown much above the ground level. In seedlings the hypocotyl as well as the young root may contract, returning the cotyledons to near the ground after they have been raised some distance into the air. Root contraction may also have some significance in countering the effect of frost heaving in cold climates.

Some, all, or none of the roots may be contractile, depending on the kind of plant. Often the contractile roots are obviously specialized as compared to the noncontractile roots on the same plant. The mechanism of contraction varies. Typically it involves a shortening and thickening of the parenchyma cells, so that the mature xylem elements assume a sinuous course. These changes may be accompanied by the death and degeneration of scattered groups of parenchyma cells, facilitating the readjustment of the remaining tissues. The region just behind the root-hair zone is often more contractile than the mature parts of the root, and specialized contractile roots frequently have only a small amount of mature xylem in this region. The contractile part of a root may lose as much as two thirds of its length within a few weeks in some kinds of plants.

MYCORHIZAE

The roots of many vascular plants harbor a filamentous fungus, forming a fungus-root combination called a **mycorhiza**. Mycorhizae commonly have shorter, thicker, and frequently more crowded branches than ordinary roots, and they have few or no root hairs. Some, all, or none of the smaller roots of a plant may be mycorhizal, depending on the species and the environmental conditions. Often the roots in the upper part of the soil, where organic matter is abundant, are mycorhizal, while those in the underlying mineral soil are not. The roots of some kinds of plants are always and necessarily mycorhizal; some are or are not, with varying degrees of benefit and harm, according to the circumstances, and others are never so. Probably more than half the kinds of vascular plants usually have mycorhizae under natural conditions. The conifers (especially pines), orchids, and heaths (Ericaceae) are usually mycorhizal, and successful cultivation of species of these groups generally requires the maintenance of conditions favorable for the growth of the fungus.

The fungi involved in mycorhizae include various kinds of basidiomycetes, ascomycetes, and phycomycetes, especially the hymenomycetous basidiomycetes. The fungus may also occur independently of the mycorhizae, or it may be largely or wholly restricted to mycorhizal associations. The host may bear only one or several different kinds of fungi, often more than one in the same root. Often a particular mycorhizal fungus is limited to only one kind or a few closely related kinds of hosts. Truffles and many kinds of mushrooms are especially noteworthy in this regard, although the common field mushroom, *Agaricus campestris*, is not mycorhizal. The association of certain fungi with the roots of oaks was known to Theophrastus (372?–287? B.C.), the Greek Father of Botany.

The mycorhizal fungus is partly in the soil and partly in the root, often forming a tangle of filaments (the mantle) over the surface so that the root is not in direct contact with the soil (Fig. 25.15). The mantle formed on tree roots by truffle fungi was noted by the French mycologist

Louis René Tulasne (1815–1885) in 1841. The fungus mantle often has numerous, short, radiating branches that resemble root hairs. Mycorhizae are said to be ectotrophic or endotrophic, according to whether the principal development of the filaments which penetrate the host is between the cells or within them. The filaments of ectotrophic mycorhizae commonly form a distinctive network (called the Hartig net, after its discoverer, who did not understand what he saw) envelop-

Fig. 25.14. Indian pipe (*Monotropa uniflora*), a plant which has become dependent on its mycorhizal fungus for food. (Photo courtesy of J. Arthur Herrick.)

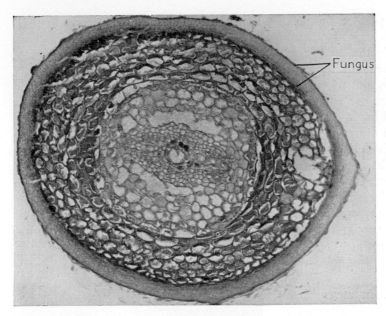

Fungus

Fig. 25.15. Cross section of root of Indian pipe, with its fungus mantle. (Photo courtesy of J. Arthur Herrick.)

ing the individual cells of the root, but they may also send some short branches into the protoplast of the root cell.

The fungus is typically limited to the outer part of the root, not extending into the endodermis. The filaments are tolerated in the outer tissues but are digested and absorbed by the host as they extend inward or into areas of greater metabolic activity (such as the apical meristem). In some plants, however, the fungus permeates most of the host, and indeed the presence of the fungus in the seed coat is necessary for germination of some kinds of orchids under natural conditions.

The ecological relationships between the fungus and the root vary according to the species and the environmental conditions. Typically the fungus digests starch grains stored in the host cells, absorbing the digestion products and using them in its own metabolism. Water and minerals are absorbed from the soil by the fungus and passed on to the host. Mycorhizal ab-

sorption is often more efficient than that which would be carried on by the unaided root. The increased absorbing surface provided by the extensive development of the mycorhizal fungus in the soil is believed to be necessary under natural conditions for many forest trees, to supply enough water to balance the loss by evaporation.

Mycorhizal fungi can also tap a mineral supply that would not be available to the unaided host. Nitrogen, phosphorus, and calcium, among other necessary elements found in humus, are not directly available to plant roots until the complex organic compounds in which they occur have been broken down to yield soluble inorganic compounds. Mycorhizal fungi attack the humus, however, digesting and absorbing the organic compounds. Digestion of some of the internal filaments of the fungus by the root releases compounds. which are then used by the host. Under experimental conditions, the absence of mycorhizal fungi in pines and some other plants can be compensated for by fertilization of the soil.

Mycorhizae evidently originated, in an evolutionary sense, by change from a simple host-parasite relationship to a modified sort of parasitism in which the fungus more or less compensates for the food it uses by providing an increased supply of water and/or necessary elements. Doubtless the relationship is often even more complex, with each symbiont having become dependent on the other for certain substances which it has lost the ability to produce for itself. In some orchids, such as a coralroot (*Corallorhiza*), and certain heaths, such as Indian pipe (*Monotropa*) (Fig. 25.14) and pinedrops (*Pterospora*), the flowering plant lacks chlorophyll and is wholly dependent on the fungus for its food supply as well as for water and minerals. The role of the fungus in this type of mycorhiza was first suggested by the German botanist Wilhelm Pfeffer (1845–1920) in 1877. The benefit, if any, derived by the fungus in such cases is obscure; recent evidence suggests that it may depend on its "host" for certain vitamins or enzymes.

OTHER MODIFIED ROOTS

The function of some fleshy roots as reproductive structures has already been mentioned. Slender roots may also serve a reproductive function. The Canada thistle (*Cirsium arvense*, a native of Eurasia) and many other plants, including a number of noxious weeds, have long, slender, deep-seated, horizontal roots which function in the same way as creeping rhizomes, sending up stems at intervals (Fig. 25.16). The stems arise adventitiously from internal tissues, in much the same way as branch roots. Black locust (*Robinia pseudoacacia*) and silver poplar (*Populus alba*) are familiar trees which produce adventitious stems from some of the roots. Some plants which do not ordinarily produce root sprouts can be in-

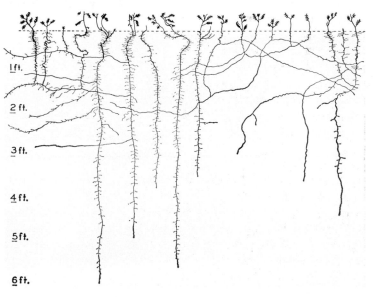
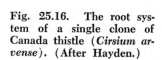

Fig. 25.16. The root system of a single clone of Canada thistle (*Cirsium arvense*). (After Hayden.)

Fig. 25.17. Prop roots of a tree (*Socratea*) in the rain forest of Colombia. (Photo courtesy of José Cuatrecasas.)

duced to do so by injury. Red raspberries, the common barberry, and some kinds of roses develop adventitious stems if the plant is cut back to the ground. Roses, blackberries, and a number of other plants are commonly propagated by root cuttings.

Many plants have adventitious prop roots. In maize these develop in whorls at the lower nodes of the stem, spreading out and entering the soil at an angle. Mangroves and some other tropical trees (Fig. 25.17) commonly have large prop roots as much as several meters long, which help to anchor the trees firmly in the marshy soil in which they grow. Prop roots of the banyan tree (*Ficus benghalensis*) descend vertically from the widely spreading branches and become columnar supports resembling ordinary trunks.

Poison ivy and many other climbing plants have numerous, short, adventitious roots on the aerial stems. As noted in Chapter 24, these roots tend to penetrate the crevices and cracks in the bark of trees, or in brick or stone walls, and may be provided with small adhesive terminal disks.

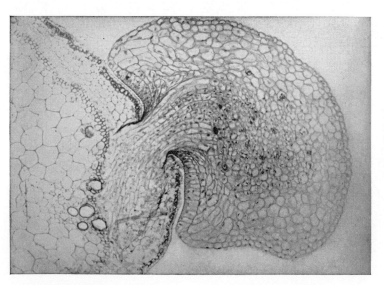

Fig. 25.18. Section showing attachment of the haustorium of dodder to the host. (Copyright by General Biological Supply House, Inc., Chicago.)

Tropical epiphytes often have slender, hanging, aerial roots with a more or less modified epidermis. In many orchids and aroids the epidermis of these roots is developed into a multiseriate layer called the velamen, consisting of compactly arranged dead cells with thickened walls. The velamen absorbs rain or dew deposited on it, and the internal tissues absorb water from the velamen. During dry weather the cells of the velamen dry out and are filled with air.

Parasitic plants such as dodder (*Cuscuta*) and mistletoe have modified roots, called **haustoria** (Fig. 25.18), which enter the tissue of the host, establishing connection with its vascular system and absorbing nutrients. Dodder is wholly dependent on the host for food as well as for water and minerals. Mistletoe, on the other hand, is green and makes at least some of its own food, depending on the host chiefly for water and minerals. The term *haustorium* is also applied to root-like hyphae of parasitic fungi which penetrate the cells of the host and absorb food.

SUGGESTED READING

Kelley, Arthur P., *Mycotrophy in Plants*, Chronica Botanica, Waltham, Mass., 1950, 223 pp. On the technical rather than the popular side.

Angiosperms: Leaves

CHAPTER 26

EXTERNAL STRUCTURE AND ARRANGEMENT

GENERAL FEATURES

Leaves (Fig. 26.1) are the characteristic photosynthetic organs of most vascular plants. They are appendages of the stem, usually having a distinct stalk, the **petiole**, and a thin, flat, expanded **blade** with an upper (adaxial) and a lower (abaxial) surface. Leaves in which the blade is attached directly to the stem, without a petiole, are **sessile**. Often there is a pair of small appendages at the base of the petiole, one on each side; these are the **stipules**.

A large proportion of monocots have sessile leaves with a relatively broad, more or less sheathing base that extends most or all of the way around the stem. In the grasses and sedges, this sheathing base is developed into a well-defined **leaf sheath** which encloses the stem for some distance above the node. The point of departure of the blade from the sheath is commonly

◄
Insect-catching leaves of pitcher plant, *Sarracenia flava*. (About ½ natural size.) (Photo by W. H. Hodge.)

521

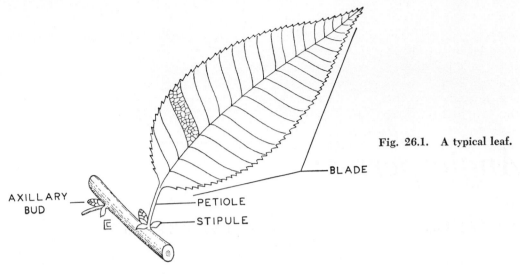

Fig. 26.1. A typical leaf.

BLADE

AXILLARY
BUD

PETIOLE

STIPULE

marked by a short, adaxial appendage that extends across the width of the leaf. This appendage, the **ligule,** has no very obvious function, but differences in its form and size are often useful in identifying species. Ontogenetically it is a projection from the top of the sheath. A number of dicots, such as celery and plantain, also have the base of the petiole expanded and more or less sheathing, and a few have sheathing sessile leaves.

There is some correlation between the nodal anatomy of the stem and the structure of the leaf. Leaves with a sheathing base are generally exstipulate (without stipules) and almost always arise from multilacunar nodes. Leaves that are not sheathing usually arise from unilacunar or trilacunar nodes. Leaves from trilacunar nodes usually have stipules, whereas those from unilacunar nodes usually lack them, but there are many exceptions.

ARRANGEMENT

The leaves on a stem are usually arranged in a definite pattern and are typically oriented so that each leaf is exposed to the light with a minimum of interference from its neighbors. The exact pattern of arrangement varies from species to species, and sometimes even on different parts of the same individual. Leaves are said to be **alternate, opposite,** or **whorled,** according to whether one, two, or more than two are borne at each node.

An imaginary line drawn through the bases of several successive alternate leaves usually forms a regular spiral, with the leaves inserted at regular intervals. Viewed from above, so that the vertical distance from one leaf to the next is ignored, the arc of the stem from one leaf base to the next commonly approximates a definite fraction of the circumference. The most common of these fractions are $\frac{1}{2}$, $\frac{1}{3}$, $\frac{2}{5}$, $\frac{3}{8}$, $\frac{5}{13}$, $\frac{8}{21}$, etc. The numerator of each succeeding fraction, as the series progresses, is the sum of the two immediately previous numerators, and the denominator is the sum of the two immediately previous denominators. Another way of explaining the same set of fractions is to say that the numerator represents the number of turns around the stem, and the denominator the number of leaf bases, before one leaf is directly over another. Thus in a ⅖ **phyllotaxy** (from Greek *phyllon*, leaf, and *taxis*, arrangement), leaf #6 is approximately over leaf #1; a spiral from leaf #1 through leaf #6 would pass twice around the stem and through 5 successive leaf bases; and the arc between each 2 successive leaf bases (or the angle of divergence between successive leaves) is 144°, which is ⅖ of 360° (Fig. 26.2). In phyllotaxies higher than ⅖, the angle of divergence quickly approaches an ultimate figure of slightly more than 137.5°.

The conformity of the actual position of the leaves to that which would theoretically be expected is often less than perfect. The stem may twist during its growth, obscuring the arrangement. The angle of divergence may be consistently a little more or a little less than the theoretical value, so that a line drawn through a series of leaf bases which should be directly over one another actually forms an elongate spiral. The phyllotaxy may differ on different stems of the same plant or may change during the growth of a given shoot. In spite of these variations, the tendency toward a phyllotaxy which can be expressed in the indicated fractions is well established.

It will be noted that all the numbers in the fractions of the phyllotactic series belong to the mathematical series 1, 1, 2, 3, 5, 8, 13, 21, 34, etc., in which each successive number is the sum of the two previous numbers. This series is called the **Fibonacci series,** after its inventor, Leonardo Fibonacci (1180?–1250), an Italian mathematician. The reason for the close relationship between the phyllotactic series and the Fibonacci series is not clear. Attempts at explanation usually center

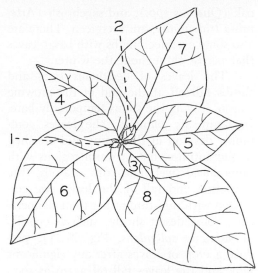

Fig. 26.2. **Vertical view of a tobacco shoot, with ⅖ phyllotaxy. The numbers indicate the relative age of the leaves. (Adapted from Esau.)**

about the geometry of close packing, sometimes with recourse also to hormones which are supposed to be produced by the leaf primordia in the bud and to inhibit the initiation of new primordia immediately adjacent to the existing ones.

Duration

Leaves have an inherently limited life span, usually only a single growing season (or part of one), seldom more than a few years. Woody plants, in which the aerial stems persist year after year, may be classed as **evergreen** or **deciduous,** according to the duration of the leaves. In evergreen plants, the leaves formed during one season persist at least until the leaves of the following season are produced; in some evergreens the leaves last several years. Nearly all conifers are evergreen, as are most angiosperm trees of moist tropical regions. Only a few angiosperms of temperate regions, such as holly (*Ilex*), live oak (*Quercus spp.*), and sagebrush (*Artemisia tridentata*), are evergreen. There are also some evergreen herbs with basal leaves that persist throughout the winter.

The leaves of deciduous trees and shrubs fall off at the end of the growing season, leaving the stems temporarily bare. In temperate climates, the leaves commonly develop in the spring and are shed in the autumn, but in warm regions with pronounced wet and dry seasons, the formation and fall of the leaves are correlated with moisture rather than temperature. Some desert shrubs, such as ocotillo (*Fouquieria splendens*, Fig. 27.11), produce a crop of leaves after any significant rain, and the leaves fall off again as soon as the soil moisture becomes inadequate to maintain them.

ABSCISSION

Leaves of most vascular cryptogams and herbaceous angiosperms usually wither on the stem and are eventually shed through decay and external causes. Leaves of most gymnosperms (especially conifers) and woody angiosperms (with the notable exception of some woody monocots), on the other hand, are generally shed as a result of changes in a specialized transverse **abscission zone** (Fig. 26.3) at the base, often before the leaf has died. The abscission zone generally contains a high proportion of parenchyma cells, and relatively few thick-walled cells, so that it is the weakest part of the petiole (or of the blade, in sessile leaves). It is usually externally evident as soon as the leaf is mature, showing as a shallow furrow, or as a line of different color or texture around the base of the petiole.

The abscission zone sooner or later becomes differentiated into two layers, a protective layer several cells thick on the side toward the stem, and a **separation layer** two to several cells thick on the side toward the leaf. Sometimes there are three layers, with the separation layer sandwiched between two protective layers, but the protective layer on the side toward the leaf has no apparent functional significance. These layers can often be detected microscopically early in the season, their further development being arrested until later.

The eventual changes which result in the abscission of the leaf and the formation of a leaf scar may or may not be immediately preceded by a series of cell divisions. In either case the middle lamellae, and often also the primary walls of the cells of the separation layer, generally swell and become gelatinous, due largely to a change of the calcium pectate component to pectic acid and thence to water-soluble pectin. The weight of the leaf and the force of wind, rain, etc. then break the leaf away from the stem along this separation layer. The term *abscission layer* is frequently used in the strict sense to apply to the separation layer after it has begun to undergo the changes which result in the fall of the leaf.

Changes in the protective layer usually proceed more or less concomitantly with those in the separation layer, although there may be a time lag in either direction. The protective layer is waterproofed by a deposit of suberin, which forms a sheet covering the inner surface of the wall of each cell and is strengthened by a deposit of a lignin-like substance which permeates the cell walls and intercellular spaces, often filling the lumina of the vessels as well. This substance may be identical with the wound gum often deposited in injured tissues as part of the

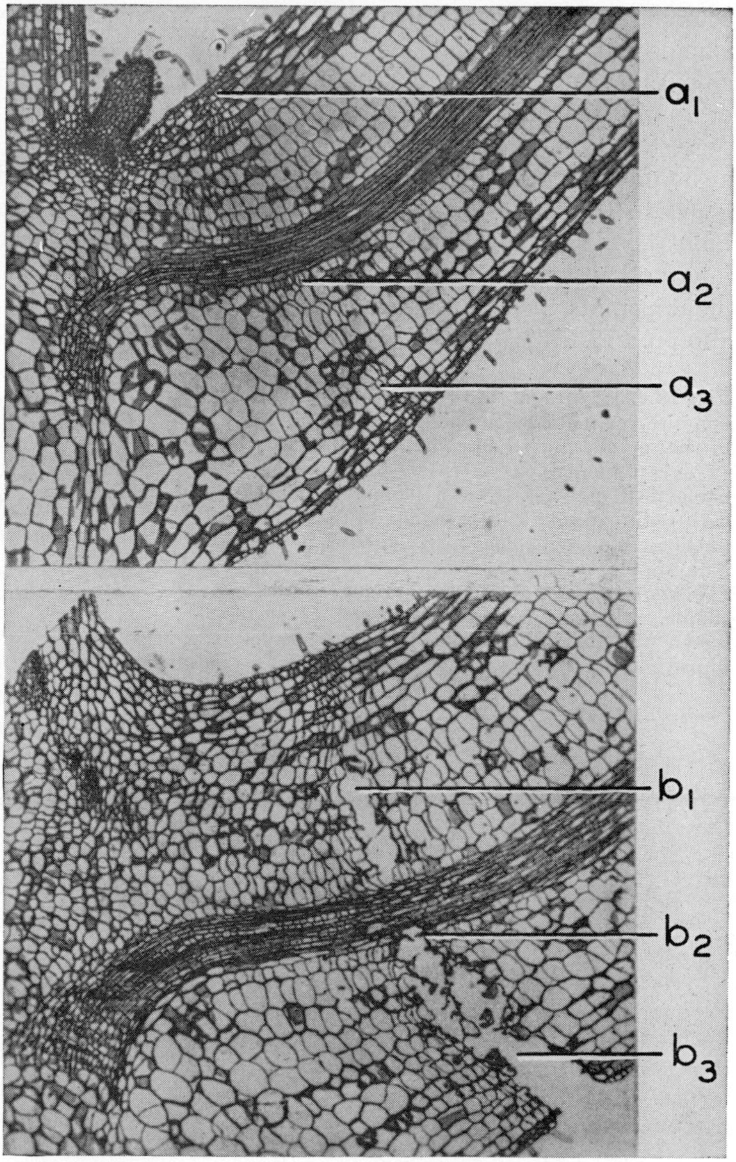

Fig. 26.3. Abscission in petiole of *Coleus*. Developing abscission layer (small cells) at a_1, a_2, a_3. Abscission in progress at b_1, b_2, b_3. Note beginning of destruction of vascular tissue at b_2. (Photomicrographs by Tillman J. Johnson, from *An Introduction to the Anatomy of Seed Plants*, by Ernest L. Stover. Copyright 1951 by D. C. Heath.)

healing process. Maturation of the protective layer of the abscission zone is commonly followed (or accompanied) by the formation of a periderm continuous with the periderm of the rest of the stem.

Abscission of the leaves can be brought about, at least in many plants, by any of several environmental factors, including water deficit, low temperature, reduced light intensity, and decreased day length. Abscission can also be induced by destroying a large part of the blade, or by treating it with various chemicals, such as ethylene and carbon tetrachloride. Several common growth-regulating substances, including indole-acetic acid, tend to inhibit abscission when applied to the leaf blade or to the debladed petiole. It has been suggested that under normal conditions a hormone produced in the blade migrates to the base of the petiole and inhibits abscission, and that any prolonged interruption of the supply of this hormone permits the abscission to occur (see also pp. 655–656).

Fig. 26.4. Types of dicot leaves. Upper left, opposite, palmately compound, exstipulate leaf of horse chestnut (*Aesculus hippocastanum*) (×1/12); upper right, alternate, pinnately compound leaf of black locust (*Robinia pseudoacacia*), with opposite leaflets, and with the stipules modified into short spines (×1/4); lower left, alternate, simple, sessile, exstipulate leaf of goldenrod (*Solidago rugosa*) (×1/3); lower right, alternate, simple, subsessile leaf of smartweed (*Polygonum*), with sheathing stipules (×1/3): lfl., leaflet; p., petiole; r., rachis; s.s., sheathing stipules.

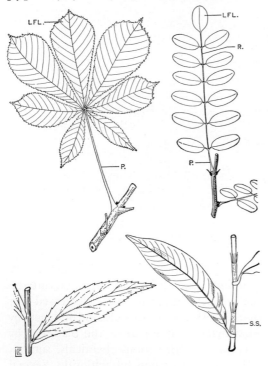

SIMPLE AND COMPOUND LEAVES

The form and structure of the leaf blade vary in different kinds of plants (Figs. 26.4–26.9), and even to some extent on the same plant or on different individuals of the same kind. An extensive terminology has been developed to describe the kinds of leaves, due to the usefulness of these characters in recognizing and distinguishing different species; only the more important of these terms are given in the following pages. If the blade is all in one piece, the leaf is said to be **simple;** if it is composed of several separate **leaflets,** it is **compound.** The stalks of the individual leaflets are the **petiolules.** Compound leaves in which the leaflets are attached nearly at the same point, as in the horse chestnut (*Aesculus hippocastanum*), marijuana (*Cannabis sativa*), and lupines (*Lupinus*), are **palmately compound.** Compound leaves in which the leaflets are attached on opposite sides of an elongate rachis, as in walnuts (*Juglans*), hickories (*Carya*), ashes (*Fraxinus*), roses (*Rosa*), and black locust (*Robinia pseudoacacia*), are **pinnately compound.** Usually the lateral leaflets are paired, with the members of the pair directly opposite each other; sometimes they are more or less offset. Pinnately compound leaves which have a terminal leaflet in addition to the lateral ones usually have an odd number of leaflets and are **odd-pinnate;** when there is no terminal leaflet, the leaf is **even-pinnate.** Pinnately compound leaves, such as those of the honey locust (*Gleditsia triacanthos*), in which the primary divisions are themselves compound, are **pinnately bicompound** or **tricompound.** The term **pinnately decompound** covers all degrees of dissection from bicompound on up. **Trifoliolate** leaves, with three leaflets, may be either pinnately compound, as in poison ivy (*Rhus toxicodendron* and related species), or palmately compound, as in white clover (*Trifolium repens*), according to whether or not there is a definite rachis extending beyond the two lateral leaflets. A compound leaf like that of the carrot, in which the ultimate segments are very numerous and more or less confluent, is said to be **dissected**.

DISTINCTION BETWEEN COMPOUND LEAVES AND LEAFY STEMS

Compound leaves may sometimes be confused with leafy stems, but the distinction is not usually difficult. Compound leaves bear axillary buds just as do simple leaves, but the leaflets do not. The position of the axillary buds, therefore, can be used to mark the base of the leaf. Axillary buds of some plants are so small as to escape notice, however, and in some trees, such as the sycamore (*Platanus*), the bud is enclosed by the expanded base of the petiole.

A stem typically ends in a terminal bud with an apical meristem, although in

Fig. 26.5. Trifoliolate leaves of poison ivy (*Rhus radicans*). (New York Botanical Garden photo.)

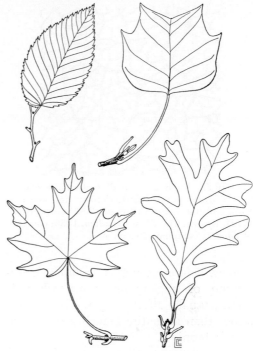

Fig. 26.6. Form and venation of dicot leaves. Upper left, American elm (*Ulmus americana*) with ovate, acute, pinnately veined, doubly serrate leaves; upper right, tulip tree (*Liriodendron tulipifera*), with pinnately veined, broadly retuse, four-lobed leaves; lower left, sugar maple (*Acer saccharum*), with palmately veined, palmately lobed and coarsely toothed leaves; lower right, white oak (*Quercus alba*) with pinnately veined, pinnately lobed leaves.

some woody plants the tip is abscised so that the stem ends abruptly just above one of the axillary buds. Compound leaves, on the other hand, never have terminal buds, and in seed plants they almost never have an apical meristem. Very often a compound leaf has a terminal leaflet like the other leaflets.

Leaves of woody plants are eventually deciduous, usually leaving a characteristic scar on the stem, although the leaflets of a compound leaf may be separately de-

Angiosperms: Leaves 527

Fig. 26.7. Veins in a small part of the leaf of lime (*Citrus aurantifolia*), showing the fine network and blind ends of the smallest veins. (From W. H. Brown, *The Plant Kingdom*, 1935; courtesy of Ginn & Company, Boston.)

The very smallest veins of dicot leaves commonly end blindly in the areolae between the veins of next larger size. Pinnately veined leaves, such as those of elms and beeches, have an evident central midvein, with the primary branches departing at intervals along its length. Palmately veined leaves, such as those of maples, sycamores, and begonias, have several main veins diverging from the base, with the central one usually not much, if at all, larger than the others. The branch veins departing from the main veins of a palmately veined leaf are usually pinnately arranged; thus the leaflets of a palmately

Fig. 26.8. Characteristic monocot leaves. *A, Juncus nodosus*, with a basal sheath and a hollow, transversely septate blade; *B*, crab grass (*Digitaria*) with a basal sheath, a flat terminal blade, and a ligule where the blade joins the sheath; *C*, cat brier (*Smilax*), with a petiole, stipular tendrils, and a broad blade; *D*, Jack-in-the-pulpit (*Arisaema triphyllum*) with sheathing base, long petiole, and trifoliate blade, the leaflets pinnately veined; l.s., leaf sheath; lig., ligule.

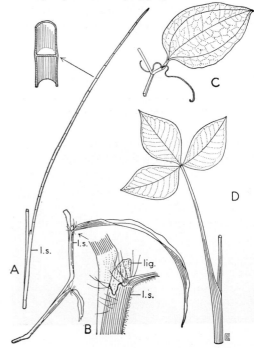

ciduous before the petiole is abscised. Abscission of angiosperm stems, when it occurs, usually affects only the branch tip rather than an entire branch, so that the scar is terminal.

VENATION

Leaves of angiosperms characteristically have a branching vascular system derived from the leaf traces of the stem. The principal veins (vascular bundles) are usually readily visible to the naked eye and very often stand out on the lower surface of the leaf. The midrib, in particular, is usually prominent. The smaller veins are evident or obscure according to the kind of plant.

The arrangement of veins in leaf blades varies in detail from species to species, with a strong tendency toward a general difference between monocots and dicots. In most dicots the main veins are either pinnately or palmately arranged, with several orders of branches, and some of the smaller veins form a more or less obvious network (Fig. 26.7). Dicots are therefore usually said to have **net venation.**

compound and palmately veined leaf are usually pinnately veined.

In most monocots the leaf has several or many nearly parallel veins which run the length of the leaf, and the branches which interconnect these longitudinal veins are very small and inconspicuous. Monocots are therefore usually said to have **parallel** venation. Most monocots have relatively long, narrow leaves, with closely spaced longitudinal veins, but some broader-leaved forms, such as *Trillium* and many aroids, do have an evident network of smaller veins between the more widely spaced main ones. Thus, although the different types of venation can usually be recognized, no hard and fast line can be drawn between the parallel and the net type, and even less between pinnate and palmate.

FORM

The shape of leaves and leaflets is described by a series of terms derived from plane geometry and other sources. Such terms as linear, elliptic, oblong, and orbicular are self-explanatory. A cordate leaf is shaped like a conventional heart, and a reniform leaf is kidney-shaped. An ovate leaf is shaped about like a long section through a hen's egg, with the broader end toward the petiole; a lanceolate leaf is likewise broadest below the middle but is distinctly narrower than ovate. Oblanceolate and obovate leaves have the broader end away from the petiole. Still other terms are used to describe other (mostly less common) forms. Often it is necessary to use more than one term, or to make hyphenated compounds, to describe the leaves of a single plant or a single species.

Leaf tips are usually rounded, obtuse, acute, or acuminate (very sharply pointed,

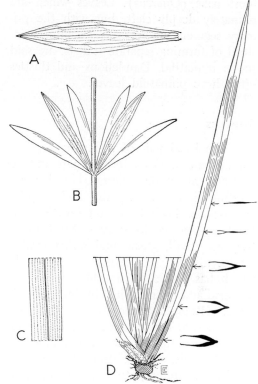

Fig. 26.9. **Characteristic monocot leaves. A, B, whorled leaves of** *Lilium philadelphicum.* **(X½ and X⅓.) C, D,** *Iris sp.* **(X⅔ and X⅓.)**

typically with concave sides). Less often they are truncate (with the broad apex forming a line at right angles to the axis) to retuse (notched), or even obcordate. An abrupt small point at the tip of a leaf is a mucro; leaves with an otherwise rounded tip are often mucronate.

The margins of a leaf are usually entire, toothed, or lobed. Leaves with sharp, forward-pointing teeth, like those of basswood (*Tilia*), are serrate; leaves with rounded, forward-pointing teeth, like those of mulberry (*Morus*), are crenate. Mulberry leaves are often irregularly lobed as well as crenate. Lobed leaves are usually either palmately lobed, as in most maples (*Acer*), or pinnately lobed, as in most oaks (*Quercus*). Leaves which are pinnately deeply cleft, but with the primary segments more or less confluent instead of forming separate leaflets, are said to be pinnatifid. Dandelions and thistles often have pinnatifid leaves.

STIPULES

The basal pair of appendages called stipules are a characteristic part of the leaves of many angiosperms, but they are wanting from gymnosperms and vascular cryptogams. Their form and function differ from species to species. Most often they are small, green, and rather weakly photosynthetic. In bedstraw (*Galium*), which has sessile leaves, the stipules are enlarged and resemble leaf blades. In black locust (*Robinia pseudoacacia*) they are modified into short, stout spines. In *Smilax* (greenbrier, catbrier) they are modified to form tendrils. In the tulip tree (*Liriodendron tulipifera*) they form the protective scales of the terminal bud; each leaf, as it expands and diverges from the growing stem, reveals the stipules of the next leaf, which completely cover the bud. The stipules of many plants are deciduous as the leaf matures, and in many others they are very much reduced, sometimes forming mere raised lines on the stem. Often there are no stipules at all.

Angiosperms without stipules are believed to be descended from stipulate ancestors, but the evolutionary origin of the stipules is not clear. If the angiosperms are descended from ancient seed ferns, as many botanists now believe, the stipules may represent the basal pair of leaflets of a pinnately compound leaf. According to this line of thought, the other leaflets have been lost, so that only the terminal leaflet remains to form the blade. Compound leaves in modern angiosperms are believed to have been more recently derived from simple leaves.

ANATOMY

GENERAL

A leaf blade ordinarily consists of an upper and lower **epidermis**, enclosing a chlorophyllous **mesophyll** that is traversed by a **vascular system** (Fig. 26.10). These three tissue systems will be discussed in sequence.

EPIDERMIS

The nature and general structure of epidermal tissues have been discussed in Chapter 23. Epidermis of leaves generally serves a protective function, regulating the evaporation of water from the internal tissues and providing a partial barrier to infection and mechanical injury. It also contributes to the even distribution of water and solutes in the leaf. The extensive lateral contact area among the epidermal cells, as contrasted to that of mesophyll cells, is doubtless responsible for the greater conducting function of the epidermis. Sometimes the epidermal cells are thick-walled and add significantly to the strength and rigidity of the leaf.

Leaf epidermis is ordinarily covered by a definite cuticle (see Chapter 23), which retards the evaporation of water. The cuticle is usually thicker on the upper epidermis than on the lower, and thicker on plants grown in sun than in shade. Often the epidermis is also provided with trichomes of one sort or another. In many plants, such as mullein (*Verbascum thapsus*), the pubescence is so dense as to hide

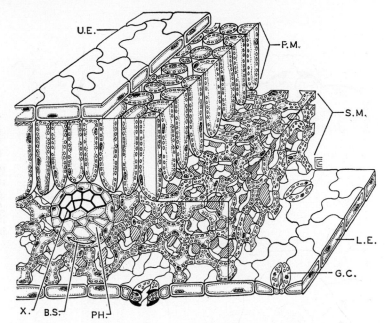

Fig. 26.10. Three-dimensional diagram of a typical leaf, with successive layers stripped away: b.s., bundle sheath; g.c., guard cell; l.e., lower epidermis; ph., phloem; p.m., palisade mesophyll; s.m., spongy mesophyll; u.e., upper epidermis; x., xylem.

the surface. A dense covering of pubescence tends to retard evaporation of water under some conditions, but often the trichomes have no evident function.

The only intercellular spaces in the epidermis of most leaves are the **stomates** (from Greek *stoma*, a mouth). Each stomate (Fig. 26.11) is bounded by a pair of specialized cells, the **guard cells,** which regulate the size of the opening. The cells adjoining the guard cells may be ordinary epidermal cells, or they may be more or less differentiated as **supporting cells.** In the strictest sense, the term *stomate* applies only to the space between the guard cells, and the stomate plus the guard cells and any supporting cells constitute the **stomatal apparatus.** The term *stomate* is often more loosely and conveniently used, however, to apply to the whole stomatal apparatus.

The guard cells, which are usually rather narrowly kidney-shaped or broadly sausage-shaped, are placed side by side.

When the guard cells are turgid, they are bowed apart in the middle, leaving a definite opening between them. When they lose their turgidity, they become appressed to each other throughout their length, closing the opening. The walls of guard cells are strongly and unevenly thickened, often with ledges along the upper and lower margins next to the aperture. Unlike ordinary epidermal cells, guard cells contain chloroplasts, and these are indirectly involved in the mechanism of opening and closing the stomates under some conditions (see pp. 554–555).

Stomates of grasses and sedges have guard cells of an unusual type. The thin-walled, bulbous ends swell and contract with changes in turgor, separating or bringing together the straight, thick-walled median portions.

In precise anatomical comparisons, stomates are classified into several groups by the structure of the guard cells, the presence or absence of supporting cells,

Angiosperms: Leaves 531

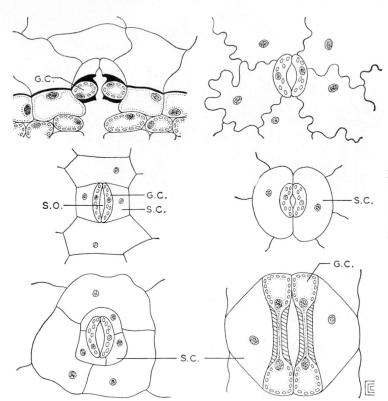

Fig. 26.11. Characteristic types of stomates—that of grasses at the lower right; g.c., guard cell; s.c., supporting cell; s.o., stomatal opening.

Fig. 26.12. Epidermis of *Sedum* leaf, showing stomates. (Copyright by General Biological Supply House, Inc., Chicago.)

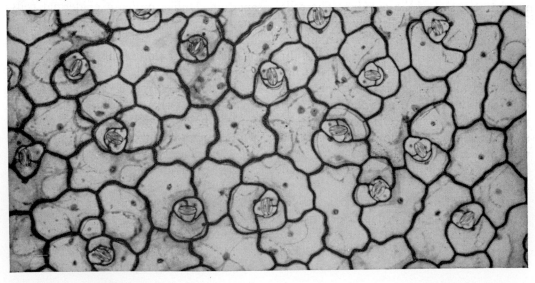

the arrangement of the supporting cells, and sometimes by the ontogeny of the stomatal apparatus. The simplest type, with more or less kidney-shaped guard cells and without supporting cells (Fig. 26.12), is called the ranunculaceous type, from its common occurrence in the genus *Ranunculus* (buttercup), although it also occurs in many other genera of various families.

The stomates may be equally abundant on both sides of the leaf, but usually they are more numerous on the lower surface than the upper; often the upper surface lacks stomates entirely. Floating leaves such as those of water lilies, on the contrary, have all the stomates on the upper surface. In dicots the stomates are generally scattered at more or less regular intervals over the leaf surface, but in monocots they commonly occur in longitudinal lines between the veins. The needle leaves of conifers often have the stomates in longitudinal lines or bands. Stomates of xerophytes (plants adapted to dry conditions) are often individually sunken or grouped in sunken stomatal pockets.

The number of stomates per unit area varies rather widely on different leaves and different individuals of the same species, according to the environment, as well as from species to species. Common figures for the lower epidermis are about 15–1000 per square mm, the lower numbers typically occurring in plants with larger stomates. Figures as low as 10 and as high as 1300 per square mm have been recorded. The stomatal opening is very small, commonly 7–40 microns long and 3–12 microns wide when fully open. The fully open stomates usually cover about 0.5–2 percent of the lower epidermis. As noted in Chapter 27, the total gaseous diffusion possible through a number of small openings is much greater than that through a single large opening of the same total area, and evaporation of water through the stomates often proceeds at a rate more than half as great as would occur from a free water surface the size of the leaf.

The epidermal cells, other than those of the stomatal apparatus, may be all alike, or there may be one or more specialized types in addition to the ground mass. Scattered cork cells, fibers, secretory cells, and crystal-containing cells are not uncommon. Most monocot leaves have some **bulliform** (bubble-shaped) **cells** scattered over the surface or arranged in longitudinal strips. Bulliform cells are relatively large, with thin walls, large vacuole, and little solid content. In some species, changes in the turgor of the bulliform cells govern the longitudinal rolling and unrolling of the leaf under varying moisture conditions, but in others they have no apparent function.

Mesophyll

The mesophyll of a leaf usually consists largely or wholly of chlorenchyma, i.e., chlorophyll-bearing parenchyma. Typically it is rather sharply differentiated into an upper layer, the **palisade parenchyma** (palisade chlorenchyma, palisade mesophyll), and a lower layer, the **spongy parenchyma** (spongy chlorenchyma, spongy mesophyll).

The palisade parenchyma typically consists of one or two tiers of elongate, more or less cylindric or prismatic cells, just beneath the upper epidermis and perpendicular to it. The cells are fairly closely set, but usually more of the wall adjoins intercellular space than adjoins

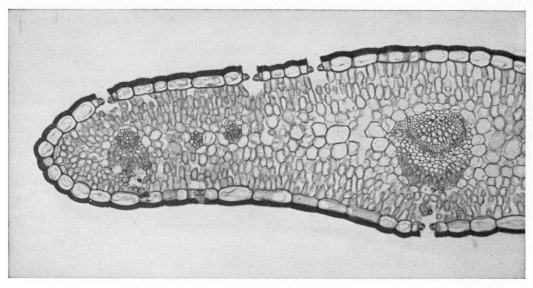

Fig. 26.13. Leaf of *Dianthus*, in cross section. This leaf, standing nearly erect in life, has stomates and palisade tissue on both sides, but the palisade tissue is not strongly differentiated from the spongy tissue. (Copyright by General Biological Supply House, Inc., Chicago.)

other cells. Often the cells taper toward the base, so that the intercellular spaces are wider near the spongy parenchyma than near the upper epidermis.

The spongy parenchyma typically consists of irregularly shaped cells, with a high proportion of intercellular space. Many of the cells have knobs or arms which extend out and adjoin other cells. Commonly there is an extra large space, the stomatal chamber, next to each stomate. The spongy layer is usually more than one cell thick, but the cells are not arranged in definite tiers. Cells of the spongy parenchyma generally contain fewer chloroplasts, in proportion to their size, than those of the palisade layer.

The proportions and arrangement of the palisade and spongy tissues vary according to the species and the environment. Leaves which droop or which stand vertically often have a palisade layer on each side, with the spongy layer sandwiched in between (Fig. 26.13). Grass leaves usually have a compact mesophyll with little or no differentiation into palisade and spongy layers; often the cells are nearly isodiametric. Plants which characteristically grow in deep shade often have the palisade layer poorly developed and not much differentiated from the spongy tissue. Many plants of dry sunny habitats have two tiers of palisade, and in *Eucalyptus* the entire mesophyll generally consists of palisade cells. In some plants, such as apples (*Pyrus malus*), leaves which differentiate and develop in shade have a single tier of palisade, whereas those formed in bright sunlight have two tiers.

In addition to being traversed by a vascular system, the mesophyll may also contain laticifers, lysigenous or schizogenous resin ducts, or oil cavities. It may also contain scattered idioblasts of one sort or another. An idioblast is any single cell that is very different from the cells surrounding it. The functions of idioblasts are varied and often obscure.

Mesophyll is structurally well adapted to the primary function of leaves, which is photosynthesis. The densest tissue and the greatest concentration of chloroplasts is toward the upper surface, which receives the most light. The intercellular space is greatest near the stomates, which are the gateway to the outer air, and diminishes progressively toward the upper surface. Since essentially all the CO_2 used in photosynthesis enters through the stomates and is distributed through the intercellular spaces, the need for intercellular space as a passageway is greatest near the stomates and diminishes progressively toward the upper surface. Evaporation from the palisade cells, which receive more light than the spongy tissue, is partly checked by the relatively small amount of wall surface that is in contact with intercellular space; it is from these exposed wall surfaces that the evaporation takes place.

The characteristic modifications in the structure of the mesophyll induced by the environment may also be interpreted as adaptive, although there is more room for argument here. The double palisade layer of many sun leaves absorbs light efficiently, and the smaller proportion of intercellular space reduces the evaporating power of the sun, but distribution of the necessary CO_2 to the upper palisade cells is also restricted. In any case the leaf does not directly attempt to adapt its structure to the environment. Differences in the environment influence the chemical and physical processes occurring in the cells of the growing leaf, and changes in these processes affect the structure of the mature leaf. Insofar as these responses are beneficial, they have survival value and tend to be preserved (by natural selection) during the course of evolution.

VASCULAR SYSTEM

The veins of angiosperm leaves generally form an interconnected branching system, as noted on p. 528. A vein typically consists of a strand of xylem and a strand of phloem, collectively surrounded by a **bundle sheath.** The phloem is usually on the lower (abaxial) side and the xylem on the upper. Plants with bicollateral bundles in the stem commonly have phloem on both the upper and the lower side of the larger veins of the leaf, with the xylem in the middle; the smaller veins of these species generally do not differ from those of other plants.

Most veins consist only of primary tissue, but the larger veins of many dicots show some secondary growth. The number of phloem and xylem elements making up the vein decreases progressively with the size of the vein. The smallest veins, as seen in cross section, often have only a single tracheid, with the phloem represented by a single modified parenchyma cell.

The midrib and often also some of the larger lateral veins of the leaf are usually embedded in a mass of compact parenchyma, rather than being surrounded by a mere bundle sheath. Often there is some strengthening tissue, usually collenchyma, sometimes sclerenchyma, associated with the parenchyma. It is generally the parenchyma and the supporting tissues which stand out on the lower surface of the leaf and mark the position of the vein. The remainder of the veins usually have a distinct bundle sheath and are embedded in the upper part of the spongy mesophyll, just beneath the palisade layer.

The bundle sheath is ontogenetically part of the mesophyll, but it is usually discussed along with the vascular system because of its close morphologic and physiologic connection to that system. Usually it consists of a single layer of elongate, thin-walled, living cells, completely surrounding the vein, and covering the ends of those veins which end blindly. The long axis of the cells parallels that of the vein, and there are no evident intercellular spaces. Except for the usual lack of Casparian strips, the bundle sheath is suggestive of an endodermis. Chloroplasts are present or absent according to the species. The bundle sheath may be thought of as a means of increasing the area of contact between the vascular elements and the more loosely arranged mesophyll cells. Its principal function is to facilitate the conduction of water and solutes from the veins to the mesophyll, and also of solutes from the mesophyll to the veins.

In many dicots, plates of cells similar to those in the bundle sheath extend part way or completely to one or both epidermises. Experimental evidence confirms the obvious suggestion that these bundle sheath extensions are involved in the conduction of water and solutes, forming a pathway between the veins on the one hand and the mesophyll and epidermis on the other. In some species the bundle sheaths or their extensions, or both, are thick-walled (collenchymatous or sclerenchymatous) and contribute to the mechanical strength of the leaf.

Hydathodes

Leaves of many kinds of plants have special structures called **hydathodes** which permit the extrusion of liquid water under conditions of high water intake and low evaporation. The **guttation drops** which form at the hydathodes are usually seen in the early morning after a cool night and are often mistaken for dew. Hydathodes commonly occur along the margins and tips of leaves; sometimes they form definite teeth, but most leaf teeth are not hydathodes. Each hydathode has one or more pores which more or less resemble large stomates, except that they are permanently open. The nature and arrangement of the tissue beneath the pore vary in different species. Typically a small vein containing only tracheids ends blindly in the loose parenchyma of the hydathode, and there is a large intercellular space, resembling a stomatal chamber, just beneath the pore. Guttation water is further discussed in Chapter 27.

SPECIALIZED LEAVES

We have noted that the principal function of most leaves is photosynthesis. Photosynthetic leaves sometimes also have subsidiary functions, such as storage of food or water. Sometimes the additional functions become more important than photosynthesis, and some highly specialized leaves are not photosynthetic at all. Some specialized types of leaves are discussed in the following paragraphs.

Storage Leaves

Members of the family Crassulaceae and some other families commonly have strongly thickened, succulent leaves with water-storage regions consisting of large parenchyma cells with big central vacuoles that contain hydrophilic colloids. Such storage leaves resist desiccation, and many plants with succulent leaves occur in dry habitats. Some succulents, however, are just as susceptible to drought as other plants.

The ordinary photosynthetic leaves of daffodils and many other plants, particularly of the lily family, are enlarged at the base to form food-storage organs. Bulbs, consisting of a short, erect stem with thickened scale leaves or leaf bases, have been discussed in Chapter 24. Cotyledons, which often serve as storage organs, are discussed in Chapter 31.

REPRODUCTIVE AND FLORAL LEAVES

A few kinds of plants, such as *Kalanchoe*, produce adventitious buds along the margins of the leaves. These buds drop off, develop roots, and grow into new plants. A somewhat similar phenomenon is the development of bulbils or bulblets in the leaf axils, or among or in place of the flowers. These bulbils, consisting of a short bit of stem with one or more small, thickened, modified leaves, drop off and develop into new plants. Many plants can be propagated by leaf cuttings (Fig. 26.14).

The sepals, petals, stamens, and carpels of flowers are modified leaves. These are discussed in Chapter 30. Some plants, such as *Poinsettia*, in which the sepals and petals are very small or absent, have brightly colored, petal-like leaves surrounding the flower clusters.

CLIMBING LEAVES

Peas (*Pisum sativum*), sweet peas (*Lathyrus odoratus*) and some other legumes have some of the leaflets of a compound leaf modified into slender, twining tendrils. The stipular tendrils of *Smilax*

Fig. 26.14. Leaf cutting of African violet (*Saintpaulia*) which has taken root in a pot of soil. (Photo courtesy of T. H. Everett.)

have already been noted. Similar climbing leaves occur in various other less familiar plants.

INSECT-CATCHING LEAVES

Plants of several families which are only distantly related have modified leaves which entrap insects that are then digested and partly absorbed. These insectivorous plants commonly grow in marshy or aquatic habitats, in which the supply of available nitrogen is severely limited. Nothing larger than an insect is in any danger from them, and stories of man-eating trees are pure fabrication.

Sarracenia, the pitcher plant (Fig. 26.15), has pitcher-shaped leaves lined with stiff, downward-pointing hairs which lead unwary insects down into the basal pool of water which contains digestive enzymes.

Utricularia, the bladderwort (Fig. 26.16), is an aquatic with finely dissected leaves. Some of the segments have small bladders, up to a few millimeters in diameter, with a complex trap-door opening that permits small aquatic insects and other animals to enter but prevents their escape. The leaves of sundew (*Drosera*) are covered with long, stout, spreading hairs, each hair being tipped by a shining, sticky globule containing digestive enzymes. An insect alighting on the leaves is held fast by the sticky secretion of the hairs it touches, and the nearby hairs bend over and often com-pletely cover it. After the insect has been digested, the hairs return to their normal position. *Dionaea*, the Venus's-flytrap (Fig. 1.3), has the leaves "hinged" along the midrib. When one of the several trigger hairs on the surface of the blade is touched, the leaf snaps shut and the fringed margins interlock. The motion of insect-catching leaves is further discussed in Chapter 32.

PROTECTIVE LEAVES

Winter buds of most deciduous trees are covered by small, modified leaves called

Fig. 26.15. Pitcher plant (*Sarracenia purpurea*). (New York Botanical Garden photo.)

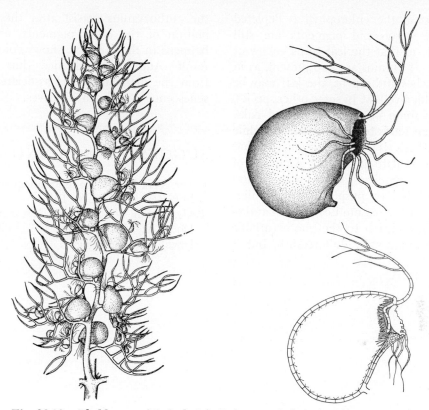

Fig. 26.16. Bladderwort (*Utricularia*). Left, part of plant (×1½); upper right, surface view of bladder (×7); lower right, section of bladder (×7). (From W. H. Brown, *The Plant Kingdom*, 1935; courtesy of Ginn & Company, Boston.)

bud scales. Bud scales are usually firmer than ordinary leaves, with more sclerenchyma and without chlorophyll. Often they are resinous. When the meristem resumes activity in the spring, the bud scales generally fall off, leaving a ring of closely set bud-scale scars around the twig.

The leaves of some kinds of plants, such as cacti, are modified into slender, sharp spines which protect the plant from grazing animals. The spines of many cacti are so numerous and so oily that they can readily be burned off, leaving an unprotected plant body which is palatable to livestock.

AUTUMNAL COLORATION

Leaves of deciduous trees in the temperate zone gradually cease to function as autumn advances, and eventually they are abscised, as described on p. 524. A severe frost will kill the leaves of most angiosperms at any time, but the autumnal senescence often occurs well in advance of killing frosts. Leaves of many woody plants take on yellow to red colors during this time, especially if there is a prolonged period of warm sunny days and cool nights.

Senescence of the leaf commonly does not affect all parts at an equal rate. In many species the chlorophyll is depleted while the carotenoid pigments are still abundant, so that the leaf turns yellow or yellowish. If tannins are also present, as in some beeches and aspens, the leaf may be bright golden-yellow. In some other species, especially some of the maples and oaks, the phloem tends to become inactive while photosynthesis is still going on, so that sugars accumulate in the leaf. An excess of sugars is commonly associated with the formation of red or purplish anthocyanins, regardless of the season. Leaves with anthocyanins in addition to the photosynthetic pigments are usually dull reddish, but if the anthocyanins persist after the deterioration of the other pigments, as often happens in the fall, very showy colors may result. Autumnal brilliance thus results from the maladjustments associated with senescence and death of leaves.

SUGGESTED READING

Ryder, Vera L., On the morphology of leaves, *Bot. Rev.* 20:263–270. 1954.

Teale, Edwin Way, *Autumn Across America*, Dodd, Mead, New York, 1956, 386 pp. A lyrical nature travelogue.

CHAPTER 27

Angiosperms: Water Relations

CHAPTER 27

INTRODUCTION

Water is the chief component of all physiologically active protoplasm. The volume of water in the vacuole of a normal cell usually much exceeds the volume of the protoplast itself, and any great loss of water from the vacuole generally sends the protoplast into a state of relative inactivity, if it is not actually fatal. Under normal atmospheric conditions, water evaporates from any exposed moist surface, living or dead. The exchange of gases necessary for photosynthesis requires (in land plants) that moist cell surfaces be exposed to the air, thus inevitably resulting in some loss of water. The means by which water is absorbed and translocated, and by which its evaporation is retarded or prevented, are therefore highly important in the physiology of the plant.

DISTRIBUTION OF WATER IN THE SOIL

In any reasonably moist climate, a hole dug in the ground will eventually, if the

Rosettes of *Echeveria,* a succulent. Plants of the family Crassulaceae, to which *Echeveria* belongs, are typically thick-leaved succulents, very resistant to desiccation. (Photo by W. H. Hodge.)

543

soil is deep enough, reach a zone in which all the interspaces among the soil particles are filled with water, i.e., the soil is saturated. The upper boundary of this zone is called the **water table.** The depth of the water table varies according to the site and fluctuates according to the rainfall, evaporation, and other factors. In general, the water table forms a subdued image of the surface topography, being nearer to the surface in the low spots, and farthest from the surface on the hilltops. Other factors, such as rock strata or impervious hardpan layers in the soil, govern local irregularities in the depth of the water table, sometimes causing temporary or permanent suspended water tables, in addition to the true one. Where the water table reaches the surface, a spring, swamp, pond, lake, or stream is formed.

For some distance above the water table, the soil is moistened by capillary rise of water. Capillary action is a physical phenomenon resulting from the attraction between water and solid particles of other kinds, in this case particles of soil. The water forms a film around each of the soil particles, filling the smallest interspaces but not the larger ones. Capillary rise of water in the soil is opposed and eventually limited by gravity. The distance to which any significant amount of water rises varies with the kind of soil but is, in any case, seldom more than a few feet.

The roots of most kinds of plants in most sites do not penetrate deep enough to reach the soil that is kept moist by capillary rise above the water table, and therefore most plants are more directly dependent on rain or irrigation.

Rainwater (or irrigation water) tends to sink into the ground, being distributed downward by the combined action of gravity and capillarity. At first all the spaces among the soil particles near the ground surface are filled with water, and the soil is saturated. The water in the larger interspaces, not being held by capillary attraction, continues to sink through the soil until it, too, becomes held by capillary attraction, or until it reaches the water table. If the zone of soil moistened by the rain does not extend all the way down to the zone moistened by capillary rise from the water table, there is a rather sharp boundary between the moistened soil and the dry soil beneath it.

At the stage when further descent of moisture has virtually ceased, due to a near-equilibrium between gravity and capillary action, the moistened soil is said to have reached its **field capacity.** The field capacity is the amount of water held in the soil by capillary attraction against the pull of gravity. Expressed in per cent of water relative to the dry weight of the soil, it varies from about 5 per cent in sandy soils to as much as 45 per cent in heavy clays. Most soils reach their field capacity within a day or so after a rain.

ABSORPTION BY ROOTS

Roots are the organs of vascular plants through which most or all of the water is generally absorbed. The expanded absorbing surface provided by the root hairs has been noted in Chapter 25, and the root-hair zone is the most important absorbing part of the root. Above the root-hair zone, the surface of the root is usually cutinized or suberized, and below it absorption is limited by the smaller surface area and the smaller volume of soil which can be effectively exploited.

We have seen in Chapter 2 that water tends to diffuse through any wall or limiting membrane which is permeable to it. Molecules of water bounce against the wall and exert a *diffusion pressure* on it. This diffusion pressure, which expresses itself in a tendency of molecules to pass through the limiting membrane, can be increased by subjecting the water to pressure (as by a piston or by increasing the atmospheric pressure) and can be decreased by subjecting it to tension or by the presence of solutes or hydrophilic colloids in the water. Water which contains solutes or hydrophilic colloids thus has a smaller diffusion pressure than pure water, and the difference between the diffusion pressure of any solution and that of pure water is called the **diffusion pressure deficit** of the solution. This diffusion pressure deficit is commonly measured in terms of atmospheres; i.e., how many atmospheres of pressure would have to be exerted on the solution to bring its diffusion pressure up to that of pure water at ordinary atmospheric pressure. Other things being equal, the net movement of water between two solutions separated by a differentially permeable membrane will be in the direction of the one with the greater diffusion pressure deficit. The osmotic potential of a cell (see Chapter 2) is thus largely a reflection of the diffusion pressure deficit of the cell sap.

Absorption of water by the roots is due chiefly to a diffusion-pressure-deficit gradient between the cell sap and the soil water, but it is also influenced by other factors. The concentration of solutes in the cell sap is ordinarily higher than in the soil water. The osmotic potential of root-hair cells and other epidermal cells of roots is commonly about 3–5 atmospheres, while that of the soil solution is seldom more than a fraction of an atmosphere.

When the amount of water in the soil is near the field capacity, absorption by the roots takes place readily if there is the usual difference in concentration of solutes in the soil water and the cell sap. As the plant continues to draw water from the soil, and as natural evaporation continues, the film of water around each soil particle becomes progressively thinner and more tightly held. Eventually the water which remains is so strongly held that it cannot be absorbed by the plant, regardless of the relative concentrations of solutes. A convenient and important measure which approximates or just precedes this stage is the **permanent wilting percentage, or wilting coefficient,** defined as the percentage of water (in relation to dry weight) to which a soil is reduced when the plants growing in it have just reached a condition of "permanent" wilting. A "permanently" wilted plant is one that will not recover its turgidity unless water is supplied to the soil. It should be understood that leaves with a high proportion of mechanical tissue, such as those of many broad-leaved evergreens, can be "wilted" in a physiological sense without showing the characteristic flaccidity of other wilted leaves. Some desert plants can maintain life and slowly withdraw water from the soil for some time after "permanent" wilting has occurred, but not much water is removed from the soil under these conditions.

Although the amount of water in the soil at the permanent wilting point varies greatly in different soils, it does not vary much for different kinds of plants growing in the same soil (except in highly alkaline soils, discussed on p. 546). Individual species seldom diverge as much as 10 per cent from the general average in the amount of water they leave in the soil when the permanent wilting point is reached. These small differences among species do not seem to be correlated with the environment in which the plant normally grows (again excepting alkaline soils). Xerophytes (plants of dry habitats) as a group are not evidently more efficient in withdrawing water from the soil than mesophytes. Some plants with scanty root systems do not fully exploit the soil, but even these reduce the soil directly adjacent to the absorbing portions of the roots to about the expected percentage of moisture. Capillary action is very slow in soils in which the amount of water approaches the wilting coefficient.

The reason for the similarity of different kinds of plants in their ability to withdraw water from the soil is clear. The tenacity with which the water is held in the soil, as measured by the diffusion pressure deficit, begins to increase rapidly as the wilting percentage is approached, and beyond the wilting percentage it increases very rapidly indeed. A large increase in the diffusion pressure deficit of the cell sap is, therefore, necessary to effect only a slight reduction in the permanent wilting percentage; any very significant reduction of the wilting percentage would require an impossibly large diffusion pressure deficit in the cell sap.

HALOPHYTISM

In most soils under ordinary conditions, there are not enough solutes in the water to interfere much with the absorption of water by the roots. The diffusion pressure deficit of the soil water at field capacity is usually only a fraction of an atmosphere, and even at the wilting point the part of the diffusion pressure deficit that is due to the solutes seldom amounts to more than 1–2 atmospheres. The osmotic potential of the cell sap of epidermal cells of roots is, as we have noted, commonly 3–5 atmospheres.

The concentration of solutes in the soil moisture of alkaline or saline soils, on the other hand, is often greater than that of the cell sap of most plants. Plants which have a relatively high diffusion pressure deficit in the cell sap, enabling them to grow in such soils, are called **halophytes.** The high diffusion pressure deficit of the cell sap in halophytes is due partly to the

Fig. 27.1. Hummocks of pickleweed (*Allenrolfea*) on salt flats in Utah. (Photo by H. L. Shantz.)

high concentration of solutes, and partly to the presence of hydrophilic colloids. As might be expected, there are varying degrees of halophytism in different kinds of plants. Species of shad scale (*Atriplex*), greasewood (*Sarcobatus vermiculatus*), and winter fat (*Eurotia lanata*) are important moderate halophytes in desert areas of the interior western United States. In more salty areas, these give way to extreme halophytes such as samphire (*Salicornia*) and pickleweed (*Allenrolfea*, Fig. 27.1); and in much of the extensive salt flats west of Great Salt Lake in Utah no plants at all are found.

A high concentration of solutes and consequently high diffusion pressure deficit can be brought about in ordinary soils by too heavy fertilization, or by applying salt to the soil. Under such conditions, absorption of water by the plant is impeded, and there may even be a net movement of water from the plant into the soil solution, followed by wilting and death. Salt is fine for melting snow on sidewalks, but it is bad for the lawn alongside. Similarly, chemical fertilizers, a boon to the careful gardener, will kill plants if applied too heavily.

METABOLIC FACTORS IN WATER ABSORPTION

Absorption of water by roots has been discussed in the foregoing paragraphs as a purely passive process resulting from differences in diffusion pressures, but that is not the whole story. A number of experimental studies have shown a positive correlation between the rate of respiration and the rate of water absorption by roots. One reason for this correlation is now fairly well established, and there may be other reasons as well. The intake of minerals (as we shall see in Chapter 28) is accomplished against the concentration gradient by the expenditure of energy. The water which rises in the xylem carries some of the absorbed minerals with it, and respiration supplies the energy necessary for the maintenance of the requisite concentration of minerals in the absorbing cells. It may also prove to be true, at least in some instances, that there is a direct expenditure of energy in the absorption of water, just as in the absorption of minerals, but the evidence so far available is contradictory and inconclusive.

Another factor which may modify the results that might otherwise be expected is that the plasma membrane, or perhaps the whole cytoplasmic membrane (i.e., the layer of cytoplasm between the cell wall and the vacuole) may not be equally permeable in both directions. Water apparently enters from the soil more readily than it passes out again. Whether or not a directional difference in permeability really exists is still a matter of controversy, which can be resolved only by further experimental studies.

As a result of the interaction of all factors affecting water intake, epidermal root cells with a formal osmotic potential of only 3–5 (seldom as much as 10) atmospheres commonly absorb water from the soil until the diffusion pressure deficit of the soil solution reaches 10–15 or even 20 atmospheres.

ABSORPTION BY PLANT PARTS OTHER THAN ROOTS

Although roots are the organs through which water is usually absorbed, any plant organ which is not thoroughly waterproof may absorb water when wet. It has been experimentally demonstrated that wilted seedlings of Coulter pine (*Pinus coulteri*) can absorb water vapor from saturated or nearly saturated air, and this ability is doubtless shared by some other species. It is believed that the leaves of redwood (*Sequoia sempervirens*) absorb water from the fog in which they are frequently bathed along the California coast, although this has not yet been experimentally demonstrated.

ASCENT OF THE SAP

A consideration of the mechanism by which water moves from the absorbing cells of the root into the xylem is best postponed until after a study of the factors governing the ascent of the sap in the xylem.

The mechanisms by which the xylem sap is raised from the roots to the leaves have been intensively and repeatedly studied. Most botanists are agreed that a theory developed largely by the British botanist H. H. Dixon (1869–1953) and

Fig. 27.2. H. H. Dixon (1869–1953), British botanist, whose theory of cohesion has been generally accepted as the principal explanation of the rise of water in plants. (Courtesy of the University of Dublin.)

expounded in a series of papers dating from 1894, is essentially correct, although root pressure also has some significance, especially in plants that are not over a few feet tall. Other mechanisms which have been suggested are probably negligible, although the possibility cannot yet be excluded that the living parenchyma cells of the xylem are an essential accessory in the process.

DIXON'S THEORY OF COHESION

The basic principle behind Dixon's theory of cohesion is the attraction of water molecules for each other. In large masses of water this attraction is not very obvious, but in long, slender tubes it is readily demonstrable, becoming greater as the tube grows more slender. A column of water in a tube the thickness of a xylem vessel has a strong resistance to being broken, and a pull at the top of the column is transmitted throughout its length. The water can thus be pulled upward, much as a rope can be pulled up through a pipe. The loss of any water from the cells of the leaf, either by evaporation, or by use in photosynthesis or other metabolic processes, transmits a strain to the adjacent cells and thus eventually to the water columns in the xylem, so that the water tends to move up through the xylem and from cell to cell of the leaf, replacing the loss.

There is no doubt that the water in the xylem is often in a state of tension. This can be demonstrated in living plants by jabbing an individual vessel of an appropriate herb with a fine needle, after careful dissection to expose the xylem. The water column can be observed under the microscope to jerk apart at the point of rupture, indicating that it had been under tension. Tension in the xylem sap can also be demonstrated by other means, but it is difficult to measure.

If water is to move up through the xylem as postulated by Dixon, its cohesive strength must, of course, be great enough to withstand the stresses to which it is subjected. These come principally from the pull of gravity and the resistance to movement imposed by the walls of the xylem elements.

The tallest trees are less than 400 feet high, so that even when the depth of the roots is also considered, the maximum rise of water in plants is not over 400 feet. The pull of gravity on a column of water 400 feet high is equal to about 12 atmospheres of pressure.

The resistance to movement imposed by the walls of vessels and tracheids is partly due to simple friction, and partly to the attraction between the molecules of water and the molecules of the walls. It should be understood that the walls of the xylem elements are permeable to water, and the resistance imposed by the end walls of the tracheids is, therefore, basically of the same type as that imposed by the lateral walls. It has been shown that in the wood of yew (*Taxus*) the resistance to movement due to the walls of the xylem elements, at ordinary rate of transpiration, is about equal to the pressure required to support a column of water to the height of the plant. At higher rates of conduction, the resistance may be several times as great. The detailed structure of the xylem differs in different kinds of plants, and the resistance to water movement, of course, varies accordingly. Most conifers are probably not much different from *Taxus*, since all of them lack vessels and depend on tracheids for the transport of water. Angiosperms, which generally have vessels in addition to the tracheids, may be expected to have less resistance to water

movement through the xylem than do most gymnosperms.

Adding the gravitational stress to the resistance from the walls of the xylem elements, we see that even in tall trees the total stress against the cohesion of the water columns in the xlyem is seldom more than 25–50 atmospheres, and probably never much more than 100 atmospheres. Experimentally determined values of the cohesive strength of water vary greatly according to the apparatus used, and probably most experimental values fall well short of the actual value in the plant. The higher experimental values, ranging up to 350 atmospheres, seem more than adequate to meet the greatest stress to which the water columns in the living plant are thought to be subjected.

SIGNIFICANCE OF XYLEM PARENCHYMA IN THE ASCENT OF THE SAP

The water columns in the xylem of woody plants do finally break after a period of years, and the older sapwood is progressively converted into nonconducting heartwood, as described on p. 479. The precise causes of these changes are not yet fully understood. A point of view once held by many botanists is that the living parenchyma cells of the xylem have some essential function in keeping the conducting cells in operative condition, or even in the actual conduction, and that the eventual senescence and death of these parenchyma cells necessarily results in cessation of conduction. The characteristic structure of xylem, with every conducting cell in contact with at least one parenchyma cell, certainly lends support to this view, but attempts at a more direct demonstration of this function have given negative or inconclusive results, and botanists now tend to be skeptical about the whole idea. The converse interpretation, that it is the breakage of the water columns in the vessels and tracheids that leads to degeneration and death of the associated parenchyma cells, is also worth consideration.

ROOT PRESSURE

Under conditions of ample moisture, adequate soil aeration, and low transpiration, water may be absorbed so vigorously by the roots that a positive pressure, rather than a tension, develops in the xylem sap. This pressure, called **root pressure,** causes the sap to rise in the xylem. When the sap is under pressure, it will exude from any cut surface, and often from hydathodes and stomates as well. The formation of guttation drops is commonly due to root pressure. Measurements of the pressure of xylem sap seldom exceed 2 atmospheres, and even this amount cannot be maintained when there is much transpiration. Root pressure, therefore, must be regarded as of relatively minor importance in the rise of the sap, superseding the Dixon mechanism only under favorable conditions, and even then not causing the sap to rise more than a few feet.

Conditions favorable for the development of root pressure in woody plants (and consequent exudation from cuts) often occur early in the spring, before the leaves have expanded, thus giving rise to the popular idea of a rise of sap in the spring.

MOVEMENT OF WATER INTO THE XYLEM

Most of the water absorbed by the epidermal cells of the root is passed from cell to cell across the immature cortex and into the conducting elements of the xylem. The mechanism of the transfer is not yet fully understood. When there is no root pressure, the tension of the xylem sap probably contributes to the development of a progressive gradient of diffusion pressure deficits from the epidermal cells to the xylem. The force necessary to pull the water from the epidermal cells to the xylem is an additional stress against the cohesion of the water columns in the xylem, but this extra stress probably does not amount to more than a few atmospheres.

Under conditions of root pressure, the mechanism by which water is transferred from the absorbing cells to the xylem is more obscure. Simple osmosis is not a sufficient explanation, because the diffusion pressure deficit in the epidermal cells is higher than that of the xylem solution. The xylem solution does generally have a higher osmotic pressure (commonly 1–2 atmospheres) than that of the soil solution, however, and a rough analogy might be made to a siphon, which will lift water over a hump, as long as the point at which water leaves the tube is lower than the point at which it enters. Possibly the directional difference in permeability of the cytoplasmic membrane (referred to on p. 547), contributes to the movement.

TRANSPIRATION

Only a very small fraction of the water absorbed from the soil is permanently retained by the plant. The rest is lost, chiefly by evaporation into the air. Evaporation and consequent loss of water from a living plant is called **transpiration.**

PHYSICAL BASIS OF TRANSPIRATION

Evaporation is a physical phenomenon which results from the escape of more molecules of water (or any other liquid) into the air than are returned to the evaporating surface from the air. When a balance is reached, so that as many molecules return from the air to the liquid as escape from the liquid into the air, the air is said to be saturated. Under ordinary conditions, the walls of living plant cells, unless cutinized or suberized, are permeated with water and present a moist surface to any intercellular spaces. The air in the intercellular spaces, in turn, is nearly or quite saturated with water vapor.

The part of the air pressure that is due to water vapor is called the actual vapor pressure; the vapor pressure at the saturation point is called the saturation vapor pressure. The ratio between the actual vapor pressure and the saturation pressure under the same conditions is called the relative humidity and is usually ex-pressed as a percentage figure. The saturation vapor pressure of water increases directly with the temperature, although the relationship is not strictly linear; an increase in temperature from 20° to 30° C nearly doubles the saturation vapor pressure. The saturation vapor pressure also varies with the air pressure, being less at lower pressures (and thus at higher altitudes).

RATE OF TRANSPIRATION

Most of the evaporation of water from living plant tissues occurs into the air of the intercellular spaces. The water vapor of the intercellular spaces then diffuses out into the air through the stomates, lenticels, or any other openings to the surface which may exist (Fig. 27.3). The speed of diffusion through a given opening is governed largely by the steepness of the gradient between the vapor pressure of the air in the intercellular spaces and that of the outside air. It also increases directly with

Fig. 27.3. Diagrammatic section of a stem and leaf, showing (arrows) paths of movement of water molecules. (From Transeau, Sampson, and Tiffany, *Textbook of Botany*, Rev. Ed., Harper 1953.)

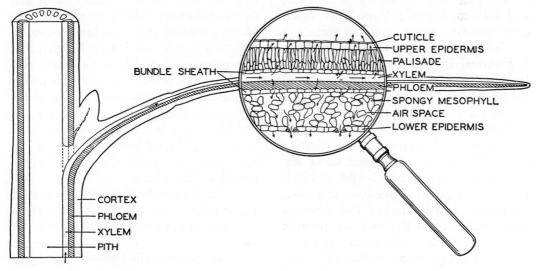

Angiosperms: Water Relations 551

the temperature, rising about 20–30 percent with every increase in temperature of 10° C. Thus the potential rate of transpiration, under a given condition of relative humidity, increases very markedly with the temperature, because of the greater difference between the actual vapor pressure and the saturation pressure at higher temperatures, and also because of the greater speed of the molecules at higher temperatures. The relationship between temperature and saturation vapor pressure is itself a reflection of the differing speeds of molecules at different temperatures.

Any part of the plant, even the roots, may transpire under appropriate conditions, but by far the greatest amount of transpiration usually occurs through the leaves, due to the presence of stomates and to the large surface area exposed to the sun and air. The epidermis of many stems also has stomates, but the surface area of stems is generally less than that of leaves, and older stems commonly develop a more or less waterproof periderm marked by scattered lenticels which permit only minimal transpiration. The older parts of roots are also protected by a waterproofing layer, and soil conditions seldom favor much evaporation from the absorbing parts.

The rate of transpiration from leaves is governed by the environmental conditions and by the structure and physiological condition of the leaf. The factors relating to the structure and condition of the leaf are noted on p. 553. The environmental factors are the same as those affecting evaporation from any exposed water surface. High temperature, bright sunlight, low humidity, high air pressure, and wind, all favor high transpiration. The effects of temperature, humidity, and air pressure have already been discussed. Sunshine raises the temperature of the leaf somewhat above that of the surrounding air and also supplies directly some of the energy that is required to change water from a liquid to a gaseous state. Wind removes the layer of more or less saturated air that would otherwise develop around the leaves and retard transpiration.

Under conditions favorable for transpiration, the rate in most angiosperms is 0.5–2.5 (rarely 5) grams per square decimeter of leaf area per hour. The leaf area is calculated by simple length-width measurements, disregarding the additional surface presented by the opposite side of the leaf. Many herbaceous plants will transpire several times their own volume of water in a single day. It has been estimated that a field of corn may transpire enough water during the growing season to cover the field to a depth of 15 inches, and the rate of transpiration from a deciduous forest is probably even higher.

IMPORTANCE OF TRANSPIRATION

The universal occurrence of transpiration in land plants has led to the supposition that it must have some value, and several values have been suggested. None of the suggested uses withstands examination, however, and it is now believed that transpiration is merely a necessary evil. The exchange of gases necessary for photosynthesis requires the exposure of moist cell surfaces to the air, and this exposure inevitably results in transpiration. Instead of being useful, transpiration is one of the most serious environmental hazards to the growth of land plants.

The supposed value of transpiration which most nearly holds true is the transportation of minerals from the roots to the stems and leaves. The minerals are carried along as solutes in the transpiration stream and tend to become concentrated in the leaves as the water evaporates. Experimental studies indicate that minerals also move freely in the phloem, however, and there is no evidence that plants ever suffer from lack of minerals due to insufficient transpiration, even when growing in a saturated atmosphere.

It has also been thought that the cooling effect of transpiration is useful. The cooling is undisputed, but its importance seems to be negligible. Even in the virtual absence of transpiration, leaves readily transmit back to the air most of the radiant energy which they absorb from the sun, and the temperature seldom approaches the thermal death point even under the most extreme natural conditions.

CONTROL OF TRANSPIRATION

The features of the plant which influence the rate of transpiration per unit area are chiefly the size, number, position, and degree of opening of the stomates, the thickness of the cuticle, the amount and distribution of intercellular spaces in the mesophyll, and the proportion of hydrophilic colloids in the cell. The stomates are the principal avenues through which water vapor escapes from the plant. Although the cuticle of the epidermis and the suberized layers of stems and roots are not absolutely moistureproof, the amount of transpiration which they permit is small compared to that permitted by the open stomates. It has been pointed out in Chapter 26 that numerous small openings permit more rapid diffusion than a single large opening of the same total area, with the result that the diffusive capacity of the stomates of a leaf surface often approaches that of an opening the size of the leaf.

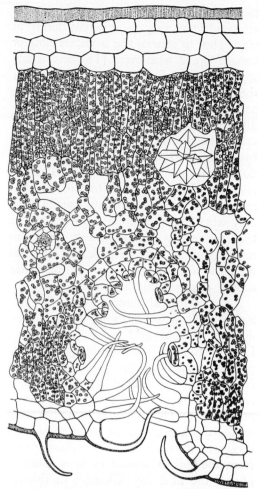

Fig. 27.4. Cross section of part of a leaf of oleander (*Nerium*), a sclerophyll well-adapted to minimize transpiration. The epidermis is three cells thick and has a heavy cuticle; the palisade tissue is two or more rows deep and is present at the bottom as well as the top; the stomates are grouped in sunken pockets which are protected from the wind by tangled hairs. (From W. H. Brown, *The Plant Kingdom*, 1935; courtesy of Ginn & Company, Boston.)

Transpiration through the stomates is so great that most plants could not long survive under natural conditions if the stomates were permanently open; the stomates are, in fact, closed much of the time. The precise responses to environmental conditions vary in different kinds of plants, but in general the stomates close or remain closed whenever: (1) there is any serious water deficiency in the leaves; (2) there is little or no light; or (3) the temperature is low. Any one of these three conditions usually induces and maintains closure of the stomates, regardless of the other two, although the stomates of some plants do remain open on warm nights. The net result of these responses to the environment is that the stomates are usually open only when the metabolic processes of the leaf (especially photosynthesis, but also respiration) require an exchange of gases with the air, and then only if the water supply is reasonably adequate.

On a typical summer day, the stomates open in the morning under the influence of light and rising temperature. Later in the day, the absorbing and transporting capacity of the plant is likely to fall behind the rate of transpiration, so that the leaves wilt slightly and the stomates close. The stomates remain closed during the night, and the plant regains its turgor as it continues to withdraw water from the soil. A similar cycle is then repeated the next day. Changes in the environmental conditions, of course, cause changes in the cycle. For example, when moisture is abundant and transpiration not too rapid, the stomates may remain open all day. Under conditions only slightly less favorable, the stomates may open in late afternoon after a period of closure during the hotter part of the day, closing again at night.

The means by which the environmental factors govern the changes in the guard cells have been intensively investigated, with only partial success. It is clear that in general they induce changes in the osmotic pressure of the guard cells, resulting in changes in turgor, which in turn cause changes in shape. An increase in turgor of the guard cells, either absolutely or with respect to that of the other epidermal cells, causes the stomatal opening to widen, and vice versa. The kinds of guard cells and the changes in their shape induced by changes in turgor have been discussed in Chapter 26. It should be noted that the stomates must be nearly or quite closed before they diminish the rate of transpiration very much. Because of the relatively greater effectiveness of small openings as diffusion channels, a half-open stomate permits a good deal more than half as much transpiration as a fully open one.

Changes in the osmotic pressure of the guard cells, when the supply of water is adequate, are due principally to changes in the concentration of solutes, especially in the proportion of soluble to insoluble carbohydrates. The guard cells, unlike ordinary epidermal cells, regularly have chloroplasts, and it is to be presumed that they carry on photosynthesis. In any case they contain a considerable amount of carbohydrate, and changes in the proportion of soluble to insoluble carbohydrates influence the concentration of solutes and thus the osmotic pressure.

The change from soluble to insoluble carbohydrates and vice versa is a reversible reaction, and the balance depends on a number of factors as yet poorly understood. One of the factors which appears to have some effect is the pH (i.e., the acid-alkaline balance) of the cell sap and protoplast; the higher the pH (corresponding to a more alkaline reaction), the less starch. One of the factors influencing the changes in the pH of the guard cells is the concentration of carbon dioxide. A scarcity of CO_2 in the guard cells, induced by photosynthesis in the guard cells or in the adjacent mesophyll, shifts the pH toward the alkaline side. It has been suggested that a low concentration of carbon dioxide, resulting from photosynthesis, is the principal cause of the opening of the stomates in the morning, but the experimental evidence so far available is inconclusive.

There is some evidence that reduction in water content of the guard cells, such as occurs during incipient wilting under excessive transpiration, causes a decrease in the pH of the cell sap, which in turn causes some of the soluble carbohydrates to be reconverted to insoluble starch. The lowered osmotic potential of the guard cells results in a further osmotic flow of water from them into the adjacent epidermal cells, causing the stomates to close before the leaf is irreparably damaged.

The effects of the structural and physiological features of the plant on the rate of transpiration are for the most part fairly obvious. A thick cuticle, a high proportion of hydrophilic colloids, and a low proportion of cell-wall surface exposed to intercellular space all tend to reduce the rate. The size and distance apart of the stomates have some effect, but not as much as might at first be expected, partly because the two tend to offset each other, and partly because the diffusive capacity does not increase in direct proportion to the size. Restriction of the stomates to the lower surface of the leaf, which occurs in many plants, minimizes the direct effect of the sun in promoting transpiration. Protection of the stomates by a layer of hair on the leaf or by their restriction to sunken pockets doubtless has some effect, at least in some plants, but experimental evidence suggests that it is not usually very important. Features which tend to restrict transpiration are further discussed on pp. 559–560 in connection with xerophytes.

GUTTATION

Under conditions of root pressure, liquid water often exudes from hydathodes

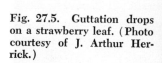

Fig. 27.5. Guttation drops on a strawberry leaf. (Photo courtesy of J. Arthur Herrick.)

(see p. 536) or ordinary stomates, and perhaps even through the cuticle, forming **guttation drops** (Fig. 27.5). Guttation water carries some solutes, but not necessarily in the same proportions as the xylem sap or the cell sap of the leaves. The proportion of sugars in the guttation water is apt to be lower than that in the cell sap, but the proportion of some minerals may be higher. It has been suggested that guttation water sometimes serves to excrete an excess of certain minerals, but the functional significance of the excretion remains to be demonstrated. The concentration of minerals obtained at the surface of the leaf or stem by evaporation of guttation water sometimes becomes great enough to damage the tissue and has been blamed for the tip burn of the young leaves of some crop plants under certain conditions.

HYDROPHYTES, MESOPHYTES, AND XEROPHYTES

Plants may be classified ecologically as **hydrophytes, mesophytes,** or **xerophytes,** according to the abundance of water in their habitat. Hydrophytes grow in water; xerophytes grow in very dry places. Mesophytes grow on land but not in extremely dry sites. The vast majority of angio-

Fig. 27.6. Hydrophytes at the New York Botanical Garden. Parrot's feather (*Myriophyllum brasiliense*), in the immediate foreground; water hyacinth (*Eichhornia crassipes*), behind the *Myriophyllum;* papyrus (*Cyperus papyrus*), the tall plants toward the rear; water lily (*Nymphaea*), left foreground; Oriental lotus lily (*Nelumbo*), emergent leaves toward the rear at the left. (New York Botanical Garden photo.)

Fig. 27.7. Royal water lily (*Victoria cruziana*) in the conservatory of the New York Botanical Garden. (New York Botanical Garden photo.)

sperms are mesophytes. There is every degree of transition between hydrophytes and mesophytes and between mesophytes and xerophytes, but it is possible to note some features characteristic of each group.

Hydrophytes (Fig. 27.6) have an abundant supply of water but a scanty supply (at least for the submerged parts) of oxygen. Their structure generally reflects an adaptation to these conditions. The submerged parts usually lack stomates and have little if any cutin, but they commonly have an extensive system of air cavities, often reaching even into the roots. Much of the oxygen relased in photosynthesis is retained in the air cavities and is available for use in respiration.

The roots of hydrophytes and near-hydrophytes (i.e., terrestrial plants which occur in saturated soils) readily grow in saturated soil and absorb water from it, but the roots of most mesophytes and xerophytes do not penetrate very far into saturated soil and absorb little or no water while the soil is saturated. The inability of mesophytes and xerophytes to grow and absorb in saturated soils is apparently due to the low oxygen supply and consequent interference with respiration and other metabolic processes which maintain conditions favorable for absorption. The ability of roots of hydrophytes and near-hydrophytes to grow in and absorb from saturated soils is apparently due, in some cases, to an aerating system, and in others to a greater ability to carry on anaerobic respiration, or to a combination of these two factors.

The aerial parts of hydrophytes are subject to environmental conditions approaching those of mesophytes, and the similarity of environment is reflected in the structure. Cuticle and stomates are usually well developed, and aerating tissue is generally much less prominent.

Xerophytes face, in an exaggerated form, the same type of conditions which confront mesophytes: the supply of soil moisture is likely to be inadequate, and the aerial parts need some protection from evaporation which will not also prevent exchange of gases with the atmosphere. The standard adaptation to these conditions, in both mesophytes and xerophytes, is the protection of the photosynthetic tissues by an epidermis that is covered by a cuticle and interrupted by stomates. Older or nonphotosynthetic tissues are frequently covered by a periderm with scattered lenticels. Most xerophytes also have some additional means of combating drought, as indicated below.

Fig. 27.8. *Monoptilon bellidiforme,* an ephemeral annual which completes its life cycle in a few weeks in the spring, growing in the Mojave desert of California. (Photo by Rupert C. Barneby.)

Xerophytes, which face the more extreme conditions of water scarcity, may mostly be divided into three groups: (1) ephemerals, (2) succulents, and (3) drought-enduring species. Ephemerals (Fig 27.8) are short-lived annuals which complete their life cycle within a few weeks when the soil is moist (usually in the spring) and survive the dry period as seeds. They are a conspicuous feature of the landscape in the spring during a good year in the southwestern United States and in similar areas elsewhere in the world. During their period of activity, ephemerals are no more drought-resistant than typical mesophytes, and they are often classified as drought-escaping mesophytes. The ephemerals belong to many different taxonomic families, all of which also contain many ordinary mesic species.

Succulents (Fig. 27.9) are characterized by the accumulation of reserves of water in the fleshy stems or leaves, due largely to the high proportion of hydrophilic colloids in the protoplasm and cell sap. Some of them, such as the cacti, also have much reduced leaves, and the photosynthetic parts generally have a very thick cuticle. During dry weather, many succulents have the stomates open only at night. This severely restricts photosynthesis as well as cutting down the amount of transpiration. The Cactaceae, Crassulaceae, and Aizoaceae are characteristically succulent, and the Euphorbiaceae, Liliaceae, and Amaryllidaceae also contain many succulent species. The Aizoaceae and the succulent members of the Euphorbiaceae are principally African; the Cactaceae are wholly American (though they have been widely introduced into the Old World).

Drought-enduring species are characterized by the ability to endure desiccation without irreparable injury. Creosote bush (*Larrea tridentata*), a characteristic species of the deserts of the southwestern United States, is highly drought-enduring. It is evergreen, retaining many of its small, firm

Fig. 27.9. Miscellaneous succulents. From left to right, *Opuntia, Aloe obscura, Echeveria corderoyi, Crassula argentea, Agave horrida.* **(New York Botanical Garden photo.)**

leaves throughout the dry season. During dry periods, the water content of the leaves may sink to less than 50 percent of their dry weight, in contrast to the leaves of most woody mesophytes, in which the water content generally ranges from 100–300 percent of the dry weight. Under such conditions the leaves are of course largely dormant; only when the water supply again becomes adequate do they return to physiological activity.

A variety of other adaptations aid drought resistance of some species. Frequently the aerial part of the plant is very small in proportion to the root system. The cuticle is commonly rather thick, and the stomates may be sunk in pockets or protected by pubescence. (Pubescence is not restricted to xerophytes, however, and its significance in restricting transpiration has been overestimated.) The leaves sometimes fall off during the dry season, minimizing the loss of water during the period of shortest supply.

Many drought-enduring species have firm leaves with a high proportion of sclerenchyma or other strengthening tissue. Such plants are called sclerophylls. It was once thought that the sclerophyllous structure minimized transpiration, but this idea has not been borne out by experimental studies. These tend to show, instead,

Fig. 27.10. Saguaro cactus (*Cereus giganteus*) in the desert of Arizona. (New York Botanical Garden photo.)

560 *Introductory Botany*

Fig. 27.11. Ocotillo (*Fouquieria splendens*—the long slender stems in the center) and prickly pear cactus (*Opuntia* — the branching stems just to the left of the center) in the desert near Tucson, Arizona. The leaves of prickly pear are reduced to spines, and photosynthesis occurs in the stem. Ocotillo produces normal green leaves after a rain and sheds them when the soil dries.

that when moisture is plentiful there is no great difference in the transpiration rates of sclerophylls, most other xerophytes, and typical mesophytes. Possibly the strengthening tissue merely serves to prevent mechanical injury while the leaf is physiologically wilted during periods of drought. The ability to endure desiccation is evidently the basic factor in drought endurance.

PHYSIOLOGICAL DROUGHT

When a considerable amount of water is present in the soil but not readily available for absorption, there is said to be a **physiological drought**. A high concentration of solutes in the soil water, as discussed on pp. 546–547, is a typical cause of physiological drought. Another is the freezing of the soil water in the winter. Some transpiration continues to occur even from the bare branches of deciduous trees in the winter, and winter killing of trees in the northern United States and Canada is often due to physiological drought rather

than to the direct effect of low temperature on the protoplasm.

SUGGESTED READING

Brown, J. R., *Unusual Plants*, Abbey Garden Press, Pasadena, Calif., 1954. 110 spectacular photographs of succulents.

Crafts, A. S., H. B. Currier, and C. R. Stocking, *Water in the Physiology of Plants*, Chronica Botanica, Waltham, Mass., 1949, 240 pp. A reference work for the student who wishes to know more about the subject.

Hazelton, Scott (Ed.), *Succulents for the Amateur*, Abbey Garden Press, Pasadena, Calif., 1939, 167 pp. Many photographs.

Muenscher, W. C., *Aquatic Plants of the United States*, Comstock Publishing Company, Ithaca, New York, 1944, 374 pp. A manual for identification, with many line drawings.

Parker, Johnson, Drought resistance in woody plants, *Bot. Rev.* 22:241–290. 1956. On the technical side.

Uphof, J. C. T., Halophytes, *Bot. Rev.* 7:1–58. 1941. On the technical side.

Angiosperms: Mineral Nutrition

CHAPTER 28

INTRODUCTION

The elements essential for plant growth and their roles in cellular metabolism have been discussed in Chapter 2. Among land plants, the soil is the usual source for all these elements except carbon and some of the oxygen. The carbon is obtained directly from the air, as carbon dioxide. Some of the necessary oxygen is obtained from the carbon dioxide and some from the water and other substances in the soil. The ability of many legumes and some other higher plants to augment their supply of nitrogen through symbiosis with nitrogen-fixing bacteria is well known, as is also the insectivorous habit of some bog plants, but the majority of land plants are directly dependent on the soil as the sole source of nitrogen.

In plant physiology it is customary to apply the term **minerals** to the inorganic substances, except water, that are ordinarily obtained from the soil. In this chapter we shall consider the occurrence, ab-

◀

Effects of calcium deficiency on young plants of Romaine lettuce. Normal plants at left, in each photograph, calcium-deficient plants at right. (Photo courtesy of James Vlamis.)

563

sorption, and transportation of minerals, and something of their roles in the metabolism of the plant.

Most minerals are absorbed in the form of ions, which are electrically charged particles that result from dissociation of molecular components in solution. Some molecules of the compound calcium nitrate $(Ca(NO_3)_2)$, for example, dissociate in solution to form calcium (Ca^{++}) and nitrate (NO_3^-) ions. Ions with a positive electric charge, as indicated by the $+$ signs, are called cations, and those with a negative charge, as indicated by the $-$ signs, are called anions.

THE MEANING OF pH

One of the important factors influencing the availability of minerals is the degree of acidity or alkalinity of the soil solution. A very small fraction of the molecules of water dissociate to form H^+ and OH^- ions. H^+ ions are the essential particles of an acid, and OH^- ions are the essential particles of a base. When there is an equal number of H^+ and OH^- ions in solution, as in pure water, the solution is neutral; if there are more H^+ than OH^- ions, it is acid; and if there are more OH^- than H^+ ions, it is basic. In pure water the fraction of molecules which dissociate is about 1/10,000,000, a figure which may be more conveniently expressed as $1/10^7$. If more H^+ ions are added from any source, the number of OH^- ions diminishes, because some of the OH^- ions become bound to the new H^+ ions. If more OH^- ions are added, the number of H^+ ions decreases. The ratio of H^+ ions to intact molecules of water can thus be used as an indicator of the degree of acidity, or alkalinity (basicity) of a solution. The power

of 10 represented by the denominator of the fraction is used as a convenient measure of the proportion of H^+ ions, and is called the **pH** (an abbreviation for "*Potenz* [=power] Hydrogen"). Thus a pH of 7 indicates a neutral solution, with a ratio of $1/10^7$ (=1/10,000,000) between H^+ ions and molecules of intact water. A pH of less than 7 indicates an acid solution, and a pH of more than 7 indicates a basic solution. The higher the pH, the fewer the H^+ ions in solution, and vice versa.

It should be noted that pH is a logarithmic rather than a simple arithmetical measure. At a pH of 6, there are 10 times as many H^+ ions as at a pH of 7, and at a pH of 5, there are 100 times as many H^+ ions as at a pH of 7; likewise pH's of 8 and 9 indicate concentrations only $\frac{1}{10}$ and $\frac{1}{100}$ as great, respectively, as a pH of 7.

Different kinds of acids and bases differ in both their degree of solubility in water and in the extent to which they dissociate in solution. A strong acid or base is one in which a high proportion of the molecules dissociate, thus releasing a high proportion of H^+ or OH^- ions.

OCCURRENCE OF MINERALS

Soil ordinarily consists of a mixture of organic and inorganic solid particles, together with some water, organic and inorganic solutes, and air. In a broad sense, all inorganic material in the soil is mineral matter; thus a soil with little or no organic matter is called a mineral soil. Only particles of molecular and submolecular size can be absorbed by plants, however, and it is with these very small particles that we are here concerned.

Mineral ions occur in the soil both

free in solution and adsorbed to soil particles of colloidal size. The adsorption of ions is due to the electric imbalance (charge) of the clay particles and organic compounds which make up the colloidal fraction of the soil. The imbalance of the clay particles is usually due to an oversupply of electrons, and these particles, therefore, have a particular affinity for the cations of the soil solution. These cations sometimes occur within the latticework of the crystalline structure of the clay particles, as well as at the surface.

The principle cations found in most soils are H^+, Ca^{++}, Mg^{++}, K^+, and Na^+, here given in the usual order of decreasing tenacity with which they are held by the soil particles. Many other cations, including those of copper, iron, manganese, molybdenum, and zinc are generally present in small amounts. It will be noted that Ca^{++} is one of the ions most tenaciously held by the clay particles. One effect of the addition of lime to the soil is the replacement of some of the other adsorbed ions by calcium ions; the displaced ions are released into the soil solution, from which they are more readily taken into the roots.

The principal anions found in most soils are Cl^-, SO_4^{--}, HCO_3^-, $H_2PO_4^-$, NO_3^-, and OH^-. Except for phosphates, most anions readily leach out of the soil. In neutral and alkaline soils, the phosphate ions generally combine with calcium or magnesium to form compounds that are not highly soluble. In acid soils, the $H_2PO_4^-$ ions tend to replace OH^- ions in the mineral kaolinite and in hydrated oxides of iron and aluminum.

The supply of a particular element available to a plant varies in different kinds of soils and under different conditions. Boron, iron, manganese, and zinc tend to

Fig. 28.1. Effect of copper deficiency in tobacco. (Photo courtesy of R. A. Steinberg, U.S. Dept. of Agriculture.)

be converted to insoluble or otherwise unavailable forms in soils with a pH of 7 or above. Available copper is often deficient in soils with a high proportion of organic matter, especially if they are alkaline and have a considerable amount of ferrous (divalent) iron. Waterlogged soils are usually deficient in available nitrogen, although the total nitrogen content is often much greater than in ordinary soils. Phosphorus is most available in nearly neutral or slightly acid soils and becomes progressively less available in more basic or more strongly acid soils. Addition of phosphate to the soil may bring on an iron shortage, by the formation of insoluble iron phosphate. Deficiency of molybdenum under natural conditions has been reported only for soils derived from serpentine rock. Serpentine soils are usually also very low

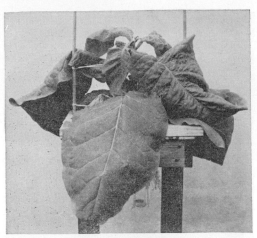

Fig. 28.2. Effect of boron deficiency in tobacco. Plants of this same age, supplied with a full nutrient solution, were in bloom. (Photo courtesy of R. A. Steinberg, U.S. Dept. of Agriculture.)

in calcium. Under continuous farming without fertilization, the supply of all mineral nutrients is depleted, but deficiencies in nitrogen, phosphorus, and potassium are likely to be the most serious, partly because these elements are used in such large quantities.

ABSORPTION

DIFFERENTIAL ABSORPTION

Ions may be absorbed by the roots either from the soil solution, or (probably with greater difficulty) directly from the soil particles to which they had been adsorbed. They are not generally absorbed in the same proportions as they are present in the soil solution or on the colloidal surfaces. Some ions, on the contrary, are much more vigorously absorbed than others, and different kinds of plants sometimes differ greatly in their affinity for various kinds of ions.

Differential absorption is strongly sup-

ported by circumstantial evidence, as well as having been experimentally demonstrated with radioactive isotopes. Some plants which require selenium for proper growth may have more than 1000 parts per million Se when growing in soil containing only 1 or 2 parts per million. Other kinds of plants growing in the same soil may have only minimal amounts of selenium. The selenium in the plant is mostly not in ionic form, of course, as it substitutes for sulfur in various proteins and other organic compounds, but such high concentrations could not be obtained if the element were absorbed only in proportion to its concentration in the soil.

The rate of absorption of individual kinds of ions is also influenced by the kind and amount of other ions present in the soil solution and in the cell. For example, the presence of divalent cations such as Ca^{++} in the soil solution tends to increase the rate at which monovalent cations such as K^+ are absorbed.

Differential absorption is only partly effective in governing the amounts and proportions of minerals absorbed. The higher the concentration of a particular kind of ion, the more of it is likely to be absorbed. Toxic concentrations of the trace elements are easily obtained experimentally and sometimes occur in nature as well.

ELECTRICAL BALANCES

Cations and anions are probably absorbed in about equal amounts (as measured by the electrical charge), so that there is no significant change in the electrical balance of the plants or of the soil. Even if an excess of cations were absorbed, however, or vice versa, the effect might not be obvious. Both the soil and the protoplasm of the cell are buffered to some extent against electrical changes.

The colloidal fraction of the soil probably seldom, if ever, holds as many adsorbed ions as its theoretical capacity, and any change in the proportions of anions and cations in the soil solution would tend to be balanced by changes in the amount of adsorbed ions. Any electrical change in the soil due to differential absorption of cations and anions would be minor compared to the changes brought about by other factors, notably the weather, and any very strong electric imbalance is eventually adjusted by a flow of electrons into or out of the air. The occurrence of such a flow should be familiar to anyone who has ever seen a thunderstorm or a lightning rod.

Protoplasm is also a colloidal system which permits some variation in the amount and proportions of adsorbed ions. The cell sap, however, is maintained in an electrostatically neutral condition. Often a measurement of the inorganic ions alone shows a large excess of cations, but this is balanced by organic anions (chiefly of organic acids) synthesized in the cells. In some instances the excess of inorganic cations is due to the quick use of the corresponding anions (notably NO_3) in the formation of organic compounds.

MECHANISMS OF ABSORPTION

The mechanisms by which minerals are absorbed from the soil are only partly understood. Simple diffusion is not an adequate explanation, inasmuch as the concentration of mineral solutes in the cell sap is generally greater than that in the soil solution.

After a great deal of study, it has become clear that the bulk of mineral ab-

sorption occurs against the concentration gradient and that respiratory energy is used in the process. Either aerobic or anaerobic respiration is effective, as long as energy is released beyond that required for other metabolic processes. In most land plants, however, anaerobic respiration does not provide enough energy for rapid absorption, and plants which normally grow in well-aerated soils do not usually absorb either water or minerals freely when the soil is saturated with water.

Under ordinary conditions, and other things being equal, the rate of mineral absorption commonly rises by a factor of about 2 or 3 for each rise in temperature of 10°C. The influence of temperature is due partly to its effect on respiration and partly to its effect on the mobility of ions.

Experiments under conditions of moderate or slow respiration have usually indicated that the cytoplasmic membrane is not very readily permeable to most mineral solutes. Under conditions of more rapid respiration, however, it evidently permits the entry of many solutes, while restricting their exit. It is thus clear that a directional difference in the permeability

Fig. 28.3. Effect of iron deficiency in tobacco. Plants of this same age, supplied with a full nutrient solution, were in bloom. (Photo courtesy of R. A. Steinberg, U.S. Dept. of Agriculture.)

of the cytoplasmic membrane is maintained by the expenditure of respiratory energy, but the means by which the energy exerts its effect remains obscure. The relative amounts of the various ions found in plant cells seem not to be correlated with the lipoid solubility, kinetic activity, or physical dimensions of the ions. The inference has been drawn that the effect of respiration on permeability involves the temporary formation of compounds of the entering ions with some protoplasmic constituents, but the validity of the inference remains to be determined.

The general term *cytoplasmic membrane* is used advisedly in the preceding paragraph, because the roles of the plasma membrane, vacuolar membrane, and the intervening cytoplasm are not yet clear. One hypothesis is that energy is expended at the surface of the plasma membrane to incorporate the ions into compounds which migrate through the cytoplasm (by diffusion and cytoplasmic cyclosis) to the vacuolar membrane, where they break down, releasing energy and liberating the ions into the vacuole. The hypothesis is in accord with some recent evidence that, in the absence of active absorption, minerals in the cytoplasm are easily lost to the soil solution whereas those in the vacuole are more firmly retained.

The supply of cations for absorption into the cytoplasm is governed to some extent by an ionic exchange mechanism. Actively absorbing roots are actively respiring and consequently liberating carbon dioxide. Some of this carbon dioxide reacts with the water of the soil solution to form carbonic acid, H_2CO_3, which in turn dissociates to some extent, liberating H^+ ions. The root surface and the soil water immediately surrounding it, therefore, have a relatively high supply of H^+ ions. Some of these replace other cations that had been adsorbed to the colloidal soil particles, transferring these other ions to the soil solution or directly to the root surface, as the case may be. Some of the H^+ ions at the root surface are also exchanged for mineral cations of the surrounding soil solution.

Mineral cations adsorbed to the outer surface of the cell wall of the absorbing part of the root are believed to be transferred through the wall by further exchange with H^+ ions, in a process somewhat similar to diffusion, except that the movement of the ions is restricted to a very small orbit adjacent to the adsorbing surface. It will be recalled that the cell wall is not a homogeneous layer but rather is composed of overlapping micelles with a good deal of interspace.

The supply of anions for absorption by the root may also be influenced by an ionic exchange mechanism, but the situation here is less clear.

EFFECT OF ABSORPTION ON pH

The pH of the soil solution is governed by a complex balance of factors relating especially to the kinds, amounts, and proportions of anions and cations with which the H^+ and OH^- ions may associate, the extent to which the molecules dissociate in solution, and the degree of solubility of the intact molecules. Differential absorption of ions by the roots modifies this balance and consequently affects the pH of the soil solution.

Plants growing in experimental culture solutions may change the pH in either direction, depending on the kind of plant and mineral nutrients supplied, and indeed it is often difficult to maintain the pH in such solutions at a level which will permit normal absorption and growth. Under ordinary farm and garden conditions, with some part of the plant being harvested and removed from the soil, the net effect of the absorption is almost always to decrease the pH. The various mineral cations adsorbed to the clay particles are progressively replaced by H^+ ions, making the soil more acid. The clay micelle with its adsorbed ions may be thought of as a chemical compound, an acid which dissociates to some extent to provide the H^+ ions which are the essential constituents of an acid.

Differential absorption would also modify the pH of the protoplasm and the cell sap, except that the plant has a delicate and effective buffer system which tends to counteract any such changes. Any change in the pH shifts the equilibrium in some reversible reactions among the cell constituents, resulting in the restoration of the pH nearly or quite to the original point. A similar but less sensitive buffer system exists in most soils.

CONTROL OF SOIL pH

Under natural conditions the pH of most soils is relatively stable, undergoing only minor changes from season to season and under varying moisture conditions. The ionic factors which immediately govern the pH of the soil are controlled principally by the size, kind, and proportions of mineral particles, the kinds and amount of organic matter, the kinds and amounts of solutes, and the amount of moisture in the soil. These factors in turn are influenced by the climate, the nature of the parent material from which the soil is derived, the vegetation, and the topography. The vegetation and the topography are themselves influenced by the climate,

and, given sufficient time, the effect of the climate also tends to overcome even the effect of the parent material. Climate is thus the most important factor governing not only the pH but also the other characteristics of the soil, but its effect is tempered and sometimes even outweighed by other factors.

Soils of arid regions usually have a higher pH than those of moist regions; soils of warm regions tend to have a higher pH than those of cooler regions; soils with a considerable amount of organic matter usually have a lower pH than mineral soils; and mineral soils derived from acid rocks, such as granite, usually have a lower pH than those derived from basic rocks, such as basalt. The most fertile soils, in reasonably moist regions of the temperate zone, usually have a pH of from 6 to 6.5 or nearly 7. Readings as low as 4 and as high as 11 have been obtained in some less common types of soils.

Continuous cropping of soils, especially in regions suitable for farming without irrigation, tends to decrease the pH progressively and to exhaust the supply of mineral nutrients. As the pH decreases, the phosphate and probably some other anions become progressively less available, and the concentration of aluminum ions often reaches toxic proportions.

In order to maintain soil fertility under such conditions, it is necessary periodically to raise the pH to about 6 or 6.5 and to replenish the supply of minerals. Usually the pH is increased by adding calcium carbonate ($CaCO_3$) to the soil. Lime ($Ca(OH)_2$) is equally effective but more expensive. In farming practice, it is customary to expand the term *lime* to include calcium carbonate.

When a soil is limed, the calcium carbonate dissociates to some extent in the

Fig. 28.4. Effect of molybdenum deficiency in tobacco. (Photo courtesy of R. A. Steinberg, U.S. Dept. of Agriculture.)

soil solution, forming Ca^{++} ions and CO_3^{--} ions. Some of the H^+ ions of the clay micelles are then exchanged for Ca^{++} ions. The H^+ ions released from the clay combine with the carbonate ions of the solution to form carbonic acid (H_2CO_3), a weak acid which tends to break up into water and carbon dioxide. The H^+ ions are thus progressively removed from the soil solution, and the pH increases.

If the clay is, for convenience, represented by the symbol Z, and the clay with adsorbed hydrogen ions by HZ, the reac-

tions may be indicated in the following set of reversible equations:

$$HZ + CaCO_3 \rightleftharpoons CaZ + H_2CO_3.$$
$$H_2CO_3 \rightleftharpoons H_2O + CO_2.$$

It should be noted that HZ and CaZ are not precise chemical formulas, inasmuch as each clay micelle ordinarily has a number of adsorbed ions, not all of the same kind. The calcium, hydrogen, and clay, therefore, do not have to be balanced on opposite sides of the first foregoing equation.

As the exchange of H^+ and Ca^{++} ions continues, the supply of H^+ ions for replacement decreases, and the supply of Ca^{++} ions to replace them also decreases. Eventually a balance is reached, with some H^+ as well as Ca^{++} and other ions adsorbed to the clay. The more heavily the soil is limed, the more H^+ ions of the clay are replaced and bound up in water, and the higher the pH becomes.

Too high a pH of the soil solution is as much to be avoided as too low. At a pH of more than 7, the iron, manganese, boron, and zinc tend to be converted to unavailable forms. Deficiency of available iron is one of the most common causes of chlorosis (yellowing of the leaves) in basic soils.

MINERAL-ABSORBING CAPACITY OF DIFFERENT KINDS OF CELLS

The ability to absorb minerals against the concentration gradient by the use of respiratory energy seems to be confined largely to meristematic or immature cells. As the cells mature and lose their capacity for growth and division, they usually also lose their capacity to absorb minerals against the gradient. The only rapidly growing cells of the root that are exposed to the soil are the outer (pre-epidermal) cells of the region of elongation, and it is in this region that most absorption of minerals occurs. Young, rapidly enlarging root hairs at the base of the region of maturation may also be expected to absorb minerals.

ROLE OF MYCORHIZAE IN MINERAL ABSORPTION

Experimental work on mineral absorption by vascular plants has been done almost entirely with plants that do not have mycorhizae under the conditions of the experiment. In mycorhizal plants much of the mineral absorption is presumably carried on by the fungus, especially if the fungus forms a mantle over the root surface. The elements usually absorbed by higher plants in mineral form are also absorbed by the fungus as components of more complex organic compounds, and doubtless some of these compounds, or their metabolic descendents, are often transferred to the higher plant symbiont.

MINERAL ABSORPTION BY AERIAL ORGANS

Absorption of minerals by aerial organs of most plants is ordinarily insignificant under natural conditions. Epiphytes such as Spanish moss (*Tillandsia usneoides*), which absorb water from the exposed aerial surface when wet, are, of course, dependent on the solutes of that water for their minerals.

Elements which are needed only in small amounts can be effectively supplied to many plants by spraying the leaves with

Fig. 28.5. Effect of zinc deficiency in tobacco. Plants of this same age, supplied with a full nutrient solution, were in bloom. (Photo courtesy of R. A. Steinberg, U.S. Dept. of Agriculture.)

a dilute solution of the proper salt. Entry of the mineral into the plant under these conditions does not require absorption against the concentration gradient. Chlorosis caused by iron deficiency can be overcome by spraying with ferrous sulfate. Pineapples in Hawaii and citrus fruits in California are among the crops frequently so treated. Copper, manganese, boron, and zinc are also supplied to some crops in some areas by spraying.

TRANSPORTATION

Minerals move upward from the roots in the xylem and, to a usually lesser extent, in the phloem. The means by which they pass from cell to cell and into the sieve tubes and xylem elements are obscure. It has been suggested that the plasmodesmata may be avenues of movement. That the transfer is largely metabolic, requiring a continuous expenditure of energy, has also been suggested. The concentration gradient of minerals between the relatively high concentration of the absorbing cells and the relatively low concentration of the xylem sap has been thought to be due to decreased aeration of the root inward from the surface, resulting in decreased capacity of the metabolic mechanism to absorb and hold mineral ions and transport them across the cytoplasmic membranes. The concentration gradient and the movement of ions have also been interpreted in terms of simple diffusion, aided perhaps by cyclosis. All these attempted explanations are subject to serious question, but the fact remains that the minerals do move progressively inward to the xylem and phloem, in which they are carried upward to the rest of the plant.

Experimental and circumstantial evidence indicates that most of the upward movement of minerals ordinarily occurs in the xylem sap. Once they enter the xylem sap, the mineral ions are passively carried upward in the transpiration stream. Experiments have clearly shown, however, that when movement through the xylem is artificially interfered with, the minerals move upward freely in the phloem. Phloem is primarily a food-conducting tissue, and the mechanics of movement of solutes through it are discussed in Chapter 29.

Most minerals move upward and are distributed in the same form in which they enter the plant. Nitrogen and probably also phosphorus and sulfur, however, are carried both as inorganic ions and as organic compounds that have been made in the roots. The organic compounds as well as the mineral ions move in both the phloem and the xylem.

FUNCTIONS OF THE NECESSARY MINERAL ELEMENTS

The functions of the elements necessary for plant growth have been discussed, at the cellular level, in Chapter 2. The division of labor in a multicellular plant causes a greater requirement for certain elements in some tissues than in others, and in these plants an insufficiency of any particular element causes characteristic visible symptoms. Our knowledge of the special roles of the various elements in the metabolism of the plant as a whole has been gained largely by observations of these symptoms in experimental cultures with one or another of the elements in short supply. More recently it has become possible to follow the distribution of the individual elements by the use of radioactive isotopes.

The roles of the various necessary elements are interrelated in a very complex way, so that increase or decrease in the supply of any one element influences directly or indirectly the need for one or several others. Sodium, although not itself considered necessary, can substitute for part of the necessary potassium. An inadequate supply of phosphorus can be partly compensated for by an extra supply of magnesium. An increase in the supply of calcium increases the need for boron, copper, magnesium, manganese, and potassium; and an inadequate supply of calcium interferes with the absorption of nitrates. Many other such correlations could be listed. The exact concentrations and proportions of the various minerals necessary for optimum growth of any particular spe-

Fig. 28.6. Effects of mineral deficiencies in tobacco: *1*, nitrogen; *2*, phosphorus; *3*, potassium; *4*, calcium; *5*, magnesium; *7*, boron; *8*, sulfur; *9*, manganese; *10*, iron. Number *6* was supplied with a full nutrient solution. (Photo courtesy of J. E. McMurtrey, Agricultural Research Service.)

cies are probably seldom, if ever, attained, but there is usually a considerable range of variation within which reasonably normal growth occurs.

Species and individuals differ in the amount of a particular element necessary for best growth, and in the vigor with which they absorb it from the soil. An amount of available iron which permits normal growth of alfalfa (*Medicago sativa*) will result in chlorosis in garden beans (*Phaseolus vulgaris*), and a supply of potassium just adequate for an apple orchard is not enough for peaches. Different strains of maize differ considerably in the concentration of soil calcium necessary for proper growth, and doubtless similar variations occur in other species.

Some elements are more readily removed from the tissues in which they are being used than others. Deficiencies of relatively immobile elements such as calcium, iron, and manganese usually show up first in the younger, more rapidly growing parts, such as the apical meristems and young leaves. The more mobile elements, such as potassium and magnesium, tend to be carried away to the growing tissues when in short supply, and the symptoms of the deficiency show up first or most prominently in mature leaves.

Nitrogen is one of the elements often in short supply. Plants deficient in nitrogen are unthrifty, with yellowish-green rather than rich green leaves, and the plants tend to mature early, while the aerial part is still poorly developed. A common symptom of less severe shortage is the firing (development of a reddish-brown color, followed by death) of the lower leaves, although species differ in this regard, and loss of the lower leaves is normal for many species.

Nitrogen is necessary for the synthesis of proteins, and a shortage, therefore, interferes directly with the formation of new protoplasm that is necessary for growth. Nitrates are more rapidly converted into organic compounds than most other minerals that enter the root, and, in case of shortage, they are mostly used in the root, so that the symptoms of shortage appear first in the shoot. Plants deficient in nitrogen, therefore, tend to have the root system excessively developed, as compared to the shoot. The total growth of the root system may still be less than that of a normal plant, however, because the poorly developed shoot does not produce enough carbohydrate to supply the energy necessary for best root growth.

The visible symptoms of *sulfur* deficiency are usually rather similar to those of nitrogen deficiency, although sulfur deficiency is much less common. Sulfur, like nitrogen, is necessary for protein synthesis and other metabolic processes, and when the sulfur supply is inadequate amino acids tend to accumulate without being converted into proteins. The yellowish color of the leaves associated with deficiency of nitrogen or sulfur is usually fairly uniform, or more prominent toward the tip than the base, unlike the characteristic mottled chlorosis resulting from some other mineral deficiencies. Stems of sulfur-deficient plants, in contrast to those of plants deficient in nitrogen, phosphorus, or potassium, usually elongate freely.

Plants deficient in *phosphorus* usually have deep-green leaves, but they grow slowly and maturity is delayed. Flowers and fruits develop poorly or not at all. The roles of nitrogen and phosphorus in metabolism are somewhat antagonistic, so that an oversupply of one causes a relative

Fig. 28.7. Relative growth of tops and roots of squash and wheat seedlings that grew in cultures with insufficient nitrogen, and with adequate nitrogen (N). (Photos courtesy of Mary E. Reid, Boyce Thompson Institute for Plant Research.)

Fig. 28.8. Effect of mineral deficiencies in petunia. Plant at upper left was provided with a full nutrient solution, including boron, calcium, copper, iron, magnesium, manganese nitrogen, phosphorus, potassium, sulfur, and zinc. (Photos courtesy of the Vigoro Department, Swift & Company.)

deficiency of the other. An excess of nitrogen over phosphorus favors vigorous vegetative growth and delay or suppression of flowering and fruiting, whereas an excess of phosphorus over nitrogen favors early maturity and vigorous flowering and fruiting. A fertilizer for flower gardens should have a higher proportion of phosphorus, in relation to nitrogen, than one for lawns.

Much of the phosphorus of a mature plant is concentrated in the seeds and fruits, where it accumulates during their development.

Potassium, another element which is often in short supply, plays such varied roles in metabolism that the symptoms differ considerably under varying degrees of shortage. A mild shortage tends to interfere with protein synthesis, without affecting photosynthesis, so that carbohydrates accumulate in the leaves. The excess of carbohydrates causes the development of anthocyanins, so that the leaves often turn dark reddish. More severe potassium shortage also interferes with photosynthesis.

Calcium and *boron* play antagonistic roles, especially in meristematic and immature tissues. Any shortage of one of these elements, or oversupply of the other, upsets the delicate balance necessary for proper growth, often killing the terminal buds and the root tips. Any lateral buds which may be stimulated by the death of the terminal buds also fail to develop properly and eventually die, so that the plant often becomes much branched and bushy. Less severe imbalance causes contortions and malformations of the leaves without killing the meristems. The exact symptoms of boron deficiency (or calcium excess) usually differ from those of calcium deficiency (or boron excess) in any given species, but these differences are not consistent from one species to another.

Deficiency of *iron, magnesium,* or *manganese* usually causes a mottled chlorosis, with green strips along the veins and yellowish or whitish interveinal areas. When shortage is severe, the chlorotic areas often die and disintegrate. The exact symptoms differ according to the deficient element and the species. One of the commonest symptoms of *zinc* deficiency is abnormally small leaves.

Symptoms of severe deficiency of any of the necessary elements always include some dwarfing. Otherwise, as should be clear from the foregoing résumé, they differ according to the element and the kind of plant. The effects of deficiency of a particular element tend to be similar in different kinds of plants, but observations made on one species cannot safely be used to diagnose deficiencies in another species.

The symptoms of deficiencies of a number of elements in tomato plants are presented in the following key, slightly modified from that published by J. T. Woolley and T. C. Broyer in 1957.

KEY TO SYMPTOMS OF NUTRIENT DEFICIENCY IN TOMATO PLANTS

1. Symptoms appearing first or most severely on youngest leaves
    2. Interveinal chlorosis present on young leaves
        3. Black spots appear next to the veins; smallest veins remain green; older leaves may develop interveinal brown necrotic spots 2–4 mm wide near the main veins
                                                                Manganese
        3. Black spots do not appear; smallest veins do not remain green; necrotic areas, if present, not associated with any particular part of the blade   *Iron*
    2. Young leaves do not show *interveinal* chlorosis, but the central basal part of the young leaflets may be chlorotic
        4. Upper side of young leaflets purplish on both the veins and the interveinal areas, the lower side very dark green; leaflets small and curled downward; oldest leaves may show slight interveinal chlorosis and necrosis   *Phosphorus*
        4. Upper side of young leaflets not purple, and the lower surface often with central basal chlorosis; very young growing tissue shows necrosis, and growth may be distorted; interveinal necrosis often appears at base of young leaflets
            5. Plant tissues very brittle, especially under conditions of low stress for water; growth

---

accompanying recovery from this deficiency usually twisted, asymmetrical, and otherwise distorted   *Boron*

   5. Plant tissues soft and often flaccid even under conditions of low stress for water; leaflets developing after onset of the deficiency are narrow and cupped downward, but there is not usually much twisting either under deficiency conditions or on recovery   *Calcium*

1. Symptoms about equal over the entire shoot, or most severe on oldest or recently matured leaves, neither appearing first nor being most severe on youngest leaves

   6. Interveinal chlorosis present, sometimes only as a mild mottling

      7. Oldest leaves most chlorotic

         8. Chlorosis definitely interveinal, so that at least the main veins remain green; plants not usually spindly

            9. Chlorosis the first visible symptom; leaf edges curl upward when deficiency is severe

               10. Necrosis appears as sunken necrotic spots which look shiny from the back of the leaf, the spots having no particular location with respect to the veins; chlorotic leaves often bright yellow or orange   *Magnesium*

               10. Necrosis occurs as gradual drying of interveinal areas followed by drying of the remaining tissues; chlorotic leaves seldom brightly colored   *Molybdenum*

            9. Chlorosis not the first visible symptom; leaf edges do not usually curl upward

               11. Tip and marginal necrosis present on older leaves of mildly affected plants, appearing as a "scorch"; old or recently matured leaves may show interveinal chlorosis; leaflets sometimes show small, black, interveinal, necrotic dots; neither excessive guttation nor "water-soaking" is present   *Potassium*

               11. Tip and marginal necrosis absent; only the oldest leaves of severely damaged plants show chlorosis; necrosis appears as irregular sunken necrotic spots which may be veinal, interveinal, or next to the veins; young leaflets sometimes show small, black, interveinal, necrotic spots; excessive guttation and "water-soaking" of leaf tissues may be observed at times of low stress for water   *Zinc*

         8. Chlorosis general, so that the veins do not remain green; plants often spindly

            12. Veins bright red; petioles and petiolules tend to be twisted and/or vertically disposed   *Sulfur*

            12. Veins yellow or sometimes pinkish; petioles and petiolules not twisted or vertically disposed   *Nitrogen*

      7. Oldest leaves not most chlorotic, the chlorosis appearing as interveinal mottling on recently matured leaves; small, black, necrotic dots appear on young or recently matured leaves

         13. Tip and marginal necrosis present on older leaves of mildly affected plants, appearing as a "scorch"; old or recently matured leaves may show interveinal chlorosis; leaflets sometimes show small, black, interveinal, necrotic dots   *Potassium*

         13. Neither tip nor marginal necrosis present on older leaves until the entire plant is severely affected, although some tip necrosis is often present on the youngest leaves; younger leaflets often show small, black, interveinal, necrotic spots,

        especially next to the main veins; necrosis usually confined to interveinal tissues next to the main veins   *Manganese*

6. Interveinal chlorosis not present

    14. Leaf margins and tips wilt easily, and the leaves do not show excessive guttation; necrotic spots, when present, sharply delimited and sunken; margins of old leaflets roll stiffly upward; petioles and petiolules often bend abruptly and stiffly downward   *Copper*

    14. Leaves show no excessive wilting except in cases of petiole necrosis, and the wilting, if present, not confined to the tips and margins of the leaflets; excessive guttation occurs under conditions of low stress for water, often accompanied by the appearance of water-soaked areas on the backs of the leaves; necrotic spots usually irregular; petioles and leaf margins not markedly turned downward   *Zinc*

SUGGESTED READING

Black, C. A., *Soil-Plant Relationships*, John Wiley & Sons, New York, 1957, 332 pp.
For the student who would know more.

CHAPTER 29

Angiosperms: Manufacture, Translocation, and Storage of Food

◄
Germinating coconuts. The seeds of coconuts and some other palms have a larger supply of stored food than have seeds in other families. (Photo by W. H. Hodge.)

CHAPTER 29

PHOTOSYNTHESIS

INTRODUCTION

The formation of food from raw materials, using light as the source of energy, is called photosynthesis. Photosynthesis occurs only in chlorophyll-bearing plants and in some chlorophyllous microorganisms on the indefinite border between plants and animals. With the minor exception of the food made by chemosynthetic bacteria, all organisms are directly or indirectly dependent on photosynthesis for their food supply.

The chemistry of photosynthesis has been discussed in Chapter 2. The present discussion deals primarily with photosynthesis in angiosperms, although similar considerations hold for most other vascular plants.

The leaves are the principal photosynthetic organs of most angiosperms, although the stems, and sometimes even exposed parts of the roots, may also be green and photosynthetic. Water and carbon dioxide are the raw materials of carbohydrate synthesis, and light is the source of energy. The water is ordinarily obtained from the soil, but the carbon dioxide must be obtained from the air. (Hydrophytes can also use dissolved bicarbonate ions as a source of carbon dioxide.)

WATER

Most of the water absorbed by land plants is lost through transpiration. Some of the remainder is used in various metabolic processes and as a principal constituent of any new protoplasm and cell sap that is formed. Only a relatively small amount, usually less than 1 percent of the water absorbed, is used directly in photosynthesis. Under conditions which permit reasonably normal physiological activity, there is probably never a significant direct shortage of water as a raw material for photosynthesis. Shortage of water does indirectly retard the rate of photosynthesis, however, even if all other conditions are favorable. Furthermore, water shortage usually causes the stomates to close, thus reducing the rate of entry of carbon dioxide, the other essential raw material for photosynthesis.

CARBON DIOXIDE

Carbon dioxide makes up only a small proportion of the air, about 0.03 percent

on the average. The actual concentration in plant habitats varies from about half to several times this value, due to local influences, such as removal of CO_2 by photosynthesis and addition of CO_2 by respiration—especially of soil microorganisms.

Carbon dioxide is absorbed chiefly through the cell walls of the mesophyll. It dissolves in the water at the surface of the cell walls, entering the protoplasm both directly and as H_2CO_3, the unstable acid formed by reaction with water. Much of the CO_2 and H_2CO_3 is transformed immediately into other unstable compounds on entry into the protoplast, so that there is probably no need to absorb against a concentration gradient. These compounds in turn readily give up CO_2 at the surface of the chloroplast, where it is used in photosynthesis.

Some carbon dioxide is absorbed directly through the epidermal cells, in spite of the cuticle. The amount of wall surface that abuts on intercellular space in the mesophyll is generally greater, however, than the total epidermal surface presented to the air, usually on the order of 10 or 15 times as great, and direct absorption through the epidermis is not usually very important. We have already noted that the rate of gaseous diffusion through stomates is higher than their total area would suggest, and the concentration of CO_2 in the intercellular spaces of the mesophyll is, therefore, usually not much different from that of the outside air, when the stomates are open.

Physiological processes of any sort are generally governed by several or many interacting environmental factors. Under a given set of conditions for all factors but one, the remaining factor has a minimum below which the process does not occur, an optimum at which it occurs fastest or best, and a maximum above which it does not

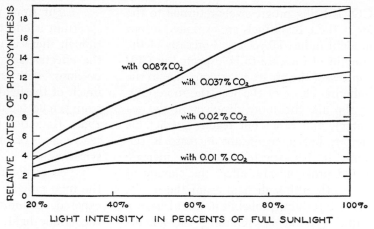

Fig. 29.1. Rates of photosynthesis in relation to light intensity and the concentration of carbon dioxide. (Data from W. H. Hoover, E. S. Johnson, and F. S. Brackett. From Transeau, Sampson, and Tiffany, *Textbook of Botany*, Rev. Ed., Harper, 1953.)

occur. The minimum effective value for any particular factor or set of factors is often called the **threshold.** The optimum value for a factor differs under different conditions, and even the minimum and maximum are subject to some change. Thus the optimum light intensity for photosynthesis is higher for plants well-supplied with water or CO_2 than for plants inadequately supplied.

If none of the factors governing the rate of a process is very far from the optimum, improvement of any one or several factors increases the rate of the process. Any factor which is too far from the optimum, however, may limit the rate, regardless of how much the other factors are improved. The factor which, through being too far from the optimum, exerts the most drag on the rate of a process, under a given set of conditions, is often called the **limiting factor.**

The amount of CO_2 in the air is often the limiting factor for photosynthesis. Under conditions of rapid evaporation, water may be the limiting factor. On a summer day, decreasing light becomes the limiting factor as the sun goes down and darkness follows; the rate of photosynthesis falls progressively with increasing darkness

until the amount of light falls below the threshold, and no further photosynthesis occurs until the next day. On a winter day in an evergreen forest, temperature is commonly the limiting factor for photosynthesis.

Moderate increase in the CO_2 content of the air, up to several times as great as normal, usually results in an increased rate of photosynthesis, if other conditions are reasonably favorable. Much higher concentrations tend to retard photosynthesis, the optimum varying according to the kind of plant, the length of the experiment, and the environmental conditions. Concentrations of more than 0.5 percent are harmful to most species, and a concentration of 0.3 percent (10 times normal) was found to be harmful to tomato plants within 2 weeks, after an initially favorable effect. Plants in greenhouses and even in open fields can be effectively "fertilized" by addition of CO_2 to the air, often increasing the yield by as much as 100–200 percent, but such treatment is uneconomical except possibly for a few greenhouse crops in some areas.

A tremendous amount of potential carbon dioxide is locked up in deposits of coal and oil from past geologic ages. This

Angiosperms: Manufacture, Translocation, and Storage of Food 583

CO_2 is being progressively returned to the air as these fossil fuels are exploited in our modern industrial society. Forecasts of the amount of increase to be expected in CO_2 content of the air are hazardous, due to the buffering effect of the sea (the more CO_2 in the air, the more dissolves in the sea water), and other not readily predictable factors, but a significant increase is certainly to be expected. Such an increase would probably also affect the climate of the earth, although here again the results are not certain; probably it would have a warming influence, retarding the reradiation and escape of heat.

LIGHT

Sunlight is ordinarily the source of energy for photosynthesis, although artificial light is also effective. The energy which reaches the earth's surface as solar radiation varies in wavelength from about 300 mμ to about 2600 mμ. (The symbol mμ indicates millimicron.) Wavelengths from about 390–760 mμ make up the visible spectrum. The color of light varies according to the wavelength. The shortest visible rays are violet, and the longest are red, the series running from violet to blue, blue-green, green, yellow, orange, and red. Wavelengths too short to be seen are called ultraviolet, and those too long to be seen are called infrared. Under ordinary conditions about 40 percent of the radiant energy which reaches the earth's surface is in the visible spectrum.

Light from practically all the visible spectrum is effective in photosynthesis, although there is usually a marked drop in the effectiveness of the green and yellow portions, between 500–600 mμ, because much of the light in this part of the spectrum is reflected rather than absorbed (Fig. 29.2). Radiation in the ultraviolet or infrared range is of little or no value in photosynthesis.

Leaves commonly absorb about half the total radiant energy to which they are exposed, including about 80 percent of the visible light. The exact proportion of the visible light absorbed varies according to the thickness of the leaves and other factors but is seldom less than 60 percent or more than 90 percent. The remainder is partly reflected, and partly transmitted through the leaf.

The intensity of sunlight varies with the latitude, the season, the time of day, the altitude, and the atmospheric conditions. Clouds, dust, and water vapor in the air all cut down the light intensity. The exposure and pitch of a slope have obvious effects on the amount of light hitting a given area of ground surface. The quality of light (i.e., the distribution of wavelengths over the spectrum) is influenced by most of these same factors, but under natural conditions the differences in intensity are far more important.

The intensity of sunlight at noon on a clear summer day in the temperate zone commonly ranges from about 8000–10,000 or even 12,000 foot candles. In midmorning

Fig. 29.2. The spectrum of radiant energy; figures represent millimicrons (mμ).

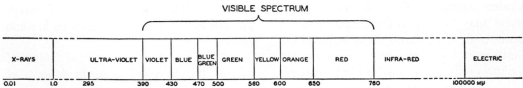

584 *Introductory Botany*

or midafternoon it is often only half as great. On a cloudy winter day, it is often less than 1000 foot candles, even at noon. Under a tree with a rather open crown, the light intensity is usually from about $\frac{1}{10}$ to $\frac{1}{20}$ that of full sunlight.

The optimum light intensity for photosynthesis in individual leaves of ordinary land plants commonly ranges from about $\frac{1}{10}$ of full summer sunlight in shade species to $\frac{1}{3}$ or $\frac{1}{4}$ of full sunlight in maize and in trees, such as apples and pines, if other conditions are reasonably favorable. The optimum light intensity for the whole plant, however, is often markedly higher than that for individual leaves. The interior leaves of a densely leafy tree may receive less than 1 percent as much illumination as the upper ones. The rate of photosynthesis for the whole plant increases with the light intensity until the reduction in rate by overilluminated leaves counterbalances the increase in rate by underilluminated ones. The optimum light intensity for many trees approaches or equals that of full summer sunlight, if other factors do not intervene.

Too high an intensity of light may depress the rate of photosynthesis in several ways. One way is through increasing transpiration, causing the stomates to close and cut off most of the CO_2 supply. Prob-ably the most important depressing effect is through a progressive replacement of photosynthesis by a process known as **photo-oxidation.** Photo-oxidation resembles respiration in that organic compounds are broken down, oxygen is used, and CO_2 is released. It differs from ordinary respiration in that essential protoplasmic constituents, including eventually chlorophyll itself, are oxidized, and in that the mechanism is in some way intimately related to the mechanism of photosynthesis. Some degree of photo-oxidation apparently occurs in the leaves of many species of plants when the solar radiation approaches that of full sunlight, but the condition does not persist for more than a few hours each day. Any significant rate of photo-oxidation for more than a few hours at a time is distinctly harmful, and, if it is long continued or severe, it kills the cells.

Only a small proportion of light absorbed by leaves is changed into potential chemical energy by photosynthesis. The proportion varies according to the quality and intensity of the light, the other environmental factors, and the kind of plant. At light intensities somewhat less than the optimum, as much as 10–20 per cent of the absorbed light energy may be fixed by photosynthesis. In full sunlight the efficiency of individual leaves may be only a

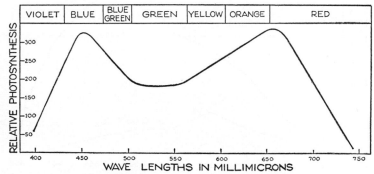

Fig. 29.3. Action spectrum of light in photosynthesis (i.e., the relative rates of photosynthesis in different wavelengths of light of equal intensity). (After B. S. Meyer and D. B. Anderson. From Transeau, Sampson, and Tiffany, *Textbook of Botany*, Rev Ed., Harper, 1953.)

Angiosperms: Manufacture, Translocation, and Storage of Food 585

fifth or a tenth as great. These figures reflect the net energy gain of the leaves, as determined experimentally by the heat of combustion, and thus really measure the excess of photosynthesis over respiration and photo-oxidation (if any), rather than the total amount of photosynthesis.

We have noted that leaves commonly absorb only about 80 percent of the visible light which falls on them, that only about 40 percent of the radiant energy from sunlight is in the visible spectrum, and that only the energy of the visible spectrum is available for photosynthesis. Thus the efficiency of the leaf in using the radiant energy to which it is exposed is roughly only a third as great as its efficiency in using the light it has absorbed. Actual figures of the photosynthetic efficiency of individual leaves in terms of the total radiant energy to which they are exposed ranged from 0.6 to 7.7 percent in one set of experiments using several different kinds of common plants under varying light intensity.

The efficiency of natural vegetation or a cultivated crop in fixing solar energy depends on the proportion of light which falls on the plant rather than on the ground surface, as well as on the efficiency with which the light that falls on the plant is used. The effect of respiration must also be considered for the entire plant, rather than just for the chlorophyllous part. The efficiency of plants is low indeed when measured in these terms.

Maize is one of the most efficient crops. It has been calculated that an acre of maize in north central Illinois fixed about 1.2 percent of the solar energy that fell on an acre during a growing season of 100 days, after allowing for the loss by respiration and photo-oxidation. About one-third the net photosynthetic product is in the grain, so that the efficiency of maize in converting solar energy into chemical energy of the grain is only about 0.4 percent. Measured on an annual basis, the efficiency is even less, since the crop occupied the field for less than a third of the year. The average annual efficiency of most crops and deciduous forests in the temperate zone, measured by the total net production of organic matter, is only about 0.1–0.2 percent.

TEMPERATURE

The low-temperature threshold for photosynthesis varies from as low as —35°C in some northern conifers to about

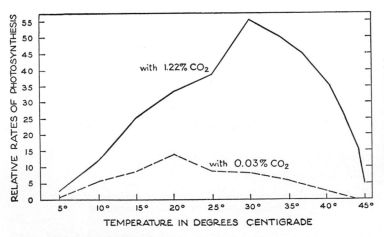

Fig. 29.4. Rates of photosynthesis in potato leaves in relation to temperature and the concentration of carbon dioxide. (Calculated from data by H. G. Lundegardh. From Transeau, Sampson, and Tiffany, *Textbook of Botany*, Rev. Ed., Harper, 1953.)

5°C in many tropical angiosperms. In the winter, temperature is doubtless often the limiting factor for photosynthesis in evergreen angiosperms and conifers, but during the ordinary growing season, some other factor is almost always limiting, and variations in temperature have less effect.

Under experimental conditions, with a plentiful supply of CO_2 and with all other factors maintained in a favorable balance, the effect of variation in temperature is very evident. The optimum then varies not only with the species but also with the duration of the experiment. The highest initial rate is often attained at temperatures as high as 35°C, but the rate falls off if such temperatures are maintained for even a few hours. The cause of the decline is not fully understood; one suggestion is that the initially favorable effect of high temperature, due to the general principal that the speed of a chemical reaction tends to increase with the temperature, is eventually counterbalanced by the progressive destruction or inactivation of some of the necessary enzymes.

TRANSLOCATION OF FOODS

INTRODUCTION

Under reasonably favorable conditions, the products of photosynthesis accumulate more rapidly during the day than they can be used or removed to other parts of the plant. Glucose, the usual primary product of photosynthesis, is soluble in water and thus affects the osmotic balance of the cell. In most angiosperms, much of the glucose is converted into starch as rapidly as it is produced. Starch is insoluble and does not affect the osmotic balance of the cell. During the night much of the starch is reconverted to glucose or other soluble sugars and carried away to the nonphotosynthetic parts of the plant.

PHLOEM

Glucose and other organic solutes are usually translocated through the phloem. The mechanism of the movement is not fully understood. It is clear that the movement results from a vital process in the phloem; translocation stops if the cells are killed. It is also clear that the same solute can move in opposite directions at different times, and that different solutes can move in opposite directions at the same time through the same region of the phloem. Furthermore, a relatively large amount of material is moved, at a rather rapid rate. Measurements of 20–100 cm per hour have been recorded.

Calculations in one experiment indicated that an average of 0.6 grams per hour of organic matter (measured by dry weight) passed through a pumpkin stalk and into the developing fruit over a 33-day period. A rate of 110 cm per hour would be required to carry this amount of food through the available phloem if the food moved in a 10 percent solution that occupied the whole interior of the sieve tubes. A rate of more nearly 1000 cm per hour would be required if the movement occurred only in the thin layer of cytoplasm that lines the wall of the sieve tubes.

All the hypotheses which have been advanced to explain the movement of solutes through the phloem are subject to serious difficulties, and these hypotheses are supported by inadequate evidence, beyond the fact that the solutes do move. It has recently been demonstrated that the sugar solution in sieve tubes of stems and leaves is generally under considerable pressure, commonly as much as 20 atmospheres, the pressure decreasing downward in the roots. Companion cells probably serve in getting the food solution into and out of the sieve tubes; in this connection it is perhaps noteworthy that the companion cells are especially large in the leaves. Sieve tubes commonly function only one year, although the phloem may live several years longer as a storage tissue, with the sieve tubes more or less collapsed.

Other Tissues

Not all the living cells of a plant are in direct contact with the phloem; therefore, some movement of foods must occur through cells or tissues of other kinds. The familiar principles of diffusion and cyclosis seem adequate to explain such movement, especially since the distance to be traveled is usually only a few cells wide and since the cytoplasm of adjacent cells is connected by plasmodesmata. The apical initials of stems and roots may be some distance removed from the phloem, but the plasmodesmata in the meristematic and immature regions are commonly larger and more numerous than those of mature regions. Furthermore, even the region of elongation commonly has some mature protophloem elements.

The greatest distance that food must travel outside the phloem is usually from the cambium to the innermost part of the sapwood of a tree, commonly several inches. This lateral conduction occurs largely in the wood rays, which are composed of parenchyma cells. An inadequate food supply at the end of the line may be one of the factors contributing to the progressive change of sapwood to heartwood.

Storage of sugar in the sapwood of trees during the winter and early spring easily gives rise to the misimpression that the xylem is an important food-conducting

tissue. Early in the spring, when the leaves have not yet expanded and the water supply is abundant, a considerable amount of sugary sap will often ooze out if the wood is cut into. Doubtless much of this stored sugar is later carried upward with the transpiration stream, but the total amount of food moved in the xylem is insignificant as compared with the amount in the phloem.

STORAGE OF FOOD

Introduction

Food is stored in many forms, including carbohydrates, proteins, and fats, in various organs of the plant. Many plants store some carbohydrates as soluble sugars which are freely transported; otherwise the food stored in a cell is made there from simple sugars or from these plus other components. We have noted in Chapter 2 that simple sugars are not the only immediate products of photosynthesis, but they are still the primary building blocks which are variously modified and recombined to form the major share of the organic components of the cell.

Forms of Stored Food

Carbohydrates are by far the most abundant form of stored food in angiosperms and other embryophytes, and starch is by far the most common storage product. Starch grains are formed singly within the leucoplasts, often becoming so large that the body of the leucoplast forms only a thin layer around the grain. A leucoplast with its included starch grain is often called an **amyloplast** (Fig. 29.5). Usually the grain appears to consist of a series of

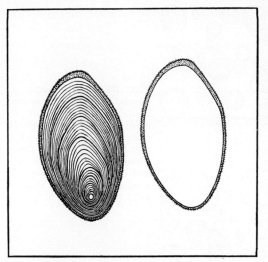

Fig. 29.5. Left: Single grain of potato starch within an amyloplast, and the amyloplast with the starch grain removed. (× about 750.) Right: Section showing a few cells of a potato tuber; the cells contain large and conspicuous starch grains and a few small granules of protein. (× about 150.) (From W. H. Brown, *The Plant Kingdom*, 1935; courtesy of Ginn & Company, Boston.)

concentric layers, with the inner part of each layer denser than the outer part. The shape of the grain varies with the species, and the source of the starch in flour can often be identified by microscopic examination, especially with polarized light.

Some plants store polysaccharides derived from fructose. The most common fructosan, as such compounds are called, is inulin, a white, powder-like substance which forms a colloidal sol in water and is dispersed in the cell sap of the cells in which it accumulates. Inulin is especially common in the family Compositae, being found for example in dahlia, dandelion, goldenrod, Jerusalem artichoke, and salsify. Inulin is more often found in roots and tubers than in aerial stems, and some plants which store inulin in the roots also store starch in the stems.

The hemicelluloses (polysaccharides which are common constituents of cell walls) are often used as reserve food, especially by the germinating embryo of a seed.

The hemicellulose of cell walls in the xylem of trees is also often used as food when growth is resumed in the spring.

Monosaccharides, disaccharides, and trisaccharides are also often stored and used as food. Sweet corn is rich in glucose, a monosaccharide. Fructose, another monosaccharide, is stored in the flesh of many fruits, as well as elsewhere. As much as 20 percent of the fresh weight of the roots of sugar beet and the stems of cane sugar may consist of sucrose, a disaccharide which yields one molecule of glucose and one of fructose when digested. Raffinose, a trisaccharide which yields one molecule each of glucose, fructose, and galactose, is also stored in many plants.

The very numerous proteins and fats which are stored as food by plants are not readily classified into groups comparable to the groups of carbohydrates. In any individual instance the fats can be analyzed and their structure determined, since each fat molecule can be hydrolyzed into 1 mole-

Angiosperms: Manufacture, Translocation, and Storage of Food 589

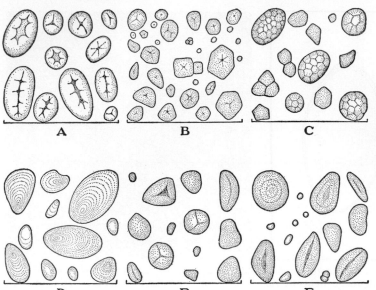

Fig. 29.6. Diagrams of starch grains from several kinds of plants: A, bean; B, corn; C, oats; D, potato; E, rice; F, wheat. (Adapted in part from Leffmann & Bean. From Transeau, Sampson, and Tiffany, *Textbook of Botany*, Rev. Ed., Harper, 1953.)

Fig. 29.7. Baobab (*Adansonia digitata*), an African tree which stores food in the swollen trunk. (Photo by W. H. Hodge.)

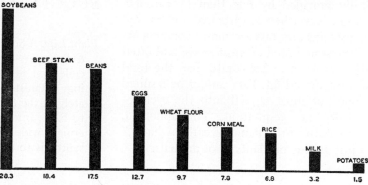

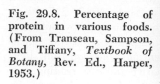

Fig. 29.8. Percentage of protein in various foods. (From Transeau, Sampson, and Tiffany, *Textbook of Botany*, Rev. Ed., Harper, 1953.)

cule of glycerin and 3 molecules of fatty acid. The proteins, though composed of a limited number of kinds of amino acids, are so much more complex in structure that it is not yet generally possible to devise structural formulas for them.

ORGANS IN WHICH FOOD IS STORED

Food may be stored in any organ of the plant, although there is not ordinarily much storage in the flower parts. The storage organ may or may not be obviously modified. Temporary storage of starch in the leaves is a normal corollary of photosynthesis. The stems and roots of trees, and the roots or underground stems of perennial herbs, necessarily store some food, which is called on when the plant resumes growth after a period of dormancy.

Many plants have special modified roots, stems, or leaves, usually underground, which serve as storage organs. The scales of an onion bulb are modified leaves; the Irish potato is a familiar underground stem, and the sweet potato is an underground root. Many familiar biennials have storage roots (sometimes joined to a massive hypocotyl). Underground storage organs are usually high in carbohydrate, which is readily digestible and available, and low in protein and fat, which are more

economical of space; space is not generally at a premium in such organs.

Fleshy fruits commonly have a supply of stored carbohydrates. Often, especially in plants of temperate regions, the amount of food stored in the fruit is not very great, and the sweetness is provided chiefly by fructose, a monosaccharide that is much sweeter than glucose or sucrose. Food stored in the pericarp of a fruit is not generally used directly by the plant but serves instead as part of the attraction to the animals which distribute the seeds.

Seeds, in which space is usually at a premium, commonly have a higher proportion of proteins and fats than do vegetative storage organs. Proteins and fats have more potential energy, per unit of volume or weight, than carbohydrates. Protoplasm is essentially proteinaceous, with a considerable fat content as well. If the seed had little or no stored protein and fat, it would be necessary to use carbohydrates in their manufacture, and also as a source of energy for the process. If the manufacture is carried out before the seed is mature, the need for stored carbohydrate as an energy source is reduced. Even with some of the necessary proteins and fats already provided, the germinating seed requires a supply of stored energy. In terms of space and weight, this is more economically provided by fats than by carbohy-drates. Nevertheless, carbohydrates as well as proteins and fats are major components of the stored food of most seeds, and often there is more carbohydrate than the total of protein and fat. Fats cannot be respired alone but must be fed into the cycle of carbohydrate respiration. The aphorism, "Fats burn in the flame of carbohydrates," is just as true of plants as of animals.

SUGGESTED READING

Plant Life. A Scientific American Book, Simon & Schuster, New York, 1957, 237 pp. A collection of popular articles by outstanding botanists, originally appearing separately in the *Scientific American* from 1949 to 1957. Informative and easy reading, covering a wide variety of topics, from photosynthesis to strangler trees to hybrid corn.

CHAPTER 30

Angiosperms: Flowers

INTRODUCTION

A **flower** is a specialized short shoot with modified leaves. Some of these leaves characteristically produce sexual reproductive structures, leading ultimately to the formation of seeds. A flower bud differs from an ordinary vegetative bud in the kind of leaves it produces, and in that its terminal growth is limited because the apical meristem either ceases to function or matures into some other kind of tissue. The floral leaves lack axillary buds, and the internodes of the flower always remain very short.

Flowers are important to the plant because of their essential role in the production of seeds. They are important to man for other reasons as well. Many of them are large and showy, causing the plants to be cultivated for ornament, although others are so small and inconspicuous that they would never be noticed by one not searching for them. Experience of taxonomists during the past several centuries has

Trillium erectum. (×3.) (Photo by Leonard Lee Rice, from National Audubon Society.)

shown that differences in the structure of the flower furnish some of the most reliable guides to identification and relationships in the angiosperms. Some of these differences used in classification are obviously important to the plant itself; others, although very useful taxonomically, are of little or no apparent significance to the plant.

INITIATION OF FLOWERS

Most vegetative buds, if they remain active, sooner or later change into flower buds. Even the terminal bud of a rhizome is not always permanently vegetative; in *Iris* and many other rhizomatous plants, the terminal bud turns up into the air each year and eventually becomes a flower bud, the rhizome continuing to elongate by the development of an axillary bud. In many plants, such as tulips, all active buds sooner or later become flower buds, so that each stem is terminated by a flower or an inflorescence (cluster of flowers). In many other plants, some buds are permanently vegetative, and only certain buds, often in particular positions, become flower buds.

The physiological factors which cause a vegetative bud to change into a flower bud are only partly understood. In soybeans and some other kinds of plants, if one branch is exposed to a length of day favoring floral growth while the remainder of the plant has a length of day favoring vegetative growth, only the one branch will flower. If the leaves are stripped from the branch exposed to flower-inducing conditions, no flowers are produced; but if the leaves are stripped instead from the remainder of the plant, flowers develop on all the branches. The inference to be drawn is that the environmental condi-

tions favoring vegetative growth, on the one hand, and floral growth, on the other, operate through two different, mutually antagonistic hormones produced in the leaves.

In cocklebur, on the other hand, exposure of one branch to flower-inducing conditions causes the whole plant to flower. It would seem that flower-inducing hormones are produced in cocklebur, but flower-inhibiting ones are not.

The presumed hormones that induce plants to flower have been called florigens, but until recently nothing that could be called a florigen had been extracted and identified. Some experimental studies now suggest that at least in some plants gibberellin acts as a florigen. Gibberellin (see Chapter 32) is a plant hormone with multiple effects on growth. It remains to be seen whether it will prove to be the hitherto elusive florigen of angiosperms in general.

In some kinds of plants, the internal factors governing the transformation of vegetative buds into flower buds are not much influenced by environmental conditions, so long as these permit growth to occur. The bud produces a more or less limited number of leaves and then changes into a floral bud that produces a flower or an inflorescence. In many other kinds of plants, the duration of the vegetative period and the change from vegetative to floral growth can be markedly hastened or retarded by changing the environment.

EFFECT OF THE PHOTOPERIOD

The environmental factor that most often governs flowering is the length of day, or **photoperiod.** The effect of the photoperiod was first demonstrated by the American botanists W. W. Garner (1875–1956) and H. A. Allard (1880–1963) in

Fig. 30.1. H. A. Allard (1880–1963), left, and W. W. Garner (1875–1956), right, American botanists, who discovered photoperiodism. (Courtesy of the U.S. Agricultural Research Service.)

1920, and later studies by these and other botanists have shown the general importance of photoperiodism. In such studies, the natural day length is extended by artificial light or shortened by covering the plants or placing them in a dark room. The supplemental light need not be very strong; in most cases 1/500 to 1/2000 of the light intensity of a bright summer day is enough, and sometimes an intensity only a few times higher than that of bright moonlight is effective.

Some plants are short-day plants, in which flowers are initiated as soon as the day length falls below a critical photoperiod of usually about 12–14 hours. Short-day plants usually bloom in the fall or the spring. The flowers of spring-blooming plants are often initiated in the fall, the buds remaining dormant over winter.

Chrysanthemums, poinsettias, and violets are familiar short-day plants. Commercial growers of chrysanthemums carefully control the effective day length for the plants, using black covering cloths or electric lights as necessary to bring them into flower on any chosen day of the year. Poinsettias and Easter lilies can be managed in the same way, but more often the temperature is controlled, under natural daylight, to prepare them for sale at the proper time.

Long-day plants, such as lettuce, clover, potatoes, and most grains, initiate and produce blossoms only when the day length is more than a critical period of usually about 12–14 hours. Under artificial conditions, long-day plants flower even when continuously illuminated, with no night. Long-day plants usually bloom in the summer.

Angiosperms: Flowers   597

Fig. 30.2. Effect of the photoperiod. Above, lettuce, a long-day plant; below, scarlet sage (*Salvia*), a short-day plant. (Photographs courtesy of the Boyce Thompson Institute for Plant Research.)

Intermediate-day plants, such as Indian grass (*Sorghastrum nutans*) and some other grasses, bloom only when the day length is within a certain range, remaining vegetative if the day is too long or too short. Such plants have two critical photoperiods, an upper one and a lower one, rather than only one.

Day-neutral plants, such as dandelions, tomatoes, and cotton, bloom during a wide variety of day lengths. Like long-day plants, they actually have a critical photoperiod below which they will not flower, but this period is usually shorter than the day lengths which occur during the growing season.

Short-day plants might perhaps better be called long-night plants, and long-day plants called short-night plants, because it is the length of the night, rather than the day, that is generally controlling. Short-day plants will flower under artificial conditions of long night, whether the day is long or short, and long-day plants will flower under artificial conditions of short night, regardless of the day length. The long night for short-day plants must be essentially continuous; interruptions of only a few minutes interfere with flowering. Street lights may also interfere. Long-day plants, on the other hand, may be induced to bloom by interrupting the night with a short period of illumination, even though the days remain short.

Any photoperiodic cycle which induces initiation of flowers is called a photoinductive cycle. An 8-hour photoperiod alternating with a 16-hour dark period, for example, is a photoinductive cycle for cockleburs. In some plants, a few successive photoinductive cycles act as a trip mechanism, which induces flowering even if the plant is thereafter subject only to nonphotoinductive cycles. Even a single

photoinductive cycle eventually induces some flowering in cockleburs. In some other kinds of plants, as many as 25 photoinductive cycles may be required for the initiation of flowers, and flower buds which have been formed may fail to mature unless the photoinductive cycles are continued. Usually there is a more or less cumulative effect; one or a few photoinductive cycles may eventually cause some flowers to be produced, but the most vigorous and rapid flowering and fruiting occur when the photoinductive cycles are continued without interruption.

The distribution of some species is limited partly by their photoperiodic response. Short-day plants, for example, are not suited to arctic regions, in which the photoperiod during the growing season is always relatively long. Species with a wide latitudinal distribution commonly show some variation in photoperiodic response in different parts of their range, and often there is some variation even within a local area, so that some individuals bloom well before others. The same species may even include short-day, long-day, and intermediate-day races. Cultivated crops often include a number of races with different photoperiodic responses. If successive sowings of a single variety of a short-day plant are made at intervals during the season, they will all bloom at about the same time, regardless of the degree of vegetative development they have attained, but different varieties may bloom at different times, even if sown at the same time and treated in the same way.

Different stages in reproductive growth often have different photoperiodic requirements. In some short-day plants, the critical photoperiod is progressively shorter for the initiation of flower buds, the actual development of the flowers, and the setting of fruit; these are necessarily fall-blooming plants. Such differences emphasize the complex and constantly changing nature of the chemical balances which govern growth and reproduction.

EFFECT OF TEMPERATURE

The second most important environmental factor influencing flowering is temperature. Aside from the photoperiodic response, some plants flower only (or best) at relatively high temperatures, some at relatively low temperatures, and some at

Fig. 30.3. Foxglove (*Digitalis purpurea*), a plant which requires exposure to cold for the initiation of flowers. The plant at the left was held continuously in a greenhouse; the plant at the right was removed to a dark room at 50°F each night from May 14 to September 30, then exposed to long days in a greenhouse. Pictures taken November 18, 1938. (Courtesy of the Boyce Thompson Institute for Plant Research.)

intermediate temperatures, while others flower under a wide range of temperature conditions. The temperature of the night is often more important than that of the day. A regular cyclical variation, corresponding to the usual variation between day and night, is necessary in some plants. Blooming of lettuce, some species of phlox, and peppers is favored by high temperatures, whereas blooming of celery, beets, onions, and carrots is favored by low temperatures. Beets, which are ordinarily biennial may be induced to flower and set seed the first season by growing them at relatively low temperatures (10°–16°C, for some varieties).

The photoperiodic response of plants may be modified or even reversed by changes in temperature. In one experiment, Heavenly Blue morning-glory behaved as a long-day plant at a night temperature of 13°C, as a short-day plant at a night temperature of 20°C, and as a day-neutral plant at a night temperature of 18°C.

The complex relationship between the effects of temperature and the photoperiod points up the fact that environmental factors governing plant growth act by favoring certain chemical reactions in the protoplasm, at the expense of others. The behavior of the plant is determined by the chemical reactions which occur under a given set of environmental conditions. The effect of a change in one environmental factor may be reinforced, or diminished, or overwhelmed by a change in some other factor. Under a particular set of conditions, a change in some one factor may cause a change in behavior, but it is only a convenient oversimplification to say that a particular environmental factor, by itself, causes some action or change.

The effect on flowering of the ratio between available nitrogen and available phosphorus has been noted in Chapter 28. A relatively high proportion of phosphorus favors early change from vegetative to reproductive growth, whereas an excess of nitrogen favors vigorous vegetative growth and delay or suppression of flowering and fruiting.

A number of chemical compounds influence flowering when applied to the plant externally. Maleic hydrazide has a pronounced inhibitory effect. Acetylene and ethylene promote flowering in pineapples and some other plants. Small amounts of indole-acetic acid promote flowering, at least in some plants, while larger amounts inhibit it. 2, 4-D, a herbicide that acts by disrupting the normal balance of growth regulating hormones, induces flowering and early fruiting in many plants when used in small amounts.

Many kinds of plants, such as pansies, produce more flowers, over a longer period of time, if the old flowers are plucked off without being allowed to produce seed. Our understanding of the mechanism of this response is still very rudimentary. It is thought that the developing fruits may produce a growth-regulating substance which causes the meristematic tissues of the shoot to mature into non-meristematic tissues. The chemical nature of this growth-regulating substance is obscure.

STRUCTURE OF FLOWERS

The Floral Organs

A typical flower has four kinds of modified leaves, the sepals, petals, stamens, and carpels, attached to a stem tip called the **receptacle.** The sepals are on the outside, the petals next, the stamens next, and the carpels are in the center. One or more of these may be missing, but the order (in normal specimens) is invariable.

The **sepals** are the outermost set of floral leaves. Typically they are green or greenish, and more or less leafy in texture. They cover and enclose the other flower parts before the flower has opened, protecting the internal parts from injury. In some plants, especially members of the lily and iris families, such as tulips, iris, and gladioli, the sepals are brightly colored and much like the petals.

The most common numbers of sepals are three, four, and five, but larger or smaller numbers occur, and some kinds of flowers (e.g., pussy-willows) lack sepals entirely. The sepals commonly seem to form a single whorl, but on close examination it can often be seen that they are really in a compressed spiral. When there are five sepals, they are very often arranged in a $\frac{2}{5}$ phyllotaxy, with an angle of divergence of about 144°.

All the sepals collectively are called the **calyx.** Not infrequently the sepals are joined toward the base by their lateral margins, forming a calyx tube with terminal calyx lobes or calyx teeth.

The **petals** characteristically form the second set of floral leaves, just internal to the sepals. Typically they are brightly colored (or white) and attract insects or birds to the flower. The function of insects and birds in transferring pollen is described on pp. 618–619.

The petals are usually of the same number as the sepals and also commonly arranged in a spiral so tight that they seem to form a single cycle. In a few flowers the spiral forms a direct continuation of the

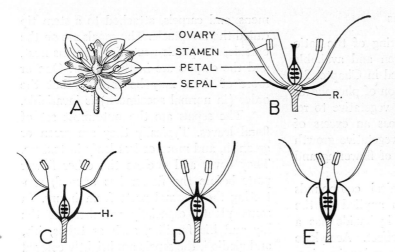

OVARY
STAMEN
PETAL
SEPAL

A

B — R.

C — H.

D

E

Fig. 30.4. Characteristic types of flowers: A, B, hypogynous; C, perigynous; D, epigynous; E, epigynous with prolonged hypanthium: h., hypanthium; r., receptacle.

spiral of sepals, but much more often the two spirals are distinct and are offset so that the petals alternate with the sepals. All the petals are attached nearer to the center of the flower than are any of the sepals, but otherwise the sepals and petals alternate in position.

All the petals are collectively called the **corolla.** The petals are typically separate from each other and individually attached to the receptacle, forming a polypetalous corolla, as in buttercups, roses, and magnolias. Often, however, they are laterally joined to each other, forming a sympetalous corolla with a basal corolla tube and terminal corolla lobes, as in petunias and snapdragons. Sometimes, as in morning-glories, the petals are so completely joined that not even the tips are separate.

If all the petals are about alike and arranged in a radially symmetrical pattern, as is true in most flowers, the corolla is **regular;** if they differ among themselves the corolla is **irregular.** Irregular corollas may be sympetalous, as in snapdragons, or polypetalous, as in sweet peas. The calyx also may be irregular, but this situation is

less common, and when a flower is said to be irregular, it is usually the corolla that is referred to.

The corolla and the calyx are collectively called the **perianth,** and any perianth member is called a **tepal.** These terms are used especially when the perianth is not clearly differentiated into sepals and petals, or when the sepals and petals are much alike. When the perianth consists of only a single whorl, it is customary to call it a calyx and call its parts sepals, unless, by comparison with related species or genera, it is clear that the sepals have been lost and that the single remaining perianth whorl consists of petals.

The **stamens** are in effect the male organs of the flower. Each stamen usually consists of a slender **filament** and a terminal **anther.** The anther usually consists of two **pollen sacs,** joined by a slender **connective,** which is merely a prolongation of the filament. The development and function of the pollen, which is borne in the pollen sacs, are discussed on pp. 615–621. In some of the more primitive kinds of angiosperms, the stamen is not divided into filament and anther, and the pollen sacs are

Fig. 30.5. Fly honeysuckle (*Lonicera canadensis*). The flowers are sessile in pairs on the end of a common stalk; the corolla is sympetalous and irregular, with a prominent spur at the base; the stamens and style can be seen protruding from the corolla. (Photo courtesy of J. Arthur Herrick.)

embedded in the broad, petal-like blade of the stamen.

All the stamens of a flower are collectively called the **androecium** (from Greek *andros*, man, and *oikos*, house). The number of stamens per flower differs in different kinds of plants. In flowers such as buttercups and wild roses, there are many stamens, and in buttercups it can fairly readily be seen that they form several turns of a close spiral. In many other flowers, there is only one whorl (or whorl-like spiral) of stamens, which alternate with the petals (although slightly farther toward the cen-

ter of the flower). Or there may be two or more successive whorls of stamens, the members of each whorl alternating in position with those of the next outer whorl. Thus the outermost whorl of stamens is alternate with the petals (and opposite the sepals), the next inner whorl is opposite the petals, and the third whorl is again alternate with the petals. In the relatively few kinds of flowers in which the outermost (or only) whorl of stamens is opposite the petals (e.g., primroses), it is believed that the original outermost whorl has been lost in the course of evolution.

Angiosperms: Flowers 603

Fig. 30.6. Tulip flower. The sepals and petals are very much alike; the three-parted stigma is sessile on the ovary, without a style. (New York Botanical Garden photo.)

In sympetalous flowers the filaments are often joined with the corolla toward the base, so that they seem to arise from the corolla rather than directly from the receptacle. The stamens are then said to be epipetalous. More rarely the stamens of polypetalous flowers are also epipetalous.

In many plants one or more of the stamens are modified in one way or another and lack functional anthers. Such a modified stamen is called a **staminode**. In the commonest type of staminode, the filament is expanded to form a petal-like blade; the extra petals of many "double" flowers, such as cultivated roses, are actually staminodes.

Evidence from comparative morphology suggests that petals were not a part of the primitive angiospermous flower, but that they did originate early in the evolutionary history of the group, in two ways: (1) as staminodes, and (2) by differentiation of the inner members of a previously undifferentiated perianth. Most presently existing plants with apetalous flowers (lacking petals), however, evidently had petaliferous ancestors.

The **carpels** are in effect the female organs of the flower. In its most typical form, the carpel is a modified leaf, bearing a row of ovules along each edge, and folded lengthwise so that the ovules are enclosed rather than being exposed to the air. The development of the ovules into seeds is discussed on pp. 621–623.

All the carpels of a flower are collectively called the **gynoecium** (from Greek *gynē*, woman, and *oikos*, house). The flower may have one to several or many carpels, and these may be separate from each other or joined together. Each carpel (if the carpels are separate) or the group of carpels (if the carpels are united) is called a **pistil.**

The simplest situation is illustrated by peas and other legumes, in which the gynoecium consists of a single carpel folded together to form a simple pistil. If a pea pod is carefully opened along the seed-bearing suture and laid out flat, it can be seen that half the ovules (peas) are attached along one side, and half along the other. The suture which does not bear seed is the midrib of the carpel.

In some plants, especially members of the buttercup family and the rose family, the gynoecium consists of several or many separate carpels, each forming a simple pistil containing one or more ovules. The pistils are individually attached to the receptacle, and separate from each other. In any flower with more than one pistil, the individual pistils are always simple (i.e., composed of a single carpel).

In well over half the kinds of angiosperms, the gynoecium consists of a single compound pistil, composed of two or more united carpels. Most compound pistils consist of two or three carpels, but four-carpellate and five-carpellate pistils are not uncommon, and in the mallows the pistil often consists of ten or more carpels. Tulips and other lilies have three-carpellate pistils. If three pea pods were joined together with the seed-bearing sutures of all three juxtaposed, the resulting compound structure would be com-

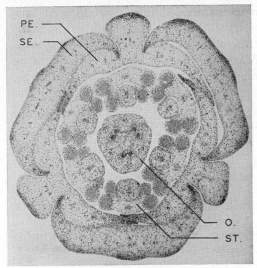

Fig. 30.7. Cross section of flower bud of lily: o., ovary; pe., petal; se., sepal; st., stamen. (Copyright by **General Biological Supply House, Inc.,** Chicago.)

parable to the three-chambered pistil of a tulip.

A pistil of any kind is ordinarily differentiated into three externally visible parts, the ovary, style, and stigma. The **ovary,** at the base, contains the ovules. The **stigma,** which receives the pollen, is usually elevated above the ovary on a slender **style.** Sometimes there is no style, and thus the stigma is sessile at the top of the ovary.

A simple pistil has only one style and one stigma. The carpels of a compound ovary may be separated at the top, so that the single ovary has several styles, each with its own stigma, or the single style has several stigmas. In many kinds of flowers with compound pistils, on the other hand, the carpels are so thoroughly joined that even the stigmas are fused into one. When there is more than one style or stigma, the number is usually a reliable guide to the number of carpels making up the pistil.

An ovary may or may not be internally subdivided into separate seed cavities, called locules. Simple pistils and many compound pistils have only a single locule. Many other compound pistils have as many locules as carpels. The locules are sometimes called cells, but cells in this sense are not comparable to cells in the usual biological sense.

PLACENTATION

The tissue of the ovary to which the ovules are attached is called the **placenta**.

Fig. 30.8. **Types of placentation:** *A*, parietal in a simple pistil; *B*, axile in a pistil with two or three carpels; *C*, *D*, parietal in a compound pistil with two or three carpels, the placentas intruded in *C*; *E*, free central; *F*, basal.

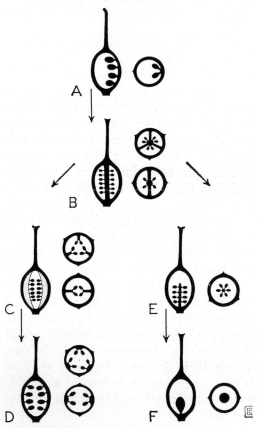

The placentation, i.e., the position of the placentae, differs in different kinds of plants. The most common types of placentation (Fig. 30.8) are parietal, axile, free-central, and basal. These types are described in the following paragraphs.

Simple pistils usually have **parietal** (along the wall) or **basal** placentation, although these types are also found as evolutionary modifications in compound pistils. Simple pistils with parietal placentation typically have a single, long placenta running the length of the wall along one suture, as in peas and other legumes. This single parietal placenta is actually formed by the two joined margins of the carpel. Sometimes the parietal placenta of a simple pistil is rather short and bears only one or two ovules. It is only a small step from this type of parietal placentation to basal placentation, with one or two ovules borne essentially at the base of the ovary.

Compound pistils are derived by fusion of two or more adjacent simple pistils. In the least modified condition, a compound ovary has as many locules as carpels, and the placentae of the carpels are joined to form a central axis in the ovary. The ovary is said to have **axile** placentation, as in tulips and many other plants. Except in the mustard family, which has a highly modified carpellary structure, pistils with two or more locules practically always have axile placentation.

Unilocular compound pistils are usually derived by evolutionary modification from plurilocular ones. In primroses, carnations, and some other plants, the placenta remains as a central column, but the partitions fail to develop, so that the ovary is unilocular. In such plants, the placenta generally does not reach the top of the ovary and is attached only at the base. The placentation is then said to be **free-**

central. Basal placentation in a compound ovary is sometimes (as in buckwheat) derived from free-central placentation by reducing the central column to a mere basal nubbin.

Parietal placentation in a compound ovary is generally derived by modification from axile placentation. The partitions fail to reach the center of the ovary, so that no common central axis is established. The ovules are attached to the inner margin of each of the partial partitions, which extend part way from the outer wall toward the center. In the more extreme types of parietal placentation, the partial partitions are reduced to mere low ridges to which the ovules are attached, and the ovary is obviously unilocular. Parietal placentation in a compound ovary can also be arrived at by abortion of all but one of the carpels, so that only one locule develops, and the basically axile placenta appears to be along one wall of the ovary.

TYPES OF FLOWERS

In flowers having the most typical structure, the sepals, petals, stamens, and carpels, although all very close together, are attached progressively farther toward the center and progressively higher on the receptacle. All the other parts are beneath the ovary, which is central and terminal. Such a flower is **hypogynous** (Greek, beneath + female), and the ovary is **superior**.

In some kinds of flowers, such as cherry blossoms, the sepals, petals, and stamens are attached to the margin of a saucer-shaped or cup-shaped **hypanthium** which surrounds the ovary but is not attached to it. Such flowers (Fig. 30.9) are **perigynous** (Greek, around + female), and the ovary is still superior. The margin of the hypanthium may rise above the ovary, but the ultimate attachment is beneath the ovary. Often the hypanthium is much like the sepals in texture, and probably it

Fig. 30.9. *Prunus* (cherry) flower in long section. Note the well-developed, cup-like hypanthium; this flower is perigynous. (New York Botanical Garden photo.)

Angiosperms: Flowers 607

is properly to be considered as the more or less modified base of the calyx, to which the bases of the petals and stamens have become fused.

In a third group of flowers, exemplified by apple blossoms, the sepals, petals, and stamens are attached at or near the tip of the ovary. Such flowers are **epigynous** (Greek, upon + female), and the ovary is inferior. Many kinds of epigynous flowers are derived from perigynous ones by fusion of the hypanthium with the ovary wall. Often the upper part of the hypanthium projects well beyond the top of the inferior ovary. In some other flowers, epigyny is thought to have been derived by submergence of the ovary in the enlarged receptacle.

A flower which has all the ordinary parts, i.e., sepals, petals, stamens, and carpels, is said to be **complete**; if any of these parts is missing, it is **incomplete.** A flower which has both stamens and carpels is **perfect,** regardless of whether or not it has sepals and petals. **Imperfect** flowers are **staminate** if they have stamens but no pistil, and **pistillate** if they have a pistil (or pistils) but no stamens. A few kinds of plants, such as the cultivated *Hydrangea,* have some of the flowers **neutral,** lacking both stamens and pistils.

Monoecious (Greek, one household) plants, such as corn, have imperfect flowers, with both types borne on the same individual. An ear of corn is a group of pistillate flowers which lack a perianth. The individual corn grains are the ovaries, and the silk consists of the styles. The tassel of the corn plant is a group of staminate flowers. **Dioecious** (Greek, two households) plants, such as willows and cottonwoods, have imperfect flowers, with the two types borne on different individuals.

NECTARIES

Most flowers produce nectar, a sweet liquid gathered and eaten by insects or other animals. The structures or tissues which produce nectar are called **nectaries.** The nature of the nectaries differs in different kinds of flowers. In buttercups and some other plants, the basal part of the petal is the nectary. In many other plants, the nectaries appear to be more or less reduced and modified stamens, often forming a thickened rim just outside the base of the ovary. Parts of the ovary, receptacle, sepals, or hypanthium may also be differentiated as nectaries. Some kinds of plants even have nectaries on ordinary leaves.

INFLORESCENCES

Some kinds of plants have solitary flowers, but more often the flowers are borne in clusters called **inflorescences.** The shape, structure, and developmental sequence of inflorescences are almost infinitely variable, and no existing classification of them is even approximately satisfactory. Nevertheless, certain characteristic types occur repeatedly, and a large proportion of the kinds of inflorescences can be divided into two general groups on the basis of sequence of flowering.

Inflorescences in which the sequence of blooming is from the outer or lower flowers to the inner or upper ones are said to be **indeterminate;** those in which the sequence is from the central or uppermost flower to the outside or the base are said to be **determinate.** These terms reflect the fact that many indeterminate inflorescences continue to elongate for some time after the opening of the first flower, in

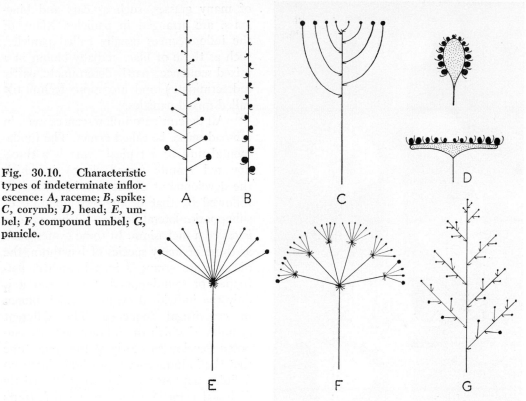

Fig. 30.10. Characteristic types of indeterminate inflorescence: *A*, raceme; *B*, spike; *C*, corymb; *D*, head; *E*, umbel; *F*, compound umbel; *G*, panicle.

contrast to determinate inflorescences in which elongation of the central axis tends to be limited by the development of the terminal flower. Determinate inflorescences may also be described as centrifugal, in contrast to indeterminate inflorescences, which are centripetal.

The basic type of indeterminate inflorescence is the **raceme,** in which the pedicels (flower stalks) arise as branches from a more or less elongate main axis. Usually each pedicel is axillary to a more or less reduced or modified leaf called a bract. The bracts are often small and inconspicuous, and sometimes they are wholly absent.

Other types of indeterminate inflorescences may, for convenience, be thought of as modified racemes, although

they may not always be so in a phylogenetic sense. All indeterminate inflorescences are said to be of a racemose type. A raceme with the flowers essentially sessile (e.g., a gladiolus) is a **spike.** A raceme with a short axis and long pedicels, so that the inflorescence is round-topped or flat-topped, is a **corymb.** If the axis is so reduced that the pedicels all seem to arise at the same point, the inflorescence is an **umbel.** The inflorescence of most members of the carrot family is a compound umbel, with the primary branches again umbellately branched to form the pedicels. A raceme in which both the axis and the pedicels are much reduced, so that the flowers are all closely crowded, as in clover and sunflowers, is a **head.**

A compact inflorescence such as a

Fig. 30.11. Part of the raceme of miterwort (*Mitella*); the petals are deeply pinnatifid. (Photo courtesy of J. Arthur Herrick.)

head or an umbel is often subtended by a whorl or cluster of bracts at the summit of the peduncle (stalk of the inflorescence). Such a group of bracts is called an **involucre.** In the sunflower family, the heads are so compact that the involucre simulates a calyx, and the outer flowers of the head often have irregular corollas which simulate the individual petals of a single flower.

A branched raceme, with the upper branches usually progressively shorter, is a **panicle.** The spikelets (very small spikes)

of many grasses, such as oats and blue-grass, are arranged in panicles. Many of the inflorescences usually called panicles, such as those of lilac, actually bloom in a mixed sequence (partly determinate, partly indeterminate) and are more technically called mixed panicles.

All determinate inflorescences may, in a broad sense, be called **cymes.** The fundamental unit of a typical cyme is a three-flowered cymule (small cyme) in which the development of the terminal flower is followed by that of the two opposite or subopposite lateral flowers. Such a cymule is called a **dichasium.** In some cymes, such as those of many species of hawthorn, the dichasia are arranged in a branched, flat-topped or round-topped cluster, and it is only the individual cymules which bloom in centrifugal sequence. The different cymules of which the inflorescence is composed develop so nearly at the same time that the inflorescence as a whole shows no definite sequence of flowering. A strictly dichasial cyme, on the other hand, starts with the development of a single terminal flower, which is subtended by two lateral branches. Each of these lateral branches in turn produces a terminal flower which is subtended by a pair of lateral branches, and the inflorescence may continue to enlarge in similar fashion indefinitely.

A **monochasium** is a cyme in which the terminal flower is subtended by only one flower, instead of two. It may be regarded as a modification of the dichasium. The branches of many compound inflorescences, such as those of species of elderberry, terminate in a mixture of dichasia and monochasia.

Many basically determinate inflorescences simulate indeterminate ones by producing a **sympodial** main axis, which is really a succession of very short, lateral branches developed in monochasial fash-

Fig. 30.12. Characteristic types of determinate inflorescence: *A*, dichasium; *B*, monochasium; *C*, dichasially branched cyme; *D*, compound cyme; *E, F*, sympodial cymes: *E*, helical; *F*, scorpioid.

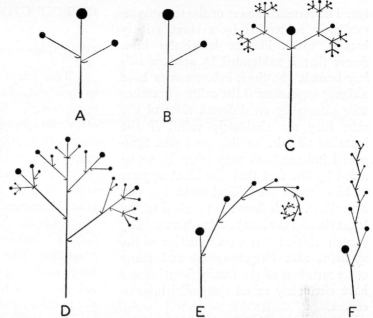

Fig. 30.13. Dogwood (*Cornus florida*). The inflorescence is a determinate head, subtended by an involucre of petal-like bracts. (New York Botanical Garden photo.)

ion. The terminal flower of the stem is immediately subtended by a short axillary branch, which likewise terminates in a flower that is subtended by another axillary branch, etc. Such inflorescences have a zigzag appearance if the axillary branches arise alternately on different sides of the axis; they are circinately rolled if the branches all arise on the same side. Sympodial inflorescences may often be recognized by the fact that the bract appears to be opposite the pedicel instead of just beneath it. Each flower is terminal to the true axis, and the bract subtends an axillary branch which forms a continuation of the apparent axis. Forget-me-nots and many other members of the family Boraginaceae have circinately rolled sympodial inflorescences.

Determinate inflorescences sometimes resemble one or another type of indeterminate inflorescence in form. Thus we have determinate umbels in onions and determinate heads in dogwood (Fig. 30.13); and the true heads of members of the sunflower family are sometimes arranged in determinate spikes or determinate heads. When used without some qualification, such as determinate or cymose, however, these terms refer to strictly indeterminate inflorescences.

Fig. 30.14. **Orthotropous (left) and anatropous (right) ovules.**

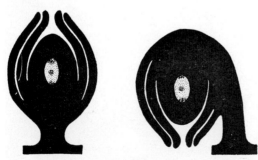

REPRODUCTIVE PROCESSES

DEVELOPMENT OF THE OVULE

The life cycle of angiosperms was worked out, and the terminology developed, before the basic homologies with other embryophytes were understood. The carpels of angiosperms are essentially megasporophylls, and the ovules which they bear are essentially megasporangia that are provided with an additional outer covering (the integuments).

An ovule that is ready for fertilization ordinarily consists of a female gametophyte, a **nucellus** (the wall of the megasporangium, enclosing the female gametophyte), one or two **integuments** partly enclosing the nucellus, and a basal stalk, the **funiculus,** by which the ovule is attached to the placenta. The evolutionary origin of the integuments is obscure. It is not at all certain that they are homologous with the seemingly similar integuments of conifer ovules. Ontogenetically, the integuments arise as rings of tissue near the base of the young nucellus. Growing faster than the nucellus, they soon completely enclose it, except for a small opening (the **micropyle**) at the tip. Unitegminous ovules (i.e., ovules with only one integument) are apparently derived from bitegminous ones, in some cases by fusion of the two integuments into one, in others apparently by abortion of one integument.

Very often the ovule is bent back on itself, so that the micropyle is alongside the stalk. The ovule is then said to be **anatropous,** in contrast to **orthotropous** ovules, which have the micropyle at the opposite end and in line with the stalk (Fig. 30.14).

Each ovule ordinarily produces only a single megaspore mother cell. The mega-

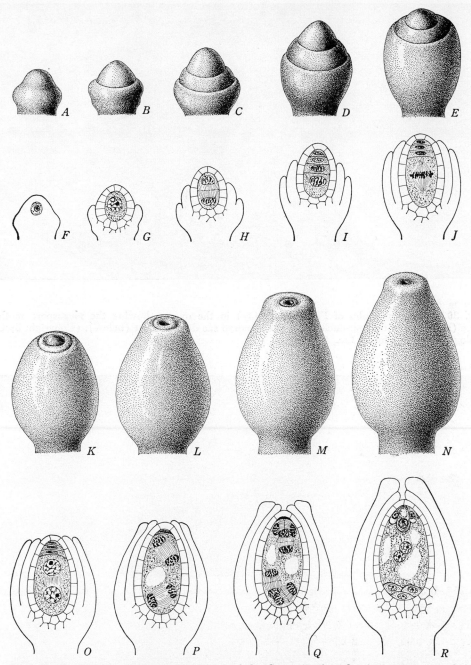

Fig. 30.15. **Diagrammatic representation of development of ovule.** *A–E, K–N,* growth of integuments; *F, G,* megaspore mother cell; *H, I,* reduction division, forming a linear tetrad of megaspores; *J,* three megaspores compressed, one enlarged, its nucleus dividing; *O,* binucleate stage of embryo sac, upper spores degenerating; *P,* four-nucleate stage; *Q,* eight-nucleate stage; *R,* mature female gametophyte, ready for fertilization; with egg and two synergid nuclei near the micropyle, two polar nuclei in the center, and three antipodal cells at the end opposite the micropyle. (From W. H. Brown, *The Plant Kingdom,* 1935; courtesy of Ginn & Company, Boston.)

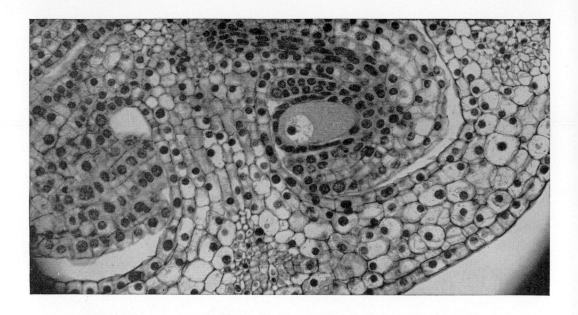

Fig. 30.16.   Young ovules of *Fritillaria* (a lily) in the ovary, showing the megaspore mother cell stage (above), and the four-nucleate stage of embryo sac development (below). (Copyright by General Biological Supply House, Inc., Chicago.)

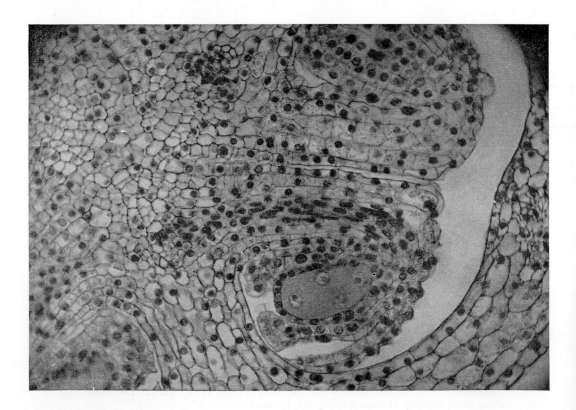

spore mother cell, which has $2n$ chromosomes and represents the last stage in the sporophyte generation, undergoes reduction division to produce four megaspores that are usually arranged in a row to form a linear tetrad. The megaspores each have n chromosomes and represent the first stage in the female gametophyte generation. Three of the four megaspores ordinarily degenerate and disappear, leaving a single functional megaspore which gives rise to the female gametophyte by a series of mitotic divisions.

The female gametophyte of angiosperms is called the **embryo sac.** Typically it consists of eight nuclei embedded in a common mass of cytoplasm, with only partial, if any, distinction into individual cells. Much of the cytoplasm is often associated with individual nuclei, and apparent cytoplasmic membranes can often be observed, but there are no definite cell walls.

The number of nuclei in the embryo sac varies according to the species, or rarely even within a species. Although 8 is by far the most common number, 4 is not rare, and numbers as high as 128 have been recorded. No species is known to have less than four as a normal number. There are some species in which more than one megaspore contributes to the formation of the embryo sac, and at least one (*Casuarina*) in which a number of embryo sacs are produced in one ovule.

Typically the two nuclei formed in the first division of the megaspore migrate to opposite ends of the developing embryo sac. Each nucleus then divides into two, and each of these two into two more, so that the embryo sac has four nuclei at each end. One nucleus from each end then migrates to the center of the embryo sac, so that three nuclei remain at each end and two lie near the center. The three nuclei

at the end farthest from the micropyle are called the **antipodal nuclei.** They have no apparent function and are usually interpreted as evolutionary vestiges of the vegetative body of the female gametophyte. The two nuclei in the center are often called the **polar nuclei,** in reference to their origin at the two ends or poles of the embryo sac. Their function is discussed on p. 621. One of the three nuclei at the micropylar end of the embryo sac is the **egg.** The other two are called **synergid nuclei,** referring to a now rejected suggestion that they somehow assist in fertilization of the egg. Presumably they represent vestiges of the archegonium or of the vegetative body of the gametophyte.

One of the most notable aberrancies in embryo-sac development is that found in many members of the lily family, discussed here because lilies became standard laboratory material for the study of ovular development before it was realized that they do not follow the usual pattern. Three of the four megaspores fuse to form a nucleus with $3n$ chromosomes. This $3n$ nucleus gives rise by mitotic divisions to the antipodal nuclei and one of the two polar nuclei, while the egg, the synergids, and the other polar nucleus are derived mitotically from the remaining megaspore. In ordinary microscopic preparations, the four triploid nuclei of the embryo sac are visibly larger than the four haploid nuclei.

DEVELOPMENT OF THE POLLEN

The stamen is essentially the microsporophyll of an angiosperm, and the pollen sacs are the microsporangia. Usually there are two pollen sacs, each of which is divided by a lengthwise partition so that the anther contains four locules or pollen chambers. Each pollen chamber in the

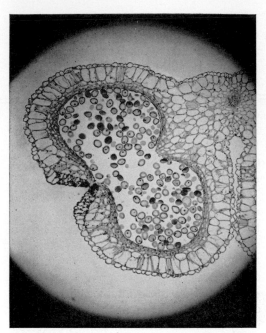

Fig. 30.17. Cross section of part of lily anther, showing one pollen sac, with pollen ready to be discharged; the partition between the two chambers of the pollen sac has broken down, and the pollen sac is ready to dehisce. (Copyright by General Biological Supply House, Inc., Chicago.)

early stages of development has a central vertical strand (one to several cells thick) of microspore mother cells surrounded by a single layer of specialized nutritive tissue, the **tapetum.** The tapetum, in turn, is surrounded by the tissues which form the walls of the pollen chamber.

The microspore mother cells, often called **pollen mother cells,** have $2n$ chromosomes and represent the last stage in the sporophyte generation, comparable to the megaspore mother cell of the ovule. Each microspore mother cell undergoes reduction division to produce a usually spherical tetrad of microspores. The microspores have n chromosomes and represent the first stage in the male gametophyte generation.

The microspores of a tetrad usually separate from each other before developing, with little or no increase in size, into **pollen grains.** Each pollen grain is a young male gametophyte, with usually two nuclei (these being produced mitotically from the original microspore nucleus). The **generative nucleus,** with a small amount of differentiated cytoplasm around it, floats freely in the cytoplasm of the **tube cell,** which fills the grain. The generative cell, which later gives rise to the sperms, is thus enclosed within the tube cell, which later produces the pollen tube that carries the sperms to the egg. The tube cell has its own nucleus; the tube nucleus and the generative nucleus are the two nuclei of the pollen grain.

The wall of the pollen grain consists of an **exine,** or outer layer, and an **intine,** or inner layer; each of these, in turn, consists of two or more sublayers. Usually there are one or more slits or circular openings, the germ pores, in the exine, through which the intine bulges out when the grain germinates. The pollen of most dicots is tricolpate (with three germ pores), but that of most monocots and some of the more primitive dicots is monocolpate (with one germ pore). The exine is often provided with minute spines or low ridges. These and other variations in the structure of the wall, as well as the shape of the pollen grain, often provide useful taxonomic characters.

The tapetum sometimes degenerates and disappears as the pollen grains mature. In other species it remains more or less intact and functions as a secretory tissue. In either case it evidently provides nourishment for the developing pollen grains.

When the pollen grains are mature, the anther opens and releases them. Usually the partition between the two pollen chambers of each sac breaks down to some

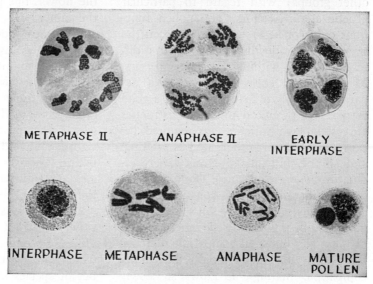

Fig. 30.18. Series of photomicrographs showing reduction division and development of pollen grains in *Trillium erectum*, a lily in which n = 5. Zygotene, pachytene, diplotene, and diakenesis are very early, early, middle, and late stages of the prophase of the first division in meiosis. (Courtesy of A. H. Sparrow, Brookhaven National Laboratory, Upton, N.Y.)

extent, and the sac dehisces (opens) along the furrow between the two pollen chambers.

POLLINATION

The transfer of pollen from the anther to the stigma is called **pollination**. Most angiosperms are normally cross-pollinated, but self-pollination is not uncommon.

Cross-pollination has the advantage of producing new and different combinations of existing genes (see Chapters 35 and 36), but self-pollination is a more certain method, not subject to the vagaries of wandering breezes or flighty insects.

Many species have special mechanisms which prevent or restrict self-pollination. The stigma may become receptive to pollen before the stamens of the same flower are

Angiosperms: Flowers **617**

mature, or vice versa. The style may be very long and the stamens very short, so that the pollen does not readily fall onto the stigma, or the stamens may extend out of the corolla, with the same result. Self-pollination is obviously impossible in dioecious plants, such as willow, and is restricted to a lesser extent in monoecious plants, such as corn.

One of the commonest mechanisms restricting *effective* self-pollination is **self-sterility.** Investigations into the genetics of self-sterility have regularly shown that the breeding population consists of several or many groups of individuals, all members of each group being alike (and different from other groups) with regard to particular genetic sterility-factors. The pollen functions only (or best) when it lands on the stigma of an individual belonging to a different group within the same species. Many of our cultivated fruit trees are partly or wholly self-sterile, so that a good crop is not produced unless two varieties are used. Two varieties are required because fruit trees are propagated by grafting, and all the individuals of one variety ordinarily belong to a single clone, with essentially identical genetic constitution.

The genes governing self-sterility commonly act by influencing the rate of growth of the pollen tube. In compatible matings, the pollen tube grows rapidly, but in incompatible matings, it grows so slowly that it fails to reach the embryo sac, or else it reaches it only after the egg has ceased to be receptive.

Insects are the most common agents of cross-pollination, but many flowers are pollinated by wind instead, and a considerable number are pollinated by birds. A few kinds of flowers are pollinated by bats, and a few others by water currents. All these pollinators sometimes also transfer the pollen merely from one flower to another on the same plant, so that the plants are still, in effect, self-pollinated.

Bees, wasps, butterflies, and moths usually visit flowers in search of nectar; often they (especially bees) gather and use pollen as well. In collecting the nectar at the base of a flower, the insect almost unavoidably brushes against the anthers and the stigma. Some of the pollen remains on the insect and may be brushed off on the stigma of some flower visited later. The stigma is generally slightly sticky, and a pollen grain that touches it is likely to remain there. The insect does not consciously or intentionally pollinate the flower, but pollination is effected just the same.

On any individual trip from the hive or nest, a bee usually visits flowers of only one kind, ignoring others, unless the supply is very restricted. The flower constancy of bees is one of the factors restricting interspecific hybridization. Many species which will produce hybrids when artificially pollinated only rarely hybridize in nature, because the pollen does not usually get transferred from one species to the other.

Some kinds of flowers attract a wide variety of insect visitors; others are usually visited by only one or a few species, to which they are especially adapted. A number of species have flowers with the odor and often the color of dung or rotten meat, attracting flies which normally lay their eggs on these substances. Some South African and Australian orchids have flowers which simulate the females of certain species of wasps, thus attracting the males, which inadvertently transfer the pollen in attempting to perpetuate their own kind. In many regions the bumblebee is the only effective pollinator of red clover; ordinary honeybees cannot reach the nectar. Charles Darwin accurately predicted the discovery of a moth with a tongue 11 inches long in Madagascar, because this length would be required to reach the nectar of a certain orchid (*Angraecum sesquipedale*) in a moth-pollinated genus.

Plants with large white flowers often attract night-flying insects, such as moths. *Yucca* depends for pollination on a moth (*Pronuba*) which shows every external evidence of knowing exactly what it is doing. It gathers the pollen, rolls it into a ball, flies to the flower of another plant, lays eggs in the ovary, and then pats the pollen onto the stigma. Some of the developing ovules are eaten by the caterpillars, but generally some remain to mature seeds.

Birds are more important as pollinators in the tropics and in the Southern Hemisphere than in north temperate regions, but even in the United States, hummingbirds are the normal pollinators for some plants, such as the red-flowered species of Indian paintbrush (*Castilleja*).

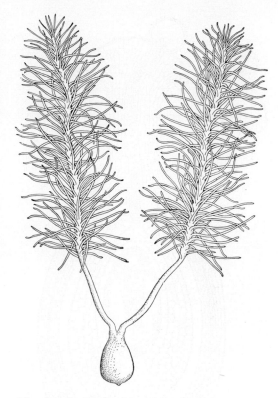

Fig. 30.19. Pistil of a grass, showing feathery stigmas adapted to wind pollination. (×100.) (From W. H. Brown, *The Plant Kingdom*, 1935; courtesy of Ginn & Company, Boston.)

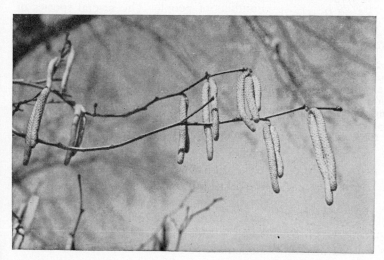

Fig. 30.20. Catkins of filbert (*Corylus avellana*), a wind-pollinated plant with much reduced flowers. A catkin is a kind of spike, characteristic of a number of mostly wind-pollinated trees. (Photo courtesy of T. H. Everett.)

Angiosperms: Flowers **619**

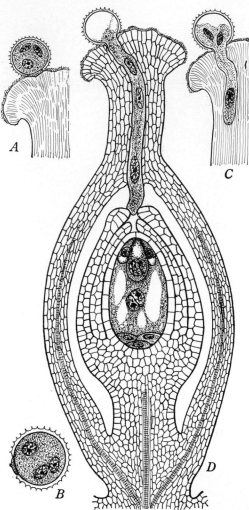

Fig. 30.21. **Diagrammatic representation of an ovary with an orthotropous ovule, showing development of the pollen tube.** *B,* a pollen grain with a tube nucleus and two sperm nuclei; *A,* pollen grain on stigma; *C,* germinating pollen grain; *D,* pollen tube entering the micropyle. (From W. H. Brown, *The Plant Kingdom,* 1935; courtesy of Ginn & Company, Boston.)

Hummingbirds also visit many kinds of flowers (e.g., gladioli) for which they are not the only pollinators.

Wind-pollinated plants generally produce large quantities of pollen, enough to overcome the tremendous waste inherent in the method. The pollen is often carried for long distances, sometimes thousands of miles. Most wind-pollinated plants have small and inconspicuous flowers (Fig. 30.20), often without petals, and many of them have relatively very large, brush-like stigmas (Fig. 30.19). Many or most grasses are wind-pollinated, although many others are self-pollinated instead.

There is some correlation between the method of pollination and the number of ovules borne in an ovary. Efficiency in wind-pollinated plants requires numerous pollen-catching stigmas, and each ovary usually produces only a single ovule. A single stigma, on the other hand, can provide for most or all of the numerous pollen grains that may be brought in by a single insect visit, and insect-pollinated plants typically have several or many ovules per ovary.

Many people show an allergic reaction, called hay fever, to the pollen of one or more kinds of plants. Probably almost any species could so affect somebody under the proper circumstances, but only wind-pollinated plants generally shed enough pollen into the air to affect large numbers of people. The several species of ragweed (*Ambrosia*) are the most serious cause of hay fever in the United States, but oaks, cottonwoods, sagebrush, certain grasses, and various other plants are important in some regions. Goldenrods, popularly reputed to cause hay fever, are relatively innocuous; being insect-pollinated, most of them release little or no pollen into the air. Possibly their bad reputation comes from the fact that they are the most conspicuous wild flowers in the eastern United States during the late summer and early fall, when the real villain, ragweed, is shedding its pollen.

Events Leading to Fertilization

The sticky fluid covering the surface of the stigma contains water, sugars, and other substances. In this environment the pollen grain germinates almost immediately. Many kinds of pollen grains can be induced to germinate by putting them in a dilute sugar solution, but others require more specialized conditions that are generally provided only by the stigma of their own species.

The intine bulges out, usually through one of the openings in the exine, producing a **pollen tube** which penetrates the stigma and grows down through the style. The protoplasm of the pollen grain flows into the tube, leaving the empty grain still perched on the stigma. The protoplast of the pollen tube produces digestive enzymes which decompose the surrounding tissue of the style. Some of the digestion products are absorbed and used as food by the protoplast of the pollen tube.

The tube nucleus (i.e., the nucleus of the tube cell) usually lies near the growing tip of the pollen tube, with the generative nucleus a little farther behind. During the growth of the pollen tube, the generative nucleus divides mitotically, giving rise to two sperms, each with a small amount of differentiated cytoplasm, but without definite walls or locomotor structures. (In some species the generative nucleus divides earlier, so that the mature pollen grain has three nuclei instead of two.) The protoplast of the tube cell, with its included sperms, continues to occupy the forward part of the growing pollen tube, and the more or less emptied rear part often degenerates, so that the pollen tube is severed from the empty pollen grain.

Eventually the pollen tube reaches and penetrates the ovule. In many species it enters through the micropyle, but in others it enters through the side or the funicular end. The micropyle in angiosperms is merely an evolutionary vestige from their gymnospermous ancestry. On reaching the embryo sac, the pollen tube bursts at the end, discharging the two sperms. The tube nucleus and the cytoplasm of the pollen tube then die and degenerate, leaving the sperms free in the embryo sac.

One of the two sperms fuses with the egg. The fertilized egg has $2n$ chromosomes and represents the first stage in the new sporophyte generation. By a series of mitotic divisions, the fertilized egg later gives rise to the embryo of the seed.

The other of the two sperms fuses with the two polar nuclei near the middle of the embryo sac, forming a **triple-fusion nucleus** with ordinarily $3n$ chromosomes. Sometimes the two polar nuclei fuse with each other before the arrival of the sperm, forming a diploid fusion nucleus which in turn fuses with the sperm. The triple-fusion nucleus, or **endosperm nucleus,** typically gives rise, by a series of mitotic divisions, to the **endosperm** of the seed, a food-storage tissue. In many plants, however, the endosperm degenerates before the seed is mature, and the food is stored in the embryo, the nucellus, or even in the seed coat.

The events following discharge of the sperms into the embryo sac are often referred to as **double fertilization,** because the true fertilization (fusion of the sperm and egg) is accompanied by the other fusion process (fusion of the other sperm with the polar nuclei or with the fusion nucleus formed from the polar nuclei), which also resembles fertilization. Double fertilization is a characteristic feature of

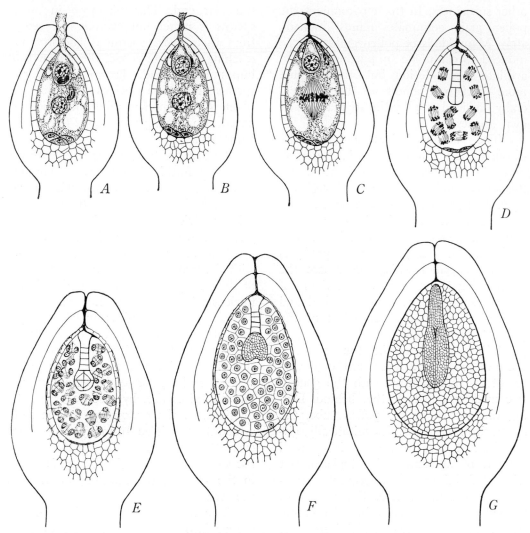

Fig. 30.22. Diagrammatic representation of fertilization and development of embryo. *A*, the pollen tube has entered through the micropyle, and a curved sperm nucleus lies in the egg just below the egg nucleus; the two polar nuclei have fused to form a single nucleus and the second sperm is near this fusion nucleus. *B*, the sperm and egg nuclei are nearly fused, and the second sperm is fusing with the nucleus formed by fusion of the polar nuclei, to form the endosperm nucleus. *C*, the endosperm nucleus is dividing. *D*, a young embryo has developed from the fertilized egg, and numerous endosperm nuclei are dividing. *E*, a more advanced stage. *F*, the cotyledons of the embryo are beginning to differentiate, and the endosperm has become cellular. *G*, a seed in which the embryo is surrounded by endosperm and this by two integuments. (From W. H. Brown, *The Plant Kingdom*, 1935; courtesy of Ginn & Company, Boston.)

angiosperms and is not known to occur in any other group of plants. The use of a triploid rather than a haploid or diploid tissue for food storage has no apparent special value and is usually thought to be a mere evolutionary happenstance. (Haploid tissue adequately performs the same function in gymnosperm seeds.) Most botanists doubt that such a process would be likely to originate and become fixed more than once (i.e., in separate evolutionary lines), and the regular occurrence of double fertilization is one of the features which contribute to the belief that the angiosperms are a truly natural group.

APOMIXIS

Some kinds of angiosperms set seed without fertilization, either regularly or as an alternative to the normal sexual process. The setting of seed without fertilization is called **apomixis**. Apomixis was first noted in 1839, in female plants of a dioecious Australian euphorbiad (*Alchornea*

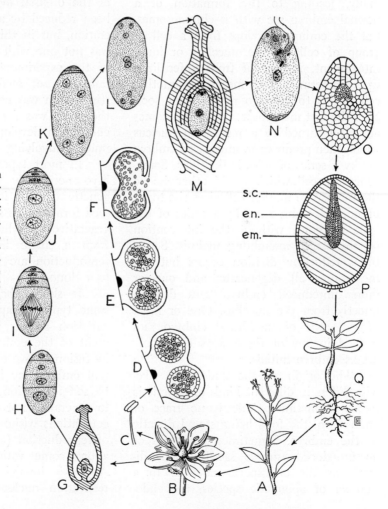

Fig. 30.23. Life cycle of an angiosperm. *A*, mature sporophyte; *B*, flower; *C*, stamen; *D–F*, development of pollen; *G*, pistil; *H–L*, development of embryo sac; *M*, growth of the pollen tube toward the embryo sac; *N*, release of the sperms into the embryo sac; *O*, developing embryo and endosperm; *P*, mature seed; *Q*, seedling: em., embryo; en., endosperm; s.c., seed coat.

s.c.
en.
em.

ilicifolia), which set seed abundantly in cultivation at Kew Gardens in England, half a world away from the male plants in Australia. Some species of a common North American (and Eurasian) genus, *Antennaria,* are represented chiefly or wholly by female plants over large parts of their range, whereas male and female plants occur together in other areas.

The mechanism of apomixis varies in different species, and sometimes even in different ovules of the same flower. Sometimes reduction division occurs normally, leading to the formation of a normal embryo sac with n chromosomes, but the embryo develops from a cell or group of cells of the nucellus or inner integument, instead of from a fertilized egg. Sometimes the megaspore mother cell begins to undergo meiosis, but soon after the first metaphase, the chromosomes are all returned to a restitution nucleus which then produces an unreduced embryo sac by a series of mitotic divisions. Sometimes the cell which would otherwise be the megaspore mother cell gives rise to an unreduced embryo sac by a series of mitotic divisions, without the intervention of any stages resembling meiosis. Sometimes reduction division occurs but the megaspores all degenerate, and one or more unreduced embryo sacs develop directly from the nucellus. One or more of the cells of unreduced embryo sacs formed in any of these ways commonly act as embryo initials.

The origin of the endosperm likewise differs in different kinds of apomictic plants. Sometimes there is no trace of endosperm, the food being stored directly in the embryo. Sometimes a nucleus of an unreduced embryo sac functions directly as the endosperm nucleus. In a number of apomictic species, the endosperm nucleus is formed by fusion of two nuclei from a reduced or unreduced embryo sac with a sperm liberated from a pollen tube; in this case pollination is necessary for seed production, even though the embryo itself is not a product of fertilization.

In one experiment, the pollen of one species of lily was transferred to the stigma of another for ten successive generations without showing any influence in the offspring. Under normal conditions of sexual reproduction, the hereditary contribution of the original ovule parent would have been reduced by about half in each generation, but in this instance, its influence was not one whit diminished at the end of the experiment. Unpollinated flowers failed to set seed, showing that pollen stimulation was necessary. The embryo of the seeds was formed asexually, but the endosperm developed only from a fusion nucleus involving a sperm.

In most types of apomixis, the embryo necessarily has exactly the same genetic constitution as the parent, and seed formation is genetically equivalent to vegetative reproduction. Plants descended from a single individual by apomictic reproduction are thus usually equivalent to a clone.

It should be noted, however, that some types of apomixis do allow some variation among the offspring. Development of the embryo from a cell formed by fusion of two cells of an otherwise normal embryo sac is genetically equivalent to self-pollination, or to self-fertilization in general. If not continued for too many generations without outcrossing, this type of reproduction (as noted in Chapter 35) allows some variation in the offspring. Apomixis involving the formation of a restitution nucleus allows some crossing over between chromosomes which pair in the first metaphase, and thus some variation among the diploid nuclei which make up the embryo sac is permitted; the possibility of variation among the embryos is therefore also established. Crossing over, i.e., the exchange of materials between chromosomes which pair during meiosis, is further discussed in Chapters 4 and 35.

The causes of apomixis are only poorly understood, but there is a clear correlation between apomixis and the occurrence of more than two complete sets of chromosomes in the nucleus. This latter condition, called polyploidy, is discussed in Chapter 35. It should be noted, however, that not all apomicts are polyploid, nor are all polyploids apomictic.

Most of the larger families of angiosperms include some apomictic species or genera. Blackberries, hawthorns, and dandelions are familiar apomictic groups. In all cases, apomixis appears to be the derived condition and sexuality the ancestral one. Many species have sexual and apomictic forms which are otherwise apparently indistinguishable, although the sexual progeny of a single individual may show as much variation as several distinct apomictic lines. Most of the habitually apomictic groups also throw at least a few sexual offspring, but in some cases apomixis appears to be wholly obligatory.

Flowers of apomictic plants usually resemble their sexual counterparts in appearance, although the showy parts are sometimes a little less well developed. The pollen of apomictic plants, especially polyploid apomicts, is often irregularly or poorly developed, and the failure to produce normal amounts of viable pollen is usually a good sign of apomixis. Hybrids between normal sexual species may also fail to produce good pollen, however, and some such hybrids reproduce so vigorously by vegetative means as to form good-sized populations. Most kinds of apomixis can readily be demonstrated by emasculating the flowers and preventing pollination, but apomixis requiring pollen stimulation can usually be detected only by prolonged experimental work or very careful cytological observations.

POLYEMBRYONY

Apomictic seeds not infrequently have more than one embryo, although normal sexual seeds rarely do. In the normal sexual cycle, only one cell, the egg, receives the stimulus (fertilization) necessary to induce its development into an embryo; in apomictic reproduction fertilization is dispensed with, and the more obscure stimuli which induce the formation of an embryo may affect several different cells. Two or more cells of an unreduced embryo sac may independently become embryo initials. Two or more embryo sacs may be formed, each giving rise to an embryo. Sometimes one embryo sac develops in the normal sexual fashion, while the others develop adventitiously from unreduced nucellar tissue; in other instances they are all unreduced. Sometimes the embryos develop directly from nucellar tissue, without relation to embryo sacs.

SUGGESTED READING

Grant, Verne, The flower constancy of bees, *Bot. Rev. 16*:379–398. 1950.

Gustafsson, Åke, Apomixis in higher plants, *Lunds Univ. Årsskr. N.F. Avd. 2. 42* (3): 1–67. 1946; *43* (2):71–179. 1947; *43*(12): 183–371. 1947. A thorough review.

Stebbins, G. L., Jr. Apomixis in angiosperms, *Bot. Rev. 7*:507–542. 1941. Less detailed than Gustafsson, but more readily understandable to a beginning student.

Angiosperms: Fruits, Seeds, and Seedlings

CHAPTER 31

FRUITS

INTRODUCTION

The ripened ovary, together with any other structures that ripen with it and form a unit with it, is called the **fruit.** It will be noted that the botanical definition of a fruit is broader than a housewife's definition. Botanically, a string bean or a corn grain is as much a fruit as is a peach or a strawberry. The old chestnut "Is a tomato a fruit or a vegetable?" raises no botanical problem. Botanically, the tomato is a fruit; so is a chestnut. Vegetable, on the other hand, is a nontechnical term, not much used botanically except in such expressions as "the vegetable kingdom."

The ovary wall of the ripe fruit is called the **pericarp.** It may be soft or hard, fleshy or dry. Often it consists of two or three distinct layers, an **exocarp** (outer layer), **mesocarp** (middle layer), and **endocarp** (inner layer). The exocarp often forms

◄
Fruits of milkweed, *Asclepias syriaca.* The fruit, consisting of a single carpel, is a follicle. The wind-borne seeds have a tuft of hairs at one end. (Photo by John H. Gerard, from National Audubon Society.)

627

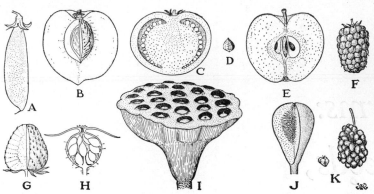

Fig. 31.1. Some types of fruits: *A*, legume (pea); *B*, drupe (peach); *C*, berry (tomato); *D*, achene (buckwheat); *E*, pome (apple); *F*, aggregate accessory (blackberry); *G*, aggregate accessory (strawberry); *H*, aggregate accessory (rose); *I*, nuts or nut-like achenes of Oriental lotus, embedded in the enlarged receptacle; *J*, multiple (syconium of fig); *K*, multiple (mulberry). (From Transeau, Sampson, and Tiffany, *Textbook of Botany*, Rev. Ed., Harper, 1953.)

a mere epidermis, or an epidermis-like covering several cells thick.

The form, texture, and structure of fruits are almost infinitely variable, and any attempt to name and classify the kinds is necessarily arbitrary and imperfect. In general, a fruit derived from a single pistil, and no other parts of the flower, is called a **simple fruit;** one derived from a single pistil, plus some other part(s) of the flower, is called a **simple accessory fruit;** one derived from several or many pistils of a single flower, but no other parts, is an **aggregate fruit;** one derived from several or many pistils of one flower, together with the receptacle or some other part(s) of the flower, is an **aggregate accessory fruit;** and one derived from several or many flowers is a **multiple fruit.**

SIMPLE AND SIMPLE ACCESSORY FRUITS

The vast majority of fruits are derived from only one pistil and thus fall into either the simple or the simple accessory type. An otherwise simple fruit derived from an inferior ovary is considered to be a simple accessory fruit, because the hypanthium (or receptacle) is joined to the ovary and ripens with it. Except for the remnants of the calyx, there is often little or nothing in the appearance of a simple accessory fruit to distinguish it from a simple fruit, and several kinds of simple fruits have close parallels among the simple accessory fruits. It is customary, therefore, to treat the two groups collectively in any further classification. Most simple and simple accessory fruits fit fairly well into the following scheme:

I. Fleshy fruits—pericarp partly or wholly fleshy
   A. Berry—pericarp fleshy throughout, or with a hard or leathery rind; carpels and seeds one or more
      1. Typical berry—pericarp fleshy essentially throughout, the exocarp forming merely a thin skin. Examples: grape, tomato, pepper, blueberry, gooseberry
      2. Pepo—a berry with a hard rind. Examples: watermelon, squash, cucumber
      3. Hesperidium—a berry with a leathery, separable rind, and with parchment-like partitions. Examples: oranges and other citrus fruits
   B. Drupe—endocarp stony, forming a pit that usually encloses a single seed; carpels one or more; less often several one-seeded pits in the fruit. Examples: cherry, peach, plum, olive, walnut
   C. Pome—endocarp papery or sometimes bony, forming a core with usually several seeds;

outer part of the fruit derived from the thickened hypanthium; carpels usually several. Examples: apple, pear, quince

II. Dry fruits—pericarp dry
   A. Dehiscent fruits—opening when ripe, releasing usually several or many seeds
      1. Legume—carpel one, generally splitting along two sutures. Examples: pea, bean
      2. Follicle—carpel one, generally splitting along only one suture. Examples: milkweed, columbine, larkspur
      3. Capsule—carpels two or more
         a. Typical capsule, usually dehiscing in one of the four following ways:
            1) Along the middle of each carpel, thus through the locules—loculicidal dehiscence. Examples: tulip and other lilies, iris
            2) Along the line of fusion of adjacent carpels, thus through the partitions—septicidal dehiscence. Example: azalea
            3) By pores, usually near the tips of the carpels—poricidal dehiscence. Example: poppy
            4) Around the middle, so that the top comes off as a lid—circumscissile dehiscence. Examples: portulaca, plantain
         b. Silique—an elongate, narrow capsule, apparently composed of two carpels, the pericarp falling off as two valves, leaving the persistent partition, which bears the seeds on its margins. Example: mustard
         c. Silicle—similar to a silique, but short, not much, if at all, longer than wide. Examples: sweet alyssum, shepherd's-purse
   B. Indehiscent fruits—remaining closed when ripe, retaining the usually few or solitary seeds
      1. Achene—fruit rather small, seldom over 1 cm long, the pericarp not especially thick and hard, not produced into a wing, the seed solitary and attached to the pericarp only by the funiculus. The most typical kind of dry indehiscent fruit, of which the others in this list (except the schizocarp) may be considered to be modified or special types. Examples: buttercup, sunflower, buckwheat, dandelion
      2. Caryopsis (grain)—like an achene, but the pericarp and seed coat firmly united, so that the seed is not loose inside the fruit. Examples: all grasses, including corn and the cereal grains
      3. Samara—like an achene, but with the pericarp produced into a thin, flat wing; sometimes composed of two duplicate halves, each with its own seed and wing. Examples: ash, elm, maple, tree of heaven
      4. Nut—like an achene, but larger, and with a thicker and harder wall. Examples: acorn, hazelnut
      5. Schizocarp—carpels two or more, splitting apart at maturity, each carpel remaining closed around its usually solitary seed. Examples: carrot, parsley, parsnip, mallow

The student will note that the botanical definitions of berry and nut do not match common usage, although there is some overlap with common usage in each case. Raspberries, blackberries, and strawberries are aggregate or aggregate accessory fruits, rather than berries in a botanical sense, and tomatoes and peppers would not be considered berries by a housewife. Most of the nuts eaten at Christmas time are not nuts in a botanical sense. Brazil nuts are seeds with a very thick seed coat; peanut shells are modified legumes, and the peanuts are the seeds. Pecans and wal-

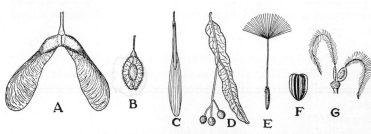

Fig. 31.2. Some simple, dry, indehiscent fruits: *A*, double samara of maple; *B*, samara of elm; *C*, samara of ash; *D*, berry-like achene or nut of basswood; *E*, achene of dandelion; *F*, achene of sun flower; *G*, achene of clematis. (From Transeau, Sampson, and Tiffany, *Textbook of Botany*, Rev. Ed., Harper, 1953.)

Fig. 31.3. Some dry, dehiscent fruits: Left, follicles of milkweed. (Courtesy of J. Arthur Herrick.) Right, capsule of *Clusia*, the outer walls of the five carpels spread away from the axile placenta. (Courtesy of José Cuatrecasas.)

nuts are atypical drupes in which the somewhat fleshy outer part of the pericarp opens to release the hard endocarp, which thus corresponds to the pit of a cherry or peach.

The drupe (Fig. 31.1) is the characteristic fruit of one subfamily of the Rosaceae but is also found in a number of other families. Cherries, peaches, and plums are typical members of this subfamily (the Drupoideae). The pome (Fig. 31.1) is the characteristic fruit of another subfamily (Pomoideae) of the Rosaceae and is not ordinarily found in other groups.

The correct definition of a legume (Fig. 31.1) is "the fruit of a member of the family Leguminosae." All legumes are unicarpellate; the vast majority of them are dry, and most of them dehisce along two sutures. Only a few fruits found in other families meet these qualifications; those which do are considered to be slightly unusual follicles.

Siliques and silicles are the characteristic fruits of members of the mustard family (Cruciferae) and are not found elsewhere. The term *silique* is sometimes loosely used to include silicles as well as true siliques. A few fruits of the Cruciferae are indehiscent, or lack a partition, but are still considered to be siliques or silicles, according to their shape.

The correct definition of a caryopsis is "the ripened ovary of a member of the family Gramineae" (the grass family). Most caryopses fit the standard characterization given in the foregoing classification, but the seed of *Sporobolus* (dropseed grass) and some other grasses is loose within the pericarp, and the fruit thus fits the standard definition of an achene.

AGGREGATE AND AGGREGATE ACCESSORY FRUITS

A relatively small proportion of angiosperms have fruits derived from several pistils of a single flower. Many or most of these, and all the best-known ones, belong to the family Rosaceae. The raspberry is an aggregate fruit, composed of a number of loosely coherent drupelets (very small drupes) that separate as a group from the hemispherical receptacle, which remains attached to the pedicel. Blackberries (Fig. 31.1) differ from raspberries in that the receptacle and its attached drupe-

lets separate from the pedicel as a unit, forming an aggregate accessory fruit. The enlarged receptacle constitutes the fleshy part of a strawberry, and the apparent seeds scattered over its surface are really small achenes, each with a single seed. The strawberry is thus an aggregate accessory fruit.

MULTIPLE FRUITS

Multiple fruits occur in a considerable number of plants, but only a few of these, such as the pineapple, mulberry, and fig, are generally familiar in the United States. Multiple fruits generally consist of a whole inflorescence, with many crowded, small, more or less reduced flowers that coalesce as they mature. The core of the pineapple is the axis of the inflorescence, and the more commonly eaten part represents the ovaries and the fused bases of the essentially sessile flowers, which are demarked by grooves in the surface of the mature fruit. In *Morus* (mulberry) the staminate and pistillate flowers are in separate inflorescences. Each pistillate flower has a single one-celled ovary which develops into an achene enclosed by the thickened, juicy calyx (there is no corolla), and the calyces of adjacent flowers become coalescent (Fig. 31.1).

The multiple fruit of figs is a special type, called a syconium (Fig. 31.1). The peduncle (stalk of the inflorescence) is enlarged and hollowed out at the end, with an opening at the top, forming a fleshy common receptacle that is lined by the very small, unisexual flowers. Staminate and pistillate flowers are borne in the same or different inflorescences, according to the species. Each pistillate flower has a single, unicellular ovary which develops

Fig. 31.4. Pineapples in Hawaii. The entire inflorescence of each plant ripens into a multiple fruit. (Photo from the U.S. Forest Service.)

into a sort of achene. The common commercial fig will mature without pollination; the achenes then remain very small and relatively undeveloped, forming the familiar tiny "seeds" of the fig.

SEED DISPERSAL

Wind, animals (including birds), water, and explosive dehiscence are the principal means of seed dispersal. The whole plant, the fruit, or only the seeds may be transported, and the structure is often evidently correlated with the means of dispersal.

Tumbleweeds, such as Russian thistle (*Salsola kali*) and Jim Hill mustard (*Sisymbrium altissimum*) are carried about by the wind during the fall and winter, dropping seeds as they go. These plants have much branched stems, commonly forming a rounded mass that has considerable wind resistance but little weight.

Fleshy fruits are commonly eaten by birds and mammals. The seeds may be dis-carded without being eaten, but more often they are eaten along with the fruit and are later passed out of the alimentary tract. The endocarp or the seed coat in many fleshy fruits is so hard and impervious to water that the seeds do not germinate readily unless they are subjected to the softening action of digestive juices, or unless the outer wall is artificially removed or broken open. Berries of some kinds of mistletoe, commonly eaten by birds, have a very sticky pulp. The birds effectively plant some of the seeds by wiping their bills on the bark of trees after eating.

Indehiscent dry fruits usually have only one or a few seeds, and seed dispersal involves the whole fruit. Samaras, such as those of maple, ash, and elm (Fig. 31.2), are adapted to distribution by wind. Most of the familiar plants with samaras are trees, and the fruit starts its journey some distance above the ground. Many kinds of achenes are also distributed by wind. Those of dandelion (Figs. 31.2, 31.6) and many other members of the family Compositae have a terminal tuft of long hairs

Fig. 31.5. Some fleshy fruits. Above gooseberry (a berry); below, cucumber (a pepo, i.e., a modified berry). (Photos courtesy of T. H. Everett.)

Fig. 31.6. Fruiting heads of dandelion, showing achenes adapted to wind distribution. (Photo courtesy of J. Arthur Herrick.)

formed by the modified calyx. In some species of *Clematis* (Fig. 31.2) and *Anemone*, the achene is tipped by an elongate persistent style that is provided with long hairs over most of its length. Some grasses likewise have a plumose awn attached to the specialized chaffy bract that surrounds the grain.

Many indehiscent fruits are adapted to distribution by animals. Achenes often have hooked or barbed projections which catch in the fur of passing animals. *Bidens*

Fig. 31.7. Schizocarp of carrot—adapted to distribution by animals. (Copyright by General Biological Supply House, Inc., Chicago.)

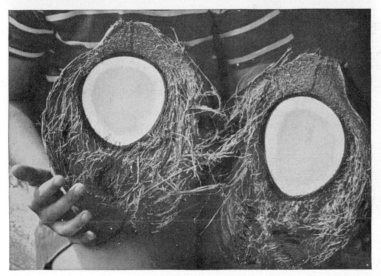

Fig. 31.8. Coconut, a fruit adapted to distribution by water. The "meat" of the coconut is endosperm; the fruit may be called a nut or a dry drupe. (Photo by W. H. Hodge.)

(beggar-ticks) is a well-known example. Other dry fruits, such as the schizocarp of the common carrot, may likewise have barbed prickles (Fig. 31.7). Cocklebur (*Xanthium*) and burdock (*Arctium*) have special types of multiple fruits in which the involucre enclosing the achenes has hooked prickles.

Acorns and some other nuts, or nut-like fruits, are commonly buried by squir-rels as a reserve food supply for use during the winter. Many of these escape redis-covery and the seeds germinate in place. Even without the interference of squirrels, nuts which fall from the tree may roll some distance down a hillside before coming to rest.

Some dry indehiscent fruits are lighter than water and are carried about by streams. The achenes of sedges (*Carex*) are enclosed in a highly modified bract called the perigynium. In many stream-bank species of Carex, the perigynium is inflated, so that the achene readily floats.

The seeds of dehiscent fruits are individually distributed by the same means as are indehiscent fruits, plus the additional means of explosive dehiscence. Tensions develop in the drying pericarp as the fruit ripens, causing it to burst open along lines of weakness. The fruits of Scotch broom (*Cytisus scoparius*), touch-me-not (*Impatiens*), and many other plants dehisce so violently that the seeds are shot several feet through the air.

Many seeds, such as those of milkweed (*Asclepias*) and cottonwood (*Populus*), are provided with a tuft or covering of long, loose hairs which help keep them afloat in the breeze. In *Catalpa* and some other plants the seed coat is produced into a broad, flat wing, so that the seed looks much like a samara. Many conifers also have winged seeds.

The seeds of many weeds are light enough to float or be carried along in water, and the distribution of such seeds by irrigation water is a serious problem in some parts of the western United States.

A few kinds of plants, such as bittersweet (*Celastrus scandens*), have dry, dehiscent fruits which open to expose seeds that have a fleshy coat. Such seeds are commonly eaten by birds, just as are fleshy fruits.

It should be noted that seeds with no very obvious specializations for dispersal manage to get around anyway. Seeds of marsh plants are often carried long distances in the mud on the feet of migrating waterfowl. Severe windstorms may carry seeds, fruits, or even whole plants that are not affected by ordinary breezes. Many plants have been introduced to America in the ballast dumped from ships.

Other things being equal, plants with the most efficient means of seed dispersal will most quickly occupy any new site that becomes available. Some of our commonest weeds do not do well in competition with undisturbed native vegetation but survive because their efficient mechanisms of seed dispersal combined with a large production enable them to quickly occupy any disturbed habitat from which the original vegetation has been removed.

Seed dispersal is, of course, only one of the factors involved in the perpetuation of a plant population. Other factors, such as longevity of the plant, number of seeds produced each year, the amount of food stored in the seed, and the ability to compete with other plants are also important. The distribution and abundance of a species are determined by a balance of all factors, and inefficiency in one respect can often be compensated for by efficiency in others.

SEED STRUCTURE

The seed is the ripened ovule. Seeds vary in size, from barely visible to the naked eye, as in many orchids, to several inches thick, as in coconuts, or sometimes even larger (Fig. 31.10). The two essential parts are the **seed coat**, developed from the integuments of the ovule, and the **embryo**, ordinarily developed from the fertilized egg. Often the embryo is embedded in or accompanied by the **endosperm**, a food-storage tissue derived from the triple-fusion nucleus of the ovule. Usually the nucellus is no longer recognizable in the mature seed, but in some plants it develops into a special food-storage tissue, the **perisperm**. Generally there is not even a recognizable vestige of the embryo sac. A little reflection will show that the seed spans three generations, the old sporophyte, the female gametophyte, and the young sporophyte.

The seed coat may be thin and papery, or hard and bony, or occasionally developed into a fleshy **aril**. The scar marking the attachment of the funiculus to the placenta is called the **hilum**. In seeds developed from anatropous ovules, the funiculus often forms a ridge, the **raphe**, along one edge leading away from the hilum. The micropyle in such seeds is next to the hilum on the side opposite the raphe. Sometimes a part of the seed coat near the micropyle is specialized to form a tumor-like spongy excrescence, the **caruncle**, which in some species absorbs water for the seed during germination.

The embryo is a miniature plant, consisting of a short axis with one or two (rarely more) attached leaves, the **cotyledons**. The part of the axis above the cotyledon(s) is the **epicotyl**, or **plumule**, which becomes the terminal bud of the seedling. The part of the axis immediately below the cotyledon(s) is the **hypocotyl**, a root-stem transition region. The hypocotyl is prolonged at the base into the **radicle**, which becomes the primary root of the seedling. The radicle may or may not be externally differentiated from the hypocotyl, and the latter term is sometimes expanded to include the radicle. Sometimes the radicle consists merely of a group of meristematic cells at the end of the hypocotyl.

Dicotyledons typically have two cotyledons (whence the name) that are essentially opposite. A few of the more primitive species sometimes have three or four cotyledons instead, and a few others have only one. Monocotyledons have only one cotyledon, and this one is often highly modified. Botanists are now agreed that the monocotyledons had ancestors with two cotyledons.

The embryo of grass seeds, including

Fig. 31.9. Long section through a young seed of shepherd's-purse (*Capsella bursa-pastoris*). The embryo, lengthwise near the bottom, has a well-developed suspensor at the left; the endosperm is beginning to degenerate and will be wanting from the mature seed. (Copyright by General Biological Supply House, Inc., Chicago.)

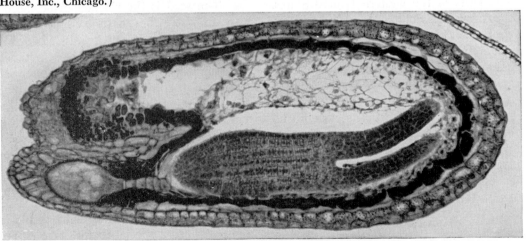

the cereal grains, is unusual in that the epicotyl is completely covered over by a sheath called the **coleoptile,** and the radicle is likewise covered by a sheath called the **coleorhiza.** The coleoptile is generally interpreted as a modified first leaf (after the cotyledon) of the embryo; the coleorhiza may perhaps represent a modified rootcap.

During its early stages, the embryo of a developing ovule becomes differentiated into a basal stalk, or **suspensor,** attached at the micropylar end of the embryo sac, and a terminal body which becomes the proper embryo of the mature seed. The suspensor may be slender and few-celled, or massive and multicellular. In either case it tends to degenerate as the seed matures, and it is represented in the ripe seed, if at all, by a mere remnant at the end of the radicle. The suspensor has no evident function in modern angiosperms; it is regarded as an evolutionary vestige from cryptogamous ancestors in which it may have served to force the embryo sporophyte deeper into the body of the female gametophyte.

The triple-fusion nucleus formed in the embryo sac typically develops by a series of mitotic divisions into the endosperm, a triploid food-storage tissue in the seed. Often, however, the endosperm degenerates before the seed is mature, and the food is stored in some other part of the seed. In peas, garden beans, peanuts, and other legumes, for instance, the food is stored chiefly in the thickened cotyledons. In most members of the Caryophyllales, including carnations and beets, the nucellus develops into a food-storage tissue called the perisperm. Perisperm is similar in appearance to endosperm, and the two can be distinguished only by careful de-

Fig. 31.10. Seed of the Seychelles palm, or double coconut (*Lodoicea maldivica*); this species has the largest seeds in the world. (Photo by W. H. Hodge.)

velopmental study or chromosome counts. It should also be noted that the so-called endosperm which is the food-storage tissue of gymnosperm seeds is actually the body of the female gametophyte.

The food stored in a seed includes proteins, carbohydrates, and fats, the proportions varying with the species. The seeds of legumes often have a relatively high protein content and are among the best vegetable sources of protein. The endosperm of corn has a hard, horny part, with a fair amount of protein, and a softer, starchy part, with a high proportion of starch; next to the seed coat and pericarp, these two regions give way to the aleurone layer of endosperm, which is only one cell thick and is largely filled with protein. In sweet corn much of the carbohydrate of the endosperm remains as sugar instead of being converted into starch.

GERMINATION

INTRODUCTION

Mature seeds of most kinds of plants normally undergo a rest period before developing into new plants. During its early stages of growth, before it has become wholly independent of the food stored in the seed, the new plant is called a **seedling.** The processes occurring from the time the embryo resumes its growth until the seedling is established are collectively called **germination.**

The length of the rest period varies according to the species and the environmental conditions. In mangroves (*Rhizophora*) there is essentially no rest period, and the seed begins to germinate while still attached to the placenta of the ovary. The hypocotyl becomes about a foot long and an inch thick before the developing embryo falls from the tree and plants itself in the soft mud (Fig. 31.11). Many kinds of seeds will germinate soon after the proper environmental conditions are provided, whereas others must undergo internal changes over a period of time before they are responsive to environmental conditions favoring germination.

CONDITIONS REQUIRED FOR GERMINATION

All seeds require a supply of moisture and oxygen for germination, as well as a suitable temperature. Some seeds also require light, although light inhibits the germination of some other kinds of seeds.

Seeds ordinarily have a relatively low water content, and the physiological processes necessary for germination occur only when the proportion of water is increased. Most seeds germinate best when the moisture content of the soil is near the field capacity, but some seeds can absorb enough water to support germination even when the water content of the soil is near the permanent wilting percentage.

Germinating seeds respire rapidly, and

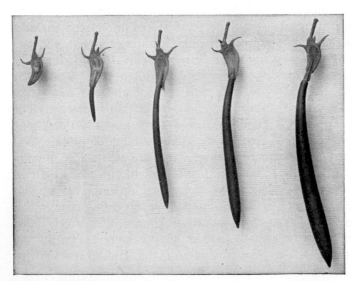

Fig. 31.11. Development of mangrove seedlings. (Photo from the Chicago Natural History Museum.)

a supply of oxygen is necessary. In garden peas and some other kinds of seeds, the seed coat is relatively impervious to oxygen even when wet, and growth during the early stages of germination is supported largely by anaerobic respiration. Even seeds of this sort eventually need oxygen, however, and aerobic respiration becomes dominant as soon as the seed coat is ruptured by the growth of the embryo.

The optimum temperature for germination varies according to the species and the environmental conditions. For any species there is a maximum and a minimum above or below which germination will not occur. The minimum for wheat is only a little above the freezing point, and the maximum is about 35°C. The maximum and minimum for corn, a species of subtropical origin, are about 10° above those for wheat.

The effect of light on germination differs in different species. A few kinds of seeds, especially those of various epiphytes, require light. Some others, including those of numerous grasses, germinate better when exposed to light than when kept in total darkness. Germination of many other kinds of seeds, such as those of onion and some other members of the lily family, is retarded or prevented by light. The effect of light may also vary according to other environmental conditions and the past history of the seed. Seeds of some species of bluegrass (*Poa*) which ordinarily respond favorably to light are indifferent to it after a period of dry storage.

DORMANCY

Freshly ripe seeds of many plants fail to germinate even under favorable environmental conditions. Such seeds are said to be **dormant.** Dormancy may be due to any

of several factors, alone or in combination. The most common of these are: (1) seed coat impervious to water, or oxygen, or both; (2) seed coat mechanically resistant to expansion of the embryo; (3) rudimentary or immature embryo; (4) necessity for further physiological changes (after ripening) in a fully developed embryo; and (5) the presence of chemicals which inhibit germination.

The seed coats of clover, alfalfa, morning-glory, and many other plants are at first impervious to water and probably to oxygen as well. The seed coats of many other plants, including a number of common weeds, such as redroot (*Amaranthus retroflexus*), are permeable to water and oxygen, but so firm that the embryo cannot expand. A bony endocarp or pericarp, such as is found in drupes and nuts, may have the same effect as a hard seed coat.

Under natural conditions seeds with impervious or very firm coats cannot germinate until the coat has softened. The softening may result from decay, from partial digestion in the alimentary tract of an animal, from changes in the colloidal structure of the cell walls caused by repeated wetting and drying, from mechanical rupture of the cells by freezing and thawing, or from any combination of these factors. Dormancy of seeds with hard or impervious coats can also be broken by cracking or deeply scratching the seed coat, a process known as **scarification.** Sulfuric acid is also used for scarification, but the treatment must be carefully controlled to avoid damaging the embryo.

In many kinds of plants the embryo does not develop as rapidly as the rest of the seed, so that the embryo in the "mature" seed is still immature. Many members of the buttercup family, in particular,

Fig. 31.12. Results of an experiment on seeds of *Rosa rubiginosa*. The seeds in the row at the left had been stored dry. Those in the other rows had been stored in moist sand for six months, at the temperatures indicated, and then planted in this flat in a greenhouse. (Photo courtesy of the Boyce Thompson Institute for Plant Research.)

have only rudimentary embryos in the newly ripe seeds, and in orchids the embryo often consists of only a few scarcely differentiated cells when the seed is shed. Such seeds are dormant—i.e., they will not germinate until the embryo has had time to develop more fully.

Many kinds of seeds with fully ripe embryos require a period of **afterripening** and will not germinate when newly ripe, even if the seed coat is removed and all external conditions are favorable. Apple, peach, hawthorn, iris, basswood, ash, dogwood, hemlock, and pine are familiar examples. Most seeds which require a significant afterripening period normally germinate in the spring, after having lain on the ground all winter. Under controlled conditions, afterripening can often be hastened by exposure to low temperatures, or by repeated alternation of high and low temperatures, thus compressing into a short time some of the environmental changes to which the seed is normally exposed during the dormant period. The actual temperatures used vary with the species.

The kinds of physiological change that occur in the seed during afterripening evidently differ in different species. In many cases, such as iris, a particular chemical which inhibits germination must degenerate, although some other changes may be necessary as well. Germination inhibitors occur in the fruits of some plants, as well as in the seeds. Tomato juice inhibits the germination of tomato seeds and many other seeds, even when considerably diluted with water.

Different seeds of the same species often differ in the length of dormancy. A single crop of seeds from a desert annual will commonly produce some seedlings each year for several years. The survival value of this variation among seeds is evident, since otherwise a single bad year with insufficient spring rains might wipe out all the annual plants in a large region. Many common weeds show a similar variability in the length of dormancy. The gardeners' aphorism, "One year's seeding is seven years' weeding," has a solid foundation in fact.

Differences in the physiological requirements of the embryo, as well as in the strength and permeability of the seed coat, contribute to the differences in dormancy of seeds. One of the two seeds in a cocklebur (*Xanthium strumarium*) usually germinates the first spring after maturity, while the other remains dormant another year. The seed coat of cockleburs is relatively impermeable to oxygen, and the two seeds differ in the concentration of oxygen required for germination.

LONGEVITY OF SEEDS

The life span of seeds varies from a few weeks to a thousand years or more, depending on the species and the environmental conditions, but is seldom more than a few decades. Seeds of silver maple (*Acer saccharinum*) ordinarily germinate soon after they are shed (in June), and the seeds which do not find suitable conditions for germination die as soon as the water content drops from an original figure of nearly 60 percent to about 30–34 percent. In nature this often happens within a few weeks.

Seeds of most of our common crop plants live only one or a few years under ordinary conditions of storage. When the seeds are stored at low temperatures and low concentrations of oxygen, respiration and other physiological processes leading to

deterioration are slowed down, and the viability may be prolonged severalfold.

In general, seeds with firm hard coats live longer in ordinary storage than other seeds. The longevity of such seeds is doubtless due in part to the low concentrations of oxygen available to the embryo, but the embryo may also be inherently longer-lived, as a reciprocal adaptation to the long period of dormancy enforced by the seed coat. The record for longevity is held by the Oriental lotus, *Nelumbo nucifera*, a member of the water-lily family with large seeds enclosed in a very hard, dry pericarp. Viable seeds taken in considerable quantities from deep in a peat deposit in Manchuria appear to be about 1000 years old by radiocarbon dating, but the nature and depth of the deposits in which they were found suggest that they may actually be several thousand years old. Fragments of wood associated with viable *Nelumbo* seeds found 20 feet underground in Japan have been dated by the radiocarbon method as about 3000 years old.

Legumes, which often have very hard seed coats, are notoriously long-lived, although they are not known to approach the record of *Nelumbo*. Seeds of a South American species of *Cassia* (a legume) collected in 1776 were successfully germinated 158 years later, in 1934.

Reports of germination of seeds recovered after thousands of years of storage in Egyptian pyramids have not been verified and are more nearly in the category of Barnumesque promotion than scientific record.

In 1879 the late Professor W. J. Beal of Michigan Agricultural College (now Michigan State University) began a continuing experiment on longevity of seeds. Seeds of 20 species of common plants were mixed with sand and buried in the soil in

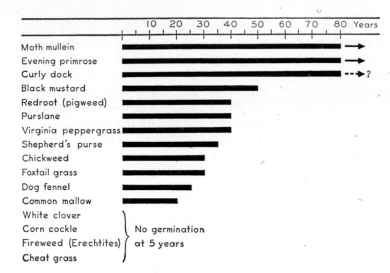

| | 10 | 20 | 30 | 40 | 50 | 60 | 70 | 80 | Years |

Moth mullein →
Evening primrose →
Curly dock --→ ?
Black mustard
Redroot (pigweed)
Purslane
Virginia peppergrass
Shepherd's purse
Chickweed
Foxtail grass
Dog fennel
Common mallow
White clover
Corn cockle } No germination
Fireweed (Erechtites) } at 5 years
Cheat grass }

Fig. 31.13. Longevity of seeds in Beal's experiment.

inverted open bottles. At intervals of 5, and later 10 years, a bottle was dug up and the seeds tested for germination. After 80 years, in 1960, moth mullein (*Verbascum blattaria*) still showed 70 percent germination, evening primrose (*Oenothera biennis*) showed 10 percent germination, and curly dock (*Rumex crispus*) showed 2 percent germination. The principal results of the experiment are shown in Fig. 31.13.

The causes of death of the embryo in stored seeds are only partly understood. Death commonly occurs long before the food supply is exhausted and while the digestive enzymes are still fully potent. Loss of water evidently kills some short-lived seeds but does not otherwise seem to have much significance, and long-lived seeds commonly have an initially low water content. Seedlings from old seeds resemble those from heat-treated or irradiated seeds and show similar aberrations in nuclear structure, but this is an expression of the deterioration, rather than its cause. The one clear lead is that conditions which increase the rate of respiration shorten the life of seeds, and conditions which de-crease the rate of respiration lengthen the life. Therefore it may be surmised that senescence and death of the embryo in seeds are due to the same factors which cause senescence and death of cells in general: physiological imbalances associated with the accumulation of waste materials.

THE GERMINATION PROCESS

Under appropriate environmental conditions, absorption of water by the seed triggers the series of changes resulting in the development of the seedling. The embryo respires rapidly and begins to grow, drawing on the food that has been stored in the seed. In endospermous seeds, the embryo produces digestive enzymes which migrate out into the endosperm and decompose it. Cell walls, protoplasm, and granules, crystals, and globules of stored food are all attacked. The digested materials are absorbed by the cotyledons and passed on to the rest of the embryo as needed. In seeds without endosperm, the digestion of the endosperm and absorption of food by the cotyledons have generally occurred before the seed was ripe, and a similar breakdown now goes on in the cotyledons; eventually the cotyledons shrivel and degenerate or fall off, although they are not resorbed to the same degree as the endosperm. In either case, the cells of the endosperm (or perisperm) degenerate concomitantly with the absorption of food by the cotyledons.

The cells of the embryo are relatively small before germination, and most of the growth, especially the early growth, during germination results from cell enlargement without cell division. The stored food available to the embryo contains proteins, carbohydrates, and fats. The proteins are used mostly in the formation of protoplasm; much of the wall material from the endosperm is reconverted into cell walls; the fats and the remainder of the carbohydrates are largely respired.

The first part of the embryo to emerge from the seed coat is generally the radicle. Emergence of the radicle may be due to elongation of the radicle itself, or to elongation of the hypocotyl, after which the radicle begins to grow. The radicle is positively geotropic, and soon turns down in its growth, regardless of its initial orientation.

The radicle regularly becomes the primary root, and the epicotyl becomes the primary shoot, but the functions of the

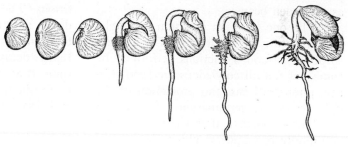

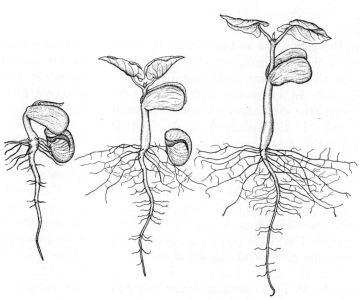

Fig. 31.14. Germination of bean seeds. (From W. H. Brown, *The Plant Kingdom*, 1935; courtesy of Ginn & Company, Boston.)

hypocotyl and cotyledons differ in different kinds of seeds. In seeds with **hypogaeous** germination, such as peas and corn, the hypocotyl remains short, the cotyledons do not emerge from the seed, and if the seed is underground, the epicotyl reaches the surface only by its own growth. In seeds with **epigaeous** germination, such as beans and castor beans, the hypocotyl elongates, bringing the cotyledons and epicotyl (and commonly the remains of the degenerating seed coat) above the ground. Cotyledons which are brought above the ground in germination may thereafter function for some time as ordinary leaves, as in castor beans, or they may show little or no photosynthetic activity and soon fall off, as in garden beans.

The one function common to cotyledons of nearly all kinds of seeds is the absorption of food. Functions performed by some but not all cotyledons are food storage, photosynthesis, and protection of the epicotyl during germination.

The hypocotyl, if it elongates at all, commonly first appears above the ground as an upside-down U, attached at one end to the developing radicle, and at the other to the cotyledons and epicotyl. The hypocotyl then gradually straightens out and pulls the cotyledons and epicotyl above the ground. In epigaeous seeds with endosperm, the cotyledons are commonly still encased in the endosperm and seed coat when they first come up.

Three or four species are commonly studied to illustrate the various types of seed germination. Corn and other grasses are hypogaeous. The hypocotyl remains very short and does not emerge from the ground. The single cotyledon absorbs food from the endosperm, passing it on to the remainder of the embryo. The radicle, covered by the coleorhiza, is the first part

of the embryo to emerge from the seed. Soon after its emergence from the grain, the radicle breaks through the coleorhiza, which plays no further part in germination; the radicle goes on to become the primary root. Shortly after the appearance of the radicle, the epicotyl emerges, still covered by the coleoptile. The coleoptile pushes above the surface of the ground, becoming green and photosynthetic. Soon it is ruptured at the tip by the first ordinary leaves that develop from the epicotyl. Meanwhile, adventitious roots develop from the hypocotyl and eventually from the base of the stem. The primary root is relatively short-lived, and long before the plant is mature, the root system is wholly adventitious. The endosperm is largely broken down and absorbed during germination; the remnants, as well as the pericarp, eventually decay. The cotyledon persists for some time after the seedling has become established, but later it, too, degenerates and disappears.

Garden peas are also hypogaeous, but there is no endosperm, the food being stored in the large, thickened cotyledons which make up most of the embryo. The hypocotyl remains short and the cotyledons do not come above the ground. The radicle is the first part to emerge from the seed coat, after which the plumule appears and develops into the shoot. The cotyledons soften and degenerate as the food is withdrawn from them by the developing seedling; eventually they decay and disappear.

Garden beans (Fig. 31.14) are epigaeous, without endosperm. The radicle emerges first, becoming the primary root. The hypocotyl then elongates, coming above the ground as an inverted U. Straightening of the hypocotyl then pulls the cotyledons and epicotyl above the ground. The cotyledons, by now considerably shrunken, spread apart, revealing the epicotyl, which gives rise to the shoot. The cotyledons become faintly green, and may carry on a small amount of photosynthesis, but they soon fall off.

Castor beans are epigaeous, with endosperm. There is a large caruncle at the micropylar end of the seed, through which water is absorbed, especially during the early stages of germination. The radicle is the first part of the embryo to emerge from the seed coat; it is followed by the hypocotyl, which comes up above the ground and pulls up the cotyledons and epicotyl, just as in the garden bean. At the time the cotyledons are pulled above the ground, they are still encased by a considerable remnant of the endosperm, which in turn is partly covered by the broken remains of the seed coat. The cotyledons spread apart, and any unused part of the endosperm falls off along with the seed coat. The cotyledons then expand considerably and become green, acting as normal leaves, although they are differently shaped from the first leaves that develop from the epicotyl.

SUGGESTED READING

Rickett, H. W., *The Green Earth. An Invitation to Botany,* Jacques Cattell, Lancaster, Pa., 1943, 353 pp. A beautifully written book which might be recommended as collateral reading for almost any chapter of this text.

Angiosperms: Growth and Movement

CHAPTER 32

THE NATURE OF GROWTH

CHARACTERISTICS

Increase in size or weight due to the formation of new protoplasm is called **growth.** Part of the increase may result directly from the absorption of water, or from the formation of cell wall materials, insofar as these changes also depend indirectly on the formation of new protoplasm. When the increase is not related to the formation of new protoplasm—as, for example, when a plasmolyzed cell returns to normal size and weight on being provided with water— it is not considered to be growth, as the term is used by biologists.

Growth is reflected, and can in part be measured, by increase in the amount of protoplasm in the cell, increase in the volume of the cell, extension of the cell wall, increase in the mass of the cell wall (e.g., by the formation of a secondary wall), and increase in the number of cells. All these increases are involved in the growth of any

◄

English Ivy, *Hedera helix*, one branch of which has reverted to the juvenile climbing form after the plant was treated with gibberellic acid. Note the adventitious roots on the juvenile branch. (Photo courtesy of William J. Robbins, New York Botanical Garden.)

tissue or organism, but, in a given cell over a short period of time, any one may be much more prominent than the others.

Growth is ordinarily permanent and irreversible, as long as reasonably normal conditions are maintained. Under starvation conditions some of the protoplasm itself may be respired, however, so that there is a net loss of weight. Volume of the cell, as an indicator of growth, must be measured under constant environmental conditions to avoid differences in turgor. The volume of the bulliform cells found in the leaves of many grasses varies greatly with the turgor, and these changes are neither growth nor loss of growth. Less extreme variation of the same sort occurs normally in other cells.

Some Chemical Aspects of Growth

Growth, like life itself, depends on a delicately balanced set of simultaneous and serial chemical processes. The chemical processes, in turn, depend on substances produced in the cell, on substances which migrate into the cell, and on environmental conditions. Changes in any of these governing factors affect the rate or nature of growth.

Most or all of the constituents of a protoplast are simultaneously involved in several or many chemical reactions, and two adjacent molecules of the same substance have quite different histories and fates. As an aid to understanding, we try to distinguish individual processes, and we are delighted when a balanced equation can be devised to express a reaction; but even these oversimplifications are often difficult to achieve. Some processes occurring in the cell can be duplicated in the test tube, but others, which require the complex and precisely balanced conditions of the cell itself, can be only roughly approximated or cannot even be approached. In spite of these difficulties, great progress has been made in the last several decades; and it is in the field of the relation of cell chemistry to growth that some of the most exciting biological discoveries are to be expected in the next several decades.

The patterns and changes in growth result from changes in the dynamic balance of interacting substances which make up the protoplasm. Any change in the proportion of a particular protoplasmic constituent has a chain of consequences, shifting the point of equilibrium for some other chemical reaction, which in turn causes other changes, etc. Any environmental change affects the chemical processes of the protoplasm unequally, thus shifting the balances and causing further changes. Some parts of the system are relatively stable; others are easily modified. Changes in some protoplasmic constituents have only minor effects on the equilibrium, whereas minute changes in the amount or distribution of others have profound effects. A by-product of some chemical reaction involved in growth may gradually accumulate, without significant effects, until it reaches a threshold level and shifts some important balance.

In addition to making their own food, most green plants can make all the other organic substances they need. Only the inorganic raw materials—water, carbon dioxide, and various minerals—must be supplied. Individual parts of the plant, on the other hand, are generally not self-sufficient. Even when provided with food and raw materials, they usually need minute amounts of complex substances produced elsewhere in the plant. Comparable substances in animal physiology can be classified as **vitamins,** which the animal cannot make and must eat, and **hormones,** which are made in particular parts of the organism—often in highly specialized, well-defined glands—and are carried in the blood stream to all parts of the body.

The distinction between vitamins and hormones in plants is not easy to make. Some animal vitamins are equally necessary for plants and are made by the plant itself, though not in equal amounts in all tissues. One tissue may make an excess, another may be barely self-sufficient, and another may be wholly dependent on a supply which migrates in from other tissues. Some of the necessary substances are strongly migratory, yet they are produced in tissues which have other functions as well, rather than in specialized glands as in animals.

Among the natural plant substances which occur in small quantities but have pronounced effects on growth, it is customary to apply the term *hormone* to distinctly migratory compounds, and the term *vitamin* to less migratory compounds, especially if these latter have similar effects in all parts of the organism, or if they are necessary for continued survival of the cells even without true growth. The distinction between the two classes is not at all sharp, and a vitamin to one botanist may be a hormone to another. The noncommittal term, **growth-regulating substance,** is often used to avoid this problem.

SOME DEVELOPMENTAL ASPECTS OF GROWTH

One of the greatest wonders of growth is that it is so precisely regulated. The organism starts as a single cell, which grows and divides. Before very many divisions have occurred, the cells begin to differentiate from each other, both in their immediate qualities and in their potentialities for further growth. They all have the same basic heredity (all coming eventually from the same zygote), and the environmental differences between two adjacent cells would not seem to be very great, yet the cells do become different, and different in a consistent pattern which is repeated in individual after individual.

The factors controlling the initial differentiation of the cells of the embryo are still obscure. Presumably, growth-regulating substances produced by the surrounding tissues of the ovule reach different parts of the embryo in differing amounts, and these slight differences shunt the cells into different paths of development.

By the time the cotyledons, epicotyl, and hypocotyl can be recognized, the embryo has its own internal system of growth regulation, although growth regulators from the surrounding tissues of the ovule may still be required for some time. Later in its development the embryo depends on the surrounding tissues only for food. By careful manipulation, the embryo can then be removed from the young seed and cultured on a nutrient medium, finally developing normally into a mature plant.

Unlike mammals and many other animals, angiosperms and most other multicellular plants continue to grow nearly throughout the life of the organism. Some parts of the plant may die and decay while other parts are still growing, so that the total size or weight of perennial herbs may not continue to increase indefinitely; and periods of growth may be interrupted by periods of dormancy. But growth is a normal and regular part of plant metabolism, and a plant which stops growing soon either goes into dormancy or dies. Dormancy cannot be prolonged indefinitely, at least under natural conditions, and a dormant plant sooner or later either resumes growth or dies. Vegetative activity is so closely linked with growth that the part of the year when plants are vegetatively active is called the **growing season.** The length of the growing season varies with the kind of plant as well as with the locality and the year.

The different parts of a plant do not always grow at the same time and relative rate. Water absorption is largely limited to the younger parts of the root, and root growth continues throughout most or all of the growing season. Most woody plants of temperate regions have a short period in the spring and early summer during which the leaves are produced and the stems elongate. After the leaves have expanded, the stem increases rapidly in thickness for a time, and then more slowly for the rest of the growing season. The tulip tree (*Liriodendron tulipifera*) of the eastern United States betrays its tropical ancestry by continuing to produce new leaves all season long, shedding the earlier ones

progressively throughout the summer. In some plants, especially annuals, the fruits and young seeds grow rapidly after growth in the rest of the plant has virtually ceased.

The differentiation of cells and tissues in higher plants is not so absolute as in higher animals, and parenchyma cells as well as meristematic cells are often said to be totipotent, i.e., to have the capacity to change into any other kind of cell, or to divide to produce any other kind of cell. Other kinds of plant cells, once they are mature, do not so readily revert to an undifferentiated type, nor do they ordinarily produce different kinds of cells by division. Under unusual conditions, however, mature plant cells of other types do sometimes revert to an unspecialized condition and become totipotent. If a flax seedling is cut off just below the cotyledons, the mature, cutinized epidermal cells of the hypocotyl will become meristematic, organizing into a bud and finally giving rise to a normal shoot.

The size of higher plants is much more subject to environmental control than is that of higher animals such as mammals. Even under reasonably normal con-

Fig. 32.1. Pine plains, on sterile sandy soil in central New Jersey. The area was burned in 1936, 22 years before this picture was taken, and the "trees" (pine and oak) developed as root sprouts. The potential height of these plants, if protected from fire, is uncertain. (U.S. Forest Service photo.)

ditions, the larger individuals of an angiosperm are commonly three or four times as tall as the smaller ones. Some of our common weeds, such as tumbling mustard (*Sisymbrium altissimum*), may mature and set seed when only an inch or so high, under unfavorable conditions, but reach a height of 3–4 feet under more favorable ones. The famous Ming trees of China, which matured when only a foot or so tall, were merely carefully tended starvelings of ordinary species, as are the more recent Bonsai of Japan. The pitch pine (*Pinus rigida*), which reaches a height of 20 m under favorable conditions, appears to be mature when only about 1 m high in the more sterile parts of the New Jersey pine barrens (Fig. 32.1). There is an inherent limit to the potential size of each plant of any kind, but it may fall far short of this limit and still appear reasonably normal.

It is a common observation that the age and degree of maturity of a plant influence the nature of its growth. We have seen in Chapter 30 that the production of flowers is strongly influenced by the environmental conditions, but the age of the plant is also an important factor; woody plants seldom flower until they are several (or even many) years old. In many kinds of plants juvenile foliage is markedly different from mature foliage. Angiosperms with compound leaves at maturity often produce simple leaves at first; the garden bean is a familar example. The common harebell (*Campanula rotundifolia*) produces short, rounded leaves at the base of the stem, and long, narrow leaves elsewhere (Fig. 32.2). Most junipers have very small, appressed, scale-like leaves at maturity, but the leaves produced during the first several years are more spreading and a little longer, suggesting the leaves of other

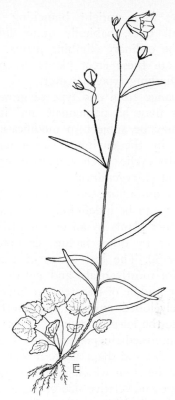

Fig. 32.2. Harebell (*Campanula rotundifolia*), showing very different basal and cauline leaves.

conifers. Young pine seedlings have the leaves spirally arranged on the stem, instead of clustered on short spur shoots as they are later.

The transition from one type of growth to another may occur at any age, depending on the kind of plant, and can often be hastened or delayed by environmental factors. Under conditions of deep shade and high moisture, harebell continues to produce juvenile leaves for some time, and flowering and fruiting are delayed. Mature plants of English ivy bear inflorescences on erect, stout branches which do not have the adventitious roots that enable ordinary branches to cling to a wall. Cuttings made from these flowering branches form upright, branching shrubs or small trees, habitally quite different from the ordinary climbing plants. Seedlings from these erect plants are of the usual climbing type, however.

Change from one type of growth to another may be permanent and irreversible, may be subject to modification or reversal by the environment, or may be inherently cyclic. Each vegetative shoot of sourwood (*Oxydendrum arboreum*) terminates in an inflorescence each year, but flowering can be indefinitely postponed in some other plants by an oversupply of nitrogen or by other factors, as noted in Chapter 30. The first leaves of a cotton plant are mostly ovate and entire; those near the middle of the stem are larger and palmately lobed; and the uppermost ones resemble the lowermost ones. Leaves occupying intermediate positions are intermediate in size and shape. Here it is the position on the stem which primarily governs the shape and relative size of the leaf, but the reasons for this position effect are still obscure.

GROWTH-REGULATING SUBSTANCES

HORMONES

During the past several decades a great deal of attention has been devoted to plant hormones. Most of the plant hormones now known can be classified as **auxins, gibberellins, lactones,** and **kinins.** Other groups and individual kinds exist as well. All these substances have complex and varying effects on growth, depending on the kind of plant, the part of the plant to which they are supplied, other internal conditions in the plant, and environmental conditions.

Probably each of these hormones is a catalyst (or, conversely, inactivates a catalyst) for some one or few chemical reactions in the protoplasm, setting off (or blocking) a chain of other reactions, each depending on the previous one. Such a series of reactions may be interrupted at any point or shunted in a new direction, depending on the environmental conditions and the other substances in the protoplasm. The cells of the root do not necessarily respond to a particular hormone in the same way as those of the stem, and the effects of a hormone may be different in the light and in the dark, or even at different temperatures.

We do not know the precise chemical action of most hormones. Our information is largely limited to their effects on particular organs of particular kinds of plants under particular environmental conditions. Some kinds of effects occur often enough to permit generalizations, but these generalizations are subject to exceptions or difficulties in interpretation, and even horticultural varieties of one species may respond differently. These difficulties are entirely expectable. All differences among cells, tissues, organs, individuals, and taxonomic groups are, in the last analysis, expressions of chemical differences.

The *auxins* are the best known and probably the most important plant hormones. The principal natural auxin is indole-3-acetic acid (often abbreviated IAA), and this is usually the substance now intended when auxin is referred to without further qualification. A series of minor chemical variants with similar physiological action, which have been isolated from some plants, are probably readily interconvertible with IAA in the cells. IAA occurs not only in higher plants, but also in bryophytes, algae, and fungi. A number of synthetic compounds related to IAA have more or less similar effects, varying in detail.

Auxins are most abundantly produced in the meristematic region of the shoot. They are also formed in root tips, leaves, and sometimes other parts of the plant, migrating through the cells so that they are present in all living tissues. Those produced in the shoot tip move principally downward toward the root; those produced in the leaves move toward the stem; and those produced in the root tip move upward toward the stem. Lateral movement of auxins is much slower than longitudinal movement, and any destruction or interruption of flow along one side of a stem, for example, is reflected in a lower concentration of auxin along that side for some distance below. Sometimes auxins apparently move as inactive chemical precursors or bound forms, rather than as active auxins. The actual quantities involved are minute, even in the shoot apex, where the concentration is generally only a few parts per million.

An optimum concentration of auxin generally stimulates growth, especially elongation, of cells, but the optimum varies widely in different tissues and under different conditions. Growth of lateral buds is strongly inhibited by concentrations which are normal for the growing apical meristem. Experimental evidence suggests that the concentrations normally present in growing shoot tips and root tips are near the optimum for cell division in these tissues but are too high for much cell elongation. The lesser concentration in the region of elongation favors cell elongation but is not enough to stimulate division.

Apical dominance has been thought to be due largely to the effect of auxins produced in the terminal bud. In many species of plants, the lateral buds mostly re-

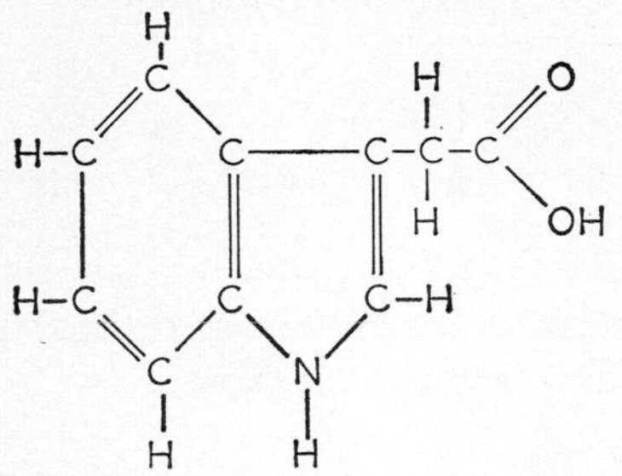

Fig. 32.3 Structural formula of indole-3-acetic acid (natural auxin).

main undeveloped as long as the terminal bud is present; or, if the lateral buds do develop, the shoots grow laterally or at an angle, rather than erect. If the terminal bud is cut off, usually one, or more, of the upper lateral buds begins to grow, or a lateral branch turns upward, re-establishing an apical dominance which inhibits or governs the growth of other lateral buds and branches. Apical dominance can be maintained even after removal of the terminal bud, if a suitable amount of auxin is applied to the cut tip. However, in at least some species the amount of auxin which must be supplied is so much greater than the amount normally produced that some other factor(s) must also be involved in maintaining apical dominance under natural conditions.

The existence of auxins was discovered through a long series of studies by different botanists on the response of plants to light. The knowledge that plants turn toward the light in their growth probably antedates recorded history, but the first significant experimental studies were reported in 1880 by Charles Darwin in his book, *The Power of Movement in Plants*. He found that the coleoptile of canary grass (*Phalaris canariensis*) turns strongly toward the light, with the curvature occurring well below the meristematic tip. (The

Angiosperms: Growth and Movement 653

Fig. 32.4. Frits W. Went (1903–), director of the Missouri Botanical Garden, who completed proof of the existence of plant hormones during his first year as a graduate student at Utrecht.

coleoptile is a modified leaf, characteristic of grass embryos, which forms a closed tube covering the epicotyl; it is the first part of the seedling to emerge from the ground.) If the coleoptile tip is covered with a small, light-proof cap, no bending occurs, even though the part which would otherwise curve is fully exposed. Darwin correctly concluded that the stimulus perceived by the tip is somehow transmitted to the lower part of the coleoptile. Experiments by the Danish botanist Peter Boysen Jensen (1883–1959) in 1910 and 1913 led him to suggest that the stimulus is transmitted by a chemical that is formed in the tip and migrates down into the region of bending. After several experiments by others which tended to support Boysen Jensen's concept, the Dutch (now American) botanist Frits W. Went (1903–)

spectacularly completed the proof in 1926 by briefly culturing decapitated coleoptile tips of oats on blocks of agar, which he then applied to the coleoptile stumps in various positions. Growth of the stump was always greatest on the side to which the agar block was applied, and when the block was symmetrically applied to the cut

Fig. 32.5. Effect of α-naphthaleneacetic acid (an auxin-like synthetic compound) on a bean seedling. Above, chemical being applied to the seedling; below, same plant 24 hours later. (Photos courtesy of John W. Mitchell, Agricultural Research Service.)

top, the coleoptile grew straight upward without bending. Went's work opened the way for careful quantitative studies on the nature and effects of auxin. Oat coleoptiles have been much used in such experiments.

Light is apparently destructive to auxin in meristems. The oat coleoptile is similar in this respect to shoot tips in general, with a light-sensitive meristem above a light-insensitive region of elongation. The greatest destruction of auxin occurs on the side that receives the most light, and the auxin deficiency on that side extends well down into the region of elongation, because the auxin moves much more rapidly downward than laterally. The darker side of the stem, having a more favorable concentration of auxin, grows faster than the illuminated side, and the stem curves toward the light.

Studies of the effect of various wavelengths of light on phototropism have focused attention on two pigments with very similar absorption spectra, β-carotene and riboflavin, as possible original receptors of the light stimulus. It has further been shown that in vitro the action of light on riboflavin triggers the chemical destruction of IAA. It seems likely that there is a complex balance in the protoplasm between IAA, riboflavin, and other substances, so that in certain cells under certain conditions light tends to destroy IAA through its effect on riboflavin, while under other conditions the destructive effect is inhibited by other substances in the cell. Knowledge of the chemical actions involved is still so fragmentary that we are much like the three blind men examining an elephant: the whole elephant cannot yet be perceived.

In addition to the effects already noted, auxin influences the development of abscission layers (leading to the fall of leaves, fruits, or other structures), adventitious roots, flowers, and fruits. Even the burst of cambial growth in woody stems in the spring may possibly be set off by the auxin produced in rapidly growing buds. The effects of auxin vary in detail according to the species, the stage of growth, and the environmental conditions.

Auxin produced in the leaf blade inhibits abscission of the leaf. If the blade is cut off, or if it becomes inactive through senescence or for any other reason, the abscission layer matures and the leaf (or its remnant) falls off. Abscission can be prevented, however, by applying auxin to the debladed petiole. If the terminal bud is also cut off when the petiole is debladed, thus interrupting the supply of auxin from

Fig. 32.6. Effect of indolebutyric acid (an auxin-like synthetic compound) on cuttings of holly. (Photos courtesy of the Boyce Thompson Institute for Plant Research.)

NOT TREATED   TREATED

the stem as well as from the leaf blade, abscission is delayed. This has been interpreted to mean that auxin reaching the petiole from the stem promotes abscission, whereas that from the blade inhibits it; but it may prove to mean instead that maturation of the abscission layer occurs only within a narrow range of auxin concentration: when the leaf is actively producing auxin the concentration is too high, but when the supply from the stem as well as from the leaf is cut off, the concentration of auxin is too low for the abscission layer to mature. Abscission of flowers and fruits is governed in part by the same factors as that of leaves, and apple trees are often sprayed with auxin to prevent premature fruit drop.

The effect of auxin in stimulating cuttings to produce adventitious roots has led to an important practical use of related synthetic compounds in commercial- and home-gardening practice. Cuttings of some kinds of plants (such as willows) root freely under natural conditions, some sparingly, and some not at all. Many species which do not ordinarily root well can be induced to do so by applying IAA or any of several synthetic chemicals. In practice some of the synthetics, such as α-naphthaleneacetic acid, are more satisfactory than IAA, and such products are now widely sold in the United States. The old folk-belief that rooting is promoted by the insertion of a germinating wheat grain in a slit in the cutting turns out to be well

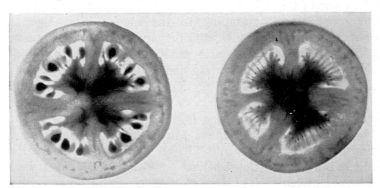

Fig. 32.7. Effect of β-naphthoxyacetic acid (an auxin-like synthetic compound) on fruit set in tomatoes. Left, fruit developed after normal pollination of an untreated flower, showing well-developed seeds. Right, fruit developed without pollination, after chemical treatment. (Photos courtesy of the Boyce Thompson Institute for Plant Research.)

Fig. 32.8. Effect of α-naphthaleneacetic acid in supressing sprouting of stored potatoes. Treated plants at right. (Photo courtesy of Wisconsin Agricultural Experiment Station.)

Fig. 32.9. Effect of 2,4-D. Upper picture, before spraying. Lower picture, after spraying; the poison ivy and Canada thistle have been killed, but the grasses are not much affected. (Photos courtesy of the American Chemical Paint Company.)

founded, the effect being due to the auxin that spreads from the grain into the cutting.

Natural and various synthetic auxins, or auxin-like compounds, are used to promote flowering and fruiting, to retard fruit drop, to induce parthenogenetic fruiting (the fruits thus being seedless), to inhibit flowering, and for other purposes (Figs. 32.6–32.8). In order to produce the desired result, without undesirable side effects, the dosage must be adjusted to the particular crop, its degree of maturity, and the environmental conditions. The amounts used in any case are relatively small, ranging from about 10 to 200 or occasionally 500 parts per million in water.

Several synthetic compounds related to IAA are used as weed killers. The most important of these is 2,4-D (2,4-dichloro-phenoxyacetic acid), which is readily absorbed from sprays or dusts applied to leaves (Fig. 32.9). Relatively minute amounts of 2,4-D derange the physiology of most plants, especially the meristems, causing metabolic abnormalities, asymmetric growth, and death. Different kinds of plants differ in their susceptibility to

2,4-D. Most monocots, especially grasses, are more resistant than most dicots, and most trees are more resistant than most broad-leaved herbs, but resistance also varies with the environmental conditions and the stage of growth, and even varieties of the same species may differ markedly.

Auxin influences so many growth processes of the plant, in such a variety of ways, that during the 1940's it was often mistakenly regarded as the only plant growth hormone, or at least the only important one. It is now clear that there are a number of other hormones, chemically not closely related to auxin, which also affect plant growth, although no one of these is known to be as ubiquitous and important as auxin. It appears, as might be expected, that every normal cell contains a number of growth-regulating substances, and that an increase or decrease in any one of these changes the balance and affects the rate or nature of growth.

The plant hormones which attracted the most attention in the 1950's were the *gibberellins*, which occur in several slightly varying forms, gibberellic acid (Fig. 32.10) being one of the most common. Gibberellin

Angiosperms: Growth and Movement 657

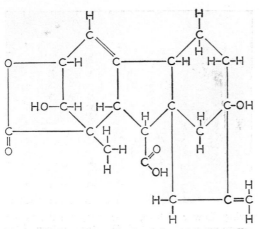

Fig. 32.10. **Structural formula of gibberellic acid.**

was discovered in 1926 by two Japanese botanists studying the cause of the foolish-seedling disease of rice. Rice seedlings, when attacked by the fungus *Gibberella fujikuroi,* grow to two or three times their normal height and then die. The fungus produces substances, now called gibberellins, which promote growth of the shoot without corresponding development of the root, and the plant grows itself to death as the root system fails to meet the demands of the shoot.

It is now known that gibberellin occurs naturally in many kinds of plants, and the foolish-seedling disease results merely from an excess. Like auxin, gibberellin influences a wide variety of growth processes, with varying effects according to the kind of plant, its stage of maturity, and the environmental conditions.

The most common and obvious effect of gibberellin is to stimulate growth of the shoot, without corresponding growth of the root. Dwarf varieties of peas and beans, among other plants, grow as tall as ordinary varieties when treated with gibberellin, although the natural gibberellin content of the dwarf plants is about the same as that of the normal tall ones.

Another common effect of gibberellin is to lower the low-temperature threshold for growth. Lawns may thus be encouraged to turn green earlier in the spring by judicious treatment. Other effects of gibberellin include breaking the dormancy of potato tubers and some kinds of seeds, promotion of early flowering and fruiting, the formation of parthenocarpic fruits, and, in a few cases, delay of flowering and fruiting. Gibberellin is widely sold in America and appears to have a bright future in agricultural practice, but the dosage and time of application must be carefully adjusted to each crop.

Lactones, another group of growth regulators, are widely distributed but not yet well understood. In general, they seem to be growth inhibitors; some of them, such as coumarin (Fig. 32.12), found in the seeds of some kinds of plants, inhibit

Fig. 32.11. **Effect of gibberellin on *Pelargonium*. The plants were the same size at the start of the experiment. The one at the right received four applications of gibberellic acid at 2-week intervals; the one at the left received similar applications of plain water. (Photos courtesy of P. P. Pirone, New York Botanical Garden.)**

germination. Different varieties of white sweet clover (*Melilotus alba*) differ greatly in the amount of coumarin in the seeds. The amount of coumarin that leaches into the soil from seeds of some varieties under natural conditions is enough to inhibit germination and growth in other varieties. Growth of excised root tips even of the high-coumarin varieties is also inhibited by the amount of coumarin which leaches from the seeds; obviously something which counters the effect of coumarin is produced elsewhere in these seedlings, and the root depends on other parts of the plant for its supply. The high coumarin content of these seeds seems to be another weapon in the endless competition for survival, but we do not yet know what disadvantages this weapon carries with it; the modifications necessary to withstand the coumarin may well have harmful side effects. Other sorts of lactones released into the soil also serve some plants (e.g., *Encelia farinosa*, of deserts in the southwestern United States) as antibiotics, inhibiting the growth of other plants in the immediate vicinity.

The *kinins*, of which kinetin (Fig. 32.13) is the outstanding example so far known, influence many of the same processes as auxin, sometimes with opposite effect. There is also some evidence linking them with the expansion and ultimately the shape of leaves. Kinetin itself is a synthetic compound, which has not yet been identified in plants, but several other kin-

Fig. 32.12. Structural formula of coumarin.

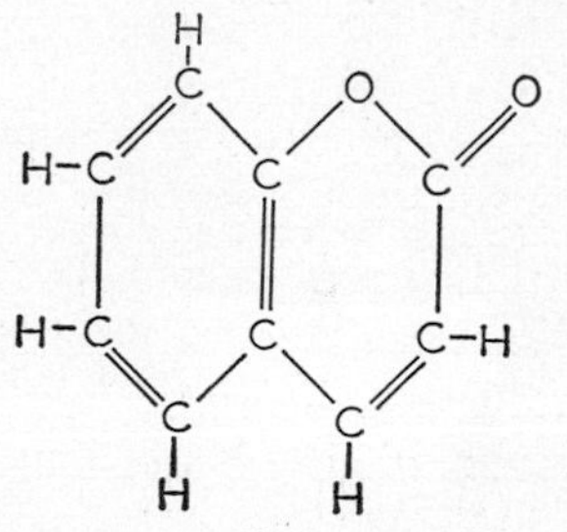

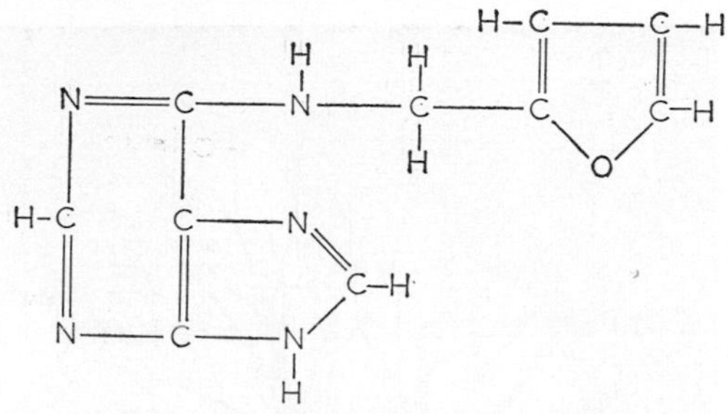

Fig. 32.13. Structural formula of kinetin.

ins do occur. The "coconut milk factor," which has attracted attention as a growth regulator, has recently been shown to consist, in part, of a kinin. Our knowledge of this group of growth regulators is still very fragmentary.

Ethylene, C_2H_4, is produced by many plants, especially in ripening fruits. It hastens ripening and is used commercially to ripen oranges, bananas, and some other fruits. Individual wrapping of pears and apples in waxed paper has more than a purely esthetic value; the ethylene formed by the fruit does not escape so readily and ripening is promoted.

Ethylene has a number of other effects on plants, often including an increased rate of respiration. Its role in normal growth is doubtful, and there has been some reluctance to consider it a hormone. It can scarcely be denied, however, that, at least in some tissues of some kinds of plants, it is an important part of the balance of growth-regulating substances, and, like other hormones, it is effective in minute amounts. As little as 1 part per million or even per 10 million of ethylene in the atmosphere, by volume, is harmful to many kinds of plants, causing asymmetric growth, abscission of leaves and flowers, and death (Fig. 32.14). The presence of ethylene in artificial illuminating gas is responsible for the well-known difficulty of growing house plants in homes where artificial gas is used

Fig. 32.14. Trees killed by artificial illuminating gas leaking under a street. (Photo courtesy of the Wisconsin Agricultural Experiment Station.)

Fig. 32.15. Effect of ethylene chlorhydrin in breaking dormancy of Azalea (*Rhododendron nudiflorum*). Photos taken January 17, after the plant at the right had been treated on December 23. (Courtesy of the Boyce Thompson Institute for Plant Research.)

for cooking; natural gas, which does not have ethylene, has in recent years largely replaced artificial gas for home use, however. Ethylene chlorhydrin, a highly poisonous derivative of ethylene, is used commercially to break dormancy of potato tubers, gladiolus corms, many shrubs and trees (Fig. 32.15), and some seeds.

Vitamins

The plant vitamins have attracted less attention than the plant hormones. Any substance which is effective in minute quantities, which is not strongly migratory, which has similar effects in different tissues, and which can be made by the organism, is not likely to be easily discovered. In practice the study of plant vitamins has been largely restricted to substances also known to be animal vitamins, especially those which are hormone-like in being migratory, with some tissues needing an outside source of supply. Thiamin (vitamin B_1) is such a vitamin. Roots of tomatoes and other plants require thiamin for growth but do not ordinarily make it in significant amounts. Excised roots in culture media must be provided with thiamin or its immediate chemical precursors if they are to survive. In the living plant, thiamin is made in the stem and migrates down into the root.

Tissue Culture

The culture of excised plant tissues in sterile media requires a carefully balanced supply of growth-regulating substances as well as ordinary nutrients. The American botanist William J. Robbins (1890–   ) reported in 1922 that the addition of yeast to the medium improved the growth of excised tomato roots, although even with this addition the roots went into a decline after a few months of diminishing growth. The techniques of tissue culture expanded rapidly thereafter. It was learned that thiamin is the principal active ingredient of yeast in promoting growth, and especially since about 1939 it has been possible to grow various tissues of many kinds of plants by providing them with the proper nutrients and growth regulators. IAA or some similar hormone is often required, depending on whether or not the particular tissue makes enough IAA for its own use. Various other hormones or vitamins are necessary in some cases, the list of essentials varying with the tissue and the kind of plant. Tissues from some kinds of plants still resist cultivation, however, presumably because they require some undiscovered growth substance made elsewhere in the plant. Tissue culture is now a very important tool in studying the nature of plant growth, including the effects and chemistry of growth-regulating substances.

ENVIRONMENTAL CONTROL OF GROWTH

Introduction

The environmental factors affecting plant growth are so intricately related that any classification is necessarily arbitrary and imperfect. Radiant energy, temperature, water, minerals, atmospheric conditions, and gravity are some of the more obvious physical factors. Water relations, mineral nutrition, photoperiodism, and the effect of CO_2 in the air have been discussed in earlier chapters, and gravity is discussed in this chapter in the section on plant movements. Certain aspects of the

Fig. 32.16. Effect of red and far-red light on seedlings of pinto bean. All plants received 8 hours of fluorescent light daily. The plant at the left received no other illumination. The center plant received an additional 5 minutes of far-red light on each of the tenth, eleventh, twelfth, and thirteenth days. The plant at the right received 5 minutes of far-red light followed by 5 minutes of red light on each of these same days. Photos taken on the seventeenth day. (Courtesy of H. A. Borthwick, Agricultural Research Service.)

effects of radiant energy, temperature, and atmospheric conditions remain to be discussed here.

LIGHT AND OTHER RADIANT ENERGY

All substances absorb and reflect light differentially, absorbing more of some wavelengths than of others. Substances with markedly differential light-absorbing properties are called **pigments**, especially if they occur in relatively small amounts in another substance or body whose color they affect. Chlorophyll, carotene, xanthophyll, and anthocyanin are familiar plant pigments. Some other plant pigments, such as cytochrome, generally occur in such small amounts as to escape the eye. The absorption of light by a pigment may be directly related to its function in the protoplast, or it may have no functional importance, as appears to be true of anthocyanin and cytochrome. (Anthocyanin in flowers attracts insect pollinators, but this is another matter.)

Different wavelengths of light have different effects on plant growth. For each response controlled by light there is an action spectrum (i.e., if the quantitative effects of successive wavelengths are plotted on a graph, a definite line with one or more peaks, comparable to the absorption spectrum of a pigment, is obtained). The only obvious explanation for this is that the initial effect is on some pigment (or pigments) in the plant. Except for the carotenoids mentioned in the discussion of phototropism, the pigments responsible for most light-controlled growth responses occur in such minute amounts that their identification and study are very difficult, and knowledge of them is still rudimentary.

One of the most interesting features of the effect of light on growth is the antagonism between ordinary red (about 650 mμ) and far-red (about 720 mμ) light. (Far-red light is at the edge of the visible spectrum, thus just short of the infrared range.) They are opposed in all reactions tested in all plants tested (up to 1960), as far as they have any detectable effect (Fig. 32.16). Red light promotes germination of seeds (when it has any effect on them); it acts against excessive elongation of the stem; it turns the cuticle of tomatoes yellow (fruits ripened in the dark lack this pigment and have a less pleasing color); it prevents flowering, when applied to a short-day plant in the middle of the night; and it promotes flowering, when so applied to a long-day plant. Far red opposes all these effects.

For any particular kind of plant under a particular set of conditions, the red and far-red parts of light exert opposite but unequal force, and the effect of one outweighs the effect of the other. With a different kind of plant, or under different conditions, the balance may be reversed and the opposite result obtained. The results may also be controlled by manipulating the proportions of red and far-red light supplied to the plant. Thus a seed which requires light for germination is most responsive to red light, and the amount of far red in natural light is insufficient to overcome the effect of the red. If the amount of far red is experimentally in-creased, germination is inhibited. A seed which seems to require darkness for germination is merely more sensitive to the inhibiting effect of far red than to the stimulating effect of red, and it germinates well if the ratio of red to far red is sufficiently increased.

Plants grown in the dark, but with an adequate food supply, develop long, weak, spindly stems; the leaves of dicots generally fail to expand, and those of monocots are commonly narrower and more attenuate than normal; the anatomical structure is also modified. The shoots remain white or pale yellowish, inasmuch as chlorophyll is not formed without light. Such plants are said to be **etiolated** (from French *étioler*, to blanch). Plants with inadequate light show similar but less pronounced effects (Fig. 32.17). Red light is highly effective in preventing the excessive elongation, but other wavelengths are more

Fig. 32.17.   Etiolated bean seedlings (*C*, grown in total darkness) alongside plants receiving 50 per cent natural light intensity (*B*) and 100 per cent natural light intensity (*A*). (Photo by F. H. Norris. From Transeau, Sampson, and Tiffany, *Textbook of Botany*, Rev. Ed., Harper, 1953.)

Fig. 32.18. Effect of the photoperiod on growth of *Catalpa*. The plant at the left was grown in a 16-hour day, that at the right in an 8-hour day. (Photos courtesy of H. A. Borthwick, Agricultural Research Service.)

effective in promoting leaf expansion and the formation of chlorophyll. Excessive elongation, without the other symptoms of etiolation, can be induced by a little extra supply of far-red light, even when the plants get normal light most of the day. Under natural conditions, etiolation occurs only in seedlings from deeply covered seeds and in the shoots arising from underground perennating organs such as rhizomes, tubers, bulbs, and fleshy or running roots. Etiolation may thus have a survival value in enabling such shoots to reach the ground surface quickly and with little damage.

The pigment responsible for growth responses of plants to red and far-red light was isolated in 1959 by a group of scientists working for U.S. Department of Agriculture. It is proteinaceous, but its structure has not yet (1960) been determined. The pigment evidently exists in two forms. Red light converts it to one of these forms, and far red to the other.

The effect of the photoperiod on flowering has been discussed in Chapter 30. Vegetative growth of some plants is also influenced by the photoperiod (Fig. 32.18). The extent and importance of this type of photoperiodism remain to be determined.

Except for the direct effects of heat, the infrared and ultraviolet rays of the sun that reach the earth's surface have little or no apparent influence on plant growth. Plants grow just as well under glass (which filters out most of the ultraviolet) as in the open, if other conditions are similar. The shorter ultraviolet rays, which are mostly screened out of natural radiation by the upper atmosphere, are destructive to plants as well as to animals. X rays are also harmful to both plants and animals (Fig. 32.19).

TEMPERATURE

Any change in temperature affects the different physiological processes in the plant unequally, with consequent effects on growth. The balance between photosynthesis and respiration, for example, is highly responsive to temperature changes. In many species of plants in temperate regions, the rate of photosynthesis under field conditions is not much higher at 30°C than at 15°C, because the CO_2 content of the air is a limiting factor. Respiration, on the other hand, is about doubled by such a change, and the higher temperature favors rapid utilization of photosynthate, rather than accumulation. We can thus envision for each species a cyclic effect of increasing

Fig. 32.19 Effect of gamma radiation on growth of *Nicotiana langsdorfii*. Plants started as small seedlings and grown for 10 weeks. Control plant at left received no artificial irradiation. Plants at right received 250, 325, and 400 roentgen units per 20 hours over a period of 10 weeks. (Photo courtesy of A. H. Sparrow, Brookhaven National Laboratory, Upton, N.Y.)

Fig. 32.20. Effects of different temperatures on the formation of potato tubers. Figures are degrees Centigrade. (Photo by John Bushnell. From Transeau, Sampson, and Tiffany, *Textbook of Botany*, Rev. Ed., Harper, 1953.)

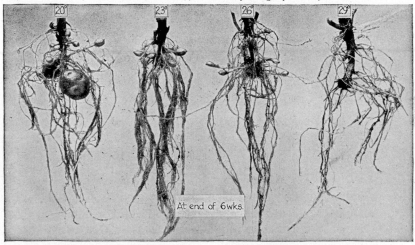

temperature, from carbohydrate depletion and eventual starvation at temperatures too low for photosynthesis, to carbohydrate accumulation but slow growth, to balanced production and use of photosynthate with rapid growth, to carbohydrate depletion and eventual starvation at temperatures so high that respiration outstrips photosynthesis. The night temperature, since it affects respiration but not photosynthesis, may be even more significant than the day temperature, under some circumstances. Other factors associated with temperature changes, or other direct effects of tempera-

Angiosperms: Growth and Movement **665**

ture, may modify the results, but the principle is still sound. Taking a practical example, it should thus be clear why potatoes produce a relatively small crop at higher than optimal temperatures, even though the plants are healthy and vegetatively active (Fig. 32.20).

High and low temperatures may limit growth or be fatal for other reasons than their effect on the balance between photosynthesis and respiration. Heat may cause various metabolic disturbances and even coagulation of the protein in the protoplasm. It also acts indirectly by influencing transpiration. Cold may also upset the metabolism, even before ice is formed. Injury due to freezing may result either from mechanical disruption of the protoplast by the ice crystals, or from metabolic disturbances associated with the loss of water or too rapid release of water in thawing.

Many plants become more resistant to frost injury after repeated exposure to near-freezing temperatures. This cold hardening is due to one or more of several changes, according to the kind of plant: (1) increase in osmotic potential and thus direct resistance to freezing; (2) increased resistance to coagulation of the proteins when desiccated; (3) increased permeability of the plasma membrane to water, permitting ice to form in intercellular spaces instead of within the cell; and (4) decreased structural viscosity of the protoplast, making it less susceptible to mechanical injury by the ice crystals.

The effect of the thermoperiod on flowering has been discussed in Chapter 30.

ATMOSPHERE

The major constituent of the atmosphere, nitrogen, is insignificant as a direct factor in the growth of most plants, being

Fig. 32.21. Copper Basin, Tennessee, showing destruction of vegetation by smelter smoke. (Photo by C. R. Hursh, U.S. Forest Service.)

absorbed only in combined forms, such as nitrates. The second most abundant constituent of the air, oxygen, is of course necessary for respiration, but variation in the oxygen content of the air is so slight as to be unimportant, except as regards the air in the soil. Poorly aerated soils may not have enough oxygen for normal root growth. Carbon dioxide and water vapor are the only other natural components of air that have any importance in plant growth; the effects of these have been discussed in previous chapters.

Wind is an important factor in increasing transpiration, as noted in Chapter 27, and the continued pressure of wind that comes chiefly from one direction may train the trunk and branches of trees to the leeward.

Various harmful chemicals are released into the air as a result of man's industrial activities. The effects of ethylene, a constituent of artificial illuminating gas, have been noted on p. 659. The hydrocarbon from automobile exhausts sometimes reaches a concentration high enough to damage plants, as well as being a prime cause of the notorious smog of many large cities. Smelters release sulfur dioxide (SO_2), and aluminum smelters release hydrogen fluoride (HF) as well. Both of these are highly toxic to plants, and in some cases all the vegetation for several miles around a large smelter is destroyed (Fig. 32.21).

HEALING OF WOUNDS

Most kinds of vascular plants respond to wounding of the stem or root by resuming growth around the wounded area, forming a callus that partly or wholly covers the wounded area before growth stops again. Experimental evidence indicates that the damaged cells produce substances which stimulate the surrounding undamaged cells to resume growth. If the wound is immediately washed, callus formation does not occur, unless wound juice is again applied. The nature of the activating substances in wound juice is still uncertain.

ABNORMAL GROWTH

We have seen that growth results from a complexly balanced set of chemical reactions in the protoplasm, and that the rate and nature of growth vary with the environmental conditions and the kind of plant. Under extreme or otherwise unusual

Fig. 32.22. Spontaneous tumors on the stem of a hybrid between *Nicotiana langsdorfii* and *N. suaveolens*. (Photo courtesy of Harold H. Smith, Brookhaven National Laboratory, Upton, N.Y.)

Fig. 32.23. Fifteen different galls on hickory leaves, caused by as many different species of insects. (Drawings by B. W. Wells. From Transeau, Sampson, and Tiffany, *Textbook of Botany*, Rev. Ed., Harper, 1953.)

environmental conditions, growth may be abnormal. Such synthetic chemicals as 2,4-D, and such natural chemicals as gibberellin, may so upset the balance that abnormal growth is quickly followed by death.

Abnormal growth may also be internally directed. A number of interspecific hybrids in *Nicotiana* (the tobacco genus) are apparently normal except for numerous small tumors along the stem (Fig. 32.22). Here the balance has obviously gone askew; some cells which should stop growing and mature into ordinary stem cells continue to grow and divide indefinitely. Doubtless other imbalances in many hybrids escape our attention.

Many insects and some bacteria that parasitize plants cause abnormal enlargements called **galls.** Often the shape and structure of the gall induced by a particular species of insect on a particular species of plant are so constant and so complex that the insect species can be identified by the plant gall. The same plant host can produce many different kinds of galls according to the kind of parasite (Fig. 32.23), and the same kind of insect sometimes in-

duces different sorts of galls on different hosts. The immediate cause of the overgrowth varies according to the parasite and, in most cases, has not been carefully studied. In general the insect probably secretes growth-stimulating substances which, in combination with the wound damage caused by feeding, subverts the host into providing a home with a built-in food supply.

Crown gall, caused by the bacterium *Agrobacterium tumefaciens*, furnishes one of the most interesting examples of abnormal growth in plants (Fig. 32.24). The bacteria usually enter the plant through a wound near the ground level, and, if they are carefully introduced without wounding the host, they grow and multiply without causing a gall. The tumor-inducing principle produced by the bacteria is formed only in the presence of wound juice. Together the wound juice and the tumor-inducing principle cause a series of irreversible changes whereby the affected cells acquire the power of virtually unlimited growth and become insensitive to the regulatory hormones produced in other parts of the plant. One characteristic of the tumor cells is a high production of auxin and other hormones and vitamins. After the primary tumor is well established, secondary tumors often develop in other parts of the plant, even without further wounding. The obvious analogy with human cancer has led some botanists to call crown gall plant cancer, but the physiological relationship remains to be determined. In spite of the more than 3500 papers on crown gall published after the causative organism was named and described by the American botanist Erwin F. Smith (1854–1927) in 1907, the physiology of crown gall is still only very incompletely understood.

MOVEMENTS

INTRODUCTION

Plants, which seem so changeless and still, are actually in continuous motion. As seen by the time-lapse camera, the stem actively twists and turns, and the flowers and leaves often repeat a series of movements like a stately dance, in a daily rhythm. Other motions may be performed but once by each of many organs, like identical routines by a series of dancers entering the stage in rapid succession.

Movements of plant parts can mostly be classified, according to the mechanism, as growth movements and turgor movements. **Growth movements** are due to differential growth; cells in one part of the affected organ grow faster than those in another part, thus changing its position. **Turgor movements** are due to differential changes in turgor (and consequently size) of the cells of the affected organ. Turgor movements are readily reversible under changed conditions. Growth movements are less easily reversed; once the cells have enlarged

Fig. 32.24. **Crown gall on sunflower stem, 3 months after inoculation. (Photo courtesy of the Wisconsin Agricultural Experiment Station.)**

or divided they do not return to their former size, and reversal of the movement can be accomplished only by a reversal in the rates of growth.

Some growth movements are self-controlled (autonomic); others are induced by external stimuli (paratonic). Nutation, the spiral twisting of the stem as it grows, is a wholly autonomic growth movement; it has been mentioned in Chapter 24. Paratonic movements are further classified as tropisms and nasties (or nastic movements). **Tropisms** are responses to stimuli which come chiefly or wholly from one direction; the direction from which the stimulus comes affects the direction of the growth response. **Nasties** are responses to stimuli which more uniformly envelop the affected organ, or which, if unidirectional, evoke the same response regardless of the direction they come from. This classification of movements is an aid to understanding, but it is not to be expected that all plant movements will fit neatly into the given categories.

TROPISMS

Geotropism (response to gravity) and phototropism (response to light) are the most familiar tropisms, but thigmotropism (response to touch), thermotropism (response to temperature), chemotropism (response to chemicals), and hydrotropism (response to water) are also well known.

Tropisms may be positive, negative, or lateral, and they may differ in different organs of the plant. Thus the primary root is usually positively geotropic, growing in the direction of gravity, and the stem is negatively geotropic, growing away from gravity. If a seed is planted upside down,

Fig. 32.25. Geotropic growth in a seedling after it was clamped in a horizontal position. (From Transeau, Sampson, and Tiffany, *Textbook of Botany*, Rev. Ed., Harper, 1953.)

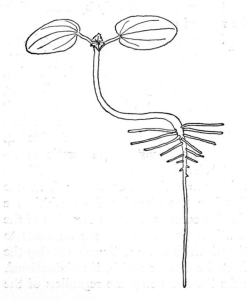

so that the emerging root points upward, the root turns as it grows, and the tip soon comes to point downward. The stem, likewise, will right itself regardless of its initial position. Creeping rhizomes are often laterally geotropic, growing at right angles to the direction of gravity, parallel to the surface of the ground. Other complex factors relating to the depth below the ground surface also influence the direction of growth of many rhizomes.

The nature and strength of a tropic response of a plant part may vary with its age and the environmental conditions, as may also the sensitivity of the affected organ to the stimulus. In species of *Arabis* (rock cress), for example, the pedicels, at first ascending, later become reflexed, or spreading, or erect, or spreading but turned up at the end, according to the species. In *Arabis* the resulting differences in position of the mature pods have no apparent importance to the plant, although they furnish useful taxonomic characters for the identification of the species. In *Trifolium subterraneum*, a Mediterranean species of clover, the stalk of the inflorescence is at first ascending but later turns and burrows into the ground, effectively planting the seeds. Many such changes in the position of flower stalks are geotropic, but some are probably phototropic instead; each species must be studied individually for the explanation.

If a potted plant is turned on its side, the tips of the stems begin to bend upward within a few days, and sometimes even the older parts of the plant are later affected (Fig. 32.25). If the tips of the main roots are examined, it will be found that they have turned downward. However, if the pot is slowly rotated on a horizontal axis after being turned sideways, so that each leaf and each point on the stem has its turn at being on the upper side as well as the lower side, no geotropic effect appears, and the plant continues to grow horizontally.

If a growing seedling is placed on a turntable, the effects of gravity can be overcome by centrifugal force. Thus on a rapidly rotating horizontal turntable, the roots grow toward the margins and the stems toward the center; but if the rotation is slower, so that the centrifugal force is less than the force of gravity, the usual geotropic responses occur.

Experimental evidence suggests that gravity is perceived through accumulation of starch grains or sometimes other bodies at the lower side of the cell. The endodermis of stems and roots seems to be particularly significant in this regard. Even when a typical endodermis with Casparian strips is not developed, a "starch sheath" with numerous starch grains often occupies its position. The starch grains of the endodermis, or starch sheath, are slow to be digested even under conditions of starvation, and when they do disappear the geotropic response is lost with them, although the plant may still be healthy enough to show normal phototropism. How the accumulation of starch grains on the lower side of the cell leads to the geotropic response is still obscure. Unequal distribution of auxin is evidently involved, but our knowledge is still too fragmentary to permit a coherent explanation.

Phototropic responses occur in most green plants. Typically the stem bends toward the light as it grows; housewives with green thumbs know that potted plants need to be turned every few days if they are to grow symmetrically. The stems of some climbing plants, such as English ivy (*Hedera helix*) are negatively phototropic; placed in a pot in a window,

they turn and grow away from the light, directly into the room. A little thought should suggest a relationship between this response to light (along with a normal negative geotropism) and the success of the plant as a climber on walls.

Different intensities of light often evoke opposite phototropic responses. The stems of Bermuda grass (*Cynodon dactylon*) and some other plants are positively phototropic at low light intensities, and negatively so at higher intensities. Such plants are prostrate when growing in open places where they are fully exposed to the sun, but they are more ascending or erect when shaded by other vegetation. Even some of the prostrate liverworts will grow upward at an angle in a terrarium with insufficient light.

Leaves as well as stems are often phototropic. The leaf blades of such vines as English ivy occupy practically the entire exposed surface of the wall, with a minimum of overlapping, fitting together in patterns called **leaf mosaics**. Most plants with large numbers of leaves show somewhat similar, though usually less accurate, patterns, making maximum use of the available light.

In many kinds of plants, the leaves or flowers assume a particular orientation with respect to the sun, changing progressively during the day. These changes are sometimes due to differential growth, as in the common sunflower (*Helianthus annuus*), in which the heads tend to face the sun. Differential turgor changes also cause such responses. In *Malva neglecta*, a common weed in which the leaf surface is directed toward the sun, it has been shown that the movement is caused by changes in the turgor of the cells at the tip of the petiole. The original light stimulus must be received by the blade, however; if the blade is covered, the movement does not take place, even when the active part of the petiole is fully exposed to the sun.

The role of auxin in phototropism has been discussed earlier in this chapter.

The most familiar examples of *thigmotropism* are shown by the tendrils of stems of climbing vines, which curl around solid objects they touch. The immediate reaction, which sometimes occurs in less than a minute (and commonly within a few minutes), is probably due to differential changes in turgor, but the changes are irreversible and are followed by differential growth, so that the tendril or stem wraps around the supporting object. Differential growth often continues in the basal part of the tendril, which becomes twisted like a coil spring, holding the plant close to the support but permitting an elastic response to the wind or other strains. Tendrils do not respond to liquids, such as raindrops, nor even to heavy liquids, such as mercury; neither do they respond to perfectly smooth solids. A slightly rough or uneven surface, providing two or more adjacent but separated stimuli, is ordinarily required. We have scarcely an inkling of the mechanism of thigmotropism.

The most familiar *chemotropism* in angiosperms is that shown by the pollen tube, which grows unerringly down through the style and into the embryo sac of the ovule in response to chemical stimuli. The nature of the chemical stimulus in this instance is not well understood.

The reaction of swimming sperms of plants and animals to chemical stimuli may also be broadly classed as chemotropism. In some bryophytes the chemical that attracts the sperm to the archegonium and the egg is sucrose, ordinary cane sugar.

The sperm of man is attracted toward a mildly alkaline solution and is repelled by acid.

When tropisms are more narrowly defined, to include only growth movements, the locomotion of whole cells or organisms in response to stimuli is called **tactic movement,** and sperms are then said to show a chemotactic (rather than a chemotropic) response. Flagellated algae are commonly phototactic, being attracted toward moderately bright light. Any tactic movement is called a taxis. Phototaxis and chemotaxis are the most commonly observed taxies, except in city streets, where Chevrolets are more common.

Hydrotropism may be regarded as a special case of chemotropism, since water is of course a chemical. Hydrotropic curvature has been demonstrated in the roots of several kinds of plants, but apparently this response is not so common as was once believed. The seeming hydrotropism of roots of many plants results from the more rapid growth and more extensive branching of roots in moist soil than in dry soil, rather than from curvature of existing roots in the direction of moisture.

NASTIC MOVEMENTS

Nastic movements, in the strict sense, are growth movements, although the term is sometimes applied also to some otherwise similar turgor movements. Some nastic movements are induced by external stimuli, like tropisms, but others are internally directed.

The growth movements of young leaves, bud scales, and petals are autonomic (internally directed) nasties. When young, these organs grow faster on the lower side than on the upper (**hyponasty**),

Fig. 32.26. Sundew (*Drosera rotundifolia*). (About natural size.) (New York Botanical Garden photo.)

so that they bend upward and inward, enclosing the tip of the axis. Later they grow faster on the upper side than the lower (**epinasty**), and consequently spread away from the axis.

The "sleep" movements of the leaves and flowers of some plants are caused by turgor changes, but others are nastic growth movements. Nastic sleep movements may be photonastic, or thermonastic, or both, according to the species.

In some species of touch-me-not (*Impatiens*) the leaves droop at night but spread out horizontally during the day. Leaves of the common pigweed (*Chenopodium album*), on the other hand, point upward at night and spread out during the day. Both these changes are photonastic growth movements. The flowers of *Oxalis* close at night in response to darkness, and those of some species of *Oenothera* (evening primrose) open in the evening as the light fades. Tulips and crocus flowers are thermonastic, opening as the temperature rises, and closing again when it falls. Crocus flowers also close if the temperature

gets unusually high, and the leaves of many tropical plants assume the "sleep" position during the hottest hours of the day as well as at night.

Both thigmonasty and chemonasty are illustrated by the tentacles of the leaves of sundew (*Drosera*), an insectivorous plant of boggy places (Fig. 32.26). The tentacles are stout, spreading hairs with proteolytic enzymes in the expanded, sticky tip. The marginal tentacles turn toward the center of the leaf, if they or the central tentacles are stimulated by the touch of a solid object or by any of several nitrogenous chemicals in solution. If the stimulus is not a digestible object, the tentacles generally recover and return to their normal position within a day, but under the continuous chemical stimulation of a trapped insect, they remain curved for a week or more while the prey is digested. In species with long, narrow leaves, it can be seen that the response of the tentacles is partly tropic rather than wholly nastic, because the direction of bending is influenced by the position of the insect on the leaf. Here, as elsewhere, it should be noted that the structures and processes of plants cannot be classified into wholly distinct categories, although the partial and imperfect classifications which can be made are very useful aids to understanding.

Closure of the leaves of Venus's-fly-trap (*Dionaea muscipula,* Fig. 1.3) seems to result from a combined growth and turgor mechanism, initiated by contact or mild pressure, and furthered by chemical stimulation with nitrogenous substances from the body of the trapped insect. Each half of the leaf has three trigger hairs on the upper side, and these are much more sensitive to the touch than is the rest of the surface. The initial closure probably results principally from a sudden transfer of water from cells near the upper surface of the leaf to cells near the lower surface, especially near the midrib, and the closure is followed by differential growth. Reopen-ing of the leaf after digestion of an insect results from epinastic growth.

TURGOR MOVEMENTS

Turgor movements of plant parts result from differential changes in turgor (and consequently size) of some cells. The effective cells are often different from ordinary cells and may be concentrated in special organs, such as the pulvinus (Latin, a cushion) at the base of the leaves and leaflets of legumes and some other plants. Turgor movements are often classed with nastic movements, because the direction is not influenced by the source of the stimulus. The rolling of the leaves of many grasses in dry weather is caused by loss of turgor and collapse of the large, thin-walled, bulliform cells that form longitudinal rows on one or the other surface. Movements of the stamens of some flowers in response to touch are

Fig. 32.27. Sensitive plant (*Mimosa pudica*). (Photo courtesy of T. H. Everett.)

caused by turgor changes; such movements may have some survival value in increasing the likelihood of cross-pollination.

Sleep movements in some plants are caused by turgor changes. The leaflets of *Oxalis*, for example, droop and partly fold at night, due to changes in the turgor of cells in the pulvini at the bases of the leaflets. Turgor changes in the pulvini of clover (*Trifolium*) leaflets cause more complex sleep movements, with the terminal leaflets turning over and covering the two lateral leaflets, which droop and twist so that their upper surfaces are brought together.

The sensitive plant (*Mimosa pudica*) is famous because the leaves or leaflets quickly droop when touched (Fig. 32.27). The speed and intensity of the movement and the amount of the plant affected vary with the intensity of the shock; the movement occurs first in the part touched and spreads progressively with diminishing force to other parts. Recovery usually takes 10–20 minutes. If a leaflet is burned in a flame, the plant reacts even more vigorously, and often all the leaves quickly droop. The movements are directly caused by differential changes in the turgor of the cells in the well-developed pulvini at the base of the leaflets and leaves, but numerous experiments have not yet clarified the mechanism of transfer of the stimulus to the pulvini, nor the chemical processes which cause the turgor changes. Hormones are very probably involved, but current hypotheses do not adequately explain the speed of the transfer. A number of other legumes are sensitive to the touch, but the reaction is less spectacular. The importance of these movements to the plant is dubious.

SUGGESTED READING

Bonner, J. T., *Morphogenesis*, Princeton University Press, Princeton, N. J., 1952, 256 pp. A high-level presentation of growth and development.

Lloyd, F. E., *The Carnivorous Plants*, Chronica Botanica, Waltham, Mass, 1942, 352 pp. Thorough and somewhat technical.

Plant Life. A *Scientific American* Book, Simon & Schuster, New York, 1957, 237 pp. Includes several articles on plant growth.

Angiosperms: Classification

CHAPTER 33

INTRODUCTION

The angiosperms, with about 200,-000 known species, make up more than half the plant kingdom and form the dominant land vegetation of most of the earth. Most botanists are agreed that the angiosperms constitute a wholly natural group, but there is still some difference of opinion as to the taxonomic rank at which the group should be received. Some botanists consider them to constitute a distinct division Anthophyta, as is done in this text; others treat them as a subdivision or class of a more inclusive division such as the Tracheophyta.

DICOTS AND MONOCOTS

The angiosperms are fairly readily divisible into two groups, the Monocotyledonae and Dicotyledonae, here treated as classes. The difference between these groups was first recognized by the English botanist John Ray (1628–1705), although he considered it less important than the

◄ **New England Aster, *Aster novae-angliae.*** Aster belongs to the family Compositae, one of the three largest families of flowering plants. (New York Botanical Garden photo.)

677

difference between woody and herbaceous plants, which is considerably downgraded as a taxonomic character in modern systems.

The several differences between the monocots and the dicots have been noted and discussed in the preceding chapters. No one of these differences is absolutely constant, but the number of cotyledons is very nearly so. The most important contrasting characters of the two groups are summarized in the following table:

DICOTS	MONOCOTS
Cotyledons 2	Cotyledon 1
Leaves mostly net-veined	Leaves mostly parallel-veined
Fascicular cambium usually present	Fascicular cambium lacking; usually no cambium of any sort
Vascular bundles usually borne in a ring which encloses a pith	Vascular bundles generally scattered, or in 2 or more rings
Floral parts, when of definite number, typically borne in sets of 5, less often 4, seldom 3 (carpels often fewer)	Floral parts, when of definite number, typically borne in sets of 3, seldom 4, never 5 (carpels often fewer)
Pollen typically of tricolpate or tricolpate-derived type, except in a few of the more primitive families	Pollen of monocolpate or monocolpate-derived type

The monocots include the grasses, sedges, rushes, lilies, iris, orchids, palms, aroids, and a number of aquatic plants. Most other familiar angiosperms belong to the dicots, which are much the larger group.

TAXONOMIC PRINCIPLES

The aim of taxonomy is to produce a natural system of classification of organisms, i.e., a system which reflects the totality of similarities and differences, as well as the path of evolution. Every characteristic of an organism is potentially important taxonomically, and no character has an inherent, fixed importance. Each character is only as important as it proves to be in any particular instance in defining a group which has been perceived on the basis of all the available evidence. Experience has shown that some characters are much more stable and thus more likely to be important than others, and that there are many essentially unidirectional evolutionary trends; but any taxonomic system which assigns a fixed and necessary value to a particular character is to that extent artificial rather than natural.

The external morphology and gross anatomy of angiosperms and other embryophytes are relatively easily studied and provide an amazing number of differences. They have, consequently, been the chief source of characters on which taxonomic systems have been based. Physiological and detailed anatomical or micromorphological characters are potentially no less important, but it is very time-consuming to study enough individuals to make sure that the observed differences are taxonomically significant.

The difficulty of obtaining some sorts of information about plants has frequently tempted botanists to base far-reaching conclusions on meager evidence, but there is no more correlation between the importance of information and the difficulty of obtaining it than there is between the efficacy of a medicine and its taste. Chromosome number is an example of an important and useful character which is subject to abuse. It is now well known that the number of chromosomes in each cell tends to be constant for all individuals of a given species, and that differences in chromosome number are likely to be taxonomically important; but unfortunately there are many exceptions. There are thoroughly documented instances of plants which differ in chromosome number but are otherwise essentially alike and interbreed freely in nature. Many legumes and other plants have cells with twice the normal number of chromosomes scattered through part or all of the plant body. Plants of one particular strain of *Xanthisma texanum*, a relative of the sunflower, have one less pair of chromosomes in the root than in the shoot, one pair of chromosomes being lost from the radicle early in the development of the embryo.

The genera and species of angiosperms frequently have a characteristic aspect, and the differences among them often reflect adaptations to particular ecological niches, such as habitat, method of pollination, method of seed dispersal, and the like. Many of these taxa are readily recognizable without formal botanical training. Oak, maple, hickory, goldenrod, ragweed, primrose, nettle, elm, tulip, Norway maple, sugar maple, silver maple, and black maple are among the many common names which closely coincide with botanical genera or species.

The families of angiosperms, on the contrary, are not usually restricted to well-defined or even approximately mutually exclusive ecological niches. The vast majority of angiosperms make and use essentially the same kinds of foods, using the same raw materials, which are obtained in the same way, and they rely on the same source of energy for food synthesis. Once the angiospermous condition has been attained, the further obvious changes which help to fit the plants to particular environments mostly occur so easily and so frequently that they tend to mark species and genera rather than larger groups. Within the single large, technically well-defined family Compositae we find herbs, shrubs, vines, and trees, self-pollinated, wind-pollinated, and insect-pollinated types, xerophytes, mesophytes, and hydrophytes, growing from below sea level (as in Death Valley) to above timberline, from tropical to arctic regions, with wind-distributed, mammal-distributed, and bird-distributed seeds, and seeds with no obvious means of dispersal.

The families, like all taxonomic categories, are or should be based on the sum of the evidence available, but in the angiosperms it is necessary to make extensive use of characters that have no evident significance in relating the plant to its environment: such things as hypogyny, perigyny, and epigyny; apocarpy and syncarpy; axile, parietal, free-central, and basal placentation; numerous or few floral parts; polypetaly and sympetaly, etc. One of the greatest difficulties in the use of these characters is that the same sort of change has occurred repeatedly in different groups (parallelism), so that the sharing of one or a few advanced characters is no guarantee of relationship.

Some botanists believe that these characters are more important to the plant than they at first seem, their significance being hidden but undiminished. Others believe them to be largely a result of internal forces governing the kinds of changes which occur. In any case, the correlation of the higher categories of angio-

Fig. 33.1. One of the massive species of *Cereus* (a cactus) in the Sonora desert of Mexico. (Photo by C. J. Chamberlain.)

Fig. 33.2. A cactus-like *Euphorbia* in semidesert in tropical Africa. (Photo from the *Belgian Congo Survey*.)

sperms with ecological niches is much less obvious than in the higher categories of land vertebrates, and the families and orders of angiosperms are correspondingly more recondite.

Only a few angiosperm families, such as the Gramineae (grasses), Palmae, and Cactaceae, stand out well enough by their gross appearance to have true common names (as opposed to the synthetic "common" names often given in books). Even these groups are not as clear-cut on the obvious characters as might at first seem. Many African members of the Euphorbiaceae are very much like the Cactaceae in general appearance (Figs. 33.1, 33.2), although quite different in floral structure; and some members of the Cactaceae (e.g., *Pereskia*) do not look much like cacti.

The emphasis on floral characters in the delimitation of families is a pragmatic development rather than a matter of principle. When the genera are arranged into groups on the basis of all that we know about them, it is usually found that the most consistent differences among the groups lie in the structure of the flowers and fruits. Other characters, such as the structure and arrangement of the leaves, the size and habit of the plant, and the special chemical compounds produced, are often also useful, but less consistently so than the floral characters.

Even the floral characters are not entirely dependable. The difference between superior and inferior ovaries usually marks groups of at least family rank, but several families, such as the Rosaceae, Saxifragaceae, and Ericaceae, run the gamut from superior to inferior ovaries. Most of the larger families that usually have a well-developed corolla also include one or more genera or species without petals. The irregular corolla is one of the outstanding features of the Scrophulariaceae, but an occasional spontaneous change in a single gene causes some snapdragons to produce regular flowers instead.

In spite of these difficulties, it has been possible to establish some 300 natural families which include practically all the known genera and species of angiosperms; and the number of genera of doubtful or controversial position is very limited. There still remains some difference of opinion as to whether certain groups should be called families or subfamilies. Some botanists, for example, recognize a family Leguminosae, with three subfamilies, the Mimosoideae, Caesalpinioideae, and Papilionoideae, whereas others recognize these same three groups as closely related families. There is general agreement, however, as to which genera should be referred to each of the three groups which collectively make up the Leguminosae. No one wishes to reshuffle the genera or to distribute them among other families outside the Leguminosae.

The classification of the families of angiosperms into orders is not yet as stabilized as the assignment of genera to families, although all systems for the past century have much in common. Even discounting the sporadic exceptions mentioned in the characters of families, it has been especially difficult to arrive at orders which are morphologically definable, and some botanists have found it necessary to accept the principle that the orders are definable only by the list of families included. Other botanists, including the author, have felt that by some rearrangement, and by the segregation of some of the larger and less coherent orders into smaller ones, natural orders with a fair degree of morphological coherence can be delimited.

HISTORY

Theophrastus (370–285 B.C.), a student of Aristotle, is often called the Father of Botany. His classification of some 500 kinds of plants was based primarily on habit (trees, shrubs, subshrubs, and herbs), with secondary use of the type of inflorescence (centripetal versus centrifugal), position of the ovary, nature of the corolla (polypetalous versus sympetalous), duration (annual, biennial, or perennial), and other characters.

Roman and medieval European botanists made no great improvement on Theophrastus' classification, although the number of kinds of plants considered gradually increased, as did also the morphological characters by which they were recognized. All these botanists generally followed a polynomial system of nomenclature; i.e., the name of a plant consisted of several Latin words, forming a brief description. The names of supposedly similar kinds of plants usually started with the same noun, which thus served as a sort of generic name, although most of these "genera" were scarcely comparable to those recognized today.

The Swiss-French botanist Jean Bauhin (1541–1631) distinguished more clearly between genera and species, and foreshadowed the binomial system of Linnaeus. In his posthumous *Historia Universalis Plantarum Nova et Absolutissima* (1650), dealing with some 5000 kinds of plants, he gave a short name to each plant, as well as a longer description. Most of his names consisted of only two words: the name of the genus, followed by the specific epithet.

The generic concept was further developed by the Swiss botanist Joseph Pitton de Tournefort (1656–1708), who is sometimes called the Father of Genera. Tournefort's genera mostly correspond well with modern concepts, and many of his names, such as *Acer*, *Betula*, *Lathyrus*, *Populus*, and *Salix*, were taken up by Linnaeus or later botanists and remain in use today. Tournefort continued to use polynomials for species, however.

The work of Linnaeus (see Chapter 5) is the greatest landmark in the history of taxonomy. His *Species Plantarum* (1753), which treated all the known genera and species of plants in a binomial system, is the formal starting point for the nomenclature of angiosperms and other vascular plants. Some of his genera and species of angiosperms have subsequently been further divided (or occasionally combined), but most of them survive with little if any change today.

Linnaeus arranged the genera of plants into 24 admittedly artificial classes. The cryptogams, in which he had little interest, were all consigned to the twenty-fourth class; and his genera and species, particularly of the nonvascular forms, bear little resemblance to those admitted today. The 23 classes of seed plants were defined largely by the numbers of stamens and carpels, thus permitting the relatively easy assignment of most genera to a particular class but often putting evidently allied genera in different classes. Linnaeus felt that the information and understanding then available were insufficient for the establishment of a natural arrangement of the genera, although in 1764 he did provide a "fragment of a natural classification" which accurately predicted a number of groups later recognized.

The first real progress toward grouping the genera of angiosperms into natural families was made by the French botanist Antoine Laurent de Jussieu. His *Genera*

Plantarum, published in 1789, recognized 100 "natural orders," many of which correspond closely to families as now recognized. The Swiss botanist Augustin Pyramus de Candolle (1778–1841) recognized 161 families which correspond even better to the families as recognized today. Subsequent improvement of the classification of genera into families has been made by a number of botanists and continues to the present.

De Candolle (Fig. 33.3) was apparently the first to perceive the major trends of floral evolution in angiosperms, although, as a pre-Darwinian, he wrote and apparently thought in terms of a series of special creations representing logically successive modifications of an original basic plan. He considered flowers with numerous free and distinct parts of all kinds (sepals, petals, stamens, and carpels) to represent the archetype. In modified or advanced types, the number of parts of each kind is reduced and stabilized, the parts of one kind become joined to each other and often to parts of another kind as well, and the parts of one kind become differentiated among themselves; in many cases, parts of a particular kind are omitted altogether. With the addition of the evolutionary concept, these same ideas prevail today (see p. 687).

The British botanists George Bentham (1800–1884) and Joseph Dalton Hooker (1817–1911) (Fig. 33.4) published a treatment of the genera of seed plants, under the title *Genera Plantarum,* in 1862–1883. The Bentham and Hooker system was essentially an elaboration and modification of the system which de Candolle did not live to complete. The families in their system correspond closely, for the most part, to the families recognized today, and they made the first real prog-

Fig. 33.3. A. P. de Candolle (1778–1841), Swiss botanist whose concepts of relationships among angiosperm families foreshadowed modern opinion.

ress toward grouping the families into natural orders, which they called cohorts. Although both Bentham and Hooker became convinced evolutionists, the basic outline of their system was conceived before Darwin's work was published, and the Bentham and Hooker system is not to be considered a phylogenetic system.

One of the great values of the Bentham and Hooker system is that their descriptions of the genera were very carefully drawn up, making use of the very large collection of specimens preserved at the Royal Botanic Gardens at Kew. Even now the descriptions of genera provided in local or regional floras are often derived directly from Bentham and Hooker.

The first avowedly evolutionary system of angiosperms was developed by the German botanist Adolf Engler (1844–

1930) (Fig. 33.5) and his associates, drawing on some principles set up by August Wilhelm Eichler (1839–1887), another German botanist. *Die natürlichen Pflanzenfamilien*, a multivolume work published from 1887 to 1899, provided a complete treatment of the divisions, classes, orders, families, and genera of plants of the world. The thoroughness of the Engler system, combined with the simplicity and apparent logic of its principles, made Engler the most influential botanist of his time; and his system became the dominant system throughout most of the world, although British botanists mostly stood by the Bentham and Hooker arrangement.

The principal flaw in the Engler system is that in general it equates the simple with the primitive, largely ignoring the significance of reduction. Although there is a certain logical satisfaction in placing plants with the simplest flowers first in the scheme and proceeding to those progressively more complex, it is now quite clear that such was not the course of evolution. The various kinds of angiosperms which lack a well-developed perianth do not form a single coherent group but represent several separate reductions from groups with the perianth well-developed. Even when there is no external evidence of a corolla or a perianth, the receptacle often contains vascular traces which end blindly and appear to be directed toward the missing parts. It is only by starting with plants of essentially the de Candollean archetype that a coherent organization can be made, starting at one point and branching out into a number of separate lines of development.

The Engler scheme postulates the repeated origin of the perianth through a series of rudimentary stages in which it can have no possible function. One of the outstanding principles of evolution, however, (see Chapter 36) is that organs do

Fig. 33.4. George Bentham (1800–1884), left, and J. D. Hooker (1817–1911), right, British botanists, authors of a *Genera Plantarum*.

Fig. 33.5. Adolf Engler (1844–1930), left, German botanist, author of a well-known system of plant classification. Charles E. Bessey (1845–1915), right, American botanist, noted for his dicta regarding evolutionary trends among the angiosperms.

not arise functionless. New organs are formed, rather, by modification of previously existing organs. It is not difficult to see sepals as modified leaves and petals as modified sepals or modified stamens; it is much more difficult to see them as totally new organs, with the first step being a blind vascular trace or a mere bump on the receptacle.

The first serious challenge to the Engler system, on an evolutionary basis, was made by the American botanist Charles E. Bessey (Fig. 33.5) in 1898. His scheme, as further elaborated in 1915, is a lineal descendant of the de Candolle and the Bentham and Hooker arrangements and shares with them the premise that the archetype of the angiosperm flower had numerous free and distinct parts of all kinds. Bessey's scheme was not nearly so

detailed as that of Engler, consisting instead of a brief synopsis of the families and orders, accompanied by a chart showing the purported relationships of the orders, and a series of evolutionary dicta which formed its philosophical foundation. Bessey's system has attracted some support, especially in the United States, but many botanists have felt that, although it is sound in principle, it needs extensive correction in detail.

The arrangements of the orders of angiosperms into a comprehensive system still arouses active and major disagreement, as does the definition of the orders themselves. Detailed studies of many families, with emphasis on vascular anatomy, embryology, and pollen structure, often supplemented by biochemical data, have clearly shown that none of the historical

Angiosperms: Classification 685

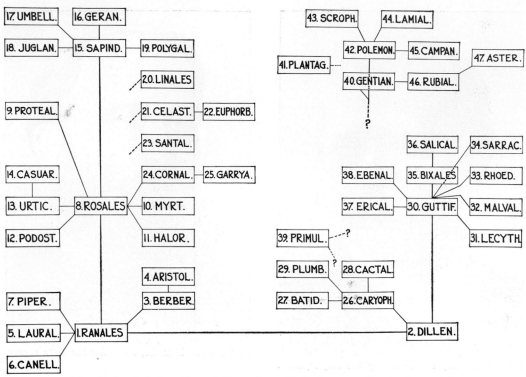

Fig. 33.6. Relationships of the orders of dicots, according to Cronquist.

systems is even approximately correct. It is generally agreed that nearly all Bessey's dicta are well founded, but the extensive parallelism among the families and orders prevented him from producing a sound system with the data then available. A recent (1957) arrangement of the dicotyledons (Fig. 33.6) by the American botanist Arthur Cronquist (1919–), making use of newer studies as well as the classical morphological characters, has attracted some support, but it remains to be seen whether this system is near enough to the ultimate truth to warrant general adoption. A rather similar system, which differs, however, in many details, was developed independently and published in 1959 (after a bare outline in 1954) by the Russian botanist Armen Takhtajan.

EVOLUTIONARY TRENDS

The evolutionary trends among the angiosperms are now fairly well understood, although much of the evidence is indirect. An interesting confirmation of the concepts about floral evolution is furnished by the comparative anatomy of the xylem. Aside from any other concepts about relationships and evolution, it is clear that vessel segments are modified tracheids, and that barrel-shaped vessel segments without end walls are more advanced than elongate, narrow vessel segments with slanting, perforated end walls. Some other trends in xylem specialization are equally clear. There is a strong statistical correlation between primitive xylem characters and the floral characters believed, on less tangible grounds, to be primitive. The correlation is not perfect, nor need it be. Evolution does not progress continuously at the same rate in all characters in all groups; in any particular group at a particular time, one character may be stable while another is rapidly changing.

In the following list, some of the characters believed to be primitive within the angiosperms are given in the left-hand column, and the contrasting advanced characters in the right-hand column. When it is desired to indicate successive stages in advancement, these are given in order in the right-hand column, separated by a semicolon.

No plant is known to have all the primitive characters listed below, but a number of tropical trees, particularly from the Malaysian region, are primitive in most respects, and *Degeneria*, the only genus of the family Degeneriaceae, is notably primitive except for having only one carpel.

PRIMITIVE	ADVANCED
1. Tropical	Temperate
2. Woody	Herbaceous
3. Cambium active	Cambium none
4. Long-lived	Short-lived
5. Vascular bundles in a cylinder, enclosing a pith	Vascular bundles scattered
6. Vessels none	Vessels present
7. Chlorophyll present	Chlorophyll none
8. Evergreen	Deciduous
9. Leaves simple	Leaves compound
10. Stipules present	Stipules none
11. Leaves net-veined	Leaves parallel-veined
12. Flowers regular	Flowers irregular
13. Flowers perfect	Flowers unisexual
14. Flowers hypogynous	Flowers perigynous; flowers epigynous
15. Floral parts of each kind many, evidently spirally arranged	Floral parts of each kind few, cyclic
16. Perianth undifferentiated	Perianth differentiated into calyx and corolla; petals and/or even sepals may thereafter be lost
17. Petals separate	Petals united
18. Stamens not differentiated into filament and anther, the pollen sacs embedded in the broad, petal-like blade	Stamens differentiated into filament and anther
19. Carpel merely folded, stigmatic along the unsealed margin	Carpel fully closed, the stigma terminal
20. Carpels separate	Carpels united, the placentation axile; placentation may thereafter become parietal, or may become free-central and then basal
21. Pollen monocolpate	Pollen tricolpate
22. Endosperm well developed	Endosperm none
23. Cotyledons several	Cotyledons 2; cotyledon 1

Fig. 33.7. Flowers of *Hepatica* (left) and *Coptis* (right), members of the family Ranunculaceae, order Ranales. These flowers are believed to be primitive in having numerous stamens and separate carpels; the perianth, although of separate parts, is not considered to be so primitive as that of some other members of the order. (Photos courtesy of J. Arthur Herrick.)

Fig. 33.8. Male (left) and female (right) catkins (inflorescences) of willow. This sort of flower, consisting of only a single pistil or a few stamens, and without perianth, was believed by Engler to be a primitive type; it is now regarded as reduced. (Photos courtesy of J. Arthur Herrick.)

The Degeneriaceae and a number of other relatively primitive families constitute the order Ranales (based on the family Ranunculaceae). It is believed that the characters of the hypothetical original angiosperm would place it in the order Ranales.

Although it is believed that several of the evolutionary trends listed here are essentially irreversible, there is no doubt that reversals of some of the others do occur. Plants of the temperate zone have certainly reinvaded the tropics in some cases; deciduous plants have become ever-green again; compound leaves have become simple by loss of all but the terminal leaflet; and parallel-veined leaves have become obviously net-veined again. On the other hand, plants that have lost their cambium do not again develop a fascicular cambium, although they may develop a cambium which does not pass through the bundles; plants that have lost chlorophyll do not again develop it; epigynous flowers do not become hypogynous; and united floral parts of any kind only rarely become separate again. In general, once a structure is lost, it is not regained in its original form, although some other structure may be modified to resemble it and perform a similar function.

CLASSIFICATION OF THE ORDERS

The synopses of the orders of dicots and monocots (given in the appendix) represent the author's own synthesis on the basis of modern knowledge. Numerous minor exceptions to the listed characters are necessarily ignored; the synopses therefore show the general organization of the classification but are not wholly trustworthy for the identification of specimens.

Some Representative Families

A. DICOTS

MAGNOLIACEAE

The Magnoliaceae, belonging to the order Ranales, consist of 10 genera and more than 100 species, widely distributed in temperate and tropical regions. They are woody plants with stipulate leaves, large, mostly perfect flowers, a well-developed perianth which is not always clearly differentiated into sepals and petals, numerous, spirally arranged stamens, and numerous, spirally arranged, separate carpels on an elongate receptacle. Many species of *Magnolia* are cultivated for ornament. *Liriodendron* (tulip tree), consisting of two closely related species, one native to the eastern United States, the other to eastern China, has valuable wood and is often also planted as a street tree. The eastern Asia–eastern United States distribution falls into a now well-known pattern believed to indicate that a large and relatively uniform deciduous forest connected these two areas through Alaska and Siberia during the Tertiary period.

ROSACEAE

The Rosaceae, with more than 100 genera and perhaps 3000 species, occur throughout most of the world but are most common in temperate regions. They have alternate, stipulate leaves, perigynous to epigynous flowers with mostly five separate petals and numerous stamens attached to the hypanthium, and the seeds generally lack endosperm. The carpels may be separate or united, and solitary to numerous. The family is also highly variable in several other respects, but the different genera all clearly belong together in one group. The Rosaceae are noteworthy for the numerous species which produce edible fruits, including the apple, pear, quince, cherry, plum, prune, peach, nectarine, apricot, blackberry, raspberry, and strawberry. A number of shrubs and small trees belonging to the Rosaceae, including hawthorn, mountain ash, and spiraea, are cultivated for ornament.

Fig. 33.9. Wild rose, from Alaska. (Photo courtesy of J. Arthur Herrick.)

Fig. 33.10. *Albizia julibrissin*, a relative of *Mimosa*, at the New York Botanical Garden. (Photos courtesy of T. H. Everett.)

LEGUMINOSAE

The Leguminosae, with more than 500 genera and perhaps 13,000 species, are one of the largest families of flowering plants. They characteristically have compound leaves, more or less perigynous flowers, five separate petals, and a solitary carpel which ripens into a dry fruit dehiscing along two sutures. Most species of temperate regions are herbs with ten sta-

Fig. 33.11. Flower structure of bristly locust (*Robinia hispida*), a legume. (New York Botanical Garden photo.)

mens and a characteristic type of irregular corolla, but many of the tropical members, such as *Mimosa*, are trees with numerous stamens and a regular corolla. All degrees of transition exist between these two seemingly very distinct types. Many legumes are cultivated: peas, beans, soybeans, and peanuts for their edible seeds; alfalfa, clover, and vetch for fodder; sweet pea, lupine, wisteria, and redbud for ornament. Several species of *Astragalus* and *Oxytropis*, occurring in the western United States, are known as loco-weed because of their effect on livestock which become addicted to them.

FAGACEAE

The Fagaceae, with 6 genera and about 600 species, occur throughout most of the world, often being dominant components of temperate forests. They are trees and shrubs with simple, alternate leaves and very much reduced, unisexual flowers, the staminate ones often in cat-

kins. The fruit is a nut subtended or enclosed by an often strongly modified involucre. Oak (*Quercus*), beech (*Fagus*), and chestnut (*Castanea*) are economically important members of the family, various species being useful for lumber, for their edible seeds, and as shade trees.

UMBELLIFERAE

The Umbelliferae, with about 125 genera and 3000 species, are most common in temperate and subtropical regions of the Northern Hemisphere. They are herbs with alternate, usually compound or dissected leaves, mostly umbellate inflorescence, and a two-carpellate, inferior ovary which ripens into a schizocarp. Many of them are aromatic. Carrot (*Daucus*), parsnip (*Pastinaca*), parsley (*Petroselinum*), and celery (*Apium*) are cultivated for food, anise (*Pimpinella*), caraway (*Carum*), dill (*Anethum*), and fennel (*Foeniculum*) for flavoring. Water hemlock (*Cicuta*) and poison hemlock (*Co-*

Fig. 33.12. Cacti in the conservatory at the New York Botanical Garden. (New York Botanical Garden photo.)

nium) are highly poisonous; the latter was used for execution in ancient Greece.

EUPHORBIACEAE

The Euphorbiaceae, with nearly 300 genera and more than 7000 species, occur throughout most of the world but are most abundant in the tropics. They are herbs, shrubs, or more often trees, usually with a milky latex. The flowers are unisexual and more or less reduced, sometimes being aggregated into small inflorescences which superficially resemble individual flowers. The ovary is superior and trilocular, each locule bearing one or two seeds with a caruncle near the micropyle and with well-developed endosperm. Economically important products of the family include rubber (*Hevea*), tung oil (*Aleurites*), castor oil (*Ricinus*), and cassava and tapioca (*Manihot*). *Poinsettia* (a subgroup of *Euphorbia*) is commonly cultivated for ornament.

CARYOPHYLLACEAE

The Caryophyllaceae, with about 80 genera and 2000 species, occur chiefly in temperate and boreal regions of the Northern Hemisphere. They are mostly herbs with simple, opposite leaves, five separate petals, free-central placentation, and centrospermous seeds; the long, narrow embryo lies just within the seed coat and curves around the copious perisperm. Carnations (*Dianthus*) and a number of other members of the family are cultivated for ornament.

CACTACEAE

The Cactaceae, with about 120 genera and 1500 species, are the only family of the order Cactales. The Cactaceae are wholly American (both North and South America), but they have been introduced in many parts of the Old World, and they are often shown in modern representations of Biblical scenes. Cacti (Fig. 33.12) are succulent, usually spiny plants, occasionally reaching tree size, with the leaves mostly very much reduced or absent. They generally have epigynous flowers with parietal placentation, numerous stamens, and numerous perianth members with little distinction between the petals and the petal-like sepals. Although they usually occur in dry places in warm regions, some species grow in forests, and one species extends as far north as Canada.

CRUCIFERAE

The Cruciferae (mustard family), with about 350 genera and 2500 species, occur chiefly in the Northern Hemisphere, especially in the cooler regions. They are mostly herbs with four sepals, four petals which spread out to form a cross, six stamens (the two outer shorter than the four inner), and a characteristic type of dry, dehiscent fruit (silique, if elongate; silicle, if short) with the ovules attached to the margins of a partition that persists on the pedicel after the walls of the fruit have fallen off. Many members of the mustard family have a mildly peppery odor or taste. Mustard, broccoli, cabbage, cauliflower, brussels sprouts, rutabagas, and turnips are familiar cultivated forms of *Brassica*. Other cultivated crucifers include radish (*Raphanus*), watercress (*Rorippa*), horse-radish (*Armoracia*), candytuft (*Iberis*), and sweet alyssum (*Lobularia*). The genera of the Cruciferae are distinguished from each other by such minor characters, and they are so thoroughly linked by transitional species that one exasperated botanist at the beginning of the twentieth century treated them all as a single genus *Crucifera*.

ERICACEAE

The Ericaceae (heath family) consist of about 80 genera and nearly 2000 species, occurring chiefly in acid soils of temperate regions and higher elevations in the tropics. Most of them are strongly mycorhizal herbs or shrubs, sympetalous or polypetalous, often evergreen, with the pollen remaining in tetrads; the anthers usually open by terminal pores and are often variously appendaged. Some members of the group, such as Indian pipe (*Monotropa*) have become so dependent on their mycorhizal associate that they no longer have chlorophyll and are unable to make their own food. Such plants are often loosely called saprophytes, although it is really the fungal component of the mycorhiza that is saprobic. Rhododendrons and azaleas (*Rhododendron*), mountain laurel (*Kalmia*), manzanita (*Arctostaphylos*), blueberries and cranberries (*Vaccinium*), and trailing arbutus (*Epigaea*) are familiar members of the family.

SOLANACEAE

The Solanaceae, with about 85 genera and perhaps 2500 species, are most abundant in tropical America, although a number of species are native to the United States. They have sympetalous, usually regular flowers with a two-carpellate, superior ovary and usually five stamens attached to the corolla tube alternate with the lobes. Well over half the species belong to the immense genus *Solanum*. "Irish" potatoes (*Solanum tuberosum*), tomatoes (*Lycopersicon esculentum*), tobacco (*Nicotiana tabacum*), peppers (*Capsicum*), deadly nightshade (*Atropa belladonna*), and petunias are well known in cultivation. Many genera contain alkaloids such as atropine, stramonium, hyoscyamine, and scopolamine—the last being one of the "truth-drugs."

SCROPHULARIACEAE

The Scrophulariaceae, a cosmopolitan family with about 200 genera and more than 3000 species, are closely related to the Solanaceae, and the distinction between the two families is not always easily drawn.

Fig. 33.13. Flowers of Scrophulariaceae: Left, moth mullein (*Verbascum blattaria*). (Courtesy of J. Arthur Herrick.) Right, beard tongue (*Penstemon*). (New York Botanical Garden photo.)

The Scrophulariaceae (Fig. 33.13) are mostly herbs with a sympetalous, distinctly irregular corolla and commonly four or only two stamens, the fifth stamen sometimes being represented by a staminode; the ovary is superior and bicarpellate, generally ripening into a capsule. Snapdragons (*Antirrhinum*) and foxglove (*Digitalis*) are commonly cultivated. *Penstemon, Mimulus,* and *Castilleja* (paintbrush) are among the most common and showy wild flowers of the western United States. Some members of the family are partly parasitic, developing haustoria which penetrate the roots of other plants. *Striga*, a recent introduction from southern Asia, which is becoming a serious pest in fields in the southeastern United States, is such a root parasite.

LABIATAE

The Labiatae (mint family), consisting of about 200 genera and more than 3000 species, occur throughout most of the world but are especially common in the Mediterranean region. They are mostly herbs with square stem and opposite leaves, generally aromatic, with an irregular, commonly bilabiate, sympetalous corolla, two or four stamens, and a characteristic two-carpellate, deeply four-lobed pistil which ripens into four achene-like, separating segments, usually called nutlets. Catnip

(*Nepeta*), sage (*Salvia*), lavender (*Lavandula*), thyme (*Thymus*), horehound (*Marrubium*), and the several kinds of mint (*Mentha*) are familiar members of the Labiatae.

COMPOSITAE

The Compositae (composite family), with nearly 1000 genera and perhaps as many as 20,000 species, are usually considered to be the largest family of angiosperms. They are mostly herbs, occurring on all continents, most abundantly in temperate and warm-temperate regions, especially in areas or habitats that are not densely forested. In most parts of the temperate zones, from 10 to 15 per cent of the species of angiosperms are composites. The family gets its name from the compact heads which simulate individual flowers; thus what appears to be a single flower is really a "composite flower." Composites have a bicarpellate, inferior ovary with a

single seed, stamens connate by their anthers, and a sympetalous corolla; the calyx, when present, is highly modified, consisting of scales, hairs, or stiff bristles. Well over half the members of the family have two kinds of flowers in each head (Fig. 33.14), the central flowers (disk flowers) being relatively small and generally perfect, with

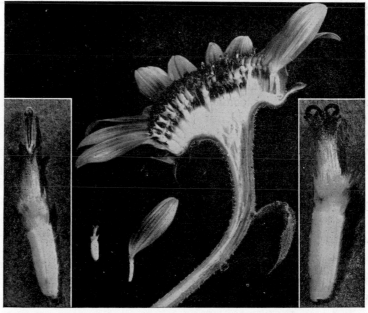

Fig. 33.14. Head and individual flowers of sunflower (*Helianthus annuus*), a member of the Compositae. (New York Botanical Garden photos.)

Fig. 33.15. Head of chicory (*Cichorium intybus*), a composite with the flowers all ray flowers and all perfect. Note the five teeth, indicating five corolla lobes, at the end of each flower. (Photo courtesy of J. Arthur Herrick.)

regular corolla, whereas the marginal flowers (ray flowers) are pistillate or neutral and have an enlarged, petal-like, strap-shaped corolla. Composites are especially important as ornamentals, because of their relatively large, showy heads. Asters (*Aster* and *Callistephus*), goldenrod (*Solidago*), chrysanthemum, dahlia, cosmos, marigold (*Tagetes*), lettuce (*Lactuca*), dandelion (*Taraxacum*), sunflower (*Helianthus*), thistle (*Cirsium* and other genera), and zinnia are familiar composites. Ragweed (*Ambrosia*) and cocklebur (*Xanthium*), with very much reduced, inconspicuous, wind-pollinated flowers, belong to a special evolutionary sideline within the family.

B. MONOCOTS

Alismataceae

The Alismataceae, a widely distributed group of about 20 genera and 70 species, are one of the most primitive existing families of monocots. They are mostly aquatic herbs with three sepals, three petals, and more or less numerous (sometimes only six) spirally (sometimes cyclically) arranged stamens and pistils. Some members differ from the dicotyledonous family Ranunculaceae chiefly in the absence of endosperm and in having only a single cotyledon. *Sagittaria* (arrowhead), is of considerable interest because some of its species show all transitions, even on the same plant, between two quite different kinds of leaves. The one type has a normal petiole and a well-defined floating blade with essentially palmate venation, and the other type consists of a submerged, flattened, bladeless petiole with parallel veins. Many botanists believe that the modern terrestrial monocots are descended from aquatic ancestors more or less similar to the Alismataceae (but with endospermous seeds), and that the characteristic narrow, parallel-veined leaf of most monocots is a flattened petiole.

LILIACEAE

The Liliaceae, as traditionally defined, have about 240 genera and 4000 species, widely distributed but especially common in tropical and warm-temperate regions that are not densely forested. They are mostly perennial herbs, often from bulbs or corms, with narrow, parallel-veined leaves, a superior, three-carpellate ovary, and three petaloid sepals that are much like the three petals (Fig. 33.16). Tulips, true lilies (*Lilium*), Mariposa lily (*Calochortus*), asparagus, and onion (*Allium*) are familiar members of the lily family. *Trillium* is unusual in the family in having green sepals that are not petaloid. Day lilies (*Hemerocallis*) and some other lilies

Fig. 33.16. Wild onion (*Allium canadense*), a member of the lily family. Note that some of the flowers are replaced by bulblets in this species; these drop off and start new plants. (Photo courtesy of J. Arthur Herrick.)

Fig. 33.17. Joshua tree (*Yucca brevifolia*), a plant of deserts in the southwestern United States, one of the most arborescent member of the lily family. (Photo courtesy of J. Arthur Herrick.)

belong to the closely related family Amaryllidaceae, distinguished by its inferior ovary, but the calla lily and some other so-called lilies belong to quite different orders. In recent years, it has been shown that the distinction between the Liliaceae and Amaryllidaceae on the basis of superior versus inferior ovary is not entirely natural, and that some realignment is necessary. Inferior ovaries have evidently been derived more than once in the group, and it will be necessary either to include the Amaryllidaceae in a more broadly defined family Liliaceae, or to recognize several smaller families in addition to these two. Those who define the Liliaceae in the narrowest sense still recognize more than 150 genera in the family.

Palmae

The Palmae, a tropical and subtropical family with about 200 genera and perhaps as many as 2500 species, differ from the vast majority of other monocots in being woody. Most of them are straight, slender, unbranched trees with a crown of very large, often pinnately compound leaves at the top (Fig. 33.18). The palms, like other monocots, lack a fascicular cambium, but some of them do have an anomalous sort of secondary thickening in which the new

Fig. 33.18. Palms. Left, inflorescence of *Guilielma*. (Courtesy of José Cuatrecasas.) Right, coconut palms in Costa Rica. (New York Botanical Garden photo.)

growth layers have scattered vascular bundles embedded in a sclerenchymatous fundamental tissue. It is generally believed that the palms are only secondarily woody, being derived from herbaceous ancestors somewhat similar to the Liliaceae. The coconut palm (*Cocos*) and date palm (*Phoenix*) are among the economically more important palms. A number of others, especially *Washingtonia*, are familiar in cultivation in Florida and southern California.

GRAMINEAE

The Gramineae (grasses), a cosmopolitan family with about 500 genera and perhaps 10,000 species, are probably the most important single family of plants, from a human standpoint. The importance of wheat as a staple food in much of the Western world is surpassed only by that of rice, another grass, in the Orient. Corn, oats, rye, barley, sugar cane, and bamboo (Fig. 33.19) are some other important grasses. The Biblical comment "All flesh is grass" reminds us also that grass is a staple food for grazing animals, which in turn are eaten by other predators and by man. The intercalary meristem at the base of the leaf blade of grasses enables them to withstand grazing better than most other plants, because the leaf continues to grow from the base after it has been cropped off at the top.

The grasses have very much reduced flowers, essentially without perianth, arranged in characteristic small, bracteate spikes called spikelets. The bracts are usually dry and papery in texture, have special names according to their position, and are the most conspicuous parts of the spikelet. The spikelets are arranged into a secondary inflorescence, most commonly a panicle, sometimes a spike or raceme. Most grasses

Fig. 33.19. Bamboo thicket in Colombia. Bamboos are the largest of all grasses. (Photo courtesy of José Cuatrecasas.)

are wind-pollinated or self-pollinated, and many are apomictic. The grasses are generally believed to be derived from lily-like ancestors with a well-developed perianth. A similar tendency toward reduction is shown by the Juncaceae, a small family with small and inconspicuous but otherwise essentially lily-like flowers.

ORCHIDACEAE

The Orchidaceae, with about 450 genera and perhaps as many as 15,000 species, are one of the largest families of plants. They are widely distributed but they are most common in the moister parts of the tropics, especially as epiphytes. The orchids are characterized by their highly modified and irregular, epigynous, often very showy flowers (Fig. 33.20), and by their very numerous, very small seeds, with

Fig. 33.20. *Dendrobium*, a tropical epiphytic orchid, in cultivation. (From Transeau, Sampson, and Tiffany, *Textbook of Botany*, Rev. Ed., Harper, 1953.)

minute and undifferentiated embryo. Most of them are strongly mycorhizal, and a few lack chlorophyll, being dependent on the fungal associate for food. Vanilla flavoring is derived from fruits of the tropical genus *Vanilla*. Otherwise orchids are important chiefly as ornamentals; *Cattleya*, in particular, is much used for corsages.

NOMENCLATURE

It has often happened that the same species has been named more than once, due to misunderstanding of the specific limits, or to ignorance of names published in other countries by other botanists, or even through dissatisfaction with existing known names. The same name has sometimes also been applied to more than one plant.

During the nineteenth century the need for a set of rules of botanical nomenclature became evident. Alphonse de Candolle, son of Augustin Pyramus de Candolle, and a group of other botanists proposed a code after an international meeting at Paris in 1867. Botanists at Kew and Berlin, the two greatest centers of taxonomy in the latter half of the nineteenth century, developed rules of their own, which differed from each other and from the Paris code in some respects. In America, Nathaniel Lord Britton (Fig. 33.21) and his associates developed still another set of rules, the American Code of Botanical Nomenclature.

Botanists from all parts of the world met in Vienna in 1905 to devise an international code, but many American botanists, dissatisfied with the results of the meeting, continued to follow the American

Code. At another botanical congress in Cambridge, England, in 1930, the differences between the American Code and the International Code were compromised, and a new, revised code was generally adopted. Only slight modifications have been made by succeeding congresses.

The code provides standards for valid publication of names and methods of choosing between competing names. One of the important requirements is that names of newly recognized taxa published since 1934 must be accompanied by a Latin diagnosis. Priority of publication is the guiding principle in choosing between competing names, but certain limitations to priority are recognized. All names published before 1753 (the date of Linnaeus' *Species Plantarum*) are disallowed; priority holds only within a given taxonomic category, e.g., a name published in varietal

status carries no priority at specific or subspecific status; and there is a Conserved List of well-known generic names which are maintained in spite of being contrary to the rules in one or another respect. The application of names is determined by the type method. The type of a species is ordinarily the particular specimen from which the original description was principally or wholly made, or a specimen designated by the author as typical. The type of a genus is the species which was central to the original author's concept, etc.

One of the most useful bibliographic tools in taxonomy is the *Index Kewensis* (*Kew Index*), which lists all names of genera and species of modern (i.e., living) seed plants from 1753 to the present, indicating the part of the world in which each species occurs and the place of publication of the name. Charles Darwin,

Fig. 33.21. Asa Gray (1810–1888), left, founder of the Gray Herbarium, and the most eminent American botanist of his time. N. L. Britton (1859–1934), right, founder of the New York Botanical Garden, sponsor of the American Code of Botanical Nomenclature.

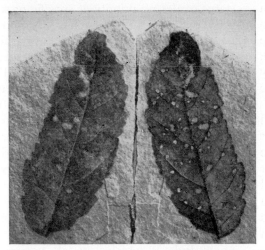

Fig. 33.22. Fossil leaves from Oligocene deposits in Montana. (Photos courtesy of Herman F. Becker.)

recognizing the need for such an index, left the money for it in his will. The compilation was done by botanists at the Royal Botanic Gardens at Kew (outside of London). The original edition, in two massive volumes, covered names published through 1885 and was published in 1895. Twelve supplements continue to the present.

The *Gray Card Index,* published by the Gray Herbarium of Harvard University, lists all the names published for vascular plants in the New World since 1885. Unlike the *Kew Index,* the *Gray Card Index* included varieties and other infraspecific taxa as well as species. Recently a start has been made toward adding the names of infraspecific taxa published before 1885. Asa Gray (Fig. 33.21) (1810–1888), for whom the Gray Herbarium is named, was the outstanding American botanist of his time. His monumental *Synoptical Flora of North America,* published in parts from 1874 to 1886, and still unfinished when he died, is the foundation for much future work on the taxonomy of North American plants.

FOSSILS

The fossil record provides very little help in deciphering the relationships and evolutionary history of angiosperms. The most abundant angiosperm fossils are leaf impressions (Fig. 33.22); seeds, dry fruits, and parts of the wood are often also fossilized. Fossil flowers are more rare and exist almost entirely as mere impressions which show the external form but not the structure. Relatively recent fossil leaves can often be identified with modern species or genera by careful comparison, but this is a risky procedure at best, and progressively more so in dealing with older fossils that are less likely to have modern counterparts. One of the common Upper Cretaceous fossils that was long referred to the modern genus *Liriodendron* (Magnoliaceae, order Ranales) has more recently been identified as a leaflet of the compound leaf of *Dalbergia* (Leguminosae, order Rosales). When fossil leaves are found associated with fruits, the identification may be fairly certain; and specialized fruits, such as those of maple, can often be identified without any other parts.

The oldest fossils that are unmistakably angiosperms are of Lower Cretaceous age, although some Jurassic pollen grains and bits of wood are very probably angiospermous. The angiosperms never constitute more than 25 per cent of the flora of known Lower Cretaceous deposits, as measured by the number of species, but they represent a wide variety of types. Both monocots and dicots are certainly represented, and the dicots have been referred to several widely separated families such as the Ebenaceae, Menispermaceae, Nymphaeaceae, and Salicaceae.

The Potomac beds of Maryland contain the most extensive known Lower Cretaceous angiosperm flora, and the proportion of angiosperms increases from the base to the top of the deposits. Angiosperm fossils also occur in Lower Cretaceous rocks in western Greenland. Many lower Cretaceous fossils have been given names suggesting a resemblance to modern genera, such as *Nelumbites, Menispermites, Sapindopsis,* and *Celastrophyllum,* and some have even been referred to modern genera, such as *Populus* and *Sassafras,* but all such identifications are doubtful.

By Upper Cretaceous time the angiosperms had become the dominant land vegetation, and they are abundantly represented in the fossil record from that time to the present. Many Upper Cretaceous fossils appear to represent modern genera, in many different families, even including such advanced families as the Compositae.

No fossils are known which tend to connect the angiosperms with any other group of plants, nor can the fossils be used to connect the modern families and orders. Concepts of relationship among the families and orders must, therefore, be based on comparison of only the living members, and the ancestry of the group can be determined only by a process of elimination. The only fossils which have the characters thought to be necessary in the forebears of the angiosperms are some of the Late Paleozoic seed ferns, and any relationship even to these must be rather remote.

SUGGESTED READING

Anderson, Edgar, *Plants, Man and Life,* Little, Brown, Boston, 1952, 245 pp. A provocative, informative, outspoken book, emphasizing the origins and classification of weeds and cultivated plants, guaranteed to hold your attention.

Peattie, Donald Culross, *Green Laurels. The lives and achievements of the great naturalists,* Simon & Schuster, New York, 1936, 368 pp. Interesting and easy reading.

Rodgers, Andrew Denny, III, *John Torrey,* Princeton University Press, Princeton, N.J., 1942, 352 pp. A biography of an outstanding American botanist of a century ago.

———, *Liberty Hyde Bailey,* Princeton University Press, Princeton, N.J., 1949, 506 pp. The life and times of the greatest American student of cultivated plants.

———, *American Botany 1873–92; Decades of Transition,* Princeton University Press, Princeton, N.J., 1944, 340 pp.

Angiosperms: Economic Importance

CHAPTER 34

INTRODUCTORY SUMMARY

Angiosperms are in a sense the foundation of our civilization. They provide man with food, clothing, and shelter. They brighten leisure, ease pain, and cure illness. They furnish the raw materials for countless industrial products. Unfortunately, they also evoke allergies such as hay fever, produce poisons which kill livestock and unwary nature-enthusiasts, and bring misery and degradation to millions trapped by drug addiction.

FOOD

The greatest importance of angiosperms is as food. Excepting fish, all the important staples of diet are either angiosperms or are derived from animals which in turn feed largely on angiosperms.

ORIGIN OF FOOD CROPS

The cultivation of angiosperms as food crops began long before recorded history.

◀ Harvesting wheat in the Palouse region of Washington. (Photo courtesy of the Spokane Chamber of Commerce.)

705

The wild ancestors of some of these plants, such as carrots, lettuce, and sunflowers, are readily identifiable, but the most important food crops, as well as many lesser ones, have been so modified under cultivation that their ancestry cannot easily be deciphered. All of them have wild relatives, but such plants as wheat, corn, rice, and many others do not seem to be direct descendants of any existing wild species. Interspecific hybridization as well as selection has undoubtedly played a part, and the hybridization has often been accompanied by polyploidy (increase in the number of complete sets of chromosomes).

In each hemisphere there were several centers in which domestication of crops principally took place, after which the crops became widely cultivated elsewhere. The important centers in America were the highlands of Mexico and the highlands of Central America and northwestern South America—the regions where the Aztec, Maya, and Inca civilizations later arose. The important centers in the Old World were southeastern Asia, the eastern Mediterranean region, the mountainous region from northern India to Asia Minor and Transcaucasia, and possibly Ethiopia —regions noteworthy also as early centers of civilization. The development of agriculture, with its associated sedentary instead of nomadic habits, is a necessary precursor and stimulus to the rise of civilization.

Only during the last several centuries has there been much exchange of crops between the Eastern and Western Hemispheres. Cassava, cocoa, common beans, corn (maize), lima beans, peanuts, pineapples, potatoes, sunflower, tobacco, and tomatoes are among the most important crops originating in the New World. Apples, bananas, breadfruit, cabbage, carrots, coffee, cherries, citrus fruits, dates, figs, flax, hemp, lettuce, olives, onions, pears, peaches, rice, rye, sorghum, soybeans, sugar cane, watermelons, and wheat are among the most important crops originating in the Old World. Different kinds of cotton were domesticated in both hemispheres. Sweet potatoes, although surely of American origin, were cultivated in the tropics of both hemispheres long before Columbus' voyage—the only significant crop common to the Old and the New World in pre-Columbian time.

The classic work on the origin of cultivated plants was published in 1883 by the Swiss botanist Alphonse de Candolle (1806–1893), son of Augustin Pyramus de Candolle. Most of his conclusions, except for many of his tentative dates of domestication, are still accepted.

CEREAL CROPS

The grass family (Gramineae) outranks all other plants combined as a source of food. Edible grains obtained from cultivated grasses are called cereals. Wheat, rice, corn (maize), oats, barley, and rye are well-known cereal crops.

The most important of all crops in the temperate regions is wheat. From long before Jesus' prayer, "Give us this day our daily bread," until well after the coinage of the medieval English aphorism that bread is the staff of life, wheat was the principal food in settled communities of Europe, temperate Asia, and the Mediterranean region. The bread demanded by the hungry mobs of Paris, and the cake supposedly offered them by Marie Antoinette, were both made from wheat. Even in modern societies with the varied diet associated with a high standard of

Fig. 34.1. Types of wheat. Left to right: einkorn, emmer, durum, and common wheat. There are also bearded forms of common wheat. (New York Botanical Garden photo.)

living, wheat is the most important vegetable food.

There are about eight principal species of wheat (*Triticum*), all annual or winter-annual grasses. Common wheat (*Triticum aestivum*) is cultivated in many varieties, including truly annual (spring wheat) and winter annual (winter or fall wheat) races, hard wheats with small grains rich in proteins, soft wheats with larger grains richer in starch, and white-grained and red-grained forms. Durum wheat (*T. durum*), with very hard, red grains rich in gluten (a sticky proteinaceous substance), is used chiefly for macaroni and similar products. The other wheats are no longer of much direct importance.

Einkorn wheat (*T. monococcum*),

emmer (*T. dicoccum*), and spelt (*T. spelta*) differ from other wheats in that the axis of the spike is jointed and shatters in threshing, and the grain does not separate readily from its enclosing bracts (the chaff). These are the oldest and most primitive known wheats, dating from the Stone Age. They do well in poor, dry soils, requiring less care than other species, but the yield is also low. Nowadays they are chiefly of historical interest, although they are grown to some extent in Europe, especially for fodder. They are also sometimes used in breeding programs because of their hardiness and vigor.

Rice (*Oryza sativa*) is the most important of all crops, from a world-wide standpoint, being the principal food of

Angiosperms: Economic Importance 707

more than half the population of the earth. It is primarily a plant of hot moist tropics and is most extensively grown in the Orient, where it dominates the social and economic structure. Rice originated in southeastern Asia, being first extensively cultivated by the Chinese in prehistoric times. All the most important varieties must be flooded for most of the growth period, but there are also upland varieties which can be grown without irrigation.

Commercial polished rice, as sold in the United States, is very rich in carbohydrates but contains only minute amounts of proteins, minerals, and fats. Unpolished rice, with the embryo still included in the grain, is much more nutritious but is still relatively low in protein. In regions where rice is the staple food, soy-

beans are commonly eaten along with it as a principal source of protein.

Maize (*Zea mays*) was the cereal of the American Indians, grown chiefly in the warmer regions, but also as far north as the St. Lawrence Valley and the Great Lakes region, and south to Chile and Argentina. It is now cultivated in all suitable parts of the world. The name Indian corn, applied to it by the English colonists in America, has been shortened in the United States to corn; but in England corn still means any cereal grain, especially wheat.

The origin of maize is even more of a mystery than that of most other crops. It is clearly from tropical America, as are most of its botanical allies, but its only close relative, teosinte (*Euchlaena mexicana*) is apparently an evolutionary sibling or descendant rather than an ancestor.

Fig. 34.2. Types of corn. Left to right: pod, flint, dent, and popcorn. (Photos courtesy of William L. Brown, Pioneer Hi-Bred Seed Company.)

708 *Introductory Botany*

The forms of corn (Fig. 34.2) are even more numerous and diverse than those of other cereals. The most primitive type, pod corn, has a husk for each grain as well as for the whole ear. The grains may resemble those of any of the other types. Because of the difficulty of threshing, pod corn has no commercial importance.

Dent corn—the most extensively cultivated type, especially in the corn belt of the United States—has a dent in the top of each mature grain because of the shrinkage of the soft part of the endosperm, the hard part being present only at the sides. Flint corn, which matures earlier and can be grown farther north than dent corn, has the starchy endosperm covered at the top as well as the sides by the horny endosperm, so that there is no dent. Dent corn and flint corn are often collectively called field corn. Field corn is used principally as food for livestock, especially hogs, but also for corn meal, breakfast cereals, salad oil, corn sirup, and as raw material for a wide variety of industrial products. Even the vegetative parts are used, both for fodder and in industry.

Sweet corn, with a high proportion of sugar instead of starch in the endosperm, does not yield so well as field corn, but it is more palatable, and the immature grains are canned as well as eaten directly from the cob. Besides sweet corn and field corn, the only other type of corn of any importance in the United States is popcorn.

NONCEREAL CROPS

Potatoes (*Solanum tuberosum*) are the world's most important noncereal crop. The total volume of potato production per year is actually greater than that of rice or any other cereal, but potatoes contain a much larger proportion of water (about 78 per cent of the total weight) than any of the grains.

Frequently called the Irish potato, because of its importance as a food crop in Ireland, *Solanum tuberosum* is actually native to the Andean region of tropical South America, where a number of other tuber-bearing species of the very large genus *Solanum* are also cultivated. Potatoes do best in rather cool, moist regions, such as central and northern Europe, where they are the principal crop, but they are cultivated in various races over much of the world, except for the tropical lowlands.

Although rich in carbohydrates, potatoes contain only a small amount of protein and almost no fat, so that alone they do not provide an anywhere nearly balanced diet. In addition to their value as food, potatoes are used as a source of carbohydrate for the production of alcohol and other industrial products, especially in Europe.

Sweet potatoes (*Ipomoea batatas*), yams (*Dioscorea* spp.), and cassava (*Manihot esculenta*) are among the most important tropical crops. Sweet potatoes are also extensively cultivated in the southeastern United States, where they have some commercial importance; elsewhere they are mostly a home-garden crop, seldom marketed, although often eaten daily. The sweet potato, a member of the family Convolvulaceae, is not very closely related to the Irish potato, which belongs to the Solanaceae. The edible organ of the sweet potato is a modified root, whereas that of the Irish potato is a true tuber, a modified stem. One type of sweet potato is often called yam in the United States, but this has nothing to do with the true yams of the tropics, which are climbing, mono-

Fig. 34.3. Left: cassava in Costa Rica; figures are meters and centimeters. (Photo courtesy of David J. Rogers.) Right: bananas in the conservatory at the New York Botanical Garden. (New York Botanical Garden photo.)

cotyledonous vines with a large storage root that often weighs as much as 40 pounds.

Cassava (Fig. 34.3), a native of tropical America, belongs to the Euphorbiaceae. It is a shrubby perennial with stems up to 12 feet tall, and with large, palmatifid leaves; many of the roots end in large, tuber-like swellings. The root contains a poisonous glucoside related to prussic acid, but the poison can be driven off by heating. In the United States cassava is known principally in the prepared form called tapioca, but in tropical America and many other tropical regions it is a dietary staple, cultivated in hundreds of varieties.

In temperate climates the fleshy fruits are important chiefly as a dietary fil-lip and as a source of vitamins. Apples (*Pyrus malus*) are the most important fruit in cool-temperate regions, and peaches (*Prunus persica*) in warm-temperate. Oranges (*Citrus sinensis*), although originally tropical, are now cultivated mostly in subtropical regions, such as Florida and southern California. In the United States some tropical fruits such as bananas (Fig. 34.3) and pineapples are also used in large quantities. Grapes (*Vitis* spp.), another temperate-zone crop, are more important, especially in Europe, as a source of wine than as a table fruit.

Several tropical fruits, including banana (*Musa paradisaica*), date (*Phoenix dactylifera*), coconut (*Cocos nucifera*), and breadfruit (*Artocarpus altilis*), are

ical coasts in general, are also noteworthy for their numerous nondietary uses, including basketry, mats, fibers, and construction timbers.

SPICES

The most important of all spices is pepper (Fig. 34.6), derived from the berry-like drupes of *Piper nigrum*, a vine native

Fig. 34.4. Left: date palms. Right: breadfruit. (Photos by W. H. Hodge.)

highly nourishing and form dietary staples in various regions. Captain Bligh's mission on the famous voyage of H.M.S. *Bounty* was to introduce the breadfruit (Fig. 34.4), a native of Malaya, into the British West Indies. (The West Indians anticlimactically found the fruit not to their liking.) The date palm (Fig. 34.4), in desert regions from North Africa to India, and the coconut palm (Fig. 33.18), in the South Sea Islands and along trop-

Angiosperms: Economic Importance 711

Fig. 34.5. Harvesting sugar cane. (Photo by W. H. Hodge.)

to southeastern Asia. Black pepper is made by grinding the whole dried fruit, white pepper from only the stone and seed; commercial pepper is often a mixture of the two types. Pepper was one of the principal items imported into Europe along the overland trade route from the Orient in Roman and medieval times, and its high price was a great stimulant in the search for a sea route to India. Red pepper, even more pungent than ordinary pepper, is produced from the berries of *Capsicum*, a member of the potato family.

Cinnamon (Fig. 34.8) is one of the most widely used of the many other spices. It is made from the bark of *Cinnamomum zeylanicum*, an evergreen shrub or small tree native to Ceylon. Nutmeg (Fig. 34.7), derived from the seed of *Myristica fragrans* (an evergreen tree) was the principal spice

Fig. 34.6. Left: harvesting pepper in Indonesia. Right: details of the leaves and fruits of pepper. (Courtesy of the American Spice Trade Association.)

of the Spice Islands (the Moluccas) of romantic fame, although cloves, the flower buds of *Syzygium aromaticum*, were also later cultivated there. Zanzibar is the principal current source of cloves.

Vanilla (Fig. 34.8), a favorite flavoring material, is obtained from the unripe, cured fruits of *Vanilla planifolia*, a climbing orchid native to the jungles of tropical America. The active principle, vanillin, develops from a nonaromatic glucoside during the carefully controlled curing process. Vanilla was introduced to Europe by the Spanish conquistadores, who found the Aztecs using it to flavor chocolate. Madagascar is now the principal source of commercial vanilla.

Fig. 34.7. Nutmeg. The aril, shown partly covering the seed and (separately) at the lower right, is the source of mace. (Photo by W. H. Hodge.)

Fig. 34.8. Left: flowering branch of cinnamon. (Photo by W. H. Hodge.) Right: harvesting vanilla in Madagascar. (Photo courtesy of Bernard L. Lewis, Inc.)

Fig. 34.9. Left: twig of coffee tree. Right: trunk and fruits of cocoa tree. Photos by W. H. Hodge.)

DRINKS

Coffee and tea are the most important hot beverages, with chocolate third. Tea is used by fully half the people of the world, but coffee, used by fewer people, is consumed in greater quantities. Both owe their popularity to the stimulating effect of the caffeine they contain. Coffee is brewed from the ground-up seeds of several species of *Coffea*, chiefly *C. arabica* (Fig. 34.9), a small tree native to Abyssinia and now cultivated in the tropics of both hemispheres (especially in Brazil). Tea is made from the dried leaves of *Camellia sinensis*, a small tree native to China or northeastern India, cultivated as a shrub in tropical and warm-temperate parts of Asia.

Chocolate and cocoa are made from the seeds of *Theobroma cacao* (Fig. 34.9),

a small tree native to the lowlands of tropical America, and now extensively cultivated in western tropical Africa as well. Cocoa differs from chocolate in having about two thirds of the natural oil (cocoa butter) extracted in the process of manufacture. Unlike coffee, tea, and most other beverages, cocoa and chocolate are highly nutritious. The seeds contain 30–50 percent fatty oil, and about 15 percent each of protein and starch. They also contain theobromine (a mild stimulant) and traces of caffeine. Chocolate is a common ingredient of candy.

Alcoholic beverages were discussed in connection with yeast on pp. 247–248. Wine is made chiefly from grapes, beer chiefly from barley, pulque from agave juice, sake from rice, and mead from honey. Our word honeymoon comes from the use of mead by Scandinavians several centuries ago in nuptial ceremonies lasting 30 days. Of the distilled beverages, whisky, vodka, and gin are made from various grains (vodka sometimes also from potatoes), brandy from grapes, and rum from sugar cane.

MASTICATORIES

The essential ingredient of chewing gum is chicle, the dried latex from the bark of the sapodilla tree (*Manilkara zapotilla* and related species), a native of tropical North America. The tree (Fig. 34.10) does not withstand tapping well, nor have efforts at large-scale cultivation met with much success. Commercial exploitation threatens it with virtual extinction in the wild, and none of the many natural and artificial substitutes and adulterants which have been tried is wholly satisfactory. Doubtless chewing gum will continue to be made, regardless of the fate of the sapodilla, but there may be some change in its nature or quality. The sapodilla is also much esteemed in tropical America for its fruit, and is often casually cultivated or encouraged in a semiwild state about dwellings.

Betel nuts (the seeds of *Areca catechu*, a palm) are chewed by more people than any other masticatory, but their use is largely restricted to tropical eastern Asia, the East Indies, and Melanesia. Slices of betel nut are wrapped in the leaves of the betel pepper (*Piper betle*), smeared with a little lime, and popped into the mouth. The mixture is esteemed as a breath sweetener and aid to digestion.

The seeds ("nuts") of the cola tree (*Cola nitida*) are commonly chewed in tropical Africa. They contain a considerable amount of caffeine, as well as kolanin,

a heart stimulant. Cola nuts are also used in the preparation of several commercial carbonated beverages, especially in the United States.

NARCOTICS

Tobacco is prepared from the dried leaves (and sometimes other parts) of *Nicotiana tabacum*, a coarse annual herb native to tropical America. A related species, N. *rustica*, was smoked by the Indians of eastern North America and was the first tobacco to be cultivated by the English colonists in Virginia, but it is no longer of much importance. Tobacco is now smoked over most of the world, most of all in the United States, because of the

Fig. 34.10. Young tree of *Manilkara zapotilla*, the source of chicle. (Photo by W. H. Hodge.)

Fig. 34.11. Foxglove (*Digitalis purpurea*). (Photo courtesy of the Boyce-Thompson Institute for Plant Research.)

phine. These drugs are habit-forming and have euphoric, analgesic, sedative, and toxic properties, heroin being the most dangerous, and codeine the least. Continued use leads to addiction, physiological deterioration, and premature death, and withdrawal of the drug causes such severe pain that an addict will do literally anything in his power to obtain it.

The opium poppy is cultivated principally in China, India, Burma, Thailand, and the Middle East, and addiction is common in those countries. China in particular has for centuries had a large proportion of addicts. The attempt of the Chinese government to prevent importation of opium from India, as part of a campaign against the use of the drug, led to the Opium War in 1840–1842, and the cession of Hong Kong to Great Britain. The present Chinese government, while attempting to repress the use of opium at home, exports the drug and fosters its use abroad.

effect of nicotine, its most important active principle, in easing nervous tension and promoting a sense of well-being. Although offensive to most of those not accustomed to its use, it is mildly habit-forming. The recent demonstration that there is a clear statistical association between the use of tobacco—especially cigarettes—and the occurrence of lung cancer and heart ailments has not as yet had any marked influence on its use.

The opium poppy, *Papaver somniferum*, is the source of the drug opium. Crude opium, the dried exudate from maturing capsules that have been bruised or slit, contains a number of narcotic alkaloids, including morphine and codeine. Heroin is a chemical derivative of mor-

MEDICINE

Angiosperms play a large but decreasing role in medicine. Once the source of practically all effective remedies for disease, they are gradually being replaced by synthetic drugs.

Digitalis is perhaps the most important therapeutic drug still obtained directly from angiosperms, the dried leaves being a standard treatment for certain types of heart disease. The drug became generally known through a report in 1785 by William Withering, an English physician, on its usefulness in treating dropsy, now known to be a symptom of circulatory disorder. Withering's interest was attracted by the success of an old woman of Shropshire in treating dropsy with an herb tea. He somehow managed to learn the components of the tea, and then, by cautious experimentation on his patients, he discovered that the active ingredient was foxglove (*Digitalis purpurea*, Fig. 34.11), and that the leaves are the most effective part of the plant. Students so-minded may be able to concoct whimsical limericks beginning, "There was an old woman of Shropshire."

Quinine, once one of the most important drugs in the world, and the only effective cure for malaria, is now being replaced by synthetics which are even more effective. As recently as World War II, when the capture of Malaya and the East Indies by the Japanese cut off the main commercial source of quinine (Fig. 34.12), the United States found it necessary to set botanists to combing the jungles of northwestern South America in search of the wild source: several species of *Cinchona* native only to that region. Quinidine, another alkaloid which occurs mixed with quinine in *Cinchona* bark, is the standard treatment for auricular fibrillation of the heart.

Some synthetics which replace natural drugs are chemically unrelated to them, but many are more or less similar to the natural product. Even when the synthetic is exactly the same as the active principle in the natural drug, the synthetic is generally preferred because the quality can be more closely controlled. The amount of the active principle in the plant varies from individual to individual, from year to year, and according to the season and method of handling. Once the drug has been synthesized and its chemical structure established, it is possible to produce numerous minor chemical variants of the same type; and frequently some of these are more effective than the original or provide a greater margin between the therapeutic and the toxic dose. Without the lead provided by the natural product, however, these improved synthetics could not be developed.

Investigation of natural drugs sometimes leads to unexpected results, just as

Fig. 34.12. Cinchona plantation in Java. (Photo courtesy of Norman Taylor.)

Fig. 34.13. Cotton field in Texas. (Photo courtesy of Elizabeth Wagner; from Transeau, Sampson, and Tiffany, *Textbook of Botany*, Rev. Ed., Harper, 1953.)

does any other type of scientific inquiry. *Simaruba glauca*, a small tree native to tropical North America, attracted interest during World War II because of the antimalarial properties of a bitter principle in the bark. The extracted drug, although inferior to many others in the control of malaria, turned out instead to be highly effective against amoebic dysentery. The latex of several species of *Ficus* proved too dangerous to live up to its original promise as an anthelmintic, but found a wholly unexpected use in clarifying beer.

FIBER

Cotton (*Gossypium* spp.) is the most important fiber plant and the world's greatest industrial crop (Fig. 34.13). The most important species, *G. hirsutum* (upland cotton) is of American origin, as is also *G. barbadense* (sea-island cotton and Egyptian cotton), but species of Old World origin are also extensively grown

in Asia. The cotton boll is the opened ripe fruit (capsule), and the cotton fibers are hairs attached to the seed coats. In 1793 Eli Whitney devised a machine, the cotton gin, for separating the fibers from the seeds (previously a time-consuming and expensive process), after which cotton soon became the dominant textile fiber of the world.

The separated seeds from the cotton boll are also utilized. Cottonseed oil is used in salad oils and in the manufacture of oleomargarine and substitutes for lard, and the residue after the oil is expressed is used as livestock food and as a raw material in many industrial processes.

Flax (*Linum usitatissimum*), once the foremost fiber plant in Europe and western Asia, has lost much of its standing to cotton but is still used for the production of linen cloth and thread, canvas, duck cloth, carpets, the strongest twine, fishline, and seines, and the finest writing paper. The flax fibers, which range up to 3 feet in length, are the outermost part

Fig. 34.14. Manila hemp plant. (Photo by W. H. Hodge.)

of the phloem of the vascular bundles. They are rotted (retted) out by submerging the stems in water for some time, or exposing them to dew. Linseed oil is obtained from the seeds of specially adapted varieties of flax which are not used for fiber.

Manila hemp, the best fiber for ropes, comes from the petioles of *Musa textilis* (Fig. 34.14) and related species, which are closely allied to the cultivated banana but have inedible fruits.

OTHER INDUSTRIAL PRODUCTS

Wood

The wood of many angiosperms is of high commercial value. Maple, oak, beech, birch, walnut, and other hardwoods are used for flooring, fine furniture, and interior finish. These same species, as well as conifers, are used in plywood. Mahogany (Fig. 34.15), a native of tropical America, is famous for its use in furniture, and many other tropical angiosperms, as yet little used, are potentially valuable. White oak is the outstanding wood for tight cooperage, i.e., for barrels which will hold liquids without imparting taste or odor. Sawmill wastes are used in destructive distillation, yielding acetic acid, wood alcohol, and other industrial chemicals. Lignum vitae, an extremely hard wood from a West Indian tree (*Guaiacum officinale*), is used for main bearings on drive shafts of submarines in preference to metal because it is less noisy and is self-lubricating.

Fig. 34.15. Mahogany (*Swietenia mahogani*). This, the Spanish or West Indian mahogany, is one of the two species, both native only to the New World, which properly bear the name mahogany. (Photo by W. H. Hodge.)

Rubber

Rubber, a coagulated latex, is obtained from the bark of several kinds of trees (Fig. 34.16), belonging to different families of angiosperms. *Hevea brasiliensis,* a member of the Euphorbiaceae native to tropical South America, is vastly more important than all other rubber-producing species combined, and it is hevea rubber (also called Para rubber, from the state of that name in Brazil) that is generally intended when the word *rubber* is used without qualification.

The name rubber, first used by Priestley in 1770, refers to the use of the substance in erasing pencil marks. A process for waterproofing cloth with rubber was developed by Mackintosh in 1823, and vulcanization was discovered by Goodyear in 1839. Thereafter rubber rapidly became one of the world's most important industrial raw materials. Its plasticity, elasticity,

Fig. 34.16. Tapping a rubber tree in Colombia. The tree is *Castilla ulei*, a member of the mulberry family; the rubber obtained from it is called caucho rubber. (Photo courtesy of José Cuatrecasas.)

resistance to abrasion and electric currents, and its impermeability to liquids and gases all contribute to its value. Automobile tires and tubes, which once took the bulk of the rubber crop, are now made mostly from synthetic rubber, as a result of the enforced improvement of quality and expansion of capacity for the synthetic product in the United States during World War II. For many other uses, including waterproofing and insulation, natural rubber remains supreme, and rubber promises to be an important crop for decades to come.

Rubber is the newest major cultivated crop. Until nearly the end of the nineteenth century, practically all commercial rubber was obtained from wild trees in the Brazilian jungles. The establishment of rubber plantations in Malaya, Ceylon, and the East Indies followed the smuggling of 70,000 seeds out of Brazil in 1876 by the British adventurer Henry Wickham. By 1914 rubber production from the cultivated crop had outstripped that from wild trees, and wild rubber has been of only negligible importance for the past several decades. Breeding programs, selection of high-yielding types, and grafting have increased the production per tree severalfold, and wild rubber can no longer compete in the market.

Dyestuffs and Tannins

Dyes made from plants have been largely replaced during the past century by synthetic products. Safflower (*Carthamus tinctorius*), a thistle-like herb, is still cultivated for the red and yellow dyes obtained from it (as well as for the oil in its seeds), but indigo (from *Indigofera*), turkey red (from *Rubia*), and many others have given way to synthetic dyes, some similar or identical to the natural product, some chemically unrelated. Haematoxylon, a red dye used on cloth and in biological stains, is obtained from the heartwood of logwood (*Haematoxylon campechianum*), a tree native to tropical America.

Tannins are a group of organic compounds, found in many plants, which act on animal skins to form leather. Quebracho (*Schinopsis*), a very hard-wooded tree of Argentina, Paraguay, and nearby areas, is the most important commercial source of tannin, but a number of other plants, notably hemlock (*Tsuga*, a conifer) and various species of oak (*Quercus*) are also much used (Fig. 34.17). The tannins obtained from different sources are not identical, and often a particular source is preferred for a particular use.

The most important inks for fountain pens also contain tannin, which unites with iron salts to form a blue-black compound. Tannin for inks is obtained mostly from insect galls formed on Aleppo oak (*Quercus infectoria*, a native of the Mediterranean region) and various other plants.

ORNAMENTALS

Angiosperms provide lawn grasses, shade trees for streets and homes, and ornamental shrubs and garden flowers. Bluegrass (*Poa pratensis*) is the most important lawn grass in cool-temperate regions. *Eremochloa* (centipede grass) and *Zoysia* show some promise for lawns in warm-temperate regions such as the southeastern United States, where until recently the choice has been between a summer lawn of Bermuda grass (*Cynodon dactylon*) and a winter lawn of winter rye (*Secale cereale*).

The choice of shade trees varies with

Fig. 34.17. Black oak (*Quercus velutina*) in New York; the source of lumber, tannin, and a yellow dye. (New York Botanical Garden photo.)

the community and the climate. Fast-growing, short-lived trees, such as poplars (*Populus* spp.), have been preferred in pioneer communities in the western United States, but these species are eventually replaced by slower-growing, longer-lived trees as the community matures. American elm (*Ulmus americana*), a graceful and once very popular street tree, is now so seriously threatened by Dutch elm disease that it is seldom planted. Various species of oak (*Quercus*) and maple (*Acer*) are persistent favorites in the United States. The tree of heaven (*Ailanthus altissima*) does well in cities under conditions unfavorable to many other species. Magnolias are often used in the southeastern United States. Palms, which are popular in tropical regions, give an exotic flavor to the streets of some cities along the southern fringe of the United States.

Thousands of species of angiosperms, belonging to many different families, are cultivated as garden flowers. The Liliaceae and immediately related families, and the Compositae stand out particularly. The Liliaceae and their allies provide such familiar flowers as tulips, hyacinths, tiger lilies, and Easter lilies (all Liliaceae), day lilies, jonquils, daffodils, narcissus, and amaryllis (all Amaryllidaceae), and iris and gladiolus (Iridaceae); all these usually have the sepals brightly colored like the petals, and the individual flowers are often very large. Asters, chrysanthemums, cosmos, dahlias, daisies, marigolds, and zinnias all belong to the Compositae. The abundance of showy species in this family is due to the fact that the individual flowers are grouped into dense heads, each of which superficially resembles a single large flower. The cultivated roses (Rosaceae) and peonies (Paeoniaceae) often have the numerous stamens of each flower transformed into petals, the resulting "double" flowers having an aspect much like that of the flower heads of composites.

POISONOUS AND ALLERGENIC PLANTS

Many angiosperms are poisonous when eaten, and a smaller number are poisonous to the touch. The Liliaceae, Umbelliferae, and Solanaceae, all of which have well-known edible species, are also notorious for their poisonous members. The Anacardiaceae are likewise infamous for their allergenic species.

Highly poisonous plants are seldom very palatable, and livestock usually avoid them if there is enough other forage. After cattle have been eating hay all winter in the barn, however, they are less choosy when first turned out to pasture. Water hemlock (*Cicuta* spp.), an umbelliferous plant somewhat similar to parsnip, causes many losses in the United States in the spring. The plant, growing in wet places along streams, is easily pulled up by an avid cow, and the shallow, tuberous-thickened roots are especially poisonous, a piece the size of a walnut being fatal.

Poison hemlock (*Conium maculatum*), a carrot-like weedy umbellifer, occasionally poisons children who make whistles from the stem. It was used for execution in ancient Greece, Socrates being the most famous victim. Children also still die from eating the bulb of death camas (*Zygadenus*), mistaking it for the nutritious sego lily (*Calochortus nuttallii*) which served the Mormon pioneers in Utah as an emergency food.

Several species of *Oxytropis* and *Astragalus* (Leguminosae), called loco weed (Spanish *loco*, insane), differ from other stock-poisoning plants in being habit-forming. Locoed horses and cattle are excitable and sickly but may survive indefinitely. They actively seek out the loco weeds and teach others of the herd to eat them too.

Poison ivy (*Rhus toxicodendron* and related spp.) is the best-known plant in America that is poisonous to the touch, the usual symptom being itching, watery blisters. It is a climbing vine or low shrub with trifoliolate leaves, the central leaflet on an evident stalk (Fig. 32.9). The leaves are brightly colored in the fall, and scarcely a year goes by that some high school class does not use it to decorate a gymnasium for a dance. Susceptibility to the poison, a nonvolatile oil, varies greatly, and many people are apparently immune. The resistance is likely to disappear, however, after repeated exposure, and those who make a show of their immunity are courting hospitalization. The poisonous effect is thus evidently due to an allergy.

A number of other members of the Anacardiaceae are also allergenic. Japanese or Oriental lacquer is derived from *Rhus vernicifera*, a close relative of poison ivy, and causes trouble to many who work with it, although the finished product is apparently innocuous. Cashew (*Anacardium occidentale*) causes a violent rash on some people, but commercial cashew nuts have been rendered harmless by roasting.

Aside from hay-fever plants (discussed on p. 620), the common cultivated primrose (*Primula obconica*) is one of the most familiar allergenic plants that does not belong to the Anacardiaceae. It causes a rash much like poison ivy in many people. Strawberries have a similar effect on some people. The list of plants to which at least a few people are allergic might be extended almost indefinitely, and probably almost any plant can be allergenic to someone, somewhere, under the proper conditions.

SUGGESTED READING

Boswell, Victor R., Our vegetable travelers, *National Geographic* 96:145–217. 1949. An informative, illustrated, easily read account of the origins and history of edible vegetables.

Brown, Andrew H., Versatile wood waits on man, *National Geographic* 100:109–140. 1951.

Dodge, Bertha S., *Plants That Changed the World*, Little, Brown & Co., Boston and Toronto, 1959, 183 pp. An accurate popular account of some of the plant products that made history, and of the men who sought them out.

Jones, Stuart E., Spices, the essence of geography, *National Geographic* 95:400–420. 1949.

Vavilov, N. I., *The Origin, Variation, Immunity, and Breeding of Cultivated Plants*, (Trans. K. Starr Chester) Chronica Botanica. Waltham, Mass., 1951, 364 pp. Selected writings by a great Russian botanist who died in a Siberian concentration camp.

Heredity

Mutation in petunia, induced by high-frequency radiation. The plant is a hybrid of a purple-flowered and a white-flowered variety, thus heterozygous for flower color, with purple dominant. The cell which gave rise to the branch at the right underwent a mutation for flower color when the young seedling was irradiated. (Photo courtesy of Robin L. Cuany, Brookhaven National Laboratory.)

INTRODUCTION

The similarities and differences between parent and offspring have interested and puzzled men throughout history. The English proverb, *Like father, like son,* is a translation from classical Latin, yet recognition of the difference between brothers is as old as the story of Cain and Abel. All sorts of circumstances relating to conception, gestation, and birth have been called on to explain sibling differences, and such beliefs die hard. Shakespeare could realize that "The fault, dear Brutus, lies not in our stars," but daily newspapers still print zodiacal charts and astrological columns, and some prospective mothers still spend long hours at the piano, hoping to exert a prenatal influence.

The upsurge of scientific inquiry ushered in by the Renaissance led to experiments directed at unraveling the mystery of heredity. For several centuries the results were contradictory and confusing, adding little to the common knowledge that both parents usually contribute about equally. The discovery of sexuality in flowering plants by the German physician Rudolf Camerarius (1665–1721) in 1694 made plants available for genetic experiments. It was soon demonstrated that hereditary variation in plants is much like that in animals, and equally puzzling.

MENDELISM

Modern genetics is founded on the work of Gregor Mendel (1822–1884) a monk at Brünn, Austria (now Brno, Czechoslovakia). (See Fig. 35.1) His classic studies on inheritance in peas, begun in 1857, were published in an obscure Austrian journal in 1866 and escaped sci-

Fig. 35.1. Gregor Mendel (1822–1884), Austrian monk, who laid the foundation of genetics. (Photo courtesy of Verne Grant.)

entific attention until 1900. In that year DeVries in Holland, Correns in Germany, and von Tschermak in Austria reported in rapid succession their own independent rediscovery of Mendel's principles. Mendel's own later experiments, on hawkweed (*Hieracium*), gave most confusing results, not at all in accord with the experiments on peas, because (as we now know and Mendel did not) the plants were partly apomictic (setting seed without fertilization), and he died without realizing the fundamental importance of his work.

Mendel succeeded, where his predecessors for centuries had failed, because he studied characters which showed sharp differences, without intermediates, because he studied each character separately as well as in combination with others, because he kept accurate pedigree records and because he worked with enough individuals to get statistically valid results. Furthermore, Mendel carefully chose a species which is normally self-pollinated but can easily be cross-pollinated. We shall see that self-pollination leads to genetic purity, and each of the original 22 varieties which he used in his garden experiments was genetically pure for all the characters studied. Mendel was also lucky in his choice of characters to be studied. Another choice might have shown contradictory results, which we can now explain, but which would have destroyed the beautifully consistent pattern he reported. Mendelian inheritance is the foundation of genetics, but not the whole structure; an understanding of Mendelism is essential to any further progress, but there are many genetic results which cannot be explained in simple Mendelian terms.

Mendel studied nine sets of characters, but three of these were so perfectly correlated that he correctly considered them as expressions of the same hereditary factor, thus reducing the number of separate characters to seven pairs. He found that the inheritance of each of the seven pairs followed the same consistent pattern, and that each was wholly independent of the others. The characters were:

1. Yellow versus green cotyledons
2. Round versus wrinkled cotyledons
3a. Purple versus white flowers
  b. Purple versus green axils in the seedling
  c. Gray to brown or purplish versus white seed coat
4. Tall versus dwarf habit
5. Axial (distributed along the stem) versus terminal flowers
6. Green versus yellow pods (before maturity)
7. Inflated versus moniliform[1] pods

As a result of his experiments, Mendel concluded that each character studied was governed by a single pair of hereditary factors: in modern terms, we would say that a single pair of genes swings the balance in each case. Mendel concluded that each seed receives one factor of each pair from the ovule parent, and the other from the pollen parent. We agree, adding that the two factors of a pair are borne on homologous chromosomes, e.g., if the factor in the sperm for pod color is on chromosome A, then the factor in the egg for pod color is also on chromosome A, and if the factor in the sperm for cotyledon color is on chromosome B, then the factor in the egg for cotyledon color is also on chromosome B.

Mendel's **prinicple of segregation,** stated in modern terms, is that *the two genes of a pair do not contaminate each*

[1] Moniliform: constricted at intervals, like a string of beads.

other but are segregated in reduction division and pass into different gametes. It is a fundamental principle of heredity.

Mendel found that one character of each opposing pair is **dominant,** showing up whenever a factor (gene) for it is present, and that the other is **recessive,** showing up only in the absence of the dominant factor. In the above list the dominant character of each pair is listed first. Thus the tall habit is dominant, and dwarf recessive: first-generation hybrids between tall and short varieties were uniformly tall, although these hybrids carried a recessive factor for dwarfness as well as a dominant factor for tallness. If the dominant factor, for tallness, is represented by T, and the recessive factor, for dwarfness, by t, then the original tall variety, being genetically pure for tallness, had the constitution TT, and the dwarf variety, being genetically pure for dwarfness, had the constitution tt. All gametes produced by the tall parent would necessarily carry the factor T, and all gametes produced by the dwarf parent would carry the factor t. The first-generation hybrids, therefore, would all have the constitution Tt; and since T is dominant over t, the plants would be tall.

It should be noted that in genetic studies any cross between individuals differing in one or more genes is called a **hybrid.** This is in contrast to common usage in which the term *hybrid* is usually applied only to crosses between different species. The first-generation offspring of a genetic hybrid are commonly called the F_1 generation, the F standing for filial. Succeeding generations derived by self-pollination or sibling matings are called the F_2, F_3, etc. A backcross is a mating between a hybrid (usually an F_1) and one of the original parental types.

The F$_1$ hybrids referred to above are tall plants with the genetic constitution Tt. When these plants are allowed to set seed naturally (by self-pollination), three-fourths of the plants in the next generation (the F$_2$) are tall, and one-fourth are dwarf. This result can be explained by considering the processes of reduction and subsequent fertilization. The two homologous chromosomes carrying the factors T and t, respectively, are pulled to opposite ends of the cell in the first division of meiosis, and each of the gametes ultimately produced therefore carries only one gene of the pair, either T or t; the two types are, of course, produced in equal quantities. The proportion of each genetic type to be expected in the F$_2$ generation can easily be seen by using a checkerboard device in which all the kinds of gametes produced by one parent are listed across the top, all the kinds produced by the other are listed along one side, and the possible matings are shown in the squares. When the plants are self-pollinated, as in the present case, the list of gametes at the side of the chart is of course the same as the list at the top, and the chart appears as follows:

	T	t
T	TT	Tt
t	Tt	tt

Thus, on the average, one-fourth of the F$_2$ plants have the constitution TT and are tall; half the F$_2$ plants have the constitution Tt and are also tall, making a total of three-fourths tall; the remaining fourth have the constitution tt and are dwarf. Successive generations derived from these dwarf plants by self-pollination would all be dwarf, since they are genetically pure for dwarfness. Successive generations derived by selfing tall plants with the constitution TT would all be tall, being genetically pure for tallness, but the next generation derived from tall plants with the constitution Tt (these being two-thirds of all the tall plants in the F$_2$) would again segregate in the ratio of 3:1, etc.

It will be seen that the 3:1 ratio of tall to dwarf plants is based on a 1:2:1 ratio of genetic constitutions. This same sort of 1:2:1 ratio can be built up by shaking 2 pennies in a jar and rolling them onto a table. About one-fourth of the throws will show two heads, another fourth will show tails, and the remaining half will show one head and one tail. This ratio is, of course, based on a large number of throws. One could not expect to get the correct ratio with only four throws (although it will sometimes happen), and the same is true of hybrid ratios.

The fact that plants of similar appearance may be genetically different necessitates some additional terms. The **phenotype** is the actual characteristic of the individual, as expressed in its form, structure, or physiology. The **genotype** is the genetic make-up. Peas with the genotype TT and those with Tt have the same phenotype, tall; those with the genotype tt all have the same phenotype, dwarf. Individuals with both factors of a pair alike are **homozygous** (from Greek *homo-*, one and the same); those with the two factors of a pair opposed are **heterozygous** (from Greek *hetero-*, other, unlike). Thus pea plants with the genotype TT are homozygous dominant; those with the genotype Tt are heterozygous; and those with the genotype tt are homozygous recessive.

A mating in which only a single pair

Fig. 35.2. Genetic segregation in corn. *A* and *B* are ears from pure lines, one of which has grains with pigmented endosperm. *C* is the F_1 hybrid between them, heterozygous for pigment, but phenotypically like the pigmented parent. *D* is the F_2 from this cross, showing a 3:1 segregation of pigmented and un-pigmented endosperm. *E* is a backcross from the F_1 to the pigmented parent; half the grains in this backcross are homozygous for pigmentation, and half heterozygous, but phenotypically they are all alike. *F* is a backcross from the F_1 to the unpigmented parent, showing a 1:1 ratio of pigmented (hetero-zygous) and unpigmented (homozygous recessive). The slight differences in intensity of color in the pigmented grains in this photo are due to environ-mental differences and to exposure to light after the ears were harvested. (Photos courtesy of G. W. Blaydes. From Transeau, Sampson, and Tiffany, *Textbook of Botany*, Rev. Ed., Harper, 1953.)

of genes is considered is called a **monohybrid.** The possible monohybrid genotypic ratios are 1:2:1, 1:1, and 1:0. The 1:2:1 ratio is obtained by crossing two heterozygous individuals, or by selfing a heterozygous individual, as shown on the previous checkerboard. Half the offspring from such a cross are heterozygous, and one-fourth represents each of the two homozygous types. For example, Tt × Tt yields ¼ TT, ½ Tt, and ¼ tt.

The 1:1 ratio is obtained by crossing a heterozygous individual with a homozygous one. Half the offspring are heterozygous, like one parent, and half homozygous, like the other. Thus Tt × tt yields ½ Tt and ½ tt; and Tt × TT yields ½ Tt and ½ TT. It should be noted that phenotypically the parents and offspring in this last example are all tall; only the genotypes show a 1:1 ratio. The mating of heterozygous to homozygous may also be shown on the following checkerboards, with the gametes of the heterozygous parent shown at the top and the single kind of gamete produced by the homozygous parent shown at the side.

The 1:0 ratio is obtained by mating homozygous with homozygous. Thus TT × TT yields only TT, tt × tt yields only tt, and TT × tt yields only Tt. The next generation obtained by selfing the Tt individuals will, of course, segregate in a 1:2:1 genotypic ratio, like any heterozygous × heterozygous mating.

DIHYBRIDS AND TRIHYBRIDS

We have noted in Chapter 4 that, during reduction division, one chromosome of each pair is pulled to one end of the cell, and the other to the other. Each of the cells produced in meiosis thus has a complete, balanced set of chromosomes. Except for this limitation, the chromosomes are randomly assorted in the process; the maternal or paternal origin of the chromosomes is immaterial. The genes are likewise randomly assorted, as long as they are borne on separate chromosomes. Each of the seven pairs of factors noted by Mendel in peas is borne on a different pair of chromosomes, and therefore, he found a completely independent assortment of characters in the hybrid progeny. From these results he deduced the principle of independent assortment, i.e., that each pair of characters is inherited independently of the others, and all combinations of characters occur in proportions governed by the mathematical laws of chance.

We should emphasize again that the operation of the principle of independent assortment is limited by the fact that it is the chromosomes, rather than the individual genes, which segregate during meiosis. Genes borne on different chromosomes are independently assorted, but genes borne on the same chromosome tend to remain together. This **linkage** of genes on a chromosome may be broken by **crossing over** (exchange of parts between homologous chromosomes) during meiosis, as explained in Chapter 4, but blocks of genes still tend to remain together. A modern restatement of Mendel's **principle of independent assortment** is that *insofar as they are borne on different chromosomes, each pair of genes is inherited independently of the others, and all combinations of genotypes occur in the offspring in the proportions governed by the mathematical laws of chance.*

In genetic studies, a **dihybrid** is a hybrid in which two pairs of genes are considered. A typical dihybrid mating, such as those recorded by Mendel, shows a 9:3:3:1 ratio in the F_2, with $\frac{9}{16}$ of the individuals showing both dominant characters, $\frac{3}{16}$ showing each of the 2 combinations of dominant and recessive, and $\frac{1}{16}$ showing both recessive characters. This ratio can be understood by determining the possible gametes and using the checkerboard to show all possible genotypes in the offspring. For example, if a pea plant with yellow, round seeds (genotype YYRR) is crossed with a plant with green, wrinkled seeds (genotype yyrr), the F_1 has yellow, round seeds, with the genotype YyRr. These F_1 plants are heterozygous for both factors and can produce four kinds of gametes, YR, Yr, yR, and yr. The checkerboard showing the F_2 is as follows:

	YR	Yr	yR	yr
YR	YYRR	YYRr	YyRR	YyRr
Yr	YYRr	YYrr	YyRr	Yyrr
yR	YyRR	YyRr	yyRR	yyRr
yr	YyRr	Yyrr	yyRr	yyrr

It will be seen that nine different genotypes are represented on the checkerboard, and that these occur in definite proportions. The genotypes YYRR ($\frac{1}{16}$ of the total), YYRr ($\frac{2}{16}$ of the total), YyRR ($\frac{2}{16}$ of the total), and YyRr ($\frac{4}{16}$ of the total) produce the round, yellow phenotype. The genotypes yyRR ($\frac{1}{16}$ of the total) and yyRr ($\frac{2}{16}$ of the total) produce the green, round phenotype. The genotypes YYrr ($\frac{1}{16}$ of the total) and Yyrr ($\frac{2}{16}$ of the total) produce the yellow, wrinkled phenotype. And the genotype yyrr ($\frac{1}{16}$ of the total) produces the green, wrinkled phenotype.

These ratios can also be obtained by simple arithmetic. Thus, $\frac{3}{4}$ of the plants in the F_2 have yellow seeds, and $\frac{3}{4}$ of that $\frac{3}{4}$, or a total of $\frac{9}{16}$, have round seeds as well. Of the $\frac{3}{4}$ that have yellow seeds, only $\frac{1}{4}$, or a total of $\frac{3}{16}$, have wrinkled seeds. One-fourth of the plants have green seeds. And three-fourths of that fourth (or a total of $\frac{3}{16}$) have round seeds, and only a fourth of that fourth (or a total of $\frac{1}{16}$) have wrinkled seeds.

The genotypic ratios can also be calculated. One-fourth of the individuals have YY; half have Yy; and one-fourth have yy. Of the fourth that have YY, only a fourth (thus a total of $\frac{1}{16}$) also have RR; another fourth (again a total of $\frac{1}{16}$) have rr; and half (a total of $\frac{2}{16}$) have Rr, etc.

It should be noted that in all these crosses it does not matter which is the pollen parent and which the ovule parent; nor does it matter how the characters are associated in the parents. A YYRR $\times$ yyrr cross gives the same results as a yyRR $\times$ YYrr cross. In the former case, the original gametes are YR and yr, and the genotype of the F_1 is YyRr; in the latter case, the original gametes are yR and Yr, and the genotype of the F_1 is still YyRr.

The F_2 derived from a trihybrid (three pairs of factors considered) normally shows a phenotypic ratio of 27:9:9:9:3:3:3:1, if the parents were homozygous and differed in all three characters. This ratio can be demonstrated with a checkerboard or calculated mathematically. If one parent is tall, with inflated, green pods (genotype TTIIGG) and the other is dwarf, with moniliform, yellow pods (genotype ttiigg), the F_1 is tall, with inflated green pods, and has the genotype TtIiGg. Eight possible kinds of gametes can be produced by this hybrid. These are TIG, TIg, TiG, tIG, Tig, tIg, tiG, and tig.

On a checkerboard with 64 squares, the possible matings among these gametes can be shown. Twenty-seven sixty-fourths of the F_2 plants ($\frac{3}{4}$ of $\frac{3}{4}$ of $\frac{3}{4}$) show all three dominant characters—tall, with inflated green pods. Nine sixty-fourths ($\frac{3}{4}$ of $\frac{3}{4}$ of $\frac{1}{4}$) show each of the three possible combinations of two dominant and one recessive character—tall, with inflated yellow pods; tall, with moniliform, green pods; and dwarf, with inflated green pods. Three sixty-fourths ($\frac{3}{4}$ of $\frac{1}{4}$ of $\frac{1}{4}$) show each of the three possible combinations of one dominant and two recessive characters—tall, with moniliform yellow pods; dwarf, with moniliform green pods; and dwarf, with inflated yellow pods. And one sixty-fourth ($\frac{1}{4}$ of $\frac{1}{4}$ of $\frac{1}{4}$) show all three recessive characters—dwarf, with moniliform yellow pods.

PROBLEMS

Given the genotype of the parents, the results of various sorts of crosses can be predicted by determining the possible kinds of gametes and using a checkerboard, or by direct calculation. One can also work backward, determining the genotype of the parents by the phenotype of one or two generations of offspring, or the genotype of one parent by the phenotype or genotype of the other plus that of one or more generations of offspring.

To determine by the checkerboard method the phenotypes produced by crossing TtRr with Ttrr, one first determines the kinds of gametes that can be produced by each parent. The TtRr parent can produce four kinds of gametes, TR, Tr, tR, and tr, but the Ttrr parent can produce only two kinds, Tr and tr. The following checkerboard can then be filled out:

	TR	Tr	tR	tr
Tr	TTRr	TTrr	TtRr	Ttrr
tr	TtRr	Ttrr	ttRr	ttrr

Three-eighths of the plants will be tall, with round seeds (genotypes TTRr and TtRr); three-eighths will be tall, with wrinkled seeds (genotypes TTrr and Ttrr); one-eighth will be dwarf, with round seeds (genotype ttRr); and one-eighth will be dwarf, with wrinkled seeds (genotype ttrr). The same results can be obtained by calculation. Three-fourths of the plants will be tall, since both parents are heterozygous for this character. Half the plants will have round seeds and half will have wrinkled seeds, since one parent is heterozygous for the character and the other is homozygous recessive. So, of the three-fourths that are tall, half, or a total of three-eighths, will also have round seeds, and the other half, again for a total of three-eighths, will have wrinkled seeds; and of the fourth that are dwarf, half, for a total of one-eighth, will have round seeds, and the other half, again for a total of one-eighth, will have wrinkled seeds.

This same problem can be worked from offspring to parent. Given $\frac{3}{8}$ tall, round, $\frac{3}{8}$ tall, wrinkled, $\frac{1}{8}$ dwarf, round, and $\frac{1}{8}$ dwarf, wrinkled, it is clear that the ratio of tall to dwarf is 3:1, and the ratio of round to wrinkled is 1:1. The 3:1 ratio shows that both parents were heterozygous for height, and the 1:1 ratio shows that one parent was heterozygous for seed texture, and the other homozygous recessive. The genotypes of the parents are, therefore, TtRr and Ttrr.

In working problems by the checkerboard method, it is of course necessary to make sure that none of the possible types of gametes has been overlooked. The number of kinds of gametes that can be produced by an individual is 2^n, if n is the number of heterozygous pairs. Thus an individual with the genotype TTIIGg has only one heterozygous pair, and can produce only two kinds of gametes, these being TIG and TIg; an individual with the genotype TTIiGg has two heterozygous pairs, and can produce four (2^2) kinds of gametes, these being TIG, TIg, TiG, and Tig; and an individual with the genotype TtIiGg has three heterozygous pairs, and can produce eight (2^3) kinds of gametes; etc. An individual with ten heterozygous pairs can produce 2^{10}, or 1064 kinds of gametes. The checkerboard method thus obviously has its limitations in working genetic problems.

OCCURRENCE OF MENDELIAN CHARACTERS

Most kinds of plants have some characters which appear to be inherited in simple Mendelian fashion, and many others which are more complex. Summer squash has been much used to illustrate Mendelism: white fruit is dominant to yellow, and disk-shaped fruit is dominant to spherical. There are no hard and fast rules as to which characters will be Mendelian and which will not, nor as to which character of a Mendelian pair will be dominant; each case must be investigated individually. Presence of a structure is usually dominant to its absence, but even here there are exceptions.

MECHANISM OF GENE ACTION

We have seen in Chapter 2 that genes apparently act by governing the kinds of molecules supplied to the remainder of the protoplasm. Some of the evidence sup-

Fig. 35.3. B. O. Dodge (1872–1960), American mycologist, the father of Neurospora genetics.

porting this concept comes from experiments with *Neurospora* (especially *N. crassa*), a mold belonging to the Ascomycetes. The usefulness of *Neurospora* in genetic studies was demonstrated in the 1930's by the American botanist B. O. Dodge (Fig. 35.3). The vegetative stage is haploid, so that the complications of heterozygosity are avoided; the plant is easily grown in pure culture and has a short life cycle; vegetative reproduction occurs freely by conidia, and parts of the mycelium can also be broken off and established as new cultures; the species *N. crassa* is heterothallic, with two mating types, and sexual reproduction occurs only when the two opposite types come into contact. The ascus produces eight ascospores in a row, and the spores are large enough so that they do not slip by each other in the ascus. By careful manipulation, the ascospores can be removed one at a time and separately cultured. It is possible, therefore, to study all the cells produced by reduction division from a single meiocyte (as it is not with higher plants, higher animals, or insects), and the principle of genic segregation in meiosis can be demonstrated directly instead of merely statistically.

About 1940 the American botanists George W. Beadle (1903–   ) and E. L. Tatum (1909–   ) and their associates gave the use of *Neurospora* a new and important turn. By exposing the fungus to X rays, they obtained mutant forms which were cultured and bred back to the wild type. Many of these mutants differed from the wild type in specific physiologic traits which segregated in Mendelian fashion when bred back to the wild type, showing that only a single gene was involved. The wild type needs only inorganic salts, a carbohydrate such as sucrose, and the vitamin biotin; from these and water it can synthesize all the more complex substances it needs. More than twenty different mutants, each lacking the ability to produce some particular substance necessary for growth, have been found. Without the necessary substance, they die; when it is provided, they grow normally. The conclusion is that a mutation in a particular gene deprives the plant of the ability to produce a particular chemical. The substances required by these mutants include various vitamins, amino acids, and other compounds. One interesting mutant is unable to synthesize the vitamin riboflavin at temperatures above 28°C, whereas the wild type can make it at temperatures up to 40°C. This mutant would remain undetected at temperatures below 28°C.

The fact that genes act by governing the kinds of molecules supplied to the remainder of the protoplasm is vital to an understanding of heredity. Any change in a particular constituent of the protoplast has a chain of side effects, influencing the reactions which occur and the products that are formed, thus ultimately influencing the phenotype of the organism. Every characteristic of the organism is governed by its total genotype, in conjunction with the environment, and any change in any gene, as well as any environmental change, potentially has some effect on every character. Any particular gene affects some characters more than others. It may swing the balance as a Mendelian factor for one character, slightly modify the expression of another character, and have no detectable effect on another. Its effects on a particular character may be strikingly different against one genic background than against another, or in one environment than in another.

When we say that the color of the cotyledons in peas is governed by a single pair of factors, what we really mean is that among the genotypes studied, under the conditions of the experiment, differences in the color of the cotyledons are caused by differences in a single pair of factors (genes). We shall see that, in some varieties of snapdragons, the environmental conditions sharply modify the effect of a particular pair of genes on flower color, and that the effect of this pair of genes also differs strongly according to the other genes present. The relative influence of heredity and environment ranges from one extreme, in which environmental differences have so little effect that they may ordinarily be disregarded, to the other extreme, in which hereditary differences are overwhelmed by environmental differences.

The Mendelian characters are those which, in the particular population studied, under the conditions of the experiment, are governed by differences in a single pair of genes. A character which is Mendelian in one population may be more complexly inherited in another population which differs in other genes, and a change in the environmental conditions may also modify or obscure the simple Mendelian ratios.

INHERITANCE WHICH DOES NOT SHOW TYPICAL MENDELIAN PHENOTYPIC RATIOS

It is perhaps paradoxical that, although Mendel's principles are essential to an understanding of heredity, it is only the exceptional character which shows typical Mendelian phenotypic ratios. The relative infrequency of simple Mendelian characters is a natural result of the mode of gene action described in the preceding paragraphs. Some aspects of this complex balance are discussed in the following paragraphs under the headings of incomplete and reversed dominance, lethal genes, multiple alleles, multiple genes, multiple effect, modifying factors, gene interaction, and linkage.

Incomplete Dominance

Dominance exists in varying degrees. Heterozygous individuals may be phenotypically so similar to the homozygous dominant as to be indistinguishable, or they may resemble the homozygous dominant but deviate slightly toward the recessive type, or they may be obviously intermediate between the two homozygous types. When the two genes of a pair govern the formation of molecules with opposite effect, the effects may counterbalance each other, or the effect of one may be more or less submerged by the other. Often the recessive factor really represents the

absence of a gene, which has been destroyed by some genetic accident in the past, or the molecules governed by one of the genes may be essentially neutral in their influence on the character under study, so that the control is exerted by only one gene of the pair. In such cases, the single active gene of the pair may or may not be effective enough to make the plant look like one which is homozygous for the active gene.

Albinism in flowers furnishes good examples of both complete and incomplete dominance. Mendel found that the factor for purple flowers in peas was dominant to the factor for white flowers. The heterozygotes were phenotypically like the homozygous dominants. In some varieties of snapdragons, on the other hand, the factor for red flowers is only incompletely dominant over a factor for ivory flowers, and the heterozygotes have pink flowers. The F_1 hybrid between a homozygous red and a homozygous ivory has pink flowers, and the F_2 generation segregates in a 1:2:1 ratio ($\frac{1}{4}$ red, $\frac{1}{2}$ pink, $\frac{1}{4}$ ivory).

Reversal of Dominance

Dominance may be affected by the environmental conditions or by the action of other genes. We have noted that snapdragons heterozygous for red versus ivory flowers have pink flowers under ordinary conditions. If the plants are grown in bright light at low temperatures, however, the flowers of heterozygous plants are red, and in shaded, warm places they are ivory. In Jimson weed (*Datura*), purple color of the stem is completely dominant over green under ordinary outdoor conditions, but only partly dominant in the greenhouse in the winter. Here the direct environmental effect is probably on the

Fig 35.4. Segregation of the lethal albino mutant in corn. Both parents in this cross were heterozygous for the albino gene. (Photo courtesy of G. W. Blaydes. From Transeau, Sampson, and Tiffany, *Textbook of Botany*, Rev. Ed., Harper, 1953.)

amount of photosynthesis; a high concentration of sugars (resulting from rapid photosynthesis) favors the formation of anthocyanins, and, at a low level of photosynthesis, the amount of sugar present in the cells does not stimulate as much production of anthocyanin in the heterozygote as in the homozygous dominant.

It has been noted in animals that some characters which are dominant in males are recessive in females, or vice versa. In some breeds of sheep, presence of horns is dominant to absence of horns in males, and recessive in females. Baldness in man has been thought to show a similar reversal of dominance, although doubtless there are other modifying factors as well. Dominance can also be reversed by genes which do not control sex. These phenomena have attracted more attention in mammals than in plants, but they exist in plants as well.

LETHAL GENES

Probably the most familiar lethal character in plants is the absence of chlorophyll. Being unable to make their own food, seedlings without chlorophyll die when the food reserve of the seed is used up. Corn is often used for laboratory demonstrations of this lethal character (Fig. 35.4). Heterozygous plants are phenotypically normal; when selfed, or crossed among themselves, they set seed which gives a 3:1 ratio of green to albino seedlings. The albinos ordinarily die from starvation within a few weeks, but if glucose is carefully supplied to the leaves, the plants can be grown to maturity. It is thus clear that a factor which is lethal under one set of circumstances is not necessarily so under another. Lethal factors also differ in the time at which they exert their effect; some plant lethals are effective at the zygote or even the gamete stage.

Some genes which are lethal when homozygous can also be recognized in the heterozygous condition. The classical example is a gene governing color of fur in the house mouse. The factor Y for yellow is dominant to all other factors for coat color, and any individual heterozygous for Y is yellow. When inbred, however, yellow mice produce yellow and nonyellow offspring in the ratio of 2:1. The embryos that are homozygous for yellow die before birth, so that a 1:2:1 ratio among the young embryos becomes a 2:1 ratio among the live offspring. All yellow mice are heterozygous for coat color. This example is especially interesting because it illustrates that a gene which is dominant in one respect (coat color) may be recessive in another (lethality).

Multiple Alleles

Any gene is an **allele** (from Greek *allēlōn*, of one another) of an opposing gene occupying the same locus (position) on a homologous chromosome. Thus in peas the factor T, for tallness, is an allele of the factor t, for dwarfness. T and t are an allelic pair. The phenotypes resulting from the actions of these genes are **allelomorphs.** A normal diploid individual has only two alleles of a given gene, but different individuals of the same species may have different alleles. The alleles for red and white flowers in snapdragons are only two in a series of at least nine alleles. Some of these produce various shades of pink, and one produces red-and-white-striped flowers. Pink-flowered snapdragons are not necessarily heterozygous for red versus ivory or white; they may be homozygous for pink. The same sort of situation holds true for many other characters in other species. It is only by pedigree records that the genotype of an individual can be determined.

Multiple Genes

It is now standard genetic theory that each hereditary character is governed by the whole genotype of the organism, in conjunction with the environment. The influence of a particular gene on a particular character may be so slight as to be negligible, however, or may become evident only under a particular set of environmental conditions. In simple Mendelian characters, a particular pair of genes regularly turns the balance governing the phenotypic expression. In many other characters the phenotypic expression is governed by several pairs of genes, each with its own effect, and the effects may be cumulative or opposed. Mendel himself discovered that the color of the flower in beans (*Phaseolus*) is governed by more than one pair of factors.

One of the simplest instances of multiple genes is provided by the color of the grain in wheat. Some crosses of red- to white-grained wheat show a simple 3:1 ratio of red to white grains in the F_2, but others show a 15:1 ratio, and still others a 63:1 ratio. Furthermore, the red grains vary in the intensity of color. In the hybrid with a 3:1 ratio in the F_2, the F_1 grains are rather pale red, paler than the red parent, and the 3:1 ratio of red to white in the F_2 is really a 1:2:1 ratio, $\frac{1}{4}$ of the grains being as dark as the original red parent, $\frac{1}{2}$ being paler, like the F_1, and $\frac{1}{4}$ being white. In the crosses showing 15:1 and 63:1 ratios, there are several degrees of redness, but it is not always possible to draw sharp lines between the classes. The 15:1 ratio is produced by the cumulative effect of 2 pairs of genes; and the 63:1 ratio by 3 pairs.

The 15:1 ratio of red to white grains in wheat may be used as a simple example of multiple factors in general. The original red parent has the genotype $R_1R_1R_2R_2$, and the white parent has $r_1r_1r_2r_2$. The red parent produces gametes of the genotype R_1R_2, and the white parent produces gametes of the genotype r_1r_2. The F_1 has the genotype $R_1r_1R_2r_2$ and has red grains which are distinctly paler than those of the red parent. The F_1 produces four kinds of gametes, R_1R_2, R_1r_2, r_1R_2, and r_1r_2. The genotypes of the F_2 are shown on the following checkerboard:

	R_1R_2	R_1r_2	r_1R_2	r_1r_2
R_1R_2	$R_1R_1R_2R_2$	$R_1R_1R_2r_2$	$R_1r_1R_2R_2$	$R_1r_1R_2r_2$
R_1r_2	$R_1R_1R_2r_2$	$R_1R_1r_2r_2$	$R_1r_1R_2r_2$	$R_1r_1r_2r_2$
r_1R_2	$R_1r_1R_2R_2$	$R_1r_1R_2r_2$	$r_1r_1R_2R_2$	$r_1r_1R_2r_2$
r_1r_2	$R_1r_1R_2r_2$	$R_1r_1r_2r_2$	$r_1r_1R_2r_2$	$r_1r_1r_2r_2$

If the two factors of a pair have equal weight, then four classes of redness may be expected in the F_2. Only $\frac{1}{16}$ of the individuals have all 4 factors for red, like the original red parent; $\frac{4}{16}$ have 3 genes for red; $\frac{6}{16}$ have 2 genes for red, and $\frac{4}{16}$ have only 1 gene for red. The remaining $\frac{1}{16}$ have no genes for red, and the grains are white.

One of the most important things about the operation of multiple factors is that some of the offspring may be more extreme than either parent. In the present example of wheat, only $\frac{6}{16}$ of the F_2's have the same shade of red as the F_1. Five-sixteenths have the grains more deeply colored than those of the F_1, and five-sixteenths have them less deeply colored. Most of the important characters of plants and animals are governed by multiple genes, with each individual being heterozygous for some genes and homozygous for others. In characters governed by multiple genes, the offspring are usually intermediate between the two parents, but they differ among themselves. In any such character, an individual may be more nearly like one parent than the other, and it may even be more extreme than either parent.

MULTIPLE EFFECT

Mendel was the first to observe multiple effects of a single gene. He found that the same factor governed the color of the flowers, the color of the seed coat, and the color of the axils of the plant; furthermore, the color of the seed coat was not the same as that of the flowers and axils. Many other examples of multiple effect are now known, and in principle every gene is believed to have some potential influence on every character. In practice it is seldom possible to identify more than about a half dozen effects of a single gene, the other effects being overwhelmed by the variation in multiple gene characters, or being so slight as to escape detection under ordinary conditions.

MODIFYING GENES

There are many genes which modify the effect of other genes, without any other obvious effect on the character concerned. Some kinds of snapdragons have a recessive dilution factor affecting the color of the flowers. Plants homozygous for this factor have paler flowers than heterozygotes or plants without this gene.

GENE INTERACTION

We have emphasized that it is really the whole genotype, rather than some one or few individual genes, which exercises genetic control over a character. Thus, in a broad sense, all heredity involves gene interaction. When a single pair of genes regularly swings the balance for a character, outweighing the effects of all other genes combined, we have Mendelian characters. When the effect of one gene is modified by another, we speak of modifying genes. When several pairs of genes have cumulative effects, differing principally in degree, we speak of multiple genes. And when we wish to emphasize that two or more pairs of genes can produce a particular effect only in combination, we speak of gene interaction.

A simple case of gene interaction is provided by flower color in sweet peas. Crosses between purple- and white-flowered races show all purple flowers in the F_1, and segregate purple to white in a 3:1 ration in the F_2. White-flowered races in general breed true, and produce white-flowered offspring when crossed among themselves. So far everything follows a simple Mendelian pattern. One particular white-flowered race, however, produces only purple-flowered offspring in the F_1 when crossed with other white-flowered races. The F_2 in such crosses segregates purple to white in a ratio of 9:7. This startling result is easily explained. Formation of anthocyanin in the flowers can be blocked at any of several places in the sequence of chemical reactions. The two white-flowered races in such a cross have different kinds of genes for white flowers, which interrupt at different places the chain of reactions leading to the formation of anthocyanin. The factor for white is, in each case, recessive to its own allele for purple (anthocyanin). Thus any individual which has at least one dominant gene at each of the loci involved develops anthocyanin in the flowers; the 9:7 ratio is really a 9:3:3:1 ratio in which the 3, 3, and 1 are phenotypically alike, being homozygous recessive for one or the other or both of the antipigment genes.

Inheritance of flower color in snapdragons provides a more complex case of gene interaction. We have already noted that red, pink, and ivory flowers can be obtained among plants differing in only one pair of genes, and that dominance is subject to environmental modification. There are many other colors in snapdrag-

ons, however, and a number of other genes affecting color. In a group of varieties adapted to greenhouse culture, it was found that four different pairs of genes can interfere with the formation of the bright-red anthocyanin pigment. One of these is merely a recessive dilution gene. Another is a recessive gene which inhibits all pigment formation in the flowers; a third is a recessive gene which, in some combinations, changes anthocyanins to nearly colorless anthoxanthins, giving ivory flowers; the fourth has varying effects according to the other genes present, and in one combination it turns the anthocyanin into a bright-yellow anthoxanthin. (Anthoxanthins are yellow or yellowish pigments chemically rather similar to anthocyanins. They are also called flavones.) Different combinations of these four pairs of genes govern the formation of white, ivory, yellow, bronze, pink, lavender, purple, and red flowers. When we remember that another botanist working with other varieties of snapdragons has found nine different alleles at one locus affecting the amount and distribution of red pigment in the flower, we see that the inheritance of flower color may be very complex indeed.

LINKAGE

Not long after the rediscovery of Mendel's work, it was found that not all Mendelian characters show independent assortment. The first satisfactory explanation of these exceptions was provided in 1910 by the American geneticist Thomas Hunt Morgan (1866–1945) (Fig. 35.5). He suggested that genes which are linked in inheritance are borne on the same chromosome—the closer together the genes, the less chance of their being separated by the

Fig. 35.5. T. H. Morgan (1866–1945), American geneticist, outstanding contributor to the development of genetic theory. (Photo courtesy of Verne Grant.)

ough studies of this type have been made on maize and the fruit fly *Drosophila melanogaster*. Several hundred gene loci have been plotted for each of these species. The sequence of genes on each chromosome appears to be strictly linear, like beads on a string. The development of a structural model of a chromosome which will integrate this fact with the other information available about the structure of chromosomes and the mechanism of gene action promises to exercise the ingenuity of cytogeneticists for some time to come.

A further complicating factor is the *position effect*. Some genes have different effects according to what genes lie next to them in the chromosome. One suggested explanation is that although the gene sequence is linear, the genes themselves are confluent; i.e., if successive parts of the chromosomes are called A, B, C, etc., parts A and B might be involved in one genic action, parts B and C in another, etc.

exchange of parts between homologous chromosomes at meiosis. (This exchange of parts, called crossing over, is discussed in Chapter 4). Each individual has as many linkage groups as pairs of chromosomes. In the garden pea, for example, there are seven pairs of chromosomes and thus seven linkage groups, and in any list of genes, the total number which can be independently assorted in inheritance is not more than seven. If Mendel had studied just one more character, whatever it might have been, its governing gene would necessarily have been on the same chromosome as that governing one of the other characters, and thus it could not have been independently assorted.

It is now possible to map the location of genes on chromosomes by the relative frequency of crossing over. The most thor-

CYTOPLASMIC INHERITANCE

A few characters are known to be inherited through the cytoplasm rather than through the nucleus. Because the egg carries so much more cytoplasm than the sperm, cytoplasmic characters are usually maternally dominated, and it is through this maternal effect that they are usually recognized. Some of the best-known cases of cytoplasmic inheritance involve plastids. In *Primula sinensis*, for example, there is a yellow-leaved form which contains less than the normal amount of chlorophyll. Pollen from yellow-leaved plants does not transmit the defect, but seeds from yellow-leaved plants produce yellow-leaved offspring, regardless of the color of the pollen parent. Differences in interspecific hybrids produced by reciprocal crosses (using each

Fig. 35.6. Hybrid segregation and crossing over in *Sordaria*, an ascomycete. Above, cluster of asci from a crushed perithecium, showing rows of ascospores, the walls of the asci not visible in the photograph. (×140.) Below, part of a cluster of asci. (×600.) These perithecia resulted from mating of gray-spored and black-spored types, the difference in color being governed by a single gene. It should be recalled that each of the four nuclei formed by reduction division within the ascus divides again, mitotically, so that ordinarily eight spores are borne in the ascus. Some asci in these photographs show results of reduction division without crossing over, so that all black spores (derived from one of the two nuclei formed in the first division of meiosis) are at one end, and all gray spores (derived from the other of the two nuclei formed in the first division of meiosis) are at the other end. Other asci show results of reduction division with crossing over. Reference to Fig. 4.3 will help to explain the arrangement of spores in these asci. (Photos courtesy of Lindsay S. Olive.)

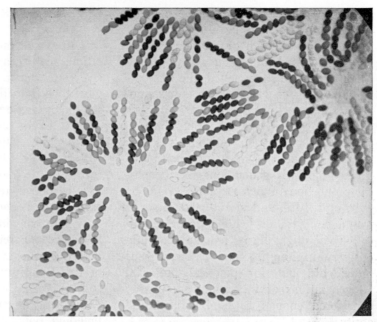

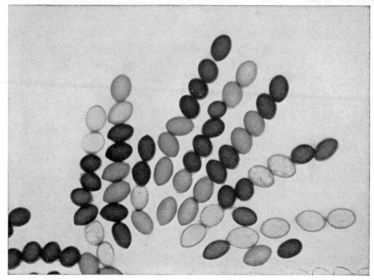

species in turn as the ovule parent, the other being the pollen parent) have also been ascribed to cytoplasmic inheritance, and intensive experimental work supports this interpretation in several cases.

RESULTS OF INBREEDING AND OUTBREEDING

PURE LINES

Inbreeding tends to eliminate heterozygosity. If an individual heterozygous for a single pair of genes is selfed, the first generation hybrids segregate in a 1:2:1 ratio, ¼ being of each of the homozygous types, and ½ being heterozygous. If all these plants are again selfed, the homozygous ones, of course, produce only homozygous offspring, but the heterozygous ones again segregate in a 1:2:1 ratio. The proportion of heterozygous individuals is thus reduced by about ½ in each generation of inbreeding. In 10 generations, the theoretical proportion of heterozygotes would be $\frac{1}{2}^{10}$, or 1/1024, and in 100 generations it would be $\frac{1}{2}^{100}$, or 1/1,048,576. Theoretically there might always remain a continuously diminishing fraction of heterozygous individuals, but for practical purposes, 10 generations of inbreeding are usually considered enough to establish homozygosity.

The same situation holds true no matter how many pairs of genes are considered: after a few generations of inbreeding, the individuals are homozygous for all characters, with an insignificant and diminishing proportion of exceptions. Obviously, if the original individual was heterozygous for many genes, then many genetically different individuals could be derived from it by selfing. Any one such line which has become essentially homozygous by selfing is called a **pure line.** Establishment of pure lines in higher animals is more difficult, because an individual cannot be bred to itself, but by close inbreeding (father-daughter, mother-son, and brother-sister matings, etc.) combined with selection, lines can be established which are homozygous for many genes. The 22 varieties of peas with which Mendel began his experiments were pure lines, since each was naturally self-pollinated. Pure lines are useful or even essential in many genetic studies.

DISCLOSURE OF RECESSIVE DEFECTS BY INBREEDING

In any characteristically outbred population, many harmful or defective recessive genes occur in low frequencies. Only when two individuals with the same recessive defect mate does the character have a chance to be expressed. Given random mating, the chance that both individuals will carry the same recessive defect is the square of the frequency of the gene. Thus, if a particular recessive defective gene is carried by 1 percent of the population, only 1 mating in 10,000 (100×100) will be between parents which both carry the defective gene, and only ¼ of the offspring of these matings (or 1/40,000 of all offspring) will be homozygous recessive. The elimination of recessive defects in an outbreeding population is thus a very slow process, and the defective genes accumulate in the population, through continued mutation, until the frequency of their elimination by natural selection equals the frequency of their origin.

If a normally outbred group is inbred, the number of homozygous recessives among the offspring is, of course, greatly increased, and many previously hidden defects are likely to appear. This is as true in plants as in animals, but its importance in domestic animals and man is greater than in plants, because of the difference in the number of offspring and the care given each. Plants generally produce large numbers of seeds, and the death of a few homozygous recessive defective phenotypes causes no great difficulty. Comparable defective human offspring fill institutions and cause much mental agony as well as expense, even without inbreeding, and there would be many more of these unfortunates if incestuous marriage were common.

Fig. 35.7. Hybrid vigor in marigolds. The Climax marigold (center) is a hybrid between the varieties shown at left and right. All these plants belong to the same species and have the same chromosome number, $2n = 24$. (Photo courtesy of the W. Atlee Burpee Company.)

All higher animals are normally outbred, but many higher plants are normally inbred through self-pollination, or they combine inbreeding with outbreeding by mixtures of self- and cross-pollination. Seriously defective mutations in inbred populations are eliminated by natural selection soon after they are produced, and the frequency of such defects in naturally inbred groups is therefore very low.

Hybrid Vigor

It has long been noted that hybrids between different races of a species, or even between different species, are often more vigorous than either parent (Fig. 35.7). The mule, although sterile, has more endurance than either a donkey or a horse. The popular ornamental shrub *Abelia grandiflora*, a hybrid between A. *chinensis* and A. *uniflora*, is hardier and flowers more freely than either of its parents. *Spiraea vanhouttei* (bridal wreath), another hybrid, is larger and more often cultivated than either of its parents. Many other such examples might be given. This **hybrid vig-** or, or **heterosis**, is often even more conspicuous in crosses between different races of an outbreeding species, such as corn. Intervarietal crosses of characteristically inbreeding species, such as wheat, seldom show marked hybrid vigor, although there are a few examples. Mendel found that the F_1 hybrids between tall and dwarf varieties of peas averaged a little taller than the homozygous tall parent, but the difference was too slight to permit accurate identification of the heterozygotes in the garden.

Two theoretical explanations have been advanced for hybrid vigor, each backed by some experimental evidence. One explanation is that the hybrid simply gets the advantage of the better genes from each parent, with minor homozygous defects in each parent being covered by dominant normal genes from the other. The second explanation is that heterozygosity itself confers an advantage, having a higher survival value than either of the opposing homozygous types. One gene, for example, might help a plant to grow well under one set of environmental conditions, while its allelic partner might help under

Fig. 35.8. George H. Shull (1874–1954), father of hybrid corn. (Photo courtesy of Mrs. George H. Shull.)

with a very low yield of grain. Hybrids between two scrawny inbred types which differ in a number of characters are often much larger and bear more heavily than the original strains from which the selections were made.

This discovery was made by the American botanist George H. Shull (1874–1954) during some experiments directed toward understanding the inheritance of the number of rows of kernels in the ear. Shull (Fig. 35.8) immediately recognized the potential importance of his discovery, and, in 1908 and 1909, he suggested that such high-yielding F_1 hybrids could be used on farms in place of the usual varieties. The difficulty with Shull's method is that the hybrid seed is necessarily produced on one of the scrawny parents, and the low yield makes the seed high-priced. The seed set in the next generation by selfing the vigorous F_1 hybrid is not satisfactory, since it reverts toward homozygosity and loss of vigor; the plants produced from such seeds also differ greatly among themselves, having a wide variety of genotypes.

Several years later another American botanist opened the door to successful commercial use of hybrid corn by replacing Shull's "single-cross" method with a "double-cross" method (Fig. 35.9). Two different F_1 hybrids produced by crossing inbred lines are themselves crossed. These plants, being vigorous and of full size, produce abundant seed. The offspring from this second cross are less uniform than those produced from single-cross hybrids, but still not so variable as ordinary open-pollinated varieties; and if the proper crosses are made, there is no significant loss of vigor. Practically all the field corn grown in the United States today is from double-cross hybrid seed, and there are

some other conditions, so that the range of conditions under which good growth might occur is greater for the heterozygote than for either of the homozygotes. The relative importance of these two suggested mechanisms for heterosis remains to be determined, but present evidence emphasizes the first one. If heterozygosity were regularly useful for its own sake, hybrid vigor might be expected to be common in normally inbred as well as normally outbred groups.

Hybrid Corn

Corn is more sensitive to inbreeding than most crops, and it shows spectacular hybrid vigor. A few generations of inbreeding lead to stunted, unthrifty, pure lines

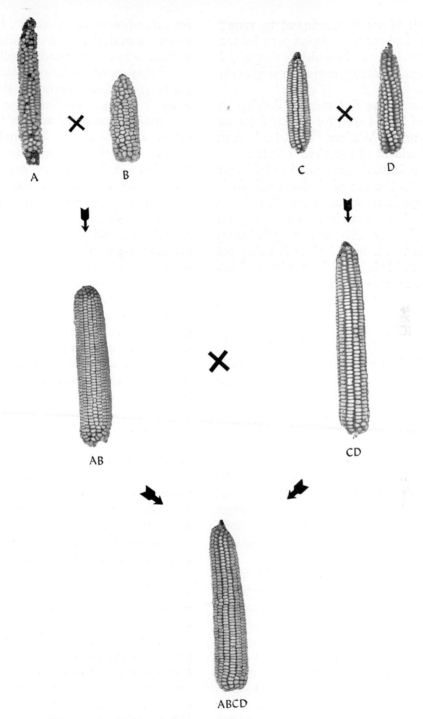

Fig. 35.9.   The double-cross method of producing hybrid corn. (Courtesy of William L. Brown, Pioneer Hi-Bred Corn Company and the Michigan State University Press.)

hundreds of varieties, adapted to various climates and purposes. Sweet corn for canning or table use, in which uniformity is important, is often grown from single-cross hybrids.

One of the first men to develop varieties of hybrid corn for regular farm use was Henry A. Wallace, who later became Vice President of the United States.

The fantastic success of hybrid corn has led to the use of similar methods in breeding other crops and domestic animals. Watermelons, squashes, cucumbers, onions, and sugar beets are among the many crops in which hybrid vigor is being put to use, and hybrid chickens, pigs, and cattle are now also commonplace.

MUTATION

Inheritance in regular patterns, as discussed in the foregoing pages, depends on the precise and regular duplication of genes in connection with mitosis, as well as on a regular pattern of meiosis and fertilization. Anything that disturbs these processes may also disturb the pattern of inheritance.

Any inheritable change in the genetic material is called a **mutation.** In the broad sense the term includes such gross changes as addition or deletion of chromosomes, chromosome segments, or whole sets of chromosomes, as well as changes in individual genes; but when a geneticist speaks of mutation, without further qualification, he normally refers to gene mutation.

Some gene mutations are actually losses and represent the absence of a gene. Others are due to faulty duplication of the original gene, so that the mutant gene is chemically different from its predecessor and has a different phenotypic effect. The mutant gene is duplicated in its new form

for generation after generation, until it too suffers a mutation, after which the new mutant is in turn regularly duplicated.

Many gene mutations with obvious phenotypic effects occur at the rate of about 1 or 2 per million gametes. A few are much commoner, and in one set of experiments on maize, 273 mutations affecting a particular gene locus were detected in 554,786 gametes, a rate of nearly 1 in 2000. A gene at this locus affects the occurrence, distribution, and abundance of red or purple pigment in the grain and herbage. No less than 22 different alleles are known for this locus, although not all of them turned up in this experiment.

Probably many gene mutations have such slight effects that they escape notice, especially when they influence characters governed by multiple factors. The frequency of such mutations is necessarily speculative, as is also their importance. They may well be very important in evolution.

The rate of mutation can be increased by exposure to extremes of heat and cold, certain chemicals, and high-frequency radiation, such as X rays and the rays given off by radioactive elements (Fig. 35.10). Observations by William C. Steere and field collaborators in northwestern Canada indicate that the mutation rate in fireweed (*Epilobium angustifolium*) is much higher on outcrops of uranium ore than on less radioactive sites. High-frequency radiation is destructive to protoplasm in general, and much of its effect on mutation probably reflects the destruction of genes.

Ultraviolet light is in a special category as a mutagenic agent. The absorption spectrum of DNA has its peak near the middle of the ultraviolet range. The energy absorbed from ultraviolet light by DNA results in chemical and physical changes in the intimate details of gene structure. Such mutations are not mere losses, as are so many mutations induced by X rays. Ultraviolet and cosmic rays are probably responsible for the increased rate of mutation observed at higher altitudes.

Some chemical mutagens, such as mustard gas, are antimetabolites which directly affect DNA. The relation of some other chemical mutagens, such as $MnCl_2$ and CH_2O (formaldehyde), to DNA is dubious.

Mutation is usually said to be at random, but this is true only in the sense that it does not seem to be directed toward specific goals. Mutations induced by extreme environmental conditions do not in general help the organism to withstand such conditions. It is conceivable that a mutation induced by low temperature might make the plant more resistant to cold, but a mutation making it less resistant to cold would be just as likely; the cause does not govern the kind of effect. On the other hand, some mutations at a particular gene locus occur oftener than others, and the rate in opposite directions is not the same. Furthermore, it has been demonstrated that the frequency and kind of mutations occurring in some genes of maize are influenced by other genes which are inherited in Mendelian fashion; and the same is doubtless true of other organisms.

Fig. 35.10. **Mutant snapdragons obtained after 4 months of irradiation of whole plants with gamma rays. The mutation affecting the flower at the right evidently occurred during the development of the flower bud; only the cells derived from the mutated cell show the mutation. (Photos courtesy of A. H. Sparrow, Brookhaven National Laboratory, Upton, N.Y.)**

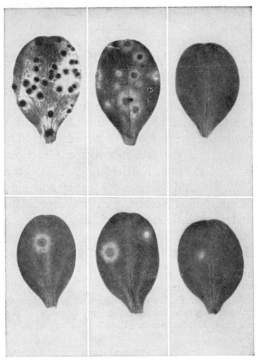

Fig. 35.11. Possible beneficial effect of radiation-induced mutations in the rust fungus *Melampsora lini*, a parasite of flax. All photos show cotyledons of flax seedlings inoculated with the same strain of the rust. Cultivar Bison (top left) is highly susceptible, and cultivar Dakota (top right) is immune to the rust, before irradiation. After the fungus has been subjected to irradiation it is less virulent to cultivar Bison (top center), but some of its mutant spores can now infect cultivar Dakota (bottom row). Each spot on a cotyledon represents a single infection from a single spore. (Photo courtesy of Erwin Schwinghamer, Brookhaven National Laboratory, Upton, N.Y.)

Many mutations are obviously harmful; many others have little or no obvious importance in survival; and a few are distinctly beneficial (Fig. 35.11). Some mutations have been shown to modify the optimum or limiting environmental conditions for the organism and are thus beneficial or harmful according to the environment. In general, the greater the obvious effect of the mutation, the more likely it is to be harmful.

Inasmuch as existing organisms necessarily have delicately balanced genic systems, which are more or less closely adapted to the environment and have had the chance to incorporate beneficial mutations during ages past, it is only to be expected that most mutations from the existing type will be more or less harmful, and only a few beneficial. The situation might be compared with the results of turning a group of undisciplined children loose on an automobile. The crayon marks on the finish do little real harm. Rolling all the windows down makes the car more comfortable on a hot day, but less so on a rainy one. The broken headlight is important only at night, and the broken windshield wipers will be missed only during rain or snow. The chewing gum, jam, and snags on the upholstery are deplorable, but minor. The extra water in the radiator is useful, but the sugar in the gas tank is disastrous.

POLYPLOIDY

We have noted repeatedly in earlier chapters that the gametophyte generation characteristically has one full set of chromosomes, and the sporophyte has two sets. The gametophytic (or gametic) number is called the n number, and the sporophytic (or zygotic) number, therefore, is $2n$. As early as 1907, it was discovered that some plants have more than two full sets of chromosomes in the sporophyte, and in 1917 the Danish botanist Oejvind Winge (1886–   ) showed that, in many groups of plants, the chromosome numbers of related taxa fall into a regular pattern of multiples of a basic (haploid) number. Plants with three or more sets of chromosomes in the sporophyte are now said to be **polyploid.** A polyploid may be triploid (three sets), tetraploid (four sets), pentaploid (five sets), hexaploid (six sets), heptaploid (seven sets), octoploid (eight sets), etc. The most common polyploids are tetraploids, and even-numbered polyploids, such as tetraploids and hexaploids, are commoner than odd-numbered ones, such as triploids and pentaploids. Numbers higher than octoploid are uncommon, but they do occur.

The dual concept of the symbol *n* as representing (1) one full set of chromosomes, and (2) the gametic number of

Fig. 35.12. Diploid (left) and haploid (right) plants of evening primrose (*Oenothera hookeri*). Only the upper part of the diploid plant is shown. Haploid sporophytes, such as the plant at the right, are rarely observed and are characteristically smaller and weaker than the normal diploid. The seed from which this haploid plant developed was formed after the ovule parent had been hand-pollinated with pollen from another species of *Oenothera*. Although the sperms from the foreign pollen evidently did not fertilize the egg in the ovule, the growth of the pollen tube may have somehow stimulated the ovule to develop into a seed. (Photo courtesy of Adolph Hecht.)

Fig. 35.13. Effect of autopolyploidy on blackberries. Polyploidy was induced by treatment with colchicine. Tetraploid above, diploid below. (Photo courtesy of J. W. Hull and the Maryland Agricultural Experiment Station.)

chromosomes, thus fails in polyploids. After some initial confusion, it has become customary to retain the symbol *n* for the gametic number, regardless of how many sets are involved. The symbol *x* has been introduced to designate one full set of chromosomes. In most plants and practically all animals, *n* and *x* represent

Fig. 35.14. Effect of autopolyploidy on black-berries. Polyploidy was induced by treatment with colchicine. Left to right: diploid, tetraploid, octoploid. (Photo courtesy of J. W. Hull and the Maryland Agricultural Experiment Station.)

the same number, but in a considerable proportion of plants n is a multiple of x.

Many species, or groups of species, have a polyploid series of chromosome numbers. Thus, if $x = 5$, one population may be diploid ($2x$), with $2n = 10$; another may be tetraploid ($4x$), with $2n = 20$; another may be hexaploid ($6x$), with $2n = 30$; and another may be octoploid ($8x$), with $2n = 40$. If only the tetraploid of this series were known, it would probably be thought to be a diploid with $x = 10$, until the chromosomes were very carefully studied.

Polyploidy influences both the characteristics of the individual and the genetic and evolutionary potentialities of the population. A very common effect on the individual is an increase in size of the cells and often an increase in the size and vigor of the whole plant. This is particularly true in newly induced polyploids (Figs. 35.13, 35.14). Natural polyploids which have existed for an indefinite

time often closely resemble the diploids, and it has been thought that natural selection may operate to restore the polyploids to the size of diploids. The larger size of the cells of polyploids is often reflected in a smaller number of stomates per unit area of the leaf, and after such a correlation has been established, the ploidy level of dried herbarium specimens, as well as living plants, can often be determined by stomate counts.

Other direct effects of polyploidy are not always predictable. Annuals may turn into perennials. There may be subtle changes in physiological characters, altering the ecological niche to which the plant is best suited. Polyploids are sometimes less highly fertile than diploids, because the pairing and segregation of chromosomes at meiosis do not always proceed normally, and some pollen grains or megaspores thus do not receive the proper complement of chromosomes.

Polyploidy introduces a barrier to interbreeding, thus allowing evolutionary divergence to occur. A tetraploid does not usually breed freely with its diploid ancestor. A first-generation hybrid between a diploid and a tetraploid will be triploid, with $3x$ chromosomes (Fig. 35.15). Meiosis in triploids is irregular, and only a small proportion of viable pollen and ovules is produced. Triploids do not leave many offspring unless they can set seed apomictically or have effective means of vegetative reproduction.

Polyploidy may also break down barriers to interbreeding. Species which produce only sterile hybrids as diploids may produce fertile hybrids at the tetraploid level. Here again meiosis is often the critical stage. In the diploid hybrid, the chromosomes from the different parents may fail to pair at meiosis, or the pairing

Fig. 35.15. Marigold hybrid (below) and parents. The "African" marigold (*Tagetes erecta*, top left, a native of Mexico) is diploid, $2n = 24$; the "French" marigold (*T. patula*, top right, also a native of Mexico) is tetraploid, $2n = 48$. The hybrid is triploid, $2n = 36$, and sterile. In these plants $x = 12$. In this instance there is no hybrid vigor, at least as regards the size of the flowers. (Photo courtesy of the W. Atlee Burpee Company.)

chromosomes may not be exact mates, so that, in either case, the resulting reduced cells do not receive a complete and balanced set of genes. In the tetraploid hybrid, on the contrary, each chromosome has an exact homologue to pair with, and meiosis proceeds more normally.

Delimitation of species in polyploid groups is often difficult, because one of the most important specific criteria, reproductive isolation, is not well correlated with the also very important criterion of morphologic differentiation. Very similar plants may fail to hybridize because of differences in ploidy level, whereas the differences between otherwise well-marked species may be bridged by fertile polyploid hybrids. The blueberries (*Vaccinium*) of the eastern United States form a well-known polyploid complex in which the identification of species is still not easy in spite of the careful and competent taxonomic attention they have received. When polyploidy is accompanied by apomixis, as it is in *Rubus* (blackberries and raspberries), *Crataegus* (hawthorn), *Antennaria*, and some other groups, the difficulties are again compounded, and it is such groups that have usually produced the greatest disagreements among taxonomists.

Sterile hybrids between species can become fertile through polyploidy. The famous Kew primrose (*Primula kewensis*) was the first plant observed to do so. The original *P. kewensis* (Fig. 35.16) was a sterile hybrid between *P. verticillata*, from Arabia, and *P. floribunda*, from the Himalayan region. It appeared as a chance hybrid in a greenhouse at the Kew Gardens in 1899 and was experimentally produced again in 1900. In 1905, 1923, and 1926, some flowers of the hybrid set seed. In each instance the seedlings were fertile and had twice as many chromosomes as the parent. These fertile tetraploids are, in effect, a new species of hybrid origin, interfertile among themselves, but not crossing readily with either

Fig. 35.16. *Primula kewensis;* **the sterile hybrid from which the fertile tetraploid can arise. (New York Botanical Garden photo.)**

of the parents or the original hybrid. Many natural species are believed to have originated in similar fashion by hybridization and polyploidy, and a few have even been experimentally duplicated.

Polyploids which originate by doubling of chromosomes of an existing species are called autopolyploids, or **autoploids,** and those which originate by doubling associated with hybridization, so that they include chromosome sets from more than one species, are called allopolyploids, or **alloploids.** The fertile derivative of *Primula kewensis* is an alloploid, or, more precisely, an allotetraploid. Many allotetraploids behave, in effect, as diploids, with the full complement of chromosomes from each parent going to make up one full set in the hybrid. Allotetraploids of this nature are often called amphidiploids, or amphiploids. Among natural populations it is often difficult to distinguish between autoploids and alloploids, and the term *amphiploid* is most likely to be used for those allotetraploids whose origin is well known.

An important evolutionary effect of polyploidy is to decrease the importance of gene mutation. If every chromosome is represented by several duplicates, a mutation in any one gene is not likely to have much phenotypic effect, or much chance of being produced in homozygous condition in future generations. The evolutionary potentialities of the group are thus severely restricted, and polyploidy is considered to be an evolutionary blind alley, even though it is often highly effective in producing new and successful combinations of existing characters. It is the diploids which provide the continuing stream of evolution.

Polyploidy originates through the suppression of meiosis, so that unreduced gametes are formed, or through the failure of anaphase migration of chromosomes during mitosis or meiosis, the duplicated chromosomes all being incorporated into a single nucleus. Under natural conditions such an occurrence is a mere accident, favored by environmental extremes such as low temperatures; polyploids are especially frequent at high altitudes or latitudes. Colchicine, an alkaloid produced by the autumn crocus (*Colchicum autumnale*), inhibits spindle formation in most other organisms and can be applied in low concentrations to induce polyploidy (Fig. 35.17). It is also a great help to botanists wishing to count chromosomes, because its interference with anaphase greatly increases the number of metaphase plates which can be seen in a single preparation.

PLANT BREEDING

Since prehistoric times, farmers have selected seed from the strongest, most desirable plants in a field, or they have selected the best seeds after harvesting. Over thousands of years, this selection, along with random crossbreeding in the fields, has had profound effects, so that, as noted in Chapter 34, it is often difficult to identify the wild ancestor of a crop plant. Selection for different purposes and in different regions led to the development of numerous varieties of each of the commoner crops, but, except in self-pollinating groups, each of these varieties was itself usually highly heterozygous, encompassing a considerable range of variability.

The development of the science of genetics during the twentieth century gave a tremendous impetus to practical plant breeding. Every important crop in the Western Hemisphere, as well as many minor ones, has been greatly improved by deliberate effort during this century. The northern limit of large-scale cultivation of wheat in Canada has been advanced hundreds of miles by the creation of new varieties which mature a few days earlier.

One of the most spectacularly successful plant breeders in America, Luther Burbank (1849–1926), had no formal botanical training, although he did acquire a working knowledge of some genetic principles. His first new variety, the Burbank potato, was the best in a group of 23 seedlings obtained from a chance fruit of another variety. (In areas away from their natural habitat, potatoes rarely mature seed and are propagated vegetatively by tubers.) Although the Burbank potato

Fig. 35.17. Diploid (left) and tetraploid (right) snapdragons, the tetraploidy induced by colchicine. (Photo courtesy of the W. Atlee Burpee Company.)

has now mostly given way to even better varieties, it was the best variety of its time and was very extensively planted for more than half a century after its introduction in 1876. Later Burbank combined hybridization with selection, and many of his varieties, notably the Burbank and other plums, are still commercially important, especially in California.

Crop improvement, using more refined techniques of the same basic type as Burbank's (hybridization and selection), is now a major activity in the United States and many other countries. Agricultural experiment stations in each of the states, in cooperation with the U.S. Department of Agriculture, are continuously producing new varieties of old crops, with higher yield, greater resistance to disease, and other desirable qualities. The effects of polyploidy and hybrid vigor are also being exploited. Colchicine-induced tetraploids of some garden flowers, such as snapdragons (Fig. 35.17) and zinnias, have larger flowers than the natural diploids. The production of hybrid corn has been discussed earlier in this chapter. In some less highly developed parts of the world, where crops have not yet received this sort of attention, Burbank's freewheeling approach could still give spectacular results.

One of the consequences of the development of improved varieties is the virtual disappearance of the older varieties of many crops. Yet these older varieties, which have survived the diseases and other environmental hazards of the past, still carry many genes which might profitably be incorporated into better varieties. The United States government, therefore, now maintains a number of farms in which the old varieties are carefully preserved as gene pools for future breeding operations.

SUGGESTED READING

Clausen, Jens, David D. Keck, and William M. Hiesey, Experimental studies on the nature of species. II. Plant evolution through amphiploidy and autoploidy, with examples from the Madiinae, *Carnegie Inst. Wash. Publ. 564.* Washington, D.C., 1945, 174 pp. An important work correlating polyploidy with taxonomy.

Crabb, A. Richard, *The Hybrid-Corn Makers. Prophets of Plenty*, Rutgers Univ. Press. New Brunswick, N.J., 1948, 331 pp. Good reading, and fair to all the many who contributed to the development of hybrid corn.

Howard, Walter L., *Luther Burbank. A Victim of Hero Worship*, Chronica Botanica 9 (nos. 5 & 6). 1946. A sympathetic biography.

CHAPTER 36

Evolution

The Principles of Evolution

HISTORY

THE PRE-DARWINIAN PERIOD

Man's urge to understand his surroundings—what they are and how they got that way—is one of the basic intellectual drives. Explanations must always, of course, be based on the information and attitudes of the time. As information increases and attitudes change, explanations which once seemed adequate cease to remain so and must be modified or discarded in favor of newer explanations. Thunder and lightning are no longer generally regarded as the voice and weapon of the gods, nor crop failure as an expression of divine wrath.

The ancient Greek philosophers, with a relatively limited body of factual knowledge, and with no authoritarian doctrine to guide them, gave free reign to speculation. Empedocles (fifth century B.C.) sug-

◄

Fruit of beggar ticks (*Bidens*), showing adaptation to seed distribution by animals. (×20.) The fruit contains only a single seed. (Photo by John H. Gerard, from National Audubon Society.)

gested that the parts of animals had arisen separately and spontaneously from the earth and had assembled themselves at random into whole animals—thus explaining why some animals look so odd. Aristotle (384–322 B.C.), on the other hand, believed that the more complex forms of life had evolved from simpler ones, though he had no clear idea of an activating mechanism. Although Aristotle's compendia of knowledge became the recognized authority in Roman and medieval times, his idea of evolution was neglected, and for many hundreds of years men were content to believe that each species of plant and animal had been separately created, remaining unchanged forever after. Apparently no conflict was felt between this belief and the also prevalent belief in spontaneous generation of mice, rats, fleas, flies, and other pests.

In the eighteenth century, a few biologists began to doubt the theory of special creation, and in 1802 the French biologist Jean Baptiste de Lamarck (1744–1829) put forward the first full-fledged theory of evolution. The activating principle of evolution, as seen by Lamarck, was the effect of use and disuse of body parts, through the inheritance of acquired characters: Giraffes have long necks because they keep reaching up into the trees to browse, and a man will have brawnier children if he becomes a blacksmith than if he becomes a musician. Although Lamarck was one of the most respected biologists of his time, well-known for his taxonomic contributions in both botany and zoology, his theory of evolution aroused relatively little interest and attracted still less support, during his own lifetime.

During the first half of the nineteenth century, the idea of organic evolution made little headway, but the increase in biological knowledge gradually prepared the way for its acceptance. De Candolle's classification of angiosperms was essentially evolutionary, as noted in Chapter 33, although expressed in terms of a series of special creations involving progressive modifications from a basic type. In 1830–1833, the British geologist Charles Lyell set forth, in his *Principles of Geology*, a correlation of the stratigraphic position and relative age of rocks with the fossils found in them. For 300 years before that time, the nature of fossils had been bitterly contested: they had variously been considered as inventions of the devil, freaks of nature, relics of the Flood, or the remains of prehistoric plants and animals. The scientific side of this controversy was laid to rest by Lyell's work, and the religious opposition to the recognition of fossils as prehistoric remains eventually dwindled to insignificance.

DARWINISM

In 1831 the young English dilettante Charles Darwin (1809–1882) obtained the unsalaried post of naturalist on the cruiser *Beagle*, which was to circumnavigate the world principally for map-making purposes. Although he suffered from violent seasickness throughout the 5-year journey, Darwin worked hard, sending home notes and collections of botanical, zoological, and geological specimens from the various stopping points. The theory of special creation and immutability of species, which he had at first accepted in orthodox fashion, became progressively unsatisfactory to him during the voyage. The 6 weeks spent on the Galapagos Islands, 650 miles off the west coast of South America, was particularly disturbing to his earlier beliefs. Here he found a fauna of distinctly South American genera, but with many strictly endemic species. Often there was a different species on each island, obviously similar to, but also obviously different from, the species on the other islands. He thought it irrational that so many very local species should have been created for such a small and desolate area, and puzzling that they should consistently belong to South American genera.

At the completion of his voyage, Darwin, now a thoroughly dedicated biologist, set to working up his collections and to reflecting on the possible explanation for his observations. Inclining toward an evolutionary explanation, he keenly felt the lack of a satisfactory mechanism but was wholly unable to accept the Lamarckian concepts of evolution through the effects of use and disuse. In search of information, he investigated the breeding of domestic animals, kept in touch with many professional breeders, and himself bred different races of pigeons for years. All this seemed to show that, under man's guidance, domestic varieties fully as distinct as natural species could be produced from an original form. Still Darwin lacked a mechanism to cause such changes in nature.

Then Darwin happened on Malthus' book, *An Essay on the Principle of Population*, which had been published in 1798. Malthus' principal point, which has only partly and temporarily been invalidated in the past century, is that the human breeding potential far outstrips potential resources, and that the limited supply leads to competition for the available goods and a struggle for existence. Here was the key to Darwin's problem, and he gladly adopted Malthus' terms *competition* and *struggle for existence*.

Fig. 36.1. Charles Darwin (1809–1882), English naturalist, who laid the foundation of modern evolutionary theory. (Photo courtesy of the New York Academy of Medicine.)

Adding to his other information Malthus' concept of population growth, Darwin (Fig. 36.1) now developed a new theory of evolution, with these salient points: (1) organisms of the same species are not all alike but differ slightly among themselves; furthermore, the offspring of a particular set of parents tend to vary around the average of the parents; (2) more individuals are produced than can possibly survive; (3) these individuals must compete with each other in a struggle for existence in order to survive; (4) as a result of this competition, the individuals best-adapted to the environment tend to survive (survival of the fittest); and (5) new species originate by this natural selection of the best-fitted individuals over a period of many generations.

Darwin now set himself to marshaling the evidence supporting his views, taking the greatest pains to substantiate each point with numerous examples as well as argumentation. In 1858, as his projected book was nearing completion, he unexpectedly received from Alfred Russell Wallace (1823–1913) a paper expressing these very same ideas. Wallace had developed his theory from years of study in the East Indies, again with emphasis on differences in the flora and fauna between islands, and again with an assist from Malthus. Embarrassed, Darwin presented Wallace's paper and a summary of his own evidence leading to the same conclusion, to a meeting of the Linnean Society of London. The following year, in 1859, Darwin's magnum opus, *On the Origin of Species by Means of Natural Selection,* was published.

Darwin's theory of evolution took the scientific world by storm. Biologists such as Huxley and Hooker in England, Haeckel in Germany, and Gray in America, as well as the geologist Lyell, were almost immediate converts. Huxley in particular defended Darwinism with untiring vigor. Within a few years the theory of special creation was abandoned by biologists, in favor of the theory of evolution.

The evolutionary concept, especially as applied to man, aroused violent religious opposition, just as Galileo's concepts about the movement of the earth with respect to the sun had done more than two centuries earlier. As great a Christian as St. Augustine had in the fourth century A.D. interpreted the first chapter of Genesis allegorically, to mean that God had bestowed on the first living thing the power to evolve into other forms, but many nineteenth-century and even twentieth-century theologians found this interpretation unacceptable. The teaching of evolution was even forbidden in some places both in the United States and

Europe. As recently as 1925, John Scopes was tried, in Tennessee's famous "monkey trial," for teaching contrary to the Bible. William Jennings Bryan acted as special prosecutor and was also called as a witness for the defense by Clarence Darrow, the defense attorney. Scopes was convicted, but Darrow won his case in the court of public opinion, and attempts to suppress the teaching of evolution waned rapidly in the United States after this episode.

The theory of evolution provided a unifying principle which explained many otherwise puzzling facts. The fossil record, with its appearance of progressively more complex types in later rocks; the useless and often vestigial structures of many plants and animals, from the appendix and ear muscles of man to the micropyle of angiosperms and the flagella of cycad sperms; the South American affinities of the Galapagos fauna; the succession of stages in the growth of embryos of man and other animals: all these and more fell into place as evidence for and results of evolution. The time was clearly ripe, and had it not been for Darwin, we would now be honoring Wallace for the discovery— although acceptance of the principle might have come more slowly. Darwin's exposition was so thorough and so carefully documented that to the modern reader it may seem to belabor the obvious, but it was exactly this approach which led to its early triumph.

NON-DARWINIAN CONCEPTS OF EVOLUTION

The principle of evolution was accepted, but doubts were felt from the beginning as to the adequacy of natural selection alone as the mechanism. The principle of survival of the fittest explains the selection of the most useful characters from among those existing, but does it explain the origin of new characteristics? The weakest part of Darwin's theory was the assumption that change through selection has no limits, because in each successive generation the offspring vary around the average of the parents. The complicated and wholly speculative mechanism that he suggested to achieve this result turned out to be so wrong that it need not be discussed here. The *Origin of Species* was published before Mendel's work, and Mendel's results did not begin to influence biological thinking until 1900.

The triumph of Darwinism, strangely enough, led to a revival of interest in Lamarck's concept of evolution through the effects of use and disuse of organs. This concept captured the popular imagination, and it still survives in nonscientific circles in spite of the consistently negative results obtained in numerous careful experiments.

Paleontologists, dealing with fossil plants and animals, and taxonomists, working on modern groups, often discerned evolutionary trends which are not readily explainable in terms of survival value and selection. From these observations came the concept of **orthogenesis**—evolution predetermined to proceed along certain lines, regardless of natural selection. The possible mechanism of orthogenesis was most obscure, but many biologists became convinced of its existence.

The genetic studies of the early twentieth century threw even more doubt on natural selection as the driving force of evolution. It was shown that selection is ineffective, once a pure line has been established. Furthermore, attention was drawn to the major mutations which occur in a group of species of *Oenothera* (evening primrose). Spontaneous polyploidy and other chromosomal irregularities whose nature was not at first recognized are unusually common in this group, causing the seeming formation of different species in single jumps.

THE MODERN PERIOD

Meanwhile, the fruit fly *Drosophila melanogaster* was discovered as an ideal tool for genetic research. These hardy little creatures with $2n = 8$ chromosomes breed like flies, producing a new generation in the laboratory about every two weeks. They require no great care and dine happily on overripe fruit. They display a number of small, but definite, differences which are inherited in Mendelian fashion. When subjected to X rays or other mutagenic agents, they undergo numerous gene mutations, some of which are evidently the same as in naturally occurring mutants. From the studies on *Drosophila* came not only the concepts of genes, linear sequence on the chromosomes, linkage, and gene mutations, but also the concept of population genetics.

Population genetics is the study of the changes in proportions of genotypes in an interbreeding population over a period of generations. In a fairly large population subjected to a uniform environment, the effects of selection are very evident. Many small characters of no obvious importance to the organism increase progressively (by differential reproduction or survival) under one set of conditions and decrease progressively under another set. Clearly, these seemingly insignificant characters do have significance in survival, either directly or through other unrecognized effects of the genes which govern them. Such studies have strongly bolstered the selectionist interpretation of evolution.

The accidents of survival become progressively more important in small populations. The proportions of a particular gene fluctuate rather widely in successive generations when the population consists of only a few individuals, and a gene may reach 100 percent frequency—or conversely may be entirely lost—regardless of its survival value, as long as it is not too strongly deleterious.

By the mid-1930's a neo-Darwinian interpretation of evolution emerged, with gene mutation as the principal source of variation, and natural selection, tempered by genetic drift in small populations, as the directing force. Neo-Darwinism provides adequately for the degeneration of unused structures as well as for the growth and elaboration of useful ones, thus undercutting the Lamarckian ideas of inheritance of acquired characters. In the neo-Darwinian view, unused structures deteriorate because of the accumulation of loss mutations. We have seen that most mutations are harmful rather than beneficial, and it is only the continuous pressure of natural selection that weeds out the defective mutants. Because each gene commonly has a number of phenotypic effects, a mutation adversely affecting a particular organ might even be beneficial in other respects.

Neo-Darwinism so clearly provides a satisfactory explanation for so much of organic evolution that one is tempted to consider it the sole explanation; and many modern students of evolution take exactly this view. Experiments with fruit flies and other organisms have shown that a character may have hidden significance in survival, either directly or through some other effect of the gene governing it; therefore, it is assumed that all evolutionary trends are based on survival value. Many ingenious and ingenuous explanations of hidden survival value have been advanced to explain evolutionary developments whose relation to natural selection is obscure.

Not all biologists accept neo-Darwinism as the sole explanation of organic evolution. Many taxonomists, especially those dealing with angiosperms, observe apparent evolutionary trends which are not easily explained in terms of survival value, and they reject the strained explanations which have been proposed. To this group of biologists, in particular, the concept of orthogenesis (see p. 761) retains its attraction.

A genetic basis for orthogenesis has been suggested but remains to be demonstrated. In effect, the proof that certain genes influence the rate and direction of mutation in other genes is assumed to reflect a rather general situation, and it is postulated that any mechanism by which mutation directors could operate would affect a number of gene loci and even cause progressive series of mutations at individual loci. Thus the mutation pressure would, in many cases, outweigh the effects of natural selection, especially since much speciation (origin of new species) is generally believed to occur in small populations, in which even mildly harmful genes might be fixed by genetic drift.

SOME CURRENT CONCEPTS

ORIGIN OF NEW STRUCTURES

One of the aphorisms of evolutionary theory is that *organs do not arise functionless.* New structures arise by modification of pre-existing structures, rather than by starting as useless bumps which acquire a function thereafter. Some function must be retained throughout the evolutionary process, although the function, just as the structure, may be gradually modified. Thus, petals may be modified stamens, or modified sepals, but they do not originate (phyletically) as useless bumps. Sepals are modified leaves, and stamens are modified microsporophylls, which are modified leaves. Leaves are modified stems, stems are modified parts of a thallus, and a thallus is a modified cell colony. Guard cells are modified epidermal cells, and epidermis is modified parenchyma.

An important evolutionary principle that has emerged from embryological and other studies is that *ontogeny* (i.e., the developmental history of the individual) *is a recapitulation of phylogeny* (i.e., the evolutionary history of the group). This principle has more numerous and more obvious applications in mammals than in plants. The human fetus, for example, has a tail throughout much of its period of development; at a fairly early stage it has gill slits, which eventually become the eustachian tubes connecting the ears to the throat; later it briefly acquires a fairly dense coating of hair, which usually disappears before birth. The fact that in sexual reproduction each individual starts its life as a single cell recalls the unicellular ancestry of all multicellular organisms. Dodder (*Cuscuta*, Fig. 1.4), a parasitic plant, has no connection with the ground at maturity, but the seed germinates on the ground in the usual way, and the basal parts deteriorate only after the twining stems have developed haustoria attaching them to the host.

The principle that ontogeny is a recapitulation of phylogeny should not be taken too literally, however. It is more nearly another aphorism expressing the fact that ancestral characters frequently persist in the developmental stages, so that the ontogeny often gives strong suggestions as to the phylogeny. Thus it is probably significant that angiosperms with compound leaves generally produce a few simple leaves in the seedling stage before producing leaves of the mature type.

The reason that ancestral features are likely to be expressed in the juvenile stages is fairly clear. Any organism necessarily has a complex genic balance more or less in harmony with the environment. The greater the phenotypic effect of a mutation, the more likely it is to disturb this balance and be eliminated by natural selection. A gradual evolutionary change has much more chance of remaining in harmony with the environment than an abrupt one. The later in ontogeny a mutation exerts its phenotypic effect, the less total effect it is likely to have, and the less likelihood there is that any possible beneficial effect will be outweighed by some harmful effect. Thus the early ontogenetic stages of an organ are the least likely to be affected by evolutionary change, and these early stages, therefore, provide evidence as to the ancestral condition.

SPECIFIC AND INFRASPECIFIC DIFFERENTIATION

THE ROLE OF ISOLATION

Most speciation probably takes place in small populations which are more or less isolated and thus have a chance to change without being swamped by a larger population with which they are interfertile. Climatic and geologic changes are constantly altering the size and outline of the area to which each species is adapted, isolating small populations in favorable locations separated from the remainder of their species. Many such local populations die out as the environmental conditions for them deteriorate; others are reunited with the main population of their species as conditions become more favorable again and the intervening area is reoccupied. A few such small populations, under pressure of selection and affected also by chance fixation of some previously uncommon genes, change so much that they retain their distinctness even when brought back into contact with the parent species. These have become new species.

The amount and stability of the differences arising under isolation vary according to the circumstances. Morphologic and physiologic differentiation tend to go along hand in hand with the development of barriers to interbreeding with the original population, but any one of these types of difference may fall behind or get ahead of the others. Thus an isolated small population may become morphologically and physiologically distinguishable from the parent population, without developing any internal barrier to crossbreeding with it, so that the two breed together freely when brought together in the garden or when natural contact is re-established. A barrier to interbreeding may likewise develop without much other change, or morphologic differences and reproductive isolation may develop without much physiologic change, or the population may remain morphologically almost unchanged after physiologic changes and reproductive isolation have been established. There is necessarily some room for difference of opinion as to whether such partially differentiated types should, in a given instance, be regarded as separate species, subspecies, or varieties, or be denied any taxonomic recognition at all.

As one of these small populations undergoes change, the area and habitats available for its exploitation also change, and it may be able to increase its geographic area. If this increase brings it back into contact with the parent population, the two may or may not interbreed freely, depending on the physical chance for transfer of pollen, the presence of internal barriers to successful development of hybrid seeds, the vigor of the hybrids, etc. If relatively free interbreeding is re-established, then the two populations may merge completely, or they may retain their individuality, occupying different habitats or different geographic areas and hybridizing along the zones of contact.

If the new population is unable to interbreed with the parent one, then its expansion of area will be unaffected by the parent species, except possibly through competition for the same habitat. The new species may then go on to develop its own series of geographic and ecologic races, if conditions favor it.

If a continuous large population is divided into two large populations (in similar habitats) by destruction of the geographically connecting part, the two do not usually diverge very rapidly. About the same kind and number of mutations will occur in each, and if the environmental conditions are similar, the effect of selection is about the same in each. Therefore, although both populations may gradually change, the changes are rather similar, and divergence is slow. Thus the deciduous forests of the southern Appalachian region of the United States contain a number of species so very similar to species from eastern Asia that it is hard to decide whether we have two closely related species or a single species with two geographically isolated segments. Yet the two populations have been separated in each case for at least half a million years, since the breakup of the Arcto-Tertiary forest at the beginning of the Pleistocene glaciation.

The southern Appalachian and Ozark regions of the United States also show many closely related species-pairs, or varieties of one species. These two areas, with somewhat similar climate and topography, have been continuously available for land-plant habitation since the Cretaceous period, in contrast to the glaciated area to the north and the coastal plain (with its Mississippi embayment) to the south and between.

Ecologic Influences

At the margins of its geographic range and ecologic tolerance, a species is subjected to the most evolutionary pressure. If the proper mutations occur, it may be enabled to occupy new territory, showing a gradual change with the geography and habitat.

Sometimes the two geographic ends of an essentially continuous population may be as different as two species. A well-known example is provided by the frog *Rana pipiens*, which occurs throughout most of the United States. The Maine and Florida segments of the population are morphologically distinguishable and intersterile. If only these two parts of the population existed, they would be called distinct species, but the change along the coast from north to south is so gradual that the whole population is necessarily treated as a single species. Thus we see a possibility that species can arise by extinction of intermediate forms connecting the differentiated ends of a population. A metaphorical comparison might be made to the reproduction by death and fragmentation which occurs in thalloid liverworts such as *Marchantia*.

Species with a wide geographic range or ecologic tolerance usually have many different genotypes and often show recognizable races correlated with the habitat. Thus *Solidago canadensis*, a common goldenrod, has one variety in the New England region and adjacent Canada, another in the deciduous forest region of the eastern United States, a third on the Great Plains, a fourth in the western cordillera, and a fifth along the coast of British Columbia and southern Alaska. Each of these varieties is adapted to the climate of its own region and differs from the other varieties in minor morphological characters; but no sharp lines can be drawn among them. Such ecologically differentiated races within a species are often called **ecotypes.** A species may have different ecotypes on different soils or at different altitudes in the same region, as well as in different geographic regions.

An important factor in the development of evolutionary diversity is the existence of habitats available for exploitation. Some plant communities may be so perfectly adjusted to the environment that there is little or no room for an invader; each ecological niche and subniche is completely occupied by its own set of species, which repulse any less well-adapted immigrants. Climatic and geologic changes do continue to disturb the balance between the vegetation and the environment, however, and, if these changes occur rapidly enough, some habitats may be left temporarily unfilled, or they will be filled by species so poorly adapted to them as to allow invasion by outsiders.

Any such unfilled or imperfectly filled niche is a powerful stimulus to evolutionary change. When the vegetation is in harmony with the environment, almost any significant mutation will probably be harmful, but when some habitats are not properly filled, some of the newly produced mutants may be able to occupy them. An extreme example is provided by oceanic islands, such as the Galapagos and Hawaiian Islands. When such islands first arise from the sea, all habitats are open. Sooner or later a few kinds of plants and animals accidentally reach them. Competition is at a minimum, and genotypes which would otherwise be eliminated have a chance to survive in one or another of the unfilled habitats. There is thus an evolutionary explosion to occupy the available habitats, and new species may arise even without initial geographic or reproductive isolation.

DISTURBANCE, HYBRIDIZATION, AND POLYPLOIDY

Man's activities also influence evolution. Man disturbs the habitat, upsetting ecological balances, and, in effect, creating new ecological niches for exploitation. Many European weeds are known only around human habitations and can continue to exist only under the disturbed conditions created by man. Some of these species have certainly originated by modification from species which continue to exist in less disturbed habitats.

One of the effects of man's disturbance is to increase the opportunity for hybridization between previously distinct species. The newly opened habitat may be invaded by species which formerly did not grow together, and the hybrids, which under natural conditions would have been quickly eliminated even if formed, may find suitable conditions for survival and reproduction. These hybrids may then breed with themselves or with either of the original parents, and genes of one species may thus be introduced into another species by this **introgression,** or introgressive hybridization.

The retreat of the glaciers after the height of the most recent glaciation (some 11,000 years ago) also provided ample opportunity for introgressive hybridization and rapid evolution on the areas laid bare. Species which are quite distinct south of the glacial boundary are sometimes difficult to distinguish north of it.

Hybridization sometimes leads to the origin of new species. This is especially true when the hybrid undergoes chance doubling of chromosomes (alloploidy); new species may then originate in a single jump, as described in the previous chapter. This type of speciation has evidently occurred repeatedly in nature, and several instances have occurred during the present century. Just as obviously, alloploidy cannot be the usual method of speciation; there is a limit to the number of chromosomes that can effectively inhabit a single cell. Origin of species by hybridization is most likely to occur under disturbed conditions in which some habitats are not adequately filled, or in dry areas where the soil is not completely covered by vegetation. Some of the hybrids or hybrid segregates may then turn out to be better adapted to the surroundings than either of the parents.

Simple doubling of chromosomes within a species (autoploidy) may also lead to speciation. Polyploidy acts as an isolating mechanism, setting the polyploid individuals off from their diploid progenitors as a small population which can undergo further change without the drag of backcrossing to the original larger population. Whether a newly produced autoploid does actually evolve into a new species depends on future events. It may do so, or it may remain so much like the diploid that taxonomic segregation is impractical.

The Evolutionary History of Plants

PRIMITIVE LIFE

The time and manner of the origin of life on earth are still matters of speculation, but the available evidence favors some lines of speculation over others. The most reasonable supposition is that organic matter was first formed early in the earth's history by happenstance chemical reactions promoted by ultraviolet light and taking place in the as yet fresh (not salty) water of the sea. Evidence from physical as well as biological sources strongly suggests that the primitive atmosphere of the earth had little if any free oxygen and permitted relatively free passage of ultraviolet rays, which are now largely screened out by the upper atmosphere. Amino acids and other organic compounds are formed from simple inorganic substances when the probable conditions of the primitive earth are experimentally duplicated.

It is thought that the organic molecules very gradually accumulated, and reactions among them led to the formation of larger molecules. Electrochemical attractions might reasonably be expected to have held some of these molecules together as colloidal particles. When such an aggregation came to include the proper chemical compounds to promote the formation of more molecules of the same type, the first organism came into being. Increase in the number of such primitive organisms may have occurred simply by failure of the mass to hold together as its volume increased.

Under this concept, the first organisms were heterotrophic, depending for their nutrition on organic compounds already in existence. As more and more of the previously formed organic molecules were incorporated into the molecule systems which represented the first organisms, a premium must have been placed on the ability to use less and less complex substances as raw materials, and finally on the ability to tap some new source of energy.

If the primitive atmosphere contained relatively little free oxygen, the primitive organisms must have been anaerobic. Any new source of energy, therefore, probably would not involve free oxygen and thus would not resemble the chemosynthesis now carried on by the iron and sulfur bacteria, which do require free oxygen. The first new source of energy may possibly have been photosynthesis resembling that of some modern bacteria, in which organic compounds are used as the source of hydrogen, and free oxygen is neither used nor released. Photosynthesis in which hydrogen is obtained from water, and oxygen is released, would, under such a hypothesis, be a later development.

Aerobic organisms (both plants and animals) characteristically contain the cytochrome system of respiratory enzymes, which are chemically related to chlorophyll. Anaerobic organisms generally do not have the cytochrome system. According to the most widely accepted current hypothesis, it was not until a considerable supply of atmospheric oxygen had been built up by the newer type of photosynthesis that the cytochrome system, which uses free oxygen, was developed by modification of chlorophyll or its chemical precursors. Under such a hypothesis, all aerobic organisms, including aerobic bacteria, would be derived from photosynthetic anaerobes more or less similar to some of the present-day photosynthetic bacteria.

Most students of bacterial cytology are now convinced that bacteria characteristically have a DNA-containing body which functions as a nucleus but which does not have the complex organization of the nucleus of higher organisms. The development of chlorophyll, the cytochrome system, and a primitive nucleus thus all occurred within the bacteria, long before the Cambrian period of geologic time.

ALGAE

INTRODUCTION

The present-day photosynthetic bacteria are mostly anaerobic and do not release oxygen in photosynthesis. We can only speculate as to whether the development of oxygen-releasing photosynthesis was directly correlated with the evolution of chlorophyll a and β-carotene. In any case, these two pigments are unknown in bacteria and are characteristic of all other photosynthetic groups; and oxygen is a normal by-product of photosynthesis among all photosynthetic organisms except bacteria. Most of these organisms also have additional chlorophylls and additional carotenoid pigments, but chlorophyll a is normally the principal chlorophyll, and β-carotene the principal carotene.

BLUE-GREEN ALGAE

The blue-green algae (Cyanophyceae) are an early offshoot from the main line of photosynthetic organisms, before a highly organized nucleus had been developed. The accessory pigments of the Cyanophyceae always include one or two phyco-bilins, which are otherwise known only among the red algae (Rhodophyta) and some of the Cryptophyceae. Phycobilin pigments are water-soluble, proteinaceous compounds, quite unlike the carotenoid pigments and chlorophylls, which are fat-soluble. The fossil record, as far as it can be deciphered, carries both the blue-green algae and the bacteria well into pre-Cambrian time, and well beyond any other groups of plants or animals.

RED ALGAE

The red algae (Rhodophyta) are apparently derived from the blue-green algae. The two groups are alike in having phycobilin pigments. They are also similar in the complete absence of flagellated cells. Furthermore, floridean starch, the characteristic carbohydrate reserve of the red algae, is chemically allied to cyanophycean starch, the characteristic carbohydrate reserve of the blue-green algae. Both these compounds are similar to glycogen and the amylopectin fraction of ordinary starch.

The red algae differ from the blue-green algae in the presence of a definite nucleus, in having definite plastids, in having chlorophyll d in addition to chlorophyll a, in the usually more complex structure of the thallus, and in being usually sexual, often with a very complex life cycle. All these features may be regarded as evolutionary advances over the condition in the blue-green algae. The sexual processes in the red algae are so different from those in other algae that a separate origin of sexuality in the red algae seems quite possible; at least the sexuality of the red algae and of other algae may have independent origins in the parasexuality of the bacteria.

In having nuclei and plastids, the red algae resemble the other groups of algae rather than the blue-greens, but these characters are such obvious steps in an evolutionary ascent that they do not carry much weight as indicators of relationship. Even if plastids and proper nuclei were considered to have arisen only once, the divergence of the red algae from the remainder of the group must have occurred barely above the level of the Cyanophyceae.

The Florideophyceae are the more advanced of the two classes of red algae, and, if only this class were known, the relationships of the group might be questionable. The Bangiophyceae, however, are less modified, and some of the genera, which have blue-green chloroplasts and lack a sexual process and a central vacuole, are very suggestive of the Cyanophyceae. Some of these genera which recall the blue-green algae occur in fresh water. The evidence suggests that blue-green algae are ancestral to the Bangiophyceae, and that the Florideophyceae are derived from the Bangiophyceae.

The origin of the Bangiophyceae from the Cyanophyceae must have occurred well before the Cambrian period, and probably in fresh water, either inland or perhaps while the ocean still had relatively little salt. The Florideophyceae probably developed by or before the Ordovician period. By Triassic time, if not before, the Florideophyceae had probably come to dominate the offshore flora of the warmer parts of the ocean, as they continue to do today.

Flagellated Groups

Flagella in all flagellated organisms except bacteria have the same basic structure, with generally nine peripheral strands surrounding a two-strand core. Bacteria, on the contrary, characteristically have flagella consisting of single strands, although there are some species with clustered flagella which suggest how the eleven-strand flagellum of other organisms may have originated.

The green algae (Chlorophyceae) and the blue-green algae evidently had a common ancestor which had flagella and nucleus and food reserves of the bacterial type, but which differed from the bacteria in having chlorophyll *a* and β-carotene. The development of a typical nucleus, of the characteristic eleven-strand flagellum, and of starch as the reserve food completed the transition to the green algae. These changes apparently all occurred in pre-Cambrian time, possibly before the sea became very salty. By the Cambrian period, types of green algae with a relatively complex thallus had been produced, and by the Devonian period, the highly specialized charoids made their appearance. Doubtless the abundance of green algae in streams and lakes dates from pre-Cambrian time.

We have noted that all flagellates have flagella of the same basic structure; there are, however, three minor variations on the general plan. The simplest type, usually called the whiplash type, lacks appendages of any sort, although the two central strands usually extend out beyond the nine peripheral ones. A second type, the pectinate type, has a single row of slender, spreading appendages. The third type, the pinnate type, has two rows of appendages, one on each side. The term *tinsel flagellum* is commonly applied to both the pectinate and the pinnate types. The tinsel flagellum is a more effective locomotor organ than the whiplash flagellum, which is presumably the ancestral type.

Excluding the Cyanophyceae and Rhodophyta, which form another line of development, the Chlorophyceae are the most primitive class of algae, from which the other types are thought to be derived. The flagella of the Chlorophyceae, whether of motile gametes, motile spores, or motile vegetative cells, are characteristically equal and of the whiplash type. Flagellated cells of other groups of algae, except the Charophyceae, generally have some or all of the flagella of the tinsel type; very often a single cell has two dissimilar flagella, one whiplash and one tinsel. The familiar chlorophycean genus *Chlamydomonas*, with its large, solitary chloroplast and two equal whiplash flagella, may well be the most primitive existing flagellate, not very much different from the hypothetical common ancestor of all existing flagellates.

If the relationships and origin of green algae, as here postulated, are correct, the possession of a cell wall is a primitive character among the flagellates, and its absence secondary. The Schizophyta, from which the Chlorophyceae are considered to be derived, characteristically have a cell wall, except for some special groups, such as the spirochaetes and the slime bacteria; all the photosynthetic bacteria have cell walls. Although the bacterial cell wall is usually nitrogenous, the chemical composition varies a great deal in different kinds of bacteria, and polysaccharides are often included. A few bacteria produce cellulose, which is also a regular constituent of the walls of the Cyanophyceae, and which is a principal constituent of the walls of green algae and most of their descendants.

An evolutionary pattern for the algal flagellates which fits the available evidence would be as follows: Chlorophycean flagellates such as *Chlamydomonas* (Fig. 9.1), with all flagella of the whiplash type, are the most primitive group. The develop-ment of a row of appendages on the flagellum, converting it into a more effective swimming organ, may have occurred only once. The euglenoids diverged from this line while the appendages were restricted to a single row, and before any significant change in the pigmentation had occurred. The gullet of the euglenoids is foreshadowed by the apical indentation around the flagella of a few green algae.

The next significant step in the evolution of the remaining group was a shift in the proportions of photosynthetic pigments, to more carotenoids and less chlorophyll, along with the development of some new kinds of carotenoids and chlorophylls. The number of flagella was stabilized at two, one whiplash and one tinsel, and the apical indentation was modified into a longitudinal ventral groove. The Pyrrophytan line diverged just after these steps, tending to retain the cellulose wall and starch-food reserves of their chlorophycean ancestors. The Cryptophyceae often retain the gullet as well as the ventral groove; the Desmophyceae tend to lose the groove altogether; in the Dinophyceae, the groove takes on a spiral and finally transverse orientation.

The next step in the evolution of the remaining group (after the divergence of the Pyrrophytan line) was the development of a second row of appendages on the tinsel flagellum, converting it to the pinnate type. Soon after this step other products were substituted for starch as food reserves.

The group then divided into two lines. One line retained cellulose as a principal wall constituent and went on to produce many multicellular plants. These are the brown algae. The other line dispensed with cellulose as a wall constituent, retaining the pectic compounds and eventually adding silica, and also dividing the cell wall into two overlapping halves. This line, which became the Chrysophyta, produced many unicellular algae, but only a few small multicellular ones. The longitudinal ventral furrow of the flagellated cells was soon eliminated in the Chrysophytan line, although the chloromonads (the least modified segment of the group) retained it. In the Phaeophytan line the furrow was modified into a broad, shallow depression by reduction of one of the flanks, and this change was associated with the change of position of the flagella from ventrally subterminal to lateral.

In all probability the major groups of flagellates were established well before the Cambrian period, and the ocean was teeming with microscopic algae then as now. The diatoms, now such a dominant part of the plankton in the cooler parts of the ocean, did not attain any importance until the Cretaceous period, although they may well have originated somewhat earlier. Characteristic types of brown algae evidently originated early in the Paleozoic era, as indicated by fossils, and probably the tidal and offshore zones in the cooler parts of the world have had much the same aspect from that time to the present, being largely dominated by brown algae.

FUNGI

The fungi appear to be derived from unicellular flagellates of Chrysophytan type, either directly or conceivably through filamentous algae similar to some of the modern Xanthophyceae. This conclusion is based largely on comparative morphology, in the absence of any significant fossil evidence.

The Phycomycetes seem to be the most primitive group of fungi, and it is this group which shows up first in the scanty fossil record. Psilophyte fossils from the Rhynie beds of Devonian age are accompanied and penetrated by fossils of coenocytic, filamentous fungi which probably represent Phycomycetes. Carboniferous and later deposits also bear occasional fossils of apparent Phycomycetes.

The Myxomycetes, if they are related to the true fungi at all, must be derived from primitive Phycomycetes or pre-Phycomycetes. The origin of the Myxomycetes may well antedate the Devonian period, but they are even less subject to fossilization than other fungi, and the fossil record is practically a blank.

The Ascomycetes probably originated from the Phycomycetes by postponement of karyogamy after plasmogamy, associated with the development of a specialized sexual sporangium, the ascus. Fossil leaves of Carboniferous and later plants sometimes have small spots resembling the fruiting bodies of powdery mildews and other Ascomycetes.

Evidence from comparative morphology suggests that the Basidiomycetes originated from the Ascomycetes by modification of the ascus into a basidium, associated with a further elaboration of the dicaryotic stage (between plasmogamy and karyogamy) in the life cycle. Here again the fossil evidence, though scanty, falls into line. Leaf spots resembling the aecial, uredinial, and telial sori of rusts occur on many fossils of Cretaceous and later age, and only doubtfully in the Carboniferous.

EMBRYOPHYTES

INTRODUCTION

Life evidently originated in the water, and adaptation to a land habitat has not been easy. The bacteria, although many of them occur on land, are still essentially aquatic. They are vegetatively active only when covered with water, but they are so small that they need only a thin film of water, which is resistant to evaporation. The algae are also mostly aquatic, although some species occur on dry land. Even the terrestrial species usually do better when the air is moist enough to permit a film of water to cover them, and they generally go into dormancy in dry weather. The fungi are mostly terrestrial rather than aquatic, but most of them still require a film of water around the individual vegetative hyphae; it is chiefly the fruiting bodies that are really aerial.

Only one group of plants, the embryophytes, has become really adapted to life on land, with aerial vegetative organs. The evolutionary history of the embryophytes is largely a story of increasing adaptation to the land, and the embryophytes are often loosely called the Land Plants.

Cambrian and Silurian deposits contain a few scattered fossils of probable land plants. Except for some lycopods and psilophytes toward the end of the Silurian, these fossils are not clearly identifiable with any of the recognized divisions. Some of them look suspiciously like brown algae, and it is conceivable that the brown algae did give rise to a temporary terrestrial line. There is ample reason to exclude the brown algae as potential ancestors of modern land plants, however; the pigmentation, food reserves, and flagellar structure all point to the green algae instead. Some of the Cambrian and Silurian fossils may be transitional between the green algae and the embryophytes, but this is not at all clear. There may even have been several groups of primitive land plants, derived from different groups of algae; if so, all but one line died out. All land-plant fossils from the Devonian period to the present (excluding fungi and terrestrial algae) are apparently embryophytes, with a common ancestry in the green algae. Some of the more complex of the present-day green algae, with similar gametophyte and sporophyte generations, may be similar to the forms which gave rise to the embryophytes.

The primitive embryophyte is now widely believed to have had similar gametophyte and sporophyte generations, and from this type evolution has proceeded in two directions. In one line the sporophyte became essentially parasitic on the gametophyte, losing much or all of its photosynthetic capacity and coming to be scarcely more than a stage in the reproduction of the gametophyte. The bryophytes represent this line of development. In the other line the sporophyte became the dominant generation, and the gametophyte was reduced, eventually becoming merely a step in the reproduction of the sporophyte. The vascular plants represent this line of development.

The characteristic stomates of the vascular plants evidently originated before the divergence of the bryophyte line from the vascular-plant line, at a time when the sporophyte had an important photosynthetic function, inasmuch as stomates are now found on the sporophytes of many bryophytes, in which they have only minor (or no) functional significance.

BRYOPHYTES

The divergence of the bryophyte line from the vascular-plant line may have occurred as early as the Cambrian or Ordovician period, inasmuch as characteristic vascular plants are known from Silurian deposits and had become common by the

Devonian. Fossils clearly identifiable as bryophytes are not known from rocks earlier than the Upper Devonian; however, because of their soft texture they are so seldom preserved, as compared to other fossils, that their apparent absence from earlier deposits may not be significant. Differentiation of the three classes of bryophytes from each other may have proceeded more slowly, however; some fossils of Triassic and Jurassic age may be intermediate between the Musci and Hepaticae, although more characteristic members of the two groups can be identified in Upper Carboniferous deposits.

PALEOZOIC VASCULAR PLANTS

In the vascular-plant line, increase in size of the sporophyte was associated with the development of a conducting system: xylem and phloem. The earliest vascular plants may well have been similar to the fossil *Rhynia*, in which the sporophyte consists of a dichotomously branching axis with a horizontal basal part and an erect terminal part, the sporangia being terminal on the branches. Plants of this general nature had evolved by the Silurian period, although *Rhynia* itself, the best example of the type, is known only from the Devonian.

Evolution from primitive psilophytes, such as *Rhynia*, apparently followed five main lines: one of these lines developed with relatively little change into the modern psilophytes. The others developed into (1) the Lepidophyta, (2) the Calamophyta, (3) the Coniferophyta, and (4) the Filicophyta, Cycadophyta, and Anthophyta. The basic changes in the structure and position of vegetative and reproductive parts incident to the evolution of the Lepidophyta, Calamophyta, and Filicophyta

Fig. 36.2. Reconstruction of *Lepidodendron*, a Carboniferous lepidophyte. (Photo courtesy of the Chicago Natural History Museum.)

are shown diagrammatically in Fig. 20.4.

The land vegetation of the early part of the Devonian period was dominated by psilophytes and to a lesser extent by club mosses. By the middle of the Devonian period, the psilophytes began to be replaced by forms transitional to the ferns, calamophytes, and Cordaitales, while the lepidophytes continued with increasing vigor. Toward the end of the Devonian, the psilophytes apparently died out, except for an insignificant fragment which has continued, without fossil record, to the present time, being represented now by only three living species.

Trees belonging to the lepidophytes, calamophytes, and the cordaitalean group of preconifers dominated the lush, luxuriant vegetation of the extensive swamps and other lowlands during the Carboniferous period, especially the Upper Carboniferous (Fig. 36.3). Ferns and seed ferns were also a prominent part of the landscape, and the smaller members of the lepidophytes and calamophytes likewise flourished. The Carboniferous period, especially the Upper Carboniferous, is the great coal age. Masses of dead vegetation accumulated in the lowlands faster than

Fig. 36.3. Reconstruction of a swamp forest of Carboniferous age. (Photo courtesy of the Chicago Natural History Museum.)

they decayed, and some of the deposits later changed into coal.

The Permian period witnessed the decline of the groups which dominated the Carboniferous landscape. The Lepidodendrales and Calamitales, representing the arborescent members of the Lepidophyta and Calamophyta, disappeared completely. The herbaceous members of these divisions persisted, and a remnant survives to this day, but these were not very important constituents of the vegetation, then or later. The seed ferns and Cordaitales dwindled, although both groups survived into the Mesozoic era. The angiosperms may have arisen from the seed ferns in uplands during the Permian period, although there are no fossils to support this speculation.

The changes in vegetation during the Permian period were associated with drastic climatic changes. The great coal swamps disappeared, and there were extensive arid uplands. In the Southern Hemisphere, there was a severe glaciation during part of the period. Permian plants in general have smaller, more leathery, and more heavily cutinized leaves than their Carboniferous ancestors. The conifers and the first clearly identifiable ancestors of the ginkgo made their appearance in the Permian period.

A very specialized flora, the *Glossopteris* flora, originated in the Southern Hemisphere during the Permian glaciation and persisted for some time thereafter. *Glossopteris* (Fig. 36.4), the most characteristic member of the flora, has simple, entire, linear or spatulate to elliptic or ovate leaves often several inches long, attached apparently to a rhizome. It is thought to be a seed fern, but its reproductive structures have not been surely identified. The similarity of the *Glossopteris* flora in such now widely separated areas as Australia, India, South Africa, and southern South America, strengthens the hypothesis held by many students that these areas were parts of a single large continent, Gondwanaland, until the close of the Paleozoic era.

Triassic and Jurassic Vascular Plants

The development of the characteristically xerophytic vegetation which was well started in the Permian period continued into the Triassic and reached its climax in the Jurassic. Three groups (the Cycadales, Bennettitales, and Caytoniales) derived from the seed ferns made their appearance in the Triassic and culminated in the Jurassic, while the seed ferns themselves dwindled and disappeared. The Cycadales and especially the Bennettitales (cycadeoids) were so abundant and varied during the Jurrasic that this period is often called the Age of Cycads. The Ginkgoales also reached their greatest development during the Jurassic period. Great forests of conifers with wood resembling the modern genus *Araucaria* existed during the Triassic and Jurassic periods

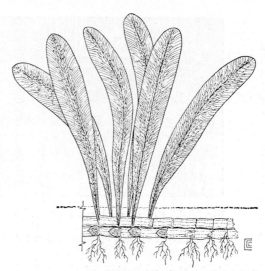

Fig. 36.4.   Reconstruction of *Glossopteris*. (X¼.)

(Fig. 36.5), and coniferous forests have continued to cover extensive areas to the present time. The conifers are evidently the direct descendants of the Paleozoic Cordaitales, and the distinction between the two groups is not easily drawn. Ferns continued to play a significant but subsidi-

Fig. 36.5.   Petrified trunks of *Araucaria*-like trees of Triassic age in Arizona. (Photo courtesy of the U.S. Natural Museum.)

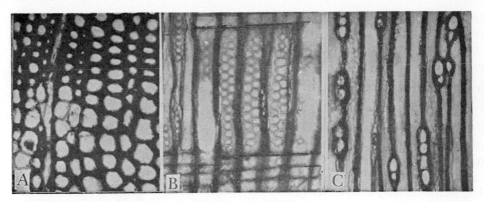

Fig. 36.6. Cross, radial, and tangential sections of petrified conifer (or Cordaitean?) wood of Triassic age from Arizona. (Photo by Lyman H. Dougherty. From Transeau, Sampson, and Tiffany, *Textbook of Botany*, Rev. Ed., Harper, 1953.)

ary role in the vegetation of the Triassic and Jurassic periods, as they have done in all periods from the Carboniferous to the present.

ANGIOSPERMS

The Cretaceous period witnessed another great vegetational change, with the angiosperms blossoming out as the dominant land flora. A few pollen grains and vegetative fragments from Jurassic deposits are apparently angiospermous, but it is not until the beginning of the Cretaceous that unmistakable angiosperm fossils are regularly found. By the middle of the Cretaceous period, the angiosperms had become the principle land vegetation, and many modern arborescent genera apparently extend all the way back to the Upper Cretaceous.

The Cretaceous angiosperms, as far as is known, were mostly trees. It is generally believed that herbaceous angiosperms have woody ancestors, and that the change has occurred independently in a number of different groups, although opinion is not unanimous. The herbaceous groups do not begin to be prominent in the fossil record until the Oligocene and Miocene periods. Bees, which are such important pollinators, especially of many herbs, also made their first appearance in the Oligocene, although beetles and some other groups of insects are much more ancient. By late Miocene time the vegetation must have had an essentially modern aspect. Many species, some genera, and probably a few families have originated since the Miocene period, but these changes are minor compared to those which preceded them.

The great climatic changes of the Pleistocene period, with its recurrent glacial and interglacial epochs, caused equally great changes in the distribution of species and whole floras in temperate and cold regions, but the evolutionary effects of these changes were mostly at the specific level. There is no evidence that large numbers of new orders, families, or even genera of angiosperms originated as a result of these stresses. The Pyrenees-Alps mountain area effectively prevented the plants of western Europe from migrating southward as the ice sheets advanced upon them, and the present flora of this region is notably poor in comparison to that of North America, where the north-south orientation of the major mountain ranges interposed no such barrier to migration. There is no reason to suppose that the aspect of the vegetation of North America was much different 500 years ago (before European colonization) from that of times with comparable climate during the most recent interglacial period.

The climate of the Tertiary period (Paleocene through Pliocene) was evidently milder than that of the present, and a large angiospermous forest apparently occupied a broad boreal belt in North America and Eurasia. This Arcto-Tertiary forest, as it is called, was broken up by the Pleistocene glaciation. Some remarkable similarities in the forest species of the unglaciated parts of eastern North America and eastern Asia, first commented on in 1859 by the American botanist Asa Gray, reflect the survival of remnants of the Arcto-Tertiary forest in these areas.

The origin of the angiosperms was an "abominable mystery" to Charles Darwin and remains hardly less so to botanists today. The Coniferae, Cordaitales, Chlamydospermae, Bennettitales, and Caytoniales have been suggested and discarded as possible ancestors. The seed ferns are the only gymnosperms without serious drawbacks as potential ancestors of the angiosperms, and even here the evidence is not at all clear. No fossils now known effectively connect the angiosperms to the seed ferns or any other group of plants. There is a considerable concentration of primitive genera and families of angiosperms in the Malaysian region, and there are excellent morphological reasons for considering the angiosperms to be origi-

Fig. 36.7. Fossil angiosperms. Main figure: *Fagopsis*, a breech-like fossil of Tertiary age from Colorado. (New York Botanical Garden photo.) Inset: A flower of Oligocene age from Montana. (Photo courtesy of Herman F. Becker.)

nally tropical. When the tropical regions are as well explored for fossils as the temperate and boreal regions, the "abominable mystery" may be solved.

EVOLUTIONARY PATTERN

The phylogeny of the land plants, especially the vascular plants, is a story of increasing adaptation to a land habitat. The development of a vascular system is obviously necessary if the plant is to rise more than a few inches above the ground. Stomates are also essential, permitting the exchange of gases necessary for photosynthesis in internal tissues, without allowing too much evaporation during periods of water shortage. The differentiation of an original dichotomously branching axis into roots, stems, and leaves with particular functions in the economy of the plant is a further adaptation to the environment.

The gametophyte, with none of the special adaptations of the sporophyte, is progressively reduced and is at first earthbound. The differentiation of the gametophytes into males and females, a specialization which ensures cross-fertilization, determines the direction of any further modifications of the gametophyte relating to the land habitat. The female gametophyte, which must provide nourishment for the young sporophyte, cannot be reduced as much as the male gametophyte, which merely needs to produce sperms.

The next important step, after reduction in the male and female gametophytes seems to have reached the limits of efficiency, is the retention of the female gametophyte on the parent sporophyte, and the transfer of the whole male gametophyte (instead of merely the sperms) by wind or other means. The female gametophyte and its associated structures now constitute the seed, and the male gametophyte is the pollen grain. Fertilization no longer depends on a film of free water for the sperms to swim in, and the sperms, not having to swim, lose (phyletically) their flagella. The further reductions which occur in the male, and especially the female, gametophyte may be merely the result of the evolutionary momentum (a form of orthogenesis) of the previously established trend toward reduction, although not all botanists would agree with this interpretation. The enclosure of the seed within the ovary is a protective measure made possible by the fact that the male gametophyte now delivers the sperm to the egg through a pollen tube which absorbs nourishment from the surrounding tissue as it grows.

Another important adaptation to the land habitat, which has been made repeatedly but which has been most effectively exploited by angiosperms, is the xylem vessel. Vessels are much more effective conducting elements than tracheids. A vessel-bearing angiosperm tree growing in the same habitat as a vessel-less conifer provides a more reliable supply of water to the leaves, especially during periods of high evaporation, enabling the angiosperm to make fuller use of the environmental resources by lessening the need for xerophytic adaptations which restrict such exploitation.

SUGGESTED READING

Anderson, Edgar, *Introgressive Hybridization*, John Wiley & Sons, New York, 1949, 109 pp. A clear and forthright presentation of hybridization as a factor in plant taxonomy and evolution.

Clausen, Jens, David D. Keck, and William M. Hiesey, Experimental studies on the nature of species. I. Effect of varied environments on Western North American plants, *Carnegie Inst. Wash. Publ. 520.* Washington, D.C., 1940, 452 pp. A classic study which profoundly influenced taxonomic thought; yet much of it is comprehensible to a general botany student.

Darwin, Charles, *Journal of researches into the geology and natural history of the various countries visited by H.M.S. Beagle,* 1839. Facsimile reprint by Hafner, New York, 1952. Good for browsing.

Eiseley, Loren, *Darwin's Century,* Doubleday, Garden City, New York, 1958, 378 pp. The background of the evolutionary concept.

Well done, neither written down nor excessively technical.

Oparin, A. I., *The Origin of Life on the Earth* (Trans. Ann Synge), Academic Press, New York, 1957, 495 pp. Much of this thorough exposition and review will be comprehensible to the better student.

Schroedinger, Erwin, *What Is Life?* Cambridge University Press, 1944. For the better student.

Stebbins, G. Ledyard, Jr., *Variation and Evolution in Plants,* Columbia University Press, New York, 1950, 643 pp. A high-level presentation containing much food for thought.

Plant Communities

CHAPTER 37

THE NATURE OF PLANT COMMUNITIES

It is a common observation that certain kinds of plants are likely to grow together. Oak and hickory; spruce and fir; lawn grass and dandelions; beech, maple, and hemlock; buffalo grass (*Buchloe*) and little grama grass (*Bouteloua gracilis*): each of these combinations occurs often enough to catch any observant eye. A little further study shows that certain kinds of shrubs and herbs are likely to be found where oak and hickory grow together; another group occurs with spruce and fir, another group with beech-maple-hemlock, and so on. Thus whole plant communities tend to repeat themselves in similar habitats. Any group of plants occupying a particular habitat at a particular place is called a **plant community**, and every plant in nature belongs to such a community.

It does not require much closer observation to see that certain kinds of animals tend to go with certain plant com-

◀

Timberline tree of limber pine, *Pinus flexilis*, in the Rocky Mountains of Colorado. (Photo by Charles J. Ott, from National Audubon Society.)

munities. In a sagebrush desert, one may expect to find jackrabbits, ground squirrels, and possibly rattlesnakes, but not snowshoe rabbits, flying squirrels, or alligators. The plants and animals occupying a particular habitat at a particular place make up a **biotic community.**

The organisms of a biotic community influence and are influenced by each other, as well as influencing and being influenced by the physical environment. Many of the shrubs and herbs of the forest floor require shade and could not survive if the trees around them were cut down. The bushy young second-growth forest which harbors a large population of deer will support only a much smaller number when the trees grow taller and there is less forage within reach.

The animal part of a natural biotic community is largely governed by the plant part, rather than the reverse. The animals depend directly or indirectly on the plants for food and cannot live without them. The plants, on the other hand, make their own food from raw materials drawn from the soil and the air. The total volume of vegetable material in a biotic community is ordinarily much greater than the volume of animal material, so that it is the plants which dominate the scene. The animals, moreover, are motile; within limits, they can directly select the habitat most suitable for them. For all these reasons it is possible (and in botanical circles customary) to consider plant communities as such, with only secondary, if any, attention to the animals.

The animals, of course, do have some effect on the nature of the plant community. Even aside from the influence of man, grazing and browsing animals can have an important influence; many kinds of flowering plants depend on insects for pollination; birds, squirrels, and parasites eat many seeds that might otherwise find a place to germinate, etc. A full understanding of the plant community, therefore, requires a consideration of the animals. Still, the **biotic** factors (other than competition among the plants themselves) generally exert less obvious control over natural plant communities than the **climatic** or even the **edaphic** (soil) **factors.**

Just as it is true that certain kinds of plants repeatedly occur together, so is it also true that no two plant communities are ever exactly alike in the species represented and the proportions in which they occur. The more carefully two similar communities are analyzed, the more differences are likely to be found between them. Each species in the community has its own geographic limits and ecological amplitude, which do not exactly match those of any other species. Since the environment of two different plant communities is never the same in all details, each community differs to a greater or lesser degree from all others.

The transition from one plant community to the next may be gradual or abrupt, and the boundary zone between them (called the **ecotone**) is correspondingly broad or narrow. The ecotone is especially likely to be narrow when the two communities are of different growth habit, as a forest and a grassland, or when there is an abrupt change in the habitat, as at the shore of a lake. On the other hand, when the environmental change is gradual, and when the two communities are of similar habit (e.g., two grassland communities, or two coniferous forest communities) the ecotone may be very broad indeed.

The ecotone is a tension zone between two communities. Just as the last straw broke the camel's back, so may a slight environmental change in the ecotone have a great effect, causing one community to give way to another. Climatic changes, even slight ones, in an ecotone region may shift the position of the ecotone as one community expands into an area previously occupied by another.

The Lawn as a Plant Community

A lawn may be taken as an example of a plant community with which the student may be familiar. Many of the environmental factors governing the lawn are under human rather than natural control, but the essential principles of competition and response to environmental factors are the same as in natural communities.

Our lawn, being reasonably well kept, consists principally of bluegrass (*Poa pratensis*), with an admixture of white clover (*Trifolium repens*). If we were naming it in the same way as we often do natural communities, we would call it a bluegrass-clover community.

In the spring the lawn begins to grow vigorously and needs to be mowed frequently. One notices that this year the clover is especially abundant in a sloping area where water runs off the driveway. Obviously there has been excessive leaching of nitrogen here, and the clover, which harbors nitrogen-fixing bacteria in its roots, has begun to crowd out the grass. In another year or so, at this rate, the clover will replace the grass in that spot completely and will begin to gain in the rest of the lawn too. So we apply fertilizer, being especially generous where the clover is most abundant. Since we are interested in vegetative growth, we use a fertilizer that is high in nitrogen, shying away from high-phosphate fertilizers, such as bone meal, that encourage flowering and fruiting.

Early in the summer some seedlings of Norway maple come up in the lawn, the winged fruits having blown in from some trees across the street. There are even one or two silver maples among them. The next block has a row of silver maples on it, and we remember learning in general botany that *the number of seeds migrating to any given distance varies inversely with the square of the distance.* The maple seedlings soon get clipped off by the lawnmower and die. Without some such lethal factor as the lawnmower, these and other seedlings of woody plants would grow up in a few years to form a forest that would cut off so much light that the lawn would die out. Exactly this same sort of competition for light occurs in nature. If the climate is moist enough to support tree growth, grasses are shaded out and play only a minor role in the community, unless some special factor operates against the trees.

As summer comes on and the weather gets warmer, the bluegrass grows more slowly and does not need mowing so often. Then we begin to notice here and there some grass sprigs with broader, paler leaves among the deep green we have been so proud of. Crab grass! This is a late-starting annual which grows vigorously all summer, especially if there is plenty of moisture. It will spread by stolons along the top of the ground, covering the bluegrass and starving it for light, if allowed to continue.

Laziness tempts us to hope that if we just stop watering the lawn all will be well. After all, bluegrass goes dormant in the summer anyway, given half a chance, and then greens up again for fall. Our neighbor, whose lawn goes brown in summer from lack of water, doesn't seem to have crab-grass trouble. But then we remember the park lawn, a few blocks away, where this policy has been in effect for twenty years. Old-timers tell us that it used to be a good lawn, too. But each year it had a little more crab grass, until now nothing else is left in the open places. It is green in the summer, and dead gray-brown all fall, winter, and spring. True, there is bluegrass under the scattered trees in the park, so in summer the lawn is green in the open and brown under the trees, and in the spring and fall it is brown in the open and green under the trees. Obviously bluegrass stands shade better than crab grass, but even bluegrass doesn't like it very well, and the turf under the trees is pretty skimpy. If the trees were clustered instead of scattered, so that light didn't get in from the side, the bluegrass would be shaded out, too.

But we are proud of our lawn, and we want it to be green all summer, as well as spring and fall, and we want it to be that way year after year. So we continue to water it, and we set the mower up a bit, to leave the grass longer so that the hot sun does not get through to the ground and parch it. We also get down on our knees and pull crab grass. Naturally we work hardest on the front lawn, which everybody can see, and here our efforts are enough. Not only does it stay green, but when fall rolls around there is hardly a blade of crab grass in it. Now the grass starts to grow vigorously again, and we set the mower back down to cut more closely and stimulate growth and branching. The front lawn has survived another season and will be in good shape next spring after its winter dormancy.

The back lawn is another matter. Somehow, after the front lawn was weeded, there never seemed to be enough time to take proper care of the back lawn. We did water it, and it stayed green, but by late summer there are big, spreading patches of crab grass. Under the crab grass, the bluegrass looks pretty sick but is perhaps not yet dead. So, late in the summer, with the weather still warm and the crab grass spreading wildly, we apply a chemical advertised as a crab-grass killer. We worry about this a bit, for we know that it is poisonous to bluegrass too, and part of its greater effect on crab grass is due merely to the fact that at this time the crab grass is growing faster than the bluegrass. With a little bit of luck, the recommended dosage turns out to be all right, and the crab grass turns yellow and dies. The bluegrass, wonder of wonders, is not yet dead, and, as the weather turns cooler, it comes back and fills in where the crab grass has been. Only a few little bare patches remain to be reseeded, but it was a close call, and we resolve to do better in the future. Perhaps next spring we shall try one of the chemicals which inhibits seed germination, and maybe the crab grass problem will be licked.

There were, of course, a few other weeds in the lawn besides crab grass, mainly dandelions and plantain. These have broad leaves which shade out the grass but lie so close to the ground that the mower misses them. Fortunately there were not very many, and the individual plants don't spread like crab grass, so we were able to keep them down by digging them out. If we ever decide to do without the clover in the lawn, we may try 2,4-D on these dicot weeds. This auxin-like chemical is much harder on most dicots than on monocots such as grasses, and we shall have to be careful not to let any of it drift onto our flowers, or into the neighbors' gardens.

From this not wholly whimsical account of some problems involved in the maintenance of a lawn, one can see that the continued existence of a particular plant community requires a delicately balanced set of environmental factors. A change in one factor favors one or more species in the community at the expense of others, and a change in some other factor favors some other species. Similar environments call forth similar plant communities, but just as no two areas ever have exactly the same environment, so are no two communities exactly alike. Individual kinds of communities may be defined as broadly or as narrowly as one wishes. All lawns may be considered as one type of community, or all bluegrass lawns, or our front lawn may be classified as different from our back lawn. Communities thus vary in size from a few square feet, or even less, to hundreds of thousands of square miles; they may be of any shape, and there may be one or many examples of a particular kind, depending on the breadth of the definition and the geographic extent or recurrence of the necessary environmental conditions.

PLANT SUCCESSION AND THE CLIMAX

PRINCIPLES

All plant communities are transitory, in terms of geologic time. Most of Canada and much of the northern United States, as well as northern Eurasia, were covered with ice only a few thousand years ago, just as the interior of Greenland is covered with ice today. There were, in fact, alternating glacial and interglacial periods during Pleistocene time, and we have no

assurance that another glaciation is not in prospect. Even the areas too far south to be glaciated have undergone great climatic changes through the ages, with corresponding changes in the vegetation. Organic evolution also affects the composition of plant communities. Many land habitats available during the Paleozoic era must have been similar to habitats existing today, but their vegetation was very different, because the angiosperms had not yet come into existence.

When time is considered in terms of decades or centuries, some plant communities are stable, perpetuating themselves indefinitely without significant change, while others are transitory, giving way to a succession of other communities before a relative stability is achieved. Even the most stable communities are actually in a delicately balanced and constantly shifting near-equilibrium, as old organisms die and are replaced by new ones. The weather is never quite the same for two years in a row, and these year-to-year differences favor first some, then other, elements of the community.

Replacement of one plant community by another on the same site with the passage of time has been observed by many people throughout past ages. The first man to observe and report an orderly, predictable succession leading to a stable community was apparently Anton Kerner (1831–1898), an Austrian botanist whose paper in 1863 on the vegetation of the Danube basin is a neglected landmark of botany. Kerner's concepts of plant succession were adopted by some of his European contemporaries and successors, but it remained for two American botanists, Henry C. Cowles (1869–1939) and Frederic E. Clements (1874–1945) to bring them to full flower. Cowles' study (1899) of the vegetation of

Fig. 37.1. Anton Kerner (1831–1909), Austrian botanist, father of the climax concept. (New York Botanical Garden photo.)

the sand dunes along Lake Michigan greatly influenced botanical thought, especially in America, and helped to inspire Clements to develop the concept of the regional **climax**, the climatically determined, stable vegetation type toward which all successional types in a region lead.

Plant succession is most conspicuous and most easily observed when a bare area is newly made available for plant colonization. On dry land this happens after retreat of a glacier, after volcanism, after severe fire, and when a fallow field is abandoned. In water it happens when a lake or pond is formed behind a natural or man-made dam. A series of plant communities starting on dry land (especially on bare rock) is known as a **xerosere**, or **xerarch succession**, and one starting in water is a **hydrosere**, or **hydrarch succession**. In each

case the habitat becomes progressively more mesic during the course of the succession.

Ideally, the stable plant community achieved after a succession of transitory communities is determined by the climate alone, regardless of the nature of the area when first exposed. Thus all xeroseres and all hydroseres in a given region should lead to the same climatically determined climax vegetation, given sufficient time.

In actuality, various factors commonly intervene to prevent or substantially delay the realization of this theoretical ideal, and there are often two or more apparently stable vegetation types on different soils or on different exposures in the same region. The soil and moisture conditions, and therefore the vegetation, of a flood plain along a river are permanently different from those of the surrounding hills, in terms of human (rather than geologic) time. In regions where moisture is a critical factor, north and east slopes may be forested, while south and west slopes are covered with grass or sagebrush, with a sharp dividing line between the two types along the crest of a ridge.

In the vicinity of Minneapolis, two equally persistent and stable vegetation types (maple-basswood and oak-hickory) occur on soils derived from the two different kinds of glacial drift found in the area. The stony and relatively sterile soil of the "red drift," derived from an ice sheet that came from the northeast, supports oak-hickory forest, whereas the more fertile, calcareous soil of the "gray drift," derived from an ice sheet that came from the northwest, supports maple-basswood forest. Elsewhere the oak-hickory climax is generally more southern, in a warmer, drier climate than the maple-basswood climax, but here the same effect is brought about by edaphic differences which have persisted since the ice age. The climatically determined climax community on each of these soil types has changed more than once since the retreat of the glaciers. As we shall see, the effect of climate ultimately tends to overcome the effect of the parent material in determining the nature of the soil, but here too the ideal situation is not always realized, and the climate itself may change before the effect of the parent material disappears.

XEROSERE

A typical xerosere begins with bare rock and leads to the climax community. The genera and species differ according to the climate and other conditions, but the broad picture is much the same in all climates. Crustose and foliose lichens are ordinarily the first inhabitants of the rock. These pioneers cause corrosion of the rock surface and catch a little dust from the wind. This first stage in the xerosere may last a very long time, especially in dry regions where the lichens must remain dormant for most of the year, growing only during the short periods when water is available.

Eventually disintegration of the rock and accumulation of small particles of debris progress to the point where mosses can get a foothold among the pioneer lichens. Fruticose lichens may become established in the moss mat or among the crustose and foliose lichens. The accumulation of wind-blown dust and the decay of older parts of the plants in the moss mats lead to the formation of a thin layer of soil on the rock surface.

Sooner or later small seed plants, especially annuals, become established in the moss mats, and the thin cover of soil gradually thickens. Then perennial herbs enter the community. In forested regions, the stage with herbs growing in the moss mat is generally followed by a shrub stage, and the shrubs in turn give way to trees. The

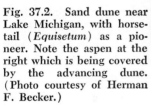

Fig. 37.2. Sand dune near Lake Michigan, with horsetail (*Equisetum*) as a pioneer. Note the aspen at the right which is being covered by the advancing dune. (Photo courtesy of Herman F. Becker.)

first trees may be the climax dominants, or they may be pioneers which later give way to other species before the climax is reached. In drier regions the herb or shrub stage may be final.

The moss mat, which played such a vital role in the earlier stages of succession, is broken up and disappears during the later stages. In the climax community, mosses are largely restricted to special habitats such as the bark of trees, fallen logs, boulders which have not yet succumbed to the soil-building process, etc.

Crevice plants also play a role in many xeroseres. Enough dust and debris may accumulate in a rock crevice, without the intervention of lichens and mosses, to permit the direct establishment of herbs, shrubs, and even trees. These species in turn give way to others as a mantle of soil is built up.

Some plants are especially adapted to talus slopes. In the long view, a talus slope is merely a transitory stage of some xeroseres, but it may last for thousands of years, until the overlooking cliff is worn away and stops adding new rocks to the talus. The stems of talus plants branch freely and sprawl among the rocks, only the tips being assurgent. Any part of the stem which gets covered by the shifting talus sends out adventitious roots and functions as a rhizome, and if the whole stem is covered, the tips grow out to the surface again. Young plants of this type, or those growing in fairly stable talus, may have a well-defined taproot. On less stable slopes, the stems eventually get separated from the taproot, and older plants have a wholly adventitious root system. Many different families contain characteristic talus species. Here, as elsewhere, we see that among the angiosperms adaptation to various habitats occurs *within* the families and genera and does not usually mark large taxonomic groups.

Completion of a xerosere may take from a few decades to many thousands of years, depending on the circumstances. On cliff faces and steep slopes, the early successional stages may be prolonged indefinitely as new bare surfaces continue to be formed by erosion. In general, the process comes to a conclusion most quickly in moist regions, especially if these are also warm.

It will be seen that the critical factor in the xerosere is the formation of soil. The soil is necessary to provide anchorage for the plants and more especially to hold a supply of ground water which the plants can absorb throughout the growing season. As the depth and quality of the soil increase, larger and larger plants invade the habitat, overtopping and crowding out their predecessors. *Each stage in the series prepares the way for the next, bringing about its own downfall.*

HYDROSERE

A hydrosere, or hydrarch succession, starts with open water and leads toward the climax community. All lakes and ponds are transitory; if other forces do not destroy them first, they are sooner or later filled by mineral sediments and organic remains. Given enough time, the former lake surface becomes dry land which supports the climax vegetation.

Several stages in a hydrosere can often be seen as concentric zones around a pond or lake. The deep water in the middle, subject to disturbance by the wind, may support only plankton algae. In shallower water nearer the shore, there is a zone of submerged aquatics, usually with linear or dissected leaves. These plants may be rooted to the bottom, but often they are free-floating, like the bladderwort (*Utricularia*). Shoreward from the submerged aquatics is a zone of aquatics with floating leaves, such as water lilies. These are rooted in the soil at the bottom, and their advance toward the middle of the pond is limited by the depth of the water. Their large leaves shade out the submerged aquatics. Nearest the shore is a zone of emergent aquatics, such as cattails; these overtop and crowd out the floating-leaved aquatics. Moisture-loving shrubs or trees grow along the shore, and on the higher ground behind these is the climax vegetation.

As the sediments and organic remains accumulate in the pond, the water becomes more shallow, and each vegetation zone moves in toward the center. A trench dug along the shore will often disclose, at progressively deeper levels, remains from each of the earlier successional stages.

A special feature of the hydrosere in many lakes of glaciated regions is the sedge mat, with shoots of sedges and other plants growing out of a densely tangled mat of rhizomes, peat, and debris. The inner margin of the sedge mat floats on the surface of the water, often for a distance of some yards, and encroaches progressively on the open water. A man can walk on the floating part with caution, but he may also break through. Toward the shore, the sedge mat is invaded by bog shrubs, which in turn give way to bog trees. The climax forest follows behind these.

A hydrosere may take from a few decades to many thousands of years, depending on the depth and turbulence of the water, rate of sedimentation, and other factors. A small oxbow lake along the Mississippi may be filled in during the lifetime of a man, but we need not fear an imminent disappearance of Lake Superior.

In the hydrosere, just as in the xerosere, we see that each stage prepares the way for the next, causing its own elimination. This is a characteristic feature of plant successions.

DISTURBANCE AND SECONDARY SUCCESSIONS

The orderly progress of a xerarch or hydrarch succession may be interrupted

Fig. 37.3. **Stages in a hydrosere. Above, a floating sedge mat in Michigan, with yellow water lily (*Nuphar*), a floating-leaved hydrophyte, in the open water. Below, a later stage, in Minnesota, with the pond completely filled in to form a bog that is being invaded by trees. (Photos courtesy of Herman F. Becker.)**

Fig. 37.4. Stages in the old-field succession in New Jersey. Top left, a field one year after being abandoned, dominated by horseweed (*Conyza canadensis*). Bottom left, 3 years after abandonment, the field is dominated by annual and perennial weedy herbs. Above, 8 years after abandonment, the vegetation consists chiefly of perennial herbs, especially grasses and composites, with a few pine seedlings showing. Right, about 70 years after abandonment, the pine forest is decadent and will soon give way to the oak and hickory which form the understory. (Photos by Jack McCormick, American Museum of Natural History; all taken July 27, 1957.)

or reversed by natural or artificial forces, with the vegetation reverting to an earlier successional stage or being wholly destroyed. Agriculture, fire, and overgrazing are three of the most important such disturbing factors. Successions which begin on soil after the natural vegetation has been destroyed are called **secondary successions**,. in contrast to xeroseres and hydroseres, which are **primary successions**.

THE OLD-FIELD SUCCESSION

The old-field succession is a common secondary succession. The first plants to invade an abandoned field are usually annual weeds. Such plants depend on their ability to invade rapidly any soil not already vegetated. They generally produce large amounts of seed and often have especially effective means of distribution. In parts of the southeastern United States, horseweed (*Conyza canadensis*) is a prominent inhabitant of newly abandoned fields. The fruits of horseweed are small and have a tuft of hairs (the pappus, a modified calyx) at one end which helps them to float in the breeze. In drier areas farther west, tumbleweeds, such as Russian thistle (*Salsola kali*), are common first invaders. A full-grown tumbleweed may blow along for miles in the fall, scattering seeds as it goes.

After one to several years, the annual

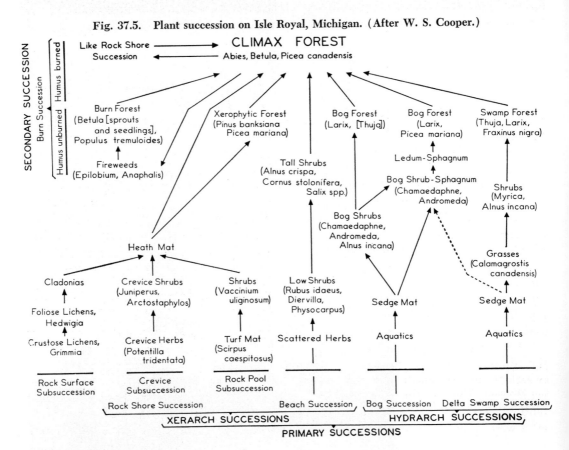

Fig. 37.5.   Plant succession on Isle Royal, Michigan. (After W. S. Cooper.)

weeds begin to give way to perennial herbs. These typically have less effective means of seed distribution but are better competitors than the annuals. The perennial herb invaders in turn give way, usually within a few years, to other plants, either trees, shrubs, or other perennial herbs.

An old-field succession may reach its conclusion in as little as a decade, under the most favorable conditions, or may take more than a century. Establishment of the climax vegetation, whatever it may be, is, of course, hastened if the climax species still persist nearby. Climax species are more noted for their competitive ability than for rapid seed dispersal. The critical factor in the old-field succession, in contrast to the xerosere, is seed dispersal.

FIRE

Fire is one of the most important catastrophic influences on vegetation. Natural fires, set by lightning, have occurred sporadically for millions of years. Furthermore, accidental and intentional fires were as much a product of aboriginal human societies as they are of our modern civilization. In pre-Columbian America, fire doubtless held the boundary between the forest and prairie some distance east of where it would otherwise have been. Likewise in the Congo region the tropical rain forest would extend much farther south, onto present savanna land, had it not been for repeated fires set by the natives.

The effects of fire vary according to the severity of the fire, the nature of the plant community, and the habitat. A severe forest fire may destroy the whole biotic community, and if the soil is thereafter washed away, the area may never (in

Fig. 37.6. Total destruction by fire in Tillamook County, Oregon. (U.S. Forest Service photo by George E. Griffith in 1941, several years after the burn.)

terms of human time) recover. In other circumstances some individuals (or seeds) survive, and the fire favors some elements of the community at the expense of others. In the Rocky Mountains, lodgepole pine (*Pinus contorta* var. *latifolia*) is known as a fire tree, which comes in rapidly after fire, but which eventually gives way to other trees in the absence of fire. The cones of lodgepole pine remain unopened on the tree for many years; they do not burn easily, but the heat of a fire makes them open. The seeds released onto the bare ground after the fire find ideal conditions for their growth, and a new forest of lodgepole pine is established. Other pines are likewise fire trees in much of the southeastern United States.

The great Douglas-fir (*Pseudotsuga menziesii*) forests of the Pacific Northwest owe their existence to fire. Douglas-fir seeds, like those of lodgepole pine, germi-

Fig. 37.7. Results of fire in Colorado. Above, near Long's Peak, aspen and some conifers have come in rapidly. Below, Jackstraw Mountain had scarcely begun to recover in 1953 from a fire of 1872. (Photos courtesy of Herman F. Becker.)

nate best in a mineral soil with little or no humus, and the seedlings do not tolerate shade. Western red cedar (*Thuja plicata*) and western hemlock (*Tsuga heterophylla*) tend to replace the Douglas fir in the absence of fire. Young trees of these species are much more shade-tolerant than Douglas fir, and the seeds germinate well in a soil rich in humus. Douglas fir, having a thicker, more fire-resistant bark than the cedar and hemlock, is more likely to survive a forest fire, and conditions after the fire are more favorable to the germination of its seeds and establishment of its seedlings.

In areas where overgrazing has resulted in increase of sagebrush at the expense of grass, as on the upper Snake River plains of Idaho, the balance may be swung the other way by fire. Fire kills the sagebrush, but most of the grasses survive. By careful management the burned area may then be maintained as productive grassland for many years. Some of the soil blows away before the grasses re-establish themselves, however, and it is not yet certain that the immediate gain in grazing value of the land will not be offset by eventual destruction of the soil if repeated burning becomes necessary to keep the sagebrush down.

Overgrazing has had disastrous effects on much of the range land in the western United States and elsewhere in the world. An early effect of overgrazing is a decrease in abundance of the more palatable plants and an increase in the less palatable ones. More severe or long-continued abuse of the range forces livestock to eat the less palatable plants, including even poisonous ones. The plant cover diminishes, and

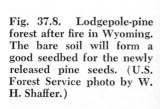

Fig. 37.8. Lodgepole-pine forest after fire in Wyoming. The bare soil will form a good seedbed for the newly released pine seeds. (U.S. Forest Service photo by W. H. Shaffer.)

Fig. 37.9. Results of fire on the upper Snake River plains of Idaho. The area at the left, unburned, is dominated by sagebrush; that at the right has developed a heavy cover of grasses after the sagebrush was burned out. (U.S. Forest Service photo.)

Fig. 37.10. Results of over-grazing. Above, in the Uintah National Forest, Utah; the area to the left of the fence, heavily grazed, supports only small scattered weedy annuals; the fenced area at the right has a dense cover of perennial wheat grass (*Agropyron trachycaulum*). Below, on the upper Snake River plains of Idaho, the ungrazed area at the left has many perennial herbs in addition to the sagebrush. (U.S. Forest Service photos.)

weedy annuals become common. In Clementsian terminology, such a community is called a disclimax.

When the plant cover is diminished or destroyed, rain water tends to run off quickly, instead of sinking in. The periodic floods which are a natural feature of the land are exaggerated, and the streams may dry up in the summer. The water running off the ground carries some of the soil with it, and erosion is thus accelerated. In hilly or mountainous regions, an erosion pavement of pebbles and stones may cover the ground surface after the upper part of the soil is washed away. A torrential rain may then cause a mudflow with a semiliquid mixture of water, dirt, rocks, and large boulders rampaging down a canyon and spilling onto the plain below. Such mudflows caused great damage in parts of Utah and California, especially during the 1930s, forcibly demonstrating the need for grazing control, and stimulating crash programs to restore the vegetation in some areas.

THE CLASSIFICATION OF PLANT COMMUNITIES

PRINCIPLES

The aim of all classification is to help us understand what we know—to relate the known facts to each other in a coherent pattern, so that the whole is actually more than the sum of its parts. A taxonomic classification permits the mere name of a plant to call up a large body of known facts about its structure, functions, and evolutionary relationships; the geographic distribution of similar individuals, the breeding behavior of the plant, and a host of other data may now be available, if the species has been carefully studied. Without the name and classifica-

Fig. 37.11. Results of overgrazing. Above, near Rawlins, Wyoming. Note how the rainwater runs off from this relatively flat, barren land, instead of sinking in. Below, in the Uintah National Forest, Utah; erosion pavement on an open slope. (U.S. Forest Service photos, the upper by D. F. Costello, the lower by I. H. Johnson.)

tion, this information could only be obtained by time-consuming study of each individual plant.

Plant communities are similarly classified so that the name of a community calls up a host of facts. Most ecologists will admit that plant communities are likely to be less sharply and more arbitrarily defined than species, but arbitrary or not, classification is essential to understanding. Some facts that can potentially be called up by such a classification are the general aspect of the community, its stability and place in succession, its floristic composition, and the geographic distribution of similar communities. Even the nature of the climate and soil can be determined with considerable accuracy from the nature of the plant community.

The classification of plant communities has developed along rather different lines in different parts of the world, due both to differences in the nature of the vegetation and to the influence of strong personalities. Reconciliation of the different schools of thought is not easy, and the classification of plant communities is still a very controversial subject.

For several decades after 1900 F. E. Clements dominated ecological thought in America. His great contribution was his emphasis of the climax community as opposed to the seral communities leading up to it, and of the climatically controlled regional climax, as opposed to the special communities in special habitats. In Clementsian ecology, the term *climax* is reserved for a single community in each region (except in mountainous areas with altitudinal zonation), and all other communities are disposed of in a complex series of categories, subclimax, preclimax, postclimax, disclimax, etc. This has the value of emphasizing the controlling nature of climate, and of concentrating attention on the prevailing natural vegetation, but it is misleading because it implies that some very stable communities are merely seral. Clements was so impressed with the myriad complex interactions among the organisms of a community that he compared the whole community to an organism, and its organisms to cells. Such a comparison makes a good simile, but most ecologists now believe that it overstates the case, and that Clements was led into serious error by building too much of his theory on the concept that "the community is an organism." Clements was also so addicted to terminology as to provoke the apocryphal quotation, "I am ready to begin work for the day. Bring me my Greek thesaurus."

Clements' concepts of the monoclimax and the organismic nature of plant communities stirred up considerable opposition, even in his own time. In America this opposition was led by H. A. Gleason (1882–   ), who propounded the individualistic concept of the plant community—i.e., that each species has its own geographic and ecologic limits, that each community differs from every other community, and that the transition between communities, although in some cases sharp, is in other cases very gradual.

The recent trend in America has been toward a synthesis of the seemingly opposite views of Gleason and Clements. Gleason's argument as to the arbitrary nature of much of the classification of communities is accepted, but the need for classification is also recognized, and

Clements' concept of the climatically determined regional climax is accepted as the foundation, or at least the starting point, for a theory of classification. The trend has also been toward a polyclimax rather than a monoclimax interpretation, but this is chiefly a matter of terminology. In monoclimax theory, there is only one true climax community in each region, and this is determined by the climate. A persistent, stable community which because of special local conditions is more xerophytic than the regional climax (such as the oak-hickory forest on the red drift in Minnesota, or such as the relatively xerophytic communities on serpentine barrens in various regions) is called a preclimax; and one which is less xerophytic than the climax (such as the band of trees along a stream in grasslands) is a postclimax. In polyclimax theory, each of these stable types is recognized as a climax, but it is admitted that in any region one of the climax types is usually more abundant than the others.

This approaching synthesis of views is, in fact, welcomed by Gleason, whose published dissents from Clementsian con-

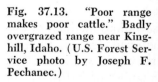

Fig. 37.13. "Poor range makes poor cattle." Badly overgrazed range near Kinghill, Idaho. (U.S. Forest Service photo by Joseph F. Pechanec.)

cepts naturally emphasized the fallacies, as he saw them, of Clementsian ecology, rather than the area of agreement.

In temperate and boreal regions, a few species or genera are usually so common and conspicuous in each community that they dominate its appearance. In America it is customary to name the community in each case for the dominant genera or species. Thus we have the beech-maple-hemlock community in New England, the live-oak–magnolia community in the southeastern United States, and the cedar-hemlock community in the Pacific Northwest. These are, of course, not the only plant communities in their respective regions, but each is a climax community of some importance.

European ecologists tend to define plant communities more narrowly than their American colleagues do. In the Scandinavian region, where a coniferous forest of monotonous sameness dominates much of the landscape, emphasis has been laid on the shrub understory in the forest as a basis for classification. Elsewhere in Europe, especially toward the south, so much of the land is farmed or otherwise occupied by man that the "natural" vegetation occurs mostly in small, scattered patches. Even in these communities, there has been so much disturbance that the original nature of the vegetation is problematical. The climax concept, which has been so useful in America and some other less-developed parts of the world, has therefore scarcely taken root in Europe. Instead the emphasis has been on detailed analyses of narrowly defined communities of limited geographic extent, even a community the size of a small classroom often being considered worthy of attention.

METHODS OF SAMPLING

In a broad-scale ecological reconnaissance, the dominant and otherwise common species may be determined by general observation, without precise sampling techniques. It requires no statistical analysis to show that ponderosa pine dominates the Kaibab plateau in northern Arizona; likewise sagebrush on the Snake River plains of Idaho.

In a more detailed analysis, in which some attention is paid to the floristic composition of the community as well as to the dominant species, some sort of sampling is necessary. Obviously it is not practical to count all the individuals of each species even in relatively small communities.

Small areas selected as samples for detailed study are called **quadrats**. Typically a quadrat is 1 meter square, but other sizes and shapes are sometimes used. A quadrat may even be round, instead of four-sided as the name would imply.

The method of locating quadrats is highly controversial. Should they be subjectively placed in "typical" spots, should they form a regular grid, or should they be mathematically at random? Should a quadrat falling on an obviously unusual spot be moved, or should one rely on a large number of quadrats to balance such abnormalities? Each of these methods has its adherents, and the results vary accordingly.

There are also various methods of taking data from the quadrats. The simplest way is merely to record the species present. More often the number of individuals or the total ground cover of each species is also recorded. For permanent quadrats, which are examined year after year to detect changes in the community, the po-

Fig. 37.14. Changes in vegetation during 38 years, due mainly to a combination of overgrazing and protection from fire. Upper picture taken in southern Arizona in 1903, the lower in 1941 from the same spot. A few small mesquite bushes which have been killed by fire can be seen toward the left of the upper picture. In the lower picture, mesquite is dominant and the grasses form only scattered tufts instead of a dense sod. (U.S. Forest Service photos.)

sition and basal area of each plant may be mapped.

The more the total floristic composition of the community is emphasized (as opposed to the few dominant species), and the more finely the communities are classified, the more important quadrat sampling becomes. It is, therefore, only to be expected that quadrats are more used in Europe than in America, and that their use in America is increasing. They have been used most of all in northern Europe, where the total number of species is small, and where the distinction between similar plant communities has been carried to its greatest extreme. The great Swiss ecologist Josias Braun-Blanquet (1884–   ), who dominated ecological thinking in Europe almost as much as Clements did in America, once referred to some Scandinavian ecologists as *Herren Quadratiker,* a name which some American ecologists might have thought appropriate for Braun-Blanquet and his associates.

Another method of sampling vegetation is to record the plants growing along a **line transect.** The transect can be treated as a very long, narrow quadrat, or as a true line with no width. Line transects are particularly useful in showing the transition from one plant community to another.

The Units of Classification

The broadest category into which plant communities are classified is the **formation.** This is also the category about which there is the most general agreement.

Formations are defined on the basis of the aspect of the vegetation rather than on the floristic composition. The same formation may occur on several continents, with different sets of dominant species in various areas. All arctic tundra land can be referred to a single formation, for example, and all tropical rain forest to another, regardless of the species present. The northern coniferous forest, which stretches around the world just south of the arctic tundra, makes up another formation. There is as yet no generally accepted scheme for classifying the major vegetation types of the world into a definite set of formations, but such a scheme is now nearly within our grasp.

Formations represent climax or near-climax communities, at least by implication. Obviously seral communities, such as the moss-mat stage in a xerosere, are excluded from consideration. A seral community which has advanced far enough so that the dominant species have the same general aspect as those of the climax community is included within the regional formation, however. Thus the deciduous-forest formation of the eastern United States includes seral swamp forests which are dominated by deciduous trees.

Formations are generally divided into **associations,** based on the floristic composition of the communities. There is a great deal of difference of opinion as to how broadly associations should be defined. In America it is customary to use a rather broad definition, based primarily on the dominant species or genera. Thus the deciduous-forest formation includes the maple-basswood association, the beech-maple association, the oak-hickory association, and several others; in each case the association is named and defined on the basis of the characteristic dominant trees.

European ecologists generally define associations more narrowly than their American colleagues do, using the herbs and shrubs of the understory as well as the trees of the forest. There is practically no limit to how finely communities may be classified by taking the whole floristic composition into account, and real agreement on how associations should be defined is not yet in sight.

In Clementsian ecology the term *association* was reserved for the climax community in a monoclimactic scheme, and the term *associes* was used for comparable seral communities. The present tendency is to avoid this distinction and to extend the term *association* to cover seral communities as well. Even the term *association* may be abandoned in favor of the more general term *plant community*, which carries no implication as to seral status, geographic extent, or floristic complexity.

Many European ecologists use a formal binomial nomenclature for plant communities, following Braun-Blanquet. In this system the "generic" name of an asso-

Fig. 37.15. Recovery of land in Mississippi. Upper picture, taken in 1948 by Dan O. Todd, shows an abandoned, eroded field. Lower picture, taken in 1957 after the field had been planted to pines; note also improvement of grass cover in the foreground. (U.S. Forest Service photos.)

ciation is formed by adding *-etum* to the stem of the most characteristic genus of the community, and the "specific epithet" is usually formed by converting into genitive form the specific epithet of the most characteristic species of that genus in the community. Thus a forest characterized by white oak (*Quercus alba*) would be a *Quercetum albae*. The associations may then be classified into groups of higher rank, with the endings *-ion* and *-alis*. A group of Quercetums would make up a Quercion, and a group of Quercions would make up a Quercalis.

The "characteristic" genera and species by which communities are named in the Braun-Blanquet system are not necessarily the most common or conspicuous plants of the community. The consistency of their presence in the community, and their absence from other similar communities, are considered more important.

The Braun-Blanquet system has not been widely accepted by American ecologists, who mostly prefer more broadly defined associations, informally named for the one or few dominant species of the community. Aside from differences of opinion on how broadly or narrowly associations should be defined, the Braun-Blanquet system has been assailed on grammatical, practical, and philosophical grounds. These arguments are perhaps beyond the scope of an elementary text designed for students in a country where the Braun-Blanquet system, important

though it is on the mainland of Europe, has made little headway.

SUGGESTED READING

Gleason, H. A., The vegetational history of the Middle West, *Ann. Assoc. Am. Geographers* 12:39–85. 1923. A classic paper.

———, The individualistic concept of the plant association, *Am. Midl. Nat.* 21:92–110. 1939. An outspoken and highly readable presentation of a point of view.

Graham, Edward H., *Natural Principles of Land Use*, Oxford University Press, London, 1944, 274 pp. Practical ecology.

McCormick, Jack, *The Living Forest*, Harper, New York, 1959, 127 pp. A botanical book so well written that it became a book-club selection.

Storer, John H., *The Web of Life*, Devin-Adair, New York, 1953, 144 pp. A simply written introduction to ecology.

Watts, May T., *Reading the Landscape. An Adventure in Ecology*, Macmillan, New York, 1957, 230 pp. An accurate popular presentation.

CHAPTER 38

Plant Geography

CHAPTER 38

INTRODUCTION

The angiosperms, which dominate most of the land vegetation of the earth, evidently originated as a group of woody plants in moist tropical regions. The tropics still harbor by far the greatest number of genera and species of angiosperms. A great many species, with comparatively few individuals of each, commonly enter into tropical climax communities.

As one travels toward the poles, the number of species in the community tends to decrease, and (short of the most barren tundra) the number of individuals of each species increases. In temperate and boreal regions, it is often possible to pick out only a few species, or even a single species, as the dominants which give the community its essential character.

The most important variable factors in the physical environment of land plants are moisture and temperature. Direct resistance to low temperature is governed primarily by physiological features of the

◄

Vertical zonation of vegetation in Spain. The dominant trees are Scotch pine (*Pinus sylvestris*) below, beech (*Fagus sylvatica*) in the middle, and mountain pine (*Pinus montana*) above (from both above and below the cliffs). (Photo courtesy of José Cuatrecasas.)

protoplasm which find little, if any, expression in the external morphology of the plant. The number of species of land plants that cannot withstand frost is much greater than the number that can, and the decreasing total number of species as one travels away from the tropics is largely a reflection of the difficulty of evolutionary adaptation to low temperature; but frost-resistant plants do not look obviously different as a group from frost-sensitive ones. Temperature does affect the aspect of the vegetation, but the effects may be indirect and are not always immediately obvious.

Adaptation to moisture conditions, in contrast to adaptation to low temperature, commonly does find a morphological expression, although the physiology, of course, is also involved. The size and longevity of the plant, and the size, shape, number, texture, duration, and position of the leaves are all more or less closely correlated with adaptation to moisture conditions. As we have pointed out in Chapter 27, moisture conditions are also influenced by temperature; even winter killing is often due to physiological drought rather than directly to low temperature. The aspect of the natural vegetation provides a good

Fig. 38.1. Recently burned savanna in the Ivory Coast of Africa. (From Pierre Dansereau, *Biogeography*, 1957. Copyright Ronald Press, New York.)

key to moisture conditions, and to some extent also to temperature conditions, in any region.

TYPES OF VEGETATION

Most of the major formations of land vegetation can be classified as **forest, grassland, desert,** or **tundra.** The borders between these types, especially the first three, are not always sharp, and there are transitional types. **Savanna** (Fig. 38.1), with widely scattered trees, is intermediate between forest and grassland.

The tundra vegetation covers arctic and alpine areas that are too cold to permit forest growth. Of course, other factors such as soil and wind enter into the matter, but it is the long, cold winter and the short, cool growing season which put the plants at such a disadvantage that other factors can turn the balance. The nature of tundra vegetation is discussed on pp. 810–813.

Outside the tundra regions, any area with adequate moisture usually supports some kind of forest formation. The potential evaporation, as well as the amount of precipitation, is important in governing the moisture conditions. Even the seasonal distribution and the rate of runoff are significant.

The most generally useful index of moisture conditions is the p/e ratio, in which p is the annual precipitation, and e is the potential annual evaporation from a free water surface. In general, a p/e ratio of about 1 or more will permit forest growth; some semidesert forests, such as the piñon-juniper association in the western United States, thrive at ratios well under 1. In subarctic flatlands, with a low potential evaporation and slow runoff, an annual precipitation of only 10–15 inches will support a dense forest; tropical regions with the same amount of precipitation are deserts.

As the *p/e* ratio decreases, forest gives way to grassland, and the grassland eventually to desert; or the forest may pass directly into the desert. Grassland generally requires not only more moisture than desert, but also a better seasonal distribution; there must be a fair supply of water through a reasonably long growing season.

Desert vegetation consists chiefly of very deep-rooted plants (often shrubs), very shallow-rooted plants (often succulents, such as many cacti) and ephemerals. The deep-rooted plants draw on a moisture supply not available to others; the very shallow-rooted plants can benefit from even the lightest rain but require such potent means of transpiration control as to restrict also the rate of photosynthesis and growth; and the ephemerals complete their life cycle in a few weeks during the most favorable part of the year.

Most grasses require less moisture than most trees, but they are not especially deep-rooted, and they generally lack the special adaptations of desert plants. If a fair amount of moisture is available during the growing season, the grasses blanket the ground and soak up the rain as it falls. They grow faster than the shallow-rooted desert types, and they do not let much moisture sink to the level worked by the deeper-rooted ones. The desert ephemerals are also crowded out, finding no bare ground to get started in. Grasses also do well under moisture conditions suitable for forests, if the trees are kept down by fire or otherwise. Forest and desert communities include some grasses, of course, but not as dominant elements.

We have noted that the climax land vegetation, in regions of adequate moisture and temperature, is generally a forest. In moist, tropical regions without a pronounced dry season, this forest consists of evergreen angiosperms. In tropical regions with alternating wet and dry seasons, the trees typically drop their leaves at the beginning of the dry season. To the northward, winter is in effect a dry season, because the ground water is likely to be frozen and not readily available for absorption. This environmental challenge is likewise met by adoption of the deciduous habit, as long as there is an adequate growing season.

As one travels still farther north and the growing season gets progressively shorter, the deciduous habit becomes progressively less adequate to meet the situation. The production of a new crop of leaves each year, only to lose them after a brief growing season, represents a tremendous waste of energy. In these colder regions the coniferous forests come into their own. The trees are evergreen, and each season's crop of leaves lasts several years. Photosynthesis is not restricted to the brief summer but occurs any day the temperature rises a little above freezing. The firm, needle-like leaves withstand desiccation in the winter as ordinary leaves could not. (The relation of the sclerophyllous habit to drought resistance is discussed in Chapter 27.)

The conifers are not restricted to the far northern woods, but this is the largest region in which their features give them a competitive advantage over angiosperms. Elsewhere conifers are mostly found in areas a little too dry for broad-leaved trees, especially where there is a summer drought, or in areas subject to repeated fire, or in the mountains at altitudes where conditions approach those of the north woods. Each species, of course, has its own set of

Fig. 38.2. *Linanthus parryae*, an ephemeral annual, in the Mojave desert of California in April; the flowers on some plants are violet, on others white. (Photo courtesy of Rupert C. Barneby.)

requirements and competitive abilities, and sometimes these permit conifers to grow intermingled with angiosperm trees, as in the beech-maple-hemlock forest of New England.

The most important single feature which gives angiosperm trees a competitive advantage over coniferous trees in so much of the world is the presence of vessels in angiosperm wood. The vessel-bearing wood of angiosperms permits a more rapid delivery of water to the leaves than does the slow-acting tracheid-system of conifers. The angiosperms can thus expose a larger transpiring (and photosynthetic) surface to the sun without suffering fatal desiccation.

LIFE FORMS

In some ecological studies, it is useful to classify plants according to the position of the vegetative buds which survive the most unfavorable part of the year. Trees and shrubs, in which the buds are well above the ground, are called **phanerophytes**. Plants with the dormant buds at or barely above the ground level are called **chamaephytes**. Plants with the dormant buds borne just beneath the soil surface

are called **hemicryptophytes. Cryptophytes** have deeply buried buds, often associated with food-storage organs such as bulbs or tubers. **Therophytes** survive the dry or cold season only as seeds; i.e., they are strictly annual.

Phanerophytes offer the least protection to the buds. The vast majority of vascular plants in tropical regions that are not too dry are phanerophytes. Phanerophytes are also abundant in temperate regions, but not to the exclusion of other types. Chamaephytes, hemicryptophytes, cryptophytes, and therophytes provide increasing degrees of protection to the parts which overwinter or survive the dry season, and they are progressively more abundant in colder or drier regions. Therophytes, which have the best protection of all, have also the disadvantage of not persisting as established plants from year to year, and they do not generally compete well with perennial plants in sites where the latter can survive. It is no accident that the only regions in which annual plants are a significant part of the climax community are deserts.

THE VEGETATION OF NORTH AMERICA

TUNDRA

The arctic tundra covers the northernmost parts of North America and Eurasia, north of the boreal forest. The most characteristic features of the arctic tundra are the absence of trees and the presence of permafrost (permanently frozen soil) at a depth of a few inches to a few feet. The depth to which roots penetrate is governed by the depth to which the ground thaws in the summer. In the moister areas the ground often cracks into rough poly-

T	TUNDRA
	BOREAL FOREST
	HEMLOCK-HARDWOOD F.
	DECIDUOUS FOREST
	S.E. EVERGREEN FOREST
G	GRASSLANDS
	DESERT GRASS AND SCRUB
	DESERT
	COASTAL FOREST
	ROCKY MT. FOREST
	WET AND DRY TROPICAL F.

SCALE OF MILES

Fig. 38.3. Distribution of the major plant formations of North America. (After Transeau.)

gons 15–25 feet across, the cracks being filled with deep ice wedges which thaw at the surface in the summer.

The growing season in the tundra region is short, generally only 2–3 months, and there may be frost any day of the year. Even in the brief summer there is often much fog and mist. During clear weather, the temperature may rise as high as on a summer day in the United States, and the long or continuous days permit rapid growth.

The precipitation in tundra regions is not high, but the potential evaporation is generally even less, and the runoff is usually slow. Much of the land is flat and poorly drained, with a sticky, typically blue-gray soil that is rich in organic matter and more or less saturated with water. Mountainous parts of the arctic pull down more snow in the winter than the lowlands and are likely to be continuously ice-covered. Even in the summer only a narrow fringe of Greenland is ice-free, and the enthusiastic Viking who named it ranks with Baron Münchhausen in his respect for the truth.

Grasses, sedges, small dicotyledonous herbs, low shrubs, lichens, and mosses are the principal elements of tundra vegetation. Toward the south the plants cover most of the soil, and shrubs, especially low evergreen members of the heath family, are not uncommon. Much of the land may have a brilliant blanket of flowers in July and August, and thickets of birch, willow, and alder may be taller than a man along the streams.

Northward the plant cover is progressively sparser. Mosses and lichens make up an increasing part of the community, not so much by an increase in their own numbers as by a decrease in the other plants. Displays of showy flowers are more restricted to south slopes or otherwise protected spots, and a willow thicket may be only an inch or so high, resembling a clover lawn. Grasses, sedges, and peat moss are common in the moister spots.

Perhaps the most characteristic single genus of the arctic tundra is *Cladonia*, the "reindeer moss," actually a fruticose lichen commonly a few inches tall. Among the true mosses, *Polytrichum* (hairy-cap moss) is common in dry places, and *Sphagnum* (peat moss) in wet ones. *Carex* and *Eriophorum* (cotton grass) are common sedges, and *Poa* (bluegrass) is a common grass. *Ranunculus* (buttercup), *Pedicularis* (lousewort), *Saxifraga*, *Draba*, and *Polemonium* (Jacob's-ladder) are common herbaceous dicots.

To the south, the arctic tundra gives way to the boreal forest in the lowlands and merges with the alpine tundra in the mountains. The timberline which marks the lower limits of the alpine tundra corresponds to the treeline of the far north. The northern treeline, however, unlike the often fairly sharp timberline of the mountains, commonly spreads over a broad belt, often 100 miles wide, in which trees are progressively restricted to the most protected habitats.

The vegetation and the environment of the alpine tundra resemble those of the arctic tundra at first glance, but there are significant differences. Alpine tundra is not generally underlain by permafrost, and the topography is generally rougher, so that much of the land is better drained. The growing season is longer, but the days are shorter. Mosses and lichens are much less prominent parts of the vegetation, and the flower-garden aspect is often even more pronounced. Many species are especially adapted to the rock crevices and talus slopes which are so abundant in the moun-

Fig. 38.4. Paramo vegetation at about 11,000 feet in Colombia; the large shrub is *Espeletia*, a composite. (Photo courtesy of José Cuatrecasas.)

tains. Most of the common genera and even many of the species of angiosperms in the alpine tundra of the United States are the same as, or closely related to, those of the arctic, and a person familiar with the flora of one would also feel at home in the other.

The alpine tundra is restricted to progressively higher elevations as one travels southward in Canada and the United States. In the east, it barely reaches the higher mountains of New England and northern New York. In the western cordillera, the mountaintops even as far south as Mexico reach above timberline. The actual elevation of the timberline varies with the snowfall as well as the latitude. Other things being equal, 1 mile of latitude equals about 4 feet of altitude, but in the dry mountains of central Idaho, the timberline is near 10,000 feet, in contrast to about 7000 feet on Mt. Hood in the moister Cascade Mountains at the same latitude in Oregon.

Even in the tropics many mountains reach above timberline and have a zone of alpine tundra, usually beginning at elevations of 12,000–15,000 feet. In the Andes of South America, such communities are called paramos (Fig. 38.4). Unlike the alpine tundra of North America, the paramos often have a sprinkling of stout, semi-woody, sparsely branched shrubs. These are a distinctive ecological type which has evolved independently in several different groups, especially members of the family Compositae.

THE BOREAL FOREST

The boreal forest forms a broad belt, up to 500 miles wide, across Canada and

Alaska just south of the tundra, extending farther north in the west than in the east, and dipping into the United States around Lake Superior. It is dominated by conifers and is often called the northern coniferous forest. The same formation extends across Siberia and into northern Europe.

Much of the boreal forest is a land of low relief, with many lakes and slow streams and extensive boggy areas. The bogs are often covered with mosses such as *Sphagnum* and *Polytrichum*, and are then called muskegs. Away from the bogs, the soil is typically pale and sandy beneath a layer of slowly decaying litter and humus. The precipitation is not very high, about 10–20 inches per year, but is still more than the potential evaporation. The growing season is only 3–4 months, and there may be frost at any time. Winters are cold and snowy, and on the coldest nights a tree may burst, with a sound like a rifle shot, as the sap freezes.

The trees of the boreal forest are small, seldom over 50 feet tall or with a trunk over 2 feet thick, but they may form a very dense cover. One mile an hour is fast—and exhausting—progress for a man making his way through such a forest, ducking under low branches, climbing over fallen trees, circling to avoid perilous muskeg, and searching for nonexistent landmarks to keep his bearings. In drier areas, on the other hand, the trees may be well spaced, with but little undergrowth.

The most characteristic tree of the boreal forest (Fig. 38.5) in America is white spruce (*Picea glauca*). East of the Rocky Mountains it is commonly associated with balsam fir (*Abies balsamea*). Black spruce (*Picea mariana*) and tamarack (*Larix laricina*, a deciduous conifer) are also abundant, especially in the wetter sites. Paper birch (*Betula papyrifera*), aspen (*Populus tremuloides*), balsam poplar (*Populus balsamifera*), and jack pine (*Pinus banksiana*) are common seral trees in the boreal forest, which often come in rapidly after fire or other disturbance, but eventually give way to spruce and fir. In some areas toward the west and north, however, some of these trees approach climax status.

The boreal forest or its ecological equivalent extends southward at increasing elevations in the Appalachian Mountains and in the western cordillera. The white spruce of the true boreal forest gives way progressively to red spruce (*Picea rubens*) in the Appalachian extension, and

Fig. 38.5. Virgin spruce-fir forest in Quebec. (From Pierre Dansereau, *Biogeography*, 1957. Copyright Ronald Press, New York.)

in the southern Appalachians *Abies balsamea* is replaced by the very closely related *A. fraseri*. This Appalachian coniferous forest, which reaches south to the Great Smoky Mountains of North Carolina, is often treated as a separate association of the boreal-forest formation, marked by the presence of red spruce. The western mountain extension of the boreal forest is, for convenience, treated as part of the Rocky Mountain forest formation, which, like the boreal forest, is dominated by conifers.

THE HEMLOCK-HARDWOOD FOREST

The hemlock-hardwood forest is the characteristic formation of most of the New England region, extending west to the Great Lakes, and south in the Appalachians to northern Georgia. The beech-maple-hemlock association (*Fagus grandifolia*, *Acer saccharum*, and *Tsuga canadensis*) is the most common climax association of the region. Beech and maple are also important elements of the deciduous forest to the south, and it is only the hemlock which gives the community a distinctive aspect that keeps it from being classified with the deciduous-forest formation.

White pine (*Pinus strobus*) forms a long-persistent subclimax associated with fire or other disturbance in much of the hemlock-hardwood forest region. Most of the once extensive stands of white pine have long since fallen to the lumberman's axe.

THE EASTERN DECIDUOUS FOREST

The deciduous forest is a complex formation which once covered hundreds of thousands of square miles in the eastern half of the United States. Many of the trees were tall and stately, well over 100 feet high. Most of this virgin forest has now been destroyed. Farms, cities, roads, and suburban homes cover much of the land. Elsewhere the forest is in various stages of secondary succession after having been cut over. In some areas the plant cover has returned to something near its original state, except that the trees are not yet so large.

The trees of the deciduous forest form an almost complete crown cover, so that very little direct sunlight reaches the ground in summer. There is generally a well-developed understory of shrubs and herbs, but walking through the forest is easy and pleasant. A number of low herbs, such as spring beauty (*Claytonia*), anemone, hepatica, trillium, and violets bloom in early spring, before the trees have leafed out, and complete most or all of their growth within a few weeks thereafter. A succession of other plants bloom throughout the season, but these are not usually abundant and showy enough to produce a flower-garden effect.

The climate of the deciduous-forest region is in general moderate. To the north, the formation is limited by the increasing severity of the winters and the shortness of the growing season, to the west by decreasing rainfall and humidity, and to the south by the sterile, sandy soil and recurrent fires which favor the pine forests.

The deciduous forest attains its most favorable development in the moist valleys and slopes in the southern Appalachian Mountains. More than two dozen kinds of trees have climax status in this mixed mesophytic forest. Among these are species of basswood (*Tilia*), beech (*Fagus*), buckeye (*Aesculus*), hickory (*Carya*), magnolia, maple (*Acer*), oak (*Quercus*), and tulip tree (*Liriodendron*).

The number of climax dominants in

Fig. 38.6. A beech-sugar-maple forest in West Virginia. (U.S. Forest Service photo.)

the deciduous forest thins out in all directions from the southern Appalachian center. To the northward, beech (*Fagus grandifolia*), and sugar maple (*Acer saccharum*) are increasingly abundant on the better soils (Fig. 38.6), with oak and hickory often occupying the drier or more exposed sites. To the far northwest, in Wisconsin and Minnesota, the *beech-maple* association (Fig. 38.6) gives way to the *maple-basswood* association as the beech drops out and is replaced by basswood. The *oak-hickory* association (Fig. 38.7), confined to the poorer sites in the beech-maple and maple-basswood regions, is the main climax community in the more southern part of the deciduous forest (outside the Appalachian region). Toward the western edge of the oak-hickory forest, as one approaches the grassland, the trees become smaller and more scattered, and toward the southwest there is some savanna vegetation with the trees widely scattered among the grasses.

East of the mixed mesophytic forest, there was once a long fringe of oak-chestnut climax, extending from Georgia to southern New England. The destruction of the chestnut since 1900 by the chestnut blight has changed much of this to an oak or oak-hickory association.

The Southeastern Evergreen Forest

The coastal plain of the Atlantic and Gulf states, from New Jersey to Florida and the border of Texas, is characterized by extensive pine forests. Northward, as in New Jersey, pitch pine (*Pinus rigida*) is the dominant species (Fig. 38.8); farther south loblolly pine (*P. taeda*), slash pine (*P. caribaea*), and longleaf pine (*P. palustris*) are more abundant. These are mostly rather small or medium-sized trees, although longleaf pine reaches a considerable size, up to 100 or even 130 feet.

The continued dominance of pines in this large area depends on repeated fires which have occurred for ages past and continue to occur. When the pine forest is dense, it may be burned to the ground, but some of the species sprout again from just below the surface. Furthermore, the fire hastens the opening of cones which have remained closed on the tree for years, and the newly released seeds germinate well in the bare mineral soil. Where the trees are more scattered, the ground is often covered by wiregrass (*Aristida*) and other low herbs which become tinder-dry in late summer and fall. Such areas may be burned every year without significant damage to the established trees.

When protected from fire, the pine

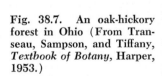

Fig. 38.7. An oak-hickory forest in Ohio (From Transeau, Sampson, and Tiffany, *Textbook of Botany*, Harper, 1953.)

forests eventually give way to angiosperm forests. Over much of the region, oak and hickory would be the climax dominants except for fire; in some areas, especially southward, live oak (i.e., evergreen oak) and magnolia would dominate instead.

Much of the coastal plain has a sterile, sandy soil which is low in mineral nutrients and does not hold water very well. In this soil the pines are at less of a competitive disadvantage vis-à-vis the broadleaved trees than they are in the better soil farther inland, and the influence of fire becomes decisive. Whether the whole forest burns down or whether the undergrowth is merely burned off, the newly burned land is more suitable for pine seeds than for those of broad-leaved trees, which generally prefer a soil with more humus and often need shade when young. The very abundance of pines insures that most of the tree seeds reaching the soil will be pines rather than angiosperms. These conditions reinforce each other, to the benefit of the pines.

In the better soils farther inland, pines

still occur in inhospitable sites and as fire trees, but fire is not enough to hold the balance permanently in their favor over large areas.

On the outer coastal plain, the water table is seldom very far below the surface and many areas are periodically or permanently flooded. Marshes with permanently standing water are usually dominated by coarse grasses and rushes (Fig. 38.9). Places where water stands most, but not all, of the year commonly support forests (Fig. 38.10) of bald cypress (*Taxodium distichum*). The irregular, knobby "knees" which grow up from cypress roots and extend above the water have sometimes been thought to be aerating organs, but their anatomy does not support this view; no special function can be certainly assigned to them. In areas flooded for a shorter period, broad-leaved trees such as gum (*Nyssa*) and ash (*Fraxinus*) are mixed with the cypress or replace it entirely. These angiospermous swamp forests in turn pass into the permanently wet but seldom flooded bogs, called pocosins, which are

Fig. 38.8. Pitch-pine forest in the pine barrens of New Jersey. A turf of *Chamaedaphne* (an evergreen shrub) was removed from the foreground about 100 years before the picture was taken; only a few pines got established in the very sandy mineral soil before litter, lichens, and mosses covered the surface. (Photo courtesy of Jack McCormick, American Museum of Natural History.)

Fig. 38.9. Marshes in Florida, with hammocks of trees where the ground rises a little higher than the average. (Photo courtesy of the Chicago Natural History Museum.)

typically dominated by evergreen shrubs and small trees, usually with a ground cover of *Sphagnum*. Burned over pocosins often grow up to a long-persistent bog forest (Fig. 38.11) of white cedar (*Chamaecyparis thyoides*).

THE GRASSLANDS

Two hundred years ago central North America was a great grassland, 1500 miles long from north to south and more than 500 miles wide over most of its length. It was bounded on the north by the boreal forest, on the south by desert, on the west by the Rocky Mountains, and on the east by the deciduous forest. An irregular and interrupted "prairie peninsula" extended eastward through the present state of Illinois and even into Ohio. Other herbs, especially various legumes and composites, were liberally sprinkled among the grasses, and there were striking changes in the seasonal aspect of the prairie as each species in turn came into bloom. Most of this former grassland is now farm land.

This central grassland is, or was, roughly divisible into three north-south

Fig. 38.10. Bald cypress swamp in the southeastern United States. (Photo by W. H. Hodge.)

strips, the tall-grass prairie to the east, the short-grass prairie to the west, and the mixed-grass prairie in between. The zonation reflects the increasing aridity from east to west.

The boundaries between the tall-grass

Fig. 38.11. White-cedar swamp, a persistent subclimax, in southern New Jersey. (Photo courtesy of Jack McCormick, American Museum of Natural History.)

and the mixed-grass, and between the mixed-grass and short-grass prairies were irregular and unstable. In the drier, more exposed sites, the short-grass type extended into the mixed-grass region, and the mixed-grass type extended into the tall-grass region; in the swales, with better moisture supply, the situation was reversed. A series of dry years would shove both boundaries east, and wet years would push them west again.

In the tall-grass prairie, the grasses formed a dense cover commonly 4–6 or even 10 feet tall, and, at least in the more favorable sites, a tough thick sod was formed. Big bluestem (*Andropogon gerardii*), little bluestem (*Andropogon scoparius*), and Indian grass (*Sorghastrum nutans*) were among the commonest of many climax dominants, but there was a great deal of local and regional variation.

The deep, dark, fertile soil of the tall-grass prairie region is as good as any soil in the world, and the original vegetation has now been almost entirely replaced by productive farms, bustling cities, and other appurtenances of civilization. Much of the corn belt of the United States lies in the tall-grass prairie region, as do millions of acres devoted to wheat, cotton and sorghum.

The high plains east of the Rocky Mountains, where the great herds of buffalo once roamed, are short-grass country (Fig. 38.12). Buffalo grass (*Buchloe dactyloides*) and little grama grass (*Bouteloua gracilis*) are the most common climax dominants. These and other common grasses in the region are generally only a few inches high, although taller species occur in the more favorable sites.

Rainfall in the short-grass region is scanty and irregular, commonly only 10–15 inches annually, and the later part of the summer in particular is often very dry. The rain water seldom penetrates more than 2–3 feet, and a hardpan layer of accumulated calcium carbonate and other salts marks the level of penetration.

The short-grass prairie is best adapted to use as grazing land. In the more favorable years it is possible to grow wheat and other crops, but such years are inevitably followed by years of drought, crop failure, and dust storms. The great drought of the early 1930's, particularly 1934, put an end to most of the farming which the United States government had encouraged in this region as an emergency measure to boost food production during World War I. Put to the plow again during World War II, the land again produced a few good crops before the dry years returned; federal aid and the absence of a really severe drought combined to permit continued cultivation of much of the short-grass region during the 1950's, with mediocre success.

The mixed-grass prairie is, as its name implies, composed chiefly of elements from the tall-grass and short-grass prairies which flank it. The climate is favorable enough to permit many tall-grass species to survive (although they do not reach full size, seldom over 4 feet) but not favorable enough to permit them to crowd out the more xerophytic, shorter species from farther west. The proportions of the various species fluctuate from year to year, principally according to the moisture conditions.

Most of the mixed-grass prairie region is suitable to the same crops as the tall-grass prairie, but the production is not so high and there is more chance of crop failure during a dry year.

At the northern edge of the great central grassland, where it adjoins the boreal forest, groves of aspen are scattered through the prairie, occupying the swales and other moister sites. Many ecologists treat this aspen-grove region (Fig. 38.13) as a separate formation distinct from both the prairie and the boreal forest.

All other grasslands of North America are much smaller than the great central grassland. Two of the most important of these smaller grasslands are the Central Valley of California and the Palouse region of southeastern Washington and adjacent Ore-

Fig. 38.12. Short-grass prairie in northeastern Colorado, dominated by buffalo grass and little grama grass. (Photo by H. L. Shantz.)

gon and Idaho. The original vegetation in both these areas has now been largely destroyed—in the Central Valley by fire and overgrazing followed in part of the area by farming, and in the Palouse by farming. Introduced annual weedy grasses, especially species of *Avena* and *Bromus*, are now the most common plants in the uncultivated parts of the Central Valley, while the Palouse is one of the great wheat regions of the nation. Both these areas have a longer summer drought than is typical of grasslands, but the Central Valley has a long spring growing season, and the deep, fertile, eolian soil of the Palouse accumulates, in the winter and spring, a good supply of moisture which it gradually gives up to the plants during the summer.

THE WESTERN CONIFEROUS FORESTS

Most of the mountains of the western United States and Canada are more or less covered with coniferous forest up to the timberline. The moister, more western part of the region, shown on our map as the coastal forest, generally has a denser stand of taller trees than the more inland area, shown as the Rocky Mountain forest.

These western forests show a prominent altitudinal zonation, often with three distinct associations at different elevations. In the Rocky Mountains of the United States one often sees an open forest of ponderosa pine in the foothills and lower reaches of the mountains, a Douglas-fir forest at middle altitudes, and a spruce-fir forest near timberline.

The Rocky Mountain spruce-fir forest occurs at progressively lower levels to the northward and merges with the boreal spruce-fir forest in Canada. The aspect of the Rocky Mountain spruce-fir forest is much like that of the drier parts of the boreal forest, with spire-topped small trees in open or dense stands, but the characteristic species are not the same. Engelmann spruce (*Picea engelmannii*) and alpine fir (*Abies lasiocarpa*) are the principal dominants of the Rocky Mountain spruce-fir forest, in contrast to *Picea glauca* and *Abies balsamea* of the boreal forest.

The Douglas fir of the Rocky Mountains is a smaller, hardier tree of higher elevations than the Douglas fir of the coastal regions and is usually considered to be a distinct variety. A true climax tree in the Rocky Mountains, it is only a fire climax west of the summits of the Cascade Mountains. The stately Douglas-fir forests of western Oregon and Washington give way to the true climax of western red cedar (*Thuja plicata*) and western hemlock (*Tsuga heterophylla*) when protected from fire.

Lodgepole pine (*Pinus contorta* var. *latifolia*) and quaking aspen (*Populus tremuloides*, an angiosperm) are the common fire trees at middle altitudes in much of the Rocky Mountain region. At lower altitudes in northern Idaho, western white pine (*Pinus monticola*) forms a persistent subclimax associated with fire.

The list of pines, firs, spruces, hemlocks, and other conifers which reach climax or near-climax status in various parts of the western coniferous forest is too long to be presented here. The Sitka spruce (*Picea sitchensis*), the common climax dominant along and near the coast of British Columbia and southern Alaska, is perhaps the most important of those not previously mentioned. The coast redwood (*Sequoia sempervirens*) of the fog belt of the north-coast ranges of California, the big tree or Sierra redwood (*Sequoiadendron giganteum*) of scattered sites at middle altitudes in the Sierra Nevada, and the sugar pine (*Pinus lambertiana*), with cones a foot or even 2 feet long, at middle altitudes in the Sierra Nevada, are among the most interesting species of the region.

The dominance of conifers instead of broad-leaved trees in so much of the West results from different causes in different localities. At higher altitudes the shortness

Fig. 38.14.   Timberline forest in the Sierra Nevada of California. (Photo by William L. Dawson, from National Audubon Society.)

of the summer is probably the most significant factor, just as in the boreal forest. At more moderate altitudes, especially inland, the summer drought discourages broad-leaved trees, without being so severe as to eliminate the conifers. In the moist coastal regions the conifers, with their central trunk and excurrent branching, grow so tall as to overtop and shade out the deliquescently branched angiosperm trees, but this is probably not the sole reason for their dominance. At any rate, most broad-leaved trees of the western coniferous-forest region, with the notable exception of aspen, are confined to wet places, such as stream banks, at middle and lower elevations.

The summer drought which characterizes so much of the western coniferous-forest region becomes increasingly prolonged and severe toward the south and at lower elevations. South of the Canadian border the forest often forms a belt across the face of the mountains, with alpine tundra above and a more xerophytic vegetation below. In California this more xerophytic vegetation is commonly of the broad sclerophyll type; farther inland it is desert.

THE COLD DESERT

Between the Cascade-Sierran axis on the west and the main Rocky Mountain axis to the east lies an area of broad valleys and scattered, narrow mountain ranges with a north-south orientation. The annual precipitation in the valleys is seldom more than about 10 inches, because the prevailing westerly winds drop most of their water in getting over the more western mountains. The heartland of this area has no drainage to the sea and constitutes the Great Basin. Creeks and small rivers flow out of the mountains, only to disappear in the desert or to reach a shallow playa lake which dries up in the summer, leaving a flat, saline playa in the middle of the valley. Great Salt Lake and a few other saline lakes in the Great Basin are permanent, but their margins fluctuate widely with the season and the year.

The Great Basin, covering western Utah, most of Nevada, southeastern Oregon, and small parts of California, Idaho, and Wyoming, is principally a desert region, with coniferous forests of the Rocky Mountain type occurring well up in the mountains. Unlike the desert farther south, it has a cold, often long winter, with frequent light snow; it is therefore called a cold desert. In addition to the Great Basin proper, the cold desert covers much of eastern Utah and far western Colorado, southern Idaho, and the lower parts of eastern Oregon and central Washington. The soil in much of the region is fertile, but it mostly requires irrigation for successful farming.

Most of the cold desert is a land of sagebrush (*Artemisia tridentata* and related species) and scattered grasses (Fig. 38.16), notably bunch wheatgrass (*Agropyron spicatum*). Overgrazing has caused a proportionate increase in sagebrush and decrease in native grasses, but the sagebrush was always (in terms of human time) an important part of the climax. Herbaceous dicots, including spring-flowering annuals, are scattered among the other plants, but they do not form such a conspicuous part of the community as they do farther south. June grass (*Bromus tectorum*), and other weedy annual grasses which mature and dry up early in the summer, have been introduced from Europe and are now very

Fig. 38.16. Sagebrush desert near Nephi, Utah; plants about 4 feet tall, 30–50 years old. (Photo by H. L. Shantz.)

abundant, doubtless due partly to overgrazing.

Sagebrush is intolerant of alkali and does not grow around the playas and lakes where salts accumulate. Members of the family Chenopodiaceae generally dominate such habitats. Where the soil is only moderately saline, low shrubs such as shad scale (*Atriplex*), greasewood (*Sarcobatus vermiculatus*), and winter fat (*Eurotia lanata*) are common. In still saltier places these give way to succulents with reduced leaves and a very high osmotic pressure, such as *Salicornia* and *Suaeda*. The most extreme habitats are desolate salt flats, bare of vegetation and fit only for automotive speed tests.

A zone of desert woodland often intervenes between the sagebrush and the montane coniferous forest of the cold-desert region. The trees are low and crooked, seldom over 20 feet tall, often as broad as high, and usually rather scattered. Piñon pine (*Pinus edulis* and related spp.) and juniper (*Juniperus osteosperma* and related spp.) are the characteristic dominants of the desert woodland, but sometimes there are small oaks instead. Piñon pines have large, wingless, edible seeds and furnish the "pine nuts" used by Indians and pioneers and now locally sold in commerce. This desert woodland might possibly be treated as part of the Rocky Mountain coniferous forest, but the trees are so small, the aspect of the community so xeric, and the associated herbaceous species so similar to those of the rest of the desert that the community is more naturally included with the desert.

The Warm Desert

The warm desert covers most of the land from the southern tip of Nevada, south through southeastern California,

eastern and southern Arizona, and well into Mexico. Like the cold desert, the area is interrupted by scattered mountain ranges which sometimes rise high enough to carry coniferous forest or even alpine tundra. Within the United States the warm desert is confined to lower elevations, mostly less than 3000 feet; some of it, such as Death Valley in California, is below sea level.

Moisture is even more deficient in the warm desert than in the cold desert. In the United States the annual precipitation of the warm desert is seldom over 5 inches. The summers are long and hot, and the winters are mild. Part of the area does have occasional frost, but there is little if any snow.

The most characteristic plant of the warm desert in North America is creosote bush (*Larrea tridentata*), a branching shrub commonly 3–4 feet tall with a very deep root system and small, firm, shiny, evergreen leaves. Over thousands of square miles in Arizona and California, creosote bushes are spaced at more or less regular intervals of 15–30 feet, with much bare ground in between (Fig. 38.17). Bur sage (*Franseria dumosa*), another low, branching shrub, is often associated with creosote bush, and cacti of various sorts are common.

Ephemeral annuals, many with showy flowers, are abundant in the warm desert. In a good year they color the landscape purple, yellow, and white for a time in the spring before the plants mature seed and disappear. If the spring rains fail, the plants may not come up at all or may wither and die before flowering. The seeds of some species will not germinate unless there is enough moisture in the soil to last through a normal cycle of growth and fruiting.

The warm-desert community under-

Fig. 38.17. Creosote bush community above Owens Valley, California, with a playa and the Sierra Nevada in the background. (Photo courtesy of Jack McCormick, American Museum of Natural History.)

goes much local and regional variation and includes many more species than its barren aspect might at first suggest. Three of the most interesting and conspicuous species that do not extend throughout the area are the giant Joshua (*Yucca brevifolia*), the saguaro cactus (*Cereus giganteus*), and mesquite (*Prosopis glandulosa*).

The giant Joshua, a very stout shrub or small tree often 10 feet tall, is the most arborescent member of the lily family. It occurs at upper altitudes in the more northern and western part of the warm desert, often forming a fringe only a mile or so wide where the land slopes down from the cold to the warm desert. In southeastern California, an area dominated by giant Joshua has been set aside as a national monument.

The saguaro (Fig. 27.10) is the largest of all cacti, reaching a height of 50 feet. It is abundant in parts of southern Arizona and northern Sonora (Mexico), where it is generally the only arborescent plant of any sort and is commonly inhabited by woodpeckers.

Mesquite, a small bushy tree of the legume family, is common in washes and other low places in the more eastern and southern parts of the warm desert, sometimes also occurring on dry slopes or even on sand dunes. It has become much more abundant, especially on upland sites away from ground water, since the beginning of extensive grazing in the Southwest. Once established, it often maintains itself even when the range is protected from grazing for many years.

THE BROAD SCLEROPHYLL FORMATION

Moist mild winters and long dry summers are typical of the foothills and lower mountains of most of California, except for the desert mountains in the southeast and the fog belt of the outer coast ranges north of San Francisco. This climate is characteristic also of much of the area bordering the Mediterranean sea, and is called a Mediterranean climate. American soldiers learned during World War II that these Mediterranean lands, famed for their sunny climate, are wet and disagreeable in the winter. In California, as elsewhere, a Mediterranean climate is associated with broad sclerophyll vegetation.

Most of the dominant species of the broad sclerophyll formation are woody angiosperms with firm, hard, evergreen leaves (see Chapter 27). In our area, there are two associations, the broad sclerophyll forest and the chaparral. The broad sclerophyll forest occurs in the less xeric habitats of the region and is commoner toward the north. It is characterized by several evergreen oaks, California laurel (*Umbellularia californica*) and madroño (*Arbutus menziesii*), among other species. The chaparral (Fig. 38.18) occupies the drier habitats, especially southward. It is characterized by evergreen shrubs, especially chamiso (*Adenostoma fasciculatum*) and

Fig. 38.20. Above, tropical forest in Colombia, with a tree fern at the left. Below, grassland in Colombia, with scattered palms. (Photos courtesy of José Cuatrecasas.)

various species of manzanita (*Arctostaphylos*).

The broad sclerophyll communities, especially the chaparral, are subject to frequent fires. Many chaparral species sprout freely from the base after a fire, and the whole community may come back to normal within 10 years.

THE TROPICAL FORESTS

The frost-free tropical forests barely enter the United States in southern Florida and Texas, but they cover much of Mexico and the West Indies. Under optimum conditions, with adequate moisture and drainage throughout the year, the community is a rain forest (Fig. 38.20), composed of many species of evergreen angio-sperm trees in several strata, with rather sparse undergrowth and few lianas, and epiphytes are not numerous near the ground. After disturbance of any sort, the impenetrable jungle of fiction and cinema develops, with dense, tangled undergrowth and numerous lianas and epiphytes (Fig. 38.19). This community is seral and gives way eventually to rain forest.

Not all tropical forest is rain forest. A recent study recognizes 27 formations in the American tropics, 10 of which are forest. Among these are the swamp forest, the seasonal-swamp forest, the dry ever-green forest, the evergreen seasonal forest, the deciduous seasonal forest, and the cloud forest. This complexity of vegetation is another reflection of the fact that the tropics are the real home of the angio-sperms.

SUGGESTED READING

Cain, Stanley A., *Foundations of Plant Geog-raphy*, Harper, New York, 1944, 556 pp. Primarily concerned with the evolutionary and taxonomic aspects of plant geogra-phy.

Good, Ronald, *The Geography of Flowering Plants*, 2nd ed., Longmans, Green, London, 1953, 452 pp. A taxonomic rather than vegetational approach to plant geography.

Harvey, A. G., *Douglas of the Fir*, Harvard University Press, Cambridge, Mass, 1947, 290 pp. The perils and achievements of an early botanical explorer.

Richards, P. W., *Tropical Rain Forest*, Cam-bridge University Press, 1952, 450 pp. A thorough ecological study.

Shantz, H. L., The saguaro forest, *National Geographic* 71:515–532. 1937. An illus-trated popular article by an outstanding ecologist.

Appendix I: Keys to the Divisions, Classes, and Orders of Plants[1]

SYNOPSIS OF THE DIVISIONS AND CLASSES OF PLANTS

1. Gametangia and sporangia, when present, generally unicellular, or sometimes multicellular with all cells fertile; zygotes generally do not develop into multicellular embryos while still attached to the parent plant; plants without xylem, and ordinarily without phloem
Subkingdom I. Thallophyta

   2. Nucleus, if present, relatively simple, lacking a nucleolus and ordinarily lacking a nuclear membrane, apparently not dividing mitotically; plants mostly asexual, sometimes with parasexual processes, perhaps rarely truly sexual; plastids wanting; food reserves generally polysaccharides which resemble glycogen
Division 1. Schizophyta

      3. Plants mostly without chlorophyll and not photosynthetic; photosynthetic forms have bacteriochlorophyll and do not release oxygen as a result of photosynthesis; carotenoid pigments do not include myxoxanthin and myxoxanthophyll; no phycobilin pigments; cell wall mostly nitrogenous, seldom containing cellulose
Class Schizomycetes

      3. Plants mostly with chlorophyll, photosynthetic and releasing free oxygen as a result; chlorophyll is chlorophyll *a*; carotenoid pigments include myxoxanthin and myxoxanthophyll, unique to this group; one or two phycobilin pigments, usually phycocyanin, always associated with the chlorophyll; cell wall of polysaccharides, including some cellulose
Class Cyanophyceae

   2. Nucleus highly organized and complex, with nucleolus, nuclear membrane, and chromonemata; plants often sexual; photosynthetic pigments, when present, generally borne on plastids; food reserves diverse

      4. Chlorophyll usually present and the plants photosynthetic (lacking chiefly among some of the unicellular flagellates); cell walls ordinarily not chitinous, mostly of polysaccharides, often including cellulose, sometimes siliceous, or wanting and the cell then bounded by a flexible, living membrane

[1] These keys are based essentially on modern forms. Fossils are included only when they have some special evolutionary significance.

5. Plants without phycobilin pigments (except in some Cryptophyceae); food reserves diverse, but not of floridean starch, and generally not glycogen-like; plants often with motile cells at some stage of the life cycle

  6. Chloroplasts grass-green, the associated pigments masked by the chlorophyll; chlorophyll of *a* and *b* types only; flagella, when present and more than one, generally all alike

    7. Cells without a gullet; plants unicellular, colonial, or multicellular, usually with cell walls, with or without flagella, the flagella when present of the whiplash type; food reserves typically starch; often sexual, sometimes asexual   **Division 2. Chlorophyta**

      8. Gametangia not surrounded by sterile jackets; thallus usually of relatively simple structure, or coenocytic when externally complex
Class Chlorophyceae

      8. Gametangia surrounded by sterile jackets; thallus relatively complex, consisting in part of an erect, multicellular axis with whorled branches
Class Charophyceae

    7. Cells with a gullet, usually solitary and flagellated, mostly naked, occasionally loricate, seldom with a definite wall; flagella pectinate; food reserves typically paramylum, a starch-like carbohydrate; asexual
Division 3. Euglenophyta (*Class Euglenophyceae*)

  6. Chloroplasts mostly yellowish to brownish, the chlorophyll generally more or less masked by the associated carotenoid pigments; chlorophyll *b* generally wanting, but chlorophyll *c* or *e* often present; flagella, when present, mostly two-several and dissimilar, typically one whiplash and one tinsel

    9. Plants unicellular to colonial or sometimes filamentous, most of the filamentous forms lacking fucoxanthin; food reserves diverse, but not laminarin

     10. Cell walls, when present, usually composed largely of cellulose, sometimes organized into two valves, but not silicified; food reserves mostly starch or starch-like substances, sometimes oils; mostly asexual, unicellular flagellates, seldom colonial or filamentous; one or both flagella usually pectinate; carotenoid pigments peridinin, dinoxanthin, and neodinoxanthin typically present   **Division 4. Pyrrophyta**

      11. Chromonemata not moniliform; cells mostly naked, often with a gullet; flagella only slightly dissimilar, at least sometimes both pectinate; phycobilin pigments sometimes present
Class Cryptophyceae

      11. Chromonemata moniliform; cells with or without a cell wall, but without a gullet; flagella distinctly dissimilar, often or always one whiplash, one pectinate; phycobilin pigments absent

       12. Motile cells with two apically inserted flagella, without a groove; cell wall, when present, of two longitudinal valves which are not divided into definitely arranged plates
Class Desmophyceae

       12. Motile cells with a transverse or spiral groove in which the two flagella are attached, one lying in the groove and encircling the cell, the other trailing; cells naked or more often with a cellulose wall, this often of interlocking plates which are seldom organized into two longitudinal valves
Class Dinophyceae

10. Cell walls, when present, seldom containing appreciable quantities of cellulose, often silicified, very often of two valves; food reserves leucosin (a polysaccharide) and/or oils, only rarely starch; plants typically unicellular or loosely colonial, sometimes (especially in the Xanthophyceae) filamentous and even coenocytic; flagella, when present, generally two and dissimilar, one whiplash, the other pinnate; often produce statospores, unique to this division; carotenoid pigments not peridinin, dinoxanthin, or neodinoxanthin **Division 5. Chrysophyta**

    13. Chloroplasts yellowish-green (or green in some Chloromonadophyceae); fucoxanthin wanting; plants, as far as known, without chlorophyll *c*; cell wall, when present, usually not highly silicified

        14. Plants unicellular flagellates without cell walls; pigments not yet analyzed *Class Chloromonadophyceae*

        14. Plants usually with cell walls, the vegetative cells seldom flagellated; vegetative cells, when without a wall, with or without flagella; plants sometimes with chlorophyll *e*, unique to this group *Class Xanthophyceae*

    13. Chloroplasts golden-brown; plants with fucoxanthin and without chlorophyll *e*

        15. Cells mostly flagellated or amoeboid and bounded by a flexible, living membrane which may bear siliceous scales, often also loricate, seldom with a definite wall, and this not highly silicified when present; plants lacking chlorophyll *c* and ϵ-carotene *Class Chrysophyceae*

        15. Cells bounded by a highly silicified wall composed of two overlapping halves, not flagellated (except some of the gametes), mostly sexual, the vegetative cells diploid; plants with chlorophyll *c* and ϵ-carotene *Class Bacillariophyceae*

9. Plants filamentous or more complex, nonmotile, with brownish chloroplasts that contain fucoxanthin and other pigments; chiefly marine, usually sexual; food reserves commonly laminarin, a soluble, dextrin-like polysaccharide; cell wall containing cellulose **Division 6. Phaeophyta**

    16. Plants with well-developed alternation of generations, both the sporophyte and the gametophyte multicellular

        17. Sporophyte and gametophyte similar *Class Isogeneratae*

        17. Sporophyte and gametophyte dissimilar, the sporophyte always the larger *Class Heterogeneratae*

    16. Plants with only the sporophyte generation multicellular; haploid stage represented only by "spores" which function directly as gametes *Class Cyclosporae*

5. Plants with one or two phycobilin pigments, including phycoerythrin, nearly always multicellular at maturity, not producing flagellated cells of any sort; principal food reserves usually floridean starch, a glycogen-like polysaccharide; chiefly marine plants **Division 7. Rhodophyta**

    18. Cells of the thallus without pit connections; cell divisions generally intercalary within the thallus, no gonimoblast filaments produced, the zygote dividing directly and probably meiotically to form either carpospores or cells which immediately divide to produce carpospores; cells usually with a single chloroplast and without a central vacuole *Class Bangiophyceae*

Appendix I: Keys to the Divisions, Classes, and Orders of Plants **833**

18. Cells of the thallus with prominent pit connections; thallus of basically filamentous construction (filaments often compacted), and cell division usually more or less restricted to the apical cells of the filaments; carpospores formed on gonimoblast filaments, the first division of the zygote typically being mitotic; cells usually with a central vacuole and often with several or many chloroplasts　　　　　　　　　　　　　　　*Class Florideophyceae*

4. Chlorophyll wanting and plants not photosynthetic; cell walls (or limiting membranes) usually chitinous (cellulose among some of the Phycomycetes, of unknown chemical composition among the Myxomycetes)　　　　　　　　　**Division 8. Fungi**

  19. Plants plasmodial and generally capable of ingesting food as well as absorbing it; flagellated cells, when produced, usually bearing two unequal whiplash flagella; spores usually numerous in a sporangium　　　　　　　　　*Class Myxomycetes*

  19. Plants consisting of filaments or cells that are usually bounded by a definite wall, obtaining food by absorption only; flagellated cells, when produced, with one or two flagella, the biflagellated forms always with one whiplash and one tinsel (usually pinnate) flagellum

    20. Filaments coenocytic or occasionally with scattered septa, or the plants unicellular; perfect stage usually consisting of a zygospore or an oöspore, not borne on a definite fruiting body; flagellated cells often produced; spores (either sexual or asexual) often numerous in a sporangium　　　　　　　　　　　　　　　　　　　　　*Class Phycomycetes*

    20. Filaments generally septate, or the plants unicellular; perfect stage usually of one or more asci or basidia that are often borne on a definite fruiting body; flagellated cells never produced; sexual spores usually few and definite in number; asexual spores never enclosed in a sporangium

      21. Sexual spores borne within a sporangium (the ascus), typically eight, seldom four, occasionally sixteen or more; filaments without clamp connections　　　　　　　　　　　　　　　*Class Ascomycetes*

      21. Sexual spores borne externally on a basidium, typically four, or the basidium sometimes failing to produce spores; filaments often with clamp connections　　　　　　　　　　　　　　　*Class Basidiomycetes*

1. Gametangia and sporangia multicellular, the outermost cells forming a sterile jacket, or the gametangia reduced and scarcely developed in some plants that usually have xylem and phloem; zygote ordinarily developing into a multicellular embryo while still attached to the parent plant　　　　　　　　　　　**Subkingdom II. Embryophyta**

  22. Plants without xylem and phloem; sporophyte partly or wholly parasitic on the gametophyte, not becoming independent　　　　　　　　**Division 9. Bryophyta**

    23. Sporophyte with a meristematic region near the base; archegonia and antheridia originating from internal cells of the thallose, dorsiventral gametophyte; chloroplasts with pyrenoids; sporophyte with stomates, and usually with a columella in the capsule　　　　　　　　　　　　　　*Class Anthocerotae*

    23. Sporophyte without a definite meristematic region; antheridia and archegonia originating from superficial cells; chloroplasts without pyrenoids

      24. Gametophyte usually dorsiventral, without a distinct protonemal stage; capsule without a columella but usually with elaters; rhizoids unicellular; stomates wanting　　　　　　　　　　　　　　　*Class Hepaticae*

      24. Gametophyte with a filamentous or dorsiventral protonemal stage, followed by the development of gametophores with phyllidia spirally and symmetrically

arranged on a caulidium; capsule without elaters but usually with a columella; rhizoids multicellular; sporophyte often with stomates *Class Musci*

22. Plants ordinarily with xylem and phloem; sporophyte physiologically independent of the gametophyte at maturity (the vascular plants)

    25. Central cylinder without leaf gaps; leaves of modern forms single-veined or veinless; modern forms not producing seeds, both generations physiologically independent at maturity.

        26. Plants without true roots, the subterranean part anatomically not much different from the aerial stem; branching chiefly dichotomous **Division 10. Psilophyta** (*Class Psilotae*)

        26. Plants with true roots that are anatomically differentiated from the stem; branching dichotomous to monopodial

            27. Leaves mostly alternate or opposite; sporangia borne in the axils of vegetative or more or less modified leaves that are often aggregated into a terminal strobilus **Division 11. Lepidophyta** (*Class Lycopodiae*)

            27. Leaves whorled; sporangia borne on highly modified sporangiophores that are aggregated into a characteristic terminal strobilus **Division 12. Calamophyta** (*Class Equisetae*)

    25. Central cylinder usually with leaf gaps; leaves (exceptions especially among the conifers) megaphylls with a branching vein system

        28. Plants not producing seeds, both generations physiologically independent at maturity **Division 13. Filicophyta** (*Class Filices*)

        28. Plants producing seeds, the gametophyte never becoming physiologically independent, the young sporophyte as well as the female gametophyte retained on the old sporophyte for some time (the seed plants)

            29. Ovules naked, not enclosed in an ovary; female gametophyte multicellular, with 500 or more cells (or nuclei), and (except in a few coniferophytes) producing definite archegonia; wood without vessels, except in a few coniferophytes; food reserves of the seed stored principally in the body of the female gametophyte; no triple-fusion cell (the gymnosperms)

                30. Leaves pinnately compound, large and more or less fern-like; plants essentially without secondary growth; modern members with ciliate sperms **Division 14. Cycadophyta** (*Class Cycadae*)

                30. Leaves simple and usually relatively small, mostly not at all fern-like; plants with more or less well-developed secondary growth, and usually with branching stems; modern members mostly with naked sperms **Division 15. Coniferophyta**

                    31. Vessels absent; male cones simple; leaves, ovules, embryos, and wood various, but usually not as in the Chlamydospermae *Class Coniferae*

                    31. Vessels present in the secondary wood; male cones compound; leaves opposite; ovules with two integuments, at least the inner forming a very long micropylar tube; embryo with two cotyledons; wood without resin canals *Class Chlamydospermae*

Appendix I: Keys to the Divisions, Classes, and Orders of Plants   835

29. Ovules enclosed in an ovary: female gametophyte of a few (typically eight) cells (or a similar free-nuclear protoplast), not producing archegonia; vessels usually present; fertilization accompanied by the formation of a triple-fusion cell, which typically gives rise to the food-storage tissue of the seed **Division 16. Anthophyta**

32. Embryo mostly with two cotyledons; plants usually with fascicular cambium; vascular bundles in herbaceous forms usually borne in a ring which encloses a pith; floral parts, when of definite number, typically borne in sets of five, less often four, seldom three; leaves mostly pinnately or palmately veined; pollen mostly of tricolpate or tricolpate-derived type *Class Dicotyledonae*

32. Embryo with one cotyledon; plants without fascicular cambium, and usually without any sort of cambium; vascular bundles often scattered; floral parts, when of definite number, typically borne in sets of three, seldom four, never five; leaves mostly parallel-veined; pollen of monocolpate or monocolpate-derived type (seldom tricolpate) *Class Monocotyledonae*

KEY TO THE ORDERS OF SCHIZOMYCETES

1. Cells bounded by a rigid wall
   2. Plants essentially unicellular, with or without flagella
      3. Plants without chlorophyll, although sometimes with other pigments; saprophytes and parasites
         4. Cell division by fission into two equal daughter cells
            5. Flagella terminal or none; cells rod-shaped to spiral — 1. *Pseudomonadales*
            5. Flagella more generally scattered over the surface; cells spherical to rod-shaped — 2. *Eubacteriales*
         4. Cell division by yeast-like budding, the daughter cell at first smaller than the parent — 3. *Hyphomicrobiales*
      3. Plants with chlorophyll, this often masked by purple or reddish associated pigments; photosynthetic — 4. *Rhodobacteriales*
   2. Plants forming multicellular filaments, without flagella except on some of the spores
      6. Filaments mostly simple, often well over 1.5 microns thick
         7. Chemosynthetic autotrophs, the filaments often surrounded by a sheath which contains iron compounds — 5. *Chlamydobacteriales*
         7. Parasites and saprophytes; filaments not ensheathed — 6. *Caryophanales*
      6. Filaments generally branched, not ensheathed, not more than about 1.5 microns thick; parasites and saprophytes — 7. *Actinomycetales*
1. Cells bounded by flexible, living membrane (or by a flexible wall in the Beggiatoales)
   8. Cells forming filaments which are motile by creeping — 8. *Beggiatoales*
   8. Cells solitary or colonial, but not filamentous
      9. Cells of moderate to large size (for bacteria), not especially fragile
         10. Cells straight or slightly curved, motile by creeping

along the substrate, tending to become colonial and
produce visible "fruiting bodies"   9. *Myxobacteriales*
    10. Cells spiral, motile by a flexous motion of the entire
body, free-swimming as individuals, not colonial   10. *Spirochaetales*
  9. Cells very small, fragile, of variable shape   11. *Mycoplasmatales*

KEY TO THE ORDERS AND SUBORDERS OF CYANOPHYCEAE

1. Plants unicellular or colonial, never truly filamentous, the cells of a
colony all about alike and generally separated from each other by
the sheath material
  2. Plants not producing endospores; reproduction by cell division
and colony fragmentation only   1. *Chroococcales*
  2. Plants producing endospores   2. *Chamaesiphonales*
1. Plants multicellular, filamentous, the filament generally provided
with a gelatinous sheath that does not separate the individual
cells; cells often not all alike   3. *Oscillatoriales*
  3. Reproduction by hormogonia delimited by separation disks; no
heterocysts or akinetes; trichomes uniseriate, unbranched   3a. *Oscillatorineae*
  3. Reproduction by heterocysts, or akinetes, or both; filaments
simple or branched, uniseriate or multiseriate   3b. *Nostochineae*

KEY TO THE ORDERS OF CHLOROPHYCEAE

1. Plants composed of uninucleate cells which are capable of vegetative
cell division
  2. Vegetative cells flagellated, motile, solitary or colonial, usually
all about alike; mostly fresh-water forms   1. *Volvocales*
  2. Vegetative cells ordinarily not motile, and not flagellate except in
some Tetrasporales
    3. Plants usually sexual, though with some notable exceptions
      4. Gametes (or at least the male gametes) flagellated
        5. Gametes and zoospores with two or four terminal fla-
gella
          6. Plants not filamentous; gametes biflagellate
            7. Plants unicellular or colonial; zoospores biflagel-
late; mostly fresh-water forms   2. *Tetrasporales*
            7. Plants multicellular; zoospores quadriflagellate;
mostly marine forms   3. *Ulvales*
          6. Plants ordinarily filamentous, sometimes unicellular;
gametes with two or four flagella; mostly fresh-
water forms   4. *Ulotrichales*
        5. Gametes and zoospores with a transverse ring of flagella
near one end; plants filamentous, occurring in fresh
water   5. *Oedogoniales*
      4. Gametes amoeboid; no flagellated cells of any type; plants
unicellular or filamentous, occurring in fresh water   6. *Zygnematales*
    3. Plants usually or always asexual and without motile cells,

Appendix I: Keys to the Divisions, Classes, and Orders of Plants   837

forming multicellular, mostly nonfilamentous thalli; fresh-water and marine forms
       7. Schizogoniales

1. Plants either without the capacity for vegetative cell division, or composed of multinucleate cells, or both
  8. Plants distinctly multicellular, each cell with at least two (usually many) nuclei and usually with a single reticulate chloroplast which extends the length of the cell and encircles the protoplast; fresh-water and marine forms
       8. Siphonocladales
  8. Plants not with the foregoing combination of characters
    9. Plants without siphonin and siphonoxanthin
      10. Plants unicellular or colonial, or of unbranched filaments, relatively simple in structure, the cells with one to many nuclei; mostly fresh-water forms
        11. Plants unicellular or colonial, not filamentous
       9. Chlorococcales
        11. Plants filamentous
       10. Sphaeroplaeales
      10. Plants forming a thallus with an erect central axis and one or more whorls of branches, the protoplast continuous until the reproductive stage, when it develops cysts that become gametangia
       11. Dasycladales
    9. Plants with the carotenoid pigments siphonin and siphonoxanthin, unique to this order; mostly filamentous or more complex, with continuous cytoplasm, scattered nuclei, and no cross walls
       12. Siphonales

Key to the Orders of Charophyceae

A single order
       1. Charales

Key to the Orders of Euglenophyceae

1. Vegetative cells flagellated, motile, with a flexible periplast
       1. Euglenales
1. Vegetative cells without flagella, nonmotile, with a firm gelatinous wall
       2. Colaciales

Key to the Orders of Cryptophyceae

1. Cells solitary, flagellated, and motile, or sometimes forming temporary colonies of nonmotile cells without flagella
       1. Cryptomonadales
1. Cells nonmotile and without flagella during the vegetative stage
  2. Vegetative cells solitary
       2. Tetragonidiales
  2. Vegetative cells colonial
       3. Phaeoplacidales

Key to the Orders of Desmophyceae

1. Cells flagellated, motile
  2. Cells without a cell wall
       1. Desmomonadales
  2. Cells with a cell wall
       2. Prorocentrales
1. Cells without flagella, nonmotile, with a cell wall
       3. Desmocapsales

1. Vegetative cells flagellated, motile, mostly solitary; mostly marine
   2. Cells bounded by a firm periplast, without a wall   1. *Gymnodiniales*
   2. Cells bounded by a definite wall
      3. Cell wall not composed of plates, or the plates numerous and not in a definite arrangement   2. *Kolkwitziellales*
      3. Cell wall composed of a specific number of plates in a definite arrangement
         4. Plates not arranged into two longitudinal valves   3. *Peridiniales*
         4. Plates arranged into two longitudinal valves   4. *Dinophysidales*
1. Vegetative cells not flagellated
   5. Cells naked, amoeboid, holozoic; marine   5. *Dinamoebidiales*
   5. Cells mostly with walls, not motile, mostly autotrophic; mostly in fresh water
      6. Unicellular, without vegetative cell division   6. *Phytodiniales*
      6. Multicellular or colonial, with vegetative cell division
         7. Plants forming palmelloid colonies, with a temporary motile stage   7. *Gloeodiniales*
         7. Plants filamentous, branching   8. *Dinotrichales*

KEY TO THE ORDERS OF CHLOROMONADOPHYCEAE

A single order   1. *Chloromonadales*

KEY TO THE ORDERS OF XANTHOPHYCEAE

1. Cell wall lacking; plants motile
   2. Vegetative cells flagellated, sometimes temporarily becoming amoeboid   1. *Heterochloridales*
   2. Vegetative cells permanently amoeboid, not flagellated, often forming a multinucleate plasmodium   2. *Rhizochloridales*
1. Cell wall (or a gelatinous envelope) present; plants nonmotile, except commonly for the zoospores or gametes
   3. Plants not filamentous, the cells solitary or colonial
      4. Zoospores formed by direct modification of vegetative cells; plants capable of vegetative cell division   3. *Heterocapsales*
      4. Zoospores formed by division of the protoplast within the wall of the vegetative cell; plants mostly incapable of vegetative cell division   4. *Heterococcales*
   3. Plants filamentous
      5. Filaments composed of uninucleate cells   5. *Heterotrichales*
      5. Filaments coenocytic, multinucleate, the vegetative part without cross walls   6. *Vaucheriales*

KEY TO THE ORDERS OF CHRYSOPHYCEAE

1. Cell naked or with a wall, but, in any case, without an internal skeleton

Appendix I: Keys to the Divisions, Classes, and Orders of Plants   839

2. Vegetative cells motile
    3. Cells generally flagellated, with only temporary or no amoeboid stage   *1. Chrysomonadales*
    3. Cells amoeboid, with only temporary or no flagellated stage   *2. Rhizochrysidales*
2. Vegetative cells nonmotile, or with only temporary motile stages
    4. Plants not filamentous
        5. Vegetative cells capable of returning directly to a motile condition, and capable of vegetative cell division   *3. Chrysocapsales*
        5. Vegetative cells incapable of returning directly to a motile condition, and usually or always incapable of vegetative cell division   *4. Chrysosphaerales*
    4. Plants filamentous   *5. Chrysotrichales*
1. Cell naked, but with an internal skeleton consisting of a framework of variously arranged siliceous rods   *6. Siphonotestales*

Key to the Orders of Bacillariophyceae

1. Valves with a longitudinally bipartite, usually bilaterally symmetrical pattern; chloroplasts usually only one or two; isogamous or anisogamous, the gametes not flagellated; vegetative cells often motile; no statospores; most abundant in fresh water, less often marine   *1. Pennales*
1. Valves with a concentric, usually radially symmetrical pattern; chloroplasts usually numerous; oögamous, the male gametes flagellated; vegetative cells nonmotile; often produce statospores; chiefly marine   *2. Centrales*

Key to the Orders of Isogeneratae

1. Thallus filamentous, the filament one or several cells thick
    2. Filaments without a prominent meristematic apical cell, the growth trichothallic or diffuse
        3. Filaments mostly uniseriate throughout, the cell divisions not localized; isogamous or anisogamous, with gametangia in clusters, and often also with clusters of neutral sporangia; sexual spores uninucleate, flagellated, more or less numerous   *1. Ectocarpales*
        3. Filaments apically uniseriate, usually multiseriate toward the base, the growth trichothallic; oögamous, the antheridia clustered, the oögonia solitary; sexual spores solitary in the sporangia and four-nucleate, not flagellated; no neutral spores   *2. Tilopteridales*
    2. Filaments with a well-developed apical meristematic cell, otherwise multiseriate; gametangia clustered; sexual spores flagellated, more or less numerous; neutral spores often formed   *3. Sphaecelariales*
1. Thallus flattened, parenchymatous, filamentous only at the tip; no neutral spores
    4. Plants with more or less distinctly trichothallic growth; anisogamous, with both types of gametangia in clusters; sexual spores 8–32, biflagellate   *4. Cutleriales*

4. Plants with an apical meristematic cell or group of cells; oögamous, or seldom anisogamous, the oögonia separate, the antheridia clustered; sexual spores four or eight, without flagella 5. *Dictyotales*

1. Sporophyte composed, at least in large part, of individual filaments, these often so closely compacted as to resemble a parenchymatous tissue, but each filament distinguishable from its neighbors and not undergoing longitudinal cell divisions; growth usually partly or wholly trichothallic
   2. Filaments of the sporophytes seldom closely compacted, not forming large, pseudoparenchymatous thalli; isogamous, as far as known; growth terminal or trichothallic 1. *Chordariales*
   2. Filaments of the sporophytes compacted into a pseudoparenchymatous, often large and complex thallus, oögamous; growth trichothallic
      3. Each branch of the sporophyte terminating in a tuft of filaments 2. *Sporochnales*
      3. Each branch of the sporophyte terminating in a single, branched filament 3. *Desmarestiales*
1. Sporophyte somewhat parenchymatous, although the central part may have more or less distinct filaments; growth not trichothallic
   4. Thallus simple or branched, with mostly cylindric branches, without differentiated stipe and blade; growth diffuse or from a single meristematic apical cell on each branch; isogamous or anisogamous 4. *Dictyosiphonales*
   4. Thallus usually divided into a holdfast, stipe, and blade, often very large; growth from intercalary meristems, usually between the stipe and the blade; oögamous 5. *Laminariales*

A single order 1. *Fucales*

A single order 1. *Bangiales*

1. Carpospores generally haploid, developing into gametophytes; tetrasporophytes only rarely formed 1. *Nemalionales*
1. Carpospores diploid, developing into tetrasporophytes
   2. Gonimoblast filaments arising directly from the carpogonium 2. *Gelidiales*
   2. Gonimoblast filaments arising from auxiliary cells
      3. Auxiliary cells intercalary
         4. Auxiliary cell an ordinary vegetative cell, or a supporting cell of the carpogonial filament 3. *Gigartinales*

Appendix I: Keys to the Divisions, Classes, and Orders of Plants 841

4. Auxiliary cell borne on a special filament which lacks chloroplasts   *4. Cryptonemiales*

3. Auxiliary cells terminal
    5. Auxiliary cell differentiated before fertilization as the terminal member of a two-celled branch from the supporting cell of a carpogonial filament   *5. Rhodymeniales*
    5. Auxiliary cell differentiated after fertilization, borne directly on the supporting cell of a carpogonial filament   *6. Ceramiales*

KEY TO THE ORDERS OF MYXOMYCETES

1. Holozoic, ingesting small organic food particles; sporangia (or spores) aerial.
    2. Sporangia without peridium and capillitium, the spores embedded in a mass of slime; cells of the "plasmodium" retaining their individual identity (although mostly without walls) throughout, or until just before the formation of sporangia; swarm cells without flagella   *1. Acrasiales*
    2. Sporangia with a peridium and usually with a capillitium, or the spores sometimes borne singly and externally; plasmodium with scattered nuclei, not divided into definite cells; swarm cells usually with flagella
        3. Spores born in a sporangium, each spore producing one, two, or rarely more swarm cells on germination
            4. Capillitium lacking or only poorly developed; peridium not calcareous   *2. Liceales*
            4. Capillitium well-developed
                5. Spores bright yellow, orange, or red; capillitium and peridium not calcareous   *3. Trichiales*
                5. Spores black or deep violet to sometimes rusty red, rarely colorless
                    6. Neither the peridium nor the capillitium calcareous   *4. Stemonitales*
                    6. Peridium, or capillitium, or both calcareous   *5. Physarales*
        3. Spores borne externally on definite stalks, each producing on germination a cluster of eight swarm cells   *6. Ceratiomyxales*
1. Parasitic, living within the cells of the host and absorbing food; sporangia, when present, produced within the individual cells of the host
    7. Plasmodium forming a compact mass rather than a net; swarm spores biflagellate; mostly parasitic on roots and stems of higher plants, seldom on algae or fungi   *7. Plasmodiophorales*
    7. Plasmodium with separate naked cells connected by long cytoplasmic strands to form a chain or network; swarm cells uniflagellate or without flagella; parasitic on algae and submerged aquatic higher plants   *8. Labyrinthulales*

KEY TO THE ORDERS OF PHYCOMYCETES

1. Plants producing flagellated spores or gametes; sexual reproduction usually involving definite

unicellular gametes and resulting in the formation of unicellular, uninucleate zygotes, or in any case not as in the Zygomycetes (Oömycetes)

2. Mycelium poorly or scarcely developed, the vegetative body with one or more enlarged regions which may or may not give rise to sparingly branched hyphae; vegetative body eventually becoming multinucleate, and each of the enlarged regions developing into one or more gametangia or sporangia; cell wall often with cellulose; typically intracellular parasites, especially of aquatic organisms, sometimes extracellular and with haustoria, or inhabiting newly dead cells of the host

    3. Motile cells biflagellate, one flagellum whiplash, one pinnate; wall of cellulose   1. *Lagenidiales*

    3. Motile cells uniflagellate

        4. Flagellum posterior, whiplash; wall sometimes chitinous, sometimes of cellulose; often sexual   2. *Chytridiales*

        4. Flagellum anterior, pinnate; wall chitinous, without cellulose; wholly asexual   3. *Hyphochytriales*

2. Mycelium more or less well-developed, coenocytic, the gametangia and sporangia formed from a relatively small part of the vegetative body; saprophytes or parasites, but not wholly intracellular

    5. Motile cells uniflagellate, the flagellum posterior, whiplash; gametes, or some of them, as well as the zoospores flagellated and free-swimming; wall lacking cellulose, usually chitinous; mostly aquatic saprophytes

        6. Isogamous or anisogamous; zygote not going into a resting stage; thick-walled asexual resting cells which eventually give rise to zoospores generally produced; plants often with an alternation of distinct gametophytic and sporophytic generations   4. *Blastocladiales*

        6. Oögamous; zygote going into a thick-walled resting stage, after which it germinates directly; no thick-walled asexual spores; no well-developed sporophyte generation   5. *Monoblepharidales*

    5. Motile cells biflagellate, one flagellum whiplash, one pinnate; only the zoospores flagellated, the sperm nuclei being transferred to the egg by a tube growing out of the antheridium; wall usually with cellulose

        7. Typically aquatic and mostly saprophytic; sporangia producing spores; seldom any conidia formed; one to several eggs per oögonium   6. *Saprolegniales*

        7. Typically terrestrial and parasitic; sporangia usually failing to produce spores and being released as conidia; one egg per oögonium   7. *Peronosporales*

1. Plants without flagellated cells of any kind; sexual reproduction involving fusion of multinucleate gametangia to form a multinucleate zygospore; gametangia similar or differing somewhat in size, coming together by growth from adjacent hyphae or hyphal branches; wall chitinous (Zygomycetes)

    8. Saprophytes, less often parasites, especially of other fungi, the zygospores chiefly aerial; outer wall of the zygospore formed by modification of the gametangial wall; sporangia with few to numerous spores, or reduced to conidia; mycelium tardily or never septate   8. *Mucorales*

8. Mostly internal parasites, especially of insects, with the zygospores produced inside the host, sometimes saprophytes in the
dung of lizards and frogs; no multispored sporangia; outer wall
of the zygospore distinct from the wall of the gametangium;
conidia present; mycelium sooner or later becoming septate   9. *Entomophthorales*

Key to the Orders of Ascomycetes

1. Asci not borne on definite fruiting bodies (subclass Hemiascomycetes
 2. Mostly saprophytes, often unicellular or with a poorly developed
mycelium; karyogamy following immediately after plasmogamy, the resulting zygote commonly maturing directly
into an ascus   1. *Endomycetales*
 2. Mostly parasites of plants; karyogamy delayed until well after
plasmogamy, the asci mostly arising from resting cells produced by mycelia in which each cell has a pair of nuclei   2. *Taphrinales*
1. Asci born on or in definite fruiting bodies; mycelium usually well-
developed
 3. Ascus unitunicate (i.e., with a single wall); fruiting body a cleistothecium, perithecium,
or apothecium, or the perithecia sometimes embedded in a stroma, but then each with
its own differentiated wall; perithecia, when present, with the ostiole lined with peri-
physes (sterile filaments) (subclass Euascomycetes)
 4. Fruiting body closed, opening only by weathering, commonly developing into a definite
cleistothecium (see also Tuberales); asci globose to broadly club-shaped, borne in
tufts or irregularly arranged, with uniformly thickened walls that lack pores
 5. Fruiting body more or less filled with asci and ascogenous
hyphae
 6. Not lichen-forming; asci only tardily degenerating   3. *Eurotiales*
 6. Mostly lichen-forming; asci soon degenerating and releasing their spores into the interior of the ascocarp   4. *Caliciales*
 5. Fruiting body not filled by asci, these arising singly or in
tufts from the basal region of the ascocarp   5. *Erysiphales*
 4. Fruiting body opening by one or more pores or slits, or open
from the beginning; asci cylindric to club-shaped, commonly
opening by an apical pore
 7. Fruiting body a perithecium (i.e., with a definite wall and
a small opening), or the perithecia sometimes embedded
in a stroma
 8. Perithecia stalked, borne on a receptacle, without prominent internal sterile hairs; minute parasites of
insects   6. *Laboulbeniales*
 8. Perithecia not stalked
 9. Asci intermingled with sterile hyphae (pseudoparaphyses) which connect to the top of the perithecium; fruiting body dull, scarcely fleshy; not
lichen-forming   7. *Hypocreales*
 9. Asci intermingled with sterile hyphae (paraphyses)
which are free at the tip; fruiting body often

brightly colored, soft, and fleshy; often lichen-
forming   8. *Sphaeriales*
7. Fruiting body an apothecium (i.e., open nearly or quite
from the first, the hymenial layer of asci and paraphyses
exposed)
   10. Lichen-forming   9. *Lecanorales*
   10. Not lichen-forming
     11. Asci opening irregularly or by a pore that does not
have a lid   10. *Helotiales*
     11. Asci operculate (the pore opening by a definite lid)
       12. Fruiting body aerial; hymenium exposed   11. *Pezizales*
       12. Fruiting body subterranean; paraphyses com-
pacted above the asci to form a definite cov-
ering, the ascocarp thus cleistothecium-like   12. *Tuberales*
3. Ascus bitunicate (i.e., with two walls, the outer wall soon splitting
and remaining as a cup around the base of the elongating inner
wall); fruiting body generally a stroma with one or more perithecium-like or cleistothecium-like cavities, these lacking differentiated walls; ostiole, if present, narrow and without peri-
physes (subclass Loculoascomycetes)
13. Fruiting body closed, opening only by weathering, divided
internally into a number of chambers, each chamber with
one ascus   13. *Myriangales*
13. Fruiting body opening by one or more pores or slits
   14. Fruiting body opening by one or more circular pores
     15. Paraphyses and pseudoparaphyses wanting; stroma
often with many perithecium-like cavities; vegetative mycelium immersed in the substrate   14. *Dothideales*
     15. Pseudoparaphyses intermingled with the asci; stroma
with only one perithecium-like cavity; vegetative
mycelium often largely superficial
       16. Hymenium covering much of the inner wall of
the fruiting body, which is not flattened at
the base; includes some lichen-formers   15. *Pleosporales*
       16. Hymenium in a basal layer within the basally
flattened fruiting body; not lichen-forming   16. *Microthyriales*
   14. Fruiting body opening by an elongate slit; pseudoparaphyses present
     17. Opening of the fruiting body remaining relatively
small; not lichen-forming   17. *Lophiostomatales*
     17. Fruiting body at maturity opening out and more or
less resembling an apothecium; often lichen-forming   18. *Hysteriales*

Key to the Orders of Basidiomycetes

1. Basidium usually septate or deeply divided, or arising from a teliospore, or the teliospore
germinating directly without forming a basidium; basidiospores often germinating by
repetition (subclass Heterobasidiomycetes)

Appendix I: Keys to the Divisions, Classes, and Orders of Plants   **845**

2. Fruiting body well-developed, with a more or less definite hymenium; basidiospores forcibly discharged from the sterigmata; saprophytes and parasites   *1. Tremellales*

2. Fruiting body scarcely developed or wanting; parasitic on vascular plants, seldom facultative saprophytes

    3. Basidiospores borne on sterigmata from which they are forcibly discharged; the four nuclei formed by meiosis within the basidium migrate directly into the four basidiospores, leaving the basidium without nuclei; spores often yellow to orange red   *2. Uredinales*

    3. Basidiospores sessile on the basidium and not violently discharged, or the basidium sometimes failing to produce basidiospores, or the teliospores germinating directly without forming a basidium; the four nuclei formed by meiosis within the basidium generally divide mitotically one or more times before some or all of the daughter nuclei migrate into the four or more basidiospores, the basidium often producing successive crops of basidiospores; spores usually black   *3. Ustilaginales*

1. Basidium always simple and not deeply divided, arising directly and without interruption from a probasidium which is not spore-like; basidiospores germinating directly to produce a mycelium (subclass Homobasidiomycetes)

    4. Fruiting body none; parasites of vascular plants   *4. Exobasidiales*

    4. Fruiting body well-developed

       5. Hymenium present, exposed before the spores are mature; basidiospores obliquely set and forcibly discharged from the sterigmata (Hymenomycetes)   *5. Agaricales*

       5. Hymenium present or absent; fruiting body remaining closed until after the spores have been discharged from the basidia, or permanently closed; basidiospores neither obliquely set nor forcibly discharged from the basidium (Gasteromycetes)

          6. Hymenium present in early stages, later losing its identity

             7. Gleba usually fleshy or waxy, sometimes slimy and fetid but then not exposed   *6. Hymenogastrales*

             7. Gleba not fleshy or waxy

                8. Gleba slimy and fetid at maturity, and exposed on an elongate or enlarged receptacle   *7. Phallales*

                8. Gleba powdery and dry at maturity   *8. Lycoperdales*

          6. Hymenium essentially wanting

             9. Gleba powdery at maturity; chambers of the gleba usually not separating from the peridium or from each other   *9. Sclerodermatales*

             9. Gleba waxy; chambers of the gleba with distinct walls, eventually separating from each other and released from the basidiocarp as individual bodies which serve as disseminules   *10. Nidulariales*

A single order   **1.** *Anthocerotales*

KEY TO THE ORDERS OF HEPATICAE

1. Sporophyte usually with a well-developed seta which elevates the capsule well above the gametophyte; capsule generally opening along four definite longitudinal lines, very rarely opening irregularly; neck of the archegonium nearly as broad as the venter; gametophyte (except usually in the Metzgeriales) with evident phyllidia, these usually in two or three rows; oil bodies usually several in every, or nearly every, cell

   2. Gametophyte somewhat moss-like, the caulidium with a naked stolon-like base and erect branches that bear three rows of equal or subequal phyllidia (or the phyllidia closely aggregated and in more than three rows at the tips of the fertile branches); rhizoids wanting; neck of the archegonium with four vertical rows of cells; jacket of the capsule one cell thick, except toward the tip, where thicker   **1.** *Calobryales*

   2. Gametophyte scarcely moss-like, dorsiventral, the lower side with rhizoids; neck of the archegonium with five vertical rows of cells; jacket of the capsule two to eight cells thick

      3. Archegonia terminal, the apical cell of the thallus used up in their formation; gametophyte distinctly "leafy," with two dorsolateral rows of well-developed phyllidia, and usually with a median ventral row of more or less reduced phyllidia   **2.** *Jungermanniales*

      3. Archegonia dorsal, the apical cell not used up in their formation; gametophyte typically thallose, sometimes "leafy" with two dorsal rows of phyllidia, but the ventral phyllidia, if present, not forming a single median row   **3.** *Metzgeriales*

1. Sporophyte with short or no seta, the capsule scarcely or not at all elevated beyond the gametophyte; jacket of the capsule one cell thick, opening in various ways, but usually not along four definite lines; neck of the archegonium much narrower than the venter; gametophyte more or less strictly thallose, usually without phyllidia; oil bodies large, borne singly in scattered cells, or seldom wanting

   4. Gametophyte with differentiated tissues and usually with air chambers, and generally with two kinds of rhizoids as well as two rows of ventral scales; antheridia and archegonia usually not individually surrounded by evident raised involucres   **4.** *Marchantiales*

   4. Gametophyte without sharply differentiated tissues and without air chambers, with only one kind of rhizoid, and without ventral scales; antheridia and archegonia individually surrounded by evident, raised, tubular involucres   **5.** *Sphaerocarpales*

KEY TO THE ORDERS OF MUSCI

1. Columella not reaching the summit of the capsule; sporophyte becoming elevated on a pseu-

Appendix I: Keys to the Divisions, Classes, and Orders of Plants   847

dopodium of gametophytic tissue, without a prominent seta; protonema broadly thallose; capsule never with an operculum fringed by a peristome

    2. Capsule opening along four longitudinal lines; caulidium not differentiated into a cortex and central cylinder; mature gametophores with numerous rhizoids along their length; cells of the phyllidia all chlorophyllous, not of two markedly contrasting types; generally several gametophores formed from each protonema   1. *Andreaeales*

    2. Capsule opening by a lid; caulidium differentiated into a cortex and central cylinder; mature gametophores without rhizoids; cells of the phyllidia of two strongly contrasting types, one with chlorophyll, one without; only one gametophore formed by each protonema   2. *Sphagnales*

1. Columella reaching the summit of the capsule and attached to it; sporophyte commonly with an elongate seta, not borne on a gametophytic pseudopodium; protonema generally filamentous, seldom broadly thallose; capsule generally opening by a lid (operculum), with a specialized peristome, or sometimes opening irregularly; mature gametophores with rhizoids at the base, or scattered along prostrate branches   3. *Bryales*

KEY TO THE ORDERS OF PSILOTAE

1. Sporangia borne on ordinary vegetative branches, simple, unilocular; ancient fossils   1. *Psilophytales*

1. Sporangia borne on specialized, very short branches, compound, three-locular; modern plants   2. *Psilotales*

KEY TO THE ORDERS OF LYCOPODIAE

1. Stem more or less elongate and usually branched; sperms (in modern forms) biflagellate; sporangia sessile or stalked, not embedded except in some Lepidodendrales, mostly lacking partitions; leaves (in modern species) seldom over an inch long

    2. Plants homosporous; leaves eligulate; plants herbaceous, with little or no secondary growth; modern and fossil forms   1. *Lycopodiales*

    2. Plants heterosporous; leaves ligulate

        3. Plants small and not very woody, with little or no secondary growth; modern and fossil forms   2. *Selaginellales*

        3. Plants woody, of tree size, usually with vigorous secondary growth; fossil forms only   3. *Lepidodendrales*

1. Stem usually very short, commonly wider than high, unbranched; sperms (in modern species) multiflagellate; sporangium incompletely divided by cross partitions, partly embedded in the sporophyll; heterosporous, with numerous megaspores in a sporangium; leaves elongate, usually at least several inches long, ligulate; plants with a unique type of secondary growth; living and fossil forms   4. *Isoetales*

1. Branching dichotomous or digitate (like the fingers of a hand); stems not always obviously jointed; leaves apically notched or cleft, or dichotomously branched; fossils only   **1.** *Hyeniaies*
1. Branches arising at the nodes, commonly whorled around the main axis; stems obviously jointed
   2. Leaves with a dichotomously branching vein system, generally toothed or cleft from the apex; stem protostelic, without a pith; fossils only   **2.** *Sphenophyllales*
   2. Leaves entire and with a single, unbranched midvein, often more or less connate into a sheath; stem with a definite, usually large and short-lived pith, and with the primary vascular tissue in the internodal regions divided into a ring of separate bundles
      3. Plants with well-developed secondary thickening in the stem and root, large and commonly attaining tree size; strobilus with alternating whorls of sporangiophores and sterile appendages; fossils only   **3.** *Calamitales*
      3. Plants without secondary thickening, always relatively small, not tree-like; strobilus (in modern species) without sterile appendages; modern and fossil forms   **4.** *Equisetales*

KEY TO THE ORDERS OF FILICES

1. Plants eusporangiate; antheridia in living forms sunken in the body of the gametophyte and producing many sperms
   2. Sporangia terminal on the ultimate segments of the leaf; fossils only
      3. Leaves scarcely differentiated, represented by slightly modified branch stem systems   **1.** *Protopteridales*
      3. Leaves well differentiated, pinnately decompound   **2.** *Coenopteridales*
   2. Sporangia borne on the leaf surface or on a projection from the leaf surface
      4. Sporangia borne in a "fertile spike" which projects from the upper surface of the leaf; leaves not circinate; modern species only   **3.** *Ophioglossales*
      4. Sporangia borne on the leaf surface, not in a fertile spike; leaves circinate
         5. Sporangia borne on the adaxial (upper) surface of the leaf, not in sori; heterosporous; fossils only   **4.** *Archeopteridales*
         5. Sporangia borne on the abaxial (lower) surface of the leaf, aggregated into sori; homosporous; modern and fossil species   **5.** *Marattiales*
1. Plants leptosporangiate; antheridia in living forms projecting from the surface of the gametophyte, seldom producing more than 32 sperms
   6. Plants homosporous; sporangia borne on vegetative or more or less modified leaves, but not enclosed in a sporocarp; terrestrial or occasionally aquatic plants   **6.** *Filicales*

Appendix I: Keys to the Divisions, Classes, and Orders of Plants   849

6. Plants heterosporous; sporangia borne in a specialized sporocarp; aquatic plants
    7. Plants rooted to the bottom; microsporangia and megasporangia in the same sporocarp   7. *Marsileales*
    7. Plants free-floating; microsporangia and megasporangia in separate sporocarps   8. *Salviniales*

KEY TO THE ORDERS OF CYCADAE

1. Microsporophylls pinnately compound, not aggregated into a strobilus, often borne on the same plant as the megasporophylls; female strobili, when present, borne on short axillary branches; fossils only
  2. Megasporophylls pinnately compound, not aggregated into strobili
    3. Ovules borne separately along the margins or on the surface of the megasporophyll; vegetative leaves usually pinnately compound or decompound; Devonian to Jurassic, but most abundant in the Carboniferous   1. *Cycadofilicales*
    3. Ovules semienclosed in groups in small pouches which are pinnately arranged along the axis of a megasporophyll; vegetative leaves usually with four subpalmately disposed leaflets; Triassic to Cretaceous   2. *Caytoniales*
  2. Megasporophylls simple, each with a single terminal ovule, aggregated into compact strobili, the strobilus commonly subtended by the more expanded microsporophylls; Triassic to Cretaceous   3. *Bennettitales*
1. Microsporophylls simple, aggregated into a definite, usually terminal strobilus, never borne on the same plant as the megasporophylls; megasporophylls usually, but not always, simple and aggregated into a terminal strobilus; modern and fossil species, known from the Triassic to the present   4. *Cycadales*

KEY TO THE ORDERS OF CONIFERAE

1. Leaves entire or slightly toothed, usually narrow, never fan-shaped; sperms naked in modern species
  2. Ovules and seeds borne in more or less definite cones; seeds not fleshy
    3. Microsporangia terminal on the microsporophylls; female cones simple (i.e., the ovules borne on the primary appendages of the cone axis); pith relatively large; fossils only   1. *Cordaitales*
    3. Microsporangia borne on the lower surface of the microsporophyll; female cones generally compound (i.e., the ovules borne on structures axillary to the primary appendages of the cone axis); pith small; modern and fossil species   2. *Coniferales*
  2. Ovules and seeds not in cones; seed with a fleshy covering; otherwise as in the Coniferales   3. *Taxales*

1. Leaves, or many of them, bilobed or palmately lobed or dichotomously dissected, commonly fan-shaped; modern species with
flagellated sperms; ovules and seeds apical on slender stalks, not
in cones; seed with a fleshy covering   4. *Ginkgoales*

KEY TO THE ORDERS OF CHLAMYDOSPERMAE

1. Leaves much reduced, scale-like; archegonium present; much
branched shrubs   1. *Ephedrales*
1. Leaves well-developed; archegonium absent
   2. Leaves more or less numerous, of ordinary size, oval, net-veined;
plant a woody vine, or sometimes a tree or branching shrub   2. *Gnetales*
   2. Leaves two, very large, much elongate, parallel-veined; plant with
a short, stout, unbranched woody main stem   3. *Welwitschiales*

SYNOPSIS OF THE ORDERS OF DICOTYLEDONAE

1. Plants either with the flowers mostly apocarpous (i.e., the carpels separate), or with the pollen
of monocolpate or monocolpate-derived type (notable exceptions in the Rosales and Berberidales); integuments generally two; petals usually separate (or absent), but the sepals
often united
   2. Stamens mostly numerous and developing in centripetal sequence; carpels most separate, two to many (one in *Degeneria*);
flowers mostly hypogynous; stamens mostly dehiscent by longitudinal slits, or sometimes irregularly dehiscent, not dehiscent
by valves   1. *Ranales*
   2. Plants generally differing in one or more respects from the
Ranales as characterized above
     3. Stamens numerous and developing in centrifugal sequence;
seeds generally arillate; calyx and corolla usually well-dif-
ferentiated; carpels separate; no specialized secretory cells
in the vegetative parts   2. *Dilleniales*
     3. Stamens either few, or numerous and developing in centripetal
sequence; seeds seldom arillate; carpels separate or united;
secretory cells present or absent
      4. Flowers not crowded into a fleshy spike, and not at once epi-
gynous and without a perianth; ovules mostly anatropous
       5. Plants generally either with separate carpels, or with
tricolpate (or tricolpate-derived) pollen, or with an
inferior ovary
        6. Flowers hypogynous; stamens two to many, often
of the same number as the petals and opposite
them; stipules mostly absent; plants herbaceous to
woody, often climbing, the woody forms mostly
with wide or very wide wood rays   3. *Berberidales*
        6. Flowers mostly perigynous to epigynous, hypogynous
only in a few Rosales; stipules present or absent;
stamens when few mostly not opposite the petals

7. Ovary mostly inferior, with united carpels; petals none or rudimentary; sepals united, the calyx often corolloid, tending to be three-lobed or irregular; carpels four to six; pollen monocolpate or acolpate; stamens often adnate to the short style; shrubs and herbs, often climbing   *4. Aristolochiales*

7. Ovary superior, or plants without petaloid calyx, or both; other characters various

    3. Perianth usually clearly differentiated into calyx and corolla, or the plants occasionally without petals; other characters various   *8. Rosales*

    8. Perianth scarcely or not at all differentiated into calyx and corolla, though often biseriate; plants woody (except in a few Proteaceae), exstipulate, generally with well-developed secretory cells in the wood

        9. Perianth consisting of a single more or less strongly corolloid cycle of mostly four members, these connate into a tube; stamens mostly four (seldom eight), dehiscent by longitudinal slits; secretory cells containing tanniferous substances; pollen mostly tricolpate; endosperm scanty or none; carpel one   *9. Proteales*

        9. Perianth not strongly corolloid, of one or more cycles or a spiral, seldom of four members; stamens seldom four, often dehiscent by valves; secretory cells containing volatile oils; pollen rarely tricolpate; endosperm present or absent; carpels one to several   *5. Laurales*

  5. Plants with a superior, syncarpous ovary and parietal placentation; stamens joined into a tube; pollen monocolpate; woody plants with secretory cells containing volatile oils   *6. Canellales*

  4. Flowers tending to be crowded into a fleshy, spike-like inflorescence, essentially without perianth, and either syncarpous or epigynous; pollen of monocolpate or monocolpate-derived type; ovules orthotropous   *7. Piperales*

1. Plants mostly with united carpels; pollen of tricolpate or tricolpate-derived type

  10. Petals mostly separate or none, seldom united; integuments usually two, occasionally (especially in the Santalales) only one or none

    11. Plants tending to be modified toward either parasitism or insect-catching; leaves mostly alternate (except some Santalales); endosperm well-developed

      12. Plants modified toward insect-catching; herbs or shrubs with perfect, regular, hypogynous flowers and loculicidal capsules   *34. Sarraceniales*

12. Plants modified toward parasitism (except some Olacaceae), often with reduced leaves, and sometimes lacking chlorophyll; ovules (except some Olacaceae) more or less simplified, with only one or no integument; flowers often unisexual, mostly without petals, and more or less epigynous; fruit indehiscent 23. *Santalales*

11. Plants neither parasitic nor insect-catching

 13. Flowers more or less strongly reduced and generally unisexual (perfect in some aquatic herbs, among others), individually mostly inconspicuous, often some of them borne in catkins; seeds not centrospermous

  14. Carpels and locules mostly three, each with one or two mostly pendulous ovules, or some locules empty; flowers not in catkins; seeds usually with endosperm; most species woody, with simple or occasionally compound leaves 22. *Euphorbiales*

  14. Flowers differing in one or usually more respects from those of the Euphorbiales as described above, seldom tricarpellate and trilocular, and often some of them in catkins

   15. Herbs, chiefly aquatic; flowers not in catkins

    16. Submerged or more often emergent aquatics, or terrestrial herbs, with inferior or naked ovary and with endosperm 11. *Haloragales*

    16. Submerged aquatics with superior or naked ovary and without endosperm 12. *Podostemales*

   15. Plants either woody, or with some of the flowers borne in catkins, or often both; mostly not aquatic

    17. Fruit indehiscent; seeds solitary or few, without long hairs

     18. Leaves simple or occasionally palmately compound, the forms with compound leaves mostly herbaceous or climbing

      19. Leaves alternate or opposite, more or less well-developed; ovules each with a single embryo sac

       20. Leaves mostly alternate (opposite-leaved forms generally have stipules, or have more than four stamens); trees, shrubs, or herbs, monoecious or dioecious, or seldom with perfect flowers 13. *Urticales*

       20. Leaves opposite, without stipules; dioecious; stamens four

        21. Ovary unilocular; leaves firm, not fleshy; integument one; shrubs and small trees; endosperm

well-developed

    21. Ovary four-locular; leaves fleshy; integuments two; subshrubs; endosperm none

   19. Leaves whorled, reduced and scale-like; ovules each with about 20 embryo sacs; trees

  18. Leaves pinnately compound or trifoliolate; trees

 17. Fruit capsular, with numerous parietally attached seeds that are provided with long hairs; leaves simple; trees and shrubs

13. Flowers usually more or less well-developed, only seldom unisexual, never borne in catkins, usually with petals (some forms with centrospermous seeds, among others, have reduced and unisexual flowers)

   22. Plants mostly with internal phloem (i.e., the vascular bundles bicollateral, or the internal strands of phloem not attached to the collateral bundles); flowers strongly perigynous to epigynous; leaves mostly opposite; stamens, if numerous, developing in centripetal sequence; placentation mostly axile, sometimes apical, rarely parietal; trees, shrubs, and herbs; seeds not centrospermous

   22. Plants mostly without internal phloem (the few exceptions limited almost entirely to the Caryophyllales, which have centrospermous seeds); flowers diverse, but mostly not presenting the combination of characters shown by the Myrtales; leaves various

    23. Seeds (except in some Polygonaceae) mostly centrospermous (i.e., the embryo elongate, peripheral or nearly so, and generally more or less curved about the usually copious perisperm or endosperm); placentation typically free-central or basal in a unilocular compound ovary; plants typically herbaceous and often more or less fleshy, less often woody

    23. Seeds generally not centrospermous, or if more or less so, then the plants mostly with parietal placentation, or differing in other respects from the Caryophyllales

     24. Plants mostly either with numerous stamens that (except in some Rhoedales, which have parietal placentation) develop in centrifugal sequence, or with parietal placentation, or both; ovules

	25. *Garryales*
	27. *Batidales*
	14. *Casuarinales*
	18. *Juglandales*
	36. *Salicales*
	10. *Myrtales*
	26. *Caryophyllales*

mostly several or numerous per carpel, seldom only one or two; flowers without a well-defined disk

25. Placentation mostly axile
    26. Flowers hypogynous or nearly so
        27. Calyx imbricate, the margins of the sepals or lobes overlapping in bud; pubescence seldom of stellate or umbrella-shaped hairs   30. *Guttiferales*
        27. Calyx valvate, the margins of the sepals or lobes merely adjacent; pubescence commonly of stellate or umbrella-shaped hairs   31. *Malvales*
    26. Flowers more or less epigynous; calyx generally valvate; pubescence not of stellate or umbrella-shaped hairs   32. *Lecythidales*

25. Placentation mostly parietal
    28. Plants more or less strongly succulent, generally with strongly reduced leaves, and usually evidently spiny; stamens numerous, centrifugal; petals and sepals mostly numerous; ovary mostly inferior; endosperm scanty or more often none   28. *Cactales*
    28. Plants not markedly succulent, usually with well-developed leaves, and seldom spiny; petals and sepals mostly of reasonably small and definite number; stamens, ovary, and seeds various
        29. Plants mostly either herbaceous, or with distinctly compound leaves, or both, and often with myrosin cells; flowers hypogynous and mostly perfect   33. *Rhoedales*
        29. Plants generally differing in one or more respects from the Rhoedales as characterized above, very often woody and simple-leaved, or with perigynous to epigynous, often unisexual flowers, and never with myrosin cells   35. *Bixales*

24. Plants seldom with more than about ten stamens (numerous in some Linales and Sapindales, and in these, as far as is known, developing in centripetal sequence); ovules very often only one or two per carpel, but sometimes more numerous, the placentation mostly axile to basal or apical; flowers often with a disk

    30. Leaves mostly compound or dissected, or simple but evidently cleft (simple and entire in a few small families and scattered genera)

        31. Ovary superior; flowers not in umbels; nodes various

            32. Plants mostly woody, seldom herbaceous   *15. Sapindales*

            32. Plants mostly herbaceous or nearly so   *16. Geraniales*

        31. Ovary inferior; flowers tending to be in umbels; nodes mostly multilacunar   *17. Umbellales*

    30. Leaves simple, entire or merely toothed

        33. Flowers mostly more or less irregular, and often with the stamens or petals partly united   *19. Polygalales*

        33. Flowers mostly regular or nearly so

            34. Ovary mostly superior; fruit and seeds various

                35. Stamens united at the base, commonly ten, sometimes more numerous, or only five in some herbaceous Linaeae; flowers without a disk   *20. Linales*

                35. Stamens mostly free, five or fewer; flowers often with a disk   *21. Celastrales*

            34. Ovary mostly inferior; fruit indehiscent; endosperm present   *24. Cornales*

10. Petals mostly united toward the base, seldom (but especially in the Ericales) wholly separate, or wanting; integuments often only one

    36. Ovary mostly superior (seldom inferior, the flowers then with mostly more than five stamens); stamens from fewer than to more numerous than the corolla lobes, and sometimes opposite them; filaments generally separate; fruits generally with more

than one seed (some notable exceptions); nodes mostly unilacunar (some notable exceptions)

37. Stamens (except in a few genera) generally either more numerous than the corolla lobes, or of the same number and opposite them; carpels (rarely two) three–many; no internal phloem

    38. Placentation generally axile, but the partition sometimes poorly developed or even wanting; stamens diverse; integuments one or two

        39. Ovules several to many per locule, rarely only one or two; herbs, shrubs, or sometimes trees, chiefly extratropical or of mountainous areas in the tropics, usually of acid soil, often (? always) strongly mycorhizal, and frequently evidently modified as a result, sometimes without chlorophyll, and often with very small leaves   **37. Ericales**

        39. Ovules one or two (rarely up to eight) per locule, rarely more than two maturing; trees or less often shrubs, chiefly tropical and subtropical, not evidently modified as a result of mycorhizal association, the leaves normally developed   **38. Ebenales**

    38. Placentation free-central or basal in one-celled ovary; stamens attached to the corolla opposite the lobes; integuments mostly two

        40. Style one, with a capitate or slightly lobed stigma; ovules generally several, sometimes only one maturing; woody or herbaceous   **39. Primulales**

        40. Style deeply five-cleft, or styles five; ovule solitary; herbs, shrubs, or vines, never trees   **29. Plumbaginales**

37. Stamens as many as the corolla lobes and alternate with them, or fewer, never opposite the corolla lobes; carpels commonly two, occasionally three or more; integument one

    41. Seeds usually either more than two per carpel, or with endosperm, or both; fruit never of four separating nutlets

        42. Corolla regular or nearly so; stamens usually as many as the corolla-lobes

            43. Corolla scarious (dry and papery); flower parts (except the carpels) mostly in sets of four; nodes trilacunar; leaves typically basal; mostly herbs, without internal phloem   **41. Plantaginales**

            43. Corolla usually petaloid, not scarious; flower parts seldom in sets of four; nodes mostly unilacunar, sometimes multilacunar; internal phloem often present

                44. Leaves chiefly opposite (Menyanthaceae excepted); carpels two; plants often tropical and woody   **40. Gentianales**

44. Leaves chiefly alternate (many exceptions among the Polemoniaceae, which generally have three carpels; fewer exceptions elsewhere); plants rarely both tropical and woody   42. *Polemoniales*

42. Corolla more or less strongly irregular; stamens usually fewer than the corolla lobes; nodes mostly unilacunar; rarely any internal phloem   43. *Scrophulariales*

41. Seeds two per carpel (or fewer by abortion), without endosperm; fruit typically of four more or less distinct (or separating) one-seeded, achene-like nutlets; nodes unilacunar; no internal phloem   44. *Lamiales*

36. Ovary inferior (superior only in a few scattered genera); stamens alternate with the corolla lobes, or fewer (fewer chiefly in herbaceous forms that either have the filaments joined into a tube or have one-seeded fruits); integument one or rarely none; nodes various; internal phloem mostly none

45. Flowers borne in various sorts of inflorescences; if borne in involucrate heads, then the ovules either pendulous or more than one

46. Leaves alternate, usually exstipulate; stamens usually free or attached to the base of the corolla; endosperm generally well-developed; seldom woody   45. *Campanulales*

46. Leaves opposite or whorled, often stipulate; stamens attached to the corolla; endosperm present or absent; plants often woody   46. *Rubiales*

45. Flowers borne in involucrate, centripetally flowering heads; ovary one-celled, with a solitary erect ovule; anthers generally united into a tube surrounding the style; endosperm none; stipules none   47. *Asterales*

SYNOPSIS OF THE ORDERS OF MONOCOTYLEDONAE

1. Carpels separate; seeds without endosperm
   2. Plants with chlorophyll, mostly aquatic or of marshy places
      3. Flowers mostly subtended by bracts; perianth in one or two whorls of three segments each, one whorl generally petaloid   1. *Alismatales*
      3. Flowers without bracts; perianth much reduced or none   2. *Najadales*
   2. Plants without chlorophyll; terrestrial   3. *Triuridales*
1. Carpels united, or if separate then the seeds usually with copious endosperm
   4. Perianth more or less well-developed, at least one series generally petaloid

5. Plants mostly herbaceous; leaves various but seldom palm-like
   6. Sepals and petals usually strongly differentiated, the sepals typically green, the petals some other color
      7. Endosperm none; placentation mostly parietal; plants aquatic   4. *Hydrocharitales*
      7. Endosperm generally well-developed; placentation and habit various
         8. Ovary superior to sometimes inferior; fertile stamens two, three, four, or most often six, not one or five; corolla regular or irregular   5. *Xyridales*
         8. Ovary inferior; fertile stamens one or five, rarely six; corolla irregular   6. *Zingiberales*
   6. Sepals and petals usually nearly alike and both petaloid
      9. Endosperm well-developed; perianth usually regular and plants chlorophyllous   7. *Liliales*
      9. Endosperm very scanty or none; perianth often irregular; plants often without chlorophyll   8. *Orchidales*
5. Plants mostly woody and with large, petiolate, either pinnately compound or simple and fan-shaped leaves   9. *Palmales*
4. Perianth more or less strongly reduced and not at all petaloid, or none
  10. Woody plants with unisexual flowers in dense spikes   10. *Pandanales*
  10. Herbs, or occasionally woody, but then generally with perfect flowers
     11. Thalloid, free-floating aquatics   13. *Lemnales*
     11. Plants with well-defined roots, stems and leaves, not free-floating
        12. Leaves, or many of them, usually divided into a petiole and a broad blade; inflorescence usually a fleshy spike
           13. Stamens many; leaves palmately veined and usually either bifid or plicate   11. *Cyclanthales*
           13. Stamens one to eight; leaves sometimes palmately veined, but not bifid or plicate   12. *Arales*
        12. Leaves not divided into blade and petiole, commonly with sheathing base; inflorescence otherwise
           14. Fruit capsular, usually with more than one seed   15. *Juncales*
           14. Fruit an achene or caryopsis, mostly with only one seed
              15. Stigma one and ovule one, or rarely stigmas two and ovules two; plants more or less aquatic; flowers unisexual, crowded in globose clusters or dense spikes   14. *Typhales*
              15. Stigmas two or three (rarely four); ovule one; plants mostly not aquatic; flowers and inflorescence various   16. *Graminales*

Appendix II:
The Mechanism of Photosynthesis[1]

INTRODUCTION

Photosynthesis is the process by which light energy is captured and transferred into the metabolic system of the cell as chemical energy. The light is absorbed by chlorophyll and accessory pigments (carotenoids and, when present, phycobilins) which are associated with chlorophyll, typically in complex cell organelles called chloroplasts. The absorbed light energy is passed into the metabolic system in a complex series of reactions following on the transfer of "excited" electrons from chlorophyll to some other substance which thereby becomes highly reactive. Carbon, hydrogen, and oxygen are assimilated and combined into organic compounds (typically carbohydrates such as glucose) in the process. The carbon in photosynthate is derived from carbon dioxide, and the hydrogen from water. Experimental evidence points to the conclusion that the oxygen contained in photosynthate is derived from carbon dioxide, and that the molecular oxygen that is typically released is derived from water; however, more conclusive experiments are needed to establish the validity of this concept. In addition to being assimilated in the process, hydrogen plays a basic role in the transfer of energy which is the essential function of photosynthesis.

The overall process of photosynthesis as carried on by algae and higher plants is usually visualized in the following equation:

$$6 \ CO_2 + 6 \ H_2O \xrightarrow{\text{visible light}} C_6H_{12}O_6 + 6 \ O_2.$$

In photosynthetic bacteria the overall process can be represented as follows:

$$6 \ CO_2 + 12 \ H_2A \xrightarrow{\text{visible and far red light}} C_6H_{12}O_6 + 12A + 6 \ H_2O.$$

In this latter equation, H_2A is an arbitrary symbol for a suitable hydrogen donor, such as H_2S or H_2, or various organic compounds which can provide hydrogen for the process. Both of these

[1] I am glad to acknowledge the very useful assistance, in the form of information, suggestions, and/or criticism, that has been provided to me in the preparation of this appendix by Ray Dawson, Albert W. Frenkel, Martin Gibbs, and Richard M. Klein. The final product is my own.

equations are useful in providing a generalized concept of the nature of photosynthesis, but both are vastly oversimplified and seriously misleading if taken literally.

Most of the discussion here will center on green plant photosynthesis, in which molecular oxygen is produced as a by-product. This process is far more common than bacterial photosynthesis and is thus of much greater significance to living organisms. The bacterial process, on the other hand, is important in helping us to understand the evolutionary origin and development of photosynthesis.

The chemistry of photosynthesis has received a great deal of study during the past several decades, and progress in our understanding has been particularly rapid since about 1950. The availability of radioactive isotopes for experimental use has been especially instrumental in this progress. Much remains to be learned, but it is now possible to present a reasonably coherent story which appears to be essentially correct. Our picture must still be painted in broad strokes, however, both because many of the details are not fully understood and because an adequate understanding of some of the details that are known requires a comprehension of biochemistry and atomic physics that can not be expected of a beginning college student. Continuing study will undoubtedly lead to changes in some of our concepts regarding photosynthesis.

CHLOROPHYLL

There are several kinds of chlorophyll, all with a similar basic structure. Chlorophyll belongs to a class of compounds called metallo-porphyrins. Porphyrins are special kinds of tetrapyrrols, and a tetrapyrrol consists of 4 pyrrols linked together. A pyrrol consists of a ring of 4 carbon atoms and one nitrogen atom, with atoms or side-chains of other elements such as hydrogen and oxygen attached to some of the carbon atoms which make up the central ring. A molecule consist-

Fig. A2.1. Absorption spectra of chlorophylls *a* and *b*. (Data of Zscheile and Comar.) The vertical axis of the chart represents a complex measurement of light absorption, the mathematics of which do not concern us here.

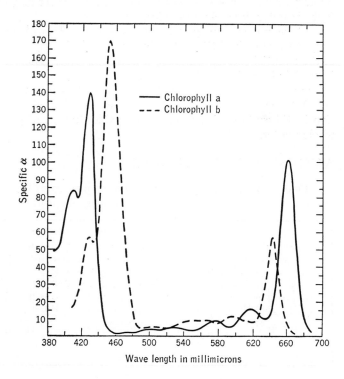

ing of 4 pyrrol units linked together is a tetrapyrrol. A tetrapyrrol with the 4 pyrrols linked together in a closed ring is a porphyrin. A porphyrin with a metallic atom at the center is a metallo-porphyrin. Chlorophyll differs from other metallo-porphyrins in that the metal at the center is magnesium, as well as in some details of the ring structure.

The several kinds of chlorophyll differ slightly among themselves in the number of hydrogen and oxygen atoms in the molecule. The most important and widespread chlorophyll is chlorophyll *a*, the structure of which is shown in Fig. 2.11. All photosynthetic organisms except bacteria contain chlorophyll *a*. Most, but not all, plants which contain chlorophyll *a* contain some other chlorophyll as well. The nature of this second chlorophyll differs among the different algal groups, and some algae do not have a second chlorophyll at all. In the green algae and in all the embryophytes the second chlorophyll is chlorophyll *b*. The ratio of chlorophyll *a* to chlorophyll *b* in green leaves varies according to the environmental conditions and according to the species, but a ratio of about 2.5 to 1 is most common. In many of the green algae the range is only about 1.4 to 1, but in others, such as *Chlorella*, the ratio is as high as 3 to 1.

The several kinds of chlorophyll found in plants other than bacteria differ only slightly in their absorption spectra (Fig. A2.1), having two large main peaks, one in the blue part of the spectrum, and the other in the red, with very low absorption in the intervening portion. Most of the bacterial chlorophylls, on the other hand, differ markedly from the nonbacterial chlorophylls in that the absorption peak near the red end of the spectrum is shifted considerably toward far red.

The efficiency of chlorophyll *a* in photosynthesis is much increased by the presence of some other chlorophyll, such as chlorophyll *b*. It is believed, however, that these other chlorophylls would not function very well if at all in the absence of chlorophyll *a*. Their normal function is apparently to increase the photosynthetic efficiency of chlorophyll *a*, rather than to carry on photosynthesis themselves. Their action in this respect may or may not be essentially similar to that of carotenoids and phycobilins.

Chlorophyll normally occurs in loose conjugation with a protein. Furthermore, recent studies suggest that much of the chlorophyll may occur in aggregate molecules composed of 2 or more of the essential chlorophyll units; i.e., the chlorophyll is more or less polymerized, with much of it possibly being in the dimer state. Preliminary evidence indicates that the polymerized molecules may be more efficient in photosynthesis than the monomers (single, unpolymerized molecules). The reason for this greater efficiency, if it in fact exists, is not yet understood. The situation is still controversial, and some very able students of photosynthesis are skeptical about the whole matter.

ACCESSORY PIGMENTS

One or more (usually more) carotenoid pigments (i.e., carotenes and xanthophylls) always occur in association with chlorophyll. The general nature of carotenes and xanthophylls has been

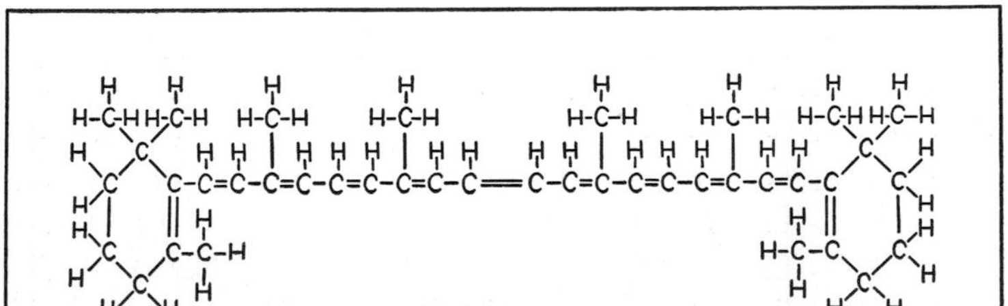

Fig. A2.2. Structural formula of β-carotene.

indicated on p. 29, and the structure of β-carotene is given in Fig. A2.2. Carotene has the empirical formula $C_{40}H_{56}$. The various kinds of carotenes differ from each other in details of the arrangements of atoms and positions of the double bonds. Xanthophylls differ from true carotenes in being partly oxidized. The most common xanthophylls, such as lutein and zeaxanthin, have the empirical formula $C_{40}H_{56}O_2$. Some of the xanthophylls, however, have more than 2 atoms of oxygen per molecule. Violaxanthin, for example, has the formula $C_{40}H_{56}O_4$.

β-Carotene is the principal carotene associated with chlorophyll in all photosynthetic organisms except the bacteria and some few of the algae. It is still present even in those algae in which it is not the principal carotene, but it is unknown among the bacteria. Lutein, zeaxanthin, and violaxanthin are among the commonest xanthophylls; lutein is regularly present in the embryophytes and in the green algae, as well as in some other algae. Many of the algae contain special xanthophylls which are not known in other groups.

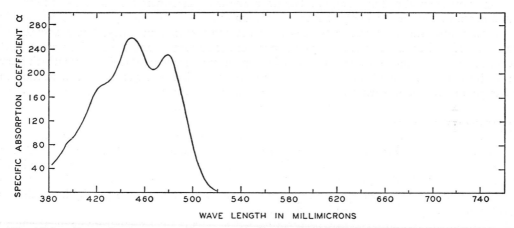

Fig. A2.3. Absorption spectrum of β-carotene. (Data of Zscheile et al.) As in Fig. A2.1, we are concerned with the shape of the curve, showing differential absorption of light of different wave lengths, rather than with the mathematics of measurement.

The common yellow carotenoids absorb light mainly between about 400 and 500 milli-microns wave length (Fig. A2.3), in the violet, blue, and blue-green range of the spectrum. Experimental determinations of the details of the absorption spectra of extracted carotenoids vary somewhat according to the technique used, especially according to the solvent. The same problem of differing results with different techniques plagues attempts to determine the absorption spectra of chlorophylls and phycobilins, but none of these differences is great enough to be significant at the level of study that concerns us here.

The metabolic roles of the carotenoids are still under active investigation, and investigators using different methods have sometimes come to different conclusions. It would seem, however, that they rather consistently have at least two major functions relating to photosynthesis: to prevent photo-oxidation of chlorophyll, and to transfer absorbed light energy to chlorophyll. Furthermore, it has been reported that they cooperate in some other, as yet unknown way, in increasing the efficiency of chlorophyll in photosynthesis. The common yellow carotenoids, such as β-carotene, have been shown to have an efficiency of about 20 percent in transferring light energy to chlorophyll. (Some other experiments indicate a higher figure, perhaps as much as 40 percent.) Fucoxanthin, a xanthophyll found in certain algae (brown algae, golden algae, and diatoms), is much more efficient, on the order of 90 percent. It has been reported that absorption of light by the accessory pigments also increases the efficiency of utilization of red light absorbed by chlorophyll *a* near its absorption limit.

Some of the algae, notably the blue-green algae and the red algae, have another class of accessory photosynthetic pigments, called phycobilins. These, like the carotenoids, absorb light energy and transmit some of it to chlorophyll. Phycobilins are highly efficient in transferring absorbed light energy to chlorophyll. It has been reported that under some conditions this efficiency may approach 100 percent.

The phycobilins are open-chain tetrapyrrols, tightly bound to a protein. As we have noted on p. 123, phycobilins are either red or blue; red phycobilins are called phycoerythrins, and blue ones are called phycocyanins. Both phycocyanins and phycoerythrins absorb well in the portion of the spectrum in which neither chlorophyll nor the common carotenoids are very effective. The phycocyanins have their absorption peak at about 600 or 625 millimicrons, in the orange-yellow or orange part of the spectrum. The phycoerythrins have their absorption peak near 560 millimicrons, about at the border between green and yellow light, and they absorb reasonably well throughout the green part of the spectrum (500 to 560 millimicrons). The absorption of green light by phycoerythrin is especially important because under most conditions green light penetrates sea water much better than light of other colors (wave lengths). Red algae which grow in relatively deep water commonly have a very high proportion of phycoerythrin in relation to other photosynthetic pigments.

CYTOCHROME

Cytochromes are metallo-porphyrins with an atom of iron at the center. The fact that iron can change from a divalent (ferrous) to a trivalent (ferric) state and back again appears to be of prime importance in the transfers of energy with which cytochrome is characteristically associated. The heme part of hemoglobin in mammalian blood is another iron porphyrin, related to cytochrome but differing in some important details.

Cytochrome has until recently been considered to be strictly a respiratory pigment and to be confined to aerobic organisms. It now turns out that neither of these beliefs is wholly correct. Cytochrome, like chlorophyll, evidently consists of a series of closely related compounds, not all of which are found in any one kind of organism. It still appears that all cytochromes may have in common the function of mediating the transfer of energy to adenosine diphosphate (ADP), with the result that another phosphate ion is added, forming adenosine triphosphate (ATP). ATP, in turn, readily reverts to ADP, giving up its third phosphate ion and liberating chemical energy into the economy of the cell.

The action of cytochrome in helping to transfer energy into newly formed ATP is in part respiratory, occurring in the mitochondria and requiring the use of free oxygen, and apparently in part photosynthetic, occurring in the chloroplasts and requiring the cooperation of chlorophyll and accessory photosynthetic pigments. In certain bacteria, such as *Desulfovibrio*, cytochrome partakes in anaerobic respiration, in which energy derived from the partial breakdown of foods is used in the formation of ATP, but no free oxygen is used. The evidence linking cytochromes to energy transfer in photosynthesis is still somewhat incomplete, but it is clear that certain types of cytochrome are consistently associated with chlorophyll, and the suggestion that in photosynthesis, as in respiration, they are involved in the formation of ATP is certainly plausible and in accord with the available information.

The classification and nomenclature of the cytochromes are still in a state of flux. On the basis of their relative activity in oxidative reactions, and on slight differences in their absorption spectra, they are usually classified into 3 general groups, called the *a*-type, *b*-type, and *c*-type.

Each of these types can be further subdivided. Cytochromes of type *a* are always (so far as known) respiratory in the strict sense, requiring the use of free oxygen. Some *b*-type cytochromes are photosynthetic, and others are respiratory; the same is true of the *c*-type cytochromes. Any given molecular species of cytochrome has only one of these functions, however, being either respiratory or photosynthetic but not both. The *b*-type photosynthetic cytochrome in higher plants is called cytochrome b_6. The *c*-type photosynthetic cytochrome in higher plants is also called cytochrome *f*.

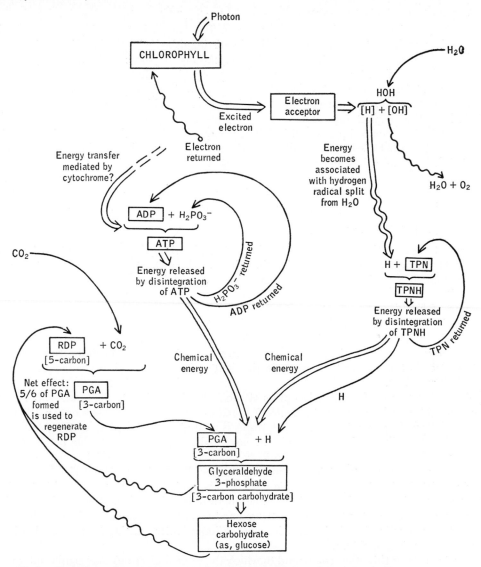

Fig. A2.4. Diagram of certain aspects of photosynthesis. (From an original design by John Cronquist.) The diagram is intended to facilitate understanding of the textual matter, and does not purport to include all of the known or postulated reactions.

CHLOROPLASTS

The chloroplasts of vascular plants are highly organized. Each chloroplast consists of a number of microscopically barely recognizable units, called grana, embedded in a relatively less differentiated mass, the whole enclosed by a membrane. In vascular plants the chloroplasts are commonly ellipsoidal or somewhat lens-shaped, and mostly 3–5 microns along the longest axis, sometimes as much as 10 microns. The number of grana per chloroplast varies from as few as 10 to as many as several hundred. Each granum consists of a series of plates (commonly called lamellae) stacked on top of each other, like a stack of coins. These lamellae are about 0.6 microns across, corresponding to the diameter of a granum. The lamellae can readily be recognized in electron micrographs, but are much too small to be distinguished with the best light microscopes.

Some of the green algae contain chloroplasts essentially like those of the vascular plants, but other algae have differently (often less complexly) organized chloroplasts, with lamellae but without grana. The blue-green algae have lamellae more or less comparable to the lamellae of a granum, but these lamellae are not organized into grana or chloroplasts. The photosynthetic bacteria have the simplest organization, with the ultimate photosynthetic particles occurring singly, or paired, or grouped into small lamellae, partly according to the genus and species. The ultimate photosynthetic particles in the bacteria are reported to be on the order of 0.2–0.5 millimicrons long and thick, and to contain chlorophyll, carotenoid pigments, and cytochrome, all conjugated to proteinaceous matter. It has been postulated, without very clear proof, that the lamellae of typical grana in the chloroplasts of higher plants are composed mainly of units comparable to these ultimate photosynthetic particles found in some bacteria.

THE LIGHT REACTIONS

Typical photosynthesis, leading to the formation of carbohydrate, can be divided into two general sets of reactions, one set following the other. In the first set, energy which is transferred from chlorophyll is used to extract hydrogen from water, and the energy and bound hydrogen are passed on to certain other compounds. Except in the bacteria, the OH radicals left by the extraction of hydrogen from water are eventually converted into water and molecular oxygen. This set of reactions can take place only in the light; they constitute the primary part of photosynthesis, in which light energy is changed into chemical energy. The second set of reactions involves the use of carbon dioxide and usually the formation of carbohydrate; these reactions can take place just as well in the dark as in the light and are discussed in a subsequent section as the dark reactions.

The series of events from the absorption of energy by chlorophyll to the formation of energy-rich compounds which can be used (in effect) to reduce carbon dioxide is still only partly understood. It is clear, however, that electron transfer is a fundamental feature of the process. The tetrapyrrolic core of the chlorophyll molecule has a balanced system of double bonds in which it is conceived that electrons are continuously circling, like horses around a race track. It is further believed that these electrons are moving less rapidly than they would if they were more closely associated with a particular atomic nucleus. These circling electrons are subject to being speeded up considerably if they are hit by a photon, or unit of light. The stimulated or "excited" electrons may then jump the track, passing from one to another of a series of adjacent chlorophyll molecules at gradually diminishing speed, or, more importantly, passing to a molecule of some other compound in the chloroplast.

The identity of this other compound to which the excited electrons may significantly pass is still uncertain. Thioctic acid was once suggested as a possibility, but later experimental work makes this unlikely. This other compound, whatever it may be, becomes highly reactive as a result of receiving the excited electron from chlorophyll. In its excited state it (or some other molecule to which it has passed on its excitation energy) extracts an atom of hydrogen from water, and it is conceived that the hydrogen is taken on as a complete atom, including its outer electron, rather than as an ion that lacks the outer electron. (Perhaps the outer electron is taken first and the hydrogen ion follows, but the end result is the same.)

The hydrogen that has been taken on by the first hydrogen acceptor is passed through one or more intermediate compounds eventually to triphosphopyridine nucleotide (generally abbreviated as TPN), forming what might be called TPNH. Each of these reactions involves the transfer of energy into the compound which accepts hydrogen. We shall return to the question of utilization of TPNH in the section on the dark reactions.

Concomitantly with the formation of TPNH, photosynthetic energy is also used in adding phosphate ion to adenosine diphosphate (ADP), forming adenosine triphosphate (ATP). This process is known as photophosphorylation. (We have noted on p. 39 that ATP readily breaks down into ADP and phosphate ion, releasing the stored energy into the metabolic system of the cell.) The immediate source of the photosynthetic energy used in the formation of this ATP is not yet clear. All that is really certain is that it is energy which has been transferred into the system from chlorophyll. It is possible that the transfer of photosynthetic energy into ATP involves or is mediated by the cytochrome that is associated with photosynthesis. This would be more or less comparable to the action of respiratory cytochrome in the mitochondria in mediating the formation of ATP from ADP and phosphate ion. The actual function of cytochrome in photosynthesis is still unknown, however, and this is not the only suggestion that has been made. The energy which has been transferred to ATP in photosynthesis is normally used up, at least in large part, in the dark reactions. If the dark reactions are artificially inhibited, ATP and some related energy-rich compounds tend to accumulate.

The OH radicals that are formed when hydrogen is extracted from water are something of a problem in the economy of the cell. They are not used, at least not to any great extent, in the formation of essential new protoplasmic constituents as are the extracted hydrogen radicals. Some way must therefore be found to dispose of the OH radicals, to convert them into harmless by-products which can be used or passed off from the cell. The OH radicals do react immediately with other constituents of the chloroplast. The identity of these other constituents is still obscure, although here again cytochrome has been suggested as a possibility. Then, through a system involving one or more enzymes that contain manganese, the OH units are converted into water and molecular oxygen. From the standpoint of chemical balances, four hydroxyl units are converted into 2 molecules of water and 1 molecule of oxygen. This is the only (or at least the principal) source of the oxygen that is released in photosynthesis, as well as the principal source of the water that is known to be reformed in photosynthesis. The energy relations of this conversion of OH radicals into water and oxygen are still obscure.

We have noted that the energy from chlorophyll is passed into the system as excited or speeded-up electrons. Obviously there must be some method for the electrons to return to the chlorophyll after they have given up their excitation energy. It is conceivable that some of them are returned to the accessory pigments instead of directly to chlorophyll, and that the passage of absorbed light energy from these pigments to chlorophyll is likewise accomplished by electron transfer, but all this is still highly speculative.

THE DARK REACTIONS

The reactions involving the use of ATP and TPNH in the assimilation of carbon dioxide can take place just as well in the dark as in the light, because at this stage the light energy absorbed by the chlorophyll has already been converted into chemical energy. These reactions are therefore generally known as the dark reactions. They are still generally considered to be a part of photosynthesis in the broad sense.

One of the most significant facts about the assimilation of carbon dioxide, and one that now seems firmly established, is that the CO_2 is taken on one molecule at a time, reacting with a 5-carbon compound in the protoplasm, rather than being condensed more directly into new carbon compounds. The American biochemist Melvin Calvin (1911—   ) received the Nobel prize in 1961 as a result of his work in the formulation and proof of this concept, which is further explained below.

In the presence of the proper enzymes, carbon dioxide reacts with a 5-carbon compound called ribulose diphosphate, forming a 6-carbon compound that immediately splits into 2 molecules of a 3-carbon compound, phosphoglyceric acid (commonly abbreviated as PGA). No input of energy is required for these two steps in the process; in fact some energy is released. PGA is a normal intermediate in the system of glucose utilization. It can react with the TPNH that has been formed in the light reactions, and, with the addition of more energy from ATP, be changed into a triose (3-carbon) carbohydrate with attached phosphate. This triose (technically, glyceraldehyde 3-phosphate) can then be transformed into glucose or other hexose sugars without further expenditure of energy. Or the PGA can continue in the normal respiratory cycle, with the release of energy into the metabolic system, leading eventually to the formation of water and carbon dioxide. Or it can be used as a building block in the formation of amino acids, fats, and other protoplasmic constituents. Under starvation conditions, the PGA formed in the dark reactions may be largely used in respiration and in the formation of other protoplasmic constituents, with little or no accumulation of glucose.

The regeneration of the ribulose diphosphate that serves as the original acceptor of CO_2 is a very complex process which is now becoming fairly well understood. A considerable part of the triose that is formed is diverted into the production of more ribulose diphosphate, rather than being converted into glucose, and some of the hexose (probably fructose rather than glucose) is also fed into the process. Diagrams representing this cyclic use and regeneration of ribulose diphosphate exist, but they are still subject to correction. Simple arithmetic indicates that five sixths of the PGA that is formed must eventually be used in regenerating ribulose diphosphate, rather than being available for other metabolic processes. If all the PGA not required for the regeneration of ribulose diphosphate were transformed into hexose, the relationship could be expressed thus: $C_1 + C_5 \longrightarrow C_6 \longrightarrow C_5 + 1/6$ hexose.

In reacting with PGA to form triose, TPNH gives up its extra hydrogen (and energy) and reverts to TPN. This TPN is then available again as a hydrogen acceptor in the light reactions of photosynthesis. The hydrogen given up by the TPNH may or may not go directly into the triose. In any case, the hydrogen in photosynthate is eventually derived from water, and the carbon and very probably the oxygen from carbon dioxide.

In many of the algae, conversion of glucose into starch takes place in a special part of the chloroplast, the pyrenoid. In higher plants starch synthesis occurs mainly or wholly away from the chloroplasts, which do not have pyrenoids. The original synthesis of glucose, however, apparently takes place mainly or wholly within the chloroplasts. Under proper experimental conditions isolated chloroplasts can carry on the complete photosynthetic process, from the reception of light to the formation of glucose.

BACTERIAL PHOTOSYNTHESIS

Photosynthesis in bacteria differs in several respects from photosynthesis in algae and higher plants, but it resembles typical photosynthesis in that chlorophyll, carotenoid pigments, and cytochrome cooperate to transform light energy into chemical energy that is used to assimilate carbon dioxide and produce new organic compounds, typically carbohydrates. It further resembles typical photosynthesis in that pyridine nucleotides serve as hydrogen acceptors, and in that much of the captured energy is transferred into ATP by photophosphorylation.

GREEN PLANT PHOTOSYNTHESIS

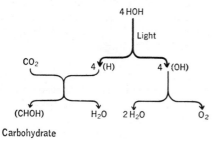

Net: $H_2O + CO_2 \xrightarrow{\text{Light}} (CHOH) + O_2$

Fig. A2.5. Diagrammatic comparison of some aspects of typical photosynthesis and bacterial photosynthesis. (From a design by Albert W. Frenkel.)

BACTERIAL PHOTOSYNTHESIS

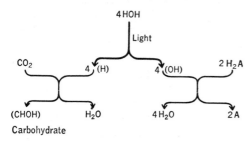

Net: $2 H_2A + CO_2 \xrightarrow{\text{Light}} (CHOH) + 2A + H_2O$

Perhaps the most important peculiarities of bacterial photosynthesis are that the bacteria require suitable hydrogen donors in addition to water, and free oxygen is not released (Fig. A2.5). Hydrogen sulfide, gaseous hydrogen, and various sulfur-containing organic compounds may serve as hydrogen donors in bacterial photosynthesis. Some of the overall equations for bacterial photosynthesis with various hydrogen donors have been given on p. 100. It has been suggested that the requirement of a hydrogen donor in addition to water relates to the difficulty of disposing of the hydroxyl radicals that are formed by the splitting of water. Algae and higher plants have acquired (evolutionarily) the ability to dispose of these hydroxyl radicals by converting them into water and oxygen. The bacteria have not.

Several genera of blue-green, green, red, and brown algae have been shown to retain the ancestral bacterial capacity to use substances other than water (such as H_2S or H_2) as hydrogen donors in photosynthesis, under special anaerobic conditions.

We have already noted that the bacteria do not have highly organized chloroplasts comparable to those of most algae and higher plants. Only the light reactions of photosynthesis are clearly associated with the chlorophyll-bearing organelles of bacteria. (In recent literature these organelles, the ultimate photosynthetic particles, have been called chromatophores, but this term is misleading because it has also been widely used for the chloroplasts of algae.) The dark reactions in photosynthetic bacteria have been reported to take place away from these chlorophyll-bearing organelles, but the matter is still controversial. These dark reactions in bacteria are apparently similar in most respects to the dark reactions in algae and higher plants, but there are evidently some differences in detail.

Appendix II: The Mechanism of Photosynthesis 869

Glossary

Note on derivations and definitions: Many botanical terms are derived from Greek, often through Latin. The Greek antecedent, being the older, is usually given instead of the Latin. When some latitude in transliteration of classical Greek to English is permissible, the form which more nearly coincides with the spelling of the modern English word is generally given. The definitions are in all cases for botanical usage. Many of the terms have a broader popular definition or a different specialized definition in some other field. For terms not included in the glossary, see the index.

achene (Gr. *a*, not + *chainein*, to gape). The most general type of dry indehiscent fruit.

adventitious (L. *adventitius*, from *ad*, to + *venire*, to come). Originating from mature nonmeristematic tissues, especially if such a development would not ordinarily be expected.

aecium (Gr. *aikia*, injury, or *oikidion*, a little house). Among rusts, a cup at the surface of the host, in which dicaryotic spores called aeciospores are borne.

akinete (Gr. *a*, not; *kinēsis*, movement). An algal spore produced by transformation of a whole vegetative cell, with the original cell wall forming part or all of the spore wall.

Algae (L. seaweed). A broad artificial group of plants, characterized by the presence of chlorophyll *a* and the absence of the characteristic multicellular sex organs or specialized water-conducting tissues of higher plants.

allele (Gr. *allelōn*, of one another). One of the two or more genes which in different genomes can occupy a particular locus on a chromosome.

amino acid. An organic acid having one or more amine (NH_2^-) groups in place of hydrogen atoms.

amitosis (Gr. *a*, not + mitosis). Nuclear division which apparently results from the constriction of the nucleus into two or more parts, without the formation of chromosomes or a spindle.

anaphase (Gr. *ana*, up + phase). The stage in mitosis in which the two chromatids of each chromosome are separated and move toward the respective poles of the spindle.

angiosperm (Gr. *angeion*, vessel + *sperma*, seed). A member of the group of plants (Anthophyta) characterized by having the ovules enclosed in an ovary.

annual (L. *annus*, year). A plant which completes its life cycle and dies in a year.

anther (Gr. *anthos*, flower). The part of a stamen, consisting of one or usually two pollen sacs (and a connective layer between them), which bears the pollen.

antheridium (Gr. *anthos*, flower + *eidos*, resemblance). A specialized cell, or a multicellular structure, within which one or more sperms are produced.

anthocyanin (Gr. *anthos*, flower + *kyanos*, dark blue). A chemical class of water-soluble pigments, ranging in color from blue or violet to purple or red, often found in the central vacuole of a cell, especially in flower petals.

apomixis (Gr. *apo*, from + *mixis*, mingling). The setting of seed without fertilization.

apothecium (Gr. *apo*, from + *thēkē*, box). An ascocarp which is open, exposing the asci.

archegonium (Gr. *arche*, beginning + *gonos*, offspring). A specialized structure, composed of more than one cell, within which an egg is produced.

ascocarp (Gr. *askos*, bladder + *karpos*, fruit). The fruiting body of an ascomycete.

ascospore. A spore produced in an ascus.

ascus (Gr. *askos*, bladder). The characteristic sporangium of the ascomycetes, within which the sexual spores (ascospores) are borne.

ATP. Adenosine triphosphate, a compound through which respiratory energy is distributed into other metabolic processes.

autoecious (Gr. *autos*, self + *oikos*, house). Among rusts, completing the life cycle on a single host.

autotroph (Gr. *autos*, self + *trophē*, nourishment). An organism which makes its own food from raw materials; opposite of *heterotroph*.

axil (L. *axilla*, armpit). The point of the angle formed by the leaf or petiole with the upward internode of the stem.

basidiocarp (basidium + Gr. *karpos*, fruit). The fruiting body of a basidiomycete.

basidiospore. A spore borne on a basidium.

basidium (L. diminutive from Gr. *basis*, base). A characteristic structure of certain fungi (the Basidiomycetes) which bears sexual spores externally.

berry. The most general type of fleshy fruit.

biennial (L. *biennium*, a period of two years). A plant which completes its life cycle and dies in two years (or more than one year but less than two).

bract (L. *bractea*, a thin metal plate). Any more or less reduced or modified leaf associated with a flower or an inflorescence, but not a part of the flower itself; in conifers, one of the primary appendages of the cone axis, in the axils of which the ovuliferous scales are borne.

budding. Unequal cell division, as in yeasts; also, a type of grafting in which a bud is used as the scion.

calyptra (Gr. *kalyptēr*, a veil). In bryophytes, the structure derived partly or wholly from the archegonium, which caps or immediately surrounds the sporophyte.

calyx (Gr. *kalyx*, cup). All the sepals of a flower, collectively.

cambium (L. *cambiare*, to exchange). A lateral meristem; specifically, the vascular cambium, which produces xylem internally and phloem externally.

capsule. The sporangium of a bryophyte; in angiosperms, a common type of dry dehiscent fruit, composed of more than one carpel.

carbohydrate. A food whose molecules consist entirely, or almost entirely, of carbon, hydrogen, and oxygen, with the ration of hydrogen to oxygen being 2:1.

carotene (*Daucus carota*, the carrot). A fat-soluble, yellow hydrocarbon, associated with chlorophyll in the photosynthetic process.

carpel (Gr. *karpos*, fruit). One of the female organs of a flower, i.e., the megasporophyll.

Casparian strip. A waxy band encircling an endodermal cell along its radial walls.

catalyst (Gr. *katalysis*, dissolution). A substance which facilitates a chemical reaction between other substances, without itself being used up in the process.

caulidium (diminutive of L. *caulis*, stem). The stem-like organ of a gametophyte of a bryophyte.

cell. An organized unit of protoplasm, bounded by a membrane or wall, and usually divisible into a nucleus and some cytoplasm: also applied to the cell wall, after the death of the protoplast.

cell sap. The watery contents of the central vacuole of a cell.

cellulose (L. *cellula*, cell). A complex polysaccharide which is the principal constituent of the cell walls of most plants.

central cylinder. The primary vascular structure of a stem or root, together with any tissue (such as the pith) which may be enclosed.

chlorenchyma (Gr. *chlōros*, green + *enchein*, to pour in). A tissue (generally parenchymatous) characterized by having chloroplasts.

chlorophyll (Gr. *chlōros*, green + *phyllon*, leaf). A green pigment which is essential for photosynthesis.

chloroplast. A plastid which bears chlorophyll.

chromatid (Gr. *chrōma*, color). One of the two longitudinal halves that make up a chromosome.

chromatin (Gr. *chrōma*, color). A complex series of substances which bear the hereditary information and are the essential constituents of a chromosome.

chromonema (Gr. *chrōma*, color + *nēma*, thread). One of the threadlike, DNA-bearing structures within the nucleus, which give rise to the chromosomes during mitosis.

chromoplast (Gr. *chrōma*, color + plastid). A colored plastid, other than a chloroplast.

chromosome (Gr. *chrōma*, color + *soma*, body). A DNA-bearing body which is organized from the chromonemata and other nuclear material during mitosis.

class. A group of related orders; a particular rank in the taxonomic hierarchy, between the order and the division.

cleistothecium (Gr. *kleistos*, closed + *thēkē*, box). An ascocarp that is completely closed at maturity, usually more or less spherical in shape, and with a differentiated outer layer.

closed bundle. A vascular bundle which has no cambium and thus lacks the potentiality for secondary growth.

coenocyte (Gr. *koinos*, in common + *kytos*, a hollow vessel). An organism which has the nuclei scattered in a continuous (usually filamentous) protoplast that is not divided into definite cells.

collenchyma (Gr. *kolla*, glue + *enchein*, to pour in). A strengthening tissue composed of living cells with thick primary walls that consist largely of cellulose.

colloid (Gr. *kolla*, glue). A suspension (usually in water) in which the suspended particles are larger than ordinary molecules but not large enough to settle out.

companion cell. A modified parenchyma cell associated with a sieve element and having a direct ontogenetic relation with it.

conidium (Gr. *konos*, offspring, or *konis*, dust). An asexual spore; in fungi, a spore (asexual) produced by differentiation and abscission of a hyphal tip.

conjugation (L. *conjugare*, to unite, or *conjugatus*, united). Fusion of isogametes.

cork. A waterproofing protective tissue, dead when functional, characterized by suberization of the cell walls.

corolla (L. little crown, diminutive of *corona*, crown). All the petals of a flower, collectively.

cortex (L. bark or rind). The tissue between the central cylinder and the epidermis of a stem or root.

cotyledon (Gr. *kotylēdon*, a cup-shaped hollow). A leaf of the embryo of a seed.

crozier (derivation complex, eventually from L. *crux, crucis*, cross). The hook-shaped hyphal tip which is the precursor to an ascus.

cryptogam (Gr. *kryptos*, hidden + *gamos*, marriage). A plant belonging to the non-seed-bearing general group: opposite of *phanerogam*.

cutin (L. *cutis*, skin). A waxy material, characteristic of epidermal cells of embryophytes, which retards evaporation of water.

cytochrome (Gr. *kytos*, a hollow vessel + *chrōma*, color). A group of important respiratory enzymes.

cytokinesis (Gr. *kytos*, a hollow vessel + *kinesis*, movement). The division of the cytoplasm (as contrasted to the nucleus) during cell division.

cytology (Gr. *kytos*, a hollow vessel + *logos*, word, discourse). The study of the protoplasmic structure of cells, including the changes which occur during cell division.

cytoplasm (Gr. *kytos*, a hollow vessel + *plasma*, a thing molded or formed). The non-nuclear part of protoplasm.

deciduous (L. *decidere*, to fall off). Falling off; dropping its leaves in the autumn.

dehiscent (L. *dehiscere*, to gape or yawn). Opening at maturity; releasing or exposing the contents.

dicaryotic (Gr. *dis*, two + *karyon*, nut). Having two nuclei (typically haploid) of different origin in each segment or cell of a filament.

dicot (Gr. *dis*, two + cotyledon). Short for dicotyledon; the Dicotyledonae are one of the two great groups of angiosperms.

dictyostele (Gr. *dictyon*, net + stele). A siphonostele with numerous and elongate leaf gaps and branch gaps, so that the primary vascular tissue forms a ring of vascular bundles.

digestion. The partial breakdown of foods, making them more soluble or more readily diffusible without significantly changing the amount of stored energy.

dioecious (Gr. *dis*, two + *oikos*, house). Producing male and female structures (in seed plants the microsporophylls and megasporophylls, or stamens and pistils) on separate individuals.

diploid (Gr. *diploos*, double). Having two full chromosome complements per cell.

division. A group of similar classes; the highest category regularly used in the taxonomic hierarchy.

DNA. Deoxy-ribose-nucleic acid; the essential constituent of chromatin.

dorsiventral (L. *dorsum*, back + *venter*, belly). Flattened, with the two flattened sides unlike; having a back side and a belly side.

ecology (Gr. *oikos*, house + *logos*, word or discourse). The study of the relation between organisms and their environment, the influence of each on the other.

egg. A nonmotile gamete which can fuse with a sperm to form a zygote; the female gamete.

embryo (Gr. *embryon*, fetus). The young sporophyte, before it has begun to take on its mature form.

embryo sac. The female gametophyte of angiosperms, within which the embryo begins to develop.

endarch (Gr. *endon*, within + *archein*, to be first). Maturing from the inside toward the outside.

endodermis (Gr. *endon*, within + *derma*, skin). A layer of specialized cells in many roots and some stems, delimiting the inner margin of the cortex.

endosperm (Gr. *endon*, within + *sperma*, seed). In the broadest sense, the food-storage tissue of a seed, other than the embryo or the seed coat; narrowly, the food-storage tissue developed from the triple-fusion nucleus of an angiosperm ovule.

endospore (Gr. *endon*, within + spore). A spore which is formed *within* a sporangium or cell wall, rather than externally.

enzyme (Gr. *en*, in + *zymē*, yeast). A catalyst produced by a living organism.

epicotyl (Gr. *epi*, upon + cotyledon). The part of the embryo of a seed which gives rise to the shoot.

epidermis (Gr. *epi*, upon + *dermis*, skin). The characteristic outermost tissue of leaves and of young roots and stems.

epigynous (Gr. *epi*, upon + *gynē*, woman). Having the perianth and stamens attached at or near the top of the ovary, rather than beneath it.

exarch (Gr. *ex*, out of + *archein*, to be first). Maturing from the outside toward the center.

family. A group of related genera; a particular rank in the taxonomic hierarchy, between the genus and the order.

fat. A food whose molecules consist entirely, or almost entirely, of carbon, hydrogen, and oxygen, with the ratio of hydrogen to oxygen being greater than 2:1.

fertilization. Fusion of a sperm with an egg.

fiber. A long, slender, thick-walled strengthening cell, usually dead when functional.

flagellate. A unicellular or colonial organism, other than a bacterium, which moves by means of flagella.

flagellum (L. whip). A slender, motile, protoplasmic projection from a cell.

flower. A specialized short shoot with modified leaves, some of which characteristically produce sexual reproductive structures, leading ultimately to the formation of seeds.

food. Any chemical compound which can be broken down by living organisms to release energy.

fructose (L. *fructus*, fruit). A sugar, found especially in fruits, which, like glucose, has the formula $C_6H_{12}O_6$, but with the atoms somewhat differently arranged.

fruit (L. *fructus*). A ripened ovary, together with any other structures that ripen with it and form a unit with it.

fruiting body. In fungi, the compact mycelium, usually of definite form and structure, associated with the perfect stage in the life cycle.

fundamental tissue. The pith, the cortex, and the primary tissue separating the vascular bundles.

gametangium (Gr. *gamos*, marriage + *angeion*, vessel). Any structure in which gametes are born.

gamete (Gr. *gamos*, marriage). Any cell which is capable of fusing with another cell to form a new individual.

gametophore (Gr. *gamos*, marriage + *pho-*
rein, to bear). In mosses, the main body of the gametophyte, on which the archegonia and/or antheridia are borne.

gametophyte (Gr. *gamos*, marriage + *phyton*, plant). The generation which has *n* chromosomes and produces gametes as reproductive bodies.

gene (Gr. *genos*, stock or race). One of the individual bits of chromatin which govern the hereditary characteristics of a cell or organism.

genera. Plural of genus.

genome. One complete set of chromosomes; i.e., a chromosome complement.

genotype. The genetic make-up of an individual; contrast with *phenotype*.

genus (L. a general kind). A group of related species; a particular rank in the taxonomic hierarchy, between the species and the family.

geotropism (Gr. *gē*, earth + *tropē*, a turning). A growth response to gravity.

germination (L. *germinare*, to sprout). The resumption of growth by any spore, seed, or other propagule, after a period of dormancy.

glucose (Gr. *glucus*, sweet). A common simple sugar with the formula $C_6H_{12}O_6$.

guard cell. One of a pair of specialized epidermal cells bounding a stomate.

gymnosperm (Gr. *gymnos*, naked + *sperma*, seed). A member of the group of plants characterized by having ovules that are not enclosed in an ovary.

haploid (Gr. *haploos*, single). Having only one full set of chromosomes (one chromosome complement) per cell.

haustorium (L. *haustor*, a drawer, from *haurire*, *haustum*, to draw to drink). A specialized organ or organelle through which a parasite extracts nourishment from its host.

herbarium (L. *herba*, herb). A collection of plant specimens, so dried and preserved as to illustrate as far as possible their characteristics.

heteroecious (Gr. *heteros*, other + *oikos*,

house). Among rusts, requiring two different kinds of hosts to complete the full sexual life cycle.

heterogamete (Gr. *heteros*, other + gamete). A gamete which can fuse only with a gamete of different form; ordinarily, an egg or a sperm.

heterosporous (Gr. *heteros*, other + spore). Producing two different kinds of spores, one of which gives rise to male gametophytes, the other to female.

heterothallic (Gr. *heteros*, other + thallus). Producing the sperms and eggs (or other gametes or nuclei which fuse with each other) on different thalli rather than on the same thallus: opposite of *homothallic*.

heterotroph (Gr. *heteros*, other + *trophe*, nourishment). An organism which does not make its own food: opposite of *autotroph*.

heterozygous (Gr. *heteros*, other + zygote). Having opposing genes on homologous chromosomes: opposite of *homozygous*.

hexose (Gr. *hex*, six). A sugar, such as glucose, with six atoms of carbon in the molecule.

holophytic (Gr. *holos*, whole + *phyton*, plant). Autotrophic, making its own food.

holozoic (Gr. *holos*, whole + *zoon*, animal). Eating (ingesting) rather than making or absorbing food.

homosporous (Gr. *homos*, one and the same + spore). Having the spores all about alike, each giving rise to a gametophyte which produces both antheridia and archegonia: opposite of *heterosporous*.

homothallic (Gr. *homos*, one and the same + thallus). Producing sperms and eggs (or isogametes or nuclei capable of fusing with each other) on the same thallus: opposite of *heterothallic*.

homozygous (Gr. *homos*, one and the same + zygote). Having identical (rather than opposing) genes on homologous chromosomes: opposite of *heterozygous*.

host. An organism which, while still alive, provides food or lodging for another organism.

hybrid. A cross between different species; in genetics, a cross between individuals differing in one or more genes.

hydrolysis (Gr. *hydōr*, water + *lysis*, a loosing). The chemical breakdown of larger molecules into smaller ones by insertion of the components of water at the point of breakage.

hydrophyte (Gr. *hydōr*, water + *phyton*, plant). A plant which grows in water.

hymenium (Gr. *hymēn*, membrane). In fungi, a layer of asci or basidia, often intermingled with sterile hyphae.

hypha (Gr. *hyphē*, web). Any single filament of a fungus.

hypocotyl (Gr. *hypo*, under + cotyledon). The part of the embryo of a seed which lies just beneath the cotyledons, connecting the epicotyl to the radicle.

hypogynous (Gr. *hypo*, under + *gynē*, woman). Having the perianth and stamens attached directly to the receptacle, beneath the ovary.

inflorescence. A cluster of flowers.

initial. One of the relatively few cells in an apical meristem which remains permanently meristematic; also, a cell which by cell division gives rise to a particular structure.

integument (L. *integumentum*, a covering). One of the one or two layers which partly enclose the nucellus of an ovule; the forerunner of the seed coat.

internode (L. *inter*, between + node). The part of a stem between two successive nodes.

interphase. The time or stage between mitotic divisions of a cell.

involucre (L. *involucrum*, a covering). Any structure which surrounds the base of another structure.

isogamete (Gr. *isos*, equal + gamete). A gamete which can fuse with another of similar appearance to form a zygote.

karyogamy (Gr. *karyon*, nut + *gamos*, marriage). Sexual fusion of nuclei (as opposed to the cytoplasm).

latex (L. fluid). A colorless to more often

white, yellow, or reddish liquid, produced by some plants, characterized by the presence of colloidal particles of terpenes dispersed in water.

laticifer (L. *latex, laticis,* fluid + *ferre,* to bear). A latex-bearing tube.

leaf. One of the primary organs of most vascular plants, typically being the principal photosynthetic organ.

leaf gap. A parenchymatous opening into a stele, left by the departure of a leaf trace.

leaf trace. A vascular bundle, from the point where it leaves the stele to the point where it enters the leaf.

lenticel (L. *lens, lentis,* a lentil). A slightly raised area in the bark of a stem or root, consisting of loosely arranged, nearly or quite unsuberized cells.

leucoplast (Gr. *leukos,* white + plastid). A colorless plastid.

lignin (L. *lignum,* wood). An essential component of the secondary walls of many cells (especially xylem), the chemical composition not yet fully understood.

lipid (Gr. *lipos,* fat, grease). Fats and some other chemical compounds which resemble fats in being insoluble in water but soluble in certain organic solvents.

locule (L. *loculus,* a little compartment). A seed cavity (chamber) in an ovary or fruit; a compartment in any container.

lorica (L. a corselet of thongs). A wall-like structure, found in certain algae, which differs from a cell wall in that most of its surface is not in contact with the enclosed protoplast, and also in that it usually does not completely enclose the cell.

lumen (L. an opening for light). The space enclosed by a cell wall: used especially in speaking of dead cells, from which the protoplast has disintegrated.

lysigenous (Gr. *lysis,* a loosing + *genesis,* origin). Originating by degeneration of tissue.

medullary ray. A parenchymatous connection between the cortex and the pith of a stem.

megaphyll (Gr. *megas,* large + *phyllon,* leaf). A leaf of the type associated with a leaf gap in the stele: opposite of *microphyll.*

megasporangium (Gr. *megas,* large + sporangium). A sporangium bearing one or more megaspores.

megaspore (Gr. *megas,* large + spore). A spore which develops into a female gametophyte.

megasporophyll (megaspore + Gr. *phyllon,* leaf). A leaf (sporophyll) bearing or subtending one or more megasporangia.

meiosis (Gr. *meion,* smaller, less). Reduction division.

meristem (Gr. *meristos,* divided). A tissue characterized by cell division.

mesophyll (Gr. *mesos,* in the middle + *phyllon,* leaf). The tissue, other than vascular tissue, between the upper and the lower epidermis of a leaf.

metabolism (Gr. *metabolē,* change). The complex set of interrelated chemical processes characteristic of life.

metaphase (Gr. *meta,* beyond + phase). The stage in mitosis during which the chromosomes become (and for a time remain) arranged in an equatorial plate.

metaphloem (Gr. *meta,* beyond + phloem). Primary phloem which matures after the protophloem, concomitantly with or after the surrounding tissues.

metaxylem (Gr. *meta,* beyond, after + xylem). Primary xylem which matures after the protoxylem, concomitantly with or after the surrounding tissues.

micelle (L. *micella,* a small crumb). A minute, slender rod: applied especially to the cellulose rods of which cell walls are commonly composed.

microphyll (Gr. *mikros,* small + *phyllon,* leaf). A leaf, usually small, with an unbranched midvein whose departure from the stele does not leave a gap; opposite of *megaphyll.*

micropyle (Gr. *mikros,* small + *pylē,* gate). The opening through the integuments of an ovule to the nucellus.

microsporangium (Gr. *mikros,* small + sporangium). A sporangium containing micro-spores.

microspore (Gr. *mikros*, small + spore). A spore which develops into a male gameto-phyte.

microsporophyll (microspore + Gr. *phyllon*, leaf). A leaf (sporophyll) which bears or subtends one or more microsporangia.

middle lamella. The thin layer, composed of pectic substances, which joins two adjacent cells.

mitochondrium (Gr. *mitos*, thread + *chondrus*, cartilage). A specialized cytoplasmic body which is concerned in respiration.

mitosis (Gr. *mitos*, thread). A complex, or-derly process of nuclear division which ordinarily results in the formation of two daughter nuclei with identical hereditary potentialities; loosely, cell division associ-ated with mitotic nuclear division.

monocaryotic (Gr. *monos*, one + *karyon*, nut). Having uninucleate segments, or having multinucleate segments with the nuclei not associated in pairs. Compare *dicaryotic*.

monocot (Gr. *monos*, one + cotyledon). Short for monocotyledon; the Monocoty-ledonae are one of the two great groups of angiosperms.

monoecious (Gr. *monos*, one + *oikos*, house). Bearing reproductive structures of both sexes on the same plant, but (in angio-sperms) not in the same flower.

monosaccharide (Gr. *monos*, one + L. *saccharum*, sugar). Any simple sugar; i.e., a sugar which cannot be broken down into smaller molecules without ceasing to be a sugar.

morphology (Gr. *morphē*, shape, form + *logos*, word, discourse). Form and struc-ture, or the study thereof, often taken to include the changes of form occurring dur-ing the life cycle.

mutation (L. *mutare*, to change). An in-heritable change in a chromosome or gene: applied especially to gene mutations.

mycelium (Gr. *mykēs*, mushroom). A mass of branching hyphae.

mycorhiza (Gr. *mykēs*, mushroom + *rhiza*, root). A symbiotic, fungus-root combina-tion; by extension, a similar association of a fungus and some other underground part of a plant.

node (L. *nodus*, knot). A place on a stem where a leaf is (or has been) attached.

nucellus (L., a small kernel). The tissue sur-rounding the female gametophyte of a seed plant; i.e., the megasporangium wall of a seed plant.

nucleolus (L., a small kernel). A specialized, more or less spherical body within the nucleus.

nucleus (L., a kernel). A protoplasmic vesicle (or body) characterized by the presence of DNA, which governs hereditary character-istics of the cell; the noncytoplasmic com-ponent of a protoplast.

ontogeny (Gr. *onta*, existing + *genesis*, ori-gin). The developmental history of an individual.

oögamous (Gr. *oon*, egg + *gamos*, marriage). Producing sperms and eggs (rather than isogametes or anisogametes).

oögonium (Gr. *oon*, egg + *gonos*, offspring). A specialized single cell within which one or more eggs are produced.

oöspore (Gr. *oon*, egg + spore). In thallo-phytes, a resting cell, usually thick-walled, formed by fusion of a sperm with an egg.

open bundle. A vascular bundle which has, or can develop, a cambium between the xylem and phloem.

operculum (L.). A little lid.

order. A group of related families; a particu-lar rank in the taxonomic hierarchy, be-tween the family and the class.

organ. A tissue or group of tissues which make up a morphologically and function-ally distinct part of an organism.

ostiole (L. *ostiolum*, a little door). A small external opening of a pouch.

ovary (L. *ovum*, egg). The structure which in angiosperms encloses the ovules.

ovule (diminutive of L. *ovum*, egg). A young seed; the megasporangium, plus the enclosing integuments, of a seed plant.

palmate (L. *palma*, the palm of the hand). Having several similar parts spreading from a common point.

paraphysis (Gr. *para*, beside + *physis*, growth). One of the sterile filaments associated or intermingled with reproductive filaments in some fungi and algae; it differs from a pseudoparaphysis in being free at one end.

parasexual. Sex-like in that new character combinations are achieved, but not strictly sexual because nuclear fusion and reduction division are not involved.

parasite (Gr. *parasitos*, eating beside another). An organism which obtains its food from another living organism.

parenchyma (Gr. *para*, beside + *enchein*, to pour in). A tissue composed of relatively unspecialized cells.

parthenogenesis (Gr. *parthenos*, virgin + *genesis*, origin). Reproduction by means of unfertilized eggs.

pectinate (L. *pecten*, a comb, *pectinatus*, comb-like). Having a single row of lateral appendages, like the teeth on a comb.

perennial (L. *perennis*). A plant that lives more than two years.

perfect. In flowers, having both stamens and pistils; in fungi, having or relating to the structures associated with nuclear fusion.

perianth (Gr. *peri*, around + *anthos*, flower). The calyx and corolla, collectively.

pericarp (Gr. *peri*, around + *karpos*, fruit). The ovary wall of a fruit.

pericycle (Gr. *peri*, around + *kyklos*, ring or circle). A tissue, usually parenchymatous, between the endodermis and the vascular cylinder.

perigynous (Gr. *peri*, around + *gynē*, woman). Having the perianth and stamens united into a basal saucer or cup (the hypanthium) distinct from the ovary.

periplast (Gr. *peri*, around + *plastos*, formed, molded). A differentiated bounding layer of a protoplast, firm but usually flexible.

perithecium (Gr. *peri*, around + *thēkē*, box). An ascocarp which is closed except for an ostiole.

petal (Gr. *petalon, a leaf*). A member of the second set of floral leaves (i.e., the set just internal to the sepals), usually colored or white and serving to attract pollinators.

petiole (L. *petiolus*, a little foot or a fruit stalk). A leaf stalk.

phanerogam (Gr. *phaneros*, visible, manifest + *gamos*, marriage). A seed plant: opposite of *cryptogam*.

phelloderm (Gr. *phellos*, cork + *derma*, skin). The tissue produced *internally* by the phellogen (as opposed to the cork or phellem, which is produced *externally*).

phellogen (Gr. *phellos*, cork + *genesis*, origin). A lateral meristem which produces cork; the cork cambium.

phenotype (Gr. *phaino*, shining, *phainein*, to show). The actual character of an individual, as expressed in its form, structure, or physiology: contrast with *genotype*.

phloem (Gr. *phloos*, bark). The characteristic food-conducting tissue of higher plants.

-phore (Gr. *phorein*, to bear). Suffix meaning a supporting stalk.

phototropism (Gr. *phōs, phōtos*, light + *tropē*, a turning). A directional growth response to light.

phycobilin (Gr. *phykos*, seaweed + L. *bilis*, bile). A class of proteinaceous, water-soluble, accessory photosynthetic pigments, red or blue in color.

phycocyanin (Gr. *phykos*, seaweed; *kyanos*, dark blue). A blue phycobilin.

phycoerythrin (Gr. *phykos*, seaweed + *erythros*, red). A red phycobilin.

phyllidium (diminutive of Gr. *phyllos*, leaf). A leaflike organ of bryophyte gametophytes.

phylogeny (Gr. *phylon*, tribe + *genos*, lineage). The evolutionary history of a group.

physiology (Gr. *physis*, nature + *logos*, word, discourse). The study of the processes occurring in living organisms and of the functions of the different parts of the organism.

pinnate (L. *pinna*, feather). Having two

rows of lateral branches or appendages, like the barbs on a feather.

pistil (L. *pistillum*, pestle). The female structure of a flower, consisting of one carpel or of several carpels joined together in a single unit.

plasma membrane. The living membrane at the outer edge of the cytoplasm.

plasmodesma (Gr. *plasma*, anything formed or molded + *desmos*, band or chain). A cytoplasmic strand connecting two adjacent cells.

plasmodium (Gr. *plasma*, anything formed or molded). A naked, multinucleate mass of protoplasm that is not divided into separate cells.

plasmogamy (Gr. *plasma*, anything formed or molded + *gamos*, marriage). The fusion of protoplasts which precedes karyogamy.

plastid (Gr. *plastos*, formed or molded). A specialized cytoplasmic body, usually associated with the manufacture or storage of food, or obviously pigmented, or both.

plumule (L. *plumula*, a little feather). The epicotyl of an embryo.

pollen (L. fine flour, dust). The mass of young male gametophytes (pollen grains) of a seed plant, at the stage when they are released from the anther.

pollination. In angiosperms, the transfer of pollen from the anther to the stigma; in gymnosperms, from the microsporangium to the micropyle.

polymer (Gr. *polys*, many + *meros*, part). A compound formed by the chemical linkage of a number of molecules of the same or closely related kinds.

polyploid (Gr. *polys*, many; *ploid* is of recent origin from the common endings of haploid and diploid). Having three or more sets of chromosomes.

polysaccharide (Gr. *polys*, many + L. *saccharum*, sugar). A substance formed by the chemical linkage of several or many monosaccharide molecules.

primary tissue. A tissue derived directly by differentiation from an apical (or intercalary) meristem.

primary wall. In cells, the outer or first-formed wall layer, in contrast to the *secondary wall*.

primordium (L. the beginning). A group of cells which is destined to develop into a particular structure; e.g., a leaf primordium.

procambium (Gr. *pro*, before + cambium). The young tissue of a root or shoot that is destined to develop into vascular tissue; more narrowly, the potential cambium between the xylem and phloem of a vascular bundle.

prophase (Gr. *pro*, before + phase). An early stage in mitosis, in which the chromonemata give rise to the chromosomes.

protein (Gr. *proteios*, primary). A food containing nitrogen (and often other elements) in addition to carbon, hydrogen, and oxygen.

prothallial cell. A cell, or one of several cells, found in some male gametophytes, which may represent an evolutionary vestige of the vegetative body of the gametophyte.

prothallus (Gr. *pro*, before + thallus). The gametophyte of a pteridophyte.

protonema (Gr. *prōtos*, first + *nēma*, thread). The filament (or flat thallus) formed by germination of a moss spore.

protophloem (Gr. *prōtos*, first + phloem). Primary phloem which matures while the surrounding tissues are still elongating; the first phloem to mature at any particular level of the stem or root.

protoplasm (Gr. *prōtos*, first + *plasma*, anything formed or molded). Living substance.

protoplast. An organized unit of protoplasm; typically, the living content of a cell.

protostele (Gr. *prōtos*, first + stele). A stele with a solid core of xylem, lacking a pith.

protoxylem (Gr. *prōtos*, first + xylem). Primary xylem which matures while the surrounding tissues are still elongating; the first xylem to mature at any particular level of the stem or root.

pycnium (Gr. *pyknos*, crowded, dense). Among rusts, a pocket at the surface of the surface of the host, in which monocaryotic spores, called pycniospores are borne.

pyrenoid (Gr. *pyrēn*, stone of a fruit, kernel). A specialized, proteinaceous part of a chloroplast, found chiefly in algae, on or around which starch accumulates.

rachis (Gr. backbone). A main axis, such as that of a compound leaf.

radicle (diminutive of L. *radix, radicis*, root). The part of the embryo of a seed which gives rise to the root.

receptacle (L. *receptaculum*, reservoir). A structure which bears or contains other parts; in flowers, the end of the stem, to which the other flower parts are attached.

reduction division. The process by which the number of chromosomes in a cell is reduced from $2n$ to n.

respiration. The chemical breakdown of foods by living organisms, resulting in release of energy.

rhizoid (Gr. *rhiza*, root). A structure of root-like form and function, but of simple anatomy, lacking xylem and phloem.

rhizome (Gr. *rhiza*, root). A creeping underground stem.

RNA. Ribonucleic acid, found chiefly in the cytoplasm and the nucleolus, and perhaps involved in the transmission of hereditary information from the nucleus to the cytoplasm.

root. One of the primary organs of most vascular plants, typically serving to anchor the plant in the soil and to absorb water and minerals.

saprophyte (Gr. *sapros*, rotten + *phyton*, plant). A plant which absorbs its food, rather than making it or eating it.

schizogenous (Gr. *schizein*, to split + *genesis*, origin). Originating by splitting or separation of tissue.

sclerenchyma (Gr. *skleros*, hard + *enchein*, to pour in). A nonvascular strengthening tissue, usually dead when functional, in which the cells have a definite secondary wall that is often lignified.

secondary tissue. A tissue derived from the cambium or other lateral meristem.

secondary wall. In cells, an inner wall layer, formed after the primary wall and often of different composition.

seed. A ripened ovule; the characteristic rest-

ing body in the reproductive cycle of many plants.

sepal (Gr. *skepe*, a covering). A member of the outermost set of floral leaves, typically green or greenish and more or less leafy in texture.

septum (L. a hedge or enclosure). A partition.

sessile (L. *sessilis*, sitting). Lacking a stalk.

sexual (L. *sexus*, sex). Relating in some way to nuclear fusion or reduction division.

shoot. The stem and leaves of a plant, collectively.

sieve element. The fundamental type of cell in phloem, being long, slender, and thin-walled, and having cytoplasm but no nucleus at maturity.

sieve plate. A perforated end wall connecting two sieve elements.

sieve tube. A phloem tube formed from several sieve elements set end to end.

siphonostele (Gr. *siphon*, tube + stele). A stele in which the vascular tissue surrounds a central pith.

solute. A component of a liquid solution, whose particles are dispersed separately from each other. Compare *solvent*.

solution. A liquid or gaseous mixture in which the dispersed particles are of ordinary molecular or ionic size.

solvent. The continuous component of a liquid solution. Compare *solute*.

sorus (Gr. *soros*, a heap). A cluster of sporangia or externally produced spores.

species (L. a particular kind). A particular kind of plant or animal, which maintains its distinctness from other kinds in nature over a period of many successive generations.

sperm (Gr. *sperma*, seed). A motile gamete which can fuse with an egg to form a zygote; the male gamete.

spindle. A structure, formed during mitosis, which is associated with the movement of the chromosomes to the poles.

sporangium (spore + Gr. *angeion*, vessel). A case or container for spores.

spore (Gr. *spora*, seed). A one-celled (seldom two-celled) reproductive structure other than a gamete or zygote; zygotes which become thick-walled and go into a resting stage, thus resembling many spores, are called zygospores or oöspores.

spore mother cell. A cell capable of undergoing reduction division to form spores.

sporophyll (spore + Gr. *phyllon*, leaf). A leaf which bears or subtends one or more sporangia.

sporophyte (spore + Gr. *phyton*, plant). The generation which has 2*n* chromosomes and produces spores (meiospores) as reproductive bodies.

stamen (Gr. *stēmōn*, thread, fiber). The male organ of a flower, i.e., the microsporophyll.

starch. A carbohydrate food reserve consisting of a mixture of amylose, amylopectin, and perhaps other substances.

statospore (Gr. *statos*, standing still + spore). A type of spore, produced by many Chrysophyta, in which the cell wall consists of two very unequal overlapping parts, the smaller part forming a plug closing a pore in the larger part.

stele (Gr. post, pillar). Same as *central cylinder*.

stem. One of the primary organs of vascular plants, typically serving to bear the reproductive structures and display the leaves.

stigma (Gr. the mark of a pointed instrument also, L. a mark or brand). The part of a pistil which is receptive to pollen.

stipe (L. *stipes*, a stock, branch, or trunk). Any stem-like structure on which some other structure is borne.

stipule (L. *stipula*, diminutive of *stipes*, stalk). One of a pair of basal appendages found on many leaves.

stomate (Gr. *stoma*, mouth). A special kind of intercellular space in epidermal tissue, bounded by a pair of guard cells which, under certain conditions, close off the space by changing shape.

strobilus (Gr. *strobilos*, cone). A cluster of sporophylls on an axis; a cone.

style (Gr. *stylos*, pillar, column). The part of a pistil which connects the stigma to the ovary.

suberin (L. *suber*, the cork oak). A water-proofing substance characteristic of the walls of cork cells.

succulent (L. *succulentus*, juicy). A plant which accumulates reserves of water in the fleshy stems or leaves, due largely to the high proportion of hydrophilic colloids in the protoplasm and cell sap.

sucrose (Fr. *sucre*, sugar). The commonest disaccharide; it has the chemical formula $C_{12}H_{22}O_{11}$ and yields equal amounts of glucose and fructose when hydrolyzed.

suspension. A mixture of water and solid or liquid particles that are of larger than molecular size.

suspensor. A cell or organ, derived from the zygote but not part of the embryo proper, which in some vascular plants pushes (by its growth) the young embryo deeper into the tissue of the gametophyte.

symbiosis (Gr. *symbiōsis*, a living together). A close physical association between two different kinds of organisms, typically with benefit to both.

sympodial (Gr. *syn*, with + *pous, podos*, foot). With the apparent main axis actually consisting of a series of usually short branches.

syngamy (Gr. *syn*, with + *gamos*, marriage). Fusion of gametes.

tapetum (Gr. *tapēs*, carpet). A nutritive tissue which degenerates during the development of spores or pollen grains.

taxon (Gr. *taxis*, order, arrangement). Any taxonomic unit of classification.

taxonomy (Gr. *taxis*, arrangement + *nomos*, law). Classification according to presumed natural (i.e., evolutionary) relationships.

telome (Gr. *telos*, end). An ultimate branch of a dichotomously branching stem.

telophase (Gr. *telos*, end + phase). The stage in mitosis during which daughter nuclei are formed.

tetrad (Gr. *tetras*, four). A group of four.

thallophyte (thallus + Gr. *phyton*, plant). A plant in which the body is a thallus; a plant group consisting of the algae, fungi, and bacteria.

thallus (Gr. *thallos*, a sprout). A complete

plant body which lacks specialized conducting tissues, especially if it is multicellular but relatively simple in form, not being divided into parts which resemble roots, stems, and leaves.

tissue. A group of cells, making up part of a unicellular organism, with similar or related function(s).

tracheid (L. *trachea*, the windpipe). The most characteristic type of cell in xylem, being long, slender, tapered at the ends, with a lignified secondary wall and without living contents at maturity.

transpiration (L. *trans*, across + *spirare*, to breathe). Evaporation and consequent loss of water from a living plant.

trichocyst (Gr. *thrix*, *trichos*, hair + *kystis*, bladder). A cell organelle, usually capable of producing a hair-like external appendage under some conditions.

tropism (Gr. *tropē*, a turning). A directional growth response to an environmental stimulus.

vacuole (diminutive of L. *vacuus*, empty). A watery vesicle within a protoplast, chemically relatively inactive and usually regarded as nonliving.

vascular (L. *vasculum*, a small vessel). Having or pertaining to a conducting system; having xylem and phloem.

venter (L. belly). The swollen base of an archegonium, containing an egg.

vessel. A xylem tube formed from several vessel segments (modified tracheids with imperfect or no end walls) set end to end.

xanthophyll (Gr. *xanthos*, yellow + *phyllon*, leaf). A carotene-like yellow pigment which contains some oxygen in addition to carbon and hydrogen.

xerophyte (Gr. *xeros*, dry + *phyton*, plant). A plant which grows in very dry places.

xylem (Gr. *xylon*, wood). The characteristic water-conducting tissue of higher plants.

zoospore (Gr. *zoon*, animal + spore). A swimming (motile) spore.

zygospore. A zygote, formed by fusion of isogametes, which secretes a thick wall and goes into a resting stage. Compare *oöspore*.

zygote (Gr. *zygōtos*, yoked). A cell formed by fusion of gametes.

Index

Numbers in italic indicate pages containing illustrations.

Carthamus, 726

Caruncle, 636

Carya, 815

Caryophyllaceae, 692

Caryophyllales, perisperm, 637

Caryopsis, 629, 631

Cashew, 723

Casparian strip, 324, *506*

Caspary, J. X. R., 506

Cassava, 709, *710*

Cassia, seeds, 641

Castanea, 691

Castilla, 720

Castor beans, germination, **645**

Catabolism, 33

Catalyst, 15

Catbrier, *528*, 530

Cations, 564

Catkin, *619*, 688

Caudex, 491

Caulerpa, *150*, 151

Caulidium, 292

Caytonia, 407

Caytoniales, 406 f.

Cedar, western red, 794, 823; white, 819

Cedar-apple rust, 268

Celastrus, 635

Cell, 21 ff., 24; division, 45 ff.; functions, 31 ff.; shape, 452; structure, 23 ff.

Cell plate, 46, 51

Cell sap, 23, 25 f.

Cell theory, 3, 21

Cell wall, 24 f., 31, 51

Cellulosan, 24

Cellulose, 24

Centipede grass, 721

Central body, 122

Central cylinder, 322, 471

Central grassland, 821

Central vacuole, 23, 25 f.

Central Valley of California, 821 f.

Centriole, 48

Centromere, 48

Centrosome, 48

Century plant, 451

Ceratopteris pteridoides, 397; *C. thalictroides*, 398

Cereal crops, 706 ff.

Cereus, 680; *C. giganteus*, *560*, 827

Chamaecyparis thyoides, 819

Chamaephyte, 810

Chamberlain, C. J., *403*

Chamiso, 828

Chaparral, 828 829

Chara, *153*, 154

Charophyceae, 152 ff.

Charophyta, 154

Checkerboard in genetic studies, 728, 730, 731

Chemistry, carbon, 15 ff.; organic, 15 ff.

Chemoautotrophs, 91, 98 f.

Chemonasty, 673

Chemosynthesis, 91, 98 f.

Chemotaxis, 672

Chemotropism, 670, 672

Chenopodiaceae, 826

Chenopodium, 673

Cherry, flower, 607

Chestnut, 691

Chestnut blight, 250

Chicle, 715

Chicory, *696*

Chitin, 7; in bacteria, 82; in fungi, 231

Chlamydobacteriales, 82, 99 See also Sheathed bacteria

Chlamydomonas, *8*, *134*, 136, *139*, 141 f., 152, 770

Chlamydospermae, 443 ff.

Chlorenchyma, 342, 452, 533

Chlorobacteriaceae, 100

Chlorobium, 100

Chloromonadophyceae, 171 ff.

Chloromonads, 171 ff.

Chloronema, 307

Chlorophyceae, 133 ff. See also Green algae

Chlorophyll, 28 f.; *a*, 28; *b*, 28; in photosynthesis, 37 f.

Chlorophyta, 133 ff. See also Green algae

Chloroplasts, 27 ff.

Chlorosis, 570, 571

Chocolate, 714

Chondriosome, 29

Chondromyces, *103*

Chondrus, 221

Chromatid, 46

Chromatin, 30

Chromonema, 30, 46

Chromoplasm, 123

Chromoplast, 27, 29

Chromosome, 30, 46 ff.

Chromulina, 179

Chrysamoeba, 179 f.

Chrysophyceae, 177 ff.

Chrysophyta, 171 ff., 770 f.

Chytridiales, 234 f.

Chytrids, 234 f.

Cibotium, 384

Cichorium, 696

Cicuta, 513, 722

Cinchona, 717

Cingulum, 182

Cinnamon, 712, *713*

Circinate, 382

Circumscissile dehiscence, 629

Cirsium arvense, 517

Cladonia, 257, 812

Clamp connections, 258 ff.

Class, 66

Classes, keys to, 831 ff.

Classification of angiosperms, 677 ff.

Clavaria, 277

Claviceps, 249 ff.

Clay, 462

Cleistothecium, 246

Clements, F. E., 785, 798 ff.

Climax community, 786, 798

Clitocybe, 224

Clone, 490

Closed bundles, 486

Clostridium, 92, 93; *C. botulinum*, 97 f.

Clover, 659, 670, 675, 783

Cloves, 713

Club fungi, 258 ff. See also Basidiomycetes

Club mosses, 334, *340*, 341 ff.

Clubroot of cabbage, 231

Clusia, fruits, 630

Cluster cups, 265

Coal, 358, 373, 398

Cobalt, 42, 43

Cocci, *81*

Coccidioides, 282

Cocklebur, 596, 599, 641

Cocoa, *714*

Coconut, 580, 634, 698, 710

Coconut milk factor, 659

Cocos, 580, *634*, 698, 710

Coenocytic, 135

Coenopteridales, 391

Coffee, *714*

Cohesion, Dixon's theory, 548 f.

Cohn, Ferdinand, 23, 80, 97

Cola, 715

Colacium, 158–159

Colchicine, 753

Cold hardening, 666

Coleoptile, 637; in auxin studies, 653 ff.

Coleorhiza, 637

Coleus, abscission of leaves, *525*

Collateral bundle, 474

Collenchyma, 452, *453*

Colletia, 489, *490*

Colloid, 14

Columella, in Anthocerotae, 296; in mosses, 311; in *Rhizopus*, 240; in slime molds, 228

Commensalism, 89
Companion cell, *454*, 459
Complete flower, 608
Compositae, *695* f.; inulin in, 589; ornamental, 722
Concentric bundle, *474*
Conceptacle in brown algae, 199, 202
Conchocelis, 215
Cones of conifers, *432* f.
Conidiophore, 232
Conidiospore, *see* Conidium
Conidium, 232; in bacteria, 86
Coniferae, 420 ff.
    See also Conifers
Coniferales, 421 ff.
    See also Conifers
Coniferophyta, 419 ff.
    See also Conifers
Coniferous forests, 809, 813 ff., 822 ff.
Conifers, 421 ff.; bark, 428 ff.; cambium, 423; cones, *432*, *433*; distribution, 421 f.; economic importance, 441 ff.; female gametophyte, 435; fertilization, 435 f.; fossils, 438 ff.; habit, 422 f.; leaves, 429 ff.; longevity, 427 f.; ovules, 433, *434*; pollen, 434 f.; pollination, 435; relationships, 442 ff.; root, 429 f.; seedlings, 437; seeds, 436 f.; stem, 423 ff.; wood, 423 ff.
Conium, 691, 722
Conjugation, 55; in bacteria, 87 f.
Connecting band, 182
Connecting filaments, 197
Connective, 602
Conyza canadensis, 790, 792
Cooperage, 719
Copper, 42, 43, *565*, 578
Coprinus, 274
Coptis, flower, *688*
Coral reefs, 220, 152
Coralline algae, 220 f.
Corallorhiza, 517
Coralroot, 517
Corda, August, 243, 260
Cordaitales, 420, 421
Cordaites, 421
Cork, 21–22, *454*, 460, 461, 484, 485
Cork cambium, 351, 429, 456
Cork oak, 484, 485
Corm, 491, *492*
Cormophyta, 289
Corn, 708 f.; efficiency in photosynthesis, 586; genetic segrega-

Corn (*Continued*)
    tion, 729; germination, 644; hybrid, 744 ff.; stem section, *485*
Corn smut, 269–270
Cornus, inflorescence, *611*
Corolla, 602
Corpus, 469
Cortex, 322, 471, 475, 507; in *Laminaria*, 198
Corti, B., 22
Corylus, catkins, *619*
Corymb, *609*
Cotton, 718
Cotyledon, 344, 436, 636
Cotyledons, functions, 644 f.
Coumarin, *659*
Cover cell, in bryophytes, 292; in ferns, 388
Cowles, Henry C., 785
Crab grass, 490, 783 f.
Crassula argentea, 559
Crassulaceae, 536, 559
Crataegus, 487, 488, 751
Crenothrix, 99
Creosote bush, 559, 826, 827
Cretaceous period, vegetation, 776
Crevice plants, 788
Crocus, thermonasty, 673
Cronartium, 268
Cronquist, Arthur, 686
Crossing over, 59, 730, 740
Crown gall, 668, 669
Crozier, 245
Cruciferae, 693; fruits, 631
Cryptogams, 375
Cryptomonads, 163 ff.
Cryptomonas, *164*
Cryptophyceae, 163 ff., 168, 770
Cryptophyte, 810
Cucumber, 633
Culture media, 97
Currants, 268
Cuscuta, 7, 8, *518* (haustorium), 763
Cuticle, 454, 325
Cutin, 454, 296, 325
Cuttings, 492, 493, 537
Cyanophyceae, 119 ff.
    See also Blue-green algae
Cyanophycean starch, 123 f.
Cyanophyta, 131
Cyatheaceae, 395
Cycadae, 404 ff.
    See also Cycads
Cycadales, 408 ff.
    See also Cycads
Cycadeoidea, *408*

Cycadeoids, 407
Cycadofilicales, 404 ff.
Cycadophytes, 401 ff.; relationships, 773
    See also Cycads
Cycads, 408 ff.; economic importance, 416; embryo, 415; female gametophyte, 412; leaves, 410 f.; male gametophyte, 414; megasporophylls, *412*; ovules, 411; pollen, 411; relationships, 416, 773; root, 409; seedlings, 415 f.; seeds, 415 f.; stem, 409 f.
Cycas, 416
Cyclosis, 34
Cyclosporae, 199 ff.; life cycle, 192 f.
Cyme, 610, *611*
Cynodon, 671, 721
Cyperus papyrus, 556
Cypress, bald, 818, *819*
Cystocarp, 211
Cytisus, 489
Cytochrome, 39, 767
Cytokinesis, 45 f., 50 f.
Cytology, 9
Cytopharynx, 157
Cytoplasm, 24, 26 ff.; function 32 f.
Cytoplasmic inheritance, 740 f.
Cytostome, 157

Dahlia, roots, *513*
Damping off, 237
Dandelion, *633*
Darrow, Clarence, 760
Darwin, Charles, 758 ff., 69, 619, 653, 701 f., 759
Date, 710, *711*
Datura, 494, 735
Dawson, John W., 327
Day length, 596 ff., 664
Day-neutral plants, 599
Death camas, 722
De Bary, H. A., 233, 266
de Candolle, Alphonse, 700, 706
de Candolle, Augustin Pyramus, 683
Deciduous, 523
Deficiency diseases in plants, 573 ff.
Degeneriaceae, 687 f.
de Jussieu, A. L., 120, 291, 682
Deliquescent branching, *477*
Dendrobium, 700
Denitrification, 91 f.
Deoxyribonucleic acid, 30
Dermatophytes, 282

Desert, cold, 824 ff.; warm, 826 f.
Desert vegetation, 809
Desert woodland, 826
Desmids, 146–147
Desmocapsa, 165
Desmomonas, 165
Desmophyceae, 165 f., 168, 770
Desulfovibrio, 95
Determinate inflorescence, 608, *611*
Deuteromycetes, 279
Devonian period, vegetation, 773
Dextrose, 16 f.
Dianthus, 534 (leaf section), 692
Diarch stele, 382
Diastase, 42
Diatomaceous earth, *184,* 185 f.
Diatoms, 181 ff.; centric, 182, *184;* classification, 185; definition, 181; distribution, 181; economic importance, 185 f.; motion, 182 f.; pennate, *182, 183;* relationships, 770 f.; reproduction, 183 ff.; structure, 181 ff.
Dicaryotic, 258
Dichasium, 610, *611*
Dicots, contrasted to monocots, 678
Dicranella, 312
Dictyophora, 278
Dictyosiphon, 196 f.
Dictyostele, 381
Dictyostelium, 230
Dictyota, 195–196
Differentially permeable membrane, 33 ff.
Differentiation in growth, 650
Diffuse-porous wood, 478, *480*
Diffusion, 14
Diffusion pressure, 545
Diffusion pressure deficit, **545**
Digestion, 4, 41 f.
Digitalis, 716 f., 600
Digitaria, 490
   See also Crab grass
Dihybrid, 730 f.
Dinobryon, 180
Dinoflagellates, 166 ff.
Dinophyceae, 166 ff., 770
Dinothrix, 167
Dioecious, 411, 432, 608
Dionaea, 7, 538, 674
Dioön, 413, 416
Dioscorea, 709
Diospyros, plasmodesmata, **26**
Diploid, 55
Disaccharide, 17
Disclimax, 796

Discomycetes, 246
Diseases, bacterial, 96 ff.
Disturbance, effects on vegetation, 789 ff.; role in evolution, 766
Division, 66
Divisions, keys to, 831 ff.
Dixon, H. H., *548*
DNA, 30
Dock, 642
Dodder, 7, 8, *518* (haustorium), 763
Dodge, B. O., 250, 733
Dogwood, inflorescence, *611*
Dominance, incomplete, 735; reversal of, 735 f.
Dominant, 727
Dormancy, in buds, 470; in seeds, 639 ff.
Dorsiventral, 293 f.
Double coconut, 637
Double fertilization, 621
Douglas fir, 432, 441, 793 f., 823
Downy mildews, 238
Dracaena, 486
Drinks, 714 f.
Dropsy, 716 f.
Drosera, 538, 673
Drosophila, 740, 761
Drought-enduring species, 559 f.
Drupe, 628
Dryopteris filix-mas, 384, 398
Dryopteris marginalis, 376
Dujardin, F., 22
Dutrochet, R. J. H., 56
Dwarfism, induced by grafting, 494 f.
Dyestuffs, 720 f.

Eastern deciduous forest, 815 ff.
Echeveria, 542, 559
Ecology, 1 f., 9 f., 781 ff.; role in speciation, 765 f.
Ecotone, 782
Ecotype, 765
Ectocarpus, 194 f.
Ectophloic siphonostele, 382
Edaphic factors, 782
Egg, 55
Ehrenberg, C., 79, 157
Eichhornia, 498, *556*
Eichler, A. W., 684
Elaters, 296, 367
Elderberry, lenticel, *483*
Electrical balances in soil, 566 f.
Elements necessary for plant growth, 42 ff.
Elm, *527* (leaf), 721
Elodea, stem tip, *468*

Embryo, 290, 635
Embryo sac, 615
Embryophyta, 71 ff., 289 f., 771 f.
Empedocles, 757 f.
Emulsion, 14
Encelia farinosa, 283, 659
Encephalartos, 400
Endarch stele, 381, 504
Endlicher, S. L., 289
Endocarp, 627
Endodermis, 322, 324, 455, 475, 505 ff., 671
Endoenzymes, 88
Endomycetales, 247
Endoplasmic reticulum, 27, 28, 30, 33
Endosperm, 621, 635, 637
Endospore, 84 ff., 124
Endothia, 250
Engler, Adolf, 683 ff.
Englerian system, 683 ff.
Enzymes, 15; digestive, 41 f.
Ephedra, 443, *444,* 445
Ephemerals, *558, 559, 810*
Epibasidium, 261
Epicotyl, 415, 636, 643
Epidermis, *453* ff.; of leaves, 530 ff.; of roots, 502 ff., 507; of stems, 475 f.
Epigaeous, 644
Epigynous, *602,* 608
Epinasty, 674
Epiphyte, 90
Epiplasm, 245
Epitheca, 182
Equatorial plate, 48
Equisetae, 362 ff.
Equisetales, 362 ff.
Equisetites, 369
Equisetum, 360, 361, 362 ff.
Eremochloa, 721
Ergot, 249 ff.
Ericaceae, 693
Erysiphe, 249
Escherichia coli, 78, 87, 88, 98
Espeletia, 813
Etapteris, 391
Ethylene, 659
Etiolation, *663*
Euascomycetes, 246
Eubacteriales, 81
Eucalyptus, leaves, 534
Euchlaena, 708
Euglena, 8, 9, *156, 158, 159*
Euglenoids, 157 ff., 770
Euglenophyceae, 157 ff.
Euglenophyta, 157 ff.
Eumycotina, 225, 231 **ff.**
Euphorbia, 680

Osmosis, 33 ff.
Osmotic potential, 36, 545
Osmotic pressure, 35 f.
Ostiole, 199, 246
Outbreeding, 741 ff.
Outer fissure in diatoms, 182
Ovary, 402, 605 f.
Overgrazing, 795 ff.
Ovule, 402; in angiosperms, 612 ff.
Oxalis, 673, 675
Oxidation, 18
Oxydendrum, 652
Oxytropis, 691, 722

Paleobotany, 10
Paleontology, 10
Paleotaxus, 439
Paleozoic era, vegetation, 773 ff.
Palisade tissue, 385, 533 f.
Palmae, 698 f.
Palms, *580, 634, 637,* 698 f., *710, 711*
Palouse region, *704,* 821 f.
Palynology, 9
Panicle, *609, 610*
Panicum, root hairs, *503*
Papaver, 716
Papyrus, 556
Parallel venation, *529*
Paramo, *813*
Paramylum, 158
Paraphyses, in Ascomycetes, 246; in Basidiomycetes, 261; in brown algae, 199
Parasexual processes, 87, 88
Parasite, 89
Parenchyma, 190 f., 451 ff.
Parthenocissus, 489
Parthenogenesis, 192
Pascher, Adolf, *120,* 163, 171
Passage cells, 507
Pasteur, Louis, *5,* 96
Pathology, 10
Patouillard, Narcisse, 260
p/e ratio, 808
Peaches, 710
Peas, germination, 644; in genetic studies, 726 ff.
Peat, 313
Peat moss, 313 ff., 812
Pectic substances, 24
Pellicle, 157
Penicillin, 282
Penicillium, 280 f., 282
Penstemon, 694
Pentaploid, 749
Pentarch stele, 382
Pentosans, 24

Pepo, *628, 633*
Pepper, 711, *712*
Perennial, 451
Perfect flower, 608
Perfect stage of fungi, 232
Perianth, 602; in liverworts, 300
Pericarp 627
Pericycle, 341, 475, 505
Periderm, 482
Peridinium, 162, 166, 167
Peridium, 228, 262, 278
Perigynous, *602, 607*
Periplasm, 236
Periplast, 157
Perisperm, 635, 637
Peristome, 311
Perithecium, 246
Permafrost, 810
Permanent wilting percentage, 545
Permeability of membranes, 33 ff.
Permian period, vegetation, 774
Peronosporales, 237 ff.
Persimmon, 26 (plasmodesmata)
Petals, 601, 604
Petiole, 376, *521, 522*
Petunia, 724
Peziza, 251 ff.
Pezizales, 251 ff.
Pfeffer, Wilhelm, 517
pH, 564, 569 f.
Phaeophyta, 189 ff.
See also Brown algae
Phaeoplax, 164 f.
Phages, 78, *106, 108, 109, 111,* 116
Phalaris, 653
Phallales, 278
Phanerogams, 375
Phanerophyte, 810
Phellem, 483
Phelloderm, 429, 482
Phellogen, 351, 429, 456
Phenotype, 728
Phenotypic ratios, 731 f.
Phloem, 320, 458 ff., 482 ff.; internal, *474;* rays, 482; role in translocation, 587 f.
Phoenix, 710, 711
Phormidium, 127
Phospholipids, 19
Phosphorescence, 166
Phosphorus, 42, 43, *573, 574, 575,* 576
Photoinductive cycle, 599
Photonasty, 673
Photo-oxidation, 585

Photoperiodism, 596 ff., 664
Photosynthesis, 37 f., 581 ff., 860 ff.; carbon dioxide in, 582 ff.; efficiency, 585 f.; light in, 584 ff.; temperature effect in, 586 f.
Phototaxis, 672
Phototropism, 670, 671 f.
Phycobilin, 123, 164, 209, 768
Phycocyanin, 123, 164, 209
Phycodrys, 210
Phycoerythrin, 123, 164, 209
Phycology, 10
Phycomycetes, 233 ff., 286, 771
Phyllidia, 292
Phyllotaxy, *523*
Phylloxera, *494*
Phylogeny of plants, 767 ff.
Phylum, 66
Physarum, 226
Physcia, 256
Physiological drought, 561
Physiology, 9
Phytophthora, 237–238
Picea engelmanni, 822; *P. glauca,* 814; *P. mariana,* 814; *P. rubens,* 814; *P. sitchensis,* 823
Pickleweed, *546*
Pigment, 662
See also Anthocyanin; Carotene, etc.
Pigweed, 673
Pileus, 272
Pine, 268 (blister rust), 422, *425* (wood), *426* (resin duct), 428, *430* (needles), *431* (needles), *432* (cone), 433 (cone), *434* (ovule), *435* (pollen), *436* (pollen), 441, 442, 651, 793, 795, 814, 815, *817, 818,* 823, 826
Pineapple, 631, *632*
Pinedrops, 517
Pinna, 383
Pinnately compound, *526*
Pinnule, 383
Pinus, 431, 432, 433, 434, 435, 436, 437, 441, 442; *P. aristata,* 428; *P. banksiana, 437,* 814; *P. caribaea,* 817; *P. contorta, 437,* 793, 795, 823; *P. coulteri,* 547; *P. edulis, 437,* 826; *P. lambertiana,* 823; *P. laricio, 430, 434, 436;* *P. monticola,* 823; *P. palustris,* 817; *P. resinosa,* cone, *432;* *P. rigida, 422,* 650, 651, 817, *818;* *P. strobus, 425, 431,* 815; *P. taeda,* 817

Scouring rushes, 361 ff.
Scrophulariaceae, 693 f.
Sea lettuce, 148 ff.
Seaweed
    See Brown algae; Red algae, etc.
Secale, 509, 721
Secondary growth, 351; in leaves, 535; in roots, 507 f.; in stems, 423 ff., 471 ff.
Secondary roots, 508
Sedge mat, 788, 789
Sedum, stomates, *532*
Seed coat, 402, 416, 635
Seed ferns, *404* ff.
Seed plants, introduction to, 401 ff.
Seedlings, 638 ff.
Seeds, 402, 635 ff.; dispersal, 632 ff., *635*, 783; dormancy, 639 ff.; food storage, 591 f.; germination, 638 f.; longevity, 641 f.; structure, 635 ff., *415* f., *436* ff.
Segregation, principle of, 727
Seifriz, W., 27
Selaginella, 345 ff., *357*, *358*
Selaginellales, 345 ff.
Selaginellites, 349
Selenium, 43, 44
Self-sterility, 618
Semicells, 146
Semipermeable membrane, **33**
Sensitive plant, *674*
Sepals, 601
Separation disk, 124
Separation layer, 524
Septicidal dehiscence, 629
Sequoia sempervirens, 423, 548, 823
Sequoiadendron giganteum, *418*, 422, 426, 823
Serpentine, 565
Sessile, 521
Seta, 292
Sex, biological significance, 61; nature of, 54 ff.
Sexual reproduction, 54 ff.
Sexual spores, 232
Shadscale, 826
Sheathed bacteria, 82, 86
    See also Chlamydobacteriales
Shepherds's purse, seed, *636*
Shoot, 320, 436, 450
Short-day plants, 597 ff.
Short-grass prairie, 819 f., *821*
Shull, George H., *744*
Sieve area, 320, *454*, 458

Sieve element, 320, 458
Sieve plate, *454*, *459*
Sieve tube, 320, *454*, **458**
Sigillaria, 353
Silica gel, 97
Silicle, 629, **631**
Silique, 629, **631**
Silt, 462
Simaruba, 718
Siphonostele, 381
Sisymbrium, 651
Skunk cabbage, *12*
Sleep movements, 673, **675**
Slime molds, 226 ff.; classification, 230 f.; distribution, 227; economic importance, 231; history, 228; life cycle, 227 ff.; relationships, 285 f., 771; vegetative features, 226 f.
Smartweed, *526* (leaf)
Smelter smoke, *666*, *667*
Smilax, *528* (leaf), 530
Smith, Erwin F., 669
Smog, 667
Smuts, 261, 269 ff.
Snapdragon, 735, 739, 747 (mutation), 753 (ploidy)
Softwood (wood of conifers), 441
Soil, 461 ff.; components, 461 f.; correlated with climate, 463 f., 569; electrical balances, 566 f.; pH (acidity and alkalinity), 564, 568 ff.; types, 462 ff.; water, 543 f.
Sol, 14
Solanaceae, 693, 722
Solanum, 693; *S. tuberosum*, 490, 693, 709
Solenostele, 381
Solidago, 507; *S. canadensis*, 765; *S. rugosa*, *526* (leaf)
    See also Goldenrod
Solute, 14
Solution, 13 f.
Solvent, 14
Sordaria, *741*
Soredia, 258
Sorghastrum, 599, 820
Sorus, 239, 385; types, 394
Sourwood, 652
Southeastern evergreen forest, 817 ff.
Soybean, 92, *94*
Spallanzani, L., 5
Spanish moss, 571
Species, 65 f.; number of, 71 f.
Species Plantarum, 69
Specific epithet, 67
Spectrum of radiant energy, *584*

Sperm, 55
Spermatangium, 209
Spermatia, in red algae, 209; in rusts, 262 f.
Spermatophyta, 70 ff.
Spermogonium, 262, **263**
Sphaeriales, 250, 254
Sphaerotilus, 99
Sphagnales, 307, 313 ff.
Sphagnum, 313 ff., *314*, 812, 814, 819
Sphenophyllales, 370 f.
Sphenophyllum, 370, **371**
Sphenopsida, 362
Sphenopteris, 405
Spice Islands, **713**
Spices, 711 ff.
Spike, *609*
Spindle, 47 f.
Spines, 488
Spirilla, 81, 83
Spirillum, 83
Spirochaetes, 101–102
Spirogyra, *145* f.
Spirulina, 127 f.
Spongy tissue, 385, 533 f.
Spontaneous generation, 5, 6
Sporangiophore, in calamophytes, 362; in fungi, 235
Sporangium, 86
Spore, 54; sexual, 58
Spore mother cell, 58, 296
Sporidia, 262
Sporobolus, 631
Sporocarp, 396
Sporogenous tissue, 311, 337
Sporophyll, 337
Sporophyte, 140
Spring wood, 427, 478
Spruce, 814, 822, 823
Spruce-fir forest, *814*, 822
Spruce-hemlock forest, 824
Stalk cell, 414
Stamen, 602
Staminate flower, 608
Staminode, 604
Stanley, W. M., 108–*109*
Stanleya elata, *43*
Starch, 40
Starch grains, *590*
Starch sheath, 475, 671
Statospore, *178*
Steere, W. C., 746
Stele, 324, 471; types, 381, 382, 484, 485, 504 f.
Stemonitis, 229
Stems, 320, 450, 467 ff.; anatomy, 470 ff.; apical growth, 467 ff.; climbing, 488 f.; com-